Elements of

PHYSICS

Elements of
PHYSICS

FOR STUDENTS OF SCIENCE AND ENGINEERING

by

George Shortley

B.E.E., PH.D., RESEARCH DIRECTOR,
APPLIED RESEARCH, INC.
FORMERLY PROFESSOR OF PHYSICS,
THE OHIO STATE UNIVERSITY

and

Dudley Williams

A.B., PH.D., PROFESSOR OF PHYSICS,
THE OHIO STATE UNIVERSITY

Second Edition

PRENTICE-HALL, INC.
Englewood Cliffs, N. J.

Library of Congress Catalog Card Number: 55-9057

First printing............*April, 1955*
Second printing......*September, 1955*
Third printing..........*June, 1956*
Fourth printing .....*September, 1957*

PRINTED IN THE UNITED STATES OF AMERICA

26873

PREFACE TO THE SECOND EDITION

IN VIEW OF the favorable acceptance accorded the first edition of this text, the publishers decided to bring out a second edition after just two years' use of the first, in order to permit the authors to take prompt advantage of the many constructive criticisms and suggestions that have been made by users of the text.

This new edition has been completely reset and incorporates extensive revisions and many additions. Subject matter in mechanics has been rearranged in more logical order; illustrative examples have been systematically included; and problem sets have been improved, expanded, and relocated at the ends of the chapters. New subjects treated include relative velocities, dynamical systems, fluid viscosity, surface phenomena in liquids, Gauss's law in electrostatics, thermionic vacuum tubes, transistors, and the newly discovered particles of modern physics. The Newtonian principle of relativity is emphasized, and the application of Newton's principles of motion in moving coordinate systems is illustrated in a number of chapters.

The text is intended for use in an introductory course for the student of science or engineering who is taking a *concurrent* course in the calculus. Mathematics is used as a tool, and no attempt is made to teach mathematics for its own sake. Plane trigonometry is used extensively from the beginning, but calculus is introduced gradually as the student acquires familiarity with this discipline.

The primary objective of the book is to provide the student with a working knowledge of the fundamental principles that describe all physical phenomena, of how they evolved, and of their scope and limitations. Emphasis is placed on the broad conservation principles, since the generalization of these principles has formed the base on which the various branches of modern physics and engineering have been built.

In modern physics and engineering, a large amount of *theory* is often interpolated between direct sensory observation and conclusions regarding the properties of the physical world. We begin with a demonstration of how sensory observations of *macroscopic* phenomena were used in the development of mechanical principles. After this beginning, the student is introduced to the methods of drawing conclusions regarding *microscopic* phenomena in heat, light, electricity and magnetism, and modern physics. We have adopted an *operational* approach and have attempted to give careful operational definitions of the various physical quantities as they are introduced.

We have specifically designated as *principles* the fundamental relationships having general application; secondary relationships having more limited application are designated as *laws*. Units for all numerical constants occurring in formulas and examples have been written explicitly in all cases, as a matter of good pedagogy. Without exception, we have attempted to give an introduction to the fundamentals of physics in which nothing will have to be 'unlearned' when the student takes up more advanced work.

Where possible, examples and problems have been chosen to illustrate the application of physical principles in the context of practical situations encountered in modern physics and engineering. The use of such practical situations in illustrative material does not mean that we attempt in any sense to teach engineering.

Two *coherent* systems of mechanical units are employed: absolute MKS units and the slug-pound-second system of British-gravitational units. In electricity and magnetism, we use only the practical MKS units in their rationalized form. In the Appendix, various systems of units are discussed, and extensive tables of conversion factors are given.

In preparing this new edition we have been guided by our own teaching experience and by that of others who have used the first edition in their classes. We wish to express our appreciation for extremely helpful comments and suggestions from all of our colleagues at the Ohio State University, and from Professors H. H. Barschall, F. L. Brown, Howard Carr, John A. Wheeler, and others who have used the text. Our thanks also go to Professors Robert Resnick, Ralph A. Goodwin, Earl W. Thomson, and I. Wallerstein, who have given detailed criticisms of our manuscripts, and to Mr. Joseph Geusic, who gave able assistance in checking the problems and examples.

Finally, we are again appreciative of the editorial help and cooperation we have received from Mr. James B. Plate, Mr. Nicholas Romanelli, and other members of the staff of Prentice-Hall, and of the excellent typographical work of Maple Press.

GEORGE SHORTLEY
DUDLEY WILLIAMS

CHEVY CHASE, MARYLAND
COLUMBUS, OHIO

CONTENTS

Part I MECHANICS

vii

Chapter 11.   PERIODIC MOTION   234

Part II   HEAT

Chapter 12.   TEMPERATURE; THERMAL EXPANSION   255

Chapter 13.   CALORIMETRY   274

Chapter 14.   HEAT TRANSFER   286

Chapter 15.   PROPERTIES OF GASES   301

Chapter 16.   SOLIDS, LIQUIDS, AND GASES   322

Chapter 17. THERMODYNAMICS 347

Part III WAVE MOTION AND SOUND

Chapter 18. WAVE MOTION 375

Chapter 19. SOUND 393

Part IV LIGHT

Chapter 20. THE NATURE OF LIGHT AND ITS PROPAGATION 425

Chapter 21. ILLUMINATION AND PHOTOMETRY 437

Part VI   MODERN PHYSICS

Chapter 37.   ELECTROMAGNETIC WAVES; PHOTONS; ELECTRONS   789

Part I
MECHANICS

CHAPTER 1

SCALAR AND VECTOR QUANTITIES;

DISPLACEMENT, FORCE, TORQUE

PHYSICS is a *quantitative* science—a science of measurement, experiment, and of systematization of the results of experiment. *Measurement* comes first, and the preferred definition, called the *operational definition*, of a physical quantity consists merely of a description of the procedure for measuring the quantity. Measurement permits the quantitative description of the results observed in an experiment. Generalization of the observations made in a number of experiments leads to a *theory* designed to predict the results of related experiments. If no contradiction to the predictions of the theory is found, the theory leads to the formulation of physical *principles*, sometimes called *laws*, that can be widely applied in predicting the results of physical experiments or the results to be achieved in engineering applications. Scientific theory is descriptive in that it attempts to explain exactly *how* nature behaves, and is not at all concerned with *why* she behaves as she does. Science studies *how* apples fall, not *why* they fall.

In this chapter we define various simple physical quantities by describing how they are measured. Before a measurement can be made, a *unit* must be chosen. For the simpler quantities this unit is quite arbitrary; thus the mile and the hour are arbitrary units of length and time. For quantities derived from the simpler quantities, it is convenient also to derive the units from the simpler units. Thus speed is defined as distance per unit time, and if distance is measured in miles and time in hours it is convenient to measure speed in miles per hour.

The magnitude or measure of a physical quantity is specified by giving both a *number* and a *unit*. To say that the length of a stick is 14 is meaningless—to say that the magnitude of the length is 14 feet, or 14 inches, is a complete description.

Many quantities encountered in the study of physics and engineering have associated with them a *direction* as well as a *magnitude*, and have a common method of composition or 'addition' that is quite different from the method of addition of dollars or gallons. Such quantities are called

1

vector quantities or simply *vectors*. Familiar examples of vector quantities are displacement, velocity, acceleration, and force. *Vector quantities* must be carefully distinguished from *scalar quantities* such as volume which are completely specified by a magnitude, and whose addition merely involves the addition of the magnitudes. Much of this chapter will be devoted to the definition of certain vector quantities and to methods of handling them in analytical discussions.

1. MEASUREMENT OF LENGTHS AND ANGLES

THE DESCRIPTION of the position and orientation of an object in space is one of the first steps in the analysis of its motion. Such a description is

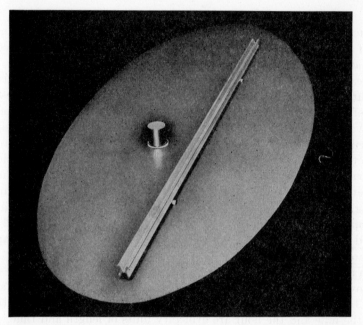

Fig. 1. Standard meter and standard kilogram kept at the National Bureau of Standards in Washington, D.C. These are the national standards of length and mass, and have been carefully compared with the international standards kept at Sèvres, France.

made in terms of lengths of lines and of angles between lines. The determination of the length of a line is one of the fundamental measurements in physical science and engineering. Everyone is familiar with such instruments as calibrated sticks, tapes, and calipers for the measurement of the distance between two points and with instruments for the measurement of angles. The precise definition of the units used for the calibration of such instruments forms a starting point for the study of physics.

The standard unit of length used for the calibration of most scientific instruments is the *meter*.

> The **meter** is defined as the distance between two fine lines ruled on the international prototype meter bar when it is at the temperature of melting ice.

This international prototype is a platinum-iridium bar kept at the International Bureau of Weights and Measures in Sèvres, near Paris. This bureau was set up by international treaty on May 20, 1875, to prepare, measure, and preserve the standards of the international metric system. The meter was originally intended to be one ten-millionth of the distance between the earth's equator and the North Pole measured along the meridian of Paris, but the original surveys were not accurate and this relation is only approximately satisfied. An accurate replica of this bar is kept in the National Bureau of Standards in Washington and constitutes the secondary standard used for calibrations in the United States. Figure 1 shows a photograph of this bar.

The meter is one of the three fundamental units in the international metric MKS (meter-kilogram-second) system of units in which the following prefixes are used to indicate multiples and submultiples:

deka-	for 10	deci-	for 0.1
hecto-	for 100	centi- (c)	for 0.01
kilo- (k)	for 1000	milli- (m)	for 0.001
mega- (M)	for 1,000,000	micro- (μ)	for 0.000001
giga-	for 10^9	millimicro- (mμ)	for 10^{-9}
tera-	for 10^{12}	micromicro- ($\mu\mu$)	for 10^{-12}

In abbreviations of the names of units, these prefixes are abbreviated as indicated in parentheses in this list.   Those prefixes for which no abbreviations are shown are seldom used in scientific work.

The commonly used metric units of length are the kilometer (km), which is 1000 m; the meter (m); the centimeter (cm), which is 0.01 m; the millimeter (mm), which is 0.001 m; the 'micrometer' or micron (μ), which is 10^{-6} m; and the millimicron (mμ), which is 10^{-9} m.

The unit of length used in most commercial transactions and in much engineering practice in English-speaking countries is the foot (ft) which is 12 inches (in) or one-third of a yard (yd).   The yard is legally defined in the United States as $3600/3937$ meter. This definition leads to the following relations among commonly used English and metric units of length:

$$
\begin{aligned}
1 \text{ in} &= 2.5400 \text{ cm} = 0.025400 \text{ m} \\
1 \text{ m} &= 39.37 \text{in} = 3.281 \text{ft} \\
1 \text{ ft} &= 30.48 \text{cm} = 0.3048 \text{m} \\
1 \text{ km} &= 3281 \text{ft} = 0.6214 \text{mi.}
\end{aligned}
$$

The statute mile (mi) is defined as 5280 ft, while the International nautical mile, which is approximately the length of one minute of latitude on the surface of the earth, is defined as exactly 1852 m, about 6076 ft.

Measurement of angles.   The angle between two lines is readily defined if any circle is drawn with its center at the intersection of the two lines as shown in Fig. 2.   The magnitude of the angle is proportional to the fraction of the circumference of the circle lying between the two lines.   By plane geometry, this fraction is independent of the radius of the circle.

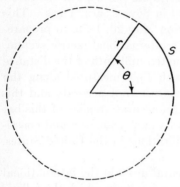

Fig. 2. Definition of an angle θ.

The *degree* (°) is the angular unit most commonly used; it is the angle subtended at the center of the circle by $\frac{1}{360}$ of the circumference.   The minute (′) is $\frac{1}{60}$°, while the second (″) is $\frac{1}{60}$′.

The *radian* (rad) is a more fundamental angular unit, which is defined as the angle subtended at the center of the circle by a portion of the circumference equal in length to the radius of the circle, that is, by the fraction $1/2\pi$ of the circumference.   The angle θ in Fig. 2 is given in radians by the relation

$$\theta = s/r$$

if the arc length s on the circumference and the radius r are both measured in the same units of length.   It follows that $\theta = 1$ rad when $s = r$, and $\theta = 2\pi$ rad when s is one circumference.

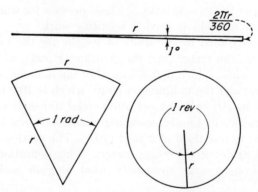

Fig. 3. The angular units: 1 degree, 1 radian, 1 revolution.

The angle subtended by the full circumference is commonly called 1 *revolution* (rev).   Thus,

$$1 \text{ rev} = 360° = 2\pi \text{ rad},$$
$$1 \text{ rad} = 57°3 = (1/2\pi) \text{ rev},$$
$$1° = (2\pi/360) \text{ rad} = 0.01745 \text{ rad} = \tfrac{1}{360} \text{ rev}.$$

These angular units are shown in Fig. 3.

2. METHODS OF SPECIFYING POSITIONS

IT IS NECESSARY in many physical problems to specify precisely the positions of points in space. In the analysis of the motion of a projectile the first essential step is the choice of a proper method of specifying the positions of successive points on the path of the projectile. The specification of position must be made in such a manner that it is easily understood and fits readily into quantitative discussions and computations. Coordinate systems like those familiar from the study of algebra or analytical geometry offer the best method of specifying positions.

A coordinate system has a fixed reference point called the origin O and fixed reference lines in terms of which the positions of points can be specified. A rectangular XY-coordinate system like that in Fig. 4(a) can be used, for example, to specify the position of the ball on a football field if

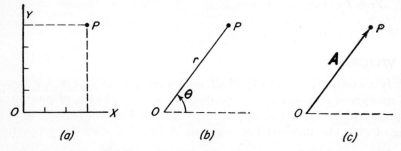

(a)   *(b)*   *(c)*

Fig. 4. (a) Rectangular coordinates of a point P. (b) Plane polar coordinates of the point P. (c) Displacement vector from O to P.

one takes the coordinate origin O at the southwest corner of the playing field, the X-axis along the south goal line, and the Y-axis along the west side of the field. When the ball is on the ground at the 40-yd line and 30 yd from the west side of the field, its position P is simply given by the statement that

$$X = 30 \text{ yd}, \quad Y = 40 \text{ yd}.$$

A third coordinate is needed for specifying positions when motion occurs in three dimensions. If the football is in the air, its position can be given in terms of an XYZ-coordinate system whose Z-axis points vertically upward from the southwest corner of the field. When the ball is 5 yd above a point on the ground which is on the 40-yd line and 30 yd from the west side of the field, its position is simply given by the statement that

$$X = 30 \text{ yd}, \quad Y = 40 \text{ yd}, \quad Z = 5 \text{ yd}.$$

It is possible to use a rectangular XYZ-coordinate system for specifying the positions of objects in any situation that we shall encounter. For example, such a system could be used for stating the instantaneous position of an airplane relative to an airport, the position of a light bulb relative to one corner of the floor of a room, and so on.

The position of a point in a plane can also be specified in terms of a plane polar coordinate system in which one gives the angular orientation and length of the line drawn from the coordinate origin to the point under consideration. The position of a point P is given by the length r and the angle θ shown in Fig. 4(b). The polar coordinates r and θ are related to the rectangular coordinates X and Y by the equations

$$X = r \cos\theta \quad \text{and} \quad Y = r \sin\theta,$$

or by
$$r = \sqrt{X^2 + Y^2} \quad \text{and} \quad \theta = \arctan(Y/X).$$

Example. *Find the polar coordinates r and θ of a football at point P in Fig. 4, at the 40-yd line and 30 yd from the west side of the field.*

From the preceding relations,

$$r = \sqrt{(30 \text{ yd})^2 + (40 \text{ yd})^2} = \sqrt{2500 \text{ yd}^2} = 50 \text{ yd},$$
$$\theta = \arctan(^{40}\!/_{30}) = \arctan 1.333 = 53°\!.1.$$

3. VECTORS

IF AN OBJECT, such as a football, moves from O to P in Fig. 4, it is said to undergo a *displacement*. The displacement or change of position is represented by the arrow-tipped line segment A drawn from O to P in Fig. 4(c). The directed line segment A has two essential properties:

(1) *magnitude*, as indicated by the length of the line segment;

(2) *direction*, as indicated by the angular orientation of the line and the placement of the arrowhead on a particular end of the line.

Displacement is an example of the type of physical quantity called a *vector quantity*, or simply a *vector*. A vector requires for its specification both a magnitude and a direction. The usefulness of the vector concept lies in the fact that those physical quantities that are called vectors have a common method of composition or 'addition,' which is identical with the method of addition of displacements that we shall discuss in Sec. 5.

> A **vector quantity** is one that is specified by a magnitude and a direction and that has a rule for composition identical with the rule for addition of displacements.

The following mechanical quantities, which will be defined later, are also vectors: *velocity, acceleration, momentum, force, weight, torque, angular velocity, angular acceleration.*   It is very important to become thoroughly familiar with the methods of handling vectors because of their frequent occurrence in mechanics and other parts of physics and engineering.

A quantity that has no direction associated with it and that can be completely specified by giving merely a magnitude is called a *scalar quantity* or simply a *scalar.*   Examples of scalars are energy, mass, volume, temperature, time, length of a string, and size of an angle.   A *scalar is completely specified by the statement of a numeral and a unit*—for example, a volume of *ten gallons.*   On the other hand, *a vector requires for its specification a numeral, a unit, and a direction*—for example, a displacement of *two feet eastward.*

A vector quantity is represented on a diagram by an arrow-tipped straight line segment having a length proportional to the magnitude of the vector and pointing in the proper direction.   It is convenient to call two vectors equal if they have the same magnitude and direction, regardless of where they are located on the diagram.   Thus, a displacement of 100 mi northeastward from the Chicago airport and a displacement of 100 mi northeastward from the Washington airport are represented by equal displacement vectors; one even goes so far as to say that they are represented by the *same* vector, namely, a vector 100 mi long pointing northeastward.   By this convention the three vectors in Fig. 5 are considered equal, or one can say that the three arrows represent the same vector.

A vector is usually denoted in print by boldface type.   For example, the symbol *A* denotes the displacement vector in Fig. 4(c).   A vector can be denoted conveniently in handwriting by underscoring the letter or by putting an arrow over it.

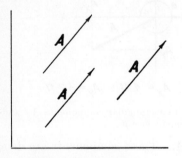
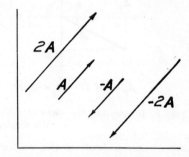

Fig. 5. Equal vectors.   **Fig. 6.** The vectors −*A*, 2*A*, −2*A*.

The *magnitude* of a vector is indicated in ordinary type; thus, *A* denotes the magnitude of the vector *A*.   The magnitude of a vector is always taken as a *positive* quantity.   Thus, if the displacement

$$A = 100 \text{ mi northeastward},$$

its magnitude $A = 100$ mi.

A negative sign before the symbol indicating a vector merely changes the sense of the direction; that is, it interchanges the head (arrow tip) and tail without changing the length or orientation of the line segment. This convention is illustrated in Fig. 6. A numerical factor before the symbol indicating a vector changes the magnitude of the vector by that factor; thus, $2A$ indicates a vector whose magnitude is twice that of A but whose direction is the same. It follows that $-2A$ indicates a vector parallel to A with the opposite sense of direction and twice the magnitude.

It is at once evident from comparison of Figs. 4(b) and 4(c) that the vector representing a displacement from O to P can be specified in terms of the polar coordinates of P relative to O. The polar coordinate r is the magnitude A of the vector A, and the angle θ defines the direction of A in the plane of the diagram.

The displacement vector A could also be specified by giving rectangular coordinates of P relative to O. In this method of specifying a vector A, the projections of the vector on the X- and Y-axes are called the

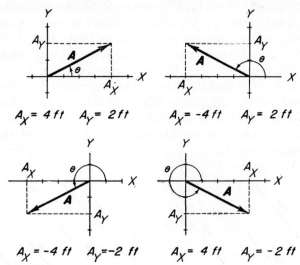

Fig. 7. Illustrating the signs attached to rectangular components A_X and A_Y of a displacement vector.

rectangular components of the vector A. These components are denoted by the symbols A_X and A_Y in Fig. 7.

> The **rectangular components** A_X and A_Y of a vector A are *scalar quantities* that specify the X- and Y-coordinates of the head of the arrow representing A when the tail is placed at the origin.

It is seen that if the angle θ is always measured counterclockwise from the $+X$-axis as in Fig. 7, the components are correctly given by the relations

$$A_X = A\ \cos\theta, \quad A_Y = A\ \sin\theta,$$

where A, the magnitude of the vector $\textbf{\textit{A}}$, is a positive number.   The components may be either positive or negative, as illustrated in Fig. 7.

The discussion above has been confined to vectors lying in a given plane.   If we desire to represent a vector pointing in any arbitrary direction in space, we choose a rectangular XYZ-coordinate system and represent the vector by three components, A_X, A_Y, and A_Z, which are its projections, taken with proper sign, on the three coordinate axes.

Example.   *Find the magnitude A and the angle θ for each vector in Fig. 7.*

In each case the magnitude

$$A = \sqrt{(4 \text{ ft})^2 + (2 \text{ ft})^2} = \sqrt{20} \text{ ft} = 4.47 \text{ ft}.$$

The *acute* angle between A and the $+$ or $-X$-axis is $\arctan(\frac{2}{4}) = \arctan 0.5 = 26\overset{\circ}{.}6$.   Placing this angle in the proper quadrant gives, in the four successive cases, $\theta = 26\overset{\circ}{.}6$; $\theta = 180° - 26\overset{\circ}{.}6 = 153\overset{\circ}{.}4$; $\theta = 180° + 26\overset{\circ}{.}6 = 206\overset{\circ}{.}6$; $\theta = 360° - 26\overset{\circ}{.}6 = 333\overset{\circ}{.}4$.

4. DISPLACEMENT

AN OBJECT is said to be *displaced*, or to undergo a *displacement*, when its position in space is changed.   The displacement of an extended object can be described by specifying the displacements of the various points of the object.   Hence this initial discussion will be confined to the description of the displacement of a point (or, as one usually says, of a *particle*, in order to imply that there is matter associated with the point).

If a man has his home in Flushing, on Long Island, and his office in Wall Street, on Manhattan Island, his task each evening is to effect a displacement of himself from office to home. In accomplishing this displacement it is immaterial, so far as net physical result is concerned, whether he

Figure 8

takes the subway, the busses, or uses his automobile.   The route he follows will be quite different in these three cases but the effect will be the same—a displacement from office to home that can be represented by the vector A in Fig. 8.

> The **displacement,** when a particle moves from point P to point Q, is measured by the length and direction of the vector whose tail is at P and whose head is at Q.   The measure of the displacement is independent of the actual path that might have been followed in the motion from P to Q.

Now let us consider how several successive displacements are combined to find the resultant displacement.   Suppose that a traveling salesman leaves home on Monday morning and visits a town to the north, ending up at a hotel 200 miles north of his home. His displacement on

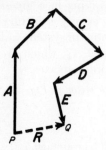

Monday is represented by *A* in Fig. 9. Tuesday he strikes off northeast and has a displacement represented by *B*. Similarly on Wednesday, Thursday, and Friday, he had displacements *C, D, E.* Having started at point *P*, he ends up at point *Q*. His *resultant* displacement from home is represented by the vector *R* connecting *P* to *Q*. The vector *R* is said to be the *resultant* or the *sum* of the vectors *A, B, C, D,* and *E.* It expresses the net displacement resulting from the several successive displacements. Mathematically, *R* is called the *sum* of the

Figure 9

vectors *A, B, C, D, E,* and written

$$R = A + B + C + D + E.$$

The **+** signs here are made heavy to indicate that this is not ordinary addition but a special kind of addition called *vector addition* that is illustrated in Fig. 9, and which we shall study in the next section.

5. ADDITION OF VECTORS

THE ADDITION OF VECTORS is the process of finding their *sum* or *resultant.* No matter whether the vectors represent displacements or any other type of vector quantity, the sum is defined just as the resultant displacement was defined in connection with Fig. 9. The rule is: to add vectors *A, B, C, D* shown at the left of Fig. 10, start at the origin and place the vectors tail to head in any order, as at the right of Fig. 10. The sum *R* is then the single vector leading from the origin to the head of the last vector in the series. That the vector *R* obtained by this procedure is independent of the *order* in which the vectors are placed tail to head will become clear from the analysis that follows.

> The **sum of several vectors** is the single vector leading from the tail of the first vector to the head of the last when the vectors are placed tail to head in any order.

The above rule is directly applicable to the graphical addition of vectors, but it may also be easily adapted to the analytical addition by expressing all vectors in terms of their components, as in the legend of Fig. 10. It is easy to show that the components of the resultant are just the sums of the components of the vectors which are added. Thus, if

$$R = A + B + C + D, \tag{1}$$

we can show that $$R_x = A_x + B_x + C_x + D_x,$$

and $$R_Y = A_Y + B_Y + C_Y + D_Y. \tag{2}$$

To prove this statement, consider the diagram at the right of Fig. 10. Since $A_x = 2$, the head of A is 2 units to the right of the Y-axis. Since $B_x = 3$, the head of B is 3 units further to the right, or $2+3=5$ units to the right of the Y-axis. Since $C_x = -4$, the head of C is back 4 units, or $2+3-4=1$ unit to the right of the Y-axis; and since $D_x = -4$, the head of D is back 4 more units, or $2+3-4-4=-3$ units to the right of the Y-axis (this means 3 units to the left). But the position of the head of D is the same as the position of the head of R, and the position of the head of R relative to the Y-axis is the X-component R_x. Hence $R_x = 2+3-4-4 = -3 = A_x+B_x+C_x+D_x$. A similar argument may be applied to the Y-component of R. Thus we see that the geometrical definition which we have given for the vector sum (1) implies the analytical relations

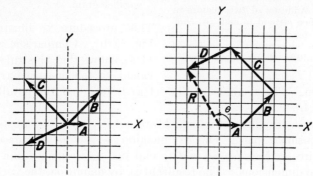

Fig. 10. Addition of vectors

$A_x =$ 2	$A_Y =$ 0	$\tan\theta = R_Y/R_X = -5/3$
$B_x =$ 3	$B_Y =$ 3	$\theta = 121°0$
$C_x = -4$	$C_Y =$ 4	
$D_x = -4$	$D_Y = -2$	$R = R_Y/\sin\theta = 5/0.857$
$R_x = -3$	$R_Y =$ 5	$R = 5.83.$

(2) between the components. In most cases we shall wish to use analytical rather than graphical methods for the addition of vectors, employing the rules contained in the equations (2):

The X-component of the sum of a number of vectors is the sum of the X-components of the vectors.

The Y-component of the sum of a number of vectors is the sum of the Y-components of the vectors.

After we have found the components R_X and R_Y, we can find the magnitude R and direction θ from simple trigonometry. A convenient procedure is first to compute the angle θ from

$$\theta = \arctan(R_Y/R_X) \tag{3}$$

and then the magnitude from either

$$R = R_Y/\sin\theta \quad \text{or} \quad R = R_X/\cos\theta. \tag{4}$$

The proper quadrant in which to put the angle may be determined from a rough sketch showing R_X, R_Y, **R**.   The magnitude R may also be determined directly from the Pythagorean relation

$$R = \sqrt{R_X^2 + R_Y^2}. \qquad (5)$$

For the addition of just two vectors, the following rule is frequently given:

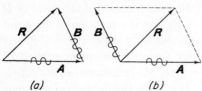

(a)   (b)

Fig. 11. Addition of two vectors by (a) laying then off end to end, (b) completing the parallelogram. The vectors **A** and **B** are 'crossed out' to emphasize that the resultant **R** completely *replaces* them.

Lay off the vectors from a common origin and complete the parallelogram.   The resultant is the directed diagonal from the origin to the opposite corner of the parallelogram.

This procedure is illustrated in Fig. 11(b).   Comparison with Fig. 11(a) shows that this rule is equivalent to the one we have previously given.   The triangle in Fig. 11(a) is just half the parallelogram of Fig. 11(b).

If we wish to add vectors which are not coplanar, we must work in three-dimensional space.   One can imagine the vectors as represented by straight wires or rods placed end to end just as we placed our directed lines in two dimensions.   The resultant is, by definition, the vector leading directly from the tail of the first vector to the head of the last.

6. RESOLUTION OF A VECTOR

THE PROCESS of resolution of a vector is the inverse of the process of vector addition in that it *replaces* a vector by two or more vectors which

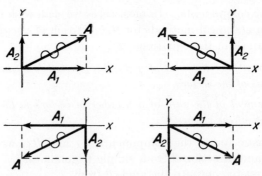

Fig. 12. Resolution of a vector into two rectangular component vectors.

have the given vector as their resultant.   The most useful type of resolution is that in which the vector is replaced by its vector projections on a set of mutually perpendicular axes.   If attention is confined to a plane we use two such axes, but if we are working in three dimensions we must use three.   These vector projections are known as *rectangular component vectors*.   Figure 12 shows a vector A resolved in two dimensions into two component vectors A_1 and A_2.

It must be emphasized that the component vectors can be used on a diagram only to *replace* the original vector, *not to supplement it*.   For this reason the original vector is shown crossed out in Fig. 12 after it has been replaced by two component vectors.

These *component vectors* are related to, but must be distinguished from the *components* previously introduced.   The components are scalar quantities.

> The **rectangular component vectors** A_1 and A_2 (see Fig. 12) are two *vectors* lying along the X- and Y-axes whose sum is A and which can together replace A.

7. FORCES

THE WORD *force* is popularly used to denote an influence that tends to produce a change in the present state of affairs.   For example, the force of public opinion tends to produce a change in the behavior of individuals. The word *force* is used in physical science and engineering with a restricted technical meaning to denote an explicitly definable vector quantity that tends to produce a change in the motion of objects.   We shall use the word *force* with this restricted meaning.

Our simplest intuitive idea of a force as a push or pull resulting from muscular exertion comes from the experience that it is necessary to push or pull on an object to change its motion.   For example, it is necessary to push or pull backward or forward on a moving object to slow it down or speed it up, and to push or pull sidewise on it to change its direction of motion.   For the present we can think of a force simply as a push or pull exerted in a particular direction by one object on another.   Force will later be precisely defined in terms of its effect on motion.

Familiar origins of forces include, in addition to muscular exertions of organisms, (a) gravitation, (b) friction, (c) elasticity, (d) electricity, and (e) magnetism.   The first three of these types of forces are treated in the branch of physics called mechanics.

It is well known from experience that the application of a force to a body does not always result in a change in its motion.   For example, the body may be fastened so that it cannot move, but an applied force can still produce an effect on the body.   The common effects which result from the application of a force to an object include (a) the balancing or counteracting of another force which is acting on the body, (b) a change in the motion of the body, and (c) a change in the size or shape of the body.   One or more of these effects is always produced when forces are applied to objects.   The balancing of forces is treated in that branch of mechanics called *statics*. The effects of forces on motions form the subject matter of *dynamics*. The effects of force on the shape and size of objects form the basis of the study of *elasticity*.

8. MEASUREMENT OF FORCE

A MEASURING INSTRUMENT for the quantitative comparison of magnitudes of forces could, in principle, be based on any one of the effects produced by forces. A familiar instrument for measuring forces is the spring balance, which consists (see Fig. 13) of a coil spring with one end

attached to a rigid case and the other end free to move a pointer along a scale on the case. The spring changes in length when a stretching force is applied to its free end but returns to its original length when the force is no longer applied. A force of given magnitude always produces the same displacement of the free end of the spring. A larger force produces a larger displacement of the free end of the spring, a smaller force a smaller displacement.

A spring balance or other device for measuring forces must be calibrated by means of a reproducible force such as the gravitational pull of the earth on a certain object at a specified location.

> The **weight** of an object is the force with which the object is pulled vertically downward toward the earth (the *force of gravity*).

Weight is an ever-present force on all objects near the earth.

> The **vertical** is defined as the direction of the force of gravity; the **horizontal** is the plane normal (i.e. perpendicular) to the vertical.

weight

Fig. 13. Spring balance (schematic) used to determine the weight of an object.

The unit of force in use in engineering practice is the *pound* (lb). The *ounce* (oz) is $\frac{1}{16}$ lb; the *ton* is 2000 lb. These so-called British gravitational units are the only ones we shall introduce until we define, in Chap. 4, the metric units that are used in most scientific practice.

While the pound is legally defined in the United States in terms of the metric units of force (just as the foot is legally defined in terms of the meter), we can for our present purposes use its original definition as the weight at a specified location of a standard cylinder of platinum kept at the Standards Office, Westminster, London. We can imagine duplicating or dividing this cylinder and hence calibrating a spring balance at the

1-lb, 2-lb, $\cdots$ points and the fractional-pound points. This operational definition of force, which specifies its method of measurement, will serve us until we study the effect of force on motion.

It is necessary to specify a standard location in defining the unit force in this manner because the weight of a given object near the earth varies somewhat with altitude and latitude. The *pound* is called a *gravitational unit* because it is defined in terms of the earth's gravitational pull on a standard sample of matter at a specified location on the earth's surface. We adopt the following tentative definition, to be corrected later to agree with the legal definition:

> The **pound** is the weight of a certain standard platinum cylinder at 45° latitude and sea level.

9. TREATMENT OF FORCES AS VECTORS

IN A TUG OF WAR it is important that each contestant not only pull with all his might on the rope but that he pull in the proper direction to

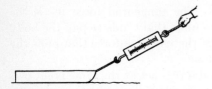

Fig. 14. A sled is pulled by a rope. The force is measured by the spring balance.

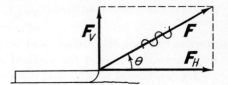

Fig. 15. Resolution of the force on the sled into horizontal and vertical component forces.

aid his own team. This example of applied forces emphasizes the fact that the effect produced by a force depends on both its magnitude and its direction. In the analysis of the effects produced by forces it is always necessary to specify both the magnitude and the direction of each force. A force is a vector quantity, and experiment demonstrates that the methods of handling vectors discussed earlier are applicable to it.

A force vector is denoted in print by F, w, or some other suitable letter in boldface type, and it is represented on a diagram by an arrow whose length is proportional to the magnitude of the force and whose direction corresponds to that of the force.

The resolution of a force vector into rectangular component vectors is illustrated in Figs. 14, 15, and 16. It must be emphasized again that the component forces can be used only to take the place of the original force, not to supplement it. For this reason the original force vector is shown crossed out in these figures in favor of the two mutually perpendicular forces that replace it. The meaning of these component forces is easy to understand in a specific example such as that in which a sled is pulled along the ground. The horizontal force F_H in Fig. 15 is the effective force pulling the sled along the ground, and the vertical force F_V is the effective force tending to lift the sled off the ground.   The resolution of a force into rectangular component forces in the above manner is very useful when the two mutually perpendicular forces can be treated independently of each other so far as their physical effects are concerned.

The weight of an object is a force w directed vertically downward.

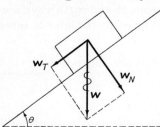

It is frequently useful, in analyzing the effect of a body's weight on its motion along an inclined plane, to resolve w into component vectors in directions parallel and normal to the inclined plane, as in Fig. 16.   The magnitude of the tangential force is $w_T = w \sin\theta$ and that of the normal force is $w_N = w \cos\theta$ if θ is the angle between the inclined plane and the horizontal and w is the magnitude of the weight.   The tangential force w_T is the effective force that tends to pull the body

Fig. 16. Resolution of a vertical force into component forces parallel and normal to an inclined plane.

downward along the incline, and w_N is the effective force that pulls the body normally against the inclined plane.

By *experiment* we find that if several forces act at the same point of a body, as in Fig. 17(a), their net effect is in all respects identical with the

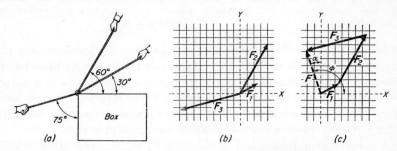

Fig. 17. Three men pull on three ropes attached to the corner of a box. In (b) and (c) the grid spacing represents 1 lb.

effect of a single force that is their vector sum determined by the same method as in the case of displacement vectors.   Thus if the three forces of Fig. 17 have the magnitudes represented in (b), they are equivalent to the single force F of (c).

> Forces acting on the same point of a body are called **concurrent forces.**

Concurrent forces are added by the rules for vector addition in Sec. 5.

Example. *Find the single force* **F** *that is equivalent to the three forces* **F₁**, **F₂**, **F₃** *in Fig. 17, when they act simultaneously at the same point of a body.* **F₁** *has magnitude 3 lb at an angle of 30° with the X-axis;* **F₂**, *8 lb at an angle of 60°;* **F₃**, *9 lb at an angle of 195°.*

The components are

$$F_{1X} = (3 \text{ lb})(\cos 30°) = (3 \text{ lb})(0.866) = 2.60 \text{ lb},$$
$$F_{1Y} = (3 \text{ lb})(\sin 30°) = (3 \text{ lb})(0.500) = 1.50 \text{ lb},$$
$$F_{2X} = (8 \text{ lb})(\cos 60°) = (8 \text{ lb})(0.500) = 4.00 \text{ lb},$$
$$F_{2Y} = (8 \text{ lb})(\sin 60°) = (8 \text{ lb})(0.866) = 6.93 \text{ lb},$$
$$F_{3X} = (9 \text{ lb})(\cos 195°) = (9 \text{ lb})(-0.966) = -8.69 \text{ lb},$$
$$F_{3Y} = (9 \text{ lb})(\sin 195°) = (9 \text{ lb})(-0.259) = -2.33 \text{ lb}.$$

The resultant has components

$$F_X = F_{1X} + F_{2X} + F_{3X} = (2.60 + 4.00 - 8.69) \text{ lb} = -2.09 \text{ lb},$$
$$F_Y = F_{1Y} + F_{2Y} + F_{3Y} = (1.50 + 6.93 - 2.33) \text{ lb} = 6.10 \text{ lb}.$$

Hence

$$\alpha = \arctan(2.09 \text{ lb}/6.10 \text{ lb}) = \arctan 0.343 = 18°.9,$$
$$\phi = 90° + 18°.9 = 108°.9,$$
$$F = 6.10 \text{ lb}/\cos 18°.9 = 6.10 \text{ lb}/0.946 = 6.45 \text{ lb}.$$

The resultant force has a magnitude of 6.45 lb at an angle of 108°.9 with the positive X-axis. The student should check that he obtains the same value of F by using Pythagoras' relation (5).

10. TORQUE ABOUT AN AXIS

IN THE CASE of forces, the point of application of the force, as well as the magnitude and direction of the force vector, has a significant influence on the effect of the force. It is common experience that the effectiveness of a force in changing the rotational motion of an object such as a door depends not only on the magnitude and direction of the force but also on the distance of its line of action from the axis of rotation. A child learns by experiment that he can open a door most readily if he pushes perpendicularly against its surface at a point as far as possible from the hinged edge. The force required to open the door is larger if he pushes on it closer to its hinged edge or along a line making an angle of less than 90° with its surface. He also learns that no rotation around the hinged edge can be produced by a force whose line of action passes through that edge (pushing on the wrong edge of a door). Experience shows that a force is most effective in producing rotation around an axis if its line of action is perpendicular to that axis and if the distance from the axis to its line of action is as large as possible.

The results of all experiments show that only the projection of a force on a plane perpendicular to an axis of rotation can be effective in changing rotational motion around that axis; a force component parallel to the axis has no effect. For example, if a man pulls with a force **F** on a string attached to a doorknob in such a way that the string makes an angle θ

with the horizontal plane through the knob, then only the horizontal projection of F, of magnitude $F \cos\theta$, can be effective in turning the door around its hinged edge.   The vertical component, which tends to *lift* the door, has no effect on its rotation.   Hence *in our study of the effect of a force on rotation about an axis, we can assume that the force is applied in a plane perpendicular to the axis of rotation.   If the force is not so applied, only the component force in such a plane need be considered.*

We now consider the relation between the effectiveness of a force in producing rotation and the distance of its line of action from the axis of rotation.   It is convenient for this purpose to define a quantity called the *lever arm:*

> The **lever arm** of a force is the perpendicular distance from the axis of rotation to the line of action of the component force in a plane perpendicular to the axis of rotation.

The distances l_1, l_2, l_3 shown in Fig. 18 are, respectively, the lever arms of forces F_1, F_2, F_3 applied to the hinged bar, where the axis of rotation of the bar is the horizontal line through its hinge and the forces act in a vertical plane.   It is important to note that the lever arm is a purely geometrical distance and is not necessarily equal to the dimension of a part of the object.

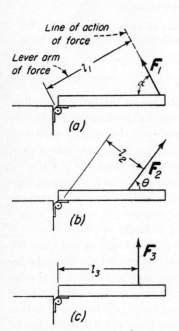

Many simple experiments can be devised to test the effectiveness of forces in producing changes of rotational motion. The hinged horizontal bar shown in Fig. 18 forms the basis of such an experiment. The force F applied to the bar in the vertical plane tends to turn the bar counterclockwise around a horizontal axis through the hinge. The force of gravity tends to turn the bar clockwise. The magnitude of F required to keep the bar from falling downward under the influence of gravity is measured for different points of application and different directions of the line of action of the force. If l denotes the perpendicular distance from the axis of rotation to the line along which F acts, it is found that the product Fl is a constant for the different cases shown in Fig. 18.   These results show that *the effectiveness of a force in producing rotation around an axis depends on the product of the magnitude of the force and the length of its lever arm.*

Fig. 18. Showing the line of action and the lever arm for several forces.

The tendency of a force F to produce change of rotational motion around an axis is measured by the resulting torque around that axis.

> The **torque** about a given axis is the product of the magnitude of the force by the lever arm of the force. This product is called the *torque resulting from the force,* or the **moment** *of the force.*

Torque is usually denoted by the letter L, thus

$$L = Fl.$$

This definition implies that a force of 10 lb with a lever arm of 2 ft will have the same tendency to change the rotation of a given object as a force of 4 lb with a lever arm of 5 ft. This definition fits the results of all experiments, such as the one shown in Fig. 18, on the effects of forces on rotation around a fixed axis.

Torques are measured in units of *force × length.* For example, a force of 10 lb applied with a lever arm of 2 ft produces a torque whose magnitude is $10 \text{ lb} \times 2 \text{ ft} = 20 \text{ lb·ft}$. Other units of torque commonly used include the pound·inch (lb·in) and the ounce·inch (oz·in).

A torque (moment of a force) is classified as *clockwise* if it tends to produce clockwise rotation or as *counterclockwise* if it tends to produce counterclockwise rotation. These designations will be useful in the next chapter, where equilibrium of forces and torques are considered. Thus, in Fig. 18(b), if $F_2 = 2.5$ lb and $l_2 = 0.6$ ft, the force F_2 exerts a *counterclockwise* torque of 1.5 lb·ft. If several forces act on a body and produce torques about an axis, the *net* or *resultant* counterclockwise torque is defined as the algebraic sum of the several torques, treating counterclockwise torques as positive, clockwise torques as negative. It is a matter of experiment that the effectiveness of a number of forces in producing rotation about an axis *depends only on the resultant torque.* Thus two different sets of forces and lever arms that give the same resultant torque will have identical rotational effects.

Since a force F, as in Fig. 19, is completely equivalent to the two component forces F_V and F_H, we can compute the moment of F by computing the resultant moment of F_V and F_H. The latter is simpler to do geometrically because the lever arms a and b are known, whereas l is somewhat complicated to calculate.

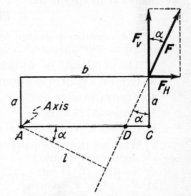

Fig. 19. The lever arm of F is l, the lever arm of F_v is b, that of F_h is a.

The counterclockwise moment of F about the indicated axis in Fig. 19 is Fl; that of F_V is $F_V b = (F \cos\alpha)b$; that of F_H is $-F_H a = -(F \sin\alpha)a$, negative because actually clockwise.

The moment of F equals the resultant moment of F_V and F_H, that is

$$Fl = F_V b - F_H a. \tag{6}$$

It is much simpler to compute the right side of (6) than the left.

In the discussion above, we have not referred to torque as a vector, although we have seen that torque is not really a scalar because we must specify whether it is clockwise or counterclockwise. Torque actually has the properties of a vector. In the case of torque about an axis, this vector is drawn along the axis in the sense shown in Fig. 20. In discussing the rotational motion of bodies that do not have a fixed axis, such as tops, gyroscopes, or airplanes, we need a more general definition of torque,

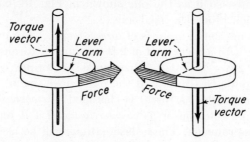

Fig. 20. Sense of the torque vector as given by the right-hand rule: *If one encircles the axis with the fingers of the right hand to indicate the direction of the tendency to rotate, the thumb points along the axis in the direction of the torque vector.*

namely, *torque about a point*, such as the point of the top. We shall return to this point in Chap. 10.

PROBLEMS*

1. The angstrom is defined by 1 angstrom $= 10^{-8}$ cm. If yellow light has a wavelength of 5900 angstroms, express its wavelength in mμ.   Ans: 590 mμ.

2. The wavelength of red light is 640 mμ. Express this in inches.

3. Express 5 ft 10 in in meters.   Ans: 1.78 m

4. Express 50 mi in km.

5. Express $17°3$ in rad.   Ans: 0.302 rad.

6. Express 0.45 rad in degrees.

7. What are the plane polar coordinates r and θ of a point having the following rectangular coordinates?
  (a) $X = 3$ cm, $Y = 4$ cm;   Ans: (a) 5 cm, $53°1$;
  (b) $X = -1$ m, $Y = 6$ m;
  (c) $X = 10$ ft, $Y = -3$ ft;   (c) 10.44 ft, $343°3$.
  (d) $X = -4$ in, $Y = -4$ in.

8. What are the rectangular coordinates of a point having the following plane polar coordinates?
  (a) $r = 5$ m, $\theta = 60°$;   Ans: (a) $X = 2.50$ m, $Y = 4.33$ m;
  (b) $r = 16$ m, $\theta = 72°$;
  (c) $r = 7$ ft, $\theta = 195°$;   (c) $X = -6.76$ ft, $Y = -1.81$ ft.
  (d) $r = 4$ ft, $\theta = 300°$

---

*The numerical data given in the problems in this book should be regarded as precise to three or four figures. All answers should be given to three figures; i.e., to "slide-rule accuracy."

9. A displacement vector A has magnitude 6 ft and makes an angle of 150° with the X-axis. Find its rectangular components.

Ans: $A_X = -5.20$ ft, $A_Y = 3.00$ ft.

10. A displacement vector B has magnitude 11 m and makes an angle of 240° with the X-axis. Find its rectangular components.

11. A displacement vector has components $C_X = 4$ m, $C_Y = -7$ m. Find the magnitude and direction of the vector.   Ans: $C = 8.06$ m, $\theta = 299°.7$.

12. A displacement vector has components $D_X = -4$ ft, $D_Y = -2$ ft. Find the magnitude and direction of the vector.

13. What are the magnitudes and directions of the two rectangular component vectors A_1 and A_2 that can be used to replace the vector A of Prob. 9?

14. Find the resultant of a displacement of 50 ft at an angle of 0° with the X-axis, one of 100 ft at an angle of 120°, and one of 120 ft at an angle of 315°.

15. Add the following vectors: 1 ft E, 2 ft NE, 3 ft N, 4 ft NW, 5 ft W, 6 ft SW, 7 ft S, and 8 ft SE.   Ans: 10.5 ft, 22°.5 west of south.

16. Add the following displacement vectors: 1 m N, 2 m W, 3 m S, 4 m E, 5 m NE, 6 m NW, 7 m SW, and 8 m SE.

17. Find the resultant R of five displacements having the following magnitudes and making the following angles, measured counterclockwise from the horizontal X-axis: A, 74 m, 350°; B, 30 m, 80°; C, 29 m, 170°; D, 63 m, 90°; E, 15 m, 180°.   Ans: 91.5 m, 67°.8.

18. A mark is put on the uppermost portion of the rim of a wheel of 2-ft radius, mounted on a fixed horizontal axle. What is the displacement of this mark when the wheel turns clockwise through ¼ rev? When it subsequently turns through ½ rev? Then when it makes 1 more whole revolution? What is the sum of these three displacements? Draw a diagram showing the three displacement vectors and their sum.

19. What is the displacement of the point of a wheel initially in contact with the ground when the wheel *rolls* forward ½ rev? Take the radius of the wheel as R and the X-axis in the forward direction.   Ans: 3.72 R at 32°.5 with the X-axis.

20. What would be the resultant of three forces, such as those in Fig. 21, if $F_1 = 4$ lb, $F_2 = 2$ lb, $F_2 = 3$ lb, and $\theta_1 = 25°$, $\theta_2 = 65°$, $\theta_3 = 140°$?

21. Find the resultant of the three forces F_1, F_2, F_3 of Fig. 21 if they have magnitudes of 37 lb, 25 lb, and 30 lb, respectively, and make angles of 30°, 60°, and 135° with the horizontal X-axis.   Ans: 65.6 lb, 69°.2.

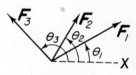

Figure 21

22. Add the forces of Prob. 21 graphically, using a protractor and a ruler.

23. In Fig. 18(a), if $F_1 = 32$ lb and $l_1 = 50$ in, what is the torque resulting from F_1, in lb·in?   Ans: 1600 lb·in counterclockwise.

24. In Fig. 18(c), if $F_3 = 1$ lb and $l_3 = 9$ in, what is the moment of F_3 in oz·in?

25. In Fig. 18(a), if the angle α is 60°, and the force vector has magnitude 16 lb, with its point of application 0.5 ft above and 2.5 ft to the right of the axis, find the torque.   Ans: 38.6 lb·ft counterclockwise.

26. In Fig. 18(b), if the force vector has magnitude 6 lb with $\theta = 50°$ and if its point of application lies 0.2 ft above and 0.7 ft to the right of the axis, find the torque.

27. By expressing l in terms of a, b, and α, verify the geometrical correctness of equation (6).

28. In Fig. 19, if $a = 1.6$ ft, $b = 3.2$ ft, $F = 40$ lb, and $\alpha = 20°$, find l and the torque Fl.   Find the same torque by adding the moments of F_V and F_H.

29. In Fig. 17, Chap. 2 (p. 44), let $F_1 - 6$ lb, $F_2 = 4$ lb, $F_3 = 7$ lb, $F_4 = 10$ lb, $l_2 = 3$ ft, $l_3 = 7$ ft, $l_4 = 10$ ft, $\theta_1 = 60°$, $\theta_4 = 40°$.   Find the resultant torque of these four forces about the point of application of F_1.   Ans: 3.28 lb·ft counterclockwise.

30. In Prob. 29, find the resultant torque of the four forces about the point of application of F_4.

CHAPTER 2

STATICS

Statics is the branch of mechanics that deals with the balance or equilibrium of forces on an object that remains at rest or in a state of uniform motion.

The principles of statics form the basis of much of the work of mechanical, civil, and architectural engineers engaged in machine, structure, and building design. These principles apply to cases in which forces act on a body in translational and rotational equilibrium. Such cases include not only truly static cases but also cases of translation with constant velocity and of rotation with constant angular velocity. In this chapter we shall state the principles of statics, learn to apply the equilibrium conditions, define the center of gravity of a body, and study the laws governing the forces of friction between the surfaces of solids in contact.

1. ACTION AND REACTION; NEWTON'S THIRD PRINCIPLE

WHEN TWO bodies A and B are in mechanical contact, in general they exert forces *on each other* across the region of contact. It is a fundamental principle that forces the two bodies exert on each other are always equal and opposite. That is, if the force exerted *by A on B* is represented by a certain vector, the force exerted *by B on A* will be represented by the negative of this vector—a vector of equal magnitude but oppositely directed. This statement is succinctly summarized in the third of Newton's three principles of mechanics:

NEWTON'S THIRD PRINCIPLE: *Action equals reaction.*

Newton called the force exerted by A on B the *action*, and the *oppositely directed* force exerted by B on A the *reaction*. In the statement above, it must be remembered that *action and reaction are oppositely directed forces exerted by two different bodies on each other*, and that in no case is it of importance which of the equal and opposite forces is considered the action and which the reaction.

The above principle holds rigorously no matter what the state of motion of the bodies may be. Various cases are illustrated in Fig. 1. This principle also holds in cases of action at a distance such as occur with gravitational, electrical, and magnetic forces. Thus, the earth exerts a downward gravitational force on any object near its surface, for example on a flying airplane. The airplane exerts an equal and opposite upward force on the earth. Although the force of the earth on the plane is of great practical importance, that of the plane on the earth is of no detectable importance in connection with the motion of the earth. The gravitational pull of the earth on the moon keeps the moon revolving around the earth just as the pull of the sun keeps the earth revolving around the sun. In the case of the earth-moon system, the reaction force exerted

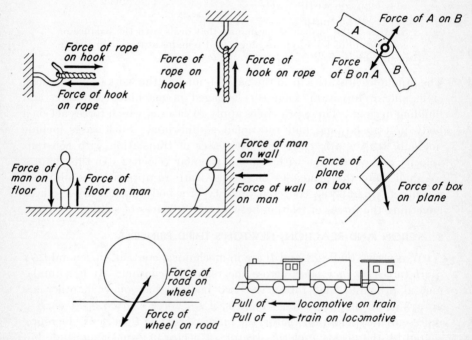

Fig. 1. Action equals reaction.

by the moon does introduce a detectable wobble into the earth's regular motion around the sun, and the gravitational pull of the moon on the waters of the earth is the principal tide-producing force.

2. NEWTON'S FIRST PRINCIPLE

BEFORE THE days of Newton it was frequently assumed that the 'natural' state of a body was one of rest and that forces or torques were required to keep the body in motion, because it was noted that all terrestrial objects come to rest when they are left alone. A box sliding on a horizontal plane or a wheel rotating on a shaft come more or less rapidly to rest. But are these objects free from forces or torques? There is a frictional force between the box and the plane acting in a direction to oppose the motion of the box, and a frictional torque in the bearings of the wheel acting in a direction to oppose the rotation of the wheel.   If efforts are made to decrease this friction—for example by lubrication, by equipping the box with steel runners and making the plane out of ice, or by using ball bearings—the state of rest is achieved much less rapidly. In order to stop an automobile more rapidly than the ordinary frictional forces would stop it, we have to apply a braking torque to the wheels, just as we have to apply engine torque to speed it up.   The braking torque is an additional retarding frictional torque.

The conclusion we draw from experience, as indicated in the discussion above, is that the 'natural' state of a body is one of *uniform motion*.   By the term *uniform motion* we mean, in the case of a particle, motion along a straight line at constant speed; in the case of a wheel mounted on a fixed axle, motion of rotation at constant angular speed (in rev/min, for example).   In the case of a ball or other object rotating about an axis of symmetry, uniform motion represents a combination of motion along a straight line at constant speed (called *uniform translational motion*) and rotation about an axis of fixed direction at constant angular speed (*uniform rotational motion*).   The 'natural' state of a free body rotating about an axis that is not an axis of symmetry is found to be somewhat more complicated; discussion of the 'natural' motion in this case will be left for more advanced treatments of mechanics.   An important special case of a state of uniform motion is the *state of rest* (no motion).

NEWTON'S FIRST PRINCIPLE: *Every body will remain in a state of uniform motion unless acted on by external forces.*

The natural tendency to remain in a state of uniform motion was termed *inertia* by Newton, and the principle we have just stated was called by Newton the *law of inertia*.   By 'external' forces, this principle refers to forces exerted by some *other* body, whether these forces arise from *contact* with the other body (pushes, pulls, friction, air and water resistance, and the like) or are of gravitational, electrical, or magnetic nature.

According to this principle, if we were to throw a ball from a rocket ship in free space where there is no air and no appreciable gravitational pull, the ball would go on indefinitely with the same translational speed along a straight line and the same rotational speed about the same axis through the center of the ball that it had when it left our hand.

It is the *resultant* force and the *resultant* torque acting on a body that determine the change in its state of motion.   As illustrated in Fig. 2, we can keep a box sliding over a horizontal plane at constant speed if we pull forward with just enough force to balance the backward dragging force of friction.   If we pull forward with more force than this, the speed increases; if we pull with less force, the speed decreases.   We can keep a wheel rotating at constant rotational speed about a fixed axis by applying just enough torque to balance the retarding frictional torque in the bearings; more torque will increase the rotational speed; less will permit the wheel to slow down. The principle that gives the rate of change of speed when a resultant force or torque acts on an object (Newton's *second* principle) will be studied in later chapters under the heading of dynamics. In this chapter we shall study cases in which the resultant

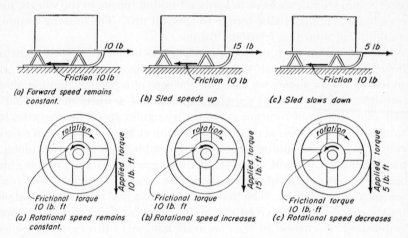

Fig. 2. A sled moving forward and a wheel rotating clockwise with (a) zero resultant force or torque; (b) and (c) non-zero resultant force or torque.

force and torque acting on a body are both *zero*, in which case the body is said to be *in equilibrium* under the system of applied forces.

3. EQUILIBRIUM CONDITIONS

THE CONDITIONS for a body to remain in a state of uniform motion (or of rest) are known as the *equilibrium conditions*. The condition for *translational* equilibrium ensures that the body will have no tendency to change its translational speed or direction of motion:

CONDITION FOR TRANSLATIONAL EQUILIBRIUM: *The vector sum of all the forces acting on the body must be zero.*

This condition applies whether or not the forces acting on the body are concurrent. The vector sum, as defined on p. 10, of *all* the force vectors must be zero (a vector of zero magnitude).

The condition for *rotational* equilibrium ensures that the body will have no tendency to change its state of rotational motion and hence no tendency to change its rotational speed:

CONDITION FOR ROTATIONAL EQUILIBRIUM: *The resultant torque acting on the body must be zero.*

In applying the equilibrium conditions, note these three requirements:

(1) Select a definite well-defined body to which the conditions are to be applied.

(2) Be sure to include in the system of forces all the forces acting on the selected body. These will be the forces exerted by all other bodies that touch the selected body, the force of gravity, and possibly electric or magnetic forces.

(3) Be sure *not* to include in your force system any forces that are acting on bodies other than the selected body. In particular do not include forces exerted by the selected body on other bodies—include only forces exerted by other bodies on the selected body.

Although in this chapter the 'body' to which we apply the equilibrium conditions will usually be a rigid solid body, it is not necessary that the body be of this nature. Later we shall apply the equilibrium conditions to a quantity of fluid (liquid or gas). It is only necessary that the 'body' be a well-defined quantity of matter.

In this chapter we shall, for simplicity, confine our attention to cases in which all the force vectors can be drawn in the same plane (the forces have X- and Y-, but no Z-components) and hence all the torques can be considered as clockwise or counterclockwise about an axis perpendicular to that plane. The condition for translational equilibrium is usually most simply applied if we replace each force by its horizontal and vertical component forces. Then the condition that the vector sum of the forces have zero horizontal component is expressed by

$$\begin{Bmatrix} \text{the sum of the magnitudes} \\ \text{of the component forces} \\ \text{acting to the right} \end{Bmatrix} = \begin{Bmatrix} \text{the sum of the magnitudes} \\ \text{of the component forces} \\ \text{acting to the left} \end{Bmatrix} ; \qquad (1)$$

and the condition that this vector sum have zero vertical component by

$$\begin{Bmatrix} \text{the sum of the magnitudes} \\ \text{of the component forces} \\ \text{acting vertically upward} \end{Bmatrix} = \begin{Bmatrix} \text{the sum of the magnitudes} \\ \text{of the component forces} \\ \text{acting vertically downward} \end{Bmatrix} \cdot \qquad (2)$$

Similarly the condition for rotational equilibrium can be written as

$$\begin{Bmatrix} \text{the sum of the clockwise} \\ \text{torques about any axis} \end{Bmatrix} = \begin{Bmatrix} \text{the sum of the counterclockwise} \\ \text{torques about the same axis} \end{Bmatrix} \cdot \qquad (3)$$

These conditions will now be illustrated by application to problems of various types. It is noted that sometimes it is convenient to take rectangular axes that are not horizontal and vertical, but, for example, parallel and perpendicular to an inclined plane; in such cases (1) and (2) undergo obvious modifications.

4. EQUILIBRIUM OF FORCES ACTING ON A PARTICLE

By *particle* we mean a body of negligible size, so that all forces acting on it can be considered as applied at the same point; that is, as *concurrent*.

In the case of a particle, rotational equilibrium does not need to be considered, because all the forces can be considered to have zero lever arm about the center of the particle and hence to exert no torque. One type of 'particle' for which we shall consider the equilibrium of concurrent forces is a knot such as the knot in the strings of Fig. 3 or the knot in the center of a tug-of-war rope.

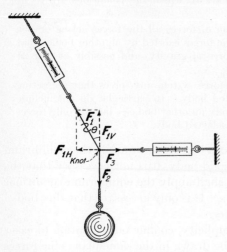

In the case of the tug of war, if the opposing teams exert equal but oppositely directed forces on their respective ends of the rope, the knot is in equilibrium and remains at rest. The knot would still be in equilibrium if the opposing teams were pulling with equal but opposite forces while riding on a steadily moving rail-

Fig. 3. A knot in equilibrium under the action of three concurrent forces.

road flatcar. In this case the knot would not be at rest but would have no tendency to change its state of uniform motion.

Example. *In the system of Fig. 3 determine the forces F_1 and F_3 in terms of the weight w of the suspended sphere and the angle θ.*

At the knot there are three strings. The vertical string pulls down on the knot with a force F_2 equal to the weight w of the suspended sphere.* The other two strings pull on the knot with forces that can be read on the spring balances. If we resolve F_1 into vertical and horizontal component forces F_{1V} and F_{1H}, equation (1) states that

$$F_3 = F_{1H}, \tag{i}$$

while equation (2) gives

$$F_{1V} = F_2. \tag{ii}$$

Since $F_{1V} = F_1 \cos\theta$, equation (ii) becomes $F_1 \cos\theta = F_2$, or

$$F_1 = F_2/\cos\theta = w/\cos\theta. \tag{iii}$$

Since $F_{1H} = F_1 \sin\theta$, equation (i) becomes $F_3 = F_1 \sin\theta$. Substitution of (iii) in this equation gives

---

* It is instructive to consider in detail the arguments involved in drawing the conclusion that the force F_2 which the vertical string exerts on the knot has the same magnitude as the weight (say w) of the sphere. By definition, the weight is the force of gravity on the sphere; therefore *gravity pulls down on the sphere with force w.* The sphere is in equilibrium; therefore *the string must pull up on the sphere with force w.* By Newton's third law (action equals reaction), *the sphere pulls down on the string with force w.* But the vertical string is in equilibrium, and so *the knot must pull up on this string with force w.* Finally, again by Newton's third law, *the string pulls down on the knot with force w.* These five steps are involved in the logical justification of the intuitive conclusion that $F_2 = w$.

$$F_3 = \frac{F_2}{\cos\theta}\sin\theta = F_2\tan\theta = w\tan\theta. \qquad \text{(iv)}$$

Equations (iii) and (iv) determine F_1 and F_3 in terms of w and θ.

Example. *If, in Fig. 3, $F_2 = 2.5$ lb and $F_3 = 1.5$ lb, determine F_1 and θ.*
From (i) and (ii),

$$F_{1H} = F_3 = 1.5\text{ lb}, \quad F_{1V} = F_2 = 2.5\text{ lb}.$$

Then $\theta = \arctan(F_{1H}/F_{1V}) = \arctan(1.5/2.5) = \arctan 0.6 = 31°0$

and $F_1 = F_{1H}/\sin\theta = 1.5/0.515 = 2.91$ lb.

In a manner similar to that used in these examples, the equations expressing the conditions for equilibrium can be written for any number of strings coming together at a knot or at a small ring.

5. EQUILIBRIUM OF COPLANAR FORCES ACTING ON A BODY WHOSE WEIGHT CAN BE NEGLECTED

ALTHOUGH WEIGHT is an ever-present force, in some cases the weight of a rigid body may be very small compared to the other forces that act on the body and hence negligible to a certain approximation. Such is the case in Fig. 4, where a light, stiff stick suspended by vertical strings at its ends carries a heavy weight exerting a force F.

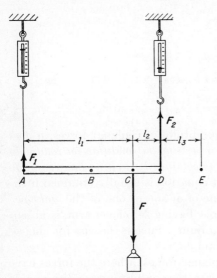

Considering the stick of Fig. 4 as the body for which we are going to write the equilibrium conditions, we see that there are no horizontal force components. Hence the condition for translational equilibrium reduces to

sum of upward forces
= sum of downward forces

$$F_1 + F_2 = F. \qquad \text{(4)}$$

The force F is assumed known, and we want to find F_1 and F_2. Equation (4) determines the sum of F_1 and F_2, but we need another equation to determine these two forces

Fig. 4. A light stick supporting a heavy weight.

individually. The second equation is determined by writing the condition for rotational equilibrium about any axis. Which axis we use is immaterial; no rotation about any particular axis implies no rotation about any axis whatsoever. We could equally well use an axis through A, B, C, D, or E, or through any point whatsoever on the page—on, beside, above, or below the bar. That an axis such as E is not on the bar does not matter—the bar could rotate about an axis at E and does not.

Using axis A, we have

$$\begin{Bmatrix} \text{sum of clockwise} \\ \text{torques about } A \end{Bmatrix} = \begin{Bmatrix} \text{sum of counterclockwise} \\ \text{torques about } A \end{Bmatrix}$$

$$Fl_1 = F_2(l_1 + l_2),$$

whence $$F_2 = Fl_1/(l_1 + l_2),$$

and from (4), $$F_1 = F - F_2 = Fl_2/(l_1 + l_2). \left.\right\} \quad (5)$$

The strings share the weight in inverse proportion to their distances from the force $\boldsymbol{F}$. This is immediately apparent if we write the condition for rotational equilibrium about point C: $F_1l_1 = F_2l_2$, or $F_1/F_2 = l_2/l_1$ (the 'teeter-totter' solution familiar to every child).

If we had used axis E, the work would have gone as follows:

$$\begin{Bmatrix} \text{sum of clockwise} \\ \text{torques about } E \end{Bmatrix} = \begin{Bmatrix} \text{sum of counterclockwise} \\ \text{torques about } E \end{Bmatrix}$$

$$F_1(l_1 + l_2 + l_3) + F_2l_3 = F(l_2 + l_3).$$

Substitution of $F_2 = F - F_1$ gives

$$F_1(l_1 + l_2 + l_3) + Fl_3 - F_1l_3 = F(l_2 + l_3),$$

or $$F_1 = Fl_2/(l_1 + l_2),$$

$$F_2 = F - F_1 = Fl_1/(l_1 + l_2),$$

as in (5).

In the solution of problems of equilibrium of coplanar forces, *it does not matter which choice of axis is used in writing the condition for rotational equilibrium, and no new information is obtained by writing this condition for more than one axis.* The simplest equation is usually obtained if the axis is chosen to pass through the line of action of one of the *unknown* forces, because then this unknown force, having zero lever arm, is absent from the equation for rotational equilibrium. Such is the case for choices A and D for the axis in the above example.

In the more general case of coplanar forces, where the forces have horizontal as well as vertical components, the equilibrium conditions give three equations which can be solved for three unknowns. In the case of the horizontal stick of Fig. 5 suspended by two strings and carrying two heavy known weights, we can solve for the unknown tensions in the two strings and the unknown angle θ of the left-hand string if we know the angle of the right-hand string. We should be unable to solve for more than three unknowns because we cannot write more than three independent equations—namely, those for horizontal and vertical translational equilibrium and one for rotational equilibrium.

Example. *Determine the unknown forces F_1 and F_2 and the angle θ in Fig. 5.*

We replace F_2 by the two component forces of magnitudes $F_2 \sin45° = 0.707\,F_2$ and $F_2 \cos45° = 0.707\,F_2$. We replace F_1 by its horizontal and vertical component forces. Since both the magnitude and the direction of F_1 are unknown, it is simplest to give new symbols to these component forces, calling them H and V. After the magnitudes H and V are determined, the values of F_1 and θ can be found trigonometrically.

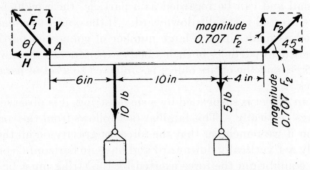

Fig. 5. A meter stick whose weight can be neglected, suspended from two strings and carrying two heavy weights.

The conditions of translational equilibrium give the equations

$$\left\{\begin{array}{l}\text{sum of magnitudes of forces} \\ \text{directed to the left}\end{array}\right\} = \left\{\begin{array}{l}\text{sum of magnitudes of forces} \\ \text{directed to the right}\end{array}\right\}$$
$$H = 0.707\,F_2; \tag{i}$$

$$\left\{\begin{array}{l}\text{sum of magnitudes of forces} \\ \text{directed upward}\end{array}\right\} = \left\{\begin{array}{l}\text{sum of magnitudes of forces} \\ \text{directed downward}\end{array}\right\}$$
$$V + 0.707\,F_2 = 10\text{ lb} + 5\text{ lb}. \tag{ii}$$

These are two equations in three unknowns, H, V, F_2. We need one further equation, to be obtained from the condition for rotational equilibrium. The best axis to use is one passing through point A, the point of application of F_1, since neither H nor V exerts a torque about this axis and our equation will have just one unknown, F_2. Equating moments about A gives

$$\left\{\begin{array}{l}\text{sum of counterclockwise} \\ \text{moments about } A\end{array}\right\} = \left\{\begin{array}{l}\text{sum of clockwise} \\ \text{moments about } A\end{array}\right\}$$
$$(0.707\,F_2)(20\text{ in}) = (5\text{ lb})(16\text{ in}) + (10\text{ lb})(6\text{ in}).$$

The moment on the left of the above equation is that of the vertical component of F_2; the horizontal component has zero lever arm. This equation gives

$$0.707\,F_2 = 7\text{ lb},$$

or $$F_2 = 9.90\text{ lb}.$$

Substitution in (i) gives $$H = 7\text{ lb},$$

and from (ii), $$V = 8\text{ lb}.$$

We then find $$\theta = \arctan \tfrac{8}{7} = 48°.8,$$
$$F_1 = 8\text{ lb}/\sin\theta = 10.63\text{ lb}.$$

The student should try using other axes in writing the moment equation in this example, verifying that he obtains the same results as above.

Verification that the torques about another axis balance out can be used as a good check on the accuracy of the solution.

6. CENTER OF GRAVITY OF AN OBJECT

AN OBJECT near the earth's surface experiences a gravitational force of attraction toward the earth called the weight of the object. If the object is very small and can be regarded as a particle, the weight is simply a single force exerted vertically downward. If the object is extended, it can be regarded as made up of a large number of connected particles; each of the constituent particles of such a body experiences a downward gravitational force, and the entire object is subjected to a set of parallel downward forces.

When an object is suspended by a single string, it is observed that the string hangs vertically. This familiar fact follows from the conditions of equilibrium if we remember that the forces of gravity on all the particles of the body act vertically downward and have no horizontal components. Hence, in equilibrium the force exerted by the string must be vertically upward and can have no horizontal component, since there would be no other horizontal component force to balance such a component.

An object suspended by a single string assumes an orientation in which it is in equilibrium. When the point of attachment of the string to the body is changed, the body assumes another equilibrium orientation. If the extended vertical line of the supporting string is marked in the body when it is in equilibrium for each of several points of attachment, all the lines so obtained are found to intersect in a common point called the *center of gravity* of the body. This point is particularly easy to find for a thin flat piece of material such as a piece of cardboard.

The center of gravity of an object is a point fixed relative to the object, but it does not necessarily lie inside the material of the object. In the case of a carpenter's square or an automobile tire, the center of gravity lies outside the material of the body. The center of gravity of a uniform regularly shaped object such as a sphere, an automobile tire, or a meter stick lies at its geometrical center, whereas the center of gravity of a tapered pole is a point on the symmetry axis between the ends but closer to the thicker than to the thinner end.

The position X_C of the center of gravity of the tapered rod in Fig. 6 is that point at which the rod will be in equilibrium under the action of the single upward force F and the downward forces of gravity on the particles of the rod. We consider the rod divided into a large number of portions of weights $w_1, w_2, w_3, \cdots$ centered at distances $x_1, x_2, x_3 \cdots$ from the end of the rod, as in Fig. 6. The larger the number and the smaller the sizes of the portions into which the rod is divided, the more accurately does such a force system represent the action of gravity.

Now apply the equilibrium conditions to the rod of Fig. 6.   Balancing the magnitudes of the vertical forces, we find that

$$F = w_1 + w_2 + w_3 + \cdots = w,$$

where we denote the whole weight of the rod by **w.**   The condition of

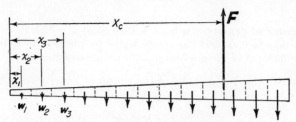

Fig. 6. A single force **F** in equilibrium with the system of forces w_1, w_2, w_3, $\cdots$.

rotational equilibrium about an axis through the left end of the rod gives the equation

$$FX_c = w_1 x_1 + w_2 x_2 + w_3 x_3 + \cdots,$$

or, since $F = w$, we have

$$wX_c = w_1 x_1 + w_2 x_2 + w_3 x_3 + \cdots. \tag{6}$$

This equation shows that *the resultant moment of the forces of gravity on the various parts of the body is the same as the moment of a single force equal to the whole weight concentrated at the center of gravity,* as in Fig. 7.

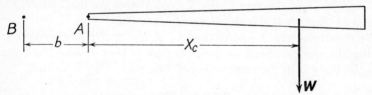

Fig. 7. The whole weight may be concentrated at the center of gravity in computing the torque resulting from gravity.

The statement in italics is true for torque about any axis whatsoever. It is proved in (6) only for an axis A through the left end of the rod, but we can readily show that the statement will hold for any other axis whatsoever.   Consider for example an axis B a distance b further to the left in Fig. 7.   Add the constant wb to both sides of (6) to obtain

$$wX_c + wb = w_1 x_1 + w_2 x_2 + \cdots + wb.$$

On the right side substitute $w_1 + w_2 + \cdots$ for w:

$$wX_c + wb = w_1 x_1 + w_2 x_2 + \cdots + w_1 b + w_2 b + \cdots,$$

or $$w(X_c + b) = w_1(x_1 + b) + w_2(x_2 + b) + \cdots. \tag{7}$$

The expressions in parentheses are the lever arms of w, concentrated at the center of gravity, and of w_1, w_2, $\cdots$, about the axis B; therefore (7) proves the statement given above in italics for any axis such as B. The statement may be similarly proved for any axis whatsoever.

These considerations lead to the most useful definition of center of gravity:

> The **center of gravity** of a body is that point at which the whole weight may be considered as concentrated for purposes of computing the moment of the gravitational forces about any axis.

According to (6), the distance X_C of the center of gravity from the left end of the rod of Figs. 6 and 7 is then given by

$$X_C = \frac{w_1 x_1 + w_2 x_2 + \cdots}{w}. \tag{8}$$

This equation is only an approximation when the rod is divided into a finite number of pieces. The center of gravity is actually the limit of this expression as the number of pieces goes to infinity and the size of each piece goes to zero.

It is not obvious from the above definition that the center of gravity is a unique point independent of the orientation of the object, as it is found to be experimentally. A proof can be given that this is so for the general three-dimensional object, but we shall be content here with proving the uniqueness of the center of gravity for a two-dimensional object such as might be cut from a sheet of metal or wood. The object of Fig. 8 is an example. In this figure, the X- and Y-axes are fixed relative to the object and turn when the object turns.

We determine the X-coordinate X_C of the center of gravity by considering the torque about an axis through O that results from gravity when the body is in the orientation of Fig. 8(a). By definition,

$$wX_C = \Sigma\, w_n x_n, \tag{9}$$

where w_n, x_n are the weight and X-coordinate of a typical small element of the body and Σ indicates a summation over all such elements. By considering the body in orientation (b), we see that

$$wY_C = \Sigma\, w_n y_n. \tag{10}$$

The question is whether, in another orientation such as (c), the torque resulting from gravity is correctly given by putting the whole weight at the point X_C, Y_C determined by (9) and (10). Let us compute this torque in (c) about the origin O by replacing each force w_n by components parallel to the coordinate axes. It is then seen that the moment of w_n about O is

$$x_n w_n \cos\alpha - y_n w_n \sin\alpha \quad \text{clockwise,}$$

and the whole torque resulting from gravity is

$$\Sigma \, x_n w_n \, \cos\alpha - \Sigma \, y_n w_n \, \sin\alpha = \cos\alpha \, \Sigma \, x_n w_n - \sin\alpha \, \Sigma \, y_n w_n \quad \text{clockwise.}$$

But by (9) and (10), this can be written as

$$w X_c \, \cos\alpha - w Y_c \, \sin\alpha \quad \text{clockwise,}$$

which is exactly the moment of the whole weight w concentrated at the center of gravity X_c, Y_c. This is what we set out to prove.

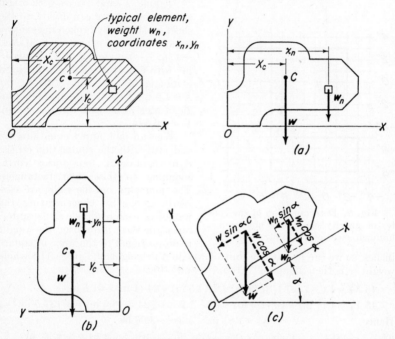

Fig. 8. If the center of gravity of a two-dimensional body is determined from two orientations (a) and (b), the same point will furnish the center of gravity in any other orientation such as (c).

In the calculus course, the student will learn to compute the position of the center of gravity of objects of various shapes by integration. Here we merely point out that many objects have sufficient symmetry so that there is an obvious geometrical center at which the center of gravity lies. This statement applies to spheres, cubes, rectangular parallelepipeds, uniform rods, plane rectangles, hoops, balanced wheels of all types, and so on. For more complex three-dimensional shapes, the three coordinates X_c, Y_c, Z_c of the center of gravity are determined by three equations similar to (9) and (10).

The center of gravity of a *composite* body can be readily determined if the center of gravity of each of its parts is known. The moment of each part about any axis is correctly given by concentrating its weight at its center of gravity. Hence the moment of the whole body and its center of gravity can be computed. Frequently an object can be artificially divided up into pieces of regular shape whose centers of gravity are known, and then treated as a composite body, as in the following example.

Example. *Determine the center of gravity of a uniform sheet of metal or plywood of the shape shown in Fig. 9.*

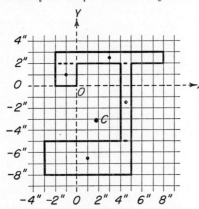

Fig. 9. Determination of the center of gravity of a piece cut from a uniform sheet of material.

Taking X- and Y-axes with origin at the point O, we can divide up the sheet as shown by broken lines into a square of area 4 in² with c.g. at $X = -1$ in, $Y = 1$ in; a rectangle of area 10 in² with c.g. at $X = 3$ in, $Y = 2.5$ in; a rectangle of area 7 in² with c.g. at $X = 4.5$ in, $Y = -1.5$ in; and a rectangle of area 24 in² with c.g. at $X = 1$ in, $Y = -6.5$ in.

We can now apply equations (9) and (10) with the summation on the right containing four terms corresponding to these four rectangles. The moments on the right are correctly given by concentrating the weight of each rectangle at its center. Since the sheet is uniform, the weight is proportional to the area in square inches, so we can use as one unit of weight the weight of 1 in². The whole weight w is then 45 units. From (9) and (10):

$$45\,X_C = 4\,(-1\text{ in}) + 10\,(3\text{ in}) + 7\,(4.5\text{ in}) + 24\,(1\text{ in}) = 81.5\text{ in},$$
$$45\,Y_C = 4\,(1\text{ in}) + 10\,(2.5\text{ in}) + 7\,(-1.5\text{ in}) + 24\,(-6.5\text{ in}) = -137.5\text{ in}.$$

Hence, $X_C = 1.81$ in, $Y_C = -3.06$ in.

These are the coordinates of the center of gravity, marked C in Fig. 9.

7. EQUILIBRIUM OF FORCES ACTING IN A COMMON VERTICAL PLANE

WE ARE NOW prepared to include the gravitational pull on the body among the forces considered in connection with the equilibrium of a body. A downward force equal to the whole weight of the body, acting at the center of gravity, represents correctly the effect of the force of gravity in regard to both translational and rotational motion. If all the other forces acting on the body lie in a common vertical plane passing through the center of gravity, we are back to the case of equilibrium of coplanar forces which was considered in Sec. 5. More general cases of noncoplanar forces do not introduce any new principles; their detailed treatment will be left to more advanced courses.

Example. *The beam of Fig. 10 is hinged at a horizontal axis near the wall and is supported by a cable making an angle of 60° with the wall. It carries* *a weight of* 60 lb *at its outer end. If the beam weighs* 200 lb, *with center of gravity* 3.6 ft *from the axis, and the cable and weight are attached at* 8 ft *from the axis, find the tension in the cable and the force exerted by the axis on the beam.*

In Fig. 10(b), the beam is isolated and all available information concerning the forces acting on the beam is entered. The forces of gravity on the particles of the beam are entirely represented, so far as any quantities entering the *equilibrium conditions*—total forces and moments—are concerned, by a single downward force of 200 lb at the center of gravity. The weight of 60 lb is represented by a downward force at the end of the beam, while the unknown tension T in the cable acts upward at an angle of 30° with the beam. The cable is a nonrigid body so it can exert only a force of pure tension in the direction of its length. The pin that attaches the beam to the wall is assumed frictionless, so it cannot exert *torque* that would assist

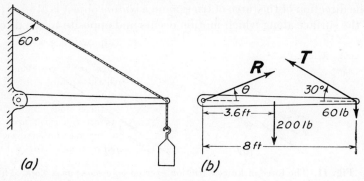

(a)   (b)

Figure 10

in keeping the beam from swinging down in the absence of the cable. However it can (and must) exert *forces both outward and upward;* the resultant of these forces is represented by the reaction vector R, unknown in both magnitude and direction. There are thus three unknowns, T, R, and θ, to be determined from the three equilibrium conditions that we can write. In place of R and θ, it will be simplest first to determine R_H and R_V, the horizontal and vertical components of R. We shall proceed to write successively the conditions for equilibrium of the horizontal components of the forces, the vertical components of the forces, and the moments of the forces about the axis at the wall:

$$R_H = T \cos 30° = 0.866\ T, \tag{i}$$
$$R_V + T \sin 30° = 200\ \text{lb} + 60\ \text{lb}, \tag{ii}$$
$$(T \sin 30°)(8\ \text{ft}) = (60\ \text{lb})(8\ \text{ft}) + (200\ \text{lb})(3.6\ \text{ft}).$$

The last equation can be solved for T directly to give

$$T = 300\ \text{lb}.$$

When this value is substituted in (i) and (ii) we obtain

$$R_H = 260\ \text{lb}, \qquad R_V = 110\ \text{lb}.$$

From the values of these components we find by the methods of the preceding chapter that

$$R = 282\ \text{lb}, \qquad \theta = 22°.9.$$

8. FRICTION BETWEEN SOLID SURFACES

EVERYONE IS familiar with the friction that is encountered whenever the surface of one solid object moves or merely tends to move along the surface of another solid object with which it is in contact.   It is friction that holds a nail in a board and keeps the individual fibers in a thread or rope from pulling apart.   Friction between the soles of our shoes and the ground or floor makes it possible for us to walk; we recall how difficult it is to walk on an icy street or a highly polished floor where the force of friction on the soles of our shoes is very small.   Friction is essential for the propulsion and the braking of an automobile.   The reduction of friction in the moving parts of machinery poses many problems in design and lubrication for the engineer.

The direction of the force of friction on a *sliding* object is always parallel to the surface along which motion occurs and opposite to the direction

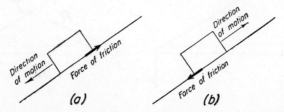

Fig. 11. The force of kinetic friction exerted *by a plane on a block*. This force is in the direction opposite to the motion of the block, as indicated. The force of friction that the *block* exerts *on* the *plane* would be opposite to the force shown here, by Newton's third law.

of motion.   This statement is illustrated in Fig. 11, in which a block is shown moving along an inclined board.   The force of friction exerted *by the surface on the block* is tangent to the surface and opposite to the direction of motion of the block along the surface.   The force of sliding friction always *opposes* the motion of one object along the surface of another object, no matter how the surface is inclined.

Two surfaces in contact exert tangential forces of friction on each other, not only when one slides past the other but also when the surfaces are stationary and one *tends* to slide past the other.   If a man leans against a heavy table and the table does not move, a horizontal force of friction exerted by the floor must oppose the horizontal force the man is exerting if the table is to remain in equilibrium.   Such a force is known as a force of *static friction* and is in such a direction as to oppose the tendency to move and to keep the body in equilibrium.   If the man pushes hard enough on the table to make it move, the force of friction exerted by the floor while the table is moving is opposite to the direction of motion of the table and is known as a force of *kinetic friction*.

A **force of static friction** is a tangential force exerted by one solid surface on another when the two surfaces *are not* sliding past each other.

A **force of kinetic friction** is a tangential force exerted by one solid surface on another when the two surfaces *are* sliding past each other.

We notice that the horizontal forces exerted by the tires of an automobile on a level road (and the equal and opposite forces exerted by the road on the tires) are usually forces of *static* friction, since the tires do not ordinarily *slide* on the road. However if the driver 'spins' the wheels in accelerating, or if the wheels are skidding, these forces become those of kinetic friction.

The laws governing frictional forces are determined by experiment. A simple experimental set-up is shown in Fig. 12, in which the forces acting on the block are the following:

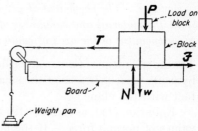

w = weight of the block,
P = downward force exerted by the load on the block,
N = normal force exerted by the board against the surface of the block,
T = tension in the string,
$\mathfrak{F}$ = force of friction.

The tension T in the string, which equals in magnitude the weight of the weight pan and its load, tends to pull

Fig. 12. Experiment to determine the force of friction.

the block forward along the surface of the board, and the force $\mathfrak{F}$ of friction is directed backward parallel to the surface of the board. When the block is in equilibrium, it either remains stationary or moves forward with constant speed. The condition of translational equilibrium requires that

$$N = w + P \quad \text{and} \quad T = \mathfrak{F}.$$

Thus, the force of friction is equal in magnitude to the tension in the string when the block is in equilibrium.

Let us start with the weight pan detached. In this case $\mathfrak{F} = 0$ because $T = 0$. Let us now attach the weight pan and start adding weights, gradually increasing T. Until T reaches a certain magnitude, the block does not move. During this period, the force of static friction is gradually increasing, since it must always equal T. Static friction is very accommodating and always exerts just enough force to keep the block in equilibrium—up to a certain maximum. If T is increased sufficiently, the block will start to move, indicating that T has exceeded the maximum force of static friction. Thus *the force of static friction is a variable quantity,* depending on how much force is needed to keep the block from moving. But there is a definite maximum force of static friction; if the magnitude T of the applied force exceeds the maximum force of static friction, the block will move.

The maximum force of static friction $\mathcal{F}_S^{\text{Max}}$ can be found from the apparatus of Fig. 12 by gradually adding weights to the weight pan until the block starts to move. If we vary the load P on the block, we shall find that the values of $\mathcal{F}_S^{\text{Max}}$ so determined are proportional to the total weight $w+P$ of load and block, which equals the normal force N between the two surfaces. Hence, we write

$$\mathcal{F}_S^{\text{Max}} = \mu_S N, \tag{11}$$

where μ_S is called the *coefficient of static friction*.

LAWS OF STATIC FRICTION: *The maximum force of static friction between two surfaces is proportional to the normal force between the surfaces. The coefficient of proportionality μ_S defined by (11) depends on the material and roughness of the surfaces but, over a wide range, is independent of the area of contact between the surfaces.*

The independence of area can be demonstrated by the apparatus of Fig. 12 by using various blocks of the same material but of different areas of contact with the plane.

Equation (11), as well as (12) below, is only true for a certain range of values of normal force. If the normal force is so great that one surface begins to dent or crush the other, the proportionality no longer applies. The laws of friction are experimental laws of great engineering usefulness over the range of values for which they are approximately valid. They are in no sense fundamental physical principles.

It is harder to get the block of Fig. 12 started than it is to keep it moving at constant velocity after it has once started. Once the weight pan has been loaded so that the block starts moving, it will be found that the block moves to the left with increasing speed, indicating that T is greater than $\mathcal{F}_K$, the force of kinetic friction exerted by the board on the moving block. Once the block has started moving, T can be reduced somewhat and the block will still continue to move, indicating that $\mathcal{F}_K$ *is less than* $\mathcal{F}_S^{\text{Max}}$. One can determine $\mathcal{F}_K$ by loading the weight pan to a value somewhat less than $\mathcal{F}_S^{\text{Max}}$, giving the block a push with the finger to start it; if it slows down and comes to rest, in indicates that $T < \mathcal{F}_K$; if it speeds up, it indicates that $T > \mathcal{F}_K$. In this way one can adjust the weight till the block moves at constant speed, once it has been started.

By varying the load P on the block, it will be found that for a given pair of surfaces, $\mathcal{F}_K$ is proportional to the normal force N between the two surfaces. Hence, we can write

$$\mathcal{F}_K = \mu_K N, \tag{12}$$

where μ_K is called the *coefficient of kinetic friction*.

LAWS OF KINETIC FRICTION: *The force of kinetic friction between two surfaces is proportional to the normal force between the surfaces. The proportionality constant μ_K depends on the material and roughness of the surfaces but over a wide range is independent of the area of contact of the surfaces and of the relative velocity of the surfaces.*

TABLE I

TYPICAL VALUES OF COEFFICIENT OF STATIC FRICTION μ_S AND OF
KINETIC FRICTION μ_K

Materials	μ_S	μ_K
Steel on steel.........................	0.15	0.09
Steel on ice...........................	0.03	0.01
Hemp rope on wood....................	0.5	0.4
Leather on wood.......................	0.5	0.4
Oak on oak............................	0.5	0.3
Wrought iron on cast iron or bronze......	0.19	0.18
Rubber tire on dry concrete road.........	1.0	0.7
Rubber tire on wet concrete road.........	0.7	0.5

Table I gives typical values of μ_S and μ_K. Note that the coefficient of static friction μ_S determines the *maximum* force of static friction but that $\mathfrak{F}_S$ can have any magnitude from zero up to this maximum. The force of static friction is $\mathfrak{F}_S^{\text{Max}}$ only when the surfaces are just on the point of starting to move relative to each other. On the other hand, μ_K determines *the* force of kinetic friction which exists *whenever* the surfaces are moving relative to each other.

Relations (11) and (12) are valid regardless of the inclination of the surfaces. For example, in Fig. 13 *the plane pushes on the block* with a force which has two components: the component normal to the plane is called the *normal force* or the *normal reaction* of the plane and is denoted by N; the component tangent to the plane is called the *force of friction* and is denoted by $\mathfrak{F}$. Relation (11) gives the maximum force of static friction, and (12) gives the force of kinetic friction, with the same

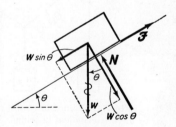

Figure 13

values of μ_S and μ_K as if the same block and plane were lying horizontally.

In Fig. 13 the force w of gravity can be resolved into components parallel and perpendicular to the plane as shown. So long as the block does not move, it is in equilibrium and

$$N = w \cos\theta, \quad \mathfrak{F}_S = w \sin\theta.$$

Thus, $\mathfrak{F}_S$ increases as the inclination θ of the plane increases. The inclination θ cannot exceed a certain value θ^{Max} which makes $\mathfrak{F}_s = \mathfrak{F}_s^{\text{Max}}$, or else the block will slide.   When the block is on the point of slipping,

$$\mathfrak{F}_s^{\text{Max}} = w \ \sin\theta^{\text{Max}} = \mu_s N;$$

also

$$w \ \cos\theta^{\text{Max}} = N.$$

Dividing the first equation by the second gives

$$\tan\theta^{\text{Max}} = \mu_s. \tag{13}$$

Thus, the plane can be raised to an angle of inclination whose tangent is μ_s before the block starts to slip.   This limiting angle is called the *angle of repose* or the *angle of slip*.

The laws of friction that we have discussed above do not apply to lubricated surfaces, where there is a continuous film of liquid between solid surfaces.   Friction between lubricated surfaces is essentially a problem in hydrodynamics that we shall not treat in this text.   We also omit from consideration a slight variation in μ_K with speed; this variation probably involves a thin air film between the moving surfaces.

PROBLEMS

1. In Fig. 14, show that if $w_1 = w_2$, then $\theta_1 = \theta_2$.

2. In Fig. 14, show that if $w_1 > w_2$, then $\theta_1 > \theta_2$.

3. In Fig. 14, if $w_1 = w_2 = 10$ lb, find θ_1 and θ_2 for the cases $w_3 = 5$ lb, 10 lb, 15 lb, 20 lb, 25 lb.   Ans: $\theta_1 = \theta_2 = 14°.5$; $30°$; $48°.6$; $90°$; no equilibrium.

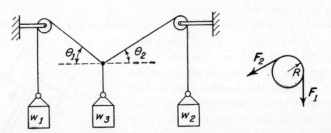

Fig. 14. A knot in equilibrium. The pulleys in this diagram are assumed to have frictionless bearings. When such a pulley is in equilibrium the tension in the string does not change as it passes over the pulley. To prove this, consider the little diagram at the right. One part of the string exerts clockwise torque F_1R on the pulley; the other part exerts counterclockwise torque F_2R. Since there is no frictional torque in the bearings, and the pulley is in equilibrium, these torques must balance, so $F_1 = F_2$. Hence in this setup, the forces exerted by the three strings on the knot have magnitudes w_1, w_2, w_3.

4. In Fig. 14, if $w_1 = w_2$, find θ_1 and θ_2 for the cases $w_3 = \tfrac{1}{4}w_1$, $w_3 = \tfrac{3}{4}w_1$, $w_3 = \tfrac{5}{4}w_1$, $w_3 = \tfrac{7}{4}w_1$, $w_3 = \tfrac{9}{4}w_1$.

5. In Fig. 14, if $w_3=20$ lb and $w_1=w_2$ so $\theta_1=\theta_2$, find the value of w_1 required to make $\theta_1=10°$; to make $\theta_1=5°$.   Ans: 57.6 lb; 115 lb.

6. In Fig. 14, if $w_3=5$ lb, $\theta_1=60°$, and $\theta_2=30°$, find w_1 and w_2.

7. In Fig. 14, if $w_1=2$ lb, $w_2=1$ lb, and $w_3=2$ lb, find θ_1 and θ_2.
                    Ans: $61°\!.1$, $14°\!.5$.

8. In Fig. 14, if w_1, w_2, and w_3 are given, show that

$$\sin\theta_1=\frac{w_1^2-w_2^2+w_3^2}{2w_1w_3} \quad \text{and} \quad \sin\theta_2=\frac{w_2^2-w_1^2+w_3^2}{2w_2w_3}.$$

9. A child weighing 60 lb sits in a swing whose ropes are 12 ft long. What horizontal force applied to the board of the swing is required to hold the child in a position where the ropes make an angle of 20° with the vertical? Neglect the weight of the swing.   Ans: 21.8 lb.

10. A cornerstone weighing 1 ton is suspended from a crane by a cable 50 ft long. A man making the final position adjustment pushes the stone 6 inches horizontally before giving the signal for the final lowering. What horizontal force did the man exert?

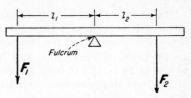

11. In Fig. 15, if the weight of the bar is negligible, $F_1=12$ lb, $F_2=15$ lb, and $l_1=5$ ft, find l_2 and the force exerted by the fulcrum.   Ans: 4 ft; 27 lb.

Figure 15

12. A man exerts a force of 30 lb downward on a pump handle at a point 4 ft from the axis. The piston rod is attached at a point 5 inches on the other side of the axis. If the 30-lb force is just sufficient to move the piston at constant speed, what is the upward force exerted on the piston?

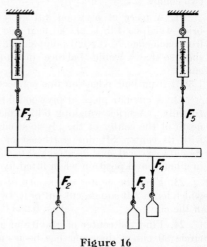

13. In Fig. 16, a rigid stick 32 in long, of negligible weight, carries weights $F_2=5$ lb, $F_3=5$ lb, and $F_4=3$ lb at points 8 in, 21 in, and 24 in from the left end. It is supported by vertical strings 2 in from the left end and 3 in from the right end. Find F_1 and F_5.
                    Ans: 5.93, 7.07 lb.

14. In Fig. 16, a rigid stick 50 in long, of negligible weight, carries weights $F_2=9$ lb, 13 in from the left end, $F_3=11$ lb, 32 in from the left end, and an unknown weight F_4 at an unknown position. The force $F_1=11$ lb is applied 3 in from the left end, and the force

Figure 16

$F_5=14$ lb is applied 5 in from the right end. Determine the magnitude of F_4 and its position of application, for equilibrium.

15. In Fig. 17, if $l_2=12$ in, $l_3=32$ in, $l_4=40$ in, $F_2=6$ lb, $F_3=9$ lb, and $\theta_1=60°$, find F_1, F_4, and θ_4, for equilibrium.   Ans: 6.93 lb, 9.64 lb, $69°\!.0$.

16. In Fig. 17, if $F_1=6$ lb, $\theta_1=60°$, $l_2=1.5$ ft, $l_3=4$ ft, $l_4=5$ ft, and $F_3=5$ lb, find F_2, F_4, and θ_4, for equilibrium.

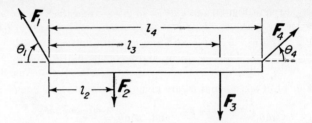

Fig. 17. Four forces act on a stick of negligible weight.

17. A bar of iron 1 in square and 10 in long weighing 47.4 oz and a bar of aluminum 1 in square and 10 in long weighing 16.2 oz are joined end to end. Find the distance of the center of gravity from the center of the resulting 20 in bar. Ans: 2.45 in.

18. A round steel bar 1 inch in diameter and 3 ft long is put into a lathe and a 1-ft length at one end is turned down to ⅝-inch diameter. Find the position of the center of gravity of the resulting shape.

19. On a uniform plank 10 ft long weighing 40 lb is placed a concentrated weight of 20 lb, at 1 ft from one end, and another concentrated weight of 15 lb, at 3 ft from this same end. Find the distance of the center of gravity of plank plus weights from this same end. Ans: 3.53 ft.

20. A steel rod 6 ft long weighing 7 lb carries a collar weighing 3 lb centered at a point 1.5 ft from one end and another collar weighing 1.2 lb centered at a point 2.5 ft from the other end. Find the center of gravity of the rod with its two collars.

21. A piece of plywood 3 ft ×6 ft weighing 10 lb is lying horizontally. A brick weighing 4 lb is placed near one corner of the piece with its center 1 ft in from each edge. At what point should a vertical cord be attached to the plywood sheet so that it would 'balance' in a horizontal position when lifted by this single cord? Ans: 2.43 ft from short edge, 1.36 ft from long edge (on line connecting center of brick with center of sheet).

22. A circular piece of plywood 6 ft in diameter weighing 20 lb is lying horizontally. A brick weighing 6 lb is placed on the piece with its center 2 ft due north of the center of the plywood circle; another brick weighing 8 lb is placed with its center 2 ft due southeast of the center of the circle. At what point should a vertical cord be attached to the plywood sheet so that it would 'balance' in a horizontal position when lifted by this single cord?

23. Find the center of gravity of a circular sheet of metal 6 ft in diameter which has a 2-ft square cut out of it, two sides of the square lying along diameters of the circle. Ans: 0.233 ft from center of circle—in what direction?

24. Find the center of gravity of a 2-m square sheet of metal from which a circle 80 cm in diameter has been cut, the center of the circle being along a diagonal of the square 70 cm from one corner of the square.

25. A uniform bar 8 ft long is bent so that a 3-ft arm makes an angle of 45° with a 5-ft arm. If the bent bar is hooked over a horizontal wire, what angle with the vertical will the long arm assume? Ans: 11°.5.

26. A uniform bar 8 ft long is bent at right angles at a point 3 ft from one end. If the bent bar is hung over a horizontal wire, what angle with the vertical will the long arm assume?

27. If the shape of Fig. 9 is 'hooked' over the edge of a table top so that the point O rests on the table, what will be the angle between the Y-axis drawn on the figure and the vertical?   Ans: 30°.6.

28. Find the center of gravity of the shape shown in Fig. 18, which is cut out of a uniform plate of metal.

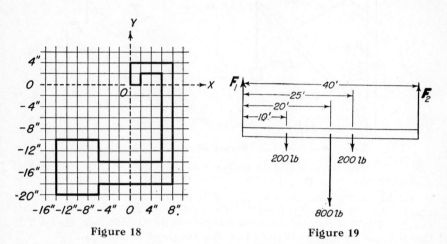

Figure 18   Figure 19

29. In Fig. 19, a uniform bar weighing 800 lb carries two concentrated loads of 200 lb each in the positions shown.   The bar is supported at the ends.   Find the magnitudes of the supporting forces F_1 and F_2.   Ans: 625 lb; 575 lb.

30. A horizontal nonuniform bar 3 ft long is supported at its ends by vertical cords attached to spring balances.   If the balances read 4.6 lb and 3.2 lb, what is the weight of the bar and where is its center of gravity?

31. When just the two front wheels of an empty four-wheel truck are placed on a platform scale, the scale reads 3500 lb.   When just the two rear wheels are placed on the scale, the reading is 2500 lb.   The wheelbase is 14 ft.   What is the weight of the empty truck, and how far ahead of the rear axle is its center of gravity?   Ans: 6000 lb; 8.17 ft.

32. When the truck of Prob. 31 is loaded, the weight on the front wheels is 5500 lb and the weight on the rear wheels is 8500 lb.   What is the weight *of the load* and where is the center of gravity *of the load?*

33. An acquaintance of one of the authors hauls his small two-wheel automobile trailer to a country coal yard to buy a ton of coal.   The dealer instructs him to place the car so that just the trailer wheels are on the platform scale. Then leaving the trailer attached to the car, the dealer reads the weight and loads the trailer with coal until the weight indicated by the scale is one ton greater.   Under what circumstances is the dealer cheating himself? cheating the purchaser?

34. The person referred to in Prob. 33, who is a physicist, has noted that the center of the pile of coal in his trailer is approximately 1 ft ahead of the trailer axle, whereas the distance from the trailer axle to the ball joint which connects the trailer to the car is 5 ft.   Approximately how much coal does he get when he buys a ton?   (He has tried in vain to tell the dealer that his method of weighing is unsound.)

35. In the derrick of Fig. 20, if the weight of the boom is $w = 2500$ lb, the load $F = 800$ lb, the center of gravity of the boom is 15 ft from its axis of rotation, the point of attachment of the supporting cable is 20 ft from the axis and that of the

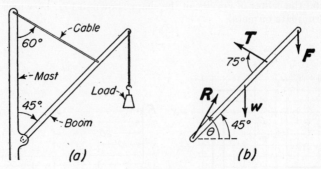

Figure 20

load is 25 ft from the axis, find the tension T in the cable and the magnitude and direction of the thrust R of the axis.   Ans: $T = 2100$ lb; $R = 2890$ lb; $\theta = 51°0$.

36. In Fig. 20, if the boom weighs 400 lb, the load F is 1200 lb, the center of gravity of the boom is 15 ft from the axis of rotation, the cable is attached 30 ft from the axis, and the load is attached 45 ft from the axis, find the tension T in the cable and the magnitude and direction of the thrust R of the axis.

37. In Fig. 21, the ladder is 20 ft long, its weight is 100 lb, and its center of gravity is 7.5 ft from its lower end. Its lower end rests on rough ground and its upper end leans at an angle of 32° against a smooth vertical wall. A man whose weight is 150 lb stands 12 ft up the ladder and exerts force F on the ladder. The smooth vertical wall can exert only a push P perpendicular to its surface against the top end of the ladder. Find the magnitude P of the push of the wall and the magnitude and direction of the force R of the ground.   Ans: $P = 79.6$ lb; $R = 262$ lb; $\theta = 72°3$.

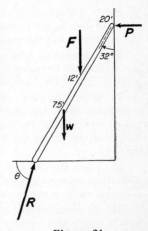

Figure 21

38. In the ladder problem of Fig. 21 and Prob. 37, find the horizontal component of the ground reaction R as a function of the slant height S (measured along the ladder) to which the 150-lb man has climbed. In particular, if 90 lb is the greatest horizontal force that the ground can exert to keep the ladder from slipping, what distance S can the man climb before the ladder starts to slip?

39. A table weighs 75 lb. The coefficient of static friction between the table legs and the floor is 0.5. If a man pushes due north on the table with a horizontal force of 25 lb, what is the force $\mathfrak{F}_s$ of static friction?   Ans: 25 lb south.

40. In Prob. 39, with what horizontal force must the man push to make the table start moving toward the north?

41. In Fig. 13, if $\mu_s = 0.5$ and $\mu_K = 0.4$, what is the maximum angle θ at which the block will remain at rest on the plane? What is the minimum angle θ at which the block will continue to move down the plane if it is given a start?
     Ans: $26°6$; $21°8$.

42. Answer the questions in Prob. 41 for the case in which $\mu_S = 0.6$, $\mu_K = 0.5$.

43. In Fig. 22, if $\mu_S = 0.6$, $w = 50$ lb, and $\theta = 30°$, find the magnitude of the pull P which is required to overcome static friction and start the block moving.   Ans: 25.7 lb.

44. In Fig. 22, show that the magnitude of the pull P, acting at an angle θ above the horizontal, which is required to overcome static friction and start the block moving is given by $P = \mu_S w / (\cos\theta + \mu_S \sin\theta)$.

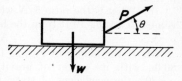

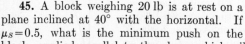

Figure 22

45. A block weighing 20 lb is at rest on a plane inclined at 40° with the horizontal. If $\mu_S = 0.5$, what is the minimum push on the block, applied parallel to the plane, which will keep the block from starting to slide down the plane? What push, applied parallel to the plane, will start the block sliding up the plane?   Ans: 5.20 lb; 20.5 lb.

46. A block weighing 12 lb is at rest on a plane inclined at 20° to the horizontal. If $\mu_S = 0.6$, what push, applied parallel to the plane, is required to start the block moving down the plane? to start the block moving up the plane?

47. In Fig. 23, if $\theta = 20°$, $\mu_S = 0.6$, and the block weighs 15 lb, what horizontal push P is required to start the block moving up the plane?   Ans: 18.5 lb.

48. In Fig. 23, show that the horizontal push P required to start the block of weight w moving up the plane is

$$P = w\, \frac{\mu_S \cos\theta + \sin\theta}{\cos\theta - \mu_S \sin\theta},$$

and that the normal force exerted by the plane is

$$N = w / (\cos\theta - \mu_S \sin\theta).$$

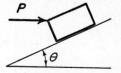

Figure 23

Show that it is impossible to start a block moving up a plane by a *horizontal* push if the angle of the plane is greater than arccotμ_S.

49. Show that the horizontal push P required in Fig. 23 to keep the block from starting to slide down the plane is given by

$$P = w\, \frac{\sin\theta - \mu_S \cos\theta}{\cos\theta + \mu_S \sin\theta}.$$

Notice that this is positive only when θ is greater than the angle of repose, because only then is a force required to keep the body from sliding down the plane.

50. What *horizontal* push P will hold a 20-lb block against a vertical wall and prevent it from sliding down if the coefficient of static friction between block and wall is 0.4?

51. In Fig. 24, what push P acting at an angle of $\theta = 30°$ is required to prevent a 15-lb block from sliding down a vertical wall if $\mu_S = 0.44$? What push is required to start the block moving up the wall?   Ans: 13.8 lb; 23.2 lb.

52. Show that it is impossible to start the block of Fig. 24 moving up the wall by any magnitude of push P if θ is greater than arccotμ_S.

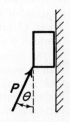

Figure 24

53. Figure 25 represents a ladder 20 ft long weighing 80 lb, with its center of gravity 7 ft from the bottom end. The base rests on a floor with $\mu_S = 0.6$.

The top leans against a smooth wall (no friction). The force F is due to the weight of a 180-lb man.

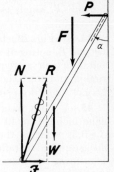

(a) What is the greatest angle α which the ladder can have and still permit the man to climb to a rung 19 ft from the base, measured along the ladder?

(b) What is the ratio $\mathcal{F}/N$ when $\alpha = 20°$ and the man climbs to a rung 19 ft from the base?

Ans: (a) $38°\!.1$; (b) 0.279.

54. If the ladder in Fig. 25 is 20 ft long and weighs 80 lb, with its center of gravity 7 ft from the base, $\alpha = 30°$, the coefficient of static friction between ladder and floor is 0.3, and the wall is frictionless, how high up the ladder can a 180-lb man climb before the ladder starts to slip? What would be the minimum coefficient of friction between ladder and floor which would permit the man to climb to a rung 19 ft from the base with the ladder at this angle?

Figure 25

55. In Fig. 26, a stiff *weightless* stick of length l is hinged at point A. It supports a weight w at its end, which is in turn supported by a string having tension T. By resolving T and w into component forces parallel and perpendicular to the length of the stick, and writing the moment equation about axis A, show that the resultant of T and w is a vector directed along the stick toward A;

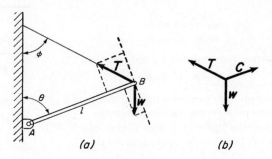

(a)　　　　　　　　　　　　　*(b)*

Figure 26

hence that the reaction of the stick at point B is a force C, directed outward along the stick, that balances $T+w$. A force C in this direction represents a pure compression in the stick. Hence the problem of Fig. 26(a) may be replaced by solution of the diagram of Fig. 26(b), with all forces known in direction but T and C unknown in magnitude. Determine C from this diagram for the case in which $\theta = 60°$, $\phi = 45°$, and $w = 150$ lb. Ans: 110 lb.

56. Show that replacement of the system of Fig. 26(a) by that of Fig. 26(b), with C representing the compression in the stick, is a *trick* that is *valid only if the stick is weightless*. Show that if the stick has weight, its reaction at point B has not only a *compressive* component parallel to the stick, but a component perpendicular to the stick in the downward direction (this component is a manifestation of the *stiffness* of the stick—the fact that it cannot be bent).

57. In Fig. 27, if $w = 60$ lb, $a = 3$ ft, $h = 2.5$ ft, and $\mu_S = 0.5$, will the table slide or tilt when F is applied? What force F is required to make it move? Find N_1 and N_2. Ans: slide; 30 lb; 5 lb, 55 lb.

58. In Fig. 27, if $w=60$ lb, $a=3$ ft, $h=2.5$ ft, and $\mu_S=0.7$, will the table slide or tilt when F is applied?   Find the value of F required to make the table move. Find $\mathfrak{F}_1$, N_1, $\mathfrak{F}_2$, N_2.

59. Show that the table of Fig. 27 will slide or tilt according to whether μ_S is less than or greater than $\frac{1}{2}a/h$.

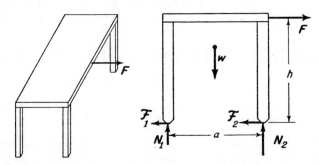

Fig. 27. The force F is applied halfway along the table, which assures sufficient symmetry so that the equilibrium problem can be handled in two dimensions, as shown in the force diagram to the right. N_1 represents the normal force on the two left legs, N_2 the normal force on the two right legs. If μ_S is low, the table will slide when sufficient force F is applied. If μ_S is high, the table will tilt rather than slide. If one assumes that the table will slide and finds that N_1 comes out negative when the table is on the point of sliding, this result indicates that the table would already have tilted with a smaller force F just sufficient to make $N_1=0$ and put all the weight on the right legs. If, on the other hand, one assumes that the table will tilt. setting $N_1=\mathfrak{F}_1=0$, and finds that $\mathfrak{F}_2$ comes out greater than $\mu_S N_2$, this result is an indication that friction is not sufficient and that the table would already have begun to slide at a lower value of F.

60. In Fig. 27, if $a=3$ ft, $h=2$ ft, what coefficient of friction is required to make the table tilt rather than slide?   Answer the same question for $a=2$ ft, $h=4$ ft.

61. A packing crate is in the form of a cube 5 ft on an edge.   It is loaded so its center of gravity is at its geometrical center.   It rests on a concrete floor with coefficient of friction $\mu_S=0.8$.   A man pushes horizontally in the middle of one face at a height h from the floor.   What is the maximum value of h in order that the cube should slide rather than overturn?   Ans: 3.12 ft.

62. Take a straight-backed chair with a heavy back and try pushing horizontally on the back of the chair at various heights from the floor, both in the direction which makes the chair move or tilt backward and in the direction which makes the chair move or tilt forward.   Explain your observations.

63. A straight-backed chair on a carpet has 16 in between its front and back feet.   A horizontal force applied to the back of the chair at a height of 24 in or more will cause the chair to tilt backward; whereas in order to cause the chair to tilt forward, a horizontal force must be applied at least 36 in from the floor. Determine the coefficient of static friction.   Ans: $\mu_S=0.267$.

64. Part of a chain 8 ft long hangs over the edge of a horizontal table.   The coefficient of static friction between chain and table is 0.45.   What is the greatest length of chain that can hang over the edge without the whole chain sliding off the table?

CHAPTER 3

KINEMATICS OF TRANSLATIONAL MOTION

Kinematics is the branch of science concerned with the quantitative description of motion.

Motion of a body of any type can be described as a continuous change in the position of each particle of the body. The scope of kinematics is limited to a mere *description of motion* and does not include a treatment of the forces and torques that cause the motion; treatment of these forces and torques is the subject matter of *dynamics*.

In this chapter we shall confine our attention to the description of the *translational motion of rigid bodies*. In Chap. 6, we shall consider the motion of fluid bodies, while in Chap. 9 we shall consider the *rotation of rigid bodies*. Any motion of a rigid body can be considered as a combination of a translation and a rotation:

A **translation of a rigid body** is a displacement of the center of gravity of the body.

A **rotation of a rigid body** is a change in angular orientation of the body.

In this chapter we describe the motion of a point. This point may represent the position of an isolated particle, the position of a particular particle of a fluid or rigid body, or, as a very important special case, may represent the position of the center of gravity of a rigid body. In order to describe the motion of such a point, it will be necessary to introduce and define certain quantities such as *speed, velocity,* and *acceleration*. We shall consider in turn the motion of a particle in a straight line, the translational motion of a projectile near the earth, and motion in a circle at constant speed.

It will be noticed from the definition above that study of the kinematics of a particle includes as a special case the study of the kinematics of the *translational* motion of a rigid body.

1. SPEED

PERHAPS the most familiar quantity used in the description of translational motion is *speed*. Everyone is familiar with the automobile speed-

50

ometer. A glance at the dial of this instrument tells the driver 'how fast the vehicle is going' at any given instant; the speedometer reading gives the instantaneous speed of the automobile in mi/hr or in some other convenient unit. In order to under-stand clearly the meaning of the term *instantaneous speed*, it will be desirable for us to define first the term *average speed*.

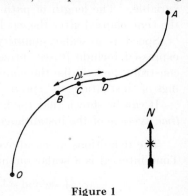

Let us consider the motion of an automobile along the curved level road-way that is shown in Fig. 1. The aver-age speed of the car in moving from point O to point A is defined as the ratio of the total path length or distance

Figure 1

traversed *along the road* to the total time that has elapsed while the motion is taking place:

> The **average speed** of traversing a given path is a *scalar quantity* defined as the total length of the path divided by the time elapsed.

The path length and the elapsed time are both scalar quantities, and hence the ratio of these quantities is also a scalar. If the total path length from O to A is l and the total elapsed time is t, the average speed between O and A will be l/t.

It should be noted that this expression gives the average speed main-tained during the entire trip from O to A but gives no information con-cerning the average speed during any shorter part of the journey. For example, a delay for refueling might result in a considerably smaller value for the average speed of the entire trip than the value of the average speed for shorter distances. To determine the average speed during the portion of the trip between points B and D, we would compute $\Delta l/\Delta t$ where Δt is the time elapsed during the motion of the car from B to D.

By considering successively smaller path lengths Δl, always including the point C, we obtain values for average speed which approach the *instantaneous speed of the car at point C:*

> The **instantaneous speed** at point C (Fig. 1) is defined as the limit of the average speed over a path length that approaches zero but always includes the point C.

In applying this definition, we note that as the path length Δl becomes smaller and smaller, the time interval Δt by which Δl is to be divided also becomes smaller and smaller, and the ratio approaches a finite limit. The instantaneous speed v is defined in calculus notation by the expression

$$v = \lim_{\Delta t \to 0} \frac{\Delta l}{\Delta t} = \frac{dl}{dt}. \tag{1}$$

This definition of instantaneous speed implies that the traversed path length l is a function of *time*, which can be regarded as the independent variable. The length of path measured from O is indeed a function of the time elapsed after the car has left point O.

Speed is a scalar quantity. The units in which it is commonly expressed include ft/sec, m/sec, mi/hr, and km/hr. It is possible to construct devices like the conventional speedometer to give direct readings of 'instantaneous' speed.

It can be shown that the average speed, as we have defined it, is the *time* average of the instantaneous speed.*

The definitions given above presuppose a definition of *time interval*. Time interval is a scalar quantity whose unit, the *second*, is defined by

$$1 \text{ second} = \frac{1}{86400} \text{ mean solar day,}$$

where

> The **mean solar day** is the average length of the day, from one passage of the sun across the meridian to the next, averaged over a long period of years.

Time intervals are measured by clocks, with which everyone is familiar. One very reproducible type of clock is furnished by the apparent revolution of the fixed stars around the earth. The time between successive meridian passages of a star is called a *sidereal day*. Since the rotational speed of the earth is constant, sidereal days do not vary in length. Solar days do vary in length because the earth moves around the sun in an elliptical path with a translational speed that varies during the course of the year. The word *day*, used without qualification, denotes the mean solar day of 24 hr, or 1440 min, or 86,400 sec.

2. VELOCITY

ALTHOUGH a knowledge of the speed of an object is an important bit of information in many situations, its value in kinematics is limited. The general problem of kinematics is one of finding the *position* of a body as a function of time. If we know the speed of an object, we know *how fast* the object is moving but have no information concerning the *direction*

---

* The proof of this statement is simple but may involve more calculus than the reader has yet studied. The time average of the instantaneous speed, between times t_0 and t_1, is

$$\frac{1}{t_1 - t_0} \int_{t_0}^{t_1} v \, dt.$$

Since $v = dl/dt$, this becomes

$$\frac{1}{t_1 - t_0} \int_{t_0}^{t_1} \frac{dl}{dt} \, dt = \frac{1}{t_1 - t_0} \int_{l_0}^{l_1} dl = \frac{l_1 - l_0}{t_1 - t_0},$$

if $l_1 - l_0$ is the path length traversed in time $t_1 - t_0$. But the last expression is just our definition of average speed.

in which it is moving.   Therefore, a knowledge of the speed of an object
is of no use whatever in finding the change of position of the object
unless other information is also available.   For example, let us consider
a car moving at a constant speed of 60 mi/hr.   We wish to find the
location of the car at the end of one hour.   Knowing the speed of the car,
we can say immediately that the total *path length* traversed by the car is
60 mi but are unable to say anything about the displacement of the
car from the starting point.   The *magnitude* of the displacement would be
60 mi if the path traversed were a straight line; zero if the car traversed a
circle of 60-mi circumference; or some intermediate value for other paths.

From the above example, it would appear desirable to define some
physical quantity which would give not only the *speed* of a body but also
the *direction* in which the body is moving.   The quantity that has these
properties is the vector quantity called *velocity*.   The *average velocity* of a
particle is defined as the ratio of its *displacement* to the length of the time
interval in which the displacement occurred:

> The **average velocity** of a particle during a specified time interval
> is a *vector quantity* defined as the displacement of the particle during
> that time interval divided by the time interval.

Since displacement is a vector and time is a scalar, the ratio is a vector
quantity that has the same direction as the displacement.

In order to understand the definition of average velocity, consider
Fig. 2(a), which shows again the path of Fig. 1.   The actual path of the

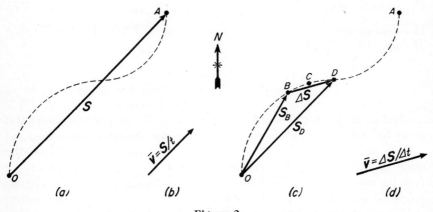

Figure 2

car is given by the dotted curve; the displacement S of the car in making
the complete trip from O to A is given by the arrow.   Denoting the
elapsed time for the trip by t, we may write the average velocity $\bar{v}$ as

$$\bar{v} = S/t. \qquad\qquad (O \rightarrow A)$$

The average velocity $\bar{v}$ can be represented by the arrow shown in (b); the length of the arrow gives a measure of the magnitude of the average velocity and the direction of the arrow is the same as that of the arrow representing S.

Let us now write the expression for the average velocity for the car in moving from B to D. As measured from the starting point, the displacement of the car at B is represented in Fig. 2(c) by the arrow labeled S_B and the displacement of the car at D is given by the arrow labeled S_D. The change in displacement of the car in going from B to D is given by the short arrow labeled ΔS. This vector ΔS must be added to the displacement S_B to obtain the displacement S_D. Since $S_D = S_B + \Delta S$, ΔS is the vector difference

$$\Delta S = S_D - S_B.$$

The average velocity of the car in moving from B to D is given by

$$\bar{v} = \Delta S / \Delta t, \qquad\qquad (B \rightarrow D)$$

where Δt is the time required for the car to move from B to D. This average velocity can be represented by the arrow shown in Fig. 2(d). The direction of this arrow is parallel to the arrow representing ΔS; the length of the arrow gives a measure of the magnitude of the average velocity.

> The **instantaneous velocity** at point C (Fig. 2) is defined as the limit of the average velocity over a path length that approaches zero but always includes the point C.

In calculus notation, considering the displacement S from O as a function of time, we can write the instantaneous velocity as

$$v = \lim_{\Delta t \to 0} \frac{\Delta S}{\Delta t} = \frac{dS}{dt}. \qquad\qquad (2)$$

Just as in the case of speed, it can be shown that the average velocity, as we have defined it, is the *time* average of this instantaneous velocity.*

The units in which the magnitude of the velocity is measured are the same as those in which speed is measured, but the statement of the velocity must include a direction. For example, the velocity of a particle might be stated as 30 mi/hr eastward or 12 m/sec upward. Hereafter, unless otherwise indicated, the term *velocity* means *instantaneous velocity*.

---

* The proof is like that for the case of speed, except that vector relations are involved. The time average of the instantaneous velocity is

$$\frac{1}{t_1 - t_0} \int_{t_0}^{t_1} v \, dt = \frac{1}{t_1 - t_0} \int_{t_0}^{t_1} \frac{dS}{dt} \, dt = \frac{1}{t_1 - t_0} \int_{S_0}^{S_1} dS = \frac{S_1 - S_0}{t_1 - t_0},$$

which is the average velocity as we have defined it.

Now let us see how we can compute the velocity of a particle if we are given its X-, Y-, and Z-coordinates as functions of time. Suppose that the particle traverses the space path indicated in Fig. 3 and we are given functions $X(t)$, $Y(t)$, and $Z(t)$ that give its coordinates at any time t. We desire to determine the velocity of the particle at a certain point P on its path. Starting from P, the particle will undergo a displacement $\Delta\boldsymbol{S}$ in a time Δt, as indicated on Fig. 3. The vector $\Delta\boldsymbol{S}$ has rectangular components ΔX, ΔY, and ΔZ as indicated. The velocity at P is defined as

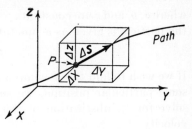

Figure 3

$$v = \lim_{\Delta t \to 0} \frac{\Delta\boldsymbol{S}}{\Delta t},$$

a vector which has components

$$v_X = \lim_{\Delta t \to 0} \frac{\Delta X}{\Delta t}; \qquad v_Y = \lim_{\Delta t \to 0} \frac{\Delta Y}{\Delta t}; \qquad v_Z = \lim_{\Delta t \to 0} \frac{\Delta Z}{\Delta t}.$$

But, by definition, these three limits are just the derivatives of the three functions $X(t)$, $Y(t)$, and $Z(t)$, and so we obtain the components of the velocity by just differentiating these three functions:

$$v_X = dX/dt; \qquad v_Y = dY/dt; \qquad v_Z = dZ/dt. \qquad (3)$$

By considering what happens in Fig. 3 as the magnitude of $\Delta\boldsymbol{S}$ becomes smaller and smaller, we see that

The magnitude of the instantaneous velocity of a particle at point P is equal to the instantaneous speed of the particle at P, and the direction of the instantaneous-velocity vector at P is the direction of the tangent to the path at that point.

Since the magnitude of the velocity is the speed, we are justified in our choice of the symbols $\boldsymbol{v}$ for velocity and v for speed.

The simplest case in which to apply these ideas is the motion of a particle along a straight line. Let us take the straight-line path as the X-axis of our coordinate system. Then there is only one non-vanishing velocity component,

$$v_X = dX/dt.$$

This can be evaluated at any point or at any time, provided the relation between X and t is known. For example, suppose that the position of the particle as a function of time is given by the relation

$$X = a + bt + ct^2, \tag{4}$$

where a, b, and c are constants. Then the X-component of the velocity of the particle is given as a function of time by

$$v_X = dX/dt = b + 2ct. \tag{5}$$

If we wish to find the X-component of the velocity when the particle is at some particular position, we substitute this position for X in (4) and solve for t; substitution of this value of t in (5) will give the desired velocity.

In the case of the motion of a particle along the X-axis, the velocity is a vector directed along this axis, in the positive sense if the component v_X is positive, in the negative sense if v_X is negative.

Example. *The position of a particle moving along the X-axis is given by*

$$X = 6 \text{ ft} + (8 \text{ ft/sec}) \, t - (2 \text{ ft/sec}^2) \, t^2.$$

Find the position and velocity of this particle at $t = 0$, 1 sec, 2 sec, and 3 sec. Find the velocity when $X = 13.5$ ft.

Differentiation of the above equation gives

$$v_X = dX/dt = 8 \text{ ft/sec} - (4 \text{ ft/sec}^2) \, t.$$

Straightforward substitution gives, at $t = 0$, $X = 6$ ft, $v_X = 8$ ft/sec; at $t = 1$ sec, $X = 12$ ft, $v_X = 4$ ft/sec; at $t = 2$ sec, $X = 14$ ft, $v_X = 0$; at $t = 3$ sec, $X = 12$ ft, $v_X = -4$ ft/sec. Thus the velocity vector points in the positive sense along the X-axis from $t = 0$ to $t = 2$ sec; at $t = 2$ sec the particle is at rest; at later times the X-component of velocity is negative, the velocity vector points in the negative sense, and the particle moves to the left if the positive sense is toward the right. It is apparent from the above computation that the particle is at $X = 13.5$ ft twice, once between $t = 1$ sec and $t = 2$ sec when it is moving toward the right, and once between $t = 2$ sec and $t = 3$ sec when it is moving toward the left. Substitution of $X = 13.5$ ft in the quadratic equation that gives X as a function of t, and solution, gives $t = 1.5$ sec and $t = 2.5$ sec as these two values of t. Substitution of these values of t in the velocity equation gives $v_X = 2$ ft/sec and $v_X = -2$ ft/sec respectively. In this example, which represents a case of constant acceleration that we shall study later in this chapter, when the particle moves to the left through a given point on the X-axis it has a velocity equal and opposite to the velocity it had when it moved through the same point to the right. The student should verify that when the particle moves back through its initial position ($X = 6$ ft) it has the velocity component $v_X = -8$ ft/sec.

The motion of a body with *constant velocity* is easily described. Since neither the magnitude nor the direction of the velocity changes in time, the motion is necessarily one with constant speed along a straight line. If we let this line be the X-axis and denote the constant X-component of velocity by v, the particle will move the distance vt in the time t. Hence if we call the position $X = 0$ at $t = 0$, the particle will be at $X = vt$ at time t. We see by differentiation that this expression correctly gives $v_X = dX/dt = v$.

3. RELATIVE VELOCITIES

All velocities are relative.

We shall show in the next chapter that it is impossible in principle to determine what would be called an *absolute* velocity of any body. The velocity of a body is always specified relative to some other body. When the other body is not specifically mentioned, it is understood to be the earth.

Consider a man walking at 3 mi/hr down the aisle of a train. This is his velocity relative to the train, but the train may be moving at 60 mi/hr relative to the surface of the earth. In turn, the surface of the earth is moving relative to the sun—at about 66,000 mi/hr because of the motion of the earth in its yearly orbit, on which is superposed a surface velocity varying from 1000 mi/hr at the equator to zero at the poles that results from the daily rotation of the earth. The sun itself is moving at about 43,000 mi/hr relative to the mean position of the stars in our galaxy—while our galaxy is moving relative to the other galaxies in the universe! It would be quite a chore to determine the absolute velocity of the man walking down the aisle of the train—if this had a meaning. Fortunately, the principles of physics (the *principle of relativity*) demonstrate that absolute velocity has no meaning whatsoever.

Relative velocities compose vectorially according to the following rule:

The velocity of body A relative to body C, denoted by v_{AC}, is the vector sum of the velocity of body A relative to body B, v_{AB}, and the velocity of body B relative to body C, v_{BC}, that is

$$v_{AC} = v_{AB} + v_{BC}. \tag{6}$$

This rule for composition of velocities follows from the fact that displacements compose vectorially. Before giving a formal proof, let us consider the particular example illustrated in Fig. 4. Here a river flows north at velocity v_{WE}, the velocity of the water relative to the earth. A boat keeps a heading directly east and is propelled by a motor at velocity v_{BW}, the velocity of the boat relative to the water. We desire to find v_{BE}, the velocity of the boat relative to the earth. Let us take the particular case where the river is one mile wide and is flowing at 8 mi/hr, while the boat is propelled relative to the water at 6 mi/hr. The boat then takes ten minutes to make the one mile across the river. So long as it keeps its head due east, it takes ten minutes to cross the river whether the water is stationary or flowing relative to the earth. During these ten minutes, the motor displaces the boat an amount S_{BW} relative to the water. But during these same ten minutes the water is displaced $1\frac{1}{3}$ mi to the north. The boat is carried with the water this distance to the north during these ten minutes independent of the progress of the boat across the stream. The net result is that the boat travels the path indicated in Fig. 4(a); is displaced $1\tfrac{2}{3}$ mi as indicated by S_{BE} in (b); and has velocity relative to the earth of magnitude 10 mi/hr in the direction indicated by v_{BE} in (c).

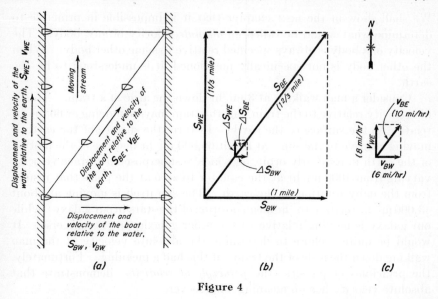

(a)   (b)   (c)

Figure 4

The proof of (6) follows from arguments similar to the above.   In any short period of time Δt,

$$\Delta S_{BE} = \Delta S_{BW} + \Delta S_{WE},$$

since displacements add vectorially.   Although Fig. 4 shows the case in which ΔS_{BW} is perpendicular to ΔS_{WE}, this vectorial relation is true for any heading of the boat.   Dividing the above equation through by Δt,

$$\Delta S_{BE}/\Delta t = \Delta S_{BW}/\Delta t + \Delta S_{WE}/\Delta t,$$

and going to the limit $\Delta t \to 0$, we find $v_{BE} = v_{BW} + v_{WE}$, as in (6).

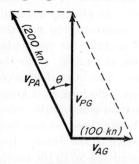

Figure 5

Example. *An airplane flies at an airspeed of 200 knots (nautical miles per hour).   At the altitude at which it is flying there is a wind of 100 knots from due west.   The plane desires to proceed due north relative to the ground.   In what direction should it head, and what will be its ground speed?*

See Fig. 5, in which P stands for plane, A for air, and G for ground.   We are given that $v_{AG} = 100$ knots east; $v_{PA} = 200$ knots at an unknown angle θ; v_{PG}, which by (6) is the vector sum of these, is of unknown magnitude but points due north.   It is apparent that the plane must head into the wind as in Fig. 5.   From the parallelogram in this figure we see that $200 \sin\theta = 100$, $\sin\theta = \tfrac{1}{2}$, $\theta = 30°$.   Hence the ground speed will be

$$v_{PG} = (200 \text{ knots}) \cos 30° = 173 \text{ knots}.$$

4. ACCELERATION

IN MOST CASES, the velocity of a moving body changes as the motion proceeds, and the body is said to move with *accelerated motion* or to have an *acceleration*. We first define the *average acceleration* of a particle:

> The **average acceleration** of a particle during a specified time interval is a *vector quantity* defined as the change in velocity of the particle during that time interval divided by the time interval.

Since the change in velocity is a vector and time is a scalar, the ratio is a vector. If v_0 is the velocity of a body at time t_0 and v_1 is the velocity of the body at time t_1, the average acceleration $\bar{a}$ during the time interval $t_1 - t_0$ is given by

$$\bar{a} = \frac{v_1 - v_0}{t_1 - t_0} = \frac{\Delta v}{\Delta t}.$$

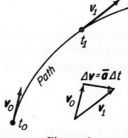

It should be remembered that this equation gives a relation between *vector* quantities. The relationship involved can be understood by considering the diagram shown in Fig. 6. In this diagram, vector Δv is the change in velocity $v_1 - v_0$ that has occurred in the time interval $\Delta t = t_1 - t_0$. The average acceleration vector $\bar{a} = \Delta v / \Delta t$ has the same *direction as* Δv. If Δv is measured in ft/sec or m/sec, the magnitude of the average acceleration is measured in (ft/sec) *per sec* or (m/sec) *per sec,* that is, in ft/sec² or m/sec².

Figure 6

The instantaneous acceleration of a body is defined in a manner analogous to that in which instantaneous velocity was defined:

> The **instantaneous acceleration** of a particle at a given point in its path is defined as the limit of the average acceleration over a path length that approaches zero but always includes the given point.

In calculus notation,
$$a = \lim_{\Delta t \to 0} \frac{\Delta v}{\Delta t} = \frac{dv}{dt}. \tag{7}$$

As in the case of speed and velocity, the average acceleration as defined above is the *time* average of the instantaneous acceleration.

Since the vector Δv has components Δv_X, Δv_Y, and Δv_Z, we conclude that in the motion of a particle along a space curve as in Fig. 3, the components of the acceleration vector are given by

$$\left.\begin{array}{l} a_X = \lim\limits_{\Delta t \to 0} \dfrac{\Delta v_X}{\Delta t} = \dfrac{dv_X}{dt} = \dfrac{d^2 X}{dt^2} \, ; \\[2ex] a_Y = \lim\limits_{\Delta t \to 0} \dfrac{\Delta v_Y}{\Delta t} = \dfrac{dv_Y}{dt} = \dfrac{d^2 Y}{dt^2} \, ; \\[2ex] a_Z = \lim\limits_{\Delta t \to 0} \dfrac{\Delta v_Z}{\Delta t} = \dfrac{dv_Z}{dt} = \dfrac{d^2 Z}{dt^2} . \end{array}\right\} \tag{8}$$

In the case of motion along a straight line, the acceleration is directed along the path and has magnitude equal to the rate of change of speed, but in the case of motion in a curved path *neither of these statements is true*, since the *velocity* changes, even if the *speed* does not change, and there is a component of the acceleration normal to the path and directed toward the concave side, as will seem reasonable by study of Fig. 6.   We shall later consider acceleration in motion along curved paths in more detail.

Let us first consider the simplest case of motion along a straight line, which we shall take as the X-axis of our coordinate system as in Fig. 7. In this diagram, the particle is at point A at time t_0 and has velocity

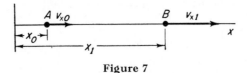

Figure 7

component v_{x0} in the direction of the positive X-axis.   At a later time t_1, the particle is at B and has velocity component v_{x1}.   The X-component of the average acceleration during this interval is given by the relation

$$\bar{a}_x = \frac{v_{x1} - v_{x0}}{t_1 - t_0} = \frac{\Delta v_x}{\Delta t}.$$

This is positive or negative according to whether v_{x1} is greater than or less than v_{x0}.   If the velocity is toward the right (v_x positive) but the speed is decreasing (dv_x/dt negative), a_x is negative and is said to represent a *deceleration*.   If the velocity is given by formula (5), the acceleration is given by

$$a_x = dv_x/dt = 2c;$$

in other words, for the motion of (4), the acceleration is constant.

In the example given on p. 56, the student should verify that the acceleration has the constant magnitude $4\,\text{ft/sec}^2$ in the negative X-direction.   The problem of rectilinear motion with constant acceleration is an important one which we shall consider in detail in the next section.

5. RECTILINEAR MOTION WITH CONSTANT ACCELERATION

THE SIMPLEST TYPE of accelerated motion is that of a body moving along a straight line with *constant* acceleration.   We shall take the X-axis along this line with a specified sense. v_x will be positive when the velocity vector points along the axis in the positive sense, otherwise negative; a_x will be positive when the acceleration vector points along the axis in the positive sense, otherwise negative.

The X-component of velocity of the body executing rectilinear motion with constant acceleration increases or decreases by the same amount in each unit of time.   The change Δv_x in any time interval Δt is given by

$$\Delta v_x = a_x \, \Delta t, \tag{9}$$

where a_x is the *constant* value of the X-component of the acceleration.

Let the body be at the origin $X = 0$ at time $t = 0$, and let the initial velocity component be v_{x0}.   At any later time t the velocity component will have changed by $\Delta v_x = a_x t$, as we see from (9), so that v_x will be

$$v_x = v_{x0} + \Delta v_x = v_{x0} + a_x t. \tag{10}$$

Similarly, the position X of the particle at any time t is given by

$$X = \bar{v}_x t \tag{11}$$

where $\bar{v}_x$ is the average velocity component during the entire time of motion t.   Now, since v_x is changing at a linear rate in (10), the average value during the time interval t equals one-half the sum of the value v_{x0} at the beginning of the interval and the value $v_{x0} + a_x t$ at the end.   Thus,

$$\bar{v}_x = \tfrac{1}{2} \, [v_{x0} + (v_{x0} + a_x t)], \qquad \text{or} \qquad \bar{v}_x = v_{x0} + \tfrac{1}{2} \, a_x t.$$

Substitution of this value in (11) gives, for the position X of the particle at any time t,

$$X = v_{x0} t + \tfrac{1}{2} \, a_x t^2. \tag{12}$$

It is sometimes useful to employ a relation that gives directly the velocity component v_x at any position X.   This relation can be obtained by solving equation (10) for t and substituting this expression for t in equation (12).   The resulting expression is

$$v_x^2 = v_{x0}^2 + 2 a_x X \tag{13}$$

where v_x is the velocity component when the particle is at point X.

6. FREELY FALLING BODIES: VERTICAL MOTION

THE MOST COMMON example of motion with very nearly constant acceleration is that of a falling body near the earth's surface.   Up to the Middle Ages it was thought that heavy bodies fall more rapidly than light bodies, and, indeed, it is a matter of ordinary casual observation that a lead shot, a feather, a snowflake, and a water droplet fall through the air at different velocities.   It remained for Galileo (1564–1642), who might be termed the first modern experimental physicist, to give a correct analysis of the problem.   Galileo introduced the clearly defined concept of acceleration and, as a result of indirect experimental measurements, concluded that *in vacuum all freely falling bodies would experience the same constant acceleration*.   This conclusion, which can easily be verified in a laboratory by modern experimental methods, was based on a series of experiments that were hampered by the fact that the only devices available for the measurement of time were crude water clocks, which had not been improved appreciably since their invention by the Egyptians and Babylonians thousands of years earlier. However, even under this handicap, Galileo arrived at a correct experimental relation describing the motion of a freely falling body.

> A **freely falling body** is one that experiences no force except that of the earth's gravity.

In principle a body falls freely only in vacuum because otherwise air resistance acts on it. In practice, the motion of a small heavy body in air, if the speed is not too great, approximates closely that of a freely falling body; in this case, air resistance is small compared to the weight of the body.

The acceleration of a freely falling body, called the *gravitational acceleration*, is usually denoted by the symbol **g**. At or near the earth's surface the magnitude of **g** is approximately 32.2 ft/sec², or 9.81 m/sec², and **g** is directed vertically downward. In the case of a rigid body, it is the *center of gravity* that has this constant translational acceleration, independent of what the rotational motion may be.

> *Near a given point on the earth's surface, all freely falling bodies have the same constant translational acceleration if air resistance is negligible.*

Since the acceleration of a freely falling body is constant, the equations of motion developed in Sec. 4 are immediately applicable if the body is released from rest or projected with an initial velocity along the vertical, so that the motion is rectilinear. Section 7 will consider freely falling bodies projected with a horizontal component of velocity.

We shall consider the rectilinear motion of a freely falling body occurring along the Y-axis of a rectangular coordinate system with the positive Y-axis pointing *upward*, so that the Y-component of acceleration is $-g$. We shall choose the origin of our coordinate system at the initial position of the body, so that $Y=0$ at $t=0$. The initial velocity component will be denoted by v_{Y0}; this is positive if the initial velocity is upward, negative if it is downward. With this notation, equations (10), (12), and (13) of the preceding section apply if we substitute Y for X and $-g$ for a_X; these equations give

$$v_Y=v_{Y0}-gt, \qquad Y=v_{Y0}t-\tfrac{1}{2}\,gt^2, \qquad v_Y^2=v_{Y0}^2-2gY. \qquad (14)$$

Example. *Suppose that a man on the top of a building 300 ft high leans over the edge of the building and throws a ball vertically upward. If the mag-*

nitude of the initial upward velocity is 64.4 *ft/sec, find the position and velocity of the ball at successive* 1-sec *intervals after it leaves the man's hand, and find the time required for the ball to reach the pavement on the ground at the side of the building.   Take* $g = 32.2$ *ft/sec²*.

Substitution in (14) gives

$$Y = (64.4 \text{ ft/sec}) \, t - \tfrac{1}{2} \, (32.2 \text{ ft/sec}^2) \, t^2 = (64.4 \text{ ft/sec}) \, t - (16.1 \text{ ft/sec}^2) \, t^2, \quad \text{(i)}$$

$$v_Y = 64.4 \text{ ft/sec} - (32.2 \text{ ft/sec}^2) \, t. \tag{ii}$$

From these equations, the following table of positions and velocities can be obtained:

Time	Position	Velocity
0 sec	0 ft	+ 64.4 ft/sec
1	+ 48.3	+ 32.2
2	+ 64.4	0
3	+ 48.3	− 32.2
4	0	− 64.4
5	− 80.5	− 96.6
6	− 193.2	− 128.8
7	− 338.1	− 161.0

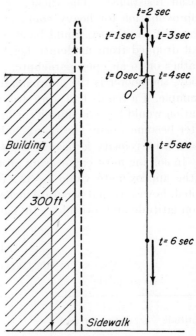

Fig. 8. The position and velocity of a ball at the end of successive one-second intervals after the ball is thrown upward from the top of a building at 64.4 ft/sec.

These values of position and velocity are shown graphically in Fig. 8.

From these results we note that the time required for the ball to reach the ground at the side of the building ($Y = -300$ ft) is between 6 sec and 7 sec.   For this value of Y, (i) gives the quadratic equation

$$-300 \text{ ft} = (64.4 \text{ ft/sec}) \, t \\ - (16.1 \text{ ft/sec}^2) \, t^2$$

or $16.1 \, t^2 - (64.4 \text{ sec}) \, t$
$$- 300 \text{ sec}^2 = 0.$$

This equation has two solutions: $t = 6.76$ sec and $t = -2.76$ sec.   Only the positive value can give the solution to the problem we are considering, so the time to reach the ground is 6.76 sec.   (The solution $t = -2.76$ sec does have an interesting physical significance: It is the time at which the ball would have to have been projected from the ground with exactly the correct upward initial velocity to have reached the top of the wall at $t = 0$ with upward velocity 64.4 ft/sec so that the ball would continue the motion tabulated above.)

Two points might be noted in connection with the results shown in the table in the previous example.   One of these is that the ball thrown upward rose for two seconds and then required two seconds to return to its original position. This result is quite general; the time of rise and time of descent to the original level are equal whenever an object is thrown upward, provided the effect of air resistance can be ignored. The second point to be noted is that the downward velocity of the ball at the time it returns to its initial position is equal in magnitude to the initial upward velocity of the ball; this result is also quite general.

It should be re-emphasized that the discussion we have given holds strictly only for the idealization of a *freely falling* body that experiences no air resistance. The theory presented does form a good first-order approximation for heavy compact bodies falling through the air. For example, the theory would be closely applicable to a lead shot or a golf ball dropped from moderate heights but would not be applicable to a feather or to an open parachute. The greater the velocity of a falling body, the poorer is the approximation given by the simple theory. For example, if a tennis ball were dropped from a great height, the approximation would be good during the first few seconds of fall but would thereafter become worse; the tennis ball would eventually attain a constant downward velocity known as the *terminal velocity*.

In solving most engineering problems, we may use for the magnitude g the approximate value $g = 32.2$ ft/sec^2 or 9.81 m/sec^2. It should be noted, however, that accurate measurements show a slight dependence of g on latitude and altitude. In Table I are given the accurate values of

TABLE I

VALUES OF THE GRAVITATIONAL ACCELERATION

At sea level   At 40° latitude

latitude	ft/sec²	m/sec²	altitude (ft)	ft/sec²	altitude (m)	m/sec²
0°	32.0878	9.78039	0	32.1578	0	9.80171
10°	32.0929	9.78195	500	32.1563	500	9.80017
20°	32.1076	9.79641	1,000	32.1547	1,000	9.79864
30°	32.1302	9.79329	2,000	32.1516	2,000	9.79554
40°	32.1578	9.80171	4,000	32.1454	4,000	9.78937
50°	32.1873	9.81071				
60°	32.2151	9.81918	8,000	32.1331	8,000	9.77702
70°	32.2377	9.82608	16,000	32.1084	16,000	9.75233
80°	32.2525	9.83059	32,000	32.0608	32,000	9.70296
90°	32.2577	9.83217				

g for sea-level stations at various latitudes and for stations at various altitudes at 40° latitude. Even these values are only mean values, and there are local variations of smaller magnitude that depend on the character of the underlying rocks.   Measurement of such local variations is a useful tool in geophysical prospecting for oil.

7. FREELY FALLING BODIES: PROJECTILES

IN CASES where the effects of air resistance can be neglected, the paths or *trajectories* of projectiles can be determined by the methods we have outlined thus far, by considering separately the horizontal and the vertical components of the translational motion.   The vertical acceleration experienced by a projectile as a result of the action of gravitational forces is not affected by horizontal motion of the projectile.   For example, if as shown in Fig. 9 a shell is shot horizontally from a gun mounted at a height h above the ground and a second shell at height h is released from rest at the instant the first projectile leaves the muzzle of the gun and falls vertically, the two shells are at any instant at the same vertical distance above the ground and reach the ground at the same time.   This result can be easily verified in the laboratory by suitable simple experimental arrangements.

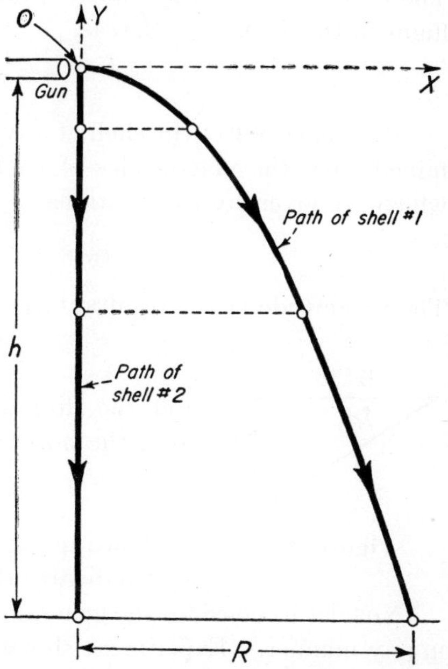

Fig. 9. A projectile fired horizontally has the same *vertical* motion as a shell dropped from rest at the instant of firing, and reaches the ground at the same instant.

The *downward* component of the motion of a shell fired horizontally is similar in all respects to the motion of the shell which was dropped from rest.   The equations previously developed are therefore applicable to the *vertical component* of the motion of the projectile fired from the gun.

Analysis of the horizontal motion of a projectile is very simple, since it is found that *the horizontal component of the velocity is constant*.

These facts can be used to determine the *range* or horizontal distance traversed by the projectile fired horizontally from the gun, provided we know the muzzle velocity of the projectile.   In determining the range let us place the origin of our coordinate system at the muzzle of the gun shown in Fig. 9.   The projectile will reach the ground when its Y-coordinate is equal to $-h$.   Substituting this value and $v_{Y0}=0$ in the center equation in (14), we may determine the time T required for the projectile to reach the ground (the *time of flight*).   This time is

$$T = \sqrt{2h/g}.$$

In the case we are considering, v_X, the constant horizontal component of the velocity, is equal to the muzzle velocity v_0. Therefore the horizontal component X of the total displacement is given by the equation

$$X = v_0 t.$$

The *range* R is given by substituting the value $T = \sqrt{2h/g}$ of the time of flight in this equation; that is,

$$R = v_0 \sqrt{2h/g}. \tag{15}$$

The velocity $\boldsymbol{v}$ of the shell at any time t during the flight can be determined from the magnitudes of its horizontal and vertical components, which are given by the relations

$$v_X = v_0; \quad v_Y = -gt.$$

The magnitude of the resultant velocity is

$$v = \sqrt{v_X^2 + v_Y^2} = \sqrt{v_0^2 + g^2 t^2},$$

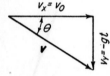

and the direction given by the angle θ measured from the horizontal is

$$\theta = \arctan(v_Y/v_X) = \arctan(-gt/v_0),$$

Figure 10   as shown in Fig. 10. The negative value of the tangent indicates that θ is below the horizontal.

Now let us consider the general case of a freely falling body projected in any manner. Experiment shows that

The center of gravity of a freely falling body has no horizontal component of acceleration and has a constant downward vertical component of acceleration.

If the projected body moves in the XY-plane, in which the X-axis is horizontal and the Y-axis vertically upward, we have $a_X = 0$, $a_Y = -g$. Equations (8) then give

$$a_X = dv_X/dt = 0, \qquad v_X = \text{constant} = v_{X0}; \tag{16}$$

$$a_Y = dv_Y/dt = -g, \qquad v_Y = v_{Y0} - gt. \tag{17}$$

Here v_{X0} and v_{Y0} are the components of the initial velocity at $t = 0$. The constant value of v_X in (16) follows from the fact that the rate of change of v_X is zero. The linear variation of v_Y in (17) follows from the constant rate of change of v_Y just as in the previous section.

Let us consider a projectile fired with muzzle velocity of magnitude v_0 at angle θ_0 above the horizontal. This situation is depicted in Fig. 11, in which a gun with muzzle located at ground level fires a shell that subsequently follows the path indicated by the broken curve, which we desire to describe.   The initial velocity has components

$$v_{X0} = v_0 \cos\theta_0; \qquad v_{Y0} = v_0 \sin\theta_0. \tag{18}$$

After the shell leaves the gun, the horizontal component v_X of the velocity remains constant at the initial value v_{X0}, and the horizontal

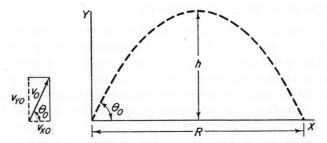

Fig. 11. Path of a projectile fired with muzzle velocity of magnitude v_0 at elevation angle θ_0.

motion is described by the relation

$$X = v_{X0}\, t. \tag{19}$$

The vertical velocity component v_Y at any time t is given by (17) and the Y-position of the shell is given, as in (14), by

$$Y = v_{Y0}t - \tfrac{1}{2}\, gt^2. \tag{20}$$

The equation
$$v_Y^2 = v_{Y0}^2 - 2\, gY, \tag{21}$$

which can be derived from (17) and (20) by elimination of t, gives the Y-component of velocity as a function of height Y.

Equations (19) and (20) are the parametric equations for a *parabola*, which is the type of trajectory followed by the shell.   These equations together with the associated velocity equations describe the motion completely.   By means of these equations such quantities as the total time of flight T, the range R, the maximum height h attained, and the velocity of the projectile at any time can be calculated.

Projectile motion in a parabola is an example of motion in a curved path, in which case, as we have noted in Sec. 4, the acceleration vector (vertically downward in this case) is not tangent to the path but points inward toward the concave side of the path.

Example.   *A gun pointed 30° above the horizontal fires a shell with muzzle velocity of 644 ft/sec.   Neglecting air resistance, find (a) the maximum height reached, (b) the time of flight, (c) the range.   Take $g = 32.2$ ft/sec².*

We have $v_{X0} = (644 \text{ ft/sec}) \cos30° = 558 \text{ ft/sec}$; $v_{Y0} = (644 \text{ ft/sec}) \sin30° = 322 \text{ ft/sec}$.

(a) At the maximum altitude, $v_Y = 0$ since the velocity (always tangent to the path) is horizontal. Equation (21) then gives, if we set $v_Y = 0$ and $Y = h$, $2 gh = v_{Y0}^2$, $h = (322 \text{ ft/sec})^2/(64.4 \text{ ft/sec}^2) = 1610 \text{ ft}$.

(b) When the shell returns to the ground, $Y = 0$. Putting $Y = 0$ in (20) and solving for t gives $T = 20$ sec, the time of flight.

(c) The range is the horizontal distance traveled in the 20-sec time of flight, which from (19) is $R = v_{X0} \cdot 20 \text{ sec} = 11,200 \text{ ft}$.

8. MOTION IN A CIRCLE AT CONSTANT SPEED

In the examples of accelerated motion considered thus far, the acceleration has resulted in a change in the *magnitude* of the velocity of a body. This is not always the case. Since velocity is a vector quantity, it is possible for acceleration to result in a change in velocity by causing a change in its *direction* without an accompanying change in its *magnitude*. This is the case when a particle moves at constant speed in a circular path.

Consider a particle moving at constant speed v in a circular path of radius R as shown in Fig. 12(a). Let us consider the motion of the particle from point A to point B in time Δt. The particle's initial and

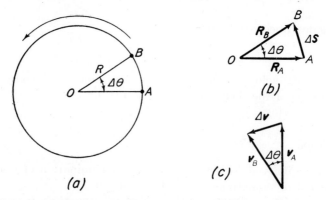

Fig. 12. (a) Particle moving at constant speed in a circular path of radius R. (b) Displacement diagram: R_A and R_B give displacements of particle from O when particle is at points A and B respectively. (c) Velocity diagram: v_A and v_B give velocities of particle at points A and B respectively.

final displacements R_A and R_B, relative to the center O, are shown in Fig. 12(b). During the time Δt required for the particle to move from A to B, the body experiences a change in displacement ΔS, equal in magnitude to the chord of the circle joining points A and B. In moving from point A to B, the particle does not, of course, pass along the *chord* but along the *arc* of length $\Delta l = v \, \Delta t$.

Now let us consider the velocity-vector diagram shown in Fig. 12(c). Here v_A and v_B represent instantaneous velocities of the particle at points A and B, respectively, and Δv represents the change in the velocity of the particle in the time interval Δt. The magnitudes of $\boldsymbol{v}_A$ and $\boldsymbol{v}_B$ are both equal to v, but vectorially $\boldsymbol{v}_B = \boldsymbol{v}_A + \Delta \boldsymbol{v}$.

In circular motion the instantaneous velocity is always perpendicular to the radius vector giving the displacement of the particle from the center. Hence, in the vector diagrams in (b) and (c), $\boldsymbol{v}_A$ is perpendicular to $\boldsymbol{R}_A$ and $\boldsymbol{v}_B$ is perpendicular to $\boldsymbol{R}_B$, hence the angle between $\boldsymbol{v}_A$ and $\boldsymbol{v}_B$ is equal to the angle $\Delta\theta$ between $\boldsymbol{R}_A$ and $\boldsymbol{R}_B$. Further, since $v_A = v_B = v$ and $R_A = R_B = R$, the velocity triangle and the displacement triangle are similar isosceles triangles. Thus, $\Delta \boldsymbol{v}$ is perpendicular to the chord $\Delta \boldsymbol{S}$ and therefore in the limit as $\Delta\theta \to 0$ is directed toward the center of the circle. Since $\bar{\boldsymbol{a}} = \Delta \boldsymbol{v}/\Delta t$, where $\bar{\boldsymbol{a}}$ is the average acceleration during time Δt, the average acceleration during any time interval Δt has the same direction as $\Delta \boldsymbol{v}$ and is also directed toward the center of the circle in the limit $\Delta\theta \to 0$.

The instantaneous-acceleration vector is the limit of the average-acceleration vector as $\Delta t \to 0$ and hence $\Delta\theta \to 0$; therefore *the instantaneous-acceleration vector is directed toward the center of the circle at every point in the motion.*

To obtain the magnitude of the instantaneous acceleration, we note that *if we let $\langle \Delta \boldsymbol{v} \rangle$ represent the magnitude of the vector $\Delta \boldsymbol{v}$ in Fig. 12,** we obtain, from similar triangles,

$$\frac{\langle \Delta \boldsymbol{v} \rangle}{v} = \frac{\Delta S}{R}, \quad \text{or} \quad \langle \Delta \boldsymbol{v} \rangle = \frac{v}{R} \Delta S.$$

If we divide both sides of this equation by Δt, we obtain

$$\frac{\langle \Delta \boldsymbol{v} \rangle}{\Delta t} = \frac{v}{R} \frac{\Delta S}{\Delta t}.$$

We now go to the limit as $\Delta t \to 0$. Since v and R are constants, this gives

$$\lim_{\Delta t \to 0} \frac{\langle \Delta \boldsymbol{v} \rangle}{\Delta t} = \frac{v}{R} \lim_{\Delta t \to 0} \frac{\Delta S}{\Delta t}.$$

But the limit on the left is just the magnitude a of the instantaneous acceleration, whereas the limit on the right is just the speed v. Hence,

$$a = \frac{v^2}{R}. \tag{22}$$

---

* We cannot simply represent the magnitude of $\Delta \boldsymbol{v}$ by the symbol Δv since we use v to represent the magnitude of the velocity, i.e., the speed, and the symbol Δv would stand for the change in speed. The change in speed and the magnitude of the change in velocity are quite different quantities, as we see from our present example, where the change in speed is identically zero, but the magnitude of the change in velocity is not at all zero.

*A particle moving in a circle of radius R at constant speed v has acceleration **a** which at each instant is directed toward the center of the circle and has magnitude v^2/R.*

This is called the *centripetal* ('center-seeking') acceleration. It is this acceleration that accomplishes the continuous turning of the velocity vector in direction, without change of speed.

In the more general case of motion in a circle with variable speed v, we shall see in Chap. 9 that the acceleration vector has two components: a centripetal component of magnitude v^2/R, which accomplishes the turning of the velocity vector; and a component tangent to the circle of magnitude equal to the rate of change of speed, which accomplishes the change in magnitude of the velocity vector.

PROBLEMS

NOTE: Where freely falling bodies are involved in the following problems, take $g = 32.2$ ft/sec^2 or 9.81 m/sec^2 and neglect air resistance.

1. A runner completes the 100-yd dash in 10 sec. Find his average speed in ft/sec and mi/hr.   Ans: 30 ft/sec; 20.4 mi/hr.

2. If the runner mentioned in Prob. 1 could maintain this average speed, what would be his time for the 220-yd dash? for a run of 1 mi?

3. A motorist makes a round trip from city A to city B, which are 120 mi apart by road. If the time required for the trip from A to B is 3 hr and the time required for the return trip is 4 hr, find (a) the average speed of the car in going from A to B, (b) the average speed of the car on the return trip, and (c) the average speed of the car for the entire trip.

Ans: (a) 40 mi/hr; (b) 30 mi/hr; (c) 34.3 mi/hr.

4. An automobile makes a round trip between two points 200 mi apart by highway. If the outward trip requires 4 hr and the return trip 8 hr, find the average speeds for the outward trip, the return trip, and the complete round trip.

5. Over a 2-sec period, the distance S traveled by a certain body is accurately described by the equation

$$S = (10 \text{ ft/sec}) \, t + (8 \text{ ft/sec}^2) \, t^2 - (2 \text{ ft/sec}^3) \, t^3.$$

Find the instantaneous speed of the body when $t = 2$ sec.   Ans: 18 ft/sec.

6. To illustrate the definition of instantaneous speed as the limit of average speed, compute accurately the average speed of the body in Prob. 5 over the time intervals 0.5 to 1.5 sec, 0.9 to 1.1 sec, and 0.99 to 1.01 sec, and compare with the instantaneous speed at $t = 1$ sec.

7. An automobile travels at 30 mi/hr for 1 hr and then at 10 mi/hr for 1 hr. What is its average speed?   Ans: 20 mi/hr.

8. An automobile travels at 30 mi/hr for 15 mi and then at 10 mi/hr for 15 mi. What is its average speed?

9. A *knot* is a unit of *speed* equal to one nautical mile (6076 ft) per hour. Show that

$$1 \text{ knot} = 1.151 \text{ mi/hr} = 1.688 \text{ ft/sec}.$$

10. Express the speed of a ship traveling at 20 knots in mi/hr and in ft/sec.

11. The motion of a steel ball rolling down an inclined plane is noted at 1-sec intervals, and the data obtained are recorded in the accompanying table. From the data given, calculate the average speed during (a) the first second, (b) the fifth second, and (c) the first 5 seconds.

Ans: (a) 2 cm/sec; (b) 18 cm/sec; (c) 10 cm/sec.

12. From the data given in the accompanying table, calculate the average speed of the steel ball during (a) the sixth second, (b) the ninth second, and (c) the last 5 seconds of motion.

13. To the data shown in the accompanying table, fit a simple equation giving the position S as a function of time. Using this equation, find the instantaneous speed of the ball at the end of the fifth second.   Ans: 20 cm/sec.

14. As in Prob. 13, find the instantaneous speed of the steel ball at $t=3$ sec, $t=6$ sec, and $t=9$ sec.

Time t (sec)	Position S (cm)
0	0
1	2
2	8
3	18
4	32
5	50
6	72
7	98
8	128
9	162
10	200

15. A car is traversing the circular racetrack shown in Fig. 13 at a constant speed of 60 mi/hr. If the circumference of the racetrack is 1 mi and if the car started at point O, find the instantaneous velocity at the end of 15 sec, 30 sec, 45 sec, and 60 sec. What is the average velocity during the first minute?   Ans: 60 mi/hr E; 60 mi/hr S; 60 mi/hr W; 60 mi/hr N; zero.

16. For the car described in Prob. 15, find the average velocity during the first 15 sec, the first 30 sec, and the first 45 sec. What is the average velocity during the first $2\frac{1}{2}$ min? During the time interval $t=30$ sec to $t=60$ sec?

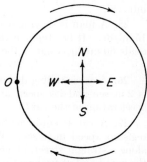

Figure 13

17. The X-coordinate of a particle at time t is given by the expression

$$X = 4 \text{ cm} + (2 \text{ cm/sec})\, t + (3 \text{ cm/sec}^2)\, t^2.$$

Find (a) the X-component of the average velocity of the particle during the first 5 seconds and (b) the X-component of the instantaneous velocity of the particle at the end of the fifth second.   Ans: (a) 17 cm/sec; (b) 32 cm/sec.

18. For the particle mentioned in Prob. 17, find the X-component of the average velocity during the first 3-sec interval and during the second 3-sec interval, and find the X-component of the velocity when $t=6$ sec.

19. In order to cross a stream flowing at 6 mi/hr in a boat that travels at 10 mi/hr, at what angle upstream should the boat be headed in order to reach the point directly opposite? What is the speed of the boat relative to the ground?   Ans: 36°9; 8.00 mi/hr.

20. An airplane with an airspeed of 200 knots desires to proceed due northwest when a wind of 100 knots is blowing from due west. In what direction should the plane head and what will be its ground speed?

21. A river 1 mi wide flows due north at 8 mi/hr. A motorboat travels at 6 mi/hr relative to the water. A man starts from the west bank in the boat and desires to reach the point on the east bank directly opposite. The boat is incapable of landing at this point because it cannot travel as fast as the water. The man must land downstream and walk back along the bank. He walks at 3 mi/hr.

(a) At what angle should he *head* the boat to reach his objective in *minimum time?* What are the times of crossing, of walking along the bank, and the total time?   (b) Compare with the case in which he *heads* due east so as to minimize the time of crossing.   (c) Compare with the case in which he heads due southeast.

Ans: (a) 33°0 south

of east; 11.9, 18.7, 30.6 min; (b) 10.0, 26.7, 36.7 min; (c) 14.2, 17.8, 32.0 min.

22. Repeat Prob. 21(a) for the case in which the boat will go 9 mi/hr, but the man still desires to minimize his time by walking along the bank.   Compare the total time with the time required if the boat proceeds directly to the opposite point on the bank.

23. An automobile is moving eastward along a straight road at a speed of 60 mi/hr when the brakes are applied.   If the car is brought to rest in 20 sec, what is the average acceleration of the car during this interval?

Ans: 4.4 ft/sec² westward.

24. A car moving northward along a straight road at a speed of 45 mi/hr is brought to rest in 30 sec.   Find the average acceleration of the car during this interval.

25. A man is driving a car eastward along a straight highway at a speed of 15 mi/hr.   If he steps on the accelerator and one minute later the speedometer reads 60 mi/hr, what is the average acceleration of the car?

Ans: 1.1 ft/sec² eastward.

26. A car is rolling down a long straight slope.   If the initial speed of the car is 2 m/sec and its speed at the end of 8 sec is 14 m/sec, what is the average acceleration of the car?

27. A car is equipped with a special speedometer that registers speed in ft/sec.   While the car is moving eastward along a straight street, an occupant of the front seat observes the speed and at various times records the data shown in the table.   From these data calculate the average acceleration (a) during the first 6 seconds of motion, (b) during the interval $t=4$ sec to $t=6$ sec, and (c) during the interval $t=6$ sec to $t=8$ sec.   Ans: (a) 3 ft/sec² eastward; (b) 4 ft/sec² eastward;   (c) −1 ft/sec² eastward or 1 ft/sec² westward.

Time (sec)	Speed (ft/sec)
0	0
2	4
4	10
6	18
8	16
10	8
12	4
14	0

28. From the data given in the table, find the average acceleration (a) during the first 4 seconds, (b) during the interval $t=8$ sec to $t=12$ sec, and (c) during the entire period of motion.

29. A train increases its speed at the rate of 15 mi/hr per minute.   Express its acceleration in ft/sec².   Ans: 0.367 ft/sec².

30. A sled starting from rest has a constant acceleration of 2 ft/sec² in a certain direction.   What is the change in velocity during the first six seconds of motion?   What is the average velocity of the sled during this time?   How far does the sled move?

31. Find the distance traveled by the sled in Prob. 30 in each of the first 8 seconds.   Ans: 1, 3, 5, 7, 9, 11, 13, 15 ft.

32. Find the average velocity of the sled in Prob. 30 in each of the first 6 seconds.

33. Two sleds are initially at the top of a steep slope.   Two seconds after starting, the first sled has moved a distance of 16 ft down the slope, and the second sled begins its descent.   If both sleds start from rest and have the same constant acceleration, what is the distance between the sleds 4 sec after the second sled starts down the slope?   Ans: 80 ft.

34. An automobile moving along a straight road at a speed of 60 mi/hr passes a motor patrolman. Just as the automobile passes, the patrolman starts his motorcycle. If the motorcycle has a constant acceleration of 1.5 ft/sec², how long will it take the patrolman to overtake the speeding motorist? What will be the speed and total displacement of the motorcycle at the time the motorist is overtaken?

35. A car starts from rest and travels eastward. If the speed of the car at the end of one minute is 60 mi/hr, how far does the car travel during this time if the acceleration is constant? What is the magnitude of the acceleration?
                                        Ans: 2640 ft; 1.47 ft/sec².

36. A car moving west at a speed of 45 mi/hr is brought to rest in 30 sec. If the acceleration is uniform, how far does the car travel? What is the magnitude of the acceleration?

37. A motorcycle moving with an initial velocity of 20 m/sec experiences a constant deceleration of 3 m/sec². How far does the motorcycle move during the first 4 seconds after its velocity begins to decrease?   Ans: 56 m.

38. A car has an initial velocity of 15 m/sec and experiences a constant deceleration of 2 m/sec². How far has the car moved by the time its velocity is reduced to 5 m/sec?

39. A car has a velocity of 60 mi/hr. If the driver applies the brakes so as to produce constant deceleration and brings the car to rest in a distance of 200 ft, what is the magnitude of the deceleration?   Ans: 19.4 ft/sec².

40. A golf ball rolls across a green and experiences constant deceleration. If the initial velocity of the ball was 3 m/sec and if the ball comes to rest after traveling 4 m, what was the magnitude of the deceleration?

41. A certain airplane taking off from a landing strip experiences a constant acceleration during its take-off run. If the plane leaves the ground with a horizontal velocity of 120 mi/hr after a run of 2000 ft, what was the magnitude of its acceleration?   Ans: 7.74 ft/sec².

42. An airplane moving at a speed of 90 mi/hr lands at the end of a runway and is brought to rest after a run of 1200 ft. If the deceleration was constant, what was its magnitude?

43. A golf ball is dropped from the top of a tall building. Find the magnitude of the instantaneous downward velocity of the ball at the end of successive half-second intervals after its release, for the first three seconds.
                 Ans: 16.1 ft/sec, 32.2 ft/sec, 48.3 ft/sec, · · · .

44. Find the magnitude of the downward displacement of the ball described in Prob. 43 at the end of successive half-second intervals for the first three seconds.

45. A baseball is batted vertically upward. If the initial upward velocity is 96.6 ft/sec, find the upward displacement and the magnitude and direction of the velocity at one-second intervals until the ball returns to its initial position.
                 Ans: $Y = 0, 80.5, 129, 145, · · ·$ ft; $v_Y = 96.6, 64.4, 32.2, 0, · · ·$ ft/sec.

46. Prove that an object projected vertically upward with initial speed v_0 (a) has again speed v_0 when it returns to its starting point, (b) takes the same time to go up to the top of its path as it does to return to its starting point.

47. A man at the top of a tall building throws a ball vertically downward with an initial velocity of 40 ft/sec. Find the downward displacement of the ball at the end of two seconds.   Ans: 144 ft.

48. Show that the average velocity of a freely falling body dropped from rest is $(n - \frac{1}{2})g$ sec downward during the nth second of motion.

49. With what velocity must a ball be thrown vertically upward in order to rise to a height of 100 ft? How long will it remain in the air? What will be the downward acceleration of the ball at the highest point reached?

Ans: 80.3 ft/sec; 4.98 sec; 32.2 ft/sec².

50. With what velocity must a ball be thrown vertically upward in order to reach a height of 20 m? How long will it remain in the air? What will be its downward acceleration at the highest point reached?

51. If a bullet is fired vertically upward with an initial velocity of 1200 ft/sec, at what height will its velocity be reduced to 600 ft/sec?   Ans: 16,800 ft.

52. What will be the velocity of the bullet of Prob. 51 at a height of 1 mile?

53. A shell is fired horizontally from a gun located 64.4 ft above a horizontal plane. The muzzle velocity of this shell is 1000 ft/sec. How long does the shell remain in the air? What is its range?   Ans: 2 sec; 2000 ft.

54. A bomb is dropped from a plane in level flight at 400 ft/sec at an altitude of 10,000 ft. Determine the distance the bomb travels horizontally before striking the target, that is, the horizontal distance of the 'bomb-release' point from the aiming point.

55. A gun pointed 30° above the horizontal fires a shell with a muzzle velocity of 640 ft/sec. If the muzzle of the gun is at ground level, find the position of the projectile at the ends of successive two-second intervals after the gun is fired, until the shell returns to earth. Plot a curve showing the path of the shell.

Ans: $X = 1108$ ft, 2217 ft, $\cdots$; $Y = 576$ ft, 1022 ft, $\cdots$.

56. Find the positions of the shell in Prob. 55 at the ends of successive two-second intervals if the gun is pointed 60° above the horizontal, and plot a curve showing the path of the shell.

57. Find the vertical and horizontal components of the velocity of the shell in Prob. 55 at the ends of successive two-second intervals.

Ans: $v_X = 554$ ft/sec (constant); $v_Y = 256$ ft/sec, 191 ft/sec, $\cdots$.

58. If the range of a gun pointed 30° above the horizontal is 15 miles, to what altitude in miles will the shell rise if the gun is pointed vertically?

59. From the parametric equations (19) and (20) for the path of a projectile, derive a single equation in X and Y for the path.

Ans: $Y = (v_{Y0}/v_{X0})X - \frac{1}{2}(g/v_{x0}^2)X^2$.

60. Find the maximum height attained by a projectile if the vertical component of the initial velocity is v_{Y0}.

61. Derive an expression giving the range R of a shell fired from ground level on a level plain with muzzle velocity v_0 at an angle θ_0 above the horizontal.

Ans: $R = (v_0^2 \sin 2\theta_0)/g$.

62. By differentiation of the equation derived in Prob. 61, show that the elevation angle θ_0 for which the range is a maximum is 45°.

63. A baseball player throws a baseball with a velocity of magnitude 96 ft/sec in a direction 30° above the horizontal. If the baseball leaves the thrower's hand at a height of 6 ft above the field, find the maximum height attained and the horizontal distance traversed by the ball before it strikes the ground.

Ans: 41.6 ft; 257 ft.

64. A baseball pitcher throws a ball whose initial velocity is horizontal. If the ball drops one foot in traveling the 60-ft distance between mound and plate, what was its initial speed?

65. During the First World War, the Germans bombarded Paris with a specially constructed long-range gun (Big Bertha). The length of the gun barrel was approximately 120 ft and the muzzle velocity was approximately 4800 ft/sec. For an elevation angle $\theta_0 = 45°$, calculate the range in the absence of air resistance. (The maximum range actually attained was about 132,000 yd with $\theta_0 = 55°$; in the case of this very high muzzle velocity, air resistance is seen to have a very important effect.)   Ans: 239,000 yd.

66. Calculate the acceleration (assumed constant) of the projectile in passing through the gun barrel and also the maximum height attained by the projectile in Prob. 65.

67. The shell fired from a trench mortar has a muzzle velocity of 300 ft/sec. Calculate two angles of elevation at which the mortar can be fired in order to hit a target 1500 ft away and at the same level as the mortar. Calculate the maximum heights and the times of flight in 'direct' and 'indirect' fire at the target.

Ans: $\theta_0 = 16°2$ and $73°8$; $h = 109$ ft and 1290 ft; $t = 5.21$ sec and 17.9 sec.

68. In Fig. 14, a gun is 'bore-sighted' on a target. At the instant the projectile leaves the muzzle of the gun, the target starts to fall from rest, vertically. Show that for any angle of elevation of the gun, any muzzle

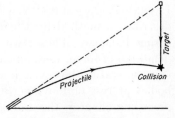

Figure 14

velocity, and any distance to the target, the projectile will always hit the target if the effect of air resistance is negligible.

69. A ball at the end of a string is whirled at constant speed in a horizontal plane. If the radius of the circle is 4 ft and the speed of the ball is 10 ft/sec, calculate the magnitude of the centripetal acceleration.   Ans: 25 ft/sec².

70. If the radius of the circle in Prob. 69 were increased to 12 ft without changing the speed of the ball, what would be the magnitude of the centripetal acceleration?

71. A car moves at a speed of 60 mi/hr around a curve of 500-ft radius. What is the acceleration of the car?

Ans: 15.5 ft/sec² toward the center of curvature.

72. If the speed of the car in Prob. 71 were reduced to 45 mi/hr, what would be the acceleration of the car?

73. The armature of an electric motor has a diameter of 2 ft and turns at 3000 rev/min. Calculate the magnitudes of the velocity and the acceleration of a point on the periphery of the armature.   Ans: 314 ft/sec; 98,700 ft/sec².

74. The flywheel on a stationary steam engine is 4 ft in diameter and makes 600 rev/min. Calculate the magnitudes of the instantaneous velocity and acceleration of a point on the rim of the flywheel.

CHAPTER 4

DYNAMICS OF A PARTICLE

IN CHAPTER 2 we stated Newton's first and third principles of motion and described a method by which forces could be measured by means of a spring balance. These two principles, together with this operational definition of force, were adequate for the treatment of problems encountered in statics; however, it will be recalled that statics dealt only with bodies at rest or moving with constant velocity. As we noted in the preceding chapter, the motion of a body generally involves *acceleration*. In order to discuss the influence of forces in producing acceleration, it is necessary to define more clearly what we mean by the term *force;* this definition is given by Newton's *second* principle of motion. The three Newtonian principles provide the basis of *dynamics*, which is the study of motion in terms of the forces that produce it.

Since Newton's principles play such an important role in the subject of mechanics, we shall discuss in detail the reasoning involved in their formulation. Briefly, we can say that *the first step was experimental*, involving observation of the motion of interacting bodies; the directly observable kinematic factors were *positions* and *times*, from which velocities and accelerations could be calculated. From accelerations occurring during interactions between pairs of bodies, Newton showed that it is possible to attribute to every body a property called its *mass*. Newton found it desirable to describe the observed interaction in terms of the three quantities *mass*, *length*, and *time*, which we call *fundamental quantities*. *The second step involved the formulation of a set of principles* giving a consistent account of the experimental observations. These principles involve certain assumptions and the introduction of a fourth quantity called *force*, which is *defined* in terms of the three fundamental quantities by Newton's second principle. That bodies can be assigned a fundamental attribute called mass is demonstrated experimentally; the second principle is essentially a very useful *definition* of a quantity called force in terms of this attribute. Since the second principle is of the nature of a definition, one cannot ask for a *proof* of this principle by experiment.

Newton formulated his principles in order to give a single coherent account of experiments actually performed. In Newton's own words,

76

"These laws must be considered as resting on convictions drawn from observation and experiment, not on intuitive perception." The real justification or 'proof' of Newton's principles is the success with which they and the relationships based upon them can be applied to the practical problems encountered in physics and engineering. Their publication occurred in 1687, and it was not until the beginning of the twentieth century that it was discovered that there were types of problems that could not be handled by the classical dynamics based upon Newton's principles. One of these types involves motion at high speeds, comparable with the speed of light (186,000 mi/sec), and must be treated by Einstein's *relativistic mechanics;* the other type involves atomic and subatomic particles, to which *quantum mechanics* must be applied. It should be pointed out that relativistic and quantum mechanics both reduce to classical Newtonian mechanics when applied to bodies such as automobiles, bullets, baseballs, and locomotives, moving at the velocities involved in ordinary engineering applications. Hence Newton's principles are applicable to the problems we shall discuss in this and most of the following chapters.

1. NEWTON'S FIRST PRINCIPLE

BY A SERIES of experiments (employing, for example, small spherical bodies rolling on a horizontal table top), Galileo and Newton were led to make the following postulate in regard to the motion of a particle:

NEWTON'S FIRST PRINCIPLE: *A particle left to itself will maintain its velocity unchanged.*

This postulate includes the case of a stationary particle, whose velocity remains zero as long as the particle is 'left to itself'; here the postulate seems obvious. In the case of moving particles the postulate is an idealization from experimental observations. For example, a marble rolling across a rug quickly comes to rest as a result of interaction with the rug; the same marble rolling across a bare floor will move for a much longer time before coming to rest because the horizontal interaction between the marble and floor is smaller than the interaction between the marble and the rug; in neither case is the marble really 'left to itself.' In no way is it possible to perform an experiment in which a body is left completely to itself, and hence, in the case of a moving object, it is clear that the above postulate is a pure idealization which cannot be realized in an experiment; the same is true in the case of a stationary particle.

Let us now introduce the concept of *force* in the manner it was introduced in the statement of the first principle given in Chap. 2:

A particle will retain a constant velocity unless acted on by external forces.

Comparison of this statement with the one given above reveals two implications: (1) *external forces* act on a body as a result of *interactions* with other bodies, and (2) *external forces* acting on a body tend to *produce acceleration*. It should be noted that the first principle leaves the quantitative relationship between the external force and the acceleration undefined. This relationship is given by the second principle.

2. MASS

THE PROPERTY of a body by which it maintains a constant velocity when 'left to itself' is called *inertia*. Newton, in formulating his principles, found it desirable to introduce *mass* as a measure of inertia.

Whenever a given particle experiences an *acceleration*, the acceleration must be attributed to the influence of other particles; this follows from the first principle. The other particles are said to *exert forces* on the particle under observation; as a result of these *external forces*, the particle is accelerated. Newton first studied the acceleration produced by interactions between *pairs* of particles.

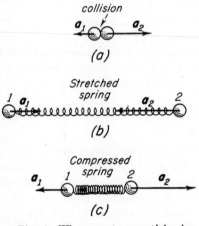

(a)

(b)

(c)

Fig. 1. Whenever two particles interact, their accelerations are oppositely directed and have a constant magnitude ratio. Since the two accelerations shown above have different magnitudes, the balls must be assumed to be of different materials, such as lead and wood.

He noted that *whenever there was an acceleration of one particle, there was also an acceleration of the other particle*. The accelerations were found to be oppositely directed, as shown in Fig. 1.

As to the magnitudes of the two accelerations, a_1 and a_2, Newton concluded *as a result of his observations* that their ratio was always a constant for a given pair of particles, provided there were no interactions with other bodies. This conclusion is found to be valid regardless of the type of interaction between the bodies studied; whether the interaction is of elastic, electrostatic, or gravitational character, the ratio of the accelerations experienced by the two interacting bodies is always the same, provided interactions with other bodies can be ignored. As we have noted before, complete isolation of a single body is impossible of experimental realization; similarly, *two* interacting bodies cannot be *completely* isolated from all other bodies, and hence Newton's conclusion involves an idealization of the experiments actually performed.

All evidence points to the fact that Newton's conclusion is correct. This conclusion may be stated in the form

$$a_2/a_1 = \text{constant} = R_{12},$$

where the ratio R_{12} has a definite constant value for any two particles, 1 and 2, as shown in Fig. 1. Newton concluded further that the accelerations experienced during an interaction were always oppositely directed. Thus, a vector equation may be written,

$$\boldsymbol{a}_2 = -R_{12}\,\boldsymbol{a}_1,$$

where the constant R_{12} is a positive number. In interpreting R_{12}, Newton proposed to assign a number m_1 to one particle and to define a corresponding number m_2 for the other particle by the equation

$$R_{12} = m_1/m_2.$$

Therefore,
$$\frac{a_2}{a_1} = \frac{m_1}{m_2},$$

or
$$m_2 = (a_1/a_2)m_1, \tag{1a}$$

where the acceleration ratio (a_1/a_2) is determinable from experimental observation. In this manner, if a number m_1, called the *mass*, is arbitrarily assigned to particle 1, the value m_2 of mass to be assigned to particle 2 is determined. Similarly, by an experiment in which particle 1 is made to interact in any manner with a third particle 3, a mass is determined for 3 by the relation

$$m_3 = (a_1/a_3)m_1. \tag{1b}$$

In this manner a value of mass may be assigned to any particle in terms of the mass assigned to the standard particle 1.

We now need to introduce another generalization from experiment that was made by Newton. If particles 2 and 3 are assigned masses m_2 and m_3 by experiments in which first one and then the other interacts with particle 1, and then particles 2 and 3 are made to interact with each other in any manner, the same values of masses may be used to determine the ratios of the accelerations in this interaction. The relation is

$$\frac{a_3}{a_2} = \frac{m_2}{m_3} \quad \text{or} \quad m_2 a_2 = m_3 a_3.$$

This experimental fact shows that the mass values determined in terms of a standard particle to which an arbitrary mass is assigned are universally applicable in determining the ratios of the accelerations in the interaction between any two particles.

The mass is said to be a measure of the inertia of a particle since in the relation $m_1 a_1 = m_2 a_2$ the particle of greater mass has the lesser acceleration in the interaction. The simple demonstration indicated in Fig. 2(a) illustrates this equation. We might place on a billard table two balls of the same diameter but composed of different materials, say wood and lead.   Attempts to set the balls in motion with the cue make it evident immediately that the mass (inertia) of the lead ball is greater than that of the wooden ball, since the lead ball has a greater tendency to remain at rest and is more difficult to accelerate than the wooden ball.   In a sense, we use the cue as a 'standard body' to interact with the two balls.   We might compare the masses of the two balls by a more direct interaction between them with the arrangement shown in Fig. 2(b).   We place the two balls in small cars connected by a light spring.   If the cars are separated by stretching the spring and then released, the acceleration of the wooden ball will be greater than that of the lead ball; again we conclude that the mass of the lead ball is greater.   A third demonstration we

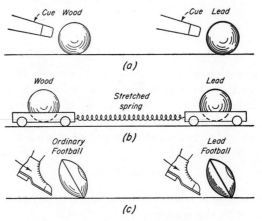

Fig. 2. Comparison of masses.

might perform is indicated in Fig. 2(c).   Here we have an ordinary football and another football made of lead; a kicker would have no difficulty in telling which ball has the greater mass and the lesser acceleration from interaction with his foot.

> The **mass** of a body is defined by the equation $m = (a_S/a)m_S$ when an experiment is performed in which the body interacts with a 'standard' body assigned mass m_S, and the body experiences acceleration a and the standard body acceleration a_S.

We shall describe later convenient and accurate methods of comparing masses.   However, in principle, equation (1) enables us to determine the mass m of any body in terms of the mass m_S of some standard body.   It is, of course, important that some one standard mass should be selected as a unit in terms of which all other masses can be measured.   The *standard unit mass is called the kilogram* (kg), and is the mass of a standard cylinder of platinum-iridium kept at the International Bureau of Weights and Measures at Sèvres, France (see Fig. 1, p. 2).   This unit mass and the *gram* (g), which is 0.001 kg, are the units used in scientific work. The mass unit commonly used in English-speaking countries is the *pound-mass:*

The **pound-mass** is legally defined as 453.5924277 g.

An important quantity associated with matter is its *density:*

Density is defined as mass per unit volume.

Data on the densities of various materials are given in Table I. Water has the density of 1000 kg/m³ = 1.0000 g/cm³. The meter and kilogram were originally designed to make this density exactly 1000 kg/m³ at the temperature at which water has maximum density (39° F); this objective was actually missed by 3 parts in 100,000. The ratio of the density of a substance to that of water is called the *specific gravity* of the substance.

TABLE I

TYPICAL DENSITIES OF LIQUIDS AND SOLIDS AT 68° F

Liquids	kg/m³	pounds-mass/ft³	Solid metals	kg/m³	pounds-mass/ft³
Water (32–50° F)...	1,000	62.43	Aluminum.........	2,700	169
Sea water..........	1,030	64.4	Cast iron..........	7,200	449
Benzene...........	879	54.9	Copper............	8,890	555
Carbon tetrachloride.	1,594	99.5	Gold..............	19,300	1205
Ethyl alcohol.......	789	49.3	Lead..............	11,340	708
Gasoline..........	680	42.5	Magnesium........	1,740	109
Kerosene..........	800	49.9	Nickel............	8,850	553
Lubricating oil......	900	56.2	Silver.............	10,500	656
Methyl alcohol.....	792	49.4	Steel.............	7,800	487
100% sulfuric acid..	1,831	114.3	Tungsten..........	19,000	1190
Turpentine........	873	54.5	Zinc.............	7,140	446
Mercury (32° F)....	13,595	848.7	Brass or bronze.....	8,700	543

Nonmetallic solids	kg/m³	pounds-mass/ft³	Woods	kg/m³	pounds-mass/ft³
Ice (32° F).........	922	57.5	Balsa.............	130	8
Concrete..........	2300	144	Pine..............	480	30
Earth, packed......	1500	94	Maple............	640	40
Glass.............	2600	160	Oak..............	720	45
Granite...........	2700	169	Mahogany........	560	35

3. NEWTON'S SECOND PRINCIPLE

WHEN TWO particles interact in such a way that they are accelerated, they are said to exert *forces* on each other. The product *ma* is taken as the measure of the force, except for an arbitrary constant factor that defines the size of the particular force unit used. *This is the fundamental definition of force.* It is convenient because the above discussion shows that, when two particles interact, $m_1\boldsymbol{a}_1 = -m_2\boldsymbol{a}_2$, so the two particles exert equal and opposite forces on each other.

Fundamentally, all forces are exerted by individual particles on each other. In practice, a given particle may experience forces from a large number of other particles simultaneously, and we need to know how these forces compound. Here we have recourse to a further generalization that Newton made from experimental observation. Suppose that three particles, 1, 2, and 3, are simultaneously interacting as in Fig. 3. Suppose that if particle 3 were not present, particle 1 would experience acceleration $\boldsymbol{a}_{12}$ owing to particle 2 alone, and that if particle 2 were not present, 1 would have acceleration $\boldsymbol{a}_{13}$ owing to 3. Then it is concluded from experience that with all three particles present, particle 1 will have acceleration

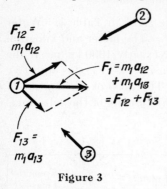

Figure 3

$$\boldsymbol{a}_1 = \boldsymbol{a}_{12} + \boldsymbol{a}_{13},$$

the vector sum. Multiplying this equation through by m_1, we obtain

$$m_1\boldsymbol{a}_1 = m_1\boldsymbol{a}_{12} + m_1\boldsymbol{a}_{13}.$$

Except for a constant common factor involved in the choice of the force unit, $m_1\boldsymbol{a}_{12}$ is $\boldsymbol{F}_{12}$, the force exerted by 2 on 1; $m_1\boldsymbol{a}_{13}$ is $\boldsymbol{F}_{13}$, the force exerted by 3 on 1; and $m_1\boldsymbol{a}_1$ is *defined* as the *resultant* force $\boldsymbol{F}_1$ acting on particle 1. Hence with this definition, forces compound vectorially and the preceding equation gives

$$\boldsymbol{F}_1 = \boldsymbol{F}_{12} + \boldsymbol{F}_{13}.$$

Thus the resultant force acting on a particle is defined as the vector sum of the various forces exerted on that particle by other particles.

The cases we have considered in the chapters on statics are those where the resultant force is zero. If the resultant force $\boldsymbol{F}$ is not zero the particle of mass m experiences an acceleration $\boldsymbol{a}$ given by

$$k\boldsymbol{F} = m\boldsymbol{a}, \qquad (2)$$

where we have explicitly written the constant k to permit various choices of size of the force unit. From equation (2) we can obtain the proportionality relation

$$\boldsymbol{a} \propto \frac{F}{m} \qquad (3)$$

which, stated in words, gives

NEWTON'S SECOND PRINCIPLE: *The acceleration of a particle is directly proportional to the resultant external force acting on the particle, is inversely proportional to the mass of the particle, and has the same direction as the resultant force.*

It is seen that Newton's first principle is really a special case of the second principle in which the force, and hence the acceleration, vanish.

In equation (2), we are free to choose any value of the constant k we please. Different choices of k correspond to different choices of the size of the unit in which F is measured. The simplest choice, $k = 1$, gives the simple relation

$$F = m\boldsymbol{a}, \tag{4}$$

according to which unit force would be defined as the force that will give unit acceleration to a unit mass.

In the MKS system of units, the unit of length is the meter, the unit of mass is the kilogram, the unit of time is the second, and the unit of force defined by equation (4) is the *newton* (nt).

> The **newton** is the resultant force that imparts to a one-kilogram mass an acceleration of one meter per second per second.

The newton is called an *absolute unit* of force because its value is defined in terms of its effect on an object quite independently of the position of the object in the universe.*

We note that the name *newton* is an abbreviation for $kg{\cdot}m/sec^2$:

$$1 \text{ nt} = 1 \text{ kg·m/sec}^2. \tag{5}$$

In solving dynamical problems in metric absolute units, forces will come out initially in kg·m/sec^2, and this fact can be used as a check on the correctness of the work. *Force* is a derived quantity of physical dimensions $mass \times length/time^2$.

The *weight* of a body is by definition the force exerted on the body in its gravitational interaction with the earth. Since this force is sufficient to give the body an acceleration $\boldsymbol{g}$, the weight is

$$w = m\boldsymbol{g}, \tag{6}$$

in nt if m is the mass of the body in kg and g is in m/sec^2.

---

* Just as the newton is defined as the absolute unit of force in the MKS system, so also we might define an absolute unit of force in the British system of units by means of equation (4) with m in pounds-mass and $\boldsymbol{a}$ in ft/sec^2. The resulting force unit (called the *poundal*) is inconveniently small and is not widely used; gravitational units are generally used in engineering applications and will be used in this text when British units are used. The gravitational force units will be defined in Sec. 5 of this chapter. A more complete discussion of the various possible systems of units is given in the Appendix.

Equation (6) shows that the weight of a body at a given position on the earth's surface is directly proportional to the mass of the body. This fact suggests immediately the possibility of comparing the *masses* of bodies by comparing their *weights*. The simplest scheme for doing this involves the use of a beam balance as shown in Fig. 4. A uniform beam is mounted with its center of gravity over the knife-edge support; a standard mass m_s and an unknown mass m are suspended from the beam and their positions are varied until the beam is balanced. When the

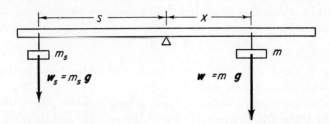

Fig. 4. Comparison of masses by means of a balance.

beam is balanced, we may make use of the condition of rotational equilibrium by taking moments about the knife-edge:

clockwise torque = counterclockwise torque,
$$wX = w_s S$$

where w and w_s are the weights of the unknown and standard bodies and S and X are the distances from the points of suspension of these bodies to the knife-edge support.

Since $w = mg$ and $w_s = m_s g$, this equation leads to $mg\,X = m_s g\,S$. Since g is the same for both bodies in a given locality, we find that

$$mX = m_s S, \quad \text{or} \quad m = (S/X)m_s.$$

The experimental determination of the unknown mass m in terms of the standard mass m_s therefore involves merely a measurement of the ratio of two distances S and X. However, it should be noted that we are really comparing the interactions of each of the two bodies with a third body— the earth itself.

Example. *What is the weight of a man of* 100-kg *mass* (a) *on a mountain near the equator where* $g = 9.76$ m/sec²? (b) *at sea level and* 60° *latitude where* $g = 9.82$ m/sec²?

The weights in newtons are obtained directly from equations (6) and (5):

       (a) $w = mg = (100 \text{ kg})(9.76 \text{ m/sec}^2) = 976$ nt;
       (b) $w = mg = (100 \text{ kg})(9.82 \text{ m/sec}^2) = 982$ nt.

These are the magnitudes of the weights; the directions are of course along the downward verticals.

4. NEWTON'S THIRD PRINCIPLE

Now THAT we have defined force by Newton's second principle, let us return to the relationship

$$m_1\boldsymbol{a}_1 = -m_2\boldsymbol{a}_2 \qquad (7)$$

that Newton used in comparing masses.   By the second principle,

$$\boldsymbol{F}_1 = m_1\boldsymbol{a}_1 \qquad (8a)$$

is the *resultant force acting on the particle of mass* m_1.   Since equation (7) assumes that only two particles are involved, we may say that $\boldsymbol{F}_1$ *is the force exerted on particle 1 by particle 2*.   Similarly,

$$\boldsymbol{F}_2 = m_2\boldsymbol{a}_2 \qquad (8b)$$

is the force exerted on particle 2 by particle 1.   Substitution of (8a) and (8b) in equation (7) leads to the result

$$\boldsymbol{F}_1 = -\boldsymbol{F}_2, \qquad (9)$$

which states that the force exerted on particle 1 by particle 2 is equal in magnitude and opposite in direction to the force exerted on particle 2 by particle 1.   Figure 5(a) gives a diagram showing the results of a repulsive

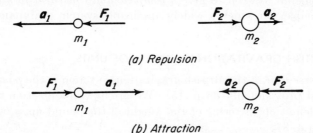

(a) Repulsion

(b) Attraction

Fig. 5. When two particles interact, the magnitude of the force exerted on the first particle by the second particle is equal to the magnitude of the force exerted on the second particle by the first. The forces are oppositely directed.

interaction between 'particle' 1 and 'particle' 2; Fig. 5(b) shows the results of an attractive interaction.   Calling the force exerted *on* particle 1 *by* particle 2 the *action* and the force exerted *on* particle 2 *by* particle 1 the *reaction*, we may state equation (9) as follows:

NEWTON'S THIRD PRINCIPLE: *To every action there is an equal and opposite reaction.*

It can be readily shown that if this principle is true for each pair of 'particles,' it is true for the more general situations depicted in Fig. 1 of Chap. 2.

Let us now give a résumé of the processes used in formulating Newton's laws.   There were four conclusions based on idealizations of experiments:

(a) The velocity of a particle is constant as long as there are no interactions with other particles.

(b) When two particles interact, they both experience accelerations. The accelerations are oppositely directed, and the ratio of the accelerations is a constant for a given pair of particles, independent of the method by which they interact.

(c) Characteristic masses can be assigned to each particle, by comparison with a standard particle, such that when *any* two particles interact the ratio of their accelerations is the inverse of the ratio of their preassigned masses.

(d) When a particle interacts with several other particles simultaneously, the acceleration it experiences is the vector sum of the accelerations it would experience by interacting with each of the other particles individually.

Conclusion (a) is the *first principle*. Conclusions (b) and (c) permit the definition of *mass*, and hence of *force* as *ma*. Conclusion (d) shows that forces obey the law of vector addition and hence permits formulation of the *second principle* in terms of resultant force. Conclusion (b) and the definition of force lead directly to the *third principle*.

It might be mentioned that many of the ideas involved in Newton's principles had been evolved by others during and before Newton's time. For example, the first principle had been stated by Galileo. However, it remained for Newton to give a *complete and consistent formulation* of three principles on which a widely applicable system of dynamics could be based.

5. THE BRITISH GRAVITATIONAL SYSTEM OF UNITS

THE *force unit* in the British gravitational system is the *pound*, which we defined provisionally on p. 15. We are now in a position to give its rigorous definition in terms of the weight of the pound-mass, which was defined on p. 81:

> The **pound** is the weight of the pound-mass at a place where the acceleration of gravity has the 'standard' value $g_0 = 32.17398$ ft/sec^2.

This gravitational force unit is of a magnitude that is convenient for most engineering applications.

However, if the pound is employed as the force unit and the pound-mass is used as the mass unit, equation (4) cannot be used for Newton's second law, and equation (2) with an appropriate value for k must be used; this is done in some engineering work. We shall adopt a different procedure which has the widest usage in engineering practice. This procedure permits us to use the convenient expression (4) for Newton's second law, with the proportionality constant k equal to unity. We may use this expression with F in lb provided we select a mass unit of proper size; this mass unit is called the *slug:*

> The **slug** is the mass of a body that experiences an acceleration of 1 ft/sec^2 when a resultant force of 1 lb acts upon it.

A procedure that involves the definition of a new mass unit, the *slug*, in terms of a force unit, the *lb*, may at first seem rather involved, particularly in view of the fact that the *lb* was itself defined in terms of the gravitational force exerted upon another mass.   However, this procedure is actually worthwhile because it permits us to use a force unit of *convenient* size in the *convenient* equation $F = ma$.   Whenever British units are used in this equation, the force should be expressed in *lb*, the mass in *slugs*, and the acceleration in *ft/sec²*.

Since 1 lb will by definition give 1 pound-mass an acceleration of 32.174 ft/sec² and will give a 1-slug mass an acceleration of only 1 ft/sec², it follows from Newton's second law in the form $a \propto F/m$ that the slug is 32.174 times the pound-mass:

$$1 \text{ slug} = 32.174 \text{ pounds-mass.}$$

From the equation $F = ma$, which is valid with F in lb, m in slugs, a in ft/sec², it follows that the pound is a unit equal to the slug·ft/sec²:

$$1 \text{ lb} = 1 \text{ slug·ft/sec}^2. \tag{10}$$

From the definition, 1 pound-mass $= 0.4536$ kg, it follows that

$$1 \text{ slug} = 32.17 \text{ pounds-mass} = 14.59 \text{ kg.} \tag{11}$$

Also, by (10) and (5):

$$1 \text{ lb} = 1 \text{ slug·ft/sec}^2 = 14.59 \text{ kg·0.3048 m/sec}^2 = 4.448 \text{ nt.} \tag{12}$$

To summarize, both of the systems of units that we shall use are based on the convenient expression

$$F = ma \qquad \begin{Bmatrix} F \text{ in nt} \\ m \text{ in kg} \\ a \text{ in m/sec}^2 \end{Bmatrix} \text{ or } \begin{Bmatrix} F \text{ in lb} \\ m \text{ in slugs} \\ a \text{ in ft/sec}^2 \end{Bmatrix} \tag{13}$$

for Newton's second law; in this equation, the proportionality factor k in (2) is unity.   When International metric units are employed, we use the MKS *absolute system*.   This system is called an *absolute* system, since the units are defined in a way that does not refer to the magnitude of terrestrial gravitation.   When English units are employed, we use the *British gravitational system*.   This system is called a *gravitational* system, since the force unit is defined in terms of gravitational effects at a specified position.

In either system, the weight of a body is

$$w = mg. \tag{14}$$

In this equation, the units must be the same as in (13).

From the definition of the lb, we see that at a point where g has its standard value, the weight of a body in lb is numerically the same as its mass in pounds-mass.   But where g does not have its standard value, this is not true.   To determine the weight we should have to divide the mass in pounds-mass by 32.174 to determine the mass in slugs and then multiply this mass by g to determine the weight in lb.   We note from the table on p. 64 that on the earth's surface g does not depart by more than a fraction of a per cent from its standard value, and hence that for most engineering purposes the weight of a body in lb may be taken as numerically equal to its mass in pounds-mass.   This numerical equality may usually be assumed in working the problems in this text.   The mass in slugs will then be numerically equal to the weight in lb divided by 32.2.

Example.   *A resultant force of* 8 lb *acts on a body weighing* 16.1 lb.   *Determine, to engineering accuracy, the resultant acceleration of the body.*

Before we can substitute in (13) to find the acceleration, we must determine the mass of the body in slugs.   We are given the weight of the body in lb, we are given no information about the exact value of g, so to engineering accuracy we can take the standard value $g = 32.2$ ft/sec². Substitution in (14) gives the mass of the body as

$$m = w/g = (16.1 \text{ lb})/(32.2 \text{ ft/sec}^2) = \tfrac{1}{2} \text{ lb·sec}^2/\text{ft} = \tfrac{1}{2} \text{ slug},$$

since, by (10), 1 slug = 1 lb·sec²/ft.

We are now ready to substitute in (13) to determine the acceleration when a resultant force of 8 lb acts on the body:

$$a = F/m = 8 \text{ lb}/\tfrac{1}{2} \text{ slug} = 16 \text{ lb/slug} = 16 \text{ ft/sec}^2,$$

since, by (10), 1 lb/slug = 1 ft/sec². The direction of the acceleration is in the direction of the resultant force.

6. EXAMPLES INVOLVING NEWTON'S PRINCIPLES

THE PROBLEMS involving freely falling bodies and projectiles which we discussed in detail in Chap. 3 are extremely simple from the standpoint of dynamics, since only constant vertical forces are involved.   This leads to a constant vertical component of acceleration and no horizontal component of acceleration, in agreement with our treatment in Chap. 3.   If we knew the type of forces produced by air resistance, we could calculate realistic values of horizontal and vertical acceleration components and determine the trajectories of actual projectiles.   Determination of the air resistance is made by wind-tunnel and other types of experimental measurements and used in the computation of 'firing tables' for military guns.   These computation are extremely complicated.   Study of actual trajectories is known as the science of External Ballistics.

We shall now work through a number of examples that illustrate the applications of Newton's principles to more complex systems.

Example.   *Determine the acceleration of the bodies in the Atwood's machine of Fig. 6 when the system is unbalanced by the addition of the 'rider' of mass* m_1.

The assumption that the pulley has *negligible mass* and is *frictionless* means that no torque is required to turn the pulley.   Therefore the tensions in the two halves of the string are equal since this is the condition for no net torque. (We shall learn in Chap. 9 how to take into account the inertia of real pulleys in problems of this type.)

In Fig. 6(a), each body is in equilibrium, there is no acceleration, and the tension T in the string just balances the weight mg of each body: $T = mg$.

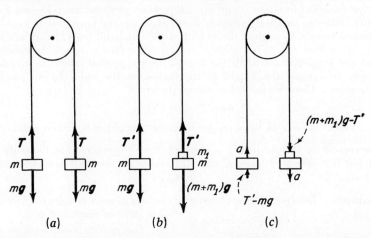

Fig. 6. Atwood's machine. The pulley is assumed to have negligible mass and to be frictionless. (a) Two equal masses. (b) A 'rider' is added on the right. (c) The resultant forces acting on the masses in (b), and the resulting accelerations.

In Fig. 6(b), the forces on the bodies are no longer balanced and acceleration will result. The masses on the right will experience an acceleration a downward and the mass on the left will experience an acceleration of equal magnitude a but directed upward. Let us now write the second principle for the bodies, taking the positive direction upward for the left-hand body and downward for the right, as indicated in Fig. 6(c); this sign convention is chosen so as to give a the same algebraic sign in the two expressions for the second principle, so that we can solve these equations simultaneously. The tension in the string will be the same throughout its length, say T'.

For the mass on the left, $T' - mg = ma$ (i)

and, for the masses on the right,

$$(m + m_1)g - T' = (m + m_1)a.$$ (ii)

Addition of these two equations gives

$$m_1 g = (2m + m_1)a, \quad \text{or} \quad a = m_1 g/(2m + m_1).$$ (iii)

Hence $m_1 g$ can be considered as the magnitude of the 'resultant force' applied to accelerate a 'system' of total mass $(2m + m_1)$.

In lecture demonstrations, the rider is of such a small size that its mass m_1 is negligible compared to the mass $2m$ of the original system, so that, although the magnitude of the resultant force is proportional to the mass m_1 of the rider, the total mass of the system experiencing acceleration is approximately the same when different riders are used. By adding riders of different mass, it can be demonstrated that the magnitude of the acceleration is approximately proportional to m_1. Since a can be kept small enough to measure readily with this apparatus, the value of g can be determined, although this determination cannot be made with high accuracy.

One further remark might be made concerning the tension T' in the string. Once a is determined from equation (iii), the tension can be determined by substitution in either (i) or (ii). Equation (i) shows that $T' = mg + ma$, which indicates that the tension is *greater* than mg, the tension that would be required merely to *support* the weight of the left-hand body, by an amount ma. Equation (ii) shows that $T' = (m+m_1)g - (m+m_1)a$ which indicates that the tension is *less* than the tension $(m+m_1)g$ that would be required merely to *support* the weight of the bodies on the right, by an amount $(m+m_1)a$. Thus, we are led to the relation:

$$mg < T' < (m+m_1)g,$$

or   weight of body on left $<$ tension in string $<$ weight of bodies on right.

The reason for this inequality is clear when we remember that the body on the left is accelerated upward while the bodies on the right are accelerated downward.

Example.   *Determine the acceleration of the body of mass m down the frictionless inclined plane in Fig. 7.*

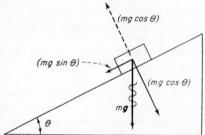

Fig. 7. Forces acting on a body on a frictionless inclined plane.

The gravitational force on the body is $m\mathbf{g}$, which we can resolve into two components, one parallel to the inclined plane, and the other normal to the plane. The component normal to the plane of the gravitational force *on the body* must be just balanced by the plane's normal reaction force *on the body*, since clearly there is no acceleration component normal to the plane. Hence, the resultant force on the body acts parallel to the plane and has the magnitude $mg \sin\theta$ as shown in Fig. 7. Therefore, the body experiences an acceleration down the plane, of magnitude a given by

$$mg \sin\theta = ma,$$

or $a = g \sin\theta.$ (i)

This equation gives the value of a in terms of g for any elevation angle θ of the inclined plane. We may check the results given by (i) for two cases with which we are already familiar. For $\theta = 90°$, equation (i) gives $a = g$. When $\theta = 90°$, the frictionless plane is upright; the body becomes a freely falling body and by definition has acceleration g, as given by (i). For $\theta = 0°$, the equation gives $a = 0$. Since, when $\theta = 0$, the plane is horizontal and there is no resultant force on the body, we see that this result is also correct.

Example.   *Determine the acceleration of the moving body in Fig. 8 if the coefficient of kinetic friction is μ_K.*

As in the case of the frictionless plane, the component of the gravitational force perpendicular to the plane is just balanced by the reaction force exerted by the plane, because there is no acceleration normal to the plane. Hence we have drawn arrows only for force components acting parallel to the plane. As before, the gravitational force component down the plane is $mg \sin\theta$. Opposing this force is the frictional force $\mu_K N$, where N is the magnitude $mg \cos\theta$ of the normal force. Hence, the resultant force F down the plane is

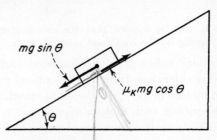

$$F = mg \sin\theta - \mu_K mg \cos\theta.$$

Thus, by Newton's second law, the acceleration down the plane is given by

$$mg \sin\theta - \mu_K mg \cos\theta = ma,$$
or $\qquad a = g(\sin\theta - \mu_K \cos\theta).$

Fig. 8. Forces acting on a body sliding down an inclined plane when there is friction.

If the body is initially moving down the plane with velocity v_0, its velocity will increase provided a is positive, that is, provided

$$\sin\theta > \mu_K \cos\theta, \quad \text{or} \quad \tan\theta > \mu_K.$$

If the acceleration is zero, the velocity will remain unchanged; this condition occurs when

$$\sin\theta = \mu_K \cos\theta, \quad \text{or} \quad \tan\theta = \mu_K,$$

as was pointed out in Chap. 2 in the discussion of kinetic friction. If the acceleration is negative, the velocity will decrease and the body will come to rest and remain at rest; this is the case when

$$\sin\theta < \mu_K \cos\theta, \quad \text{or} \quad \tan\theta < \mu_K.$$

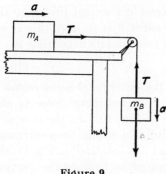

Figure 9

Example. *In Fig. 9, a body A of mass m_A lies on a flat, frictionless table top and a light string attached to the body passes horizontally to a light, frictionless pulley and thence vertically downward to a body B of mass m_B. Determine the magnitude of the acceleration experienced by the two-body system and the tension T in the string.*

Let us write the second principle for body A. The resultant force on body A equals the tension T in the string and is exerted horizontally and to the right. The acceleration a of this body has the same direction as the resultant force. Hence, we may write

$$T = m_A a. \qquad \text{(i)}$$

Now we write the second principle for body B. The resultant downward force on body B is $(m_B g - T)$, and B has the same acceleration a downward as A has to the right. The second principle gives

$$(m_B g - T) = m_B a,$$
or $\qquad T = m_B g - m_B a = m_B(g - a). \qquad \text{(ii)}$

Simultaneous solution of (i) and (ii) gives

$$a = \frac{m_B g}{m_A + m_B}; \quad T = \left(\frac{m_B m_A}{m_A + m_B}\right) g.$$

It will be noticed that the acceleration is that resulting from force $m_B g$ acting on the combined mass $m_A + m_B$.

One other problem discussed earlier in terms of kinematics merits reconsideration from the dynamical point of view. This is the problem of motion in a circle at constant speed. As pointed out in Chap. 3, a body describing such motion experiences a centripetal acceleration of magnitude $a = v^2/R$, where v is the speed of the particle and R is the radius of

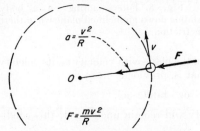

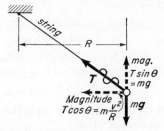

Fig. 10. A constant resultant force of magnitude $F = mv^2/R$ must act at all times on a particle moving with constant speed v in a circular path of radius R. This force is directed toward the center of the circle and is called the *centripetal force*.

Fig. 11. The force system in a vertical plane through a mass attached to a string and moving in a horizontal circle at constant speed. (This is called a *conical pendulum* since the string generates a cone as the body moves.)

the circular path. Now, according to Newton's second principle, the body must be acted upon by a force $F = ma$ if it is to have this acceleration. This force is called the *centripetal force* and its magnitude is

$$F = mv^2/R, \qquad (15)$$

where m is the mass of the body. Since the centripetal acceleration is directed toward the center of the circle, the centripetal force is also directed toward the center of the circle as in Fig. 10. In the case of a ball whirled in a horizontal circle at the end of a string, the centripetal force is produced by the tension in the string. As indicated in Fig. 11, the two components of string tension are required to balance the vertical force of gravity and to furnish the horizontal force that produces the centripetal acceleration.

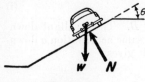

Figure 12

Example. *What is the angle of 'bank' of a highway curve of 400-ft radius in order that automobiles traveling at 60 mi/hr shall have no tendency to skid?*

'No tendency to skid' means no sidewise force of friction for the car shown in Fig. 12; the only forces acting on the car are then w

and **N**. Since there is no *vertical* acceleration $w = N \cos\theta$, $N = w/\cos\theta = mg/\cos\theta$. The horizontal acceleration to the left is $v^2/R = (88 \text{ ft/sec})^2/400$ ft $= 19.4$ ft/sec^2. The only force to the left is $N \sin\theta$, so

$$m (19.4 \text{ ft/sec}^2) = N \sin\theta = mg \sin\theta/\cos\theta,$$

from which $\qquad \tan\theta = (19.4 \text{ ft/sec}^2)/g = 19.4/32.2 = 0.603,$

$$\theta = 31°1.$$

In general, problems involving the translational motion of bodies are solved by methods similar to those applied in statics, except that the resultant force and the resultant acceleration are not in general zero. Rather, if **F** is the resultant force acting on any body, the rectangular components of **F** are related to the rectangular components of **a** by the equations

$$F_X = ma_X, \qquad F_Y = ma_Y, \qquad F_Z = ma_Z.$$

7. THE NEWTONIAN PRINCIPLE OF RELATIVITY

We stated on p. 57 that all velocities are relative and that no mechanical experiment could determine an absolute velocity. Inside a closed room in a moving train or airplane, there is no way of determining the velocity of the train or plane, so long as this velocity is constant. All mechanical experiments—the acceleration of a body down an inclined plane, the path of a projected body, etc—give the same results as if the room were at rest on the ground. Inside the room we could easily measure the *acceleration* of the train or plane, as we know from common experience, but it is impossible to measure its velocity. These ideas were formulated by Newton as the

NEWTONIAN PRINCIPLE OF RELATIVITY: *If the principles of mechanics are valid in one coordinate system, they are equally valid in a coordinate system in motion at constant velocity relative to it; hence on the basis of mechanical phenomena there is no way of determining absolute velocity; only relative velocity can be measured.*

It is not difficult to see that if Newton's principles are applicable in one coordinate system, they are applicable in a second coordinate system moving at constant velocity relative to the first; for example, the coordinate system in the moving train or plane mentioned above. Of course, different velocities are assigned to a particle in the two coordinate systems, but if a particle moves at *constant* velocity in one it moves at constant velocity in the other and would be considered as acted on by no forces in either case. Hence, Newton's first principle is satisfactory. Although different velocities are assigned to particles in the two coordinate systems, these velocities always differ by a constant which is the relative velocity of the two systems. Hence, a particle has the *same acceleration* in the two coordinate systems, and Newton's second principle assigns the *same forces*.   Since the forces are the same, Newton's third principle is valid in one system if it is valid in the other.   This proves the Newtonian principle of relativity.

It was by extension of the idea that laws of nature are the same for coordinate systems in uniform relative motion, so that no one coordinate system is more fundamental than any other, to the laws of electrodynamics, that Einstein was led to the important conclusions embodied in the Einstein theory of relativity which we shall discuss in Chap. 38.

Example.   *In Chap. 3 we found that a projectile with initial velocity v_0 at angle θ with the horizontal reached maximum height $h = v_0^2 \sin^2\theta/2g$, had the time of flight $T = 2v_0 \sin\theta/g$, and range $R = (v_0 \cos\theta)\, T$.   Let us suppose that a ball is thrown in the forward direction down the aisle of a train moving with speed V and that an observer on the train measures the quantities v_0, θ, h, T, and R.   What initial speed v_0' and angle θ' would be determined by an observer*

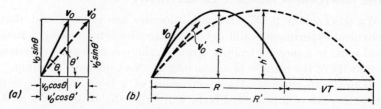

Fig. 13. Initial velocities (a) and trajectories (b) of a projectile as seen by an observer on a train moving to the right (solid lines) and by an observer on the ground (broken lines).

on the ground?   What quantities h', T', R' would the ground observer compute from the same dynamical equations?   Show that $h' = h$, $T' = T$, $R' = R + VT$, as would follow from simple geometry.

The situation is depicted in Fig. 13.   The man on the ground sees the ball start out with the same vertical component of velocity

$$v_0' \sin\theta' = v_0 \sin\theta \tag{i}$$

as the man on the train, but with horizontal velocity component greater by an amount V because of the motion of the train:

$$v_0' \cos\theta' = v_0 \cos\theta + V. \tag{ii}$$

Squaring both sides of (i) and (ii) and adding, we find

$$v_0'^2 = v_0^2 + 2V v_0 \cos\theta + V^2. \tag{iii}$$

Division of (i) by (ii) gives

$$\tan\theta' = \frac{v_0 \sin\theta}{v_0 \cos\theta + V}. \tag{iv}$$

Equations (iii) and (iv) determine v_0' and θ'.

The height h' computed by the man on the ground is, using (i),

$$h' = \frac{v_0'^2 \sin^2\theta'}{2g} = \frac{v_0^2 \sin^2\theta}{2g} = h.$$

The time of flight T' computed by the man on the ground is, using (i),

$$T' = \frac{2v_0' \sin\theta'}{g} = \frac{2v_0 \sin\theta}{g} = T.$$

The range R' computed by the man on the ground is, using (ii),

$$R' = (v_0' \cos\theta')T' = (v_0 \cos\theta + V)T = R + VT,$$

as expected because during the time of flight T, the train moves a distance VT, so that while the ball lands a distance R up the aisle of the train, it lands a distance $R+VT$ further along relative to the ground.

8. PLANETARY MOTION; UNIVERSAL GRAVITATION

PRIOR TO the time of Newton, Tycho-Brahe had made extensive observations on the motions of the planets in the sky. Kepler had analyzed these observations and formulated three laws concerning the character of the motion in relation to the shape and size of the ellipse in which the planet moves with the sun at one focus. Actually the elliptical orbits of the planets are all very close to circles with the sun at the center. In terms of the latter approximation, one of Kepler's laws states that the speeds v_P of the different planets are inversely proportional to the square roots of the radii R_P of their orbits:

$$v_P \propto 1/\sqrt{R_P} = R_P^{-1/2}. \tag{16}$$

A planet moving at speed v_P in a circle of radius R_P around the sun has acceleration v_P^2/R_P toward the sun. The sun must therefore *attract* it with the centripetal force given by (15) as

$$F_P = m_P v_P^2/R_P, \tag{17}$$

where m_P is the mass of the planet. In comparing different planets, we may substitute Kepler's observation (16) in (17) to obtain

$$F_P \propto m_P R_P^{-1}/R_P = m_P/R_P^2.$$

The force exerted by the sun on a planet is thus found to be proportional to the mass of the planet and inversely proportional to the square of the distance to the planet.

Since the force between the sun and a planet is thus found to be proportional to the mass of the planet, it is reasonable, in extending this force law to other situations, such as the earth-moon system, to set the force proportional to both of the masses in the system. By such considerations, Newton was led to formulate the law of universal gravitation, which has been amply confirmed by detailed astronomical observation:

LAW OF UNIVERSAL GRAVITATION: *Every particle of matter in the universe attracts every other particle. The magnitude of the force of attraction between two particles is proportional to the product of the masses of the particles and inversely proportional to the square of the distance between them; the gravitational forces between two particles act along the line joining the two particles.*

The equation expressing this relationship for a given pair of particles of masses m_1 and m_2 is

$$F = G\,\frac{m_1 m_2}{R^2}, \tag{18}$$

where R is the distance between the two particles and G is a proportionality constant called the *gravitation constant.* The gravitation constant G is not to be confused with g, the acceleration of a freely falling body, which represents *the gravitational force per unit mass* on a body near the surface of the earth. The gravitational pull exerted by the earth on objects near its surface is merely an example of the property of universal gravitation.

It should be noted that Newton's law of universal gravitation is *not* a defining equation like Newton's second principle of mechanics and cannot be derived from defining equations. It represents an *observed relationship,* and the gravitation constant G can be determined experimentally.

Because the standard of mass exists only in the laboratory, G cannot be determined by astronomical observation; it was first measured accurately by Cavendish in 1798 with the apparatus in Fig. 14. Two small balls, each of mass m, are attached to the ends of a light rod. The resulting 'dumbbell' is suspended in a horizontal position by a fine quartz fiber just strong enough to support it. Heavy lead balls of mass m' can be moved close to the ends of the dumbbell by sliding them along supporting rods. When the large balls are in the position shown, the gravitational forces they exert on the small balls produce a torque tending to twist the fiber. When they are moved into the position indicated by broken lines, the fiber tends to twist the other way. The angle θ through which the fiber is twisted when the balls are moved from one position to the other is measured by observing the deflection of a beam of light reflected from the small mirror attached to the dumbbell. With a knowledge of the geometry of the apparatus and the elastic properties of the supporting fiber, the value of G can be determined from the observed angle θ. At this writing the best value for G is 6.670×10^{-11} nt·m²/kg², determined by P. R. Heyl at the U. S. National Bureau of Standards.

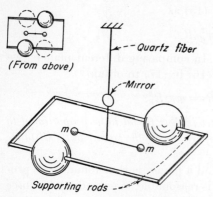

(From above)

Quartz fiber

Mirror

m m

Supporting rods

Fig. 14. The experiment of Cavendish for determining the gravitation constant G.

The extremely small magnitude of G shows that gravitational forces *between* bodies on the earth's surface are extremely small and quite negligible for all ordinary purposes.   The Cavendish experiment is a very delicate experiment indeed.   The large and important gravitational force of the earth on all bodies near its surface is accounted for by the extremely large mass of the earth, which is computed in the following example.   In this computation we shall need to use the following theorem, whose proof is merely a matter of geometry (see Prob. 50, Chap. 27):

The resultant gravitational force between two spherically symmetric bodies, whose densities may vary with radial distance from their centers but must be the same at all points in a spherical shell of given radius, is the same as if the whole mass of each body were concentrated in a small particle at its center.

Example.   *The approximate radius of the earth is* 6.4×10^6 m.   *Compute the approximate mass of the earth.*

To a very good approximation the earth can be assumed to be a sphere, since the polar and equatorial radii differ by only $\frac{1}{3}$ per cent.   We shall make this assumption and use the approximate value 9.8 m/sec^2 for the acceleration of a body near the earth's surface.   The theorem preceding then shows that the force between the earth, of mass m_E, and a body of mass m near its surface, at distance R_E from its center, is

$$F = G \frac{m m_E}{R_E^2}.$$

This force results in the acceleration (of gravity)

$$g = F/m = G m_E / R_E^2.$$

Substitution of the known quantities in this equation gives

$$m_E = \frac{g R_E^2}{G} = \frac{(9.8 \text{ m/sec}^2)(6.4 \times 10^6 \text{ m})^2}{6.67 \times 10^{-11} \text{ nt·m}^2/\text{kg}^2} = 6.0 \times 10^{24} \text{ kg},$$

where we have substituted, from (5), 1 nt $= 1$ kg·m/sec^2 in converting the units.   This figure is the mass of the earth.

From a consideration of Newton's law of gravitation, it is easy to see one reason for the variations of g with latitude and altitude as given in Table I on p. 64.   If the earth were a perfect sphere of uniform density, the magnitude of the gravitational force exerted on a particle of mass m above the earth's surface would decrease with the distance of the particle from the center of the earth.   This variation with *altitude* is observed. The observed variation of g with *latitude* is readily understood when we recall that the earth is not a perfect sphere but is an oblate spheroid, and the distance from sea level to the center of the earth becomes less as one proceeds from the equator toward the poles.   Therefore, g would be expected to show a slight increase with increasing latitude, as it does.[*]

[*] The rotation of the earth also has a small effect on the value of the acceleration of gravity; we shall omit discussion of this subject.

PROBLEMS

NOTE: Unless otherwise specified, assume that the acceleration of gravity has the standard value $g = 32.2$ ft/sec$^2 = 9.81$ m/sec^2. For values of g as a function of latitude and altitude see Table I on p. 64.

1. A 1-kg body interacts with a second body of unknown mass. At a certain instant the magnitude of the acceleration of the 1-kg body is 12 m/sec^2 and that of the second body is 2 m/sec^2. What is the mass of the second body?
Ans: 6 kg.

2. If a 1-kg body experiences an acceleration of magnitude 2 m/sec^2 when interacting with a second body and if the magnitude of the acceleration experienced by the second body is 5 m/sec^2, what is the mass of the second body? What can be said concerning the *directions* of the accelerations experienced by the two bodies?

3. A 4-kg body and a 3-kg body are connected by a stretched light spring as shown in Fig. 1(b). If the two bodies are released simultaneously and the initial acceleration of the 4-kg body is 5 m/sec^2 eastward, what is the initial acceleration of the 3-kg body?
Ans: 6.67 m/sec^2 westward.

4. During an interaction between a 12-kg body and a 4-kg body, the 12-kg body experiences an eastward acceleration of 2.5 m/sec^2. What is the acceleration of the 4-kg body?

5. A 5-kg body experiences an upward acceleration of 2 m/sec^2. What resultant external force acts on the body?
Ans: 10 nt upward.

6. A 10-kg body experiences an acceleration of 20 cm/sec^2 eastward. What resultant external force acts on the body?

7. A resultant horizontal force of 10 nt acts on a certain body, which experiences an acceleration of 2 m/sec^2 eastward. What is the direction of the resultant force? What is the mass of the body on which the force is exerted?
Ans: eastward; 5 kg.

8. A resultant force of magnitude 2 nt exerted on a certain body produces an acceleration whose magnitude is 10 m/sec^2. What is the mass of the body?

9. Find the weight of an 0.8-kg body at sea level at the following latitudes: 0°, 40°, 60°, and 90°.
Ans: 7.82, 7.84, 7.86, 7.87 nt.

10. Find the weight of a 2-kg mass at 40° N. latitude at the following heights above sea level: 0 m, 4000 m, and 16,000 m.

11. In moving a 30-kg trunk across a horizontal floor, a man exerts a horizontal force. If the trunk experiences an acceleration of magnitude 0.5 m/sec^2 and if the coefficient of kinetic friction between the trunk and floor is 0.2, what force must the man exert? What force does the trunk exert on the man? Does the man experience a resultant acceleration in a direction opposite to that of the acceleration experienced by the trunk?
Ans: 73.9 nt; 73.9 nt; no, why not?

12. A man exerts a horizontal force of 80 nt on a 30-kg box in pushing it across a level floor. If the box experiences an acceleration of 0.5 m/sec^2, find the coefficient of kinetic friction between the box and the floor. What force does the box exert on the man? What horizontal force does the box exert on the floor?

13. A 12-kg body falls freely and experiences a downward acceleration of 9.79 m/sec^2. What force does the earth exert on the body? What force does the body exert on the earth?
Ans: 117.5 nt downward; 117.5 nt upward.

14. A 4-kg body slides across a level floor. If the initial velocity of the body is 2 m/sec and if the body comes to rest in 4 sec, what is the average resultant horizontal force exerted on the body? What is the average horizontal force exerted on the floor by the body?

15. In Fig. 15, a force F is applied at angle θ to pull the box at constant speed along a horizontal surface with coefficient μ_K of kinetic friction. Find the angle θ at which the magnitude F of the required force is a minimum. For the case $\mu_K = 1$, compute F at $\theta = 0°$, $30°$, $45°$, and $60°$, and verify the correctness of your solution in this particular case.

Ans: $\tan\theta = \mu_K$, $\theta = \arctan\mu_K$.

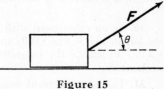

Figure 15

16. What is your own mass in slugs?

17. What is your 'apparent weight' when you are riding in an elevator accelerated upward at 16.1 ft/sec²?

18. The mass of a certain body is exactly 1.00000 slug. What is the exact weight of this body at a place where the acceleration of a freely falling body is 32.1578 ft/sec²? What would be the weight of this body at a sea-level station at the equator? at a sea-level station at the North Pole?

19. A trunk weighing 50 lb is pushed across a level floor. If the coefficient of kinetic friction between the trunk and the floor is 0.3, what horizontal force must be applied in order to give the trunk an acceleration of 2 ft/sec²? What is the mass of the trunk in slugs? What is the magnitude of the frictional force opposing motion?   Ans: 18.1 lb; 1.55 slugs; 15.0 lb.

20. A trunk weighing 120 lb is pushed across a level floor. If the coefficient of kinetic friction between the trunk and the floor is 0.24, what horizontal force must be applied in order to give the trunk an acceleration of 3 ft/sec²? What is the mass of the trunk in slugs? What is the magnitude of the frictional force opposing motion?

21. A large crate weighing 322 lb is pushed across a horizontal loading platform. If a horizontal force of 60.2 lb must be applied in order to give the box an acceleration of 2 ft/sec², what is the coefficient of friction between the box and the platform?   Ans: 0.125.

22. When a horizontal force of 10 lb is exerted on a sled weighing 60 lb, the sled experiences an acceleration of 5 ft/sec² on a horizontal surface of snow. What is the coefficient of friction between the sled and the snow?

23. An elevator cage weighing 2000 lb experiences an upward acceleration of 4.02 ft/sec². If friction is negligible, what upward force is exerted on the elevator cage by the supporting cable?   Ans: 2250 lb.

24. If the elevator cage in Prob. 23 experiences a downward acceleration of 8.05 ft/sec², what upward force is exerted by the supporting cable?

25. If the coefficient of static friction between the tires and the level road is μ_S, show that the minimum stopping distance for an automobile of mass m traveling at speed v is $v^2/2\mu_S g$.

26. If $\mu_S = 1.0$, find the minimum stopping distance of a car weighing 3000 lb and traveling at 15, 30, 60 mi/hr.

27. The coefficient of static friction between automobile tires and a dry concrete road is 1.0. What is the minimum number of seconds in which a car could possibly accelerate from rest to a speed of 50 mi/hr?   Ans: 2.28 sec.

28. Repeat Prob. 27 for the case of a car on a wet concrete road with coefficients of friction given in the table on p. 41.

29. In an Atwood's machine (see Fig. 6), the mass of each suspended body is 1.000 kg, while the mass of the 'rider' is 20 g. Assuming negligible friction and negligible mass in the pulley wheel, calculate the magnitude of the resulting upward acceleration of the left-hand body and the tension in the string.

Ans: 9.71 cm/sec^2; 9.90 nt.

30. In an experiment with an Atwood's machine, the weight of the body on the left in Fig. 6 was 8.0 lb and the total weight of the bodies on the right was 8.5 lb. Calculate the magnitude of the resulting acceleration and the tension in the string.

31. In an arrangement similar to that shown in Fig. 9, the weight of the body lying on the table top is 64.4 lb and that of the suspended body is 16.1 lb. Find the downward acceleration of the suspended body and the tension in the cord. (Ignore frictional effects.)   Ans: 6.44 ft/sec^2; 12.9 lb.

32. In an arrangement similar to that shown in Fig. 9, the mass of the body on the table top is exactly 4 kg and that of the suspended body is 1 kg. If the coefficient of kinetic friction between the table top and the body lying upon it is 0.2, calculate the tension in the cord and the magnitude of the resulting acceleration once the block is set in motion.

33. A 2-kg block is placed on a frictionless board inclined at angle of 30° with the horizontal. What is the magnitude of the acceleration experienced by the body?   Ans: 4.90 m/sec^2.

34. A box weighing 50 lb is placed on a frictionless board inclined at an angle of 45° with the horizontal. What will be the acceleration of the body down the board?

35. If the coefficient of kinetic friction between the block and the board in Prob. 33 had been 0.2, what would have been the acceleration of the block in its motion down the board?   Ans: 3.20 m/sec^2.

36. If the coefficient of kinetic friction between the box and the board in Prob. 34 had been 0.3, what would have been the acceleration of the box?

37. A shell weighing 8.05 lb is fired from a gun whose barrel is 4 ft in length. The muzzle velocity of the shell is 2000 ft/sec. Assuming that the acceleration of the shell in moving down the barrel is constant, find the average resultant force exerted on the shell while it is in the barrel.   Ans: 125,000 lb.

38. A 2.48-kg shell is fired from a gun whose barrel is 2 m in length. The muzzle velocity is 300 m/sec. Assuming constant acceleration, calculate the average force exerted on the shell while it is in the barrel.

39. A ball weighing 2 lb is swung at the end of a string at a constant speed of 6 ft/sec in a horizontal circle of radius 4 ft. What centripetal force does the string exert on the ball? What angle does the string make with the horizontal? What is the tension in the string?   Ans: 0.559 lb; 74.°4; 2.08 lb.

40. A 1-kg ball at the end of a cord travels at a constant speed of 3 m/sec in a horizontal circle of radius 1.5 m. What centripetal force is exerted on the ball? What angle does the cord make with the horizontal? What is the tension in the cord?

41. An automobile weighing 3000 lb travels around a curve of 200-ft radius. If the roadway is level and the centripetal force results from friction alone, what is the maximum speed the automobile can have if the coefficient of friction between the tires and the roadway is 0.3?   Ans: 44.0 ft/sec.

42. In the 'airplane ride' at the carnival, cars are suspended from cables 14 ft long attached to arms at points 20 ft from the vertical axis of rotation. At what angular speed of rotation will the cars swing out so that the cables make an angle of 45° with the horizontal? an angle of 30°?

43. An automobile travels around a curve of 200-ft radius at a speed of 60 ft/sec. At what angle θ with the horizontal should the roadway be 'banked' in order for the car to make the curve without depending upon friction between the tires and roadway?   Ans: 29°.2.

44. At what angle should the curve in Prob. 43 be banked if the automobile has a speed of 30 mi/hr?

45. A body of mass 3 kg is projected at initial speed 5 m/sec up a plane inclined at 20° to the horizontal, on which the coefficients of friction are $\mu_K = 0.2$ and $\mu_S = 0.3$.

(a) What is the deceleration of the block as it moves up?
(b) How far does it move along the plane before coming to rest?
(c) Show that the block will start back down after coming to rest.
(d) What is its acceleration down the plane?
(e) What is its speed when it again reaches the starting point?
        Ans: (a) 5.20 m/sec²; (b) 2.41 m; (d) 1.51 m/sec²; (e) 2.70 m/sec.

46. A body weighing 6 lb is projected at initial speed 24 ft/sec up a plane, inclined at 30° to the horizontal, on which the coefficients of friction are $\mu_K = 0.4$ and $\mu_S = 0.5$. Answer the same questions as in Prob. 45.

47. A box weighing 100 lb rests on the flat bed of a truck moving at 40 ft/sec along a level road. Because the bed of the truck is oily, the coefficient of static friction between box and truck bed is only 0.15. How rapidly must the truck decelerate in order for the box to slip forward during the deceleration?
                                                   Ans: 4.83 ft/sec².

48. If the coefficient of kinetic friction in the example of Prob. 47 is 0.12, and the truck accelerates from rest at the uniform rate of 8 ft/sec², how far has the truck gone before the box has slipped back 11 ft on the truck body, which is enough to cause it to fall off?

49. In Fig. 13, if the initial velocity of the projectile is $v_0 = 30$ ft/sec at angle $\theta = 60°$ as seen by the observer on the train, compute the height h, time of flight T, and range R. If the train is moving at 15 mi/hr, compute the initial velocity v_0', θ', as seen by an observer on the ground; also the height h', time of flight T', and range R'.   Ans: $T = T' = 1.61$ sec; $h = h' = 10.5$ ft; $R = 24.2$ ft, $R' = 59.6$ ft.

50. In the preceding problem, if the projectile had been thrown *backward* down the aisle of the train, again at an angle of 60° with the horizontal and at the same speed, make the same computations for the observer on the train and the observer on the ground.

51. In the preceding two problems, at what angle should the observer on the train throw the projectile at 30 ft/sec in order that to the observer on the ground it should appear to go straight up and down in a vertical path?
                                                   Ans: $\theta = 137°.2$.

52. A man on a train tosses an object directly across the aisle, in a direction perpendicular to the length of the train. The object is tossed at an initial angle of 45° with the horizontal and has a range of 6 ft. If the train is moving at 15 mi/hr, what is the initial speed and direction as seen by an observer on the ground? What range would the ground observer compute? Show that this range corresponds to the range observed on the train when the motion of the train is taken into account.

53. Two lead balls, each of mass 4 kg, are placed with their centers 20 cm apart. What is the magnitude of the gravitational force exerted by the first ball on the second?   Ans: 2.67×10^{-8} nt.

54. In a centrifuge, what angular velocity is required to achieve an acceleration 100 times that of gravity at a point 3 inches from the vertical axis of rotation?

55. There has been much discussion recently about creating an artificial satellite to circle the earth outside the earth's atmosphere. Assume the earth's radius to be 4000 mi and that the satellite is to be 1000 mi above the surface or 5000 mi from the center. Compute the time of revolution of the satellite in a circular orbit of this radius.   Ans: 118 min.

56. At what altitude above the earth's surface would the acceleration of gravity be approximately 16 ft/sec²? Take the radius of the earth as 4000 mi.

57. Compute the value of the mass of the sun in kg on the assumption that the earth moves in a circular orbit of radius 93,000,000 mi and has a period of revolution of 365 days.   Ans: 1.99×10^{30} kg.

58. Compute the value of the earth's mass on the assumption that the moon completes one revolution about the earth every 29½ days in a circular path of radius 240,000 mi. Compare your result with that obtained in the example in the text on p. 97.

59. The mass of the moon is 1/81.5 times that of the earth; its radius is 1/3.7 times that of the earth. What would be the acceleration of gravity in ft/sec² on the surface of the moon?   Ans: 5.41 ft/sec².

60. A dive bomber has an acceleration of 5g upward (where g is the standard acceleration of gravity) at the lowest point of its dive when its velocity is horizontal and 500 ft/sec. What is the radius of curvature of its path at this point? Determine the force between the pilot and his seat expressed as a multiple of the pilot's weight.

CHAPTER 5

WORK, ENERGY, AND POWER

IN THIS CHAPTER we shall define the quantities *work* and *energy*, which are extremely important physical concepts. We shall develop the principle of *conservation of mechanical energy* for use in mechanical problems in which neither frictional forces nor collisions are involved. Then we shall introduce a more general *conservation-of-energy* principle applicable to problems in which heat is generated. The introduction of this principle at this point may be somewhat premature, since the general principle was stated by Helmholtz and Mayer on the basis of experimental work that will be discussed in Part II of this book dealing with Heat. However, since conservation of energy is probably the most important principle in physics, it is desirable to introduce this principle immediately even though we must postpone discussion of this experimental work.

We shall see that the energy-conservation principle is very useful in the solution of dynamical problems and in the discussion of simple machines. In connection with simple machines we shall define mechanical advantage and efficiency, and we shall define *power* as the time rate of doing work.

1. WORK

IN NONSCIENTIFIC language, we use the word *work* to denote any type of activity that requires the exertion of muscular or mental effort. In physics, however, the term *work* has a definite technical definition and is used *only* in the restricted sense of this definition. In order for physical work to be done, it is necessary for a force to act on a body and for the body to experience a displacement that has a component parallel to the direction in which the force is acting.

Figure 1 represents a body moving along a horizontal surface in a direction which we shall take as the X-axis. A force F acts on the body at an angle θ with the direction of motion. The work done by this force is *defined* in the following way:

> The **work** done by a force acting on a body while the body undergoes a displacement is a scalar quantity defined as the product of the magnitude of the displacement and the component of the force in the direction of the displacement.

Thus, the work dW done by the force in Fig. 1 when the body experiences an infinitesimal displacement toward the right of magnitude dX is

$$dW = (F \cos\theta)\, dX. \tag{1a}$$

If the force is constant, the work W done in moving the body from the origin to a point X is

$$W = (F \cos\theta)\, X. \tag{1b}$$

In the special case in which the force is constant and has the same direction as the displacement, the work done by the force is equal to the product of the force and the displacement; this is the case when the angle θ in Fig. 1 is zero. If the angle θ between the force vector F and the

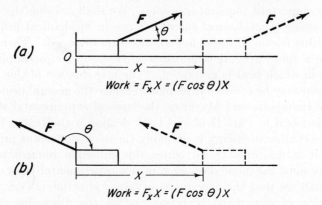

Fig. 1. A body acted on by a constant force $\boldsymbol{F}$ moves to the right a distance X.

direction of the displacement is greater than 90°, as in Fig. 1(b), $\cos\theta$ is negative and the work is negative. This is the case where a force is applied to retard the motion of a body already moving with a positive velocity in the X-direction. If θ is 180°, the work is the negative of the product of the force magnitude and the displacement magnitude. When $\theta = 90°$, no work is done.

We note that, regardless of how large a force may act, displacement must occur before work is done. Thus, although opposing teams may exert enormous forces on a rope during a tug of war, neither team performs any work unless the rope moves. Similarly, a heavy man sitting at rest may exert a downward force of 300 lb on a chair, but he does no work on the chair. Further, it should be emphasized that even if a body experiences a displacement, no work is done unless a force having a component in the direction of motion acts on the body. Thus, a man does work in lifting a suitcase vertically, since the force he exerts is in the direction of motion. However, the force he exerts on the suitcase does no work if he holds the suitcase still, or if he carries the suitcase in a perfectly horizontal line at constant velocity across the floor.

As noted above, work is defined as the *product* of a force component and the magnitude of a displacement.   Therefore, the unit used in measuring work involves the product of a force unit and a length unit.   In the British gravitational system, the force unit is the *pound* and the length unit is the *foot*.   The work unit is therefore called the *foot-pound* (ft·lb):

> One **foot-pound** is the work done by a constant force of one pound when the body on which the force is exerted moves a distance of one foot in the direction of the force.

Similarly, the work unit in the MKS system is the *meter-newton*, and this unit is defined in terms of the *newton* (nt) and *meter* (m) in the same manner as that used to define the ft·lb in terms of the foot and the pound. This work unit, the *meter-newton*, is called the *joule;* there is no single corresponding word for the ft·lb.

> One **joule** is the work done by a constant force of one newton when the body on which the force is exerted moves a distance of one meter in the direction of the force.

The following relations between work units will be found useful:

$$1 \text{ joule} = 1 \text{ m·nt} = 0.7376 \text{ ft·lb}, \qquad 1 \text{ ft·lb} = 1.356 \text{ joules}. \qquad (2)$$

2. ENERGY

JUST AS in the case of the word *work*, the word *energy* has two somewhat distinct uses.   In nonscientific language, the word *energy* is sometimes used to denote activity; for example, if a man is active in social or civic organizations, we are accustomed to describe him as a man who has 'a great deal of energy.'   In physics, the term *energy* has a precise technical meaning.   The following will serve as a general definition:

> The **energy** of a body is a measure of the capacity or ability of the body to perform work.   It is a scalar quantity and is measured in the same units as work.

Using this definition, we can immediately think of many examples of objects having energy because of their *motion*.   For example, a moving bullet, a moving automobile, and a rotating flywheel all have the ability to do work during the process of being brought to rest.   *The energy possessed by a body as a result of its motion is called kinetic energy.*

A body may also have energy as a result of its position or configuration.   For example, a cubic foot of water at the top of a waterfall can perform work in turning a water wheel or turbine as a result of its *position*, while a clockspring, when wound, can do work in operating the clock mechanism as a result of its stressed *configuration*.   *Energy possessed by a body as a result of its position or configuration is called potential energy.*   The pound of water has potential energy as a result of its position in the gravitational field of the earth; hence we sometimes refer to its energy as *gravitational potential energy*.   In the case of the clock spring, the spring is an elastic body and, when distorted, tends to regain its original shape or configuration; we can therefore think of energy as being imparted to the spring when the clock is wound.   This type of energy is referred to as *elastic potential energy*.   In Part V we shall also have occasion to discuss *electrostatic potential energy*.

In both the examples of potential energy we have given, we can think of energy as resulting from the performance of work.   In the case of the cubic foot of water, the energy is imparted to the water when *work is done* in raising it to the top of the waterfall; in the case of the spring, the potential energy is produced when *work is done* in distorting the spring. Since work must be done in setting a body in motion, we see immediately that *work is done* in giving kinetic energy to a body.   These observations suggest operational definitions of kinetic and potential energy that are more satisfactory than the general definition given earlier, but which we shall show, by means of examples, are equivalent to the general definition:

> The **kinetic energy** of a body in motion is equal to the work that must be done by a resultant force acting on the body in order to change the body from a state of rest to its state of motion.

> The **change in gravitational, elastic, or electrostatic potential energy** when a body changes from one position or configuration to another is the *negative* of the work done by the gravitational, elastic, or electrostatic forces during the change in position or configuration.

We shall first derive an expression giving the *kinetic* energy of a particle in terms of its mass m and its speed v.   In order to obtain this expression, let us compute the work that must be done in accelerating the particle, initially at rest, to velocity $\boldsymbol{v}$.   If a constant resultant force $\boldsymbol{F}$ acts on the particle, the acceleration $\boldsymbol{a}$ is constant and the displacement

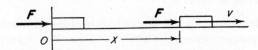

Fig. 2. The external work FX done in accelerating the body is transformed into the kinetic energy $\frac{1}{2}mv^2$ of the body.

has the same direction as the force.   Therefore, we may choose this direction as the X-axis of a coordinate system in which the particle is initially located at the origin as shown in Fig. 2.   The work W done in moving the particle to position X is

$$W = FX. \tag{3}$$

Since the initial velocity is zero and the acceleration is constant, we may substitute the value $X = \frac{1}{2} at^2$ in (3), and we may write ma for F.

Equation (3) then becomes

$$W = (ma)(\tfrac{1}{2} at^2) = \tfrac{1}{2} m (at)^2,$$

or, since $v = at$, $\qquad\qquad W = \tfrac{1}{2} mv^2.$ $\qquad\qquad\qquad$ (4)

Since the kinetic energy of a particle traveling at speed v is defined as the work W required to accelerate the body from rest to speed v, expression (4) is just the kinetic energy of the particle:

$$\text{K.E.} = \tfrac{1}{2} mv^2. \quad \left\{ \begin{matrix} \text{K.E. in joules} \\ m \text{ in kg} \\ v \text{ in m/sec} \end{matrix} \right\} \text{ or } \left\{ \begin{matrix} \text{K.E. in ft·lb} \\ m \text{ in slugs} \\ v \text{ in ft/sec} \end{matrix} \right\} \quad (5)$$

As indicated, the units in the above equations must correspond to one of the two systems in which the equation $F = ma$ is valid.

The above simple derivation of (5) is for the special case in which the particle is accelerated at a constant rate along a straight line. However, it can be readily shown by the methods of integral calculus that the same result is obtained for a particle accelerated in any manner along any type of curve. This proof is given in the footnote.* Expression (5) applies only to the case of a particle or an extended body without rotation; it is called the *translational kinetic energy*. For a rotating body there is an additional kinetic energy associated with the work required to set the body into rotation. This *rotational kinetic energy* we shall consider in Chap. 9.

Let us now obtain an expression for the change in gravitational potential energy when a particle changes its position relative to the earth's surface. Look first at the definition of this change as the *negative* of the work done by the gravitational force. If a stone moves from the top of a cliff to the bottom, it loses potential energy; that is, it loses the ability to do work by virtue of its position. In this motion the downward force of gravity does *positive* work, but the potential energy decreases; the *change* in potential energy is *negative*. But if we haul the stone at constant speed from the bottom to the top of the cliff, the force of gravity does *negative* work while the potential energy *increases*. We must pull up on the stone

---

* Let us consider a particle that changes its speed from zero to v_1 as it moves along an arbitrary path under the action of an arbitrarily varying resultant force $\boldsymbol{F}$. Let S be the distance measured along the path and dS the increment of distance. Then the component of acceleration along the path can be shown to be d^2S/dt^2, and this will be related to the component F_S of force in the direction of motion by $F_S = m\, d^2S/dt^2$. The work done by the resultant force when the particle moves along the path from $S = 0$ to $S = S_1$ will then be

$$W = \int_0^{S_1} F_S\, dS = \int_0^{S_1} m \frac{d^2S}{dt^2}\, dS = \int_0^{t_1} m \frac{d^2S}{dt^2} \frac{dS}{dt}\, dt$$

$$= \int_0^{t_1} m \frac{dv}{dt} v\, dt = \int_0^{t_1} m \frac{d}{dt} (\tfrac{1}{2}v^2)\, dt = \int_0^{v_1} m\, d(\tfrac{1}{2}v^2)$$

$$= \tfrac{1}{2}mv_1{}^2.$$

Thus we have derived the expression (5) for the kinetic energy in a manner entirely independent of the particular way in which the particle is accelerated.

with sufficient force to overcome the force of gravity. The force we exert does positive work; this is said to be work done *against* the force of gravity. When positive work is done *against* the force of gravity, the potential energy *increases;* when positive work is done *by* the force of gravity, the potential energy *decreases.* If the body is *projected* from the bottom to the top of the cliff, the force of gravity does *negative* work during the motion. The potential energy therefore *increases;* this time at the expense of the kinetic energy the body had when it was projected, as we shall see later.

A body has potential energy by virtue of its *position*, but, since the pull of gravity is directed *vertically* downward, the gravitational potential energy of the body changes only when the body experiences a *vertical* displacement. Therefore, we need only to find the work done in *raising* the body vertically to a given *height* in order to find its increase in potential energy. For example, let us consider the situation in Fig. 3 which shows

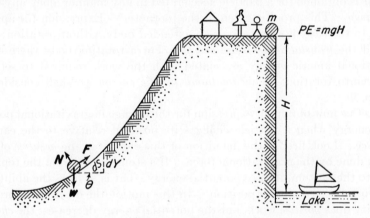

Fig. 3. At the top of the cliff, the stone has potential energy $mgH = wH$ with *respect to the lake surface.*

a large stone on a cliff at a height H above a lake; we wish to find the gravitational potential energy of the stone relative to the water surface as reference level. We may do this by finding the work done against the earth's gravitational pull when the stone is raised vertically to its position at constant speed. The force F that must be exerted is equal to the weight mg of the stone and the work done is

$$W = FH = mgH;$$

hence the stone's potential energy relative to its position at water level is equal to the work done in raising the stone:

$$\text{P.E.} = mgH = wH. \quad \begin{Bmatrix} \text{P.E. in ft·lb} \\ m \text{ in slugs} \\ g \text{ in ft/sec}^2 \\ H \text{ in ft} \\ w \text{ in lb} \end{Bmatrix} \text{ or } \begin{Bmatrix} \text{P.E. in joules} \\ m \text{ in kg} \\ g \text{ in m/sec}^2 \\ H \text{ in m} \\ w \text{ in nt} \end{Bmatrix} \quad (6)$$

The units in (6) must again correspond to one of the two systems in which the equation $w = mg$ is valid.

It will be noted from this example that the potential energy is directly proportional to the height H *above some reference level,* which in this case we have chosen as the surface of the lake. The potential energy given by (6) represents only the ability of the stone to do work as it returns the whole distance to the reference level. For example, if the stone falls over the cliff, it can do work $W = mgH$ on a sailboat on the lake surface, but the stone has *no* ability to do work on the objects on the top of the cliff. The reference level of potential energy is arbitrary; *only differences in potential energy at two different levels have physical significance.*

It is interesting to verify that the work required to pull a body up any type of inclined path is (friction being absent) just the same as the work mgH required to lift the body vertically the same vertical height. Suppose, as at the left of Fig. 3, we pull the body up a frictionless incline by applying a force just large enough to move the body without acceleration. Then, as we found in Chap. 2, we require $F = w \sin\theta$, where θ is the inclination of the hill at any stage. The work done when the body moves a short distance dS is $F\, dS = w\, dS \sin\theta$. But $dS \sin\theta = dY$, the increment in vertical height. Hence the work required to move the body a vertical height dY is $w\, dY$ independent of the inclination. Thus, the total work required to move the body up the hill of vertical height H is $wH = mgH$, independent of the shape of the incline. If there is friction, more work will be required but, as we shall see in Sec. 4, only the work wH is done against gravity and goes into increase of gravitational potential energy; the additional work done against friction goes into heat.

3. TRANSFORMATIONS OF MECHANICAL ENERGY

IT IS sometimes convenient to refer to the kinetic and potential energy of a body as the body's *mechanical energy.* It can be proved from Newton's principles that, *provided there are no frictional or other dissipative effects, the total mechanical energy of a system of bodies remains constant.* We can easily demonstrate this statement for a ball thrown vertically upward from the earth's surface. Let m be the mass of the ball and $\boldsymbol{v}_0$ the initial upward velocity of the ball. In the absence of air resistance, the ball will experience a constant downward acceleration $\boldsymbol{g}$. Let us place the origin of our coordinate system at the point at which the ball is released and consider motion along the vertical axis. Taking the upward direction as positive, the initial upward velocity component is $+v_0$ and the downward acceleration has the upward component $-g$. Therefore, from equation (14) of Chap. 3, p. 62, we may write for the magnitude of the velocity v of the ball at position Y:

$$v^2 = v_0^2 - 2gY.$$

By multiplying both sides of this equation by $\tfrac{1}{2}\,m$, we obtain

$$\tfrac{1}{2}\,mv^2 = \tfrac{1}{2}\,mv_0^2 - mgY,$$

and by transposition we obtain

$$\tfrac{1}{2}\,mv^2 + mgY = \tfrac{1}{2}\,mv_0^2. \tag{7}$$

The quantities in equation (7) can be interpreted as follows:

$\tfrac{1}{2}\,mv^2$ = kinetic energy of the ball at height Y,

mgY = potential energy of the ball at height Y, relative to the origin,

$\tfrac{1}{2}\,mv_0^2$ = initial kinetic energy of the ball.

The terms on the left-hand side of equation (7) represent the *total mechanical energy* (kinetic+potential) of the ball at any point in its path, and the term on the right-hand side represents the *total initial mechanical energy*, taking the potential energy of the ball at the origin as zero. Thus, equation (7) states that at all times *the total mechanical energy of the ball is constant.* Provided there is no air resistance, mechanical energy is *conserved.* Air resistance is of the nature of a frictional force. As indicated in Fig. 4, the initial kinetic energy is all changed to potential energy at the top of the path.

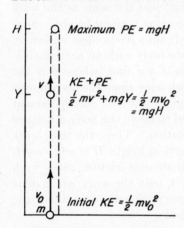

Fig. 4. The sum of the kinetic energy and the potential energy of a ball thrown vertically upward from a horizontal plane is at all times constant and equal to the initial kinetic energy of the ball.

It should be pointed out that conservation of mechanical energy is not limited to one-dimensional motion as in the case we have been considering. In order to demonstrate this fact, let us consider the motion of a projectile of mass m fired from a gun with muzzle velocity of magnitude v_0 at an angle θ_0 to the horizontal as shown in Fig. 5.

Let the horizontal and vertical components of the muzzle velocity be v_{0X} and v_{0Y}, respectively. In the absence of air resistance, v_X will at all times be equal to v_{0X}:

$$v_X = v_{0X}. \tag{8}$$

The upward acceleration in the coordinate system in Fig. 5 is equal to $-g$. Hence, from (14), p. 62, we may write

$$v_Y^2 = v_{0Y}^2 - 2gY, \quad \text{or} \quad v_Y^2 + 2gY = v_{0Y}^2. \tag{9}$$

Squaring both sides of equation (8) and adding the resulting equation to equation (9), we obtain

$$v_x^2 + v_y^2 + 2gY = v_{0x}^2 + v_{0y}^2.$$

Multiplication of both sides of this equation by $\frac{1}{2}\, m$ gives

$$\tfrac{1}{2}\, m\, (v_x^2 + v_y^2) + mgY = \tfrac{1}{2}\, m\, (v_{0x}^2 + v_{0y}^2),$$

or $$\tfrac{1}{2}\, mv^2 + mgY = \tfrac{1}{2}\, mv_0^2. \qquad (10)$$

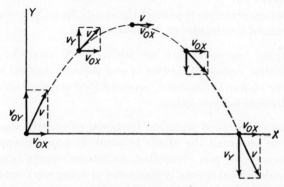

Fig. 5. Path of a projectile with velocities indicated at several points along the trajectory.

The terms in equation (10) have the following interpretation:

$\frac{1}{2}\, mv^2 =$ kinetic energy of the projectile at height Y,

$mgY =$ potential energy of the projectile at height Y, relative to $Y = 0$,

$\frac{1}{2}\, mv_0^2 =$ initial kinetic energy = total initial mechanical energy.

Hence, we see that equation (10), like equation (7), is an expression of the conservation of total mechanical energy.

4. CONSERVATION OF ENERGY

THE EXAMPLES of the preceding section demonstrated the *principle of conservation of mechanical energy* for a projectile experiencing no frictional resistance.   The same principle can readily be demonstrated in the case of a body sliding on a frictionless incline, whether or not the inclined surface is plane.   The work done by the force of gravity is, by definition of potential-energy change, the decrease in potential energy.   Since the incline is frictionless, the force of the incline on the body is normal to the direction of motion and does no work.   Hence the work done by the force of gravity is the work done by the resultant force and hence by definition is the increase in the kinetic energy.   Therefore the increase in kinetic energy equals the decrease in potential energy, and the total mechanical energy is conserved.

The same type of argument can be applied to a system of bodies connected by string and pulleys, provided there is no friction.   The Atwood's machine of Fig. 6, p. 89 is a simple example.   In this case, the tension in the string, as well as the force of gravity, does work.   But the work done by the string tension on one body is equal and opposite to the work done by the same tension on the other body, so the net work done by the string tension is zero.   Hence it can be shown that if we consider the two bodies together, the sum of the potential energies plus the sum of the kinetic energies is conserved.

The following principle is proved rigorously from Newton's principles in more advanced treatments of dynamics:

PRINCIPLE OF CONSERVATION OF MECHANICAL ENERGY: *For any system of bodies, connected together in any manner, the total mechanical energy of the system is conserved, provided there are no frictional forces and no collisions between bodies.*

In any actual physical situation frictional effects are always present; if these effects are small the above principle is a useful approximation. However, *whenever friction is involved, mechanical energy is not conserved;* we say that mechanical energy is *dissipated* in doing work against friction. Mechanical energy is also dissipated in collisions between bodies because of the presence of forces of the nature of internal friction: this dissipation of energy will be discussed in Chap. 7.

As an example of the way in which mechanical energy is dissipated against friction, let us consider the situation shown in Fig. 6.   A box of

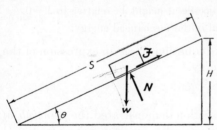

Figure 6

mass m initially at rest moves down an inclined plane from a height H above a level floor.   The potential energy of the box in the initial position (relative to the bottom of the plane) is given by mgH.   If there were no friction between the box and the inclined plane, the kinetic energy $\frac{1}{2} mv^2$ of the box on reaching the lower end of the inclined plane would be exactly equal to the initial potential energy mgH.   However, if friction is involved, some of the initial potential energy is dissipated in doing work against friction, and the kinetic energy of the box reaching the bottom of the inclined plane is less than its initial potential energy.   Let μ_K be the coefficient of friction.   Since the normal force $N = mg \cos\theta$, the frictional force $\mathfrak{F}$ has the magnitude

$$\mathfrak{F} = \mu_K mg \cos\theta,$$

and is directed up the plane, opposite to the displacement; hence the work W done by the force of friction as the block moves distance S down the plane is

$$W = -\mathfrak{F}S = -\mu_K mgS \cos\theta. \tag{11}$$

This negative work done by friction is commonly called work done against friction, if the sign is changed. We shall show that mechanical energy equal to the work done against friction disappears or is *dissipated*.

To see this, we note that the resultant force down the plane is the difference between the component of the weight and the force of friction:

$$F = mg \sin\theta - \mathcal{F}. \qquad (12)$$

This causes an acceleration down the plane of magnitude $a = F/m$. The speed at the bottom of the plane is thus given by

$$v^2 = 2aS = 2FS/m.$$

The kinetic energy at the bottom is

$$\tfrac{1}{2}\, mv^2 = FS = mgS \sin\theta - \mathcal{F}S,$$

or $\qquad\qquad \tfrac{1}{2}\, mv^2 = mgH - \mathcal{F}S. \qquad (13)$

Thus, the kinetic energy at the bottom of the plane is not as great as the potential energy mgH at the top of the plane; it is less than this potential energy by the work $\mathcal{F}S$ done against friction. Mechanical energy $\mathcal{F}S$ disappears during the motion and is said to be *dissipated in friction*.

Now let us consider the question: What becomes of the mechanical energy that is dissipated? It is recognized by everyone who has ever rubbed his hands together to warm them that work done against friction produces *heat*. However, not until more than one hundred years after Newton's death was it clearly understood that the amount of heat produced is directly proportional to the amount of mechanical energy dissipated and that *heat itself is a form of energy*. When work is done against friction, mechanical energy is converted into *heat* or *thermal energy;* in heat engines, thermal energy is converted into mechanical energy. In both cases, one form of energy is transformed into another form of energy.

Recognition of this fact led to the formulation of one of the most important principles in physical science. This principle of *conservation of energy* can be stated as follows:

PRINCIPLE OF CONSERVATION OF ENERGY: *Energy cannot be created or destroyed, although it can be changed from one form to another.*

In addition to mechanical kinetic and potential energy and heat, there are still other forms of energy, which include chemical energy, electrical energy, magnetic energy, radiant energy, and nuclear energy. The principle of conservation of energy finds application in all branches of physics. There is no formal general proof of the principle, but we have no evidence that it is ever violated.

As an example of a process in which several energy transformations occur, let us consider a projectile of mass m fired from a cannon at the top of a cliff as shown in Fig. 7. The shell leaves the barrel, describes a parabolic path, and finally sinks into the mud in the marsh at the foot of the cliff. Since the projectile eventually does work in penetrating the mud in the marsh, let us use the level at which the projectile finally stops as the arbitrary reference level from which heights are to be measured in computing potential energy. Before the shell is fired from the gun, it has

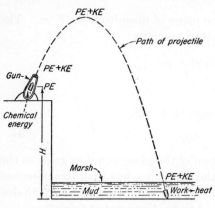

Fig. 7. Energy transformations.

potential energy mgH, and the propellant has a certain amount of chemical energy. When firing occurs, some of this chemical energy is transformed into thermal energy, and, as a result of the rapid expansion of hot gaseous combustion products, a part of this thermal energy is used in doing work on the shell, which thereby acquires *kinetic energy* $\frac{1}{2}mv_0^2$, where v_0 gives the magnitude of the muzzle velocity. As the shell rises, some of its initial kinetic energy is transformed into potential energy. As the shell starts downward from the highest point in its trajectory, its kinetic energy increases as its potential energy decreases. If there is no air resistance, the total mechanical energy of the shell remains constant from the time it leaves the muzzle of the gun until it strikes the surface of the mud. However, once the shell strikes the surface of the marsh, it begins dissipating its mechanical energy in doing work against frictional forces. As the shell plows its way into the mud, its speed gradually decreases and it eventually comes to rest at the reference level. The total work done against friction is equal to the total mechanical energy associated with the projectile at the moment it left the muzzle of the gun. The resulting thermal energy is evidenced by an increase in the temperature of the shell and the surrounding mud.

The heat produced in processes similar to the one just described is sometimes readily observable. For example, a nail becomes noticeably warmer when driven into or suddenly withdrawn from a board. Similarly, when a bullet enters a piece of wood, the walls of the resulting hole sometimes become charred as a result of the high temperatures attained, and a lead bullet sometimes melts. It is also observed that fast-moving meteors are heated to incandescence on entering the earth's atmosphere.

In closing the present discussion, it may be well to emphasize once more that the *principle of conservation of energy* is applicable in all branches of physics. The *total* energy in the *universe* seems to be constant! In the chapters that follow, we shall have many occasions to apply this principle.

Example. *In Fig. 6, the angle θ is 30°, the height H is 10 ft, the slant height S is 20 ft, the mass m is 3 slugs, and the coefficient of friction μ_K is 0.25. If the mass starts from rest at the top of the plane, determine from energy considerations its speed at the bottom.*

At the top of the plane, the potential energy (relative to the bottom) is

$$mgH = (3 \text{ slugs})(32.2 \text{ ft/sec}^2)(10 \text{ ft}) = 966 \text{ ft·lb}.$$

To get the kinetic energy at the bottom we must subtract from this initial potential energy the energy transformed into heat in friction—that is, the work done against friction. Since there is no acceleration perpendicular to the plane, $N = w \cos\theta = mg \cos\theta = (96.6 \text{ lb})(0.866) = 83.7 \text{ lb}.$ The force of friction is then $\mathfrak{F} = \mu_K N = (0.25)(83.7 \text{ lb}) = 20.9 \text{ lb}.$ The work done against friction is

$$\mathfrak{F}S = (20.9 \text{ lb})(20 \text{ ft}) = 418 \text{ ft·lb}.$$

The kinetic energy at the bottom of the incline is the difference

$$\text{kinetic energy} = (966 - 418) \text{ ft·lb} = 548 \text{ ft·lb}.$$

We can equate this kinetic energy to $\frac{1}{2} mv^2$, where v is the speed at the bottom of the incline:

$$548 \text{ ft·lb} = \tfrac{1}{2} mv^2 = \tfrac{1}{2} (3 \text{ slugs}) v^2,$$

from which
$$v^2 = 365 \text{ ft·lb/slug} = 365 \text{ ft}^2/\text{sec}^2,$$
$$v = 19.0 \text{ ft/sec}.$$

5. WORK AND ENERGY IN MOVING COORDINATE SYSTEMS

BY THE Newtonian principle of relativity, we know that the principles of mechanics are equally valid for two different observers, one of whom is moving at constant velocity relative to the other. Hence the concepts of work and energy, and the principle of conservation of energy must be equally valid and useful for the two observers. However, as we shall see in the following example, both work and energy must be measured relative to a particular frame of reference since two observers in relative motion assign not only different kinetic energies but different amounts of work done. After working through the example, we shall examine the physical significances of these differences.

Example. *A particle of mass m rests on a smooth horizontal floor on a train moving forward with constant speed V. A constant force F is applied in the forward direction on the particle and gives it acceleration a for time t. Show that the increase in kinetic energy of the particle equals the work done by the force, both as measured by an observer whose frame of reference is attached to the train and one whose frame is attached to the ground.*

The force required, which is independent of the frame of reference, is given by Newton's second principle as $F = ma$. In time t the particle increases its speed by at.

The observer on the train determines the following quantities for the particle:

initial speed $v_0 = 0$
final speed $v_1 = at$
average speed $\bar{v} = \frac{1}{2}\, at$
distance traveled $S = \bar{v}t = \frac{1}{2}\, at^2$
work done $W = FS = (ma)(\frac{1}{2}\, at^2) = \frac{1}{2}\, ma^2 t^2$
initial kinetic energy $= \frac{1}{2}\, mv_0^2 = 0$
final kinetic energy $= \frac{1}{2}\, mv_1^2 = \frac{1}{2}\, ma^2 t^2$
increase in kinetic energy $= \frac{1}{2}\, ma^2 t^2 =$ work done.

The corresponding quantities as determined by the observer on the ground are

initial speed $v_0' = V$
final speed $v_1' = V + at$
average speed $\bar{v}' = V + \frac{1}{2}\, at$
distance traveled $S' = \bar{v}'t = Vt + \frac{1}{2}\, at^2$
work done $W' = FS' = maS' = maVt + \frac{1}{2}\, ma^2 t^2$
initial kinetic energy $= \frac{1}{2}\, mv_0'^2 = \frac{1}{2}\, mV^2$
final kinetic energy $= \frac{1}{2}\, mv_1'^2 = \frac{1}{2}\, mV^2 + maVt + \frac{1}{2}\, ma^2 t^2$
increase in kinetic energy $= maVt + \frac{1}{2}\, ma^2 t^2 =$ work done.

In connection with the above example, the question arises: If work has fundamental physical significance as energy expended, why does one get different results according to the frame of the observer? What is the energy actually expended in accelerating the particle?

The answer to these questions is that the energy expended is different according to who expends the energy, and in employing the principle of conservation of energy one should use the reference frame of the person doing the work. If the man on the train pulls on the particle to accelerate it, he exerts force F through distance S and does work FS. If on the other hand, the man on the ground is imagined to have a string tied to the particle and to run along beside the train exerting force F to accelerate the particle, he must exert the force F through the much larger distance S' and do the greater work FS'.

Correspondingly, the differences in assigned kinetic energies have definite physical significances in the two frames of reference. We can think of the kinetic energy as measured by the train observer as the work the particle could do if it struck an object *stationary on the train* and was brought to rest *relative to the train*. The much larger kinetic energy assigned by the observer on the ground represents the much larger work the particle could do if it struck an object *stationary on the ground* and was brought to rest *relative to the ground*.

The case of work done against friction needs special consideration. Surely the quantity of heat generated in this case is independent of the velocity of the observer. It turns out that *work done against friction is to be computed by multiplying the force of friction* $\mathfrak{F}$ *by the distance of relative motion of the two sliding surfaces*. This distance has a definite physical significance independent of the observer. Thus two observers would assign the same amount of mechanical energy transformed into heat in

friction.   The discussion following the next example should help clarify
these ideas.

> **Example.**   *What changes occur in the results of the preceding example if we
> assume that there is a coefficient of kinetic friction μ_K between the particle and
> the floor of the train?   A force is to be applied to the particle such as to give it
> the same acceleration a for the same time t as in the previous case.*
>
> In addition to the force $F = ma$, a force $\mathfrak{F}_K = \mu_K mg$ is required to balance
> the opposing force of friction.   The man on the train does additional work
> $\mathfrak{F}_K S$; the man on the ground does additional work $\mathfrak{F}_K S'$.   There is no change
> in the initial, the final, or the increase in, kinetic energy.   Increase in kinetic
> energy no longer equals work done.

In this example, the additional work done by the man on the train is
$\mathfrak{F}_K S$, which is the amount of energy that goes into heat, since the distance
of relative motion of the particle and the train floor on which it slides is S.

Of the additional work $\mathfrak{F}_K S'$ done by the man on the ground, only the
part $\mathfrak{F}_K S$ goes into heat.   Where does the rest of the energy $\mathfrak{F}_K(S' - S)$
go?   Notice that $S' - S$ is the distance the train moves in the time t.
One suspects that work is being done *on the train*.   The man on the
ground is indeed helping to pull the train, because the box is exerting
on the train a *forward force* $\mathfrak{F}_K$, and the work done by this force, $\mathfrak{F}_K$
times the distance the train moves, relieves the engine of some of the
burden of keeping the train moving at constant speed and represents
work done on the train.   The man on the train can do *no* work on the
train; in his coordinate system the train *does not move!*   We can break
up the work done by the man on the ground into the several parts:

$$(F + \mathfrak{F}_K)S' = FS' + \mathfrak{F}_K S' = FS' + \mathfrak{F}_K S + \mathfrak{F}_K(S' - S),$$

of which the first term increases the kinetic energy of the box, the second
term appears as heat between the surface of the box and the floor of the
train, and the third term represents
work done on the train itself.

6. ENERGY OF EXTENDED BODIES

So FAR we have considered the
potential energy of a *particle* and
have seen that when it moves from
height Y_1 to height Y_2, it increases
its P.E. by $mg(Y_2 - Y_1)$.   This represents work done against gravity
and is independent of the path
followed in the motion.

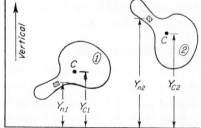

Fig. 8. A body moves from position 1 to position 2 in the earth's gravitational field.

Now let us consider (Fig. 8) an extended body that moves from one
position to another.   A typical particle, of mass m_n, changes its height
above a reference level from Y_{n1} to Y_{n2}; hence its potential energy

increases by $m_n g\ (Y_{n2}-Y_{n1})$. The whole increase in potential energy of the body is then

$$\sum_n m_n g\ (Y_{n2}-Y_{n1}) = \sum_n m_n g Y_{n2} - \sum_n m_n g Y_{n1}.$$

We recognize, by comparison with equation (10) on page 34, that the terms on the right are respectively mgY_{C2} and mgY_{C1}, where m is the total mass of the body and Y is the height of the center of gravity. Thus

$$\text{increase in P.E.} = mg\ (Y_{C2}-Y_{C1}). \tag{14}$$

The increase in potential energy of an extended body is the product of the weight of the body by the increase in height of the center of gravity of the body.

While Fig. 8 is drawn for a rigid body, the property of rigidity was not used in the proof of the theorem in italics, so this important theorem applies equally well to a non-rigid body such as a quantity of fluid.

If the nth particle of a body is moving with speed v_n, the whole body has kinetic energy

$$\text{K.E.} = \sum \tfrac{1}{2}\ m_n v_n^2, \tag{15}$$

where the summation is over all the particles of the body. In the case in which all the particles of the body have the *same* speed v_C, this expression reduces to

$$\text{K.E.} = \tfrac{1}{2}\ mv_C^2, \tag{16}$$

where m is the total mass.

In the case of a *rigid body in pure translation*, all the particles have the same velocity as the velocity of the center of gravity, and (16) gives the total kinetic energy. If the body is also rotating, the different particles no longer have the same speed, and (16), which involves the speed of the center of gravity, is called the *translational kinetic energy*. There is an additional term in the expression for the total kinetic energy, called the *rotational kinetic energy*. This term we shall consider in Chap. 9.

7. SIMPLE MACHINES

FROM THE energy-conservation principle, we are led to the conclusion that the performance of a given amount of useful work requires the expenditure of an equal amount of energy. At first glance, it might also appear that the choice of a method or procedure for performing work is immaterial; however, the question of *convenience* should be considered. For example, since

$$\text{work} = FS\ \cos\theta,$$

there is an immediately apparent choice of exerting a large force to produce a small displacement or a small force to produce a large displacement, as well as a choice of the direction θ in which the force is to be applied with respect to the displacement.

A **machine** is a device that enables us to do work more conveniently than would otherwise be possible.

In performing a given amount of work, for example in raising a large body of weight w to a height above its original position, it is *usually more convenient* for the operator to exert a small force through a large distance rather than a large force through a small distance. The operator uses a machine designed in such a manner that when he applies a small force to the machine, the machine exerts a larger force on the load. When the small applied force produces a large displacement of some part of the machine, the machine produces a small displacement of the large load. In order to have some way of comparing the relative merits of various machines, it is desirable for us to define certain pertinent quantities.

As mentioned above, one usually wishes to employ a machine that applies a large force to the load when a smaller force is applied to the machine. The quantity that is used to describe this property is called the *mechanical advantage* of the machine.

The **mechanical advantage** of a machine is the ratio of the force exerted *by* the machine to the force applied *to* the machine:

$$\text{mechanical advantage} = \frac{\text{force exerted by the machine}}{\text{force applied to the machine}}. \quad (17a)$$

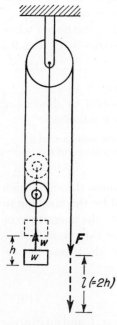

The ratio may be either greater than unity or less than unity. For example, a crowbar as normally used has a mechanical advantage greater than unity, whereas the oar of a rowboat has a mechanical advantage less than unity.

Although many machines used in engineering and industrial work are highly complicated, the principles involved in their construction and operation can be described in terms of a few devices called *simple machines*, such as the inclined plane, the lever, the pulley, the gear, the screw, and the cam. As an example to illustrate our definitions, we shall consider the simple pulley system of Fig. 9. Here a force F in the downward direction is used to lift a weight w. From the arrangement of the strings, it is seen that the force F must act through a distance $l = 2h$ in order to lift the weight a distance h.

In general, if the force applied to the machine is F, and the force exerted by the machine is w,

Figure 9
$$\text{mechanical advantage} = w/F. \quad (17b)$$

Part of the force F may represent a useful force of gravity—for example the right-hand string of Fig. 9 may carry a counterweight. In such a case we must include this force of gravity as part of the force applied to the machine.

A second quantity of importance in describing the operation of a machine is *efficiency*. Since there is always some friction in every machine, the work done *by* the machine—the *work output*—is always less than the work done *on* the machine—the *work input*. This statement is in accord with the conservation-of-energy principle, since any work done against friction is converted into *heat*.

> The **efficiency** of a machine is the ratio of the work output to the work input:

$$\text{efficiency} = \frac{\text{work output}}{\text{work input}}. \qquad (18a)$$

It is *usually* desirable for the efficiency of a machine to be as near unity (100 per cent) as possible. If there is a large amount of energy involved, a low efficiency is objectionable from two points of view: first, the dissipation of large quantities of energy is expensive; and, second, the accompanying production of large amounts of heat may result in damage to the machine itself. For example, when large amounts of heat are produced in a bearing, the bearing may 'burn out' or, in the case of a railroad car, a 'hotbox' may result. There are some special cases, however, in which low efficiency is desirable; for example, the jackscrew described below *must* have a low efficiency for successful operation.

If the force F applied to the machine acts through a distance l while the force w exerted by the machine acts through a distance h (cf. Fig. 9),

$$\text{efficiency} = wh/Fl. \qquad (18b)$$

In the case of the pulley system of Fig. 9, the efficiency is $\frac{1}{2}\, w/F$.

We shall mention one other quantity that is useful in describing machines. This quantity is called the *ideal mechanical advantage*.

> The **ideal mechanical advantage** of a machine is the mechanical advantage the machine would have if there were no friction and the parts of the machine were weightless.

This quantity can be determined in terms of the distances through which the force applied to the machine and the force applied by the machine to the load move. In the ideal case, let us use f to denote the magnitude of the force that would have to be applied to the machine; this would be less than the magnitude F of the actual force. For an ideal machine we would have

$$\text{work input} = \text{work output},$$
$$fl = wh. \qquad (19)$$

Now the mechanical advantage of this ideal machine is w/f, and an expression for this ratio can be obtained from equation (19):

$$\text{ideal mechanical advantage} = w/f = l/h. \qquad (20)$$

Thus, we see that the ideal mechanical advantage of the machine can be expressed as the ratio l/h.

In the case of the pulley system of Fig. 9, we see that the ideal mechanical advantage is $l/h = 2$. We can see that this equals w/f because in the frictionless case the tension in the string would be constant throughout and equal to f; if the lower pulley were weightless, the load w would equal twice the tension in the string, that is $w = 2f$ and $w/f = 2$. For a given weight w, the actual force F will be greater than f for two reasons: (a) force must be exerted to overcome friction in the pulleys, and (b) not only the load w but the weight of the lower pulley must be lifted. Thus the actual mechanical advantage would be less than 2.

From (19) we see that $wh/l = f$; hence from (18b) we see that

$$\text{efficiency} = f/F, \tag{21}$$

the ratio of the force required in the ideal case to that required in the actual case. Equation (21) leads to the useful relation:

$$\text{efficiency} = \frac{f}{F} = \frac{fw}{Fw} = \frac{w}{F} \div \frac{w}{f} = \frac{\text{mechanical advantage}}{\text{ideal mechanical advantage}}, \tag{22}$$

where the last expression is obtained by comparison with (17b) and (20).

In the example of Fig. 9, if $w = 100$ lb, the force required in the ideal case would be $f = 50$ lb. If the lower pulley weighs 10 lb, this must be lifted with the load, and in the absence of friction a pull of 55 lb would be required. With friction, a pull of $F = 60$ lb might be required. In this last case,

$$\text{mechanical advantage} = w/F = 100/60 = \tfrac{5}{3},$$

$$\text{ideal mechanical advantage} = w/f = l/h = 2,$$

$$\text{efficiency} = f/F = 50/60 = \tfrac{5}{6},$$

and we verify the correctness of (22).

Various other simple machines will be involved in the problems at the end of this chapter. Here we shall consider one more example:

Example. *Determine the ideal mechanical advantage of the jackscrew shown in Fig. 10.*

The jackscrew is a simple machine used to lift large loads by applying relatively small forces. One turn gives the load a vertical displacement equal to the pitch of the screw, that is, the distance p between adjacent threads. The work done is wp, where w is the weight of the load. In order to

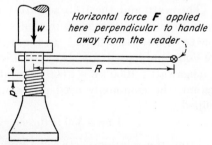

Horizontal force $\boldsymbol{F}$ applied here perpendicular to handle away from the reader

Fig. 10. The jackscrew.

produce this vertical displacement of the load, a force F is applied near the end of the handle in a direction perpendicular to the handle in the indicated manner. The point of application of the applied force must move around the circumference of the circle whose radius R is the length of the lever arm. The work done by this applied force for one turn is therefore $2\pi RF$. If there were no friction, we would have $2\pi Rf = wp$, and the ideal mechanical advantage, defined as w/f in the frictionless case, has the value

$$\text{ideal mechanical advantage} = 2\pi R/p.$$

In the jackscrew the mechanical advantage is always much smaller than this, since in a screw there is always a great deal of friction. Here this property is desirable, since a useful jack must support the load after the load has been raised; a frictionless jackscrew would unwind as soon as the applied force F ceased to act and thereby would allow the load to descend.

8. POWER

Time is not involved in any way in the definition of *work*. The same amount of work is done in raising a given weight through a given vertical distance regardless of the time required. However, the *time rate* at which work is done is an important quantity called power:

Power is the time rate at which work is done.

If ΔW represents the work performed in a time interval Δt, the average power $\bar{P}$ is defined by the relation

$$\bar{P} = \Delta W/\Delta t.$$

The power at any instant is given by the relation

$$P = dW/dt, \tag{23}$$

where this derivative (the limit of $\bar{P}$ as $\Delta t \to 0$) is evaluated at the instant in question.

The unit used for the measurement of power involves the ratio of a work unit to a time unit. Thus, in the British engineering system, we can use the ft·lb/sec as a power unit. In the MKS system, the corresponding unit is the *joule/sec*, which is given a special name: the *watt* (w).

$$1 \text{ watt} = 1 \text{ joule/sec}. \tag{24}$$

The watt and the ft·lb/sec are both inconveniently small units for many practical power measurements, and hence it has been found desirable to define larger units. In the MKS system two multiples of the watt are commonly used: the *kilowatt* (1 kw = 1000 watts) and the *megawatt* (1 megawatt = 1000 kw = 1,000,000 watts). In the British gravitational system, the commonly used power unit is called the *horsepower* (hp), defined by

$$1 \text{ hp} = 550 \text{ ft·lb/sec} = 33,000 \text{ ft·lb/min}. \tag{25}$$

From the relations between the newton, pound, meter, and foot, it can easily be shown that

$$1 \text{ hp} = 745.7 \text{ watts} = 0.7457 \text{ kw}.$$

It is convenient in making rough calculations to remember that 1 horse-power is about ¾ kilowatt.

Having defined the conveniently large *power units*, the horsepower and the kilowatt, we may now define two additional conveniently large *work units*, the *horsepower-hour* (hp·hr) and the *kilowatt-hour* (kwh).

> One **horsepower-hour** is the work done in one hour by a device working at constant rate of one horsepower.

Since such a device does 33,000 ft·lb of work per minute, the work done in one hour is 60 min·33,000 ft·lb/min = 1,980,000 ft·lb; hence

$$1 \text{ horsepower-hour} = 1.98 \times 10^6 \text{ ft·lb}. \tag{26}$$

> One **kilowatt-hour** is the work done in one hour by a device work-ing at a constant rate of one kilowatt.

Since 1 kw = 1000 w = 1000 joules/sec, and 1 hr = 3600 sec,

$$1 \text{ kwh} = (1 \text{ kw}) \times (1 \text{ hr}) = (1000 \text{ joules/sec})(3600 \text{ sec}) = 3,600,000 \text{ joules},$$

or,

$$1 \text{ kwh} = 3.6 \times 10^6 \text{ joules}. \tag{27}$$

It should be noted that the horsepower-hour and the kilowatt-hour are units of *work* or *energy, not of power.* Thus, when an electric 'power company' presents a bill to a customer, charges are actually made for *energy,* not power. In the form of electrical energy, a kilowatt-hour can be purchased at a price that varies from a few tenths of a cent to a few cents, depending upon the locality of the consumer and on the quantity of energy he purchases. Since input power requirements of electrical appli-ances are stated in *watts* and electric utility rates are stated in terms of *kilowatt-hours,* there is a popular misconception that there is something 'electrical' about a watt, a kilowatt, and a kilowatt-hour. This is not the case. These particular units occur because all electrical units and the whole of electrical engineering are based on the *metric* system, as dis-tinguished from mechanical engineering, which in the United States generally employs British-system units such as horsepower. Although electrical power is commonly measured in watts and kilowatts and elec-trical energy is usually measured in kilowatt-hours, it would be quite correct to state the power rating of incandescent lamps in horsepower and to measure electrical energy in horsepower-hours. Similarly, it would be entirely correct to rate automobile engines in kilowatts.

Let us now compute the power expended by a force acting on a moving body, that is, the *rate* at which the force does work. Suppose a force of magnitude F acting in the X-direction is exerted on a body as shown in Fig. 2 while the body undergoes a displacement dX in time dt. Then the work done is $dW = F\,dX$, and the instantaneous power is

$$P = dW/dt = F\,dX/dt = Fv. \tag{28a}$$

The rate at which a force F does work on a body moving at velocity v is
Fv if the vectors F and v have the same direction. If the force F does
not have the same direction as the velocity v, it is easy to see that the
rate at which the force does work is

$$P = Fv \cos\theta, \quad \begin{Bmatrix} P \text{ in ft·lb/sec} \\ F \text{ in lb} \\ v \text{ in ft/sec} \end{Bmatrix} \text{ or } \begin{Bmatrix} P \text{ in watts} \\ F \text{ in nt} \\ v \text{ in m/sec} \end{Bmatrix} \quad (28b)$$

where θ is the angle between the vectors F and v, as in Fig. 1.

Example. *An automobile of mass 110 slugs is accelerated from rest with the
constant acceleration of 5 ft/sec² for 10 sec. Determine the useful horsepower
delivered by the engine as a function of time during this period.*

From $F = ma$, the required force is $F = 550$ lb. From $v = at$, the speed as
a function of time is $v = (5 \text{ ft/sec}^2) \, t$. From (28), the power is

$$P = Fv = (2750 \text{ ft·lb/sec}^2) \, t.$$

Since 1 ft·lb/sec $= \frac{1}{550}$ hp, we divide by 550 to get

$$P = (5 \text{ hp/sec}) \, t.$$

The power useful in accelerating the automobile increases linearly in time
from zero at $t = 0$ to 50 hp at $t = 10$ sec.

PROBLEMS

NOTE: In these problems assume that the acceleration of gravity has the
standard value $g = 32.2 \text{ ft/sec}^2 = 9.81 \text{ m/sec}^2$.

1. By exerting a constant force of 12.0 lb on a rope attached to a sled, a
man pulls the sled across the ice on the surface of a pond. If the rope makes
an angle of 45° with the direction of motion, how much work does the man do
in moving the sled a distance of 90.0 ft?   Ans: 764 ft·lb.

2. A sled weighing 30 lb is dragged at constant velocity across a horizontal
surface. If the coefficient of friction between the sled runners and the snow is
0.12, how much work is done in moving the sled a distance of 50 ft if the applied
force is in the direction of motion?

3. An elevator cage has a mass of 1000 kg. If frictional effects are negligible,
how much work is done in raising the cage 50 meters at constant speed?
          Ans: 4.90×10^5 joules.

4. A 2-kg well bucket containing 8 kg of water is raised at constant speed
from the water surface in the well to ground level, 9 m above the water level.
How much work is done in this process?

5. An automobile weighing 3220 lb has an instantaneous velocity of 60 ft/sec
southward. What is the kinetic energy of the automobile? If frictional losses
were negligible, how much work was done in giving the automobile this velocity?
          Ans: 180,000 ft·lb; 180,000 ft·lb.

6. A truck weighing 8250 lb is moving along a highway at a speed of 60
mi/hr. What is the kinetic energy of this truck? Assuming negligible frictional
losses, calculate the work done in accelerating the truck to this speed.

7. A 7.25-kg shell fired from a gun has a muzzle velocity of magnitude
300 m/sec. What is the kinetic energy of this shell? How much work can this
shell do against retarding forces as a result of this kinetic energy?
          Ans: 326,000, 326,000 joules.

8. What is the kinetic energy of a 20-kg shell moving at a speed of 200 m/sec? How much work was done in accelerating this shell? How much work can be done by this shell against retarding forces?

9. A stone with a mass of 1.20 slugs lies at rest at the top of a cliff 360 ft high. What is the potential energy of this stone with respect to the top of the cliff? With respect to the valley floor at the foot of the cliff? Ans: 0; 13,900 ft·lb.

10. A waterfall is 33 m high. What is the potential energy of one cubic meter of water at the top of the fall with respect to the foot of the waterfall? How much work can this cubic meter of water do in a turbine located at river level below the fall?

11. A 200-kg bomb is released from an airplane flying at an altitude of 225 m. What is the initial potential energy of this bomb with respect to the ground?
Ans: 4.41×10^5 joules.

12. At the left of Fig. 3, let friction be present, and let us pull the body up the incline in any manner, with or without acceleration. Show that the work done *by the force of gravity* is $-mgH$, so the potential energy increases by mgH, in accordance with the basic definition on p. 106.

13. A body of mass 2 slugs is dropped from the top of a building 250 ft above street level. What is the potential energy of the body, relative to street level, at the instant it is released? What is the kinetic energy of the body just before it strikes the street? What is the final speed of the body?
Ans: 16,100 ft·lb; 16,100 ft·lb; 127 ft/sec.

14. A body weighing 16 lb is dropped from a height of 400 ft. What is the kinetic energy of the body just before it strikes the ground?

15. A 0.25-kg ball is thrown vertically upward with an initial velocity of 8.0 m/sec. Find (a) the initial kinetic energy of the ball, (b) the kinetic energy of the ball as it reaches its maximum height, (c) the potential energy of the ball at the highest point in its trajectory, relative to the point of release, and (d) the maximum height attained. Ans: (a) 8.0 joules; (b) 0; (c) 8.0 joules; (d) 3.26 m.

16. Two sleds, each weighing 50 lb, are initially at rest on a platform 30 ft above ground level. Sled A is pushed over the edge and allowed to fall vertically to the ground; sled B is allowed to slide down a frictionless inclined plane to the ground. The inclined plane makes an angle of 30° with the horizontal. Find the following quantities: (a) change in potential energy of sled A, (b) change in potential energy of sled B, (c) kinetic energy of sled A at the instant it reaches the ground, (d) kinetic energy of sled B at the instant it reaches the ground, and (e) the speeds of sleds A and B just as they reach the ground.

17. Two balls each weighing ⅛ lb are thrown from the top of a building 328 ft high. Ball A is thrown downward with an initial velocity of 72.0 ft/sec and ball B is thrown vertically upward with an initial velocity of 72.0 ft/sec. Find: (a) the initial potential energies of balls A and B, relative to ground level, (b) the initial kinetic energies of ball A and ball B, (c) the speeds of balls A and B two seconds after release, and (d) the final speeds of balls A and B at ground level. Ans:
(a) 41.0, 41.0 ft·lb; (b) 10.1, 10.1 ft·lb; (c) 136, 7.6 ft/sec; (d) 162, 162 ft/sec.

18. A 400-g ball is thrown horizontally at 20 m/sec from the top of a cliff 120 m high. Find (a) the initial kinetic energy of the ball, (b) the initial potential energy of the ball, relative to the bottom of the cliff, (c) the final kinetic energy of the ball just before it strikes the ground, and (d) the final speed of the ball.

19. A 2-slug shell is fired with a muzzle velocity of 1600 ft/sec. If the elevation angle is 60°, find the magnitude of the shell's velocity when it is at altitude of 10,000 ft above the earth's surface. Neglect air resistance. Ans: 1384 ft/sec.

20. What is the speed of the shell in Prob. 19 when it is 6400 ft above the ground? If the elevation angle had been 30°, what would have been the shell's speed at 6400 ft? Repeat these computations for a 3-slug shell.

21. A sled weighing 40 lb is at the top of a hill at a height of 60 ft above a level field. The sled slides down a runway to the foot of the hill and its final speed at the end of the runway is 50 ft/sec. How much mechanical energy was dissipated during the sled's descent? Ans: 848 ft·lb.

22. If the final speed of the sled in Prob. 21 had been 45 ft/sec, how much mechanical energy would have been dissipated?

23. A 150-g ball with a rough cover is thrown vertically upward with an initial velocity of 20 m/sec. The ball rises to a height of 15 m. How much mechanical energy is dissipated during the upward motion of the ball?
Ans: 7.94 joules.

24. If the final velocity of the ball in Prob. 23 when it returns to the ground is 15 m/sec, how much mechanical energy was dissipated during its downward passage?

25. An automobile weighing 3220 lb moves at a speed of 60 ft/sec along a level roadway. When the car reaches an upward slope, the driver allows the car to coast uphill until it comes to rest. If the final position of the car on the hill is 45 ft above the level of the approaching roadway, how much mechanical energy was dissipated during the car's ascent of the hill? Ans: 35,100 ft·lb.

26. If the car in Prob. 25 were allowed to roll backward down the hill and the same amount of mechanical energy were lost during descent as during ascent, what would be the speed of the car when it reached the foot of the hill?

27. A large crate weighing 400 lb is permitted to slide down a ramp inclined at an angle of 30° to the horizontal. The length of the ramp is 50 ft. If the magnitude of the acceleration of the crate is 4 ft/sec², how much mechanical energy is dissipated during descent? Ans: 7510 ft·lb.

28. What was the speed of the crate in Prob. 27 when it reached the foot of the ramp? What was the kinetic energy? What was the coefficient of friction between the crate and the ramp?

29. The 1-ton hammer of a pile driver drops from a vertical height of 10 ft, strikes a pile, and drives the pile 4 inches into the ground. Assuming that all the energy of the pile driver (at the instant of striking) is communicated to the pile, compute the average force resisting the motion of the pile. Ans: 60,000 lb.

30. Using the answers to Prob. 45, p. 101, show that the work done against friction as the body moves up the plane equals the decrease in total mechanical energy. Do the same for the motion down the plane back to the starting point.

31. In Fig. 11, body A has 1-slug mass, body B has $\frac{1}{2}$-slug mass. Body C is a board of $\frac{3}{2}$-slug mass mounted on frictionless wheels. The coefficient of kinetic friction between B and C is 0.6. Determine (a) the accelerations of A, B, C; (b) the heat generated by friction in 1 sec; (c) the loss of potential energy of body A in 1 sec; (d) the kinetic energies of bodies A, B, C after 1 sec; (e) verify that the loss of potential energy of A equals the gain in kinetic energy of A, B, and C plus the heat generated by friction. The system starts from rest. Ans: (a) 15.0, 15.0, 6.44 ft/sec²; (b) 41.5 ft·lb; (c) 242 ft·lb; (d) 113, 56.4, 31.1 ft·lb.

32. In Fig. 11, body A has 4-kg mass, body B has 5-kg mass; body C is a board of 12-kg mass mounted on frictionless wheels. The coefficient of kinetic friction between B and C is 0.4. Make the same computations as in (a)–(e) of Prob. 31.

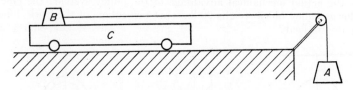

Figure 11

33. Consider the inclined plane, or ramp, as a simple machine whose useful work output consists of lifting a box of weight w through a vertical height h. Let the coefficient of sliding friction between the box and the plane be μ_K. Show that

$$\text{mechanical advantage} = 1/(\sin\theta + \mu_K \cos\theta),$$
$$\text{ideal mechanical advantage} = 1/\sin\theta,$$
$$\text{efficiency} = \sin\theta/(\sin\theta + \mu_K \cos\theta).$$

34. Discuss the claw hammer and the cutting pliers as examples of simple machines that are essentially levers. By means of diagrams, indicate how you would compute the ideal mechanical advantage in each case.

35. A ramp inclined at an angle of 30° with the horizontal is used in loading crates on a railroad car. If there were no friction involved, what would be the mechanical advantage of this ramp? The coefficient of friction between the crates and the ramp is actually 0.2. What is the actual mechanical advantage of the ramp? What is the efficiency of the ramp? If the ramp were used to raise a 1000-lb crate a vertical distance of 5 ft, how much mechanical energy would be dissipated?   Ans: 2; 1.49; 74.3%; 1730 ft·lb.

36. Determine the ideal mechanical advantage of the pulley system of Fig. 12 both by analyzing the tensions in the strings and by analyzing the geometrical motions. Assume all strings to be vertical.

37. For the jackscrew shown in Fig. 10, the pitch p of the screw is 0.50 in and the force perpendicular to the lever is applied at a point 4 ft from the axis of rotation of the screw. What is the ideal mechanical advantage of the jackscrew? When the jackscrew is used to raise a weight $w = 5000$ lb, a force $F = 50$ lb must be applied in a direction perpendicular to the lever. What is the actual mechanical advantage of the jackscrew? The screw mechanism itself including the lever weighs 200 lb. How much work is done against frictional forces in raising the load a distance of 10 in? How much useful work was done in raising the load? How much useless work was done in raising the screw?
Ans: 603; 100; 20,800 ft·lb; 4170 ft·lb; 167 ft·lb.

38. Verify the correctness of equation (22) for the jackscrew of Prob. 37.

39. The lower pulley block in the system of Fig. 9 weighs 20 lb. When the load of 200 lb is raised through a vertical distance of 2 ft, how much useful work is done in raising the load? How much useless work is done in raising the lower pulley block? How much work is done against frictional forces if $F = 133$ lb is required?   Ans: 400 ft·lb; 40 ft·lb; 92 ft·lb.

40. What is the mechanical advantage of the crank and axle type of hoist such as was used to raise the bucket in the old-fashioned well?

41. What is the ideal mechanical advantage of the pulley system shown in Fig. 13? If a force of 60 lb is required to raise a load $w = 200$ lb at constant speed, what is the actual mechanical advantage of the pulley system? the efficiency? If the lower pulley block weighs 20 lb, what percentage of the work done by F is dissipated in heat?   Ans: 4; 3.33; 83.3%; 8.33%.

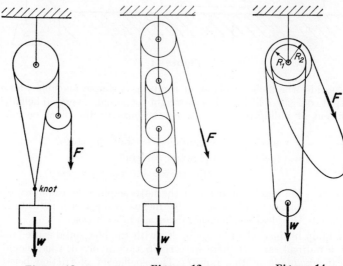

| Figure 12 | Figure 13 | Figure 14 |

42. Determine the ideal mechanical advantage of the differential chain hoist sketched in Fig. 14. The 'string' shown in this drawing is actually a chain that engages teeth in the pulleys so that it cannot slip. Determine w/f both geometrically and from consideration of rotational equilibrium of the upper pulley.

43. A man weighing 200 lb climbs a stairway in 2 min. If his upward displacement is 60 ft, how much work does he do against the pull of gravity? What is his average useful power output? Express this power output in hp.

Ans: 12,000 ft·lb; 100 ft·lb/sec; 0.182 hp.

44. A 100-kg packing box is moved 15 m across a rough floor in 1 min at constant speed. If the coefficient of kinetic friction between the box and the floor is 0.4, what power is involved in moving the box?

45. An automobile weighing 3220 lb starts from rest and attains a speed of 80 ft/sec in 40 sec. Find the total useful work done on the car and the average power output of the automobile engine that was effective in accelerating the car. Express the average power in hp. Ans: 320,000 ft·lb; 8000 ft·lb/sec; 14.5 hp.

46. If the acceleration was constant in Prob. 45, what was the maximum useful power output just before the car acquired its final speed of 80 ft/sec? If it requires 22 hp to keep the car running at a constant speed of 80 ft/sec, what was the maximum total power output of the engine?

47. Water flows over a 50-ft waterfall at the rate of 4000 ft³/min. What would be the maximum power output of a water wheel operated at this waterfall if all the energy of the falling water could be utilized? Express this power in hp and in kw.   Ans: 378 hp; 282 kw.

48. Find the power available from a waterfall 120 ft high if the flow of water is 1500 ft³/min. Express the result in hp and kw.

49. A locomotive exerts a constant drawbar pull of 4 tons (8000 lb) while pulling a freight train at 45 mi/hr on a level track. What is the drawbar power developed by this locomotive?   Ans: 5.28×10^5 ft·lb/sec = 960 hp.

50. If the locomotive of Prob. 49 is pulling 1000 tons of cars up a 1-percent grade at 45 mi/hr, what horsepower is the engine delivering if it is assumed that a force of 4 tons is still required to overcome friction?

51. A constant horizontal force of 8 lb is applied to a block of mass 2 slugs initially at rest on a frictionless horizontal surface. What instantaneous power is being developed at the end of the third second? at the end of the fifth second? What is the average power developed during the first five seconds?
                     Ans: 96 ft·lb/sec; 160 ft·lb/sec; 80 ft·lb/sec.

52. Show that the power required to give a block of mass m an acceleration a when it is moving at velocity v up a frictionless inclined plane making angle θ with the horizontal is

$$P = mva + mgv \sin\theta.$$

Derive this expression in two ways: (a) by computing the force required and using the relation $P = Fv$; (b) by determining the time rate of change of mechanical energy by differentiation of $\frac{1}{2}mv^2 + mgh$.

53. A ½-hp electric motor operates continuously at rated load for 5 hr. How much work is done by this motor? Express your answer in hp·hr, ft·lb, joules, and kwh.   Ans: 2.5 hp·hr; 4.95×10^6 ft·lb; 6.71×10^6 joules, 1.86 kwh.

54. If a 50-kw electric generator operates continuously at full capacity for 8 hours, how much energy is delivered? Express your answer in hp·hr, ft·lb, joules, and kwh.

55. An electric power company sells energy at 6 cents per kwh. How many joules can be purchased for 10 cents?   Ans: 6×10^6.

56. Buying energy from the electric company at 6 cents per kwh, a customer operates a 2-hp motor at rated load for two hours. Assuming negligible losses in the motor, calculate the cost to the customer. What is the company's charge for 1 hp·hr?

57. In Prob. 15, p. 99, at what angle θ is the minimum *power* required to pull the box at constant speed? Explain what was probably an unexpected answer.

58. An impact testing machine has a concentrated weight of 80 lb held at the end of a light 3.5-ft arm pivoted at the other end (Fig. 15). The pendulum is allowed to swing down from a horizontal position, strike the rod to be tested at the bottom of the swing, and to coast past on the far side. Find the relation between the maximum angle θ made by the pendulum on the upswing and the energy, in ft·lb, used in rupturing the specimen.

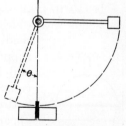

Figure 15

CHAPTER 6

MECHANICS OF FLUIDS

THE TERM *fluid* refers to a substance that does not have a fixed *shape* but that is able to *flow* and take the shape of its container; in other words, to a *liquid* or a *gas*. Although there is no sharp line of demarcation between solids and liquids (witness such materials as gelatin, heavy grease, and cold tar), we shall restrict our attention in this chapter to substances that are obviously liquid because they flow with reasonable rapidity, and to gases.

It is perhaps somewhat surprising to find that the same basic laws govern the static and dynamic behavior of both liquids and gases, in spite of their very different appearance. We shall discuss the distinction between liquids and gases in some detail in Chap. 16. In discussing the mechanical behavior of fluids we need make use only of properties that liquids and gases have in common and that are associated with their ability to flow. The first part of this chapter will be concerned with the static behavior of fluids, the latter part with their dynamic behavior.

1. FLUID PRESSURE

IT IS A MATTER of common experience that fluids exert forces on material solids with which they are in contact; examples are the forces that

Figure 1

tend to burst a high-pressure air tank and those that support a floating boat or balloon. The liquid in the pail in Fig. 1 exerts a force on the bottom which is equal and opposite to the force exerted by the solid bottom on the liquid. That the latter force exists is apparent if we consider what would happen if we took away a piece of the bottom. The liquid would no longer be in static equilibrium but would flow downward when the upward force of the bottom was removed.

Similarly, the liquid *below* the imaginary horizontal plane shown by the dashed line in Fig. 1 must be exerting an upward force on the liquid *above* this plane, because this force is required to hold the latter part of the liquid up; remove this force and the liquid above the broken line would fall to the bottom of the

130

pail. By Newton's third principle, the fluid above this imaginary plane must be exerting an opposite downward force on the fluid below the plane. Thus we conclude that not only does a fluid exert a force on a solid surface but also that if we 'draw' an imaginary plane in the fluid, the fluid on one side of this plane exerts a force across the plane on the fluid on the other side. The plane need not be horizontal. Consider the small imaginary cube sketched in Fig. 1. The liquid in this cube must exert horizontal forces across the vertical walls of the cube on the surrounding liquid, since such forces are needed to prevent the surrounding liquid from flowing in and occupying the space occupied by the liquid within the cube. The same argument applies to an imaginary cube drawn in a gas such as the air of the atmosphere.

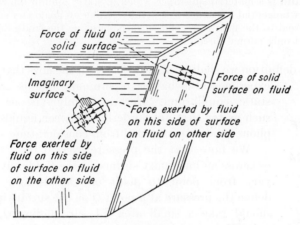

Force of fluid on solid surface

Imaginary surface

Force of solid surface on fluid

Force exerted by fluid on this side of surface on fluid on other side

Force exerted by fluid on this side of surface on fluid on the other side

Figure 2

Thus we see the general necessity for the existence of forces across any imaginary surface in the fluid as well as for forces between the fluid and solid surfaces. Experience completely justifies the assumption that *in static equilibrium these forces are normal to the surfaces* in question and are usually of the nature of a *push* rather than a *pull*. This statement is illustrated in Fig. 2. Such forces are described by giving the *pressure P*, which is defined as *normal force per unit area*. The pressure is almost always a positive quantity.*

Our description of the forces across any imaginary surface in a substance in static equilibrium applies to a solid substance (see Chap. 8, Elasticity and Strength of Materials) as well as to a fluid, *up to the point* where we assert that the force is normal to the surface and almost always compressive. We readily see that in a solid there must be both tangential

---

* Under certain very exceptional circumstances a liquid (never a gas) can withstand a tensile force (a negative pressure of the nature of a pull across a surface), but the rule that pressure is always positive is valid for nearly all engineering purposes.

forces and tensile forces. In the case of a stick protruding from the
edge of a table, there must be a vertical force across the imaginary
vertical plane drawn in the stick at the edge of the table to balance
statically the downward force of gravity on the protruding part of the
stick if the stick is in equilibrium. Thus the force system across a plane
in a solid in equilibrium can have tangential components. The properties peculiar to a fluid medium are obtained when we require that the force
across any plane be entirely of the nature of a *pressure* normal to the
plane. Obviously, a fluid could not have the configuration of a stick
protruding across the edge of a table.

For our purposes we adopt the following definition:

> A **fluid** is a material substance which in static equilibrium cannot
> exert tangential forces across a surface (either an imaginary surface
> internal to the fluid or a solid surface bounding the fluid), but can
> exert only normal forces.

From this definition we shall be able to derive all the laws that govern the
experimental behavior of ordinary liquids and gases in
static equilibrium. Certain highly viscous substances
such as tar that are borderline between liquids and amorphous solids are excluded from consideration.

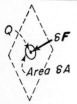

Figure 3

We note that the pressure exerted on a real surface
or across an imaginary surface in the fluid may in general
vary from point to point on the surface. Hence, to
define the pressure at a point Q on the surface in Fig. 3, we
should take a small area δA surrounding Q, on which
force of magnitude δF acts, and write

$$P = \lim_{\delta A \to 0} \frac{\delta F}{\delta A}. \tag{1}$$

Suitable units for measuring pressure are lb/in², lb/ft², and nt/m².

From the discussion so far, one would be tempted to treat pressure
as a vector quantity having the direction of the force δF in Fig. 3. We
might expect the pressure to be different for every different choice of the
plane through Q. But it is very convenient that in the case of fluids
the pressure at Q is *independent* of the direction of the plane through Q,
so that we can treat P as a scalar function associated with the point
and from it derive the vectorial force across any plane whatever through
Q. That the pressure is independent of the direction of the plane is
proved as follows:

Let the slant face of the prism in Fig. 4 be any plane whatsoever
through Q; let this plane make a dihedral angle θ with the horizontal
plane. Choose a rectangular coordinate system with the Z-axis vertical

and the X-axis parallel to a horizontal line in the plane, and construct the small prism shown in Fig. 4.

Let the average pressure on the slant face be P_1; then the force on the slant face is $P_1 a^2$. Let the average pressure on the left face be P_2; the area of this face is $a^2 \sin\theta$, and hence the force on this face is $P_2 a^2 \sin\theta$. Let the average pressure on the bottom face be P_3; the area of this face is $a^2 \cos\theta$, and hence the force on this face is $P_3 a^2 \cos\theta$. Denote the density of the fluid in the prism by ρ (*density* is *mass per unit volume*); the volume of the prism is $\frac{1}{2} a^3 \sin\theta \cos\theta$; the *weight* per unit volume is ρg; therefore the weight of the prism is $\rho g \cdot \frac{1}{2} a^3 \sin\theta \cos\theta$.

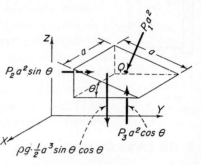

Figure 4

Now consider the equilibrium of forces on the prism. In the Y-direction we have

$$P_2 a^2 \sin\theta = P_1 a^2 \sin\theta,$$

or
$$P_2 = P_1. \tag{2}$$

In the Z-direction we have

$$P_3 a^2 \cos\theta = P_1 a^2 \cos\theta + \rho g \cdot \tfrac{1}{2} a^3 \sin\theta \cos\theta,$$

or
$$P_3 = P_1 + \tfrac{1}{2} \rho g a \sin\theta. \tag{3}$$

Equations (2) and (3) are true for any size prism; in particular they must remain true in the limit as $a \to 0$. In the limit, P_1 approaches the pressure on the slant face at Q; P_3 approaches the pressure on a horizontal surface at Q; and P_2 the pressure on a vertical surface at Q. Also, in (3), the last term approaches zero as $a \to 0$ and can be dropped. Hence in the limit we conclude that $P_1 = P_2 = P_3$, and hence that the pressure on any slant surface or any vertical surface through Q equals the pressure on a horizontal surface through Q. In other words,

At a given point in a fluid, the pressure is independent of the orientation of the surface through the point.

Because of this fact, which has no counterpart in the case of stresses in solids, it is convenient to *treat the pressure P in a fluid as a scalar function of position.*

Although the convenient instruments for measuring pressure employ fluids and hence depend for their operation on laws of fluid statics which we have not yet derived, one could conceive of constructing a little 'gadget' that would measure fluid pressure by compression of a spring, as in Fig. 5. A very flexible rubber diaphragm is backed by a plate attached to a spring. *The inside space is evacuated.* The force of the fluid on the diaphragm is measured by the compression of the spring.

Such a gadget, in the normal atmosphere, would give a pressure reading of 14.7 lb/in², independent of whether the diaphragm were pointed up, down, sidewise, or in any other orientation, in accordance with the theorem we have just proved, which says that pressure is independent of orientation. Similarly, 35 ft down in a lake, the gadget would give a constant reading of about 30 lb/in², independent of the way it was pointed.

Fig. 5.
'Gadget' for pressure measurement.

2. THE LAWS OF FLUID STATICS

IN THIS SECTION we shall state and prove a set of theorems that give the laws of fluid statics. These laws follow directly from the above definition of a fluid, and from Newton's first and third principles. In the proofs of the following laws, we shall not assume that the fluid is homogeneous; rather, it is important to consider the case where more than one type of fluid is present, as in the case of oil floating on water or the ever-present case of air 'floating' on water. After we are equipped with these laws, we shall discuss their applications in some detail.

The pressure at every point in a continuous horizontal layer of a fluid at rest is the same.

Imagine a thin square prism to be 'drawn' within the fluid with its axis horizontal as in Fig. 6. Let the Y-axis of a coordinate system be parallel

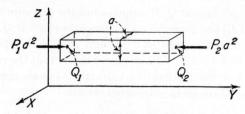

Figure 6

to the axis of the prism. The only forces acting in the Y-direction on the fluid within this prism are the normal forces on the ends. If P_1 is the average pressure on the left end, P_2, the average pressure on the right end, equilibrium requires that

$$P_1 a^2 = P_2 a^2, \quad \text{or} \quad P_1 = P_2.$$

If now a approaches zero, P_1 approaches the pressure at Q_1 and P_2 that at Q_2; therefore the pressures at Q_1 and Q_2, two arbitrary points in the same horizontal plane, are equal. This identity proves the law stated above for two points Q_1 and Q_2 that can be joined by such a prism of fluid as in Fig. 6. If, because of a solid obstruction, a straight line cannot be drawn in the fluid from Q_1 to Q_2, but if a succession of straight horizontal lines in the fluid can connect Q_1 and Q_2, the principle is clearly still true. Thus, when a solid object is completely *surrounded* by fluid, the pressure of the fluid on the object is the same at all points on the same horizontal level.

The pressure at a height h_1 in a fluid at rest is greater than the pressure at a greater height h_2 by the weight of a column of fluid of unit cross section and height $h_2 - h_1$ lying between these two levels. For a homogeneous fluid this pressure difference is $\rho g \, (h_2 - h_1)$, where ρ is the density.

Consider fluid levels a vertical distance $h_2 - h_1$ apart, as in Fig. 7. Connect them by a prism of cross-sectional area A. If the fluid in this prism has weight w, equilibrium of vertical forces requires that

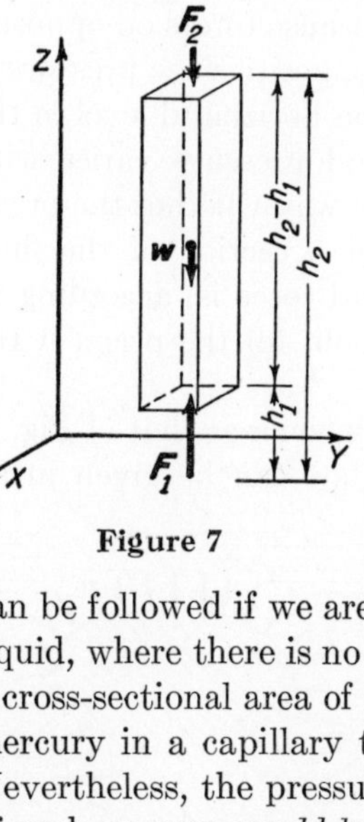

$$F_1 - F_2 = w. \qquad (4)$$

Dividing this equation through by the area A gives

$$\frac{F_1}{A} - \frac{F_2}{A} = \frac{w}{A},$$

or $\qquad P_1 - P_2 = \left\{ \begin{array}{l} \text{weight per unit cross-} \\ \text{sectional area of prism} \end{array} \right\},$

Figure 7

which proves the statement. One is tempted, in this proof, to say, 'Take a column of fluid of unit cross-sectional area.' This instruction can be followed if we are talking about the atmosphere or a large tank of liquid, where there is no difficulty in cutting out a column of fluid having a cross-sectional area of 1 in², 1 ft², or 1 m². But if we are talking about mercury in a capillary tube, we cannot cut out a column of such area. Nevertheless, the pressure difference is the weight that a column of fluid of such an area *would have*.

If the fluid is homogeneous, in that it has the same density ρ at all points, it is seen that the weight of a column of fluid of unit cross section is ρg times the volume $h_2 - h_1$.

Although the above law refers explicitly to pressures at points vertically above one another, combined use of this and the previous law, which says that the pressure is constant in a horizontal layer, enables us to relate the pressure at any two points in a fluid, as indicated in Fig. 8. If the U-tube of Fig. 8 contains a dense liquid to the left and a less dense liquid in the right-hand tube down to the level marked 'interface,' the pressure at *4* will be *greater* than at *1*, because a unit column of fluid connecting *4* and *3* will weigh less than a unit column of fluid connecting (in two steps) *1* and *3*. The liquid will stand higher in the right-hand tube than in the left.

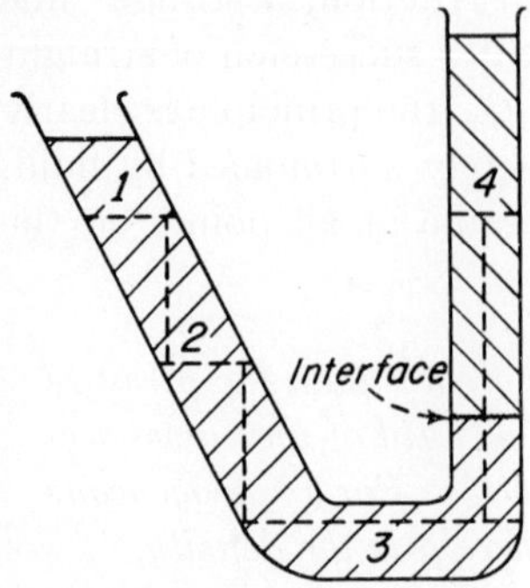

ARCHIMEDES' LAW: *A fluid acts on a foreign body immersed in it with a net force that is vertically upward and equal in magnitude to the weight of the fluid displaced by the body. (This upward force is called the buoyant force.)*

This law was first proved by Archimedes (c. 287–212 B.C.). For a foreign body of the shape of the prism of Fig. 7, we can immediately demonstrate this principle as follows: There is no resultant horizontal force on the prism because forces on opposite faces are equal and opposite since pressure is the same at the same horizontal level in the fluid. Since the fluid pressure varies with height *h* in the same way whether the prism is a foreign body or a section of the fluid itself, the net upward force is, according to (4), $F_1 - F_2 = w$, the weight of the fluid that would fill the prism if the foreign body were not present.

Fig. 8. Pressure is constant on layers *1, 2, 3,* and *4.* The pressure difference between two layers that can be connected by a vertical line is the weight of a unit column of fluid connecting these layers. The pressure at *4* is not necessarily the same as at *1*, on the same horizontal level, unless the liquid is homogeneous throughout.

For the more general case of an irregular body, such as that of Fig. 9, immersed in a fluid, the proof of Archimedes' law can be given in an equally simple fashion. The fluid pressures on the surface of the body would be unchanged if the body were not present and this surface were considered as an imaginary surface drawn in the fluid itself. When the body is replaced by a region of fluid of the same shape, the laws of static equilibrium require that the surrounding fluid exert forces whose resultant is vertically upward and equal in magnitude to the weight of the fluid in the region. Since the surrounding fluid acts with the same system of forces on the foreign body, this body also experiences a net upward buoyant force equal to the weight of the fluid that would occupy the region occupied by the body; that is, equal to the weight of the fluid displaced, as stated in Archimedes' law.

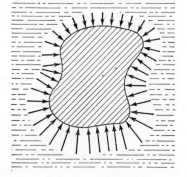

Fig. 9. Cross section of an irregular body immersed in a fluid.

3. THE BAROMETER; PRESSURE GAUGES

TORRICELLI, in 1643, first devised a method for measuring the pressure of the atmosphere by the invention of the mercury barometer. Knowledge of atmospheric pressure is fundamental to most other measurements of pressure because most pressure gauges use the atmosphere as a reference level and measure the difference between an actual pressure and atmospheric pressure. We must distinguish between *absolute* and *gauge* pressures:

> **Absolute pressure** is the actual pressure at a point in a fluid.
>
> **Gauge pressure** is the difference between absolute pressure at a point in a fluid and the pressure of the atmosphere.

Gauge pressure is stated as either above or below atmospheric. A gauge that reads pressures below atmospheric is ordinarily called a *vacuum* gauge. In this book, the word *pressure* will refer to absolute pressure unless gauge pressure is specifically indicated.

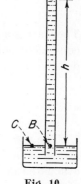

To make a simple mercury barometer, take a straight glass tube about a meter long, closed at one end. Fill the tube *completely* with mercury, close the open end with the finger, and invert the tube in a dish of mercury as in Fig. 10. The mercury column in the tube will fall to a height h of about 76 cm above the level of the mercury in the reservoir if the experiment is done at sea level.

If the barometer of Fig. 10 is properly constructed, no air will be trapped in the space above the mercury column. Hence this space must be free from substance— a vacuum.* Since a vacuum certainly exerts no pressure, the pressure at point A is zero. The pressure at point B is the weight of a unit column of mercury of height h. The pressure at C equals that at B, since these are two points at the same horizontal level in a homogeneous fluid. But the pressure at C is the pressure of the

Fig. 10.
The mercury barometer.

atmosphere. Hence the pressure of the atmosphere is the weight of a unit column of mercury of height h.

The pressure of the atmosphere is the weight of a unit column of air extending all the way to the top of the atmosphere (99 per cent of the air lies within 30 km of the earth's surface). The whole of this air, down to sea level, has exactly the weight of a layer of mercury about 76 cm thick. Atmospheric pressure decreases with altitude because there is less total weight of atmosphere above a point at higher altitude than above a point at sea level. This is the principle on which the airplane altimeter works.

* Actually, there will be a small amount of mercury *vapor* in this space; but since at ordinary temperatures the pressure this vapor exerts will be quite negligible, we can ignore it here. See Chap. 16 for a discussion of vapor pressure.

At a given location, there are day-to-day variations in atmospheric pressure which may amount to as much as five per cent. These variations have important meteorological significance.

A pressure equivalent to that exerted by exactly 76 cm of mercury at 32° F and under standard gravity $g = 32.174$ ft/sec$^2 = 9.80665$ m/sec^2 is called *one standard atmosphere* (1 atm). Since the density of mercury at this temperature is 13.5950 g/cm^3, the mass of a column 1 cm^2 in cross section and 76 cm high is 76 cm$^3 \times 13.5950$ g/cm$^3 = 1033.2$ g = 1.0332 kg. This column weighs (1.0332 kg)(9.8067 m/sec^2) = 10.132 nt. Hence standard atmospheric pressure is

$$1 \text{ atm} = 10.132 \text{ nt/cm}^2 = 1.0132 \times 10^5 \text{ nt/m}^2$$
$$= 14.70 \text{ lb/in}^2 = 2116 \text{ lb/ft}^2. \tag{5a}$$

Pressures are frequently specified in *atmospheres* (meaning standard atmospheres). They are also conveniently specified by giving the equivalent height of mercury column, as *centimeters of mercury* or as *inches of mercury* (at 32° F under standard gravity). Thus,

$$1 \text{ atm} = 76 \text{ cm of Hg} = 29.92 \text{ in of Hg}. \tag{5b}$$

They are sometimes specified in inches or feet of water by giving the equivalent height of water column. At 32° F, mercury is 13.60 times as dense as water, so that

$$1 \text{ atm} = 29.92 \text{ in of Hg} = 29.92 \times 13.60 \text{ in of water}$$
$$= 406.8 \text{ in of water} = 33.90 \text{ ft of water}. \tag{5c}$$

The pressure of the atmosphere may be measured (less accurately) by means of an *aneroid barometer*. This consists in principle of a sealed evacuated metal box, flat and circular in shape, with a corrugated top as in Fig. 11. The top is bent in by the pressure of the atmosphere, the amount of bending being a measure of the pressure. Motion of the top is amplified by a system of levers and gears and is transmitted to a pointer which reads centimeters or inches of mercury on a scale that has been calibrated against a mercury barometer.

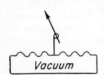

Fig. 11.
Schematic cross-section of aneroid-barometer.

The normal density of air is so small that variations in atmospheric pressure with a change in height of a few feet are ordinarily negligible, so that if one reads barometric pressure in a room, the value obtained will ordinarily apply to apparatus at any height in the room. The decrease in pressure in going up 10 ft is only 0.0004 atm, a value negligible for most purposes.

The barometers illustrated in Figs. 10 and 11 are gauges that measure the *absolute* pressure of the fluid in which they are immersed, since the vacuum exerts no opposing pressure. We shall now describe three common types of pressure gauges that measure *gauge* pressure.   One is the *manometer*, illustrated in Fig. 12.   The manometer is essentially a U-tube open to the atmosphere on one side and to the fluid whose pressure is being

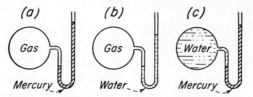

Fig. 12. Manometers; (a) would be used for high gas pressures, (b) for low gas pressures.

measured on the other, and filled with a suitable liquid.   From the difference in heights of column in the two sides, the difference between the fluid pressure and the atmospheric pressure is readily determined.

Another type of pressure gauge, used in many technical applications, is the *Bourdon gauge*.   This gauge contains a sealed spiral of flat metal tubing as in Fig. 13.   The inside of the tubing is filled with the fluid whose pressure is being measured (or with air in communication with the fluid and hence at the same pressure); the outside of the tubing is exposed to the atmosphere.   The elastic properties of such a tube are such that when the pressure inside is increased, the tube tends to 'unwind' and straighten out.   This unwinding effect is communicated to a pointer.   It turns out that the configuration of the tube and hence the position of the pointer depend only on the difference between the pressure inside the tube and the atmospheric pressure outside.   Such gauges can be constructed to cover various pressure ranges either above or below atmospheric, or both.

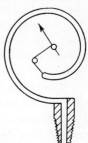

Fig. 13. The Bourdon gauge (schematic).

The hand gauge ordinarily used to measure the pressure in automobile tires is of still another type, in which the high-pressure air pushes back a piston against the force of a spring.   Since the atmosphere acts on the spring side of the piston, the compression of the spring is a measure of gauge pressure, that is, the difference between absolute pressure in the tire and atmospheric pressure.

Example.   *When the mercury manometer shown in Fig. 12(a) is connected to a gas main, the mercury stands 40 cm higher in the right-hand tube than in the left-hand.   A barometer at the same location reads 74 cm.   Determine the absolute pressure of the gas in cm of Hg, in atm, and in* lb/in².

The pressure at the top of the left-hand mercury column is the gas pressure.   This equals the pressure *at the same horizontal level* in the right-hand column.   But the pressure at this level in the right-hand column is the atmospheric pressure (74 cm of Hg) plus the pressure exerted by the additional 40 cm of mercury, or a total of 114 cm of Hg.   Hence the absolute pressure of the gas is 114 cm of Hg. Using conversion factors obtained from (5), we find for the same pressure in atm and lb/in²:

114 cm of Hg = 114 ($\frac{1}{76}$ atm) = 1.50 atm = 1.50 (14.7 lb/in²) = 22.0 lb/in².

4. BUOYANT FORCES

THE EXISTENCE of buoyant forces on bodies immersed in or floating on liquids is familiar, as well as the existence of buoyant forces on bodies such as balloons and lighter-than-air craft immersed in air. The buoyant force of the atmospheric air on solids and liquids immersed in it is for most purposes negligible compared to the weight of solid or liquid, but it must be taken into account in *very accurate* determinations of the weight of a substance.

From Archimedes' law, it is seen that a body immersed in a homogeneous fluid will sink if its own average density is greater than the density of the fluid, will rise if its density is less than that of the fluid, and will be in equilibrium only if its average density exactly equals that of the fluid.

Reexamination of the proof of Archimedes' law shows that it applies to the case of a body immersed partly in one fluid, partly in another, as a floating log is immersed partly in water, partly in air. It is seen that a body will 'float' at the interface of two fluids if the density of one fluid is greater and that of the other fluid less than the average density of the body.

The 'body' mentioned in the preceding paragraphs may be a quantity of fluid as well as a quantity of solid. A quantity of 'heavier' fluid immersed in a 'lighter' fluid with which it does not mix will sink; similarly, lighter fluid immersed in a heavier fluid will rise; until an equilibrium is reached with all the fluid of lesser density above the fluid of greater density, the two fluids being separated by a horizontal interface.

Example. *What is the area of a block of floating ice 2 ft thick that will just support an automobile weighing 3000 lb?*

The minimum-size block will be just on the point of being sunk by the weight of the automobile; hence it will be just awash and will displace water equal to its whole volume. From Table I, p. 81, water has density 62.4 lb-mass/ft³; ice has density 57.5 lb-mass/ft³. Under normal gravity these same numbers will give the weights in pounds of a cubic foot of water and ice. Hence a cubic foot of ice entirely immersed in water will experience a buoyant force of 62.4 lb. Since its own weight is 57.5 lb, it will be able to support an additional weight of only 62.4 lb − 57.5 lb = 4.9 lb. To support 3000 lb will require 3000/4.9, or 612 ft³ of ice. Since the ice is 2 ft thick, a block of area 306 ft² will be required, for example, a block of size 20 ft × 15.3 ft.

5. PASCAL'S LAW

PASCAL'S LAW: *If pressure is applied anywhere on a confined liquid, this pressure is transmitted undiminished to all portions of the confined liquid.*

This law follows from those of Sec. 2, since the pressures at different points in a confined liquid differ by amounts that are entirely determined by the differences in vertical heights and the density of the liquid. Any increase in pressure at one point must result in the same increase at all points because the pressure *differences* do not change. This argument supposes the liquid to be negligibly compressible, a supposition that is valid for all ordinary liquids.

Pascal's law furnishes the principle of operation of the hydraulic press, the hydraulic jack, the hydraulic elevator, and other hydraulic devices in which one essentially obtains hydraulic amplification of force. Consider the fluid-filled vessel of Fig. 14 equipped with two pistons, a small one of area a_1 and a larger one of area a_2. If a force F is applied to the small piston and if the fluid is in equilibrium, the gauge pressure at the piston will be $P=F/a_1$. This will require force $w=Pa_2=F(a_2/a_1)$ on the large piston to maintain equilibrium. If the force on the large piston is slightly less than this value, the large piston will move up and the small piston will move down. Thus a small force will be capable of lifting a very large weight. It will

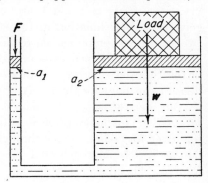

Fig. 14. Hydraulic press.

not lift it very far with one 'stroke' of the small piston; but by equipping the tubing with valves so that the large piston cannot move back down when the small piston is retracted and so that new fluid enters the vessel from a reservoir on the return stroke, the large piston can be raised as much as desired by repeated strokes of the small piston. Such hydraulic devices are *machines* designed to lift a large load by application of a small force.

> **Example.** *A hydraulic lift in an automobile service station is operated by compressed air applied directly to the end of a piston 8 inches in diameter. If the weight of lift plus automobile is 4500 lb, what gauge pressure of compressed air is required?*
>
> The area of the piston is $\pi(4 \text{ in})^2 = 50.3 \text{ in}^2$. Hence the required gauge pressure is
> $$P=F/A = 4500 \text{ lb}/50.3 \text{ in}^2 = 89.5 \text{ lb/in}^2.$$
>
> Such a pressure is easily furnished by a small compressor. This computation furnishes gauge pressure because motion of the piston is opposed by atmospheric pressure as well as by the weight of lift and load.

6. FLUID DYNAMICS

So FAR we have discussed the laws of fluids at rest—*fluid statics*. We shall now give a brief introduction to the behavior of fluids in motion—

fluid dynamics. This is the subject that furnishes the foundation material for *hydrodynamics* and engineering *hydraulics,* which are concerned with the motion of water, and for *aerodynamics,* which is concerned with the motion of air and with the motion of bodies such as airplanes, rockets, and shells through the air.

The subject of fluid dynamics is mathematically and physically very complex. Bernoulli's law, which we shall derive, is basic to the whole subject. This law is derived for an *ideal, non-viscous* fluid. For an ideal fluid, the only resistance to acceleration is inertial; no viscous (frictional) forces resist the motion of one layer of fluid past another, nor the motion of the fluid along a solid surface. Since the viscosity of air and water are very low, Bernoulli's law furnishes a good *first* approximation in the study of their flow. During the past two centuries, empirical corrections to the results given by this law have been determined experimentally. The interest in powered flight in the twentieth century resulted in the first intensive effort to develop *theory* to account for the behavior of *real* fluids.

Our derivation of Bernoulli's law assumes the fluid to be *incompressible.* This assumption is entirely valid for water, and is satisfactory even for bodies moving through air at speeds below about 350 mi/hr, but as speeds approach that of sound (about 740 mi/hr) a corrected form of the law must be used. One subject under intensive experimental and theoretical study today is that of *supersonic flow*—motion at speeds greater than that of sound. Supersonic flow is, both physically and mathematically, very different from motion at subsonic speeds.

Real fluids in motion *do* exert tangential forces on solid surfaces past which they are flowing, and also tangential forces across an imaginary plane in the fluid, if there is a velocity gradient such that the fluid is flowing faster on one side of the plane than on the other, in the direction parallel to the plane. The magnitudes of these forces are proportional to a characteristic constant of the fluid called the *coefficient of viscosity,* which we shall define. *If the fluid has zero viscosity,* as is assumed in Bernoulli's law, *there are no tangential forces.* Viscous forces on a solid surface are of the nature of frictional forces since they are parallel to the direction of motion of the fluid and directed so as to retard this motion; they result in transformation of kinetic energy of the fluid into heat.

7. BERNOULLI'S LAW

THE BASIC LAW of fluid dynamics is Bernoulli's law, which is essentially a formulation of the principle that work equals change in mechanical energy in the case where mechanical energy is conserved, that is, in the case where the heat generation by viscous friction is negligible. We shall assume that density changes resulting from the flow can be neglected and treat the fluid as *incompressible*.

We shall derive this law for the important special case in which the flow is *steady*. By *steady flow*, we mean that *the velocity and other characteristic properties of the fluid at a given point of space are constant, independent of time*. Thus in steady flow through the pipe of Fig. 16, the velocity at a given point in the pipe is constant in time, so that a definite constant volume of fluid passes a given section in the pipe in each unit of time. In order that the fluid should not 'pile up' anywhere in the pipe, or leak out, the same volume per unit time must pass every section in the pipe. The same volume per unit time enters one end of the pipe as leaves the other.

In more general steady flow, such as the flow of air around a model in a wind tunnel, we can represent the velocity directions by means of *streamlines*, as in Fig. 15. At each point X, Y, Z of space the velocity has a definite magnitude and direction which do not vary with time. The streamlines of Fig. 15 are drawn in such a way that at each point the velocity vector is tangent to the streamline. A tubular region whose generators are streamlines, as indicated near the top of Fig. 15, is called a *stream tube*. Because of the way in which streamlines are defined, the fluid contained within a particular stream tube remains within this tube, never crossing the boundary, because at no point does the fluid have a velocity component across the boundary of a stream tube. Hence the fluid in a particular stream tube behaves in all respects like the fluid flowing down the pipe of Fig. 16, and the same volume of flow crosses each section of the stream tube in each unit of time (if the density of the fluid does not change).

Now let us consider the forces that act on a definite quantity of fluid located within a stream tube, such as the quantity marked out by heavy solid lines in Figs. 15 and 16. On the 'ends' act forces $P_1\,dA_1$ and $P_2\,dA_2$ arising from the pressure of the adjoining fluid. Similarly, on the 'sides' act normal forces arising from the pressure of the adjoining fluid in Fig. 15, or from the walls of the pipe in Fig. 16. *If the viscosity of the fluid is neglected*, there will be no tangential forces on any of these surfaces. In addition, there will be the force of gravity.

We shall now compute the work done on this quantity of fluid in the time interval dt and equate this work to the increase in potential energy in the field of gravity plus the increase in kinetic energy. In either Fig. 15 or Fig. 16, in time dt, one end of our portion of fluid moves distance dl_1, the other end dl_2, related in such a way that $dl_1\,dA_1 = dl_2\,dA_2 = dV$, where dV is the volume of fluid passing any point in the stream tube in time dt. The work done by the pressure P_1 is $P_1\,dA_1\,dl_1 = P_1\,dV$; that done by P_2 is $-P_2\,dA_2\,dl_2 = -P_2\,dV$, negative because the force is opposite to the direction of the motion as the fluid moves from the position shown by the solid outline to that shown by the broken outline. The pressures on the sides of the tube do no work because they act perpendicularly to the motion. Hence, in the time dt,

$$\text{work done} = (P_1 - P_2)\, dV. \tag{6}$$

Now we compute the change in energy in the same time dt. Here the assumption of steady flow greatly simplifies the discussion, since in steady flow the energy of the fluid that happens to occupy any given region of space at one time is the same as the energy of the fluid that occupies this same region of space at a later time. Hence, the fluid that occupies a given region of space, such as the region denoted by ①, ②, or ③ in Figs.

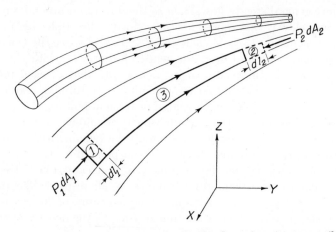

Fig. 15. Streamlines and stream tubes in the flow of an incompressible fluid.

15 and 16, has an energy that is characteristic of that particular region. Initially, the fluid bounded by solid lines has energy characteristic of regions ①+③. After time dt, the same fluid, which has moved into the space outlined by broken lines, has energy characteristic of regions ②+③. The change in energy is the energy characteristic of region ② minus the energy characteristic of region ①. Let us denote the density (mass per unit volume) of the fluid by ρ, the speeds in regions ① and ② by v_1 and v_2, and the vertical heights of regions ① and ② by Z_1 and Z_2. (In the final analysis, the tube of Fig. 15 is supposed to have infinitesimal area, so that the assignment of a single speed and height to these regions is justified. The speeds and heights assigned in Fig. 16 are some kind of average over the cross section.) The fluid in region ② has potential energy $\rho\, dV\, gZ_2$ and kinetic energy $\tfrac{1}{2}\, \rho\, dV\, v_2^2$. The fluid in region ① has potential energy $\rho\, dV\, gZ_1$ and kinetic energy $\tfrac{1}{2}\, \rho\, dV\, v_1^2$. Hence,

$$\text{change in energy} = \rho\, dV\, gZ_2 + \tfrac{1}{2}\, \rho\, dV\, v_2^2 - \rho\, dV\, gZ_1 - \tfrac{1}{2}\, \rho\, dV\, v_1^2 \tag{7}$$

in time dt.   Equating work done (6) to change in energy (7) and dividing by dV gives

$$P_1 - P_2 = \rho g Z_2 + \tfrac{1}{2}\,\rho v_2^2 - \rho g Z_1 - \tfrac{1}{2}\,\rho v_1^2,$$

or

$$P_1 + \tfrac{1}{2}\,\rho v_1^2 + \rho g Z_1 = P_2 + \tfrac{1}{2}\,\rho v_2^2 + \rho g Z_2. \qquad (8)$$

The equality in (8) expresses the law first stated by Daniel Bernoulli, a Swiss mathematical physicist, in 1738:

BERNOULLI'S LAW: *At any two points along the same streamline in a nonviscous, incompressible fluid in steady flow, the sum of the pressure, the kinetic energy per unit volume, and the potential energy per unit volume has the same value.*

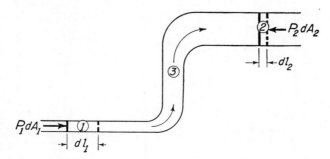

Fig. 16. Flow in a pipe of variable cross section.

In applying (8) we must use a consistent system of units, such as

P	ρ	v	g	Z
lb/ft²	slug/ft³	ft/sec	ft/sec²	ft
nt/m²	kg/m³	m/sec	m/sec²	m

Each term in (8) is seen to have the dimensions of energy/volume.

A fluid at rest is a special case of steady flow, and in this case (8) is seen to embody the law of pressure change with height.

In the case of a fluid that has frictional (viscous) forces acting, particularly in the case of flow through pipes as in Fig. 16, some of the work done goes into heat rather than into increase in mechanical energy.   In this case the change in *mechanical* energy will be *less* than the work done. Expressing this inequality leads to the conclusion that *if there are frictional forces, the value of the left side of* (8) *is greater than the value of the right side, which is evaluated further downstream.*   In the case of flow through pipes Bernoulli's law is ordinarily used with empirical corrections for the loss of mechanical energy to heat.

As a first application of Bernoulli's law, we shall derive *Torricelli's law* for the velocity of efflux of a liquid from an orifice in a tank.   Figure 17 shows three types of orifices discharging at height h below the water level in a *large* tank.   We can apply Bernoulli's law to points ①, ②, and

③, since some streamline will connect ① and ③, also ② and ③. We shall call $Z=0$ at ② and ③; $Z=h$ at ①. Since the pressure appears on both sides of Bernoulli's law, an arbitrary reference level for pressure may be used. Normally, it is most convenient to use *gauge pressure*. The gauge pressure at ①, at the free surface at the top of the tank, is zero. The gauge pressure at ③, in the stream just beyond the opening, is also zero because the sides of the stream are open to the atmosphere. We shall write P for the gauge pressure at point ② in the tank at the level of the orifice. The speeds at ① and ② can be taken as zero if the tank is

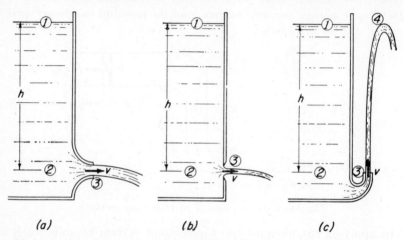

Fig. 17. Efflux from (a) a well-rounded orifice, (b) a sharp-edged orifice, showing *vena contracta*, (c) a vertical nozzle.

large. We desire to find the speed v at ③. Writing the terms in (8) for points ①, ②, and ③ successively gives

$$0+0+\rho gh = P+0+0 = 0+\tfrac{1}{2}\,\rho v^2+0.$$

This equation gives
$$v = \sqrt{2gh} \qquad\qquad (9)$$

for the velocity of efflux from a tank under 'head' h, or

$$v = \sqrt{2P/\rho} \qquad\qquad (10)$$

for the velocity of efflux of liquid from an orifice when the tank gauge pressure is P at the same elevation as the orifice. Equation (9) is called *Torricelli's law*, after Evangelista Torricelli (1608–1647), who first recognized that in Fig. 17(c) the water column reaches the level of the water in the tank. Equation (10) is useful for flow from a closed tank when the liquid is under greater pressure than just the hydrostatic head.

In the case of the vertical jet in Fig. 17(c), if we extend the application of Bernoulli's law to point ④, where the speed is again zero, we see that the vertical jet should reach just the height h. In practice, the jet falls a little short of h because of frictional losses.   This result is in accord with our remark that the expression evaluated in Bernoulli's law may in actual cases decrease (but never increase) as one goes *downstream*.   It will be noted that the velocity given by Torricelli's law is just the velocity of vertical projection required for a body to reach height h in the absence of air resistance.

To find the volume flow out of the tank, one can get a reasonably accurate result by multiplying the velocity v by the area of the opening if the opening is well rounded as in (a).   But if the opening is sharp-edged as in (b), the fluid has not completed its acceleration by the time it passes through the opening.   It continues to accelerate for a short distance in the jet, and, as the fluid speeds up, the jet contracts because the product of velocity by area must remain constant.   The jet takes on a character-istic shape called the *vena contracta*.   Torricelli's law gives the velocity after the contraction is complete.   For a sharp circular opening, the con-tracted area is approximately 62 per cent of the area of the opening, and correction for this contraction must be applied in finding the volume flow.

An interesting application of Torricelli's law is to the *siphon* (Fig. 18).   We see from arguments similar to the above that the velocity of efflux will be given by the Torricelli formula with h equal to the difference in height between the water surface in the tank and the discharging orifice. The depth of the entrance to the siphon is irrelevant.   Of course the siphon will not work unless it is filled with liquid.   The liquid column will break at the top of the siphon if the absolute pressure there falls to zero (more rigorously, to the vapor pressure

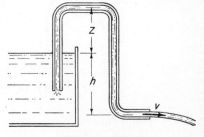

Fig. 18. Siphon.

of the liquid; see Chap. 16).   If we denote the absolute pressure at the top of the siphon by P, absolute atmospheric pressure by P_{Atm}, and the height of the top above the liquid level in the tank by Z, and em-ploy a tube of uniform bore so that the speed at the top is v, Bernoulli's theorem gives, by comparison of the top of the siphon with the top of the tank,

$$P + \tfrac{1}{2}\,\rho v^2 + \rho g Z = P_{\text{Atm}}.$$

Since for a liquid unable to withstand a tensile force, P must be positive if the column is not to break, the limiting height Z_{Max} is obtained by setting $P = 0$ to get

$$\rho g Z_{\text{Max}} = P_{\text{Atm}} - \tfrac{1}{2}\,\rho v^2 = P_{\text{Atm}} - \rho g h.$$

The greater the flow velocity, that is, the greater the head h, the less the maximum permissible value of Z.

As an important application of Bernoulli's law to the flow of gas or liquid through a pipe, we shall discuss the measurement of flow by means of the Venturi flowmeter illustrated in Fig. 19. The flow velocities in Fig. 19 will be related to the cross-sectional areas by

$$v_1 A_1 = v_2 A_2. \tag{11}$$

Bernoulli's law gives

$$P_1 - P_2 = \tfrac{1}{2} \rho \ (v_2^2 - v_1^2). \tag{12}$$

The pressure difference $P_1 - P_2$ is read directly on the differential manometer in Fig. 19. If we solve (11) for v_1 and substitute in (12), we obtain

$$P_1 - P_2 = \tfrac{1}{2} \rho v_2^2 \ (A_1^2 - A_2^2)/A_1^2. \tag{13}$$

This equation enables us to obtain the velocity of flow, and hence the volume rate of flow, merely from a measurement of the differential pres-

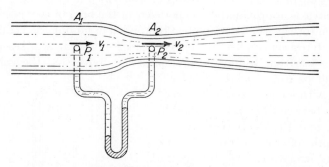

Fig. 19. Venturi flowmeter.

sure. The Venturi flowmeter is widely applied in the measurement of flows of liquids and gases in pipe lines.

If the flow of liquid through a constricted tube such as that of Fig. 19 is rapid, it is not at all difficult to get conditions in which Bernoulli's law gives a value for absolute pressure in the constricted section that is negative. Since a liquid will not ordinarily sustain a negative pressure, a phenomenon called *cavitation* ensues, in which cavities or holes are formed in the interior of the liquid. Not only does cavitation introduce a large energy loss, but it produces serious pitting on metallic surfaces, apparently owing to sudden collapse of the cavities. Such cavitational corrosion can cause destruction of turbine blades and ship propellers.

The low pressure attained in fluid flow through a constricted section is utilized in the design of suction pumps and atomizers.

Example. *In Fig. 19, if* $A_1 = 1$ ft², $A_2 = 0.5$ ft², *the differential mercury height is* 15 in, *and the fluid is water, determine the flow in* ft³/sec.

We have all the data necessary to find v_2 from (13), but we must be careful to use the consistent system of British units given on p. 145.

The differential *pressure* is *not* 15 in of Hg, because the water in the left-hand manometer tube does not have density negligible compared to that of mercury. Since mercury is 13.6 times as dense as water, the differential pressure is

$$P_1 - P_2 = (15 \text{ in of Hg}) - (15 \text{ in of water})$$
$$= (15 \times 13.6 - 15) \text{ in of water} = 189 \text{ in of water.}$$

From (5), or the pressure conversion table in Sec. 8 of the Appendix, we convert this to

$$P_1 - P_2 = 189 \ (5.20 \text{ lb/ft}^2) = 988 \text{ lb/ft}^2.$$

The density ρ of water is 62.4 lb-mass/ft^3, or

$$\rho = (62.4/32.2) \text{ slug/ft}^3 = 1.94 \text{ slug/ft}^3.$$

We are now ready to substitute in (13); from this equation,

$$v_2^2 = \frac{2(P_1 - P_2)}{\rho} \ \frac{A_1^2}{A_1^2 - A_2^2} = \frac{2 \times 983 \text{ lb/ft}^2}{1.94 \text{ slug/ft}^3} \ \frac{1}{1 - \frac{1}{4}} = 1350 \ \frac{\text{ft}^2}{\text{sec}^2}.$$

Hence $v_2 = 36.8 \text{ ft/sec,}$

and the volume of flow is

$$A_2 v_2 = (0.5 \text{ ft}^2)(36.8 \text{ ft/sec}) = 18.4 \text{ ft}^3/\text{sec.}$$

8. THE LIFT OF AN AIRFOIL

IF WE SET UP an airplane model in a wind tunnel and blow air past it at a constant oncoming speed, we get a *steady* flow that is representable by streamlines as in Fig. 15, and Bernoulli's law is applicable.

But for a plane in flight, the flow is not at all *steady* (see definition of steady flow on p. 143) if we use a coordinate system attached to the ground. However, if the plane is flying at constant velocity and we use *a coordinate system attached to the plane*, then we do get a steady-flow pattern which is identical with the pattern observed in a wind tunnel when the plane is standing still and air is blown past it. From the point of view of a coordinate system attached to the plane, the plane *is* standing still and air *is* blowing past it at high speed. *Bernoulli's law is applicable to this steady flow in this coordinate system.* This statement follows from the Newtonian principle of relativity.

Because of the validity of the Newtonian principle, Bernoulli's law furnishes a very useful first approximation in the computation of forces on the surfaces of airplanes or missiles, provided that the air speeds used in (8), or in the corrected form applicable to a compressible fluid, are measured *relative to the moving object*.

Let us now consider the origin of the *lift* of an airplane wing. A wing is called an *airfoil*, and the lift is entirely associated with the characteristics of the flow pattern that is set up around a section having the distinctive characteristic shape of an airfoil, with its sharp trailing edge and greater curvature of the top surface than the bottom surface. This shape results in a greater flow velocity past the top surface of the wing than past the bottom surface, as can be seen from the pattern of stream-lines in Fig. 20.   As the figure shows, the oncoming air divides in such a way that more than the proper share passes above the wing and less than the proper share below the wing.   This inequality results in the flow velocity past the top of the wing being greater than the oncoming velocity

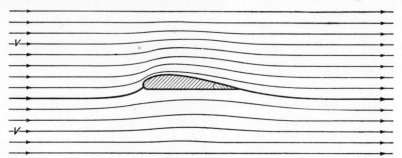

Fig. 20. Flow past an airfoil in a wind tunnel. The heavy streamline divides the flow above the airfoil from the flow below.

v, and hence, by Bernoulli's law, in the pressure on the top of the wing being *less* than the free-stream pressure P.   The reverse happens on the bottom of the wing; there the velocity is in general lower than the free-stream velocity, and the pressure is greater than the free-stream pressure. The pressure difference between the top and bottom surfaces results in a

Fig. 21. Streamlines in the flow from left to right past a cylinder rotating clockwise. A net *lift* develops. (From L. Prandtl and O. Tietjens, *Hydro- and Aeromechanik*, vol. 1: Springer, Berlin; reproduced by permission of J. W. Edwards, publisher of the American edition.)

lift which is proportional to ρv^2.   The lift can be increased by lowering the trailing edge of the wing.   Rotation of the trailing section, called the *aileron*, about a transverse axis is used to control the lift.   A different amount of rotation of the two ailerons on right and left wings causes the plane to 'roll' about a longitudinal axis.

A similar phenomenon accounts for the 'curve' of a spinning baseball or tennis ball. Look first at Fig. 21, in which the velocity of flow past the surface of the rotating cylinder is greater above the cylinder than below just as for the airfoil of Fig. 20, and for the same reason a *lifting force* results. A spinning ball *moving to the left* would develop a pattern of streamlines similar to those in Fig. 21, from the point of view of an observer moving with the ball; the ball would have a 'back spin' and would experience a lift tending to raise its normal trajectory.

9. FLUID VISCOSITY

WHENEVER the velocity of a fluid changes in magnitude as one moves in a direction perpendicular to the streamlines, viscous forces come into play. To visualize this situation, consider Fig. 22, in which we have two very large horizontal plates, the lower one at rest and the upper one moving in the X-direction at speed V. The space between the plates is filled with a fluid such as air or water. In such an arrangement, it would be found that a pattern of horizontal streamlines would be set up in the fluid, with the fluid velocity

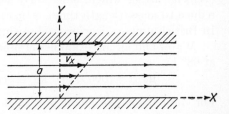

Fig. 22. A layer of fluid between a moving plate and a stationary one.

entirely in the X-direction, but with magnitude varying linearly from 0 to V as one progressed in the Y-direction. There would be no slip of the fluid at either solid surface.

The last statement is a rigorous observational conclusion. *There is no slip between a fluid and the surface of a solid.* The velocity of the fluid immediately adjacent to the solid is always the same as the velocity of the solid surface; that is, this fluid is at rest *relative to* the solid surface.

In the case of Fig. 22, the fluid in any given layer will exert a tangential force on the faster-moving fluid above it, tending to retard the motion of this faster-moving fluid. Reciprocally, in accordance with Newton's third principle, the faster-moving fluid will exert a force in the forward direction on the slower-moving fluid below it, tending to accelerate this fluid. The fluid in contact with the upper plate will exert a backward force on this plate, tending to retard it; whereas the fluid in contact with the lower plate exerts a forward force on this plate, tending to drag it along with the fluid.

The magnitude of the tangential force we have been discussing is found to be directly proportional to the velocity gradient in a direction perpendicular to the streamlines, that is, to dv_x/dY in the case of Fig. 22. The force is also proportional to the area A of the plate. The constant of proportionality, called the *coefficient of viscosity* μ, is characteristic of the fluid.   If F denotes the force,

$$F = \mu \, (dv_X/dY) \, A \qquad (14)$$

for the case of Fig. 22.   This law was first stated by Newton.   In principle, we could measure the coefficient of viscosity with the apparatus of Fig. 22 by measuring either the force per unit area required to keep the upper plate moving, or the forward drag force per unit area on the lower plate.   In practice, we cannot construct the apparatus of Fig. 22, but we can use two cylinders of large diameter with fluid in the thin annular space between.   When one of the cylinders rotates, conditions in the annular space approximate the conditions in Fig. 22.

The dimensions of μ are seen from (14) to be those of (force·length)/(velocity·area), which, since force has dimensions of mass·acceleration, reduce to mass/(length·time).   In MKS units, μ is expressed in kg/m·sec. In British units, μ is expressed in slug/ft·sec.

Water and air are examples of fluids of very low viscosity.   For water at 68° F,

$$\mu_{\text{Water}} = 1005 \times 10^{-6} \text{ kg/m·sec} = 20.9 \times 10^{-6} \text{ slug/ft·sec.} \qquad (15)$$

For comparison, we might note that olive oil has a viscosity about 100 times, and castor oil a viscosity about 1000 times, that of water.   For air at 68° F,

$$\mu_{\text{Air}} = 18.1 \times 10^{-6} \text{ kg/m·sec} = 0.376 \times 10^{-6} \text{ slug/ft·sec.} \qquad (16)$$

It turns out that in the flow of air around an object such as an airplane, *the viscous forces have an entirely negligible effect on the air motion*

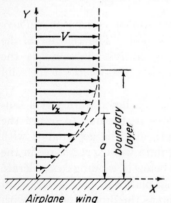

Airplane wing

Fig. 23. Velocity distribution in a boundary layer, relative to the material surface.

except in a thin layer immediately adjoining the solid surface; this layer is called the *boundary layer.*   The coefficient of viscosity is so small that the velocity gradients occurring in the bulk of the fluid do not give rise to sufficient viscous force to have any detectable effect on the motion of the fluid.   The flow is the same as that of a non-viscous fluid except in the immediate vicinity of the solid surface.   But in this immediate vicinity we must have sufficient viscous force to bring the fluid in contact with the surface to rest relative to the surface, since no slip occurs.   Thus the air might be flowing over an airplane wing at 300 ft/sec, relative to the wing. But just at the surface the speed is zero.   The layer in which the transition takes place is thin—a fraction of an inch thick in the case just mentioned.   In this boundary layer, the gradients are sufficiently large that the viscous forces exert an appreciable, though not large, viscous drag on the solid surface. This is called the *skin-friction drag*.

Fig. 23 shows the manner in which the speed changes from the free-stream speed V to the speed 0 at the surface of the solid. We give all speeds relative to the solid surface. We are now in a position to compute a typical magnitude for the skin-friction force on a wing or fuselage surface and verify that it is indeed small:

Example. *If, for a typical airplane wing or fuselage, the boundary layer has thickness a (as in Fig. 23) of $\frac{1}{10}$ inch when the plane is traveling at 300 ft/sec (about 200 mi/hr), find the tangential drag force per square foot that arises from viscous friction.*

The slope of the broken curve in Fig. 23, which is the velocity gradient at the surface, is given as

$$V/a = (300 \text{ ft/sec})/(\tfrac{1}{120} \text{ ft}) = 36,000/\text{sec}.$$

When we substitute this in (14) with the value of μ taken from (16), and $A = 1 \text{ ft}^2$,

$$F = 0.38 \times 10^{-6} \frac{\text{slug}}{\text{ft·sec}} \times 36000 \frac{1}{\text{sec}} \times 1 \text{ ft}^2 = 0.014 \frac{\text{slug·ft}}{\text{sec}^2}$$

Since $1 \text{ lb} = 1 \text{ slug·ft/sec}^2$, this is a tangential force of

$$F = 0.014 \text{ lb}$$

on each ft^2 of surface. This is small indeed. The whole drag of a plane is small compared with the lift. If it were not possible to design a plane so this were so, flight would be impossible.

Bernoulli's law is applicable to the entire flow pattern around an airplane except for that part of the fluid that lies within the thin boundary

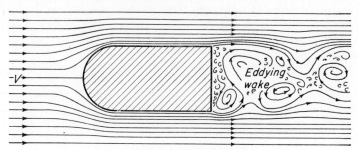

Fig. 24. Flow past a nonstreamlined body.

layer, where viscous forces have profoundly affected the flow. Actually, the pressure (normal force per unit area) on the solid surface in Fig. 23 is the same as the pressure at the outer limit of the boundary layer. Hence pressures and the resulting lift can be computed from a diagram like that of Fig. 20 in which the boundary layer is completely ignored, provided the viscosity is low and the body well streamlined so that the boundary layer is thin. If a body is poorly streamlined so that the flow does not rejoin smoothly at the rear, as in the case of the familiar bullet shape shown in Fig. 24, Bernoulli's law will not be applicable in the large eddying wake at the rear. Such a body has low pressures at the rear in comparison with the pressures at the nose, and hence has a large drag resulting from normal forces alone, whereas the streamlined airfoil of Fig. 20 has almost no drag resulting from normal forces.

PROBLEMS

Note: A table of densities of solids and liquids will be found on p. 81. Neglect the buoyant force of the air except in problems that explicitly require that it be considered.

1. If the liquid in a barometer is water, at what height in feet will the water stand when a mercury barometer reads 27 in? (Neglect pressure of vapor above the water column.)   Ans: 30.6 ft.

2. If the liquid in a barometer is carbon tetrachloride, at what height in meters will the CCl_4 stand when a mercury barometer reads 76 cm? (Neglect pressure of CCl_4 vapor above the liquid.)

3. A manometer such as in Fig. 12(b) attached to a household gas line records, typically, 10 inches difference in water level. What is the gauge pressure in lb/in^2? What is the absolute pressure in lb/in^2 and in atm if the barometer reads 27 in of mercury?   Ans: 0.361 lb/in^2; 13.6 lb/in^2, 0.927 atm.

4. In Fig. 12(c), if the mercury stands 70 cm above the bottom of the water tank in the right-hand tube and 20 cm above the bottom of the tank in the left-hand tube and if the barometer reads 73 cm, find the gauge pressure and the absolute pressure at the bottom of the water tank (a) in cm of Hg, (b) in atm, (c) in lb/in^2.

5. If the U-tube of Fig. 25 contains mercury, how many centimeters of water column must be poured into the right-hand arm to depress the mercury level 1 cm in this arm and raise it 1 cm in the other?   Ans: 27.0 cm.

6. If the U-tube of Fig. 25 contains water and if a 20-cm column of kerosene is poured over the water in the right arm, by how many cm is the water level depressed in this arm and raised in the other?

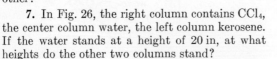

Figure 25

7. In Fig. 26, the right column contains CCl_4, the center column water, the left column kerosene. If the water stands at a height of 20 in, at what heights do the other two columns stand?
Ans: 12.5 in, 25.0 in.

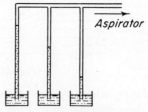

Aspirator

8. In Fig. 26, the center column contains water and stands at a height of 30 cm. The other two columns contain liquids of unknown densities and stand at heights of 41 cm and 23 cm. Determine the densities of these liquids.

Figure 26

9. In Fig. 8, the left tube and the bottom part of the right tube contain water; the rest of the right tube contains kerosene. The top of the kerosene in the right tube is 2 ft above the top of the water in the left tube. If the pressure at level *1* in the left tube is 1.5 lb/in^2 gauge, what is the pressure at level *4* in the right tube?   Ans: 1.89 lb/in^2 gauge.

10. In Fig. 8, the left tube and the bottom part of the right tube contain water, and the rest of the right tube contains kerosene. The interface is 15 ft below the top of the water in the left tube. How far below the top of the kerosene is the pressure 5 lb/in² gauge? What is the gauge pressure in the water at the same vertical height?

11. Show that the force F required to pull apart the evacuated hemispheres (Magdeburg hemispheres) of Fig. 27 is $\pi R^2 P$, where P is the pressure of the atmosphere and R the outside radius of the hemispheres. (Assume that the vacuum seal occurs at the outside radius.)

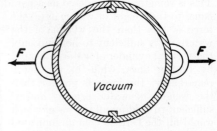

Fig. 27. Magdeburg hemispheres.

12. In 1654, Otto von Guericke, Burgomaster of Magdeburg and inventor of the air pump, gave a demonstration before the Imperial Diet at Ratisbon in which two teams of eight horses could not pull apart two evacuated brass hemispheres. If the hemispheres were 24 inches in diameter and imperfectly evacuated to 0.1 atm in the demonstration, what force would the horses have had to exert to pull them apart if the atmospheric pressure was 1 atm?

13. If the earth's atmosphere were homogeneous and of normal density 1.292 kg/m³ throughout, what would be the thickness of the atmosphere in km when the barometer read 1 atm?   Ans: 8.00 km.

14. If the glass tube of the barometer in Fig. 10 is supported by a string attached to the upper end, so that the lower end just dips below the level in the reservoir, determine the tension in the string. Analyze the forces carefully and determine whether this tension is (a) just the weight of the glass tube, (b) the weight of the tube plus the weight of the mercury it contains, or (c) some other weight.

15. Find the magnitude of the resultant force tending to open the cap on the end of a pipe of 2-ft diameter if this end is 75 ft below the surface of the water in the reservoir to which the pipe leads and if the barometer reads 14.7 lb/in².
                                                                   Ans: 14,700 lb.

16. Why should gauge pressure rather than absolute pressure be specified in giving the bursting strength of a tank?

17. Why do bottles containing liquids tend to leak if taken up in an airplane? Do they tend to leak when they are right-side-up or when they are upside-down?

18. A company manufacturing double-pane windows with a layer of air hermetically sealed between two panes of glass found the windows all broken in shipments sent by rail from the Eastern Seaboard to the West Coast. Can you explain this damage?

19. When an iceberg floats on sea water, what percentage of the iceberg is under water?   Ans: 89.5%.

20. When a block of oak of density 45.0 lb-mass/ft³ floats on kerosene, what percentage of the block is submerged?

21. When a block of material of density 950 kg/m³ floats at the interface between water and kerosene, what fraction is below the interface?   Ans: ¾.

22. When a piece of steel floats at the interface between mercury and water, what fraction of the steel is above the interface?

23. In each of the three vessels of Fig. 28, the water has the same depth and the bottom the same area. Hence the pressure and the force on the bottom is the same in all cases. If we imagine the bottom of each vessel to be a frictionless watertight piston, we would have to exert the same force F to hold up each piston. This is sometimes considered as a paradox, because while in (a) this force is just equal to the weight of water, in (c) the force is less than the weight of the water and is sufficient to hold up only the vertical cylinder of water indicated by broken lines, while in (b), more remarkably, the force is greater than the weight of water present and is sufficient to hold up all the water which would fill the vertical column indicated by broken lines.

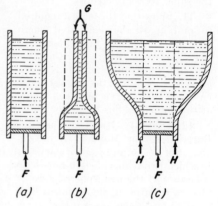

Fig. 28. Pascal's vases.

Resolve the paradox by analyzing the forces acting on the material of the sides of the vessels. Show that, over and above the weight of this part of the vessel, in (c) a lifting force H is required that is exactly equal to the weight of the excess fluid not supported by F, whereas in (b) a downward force G is required that is equal to the weight of the fluid apparently supported by F but not present.

24. If a ship displaces water weighing 10,000 tons, find the weight of the ship.

25. A floating log is in the shape of a circular cylinder, but its center of gravity is displaced from the axis. Show that independent of its depth in the water, the log will float stably with its center of gravity directly below its axis, and that the greater the displacement of the center of gravity from the axis, the greater will be the resistance of the log to rolling.

26. The total weight of a balloon (except for the lifting gas) is 3000 kg. What volume of helium of density 0.178 kg/m³ is required to lift the balloon in air of density 1.292 kg/m³?

27. The bag of a balloon is a sphere 50 m in diameter filled with hydrogen of density 0.090 kg/m³. What total mass of fabric, car, and contents can be lifted in air of density 1.292 kg/m³?   Ans: 78,700 kg.

28. A solid heavier than water is weighed in air and then suspended by a string and weighed in water. The difference between these weights is called the 'loss of weight in water.' This is a convenient method of determining the density of the solid. Show that

$$\text{density of solid} = \frac{\text{weight of solid in air}}{\text{loss of weight in water}} \times \text{density of water.}$$

29. The density of a liquid can be determined by weighing a solid in air, then in water, then in the liquid. Show that

$$\text{density of liquid} = \frac{\text{loss of weight of solid in liquid}}{\text{loss of weight of solid in water}} \times \text{density of water.}$$

30. Devise a scheme for determining the density of a solid lighter than water by tying it to a solid heavier than water, of known density, and weighing the combination under water.

31. A *hydrometer* (Fig. 29) is a convenient instrument for measuring the density of a liquid by a determination of the depth at which the hydrometer floats.

If it is desired to construct a hydrometer in which the calibration marks for 1.0 g/cm³ and 2.0 g/cm³ are 15 cm apart on a stem of 1 cm² cross section, what must be the volume of the bulb below the 2.0 mark and what must be the total mass of the hydrometer? How far from the 1.0 mark will the 1.5 mark fall?   Ans: 15 cm³; 30 g; 10 cm.

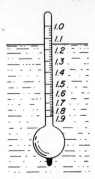

Fig. 29.
A hydrometer giving densities in g/cm³.

32. It is desired to construct a hydrometer for fluids lighter than water in which the calibration marks for 0.7 g/cm³ and 1.0 g/cm³ are 15 cm apart on a stem of 1 cm² cross section. What must be the volume of the bulb below the 1.0 mark and what must be the total mass of the hydrometer? How far from the 1.0 mark will the 0.9 and 0.8 marks fall?

33. An iron casting weighs 60 lb in air and 39 lb in water. What is the volume of cavities in the casting?   Ans: 0.202 ft³.

34. A bar of gold is balanced by brass weights totalling 10,364.8 g mass, on a precision balance in air. Determine the mass of the gold bar to an accuracy of 0.1 g, taking into account the buoyant force of the surrounding air of density 1.292 kg/m³.

35. Draw a schematic design of a valve system for the hydraulic press or jack shown in Fig. 14.

36. If it is desired to raise 3000 lb by a hydraulic jack employing a small piston of 2-inch stroke on which a force of 150 lb is applied, what must be the ratio of the areas of the two pistons? How many strokes are required to raise the 3000-lb weight a distance of 4 inches?

37. In the hydraulic press shown in Fig. 14, the area a_1 of the small piston is 1 in², and the area a_2 of the large piston is 120 in². A force $F = 2.5$ lb is required to raise a load $w = 200$ lb. From these data, calculate (a) the ideal mechanical advantage, (b) the actual mechanical advantage, and (c) the efficiency of this device.   Ans: (a) 120; (b) 80; (c) 66.7%.

38. The normal density of air is 1.29 kg/m³. Show that the pressure difference between the floor and ceiling of a room 10 ft high is approximately 0.004 atm.

39. Find the speed of flow of water from an open tank through an orifice 15 ft below the water surface.   Ans: 31.1 ft/sec.

40. Find the speed of flow of water from a closed tank if the gauge pressure at the level of the orifice is 30 lb/in².

41. Find the volume rate of flow in Prob. 39 if the orifice is well rounded, with an area of 1 in².   Ans: 0.216 ft³/sec.

42. Find the approximate volume rate of flow in Prob. 40 if the orifice is a 1-inch-diameter sharp-edged circle.

43. Find the theoretical maximum value of Z for a water siphon of uniform bore with $h = 20$ ft in Fig. 18, when the atmospheric pressure is 14 lb/in².
                          Ans: 12.3 ft.

44. Show that the theoretical maximum value of Z for a siphon can be written as $Z_{Max} = P_{Atm}/\rho g - h$. Find the theoretical maximum value of Z for a water siphon of uniform bore with $h = 40$ ft in Fig. 18, when the atmospheric pressure is 15 lb/in². Might large friction losses in a small pipe make such a siphon possibly operate with a positive Z?

45. A Venturi flowmeter in a water line has $A_1 = 4$ ft^2, $A_2 = 3$ ft^2, in the notation of Fig. 19. If the differential height reading is 10.8 in of mercury, what is the volume rate of flow of water?   Ans: 122 ft^3/sec.

46. If it is desired that a Venturi flowmeter should read a differential height of 12 inches of mercury when the flow velocity of oil of density 45 lb-mass/ft^3 in the full diameter of the pipe is 100 ft/sec, what should be the ratio of the diameter of the constricted section to the full pipe diameter?

47. In Fig. 19, if $P_1 = 20$ lb/in^2 absolute and $v_1 = 100$ ft/sec, at what area ratio A_1/A_2 will cavitation ensue in water, neglecting vapor pressure?   Ans: 1.14.

48. In Fig. 19, if the area ratio A_2/A_1 is $\frac{3}{4}$, and $P_1 = 40$ lb/in^2 absolute, at what speed v_1 will cavitation ensue in water?   Neglect the vapor pressure.

49. Neglecting friction, find the gauge pressures and speeds at ①, ②, and ③ in Fig. 30 if $h = 100$ ft, $Z = 70$ ft, $A_1 = 1$ ft^2, $A_2 = 1$ ft^2, $A_3 = 0.75$ ft^2, and the water discharges into the free atmosphere at ③.

Ans: ①: 19.0 lb/in^2, 60.2 ft/sec; ②: -11.4 lb/in^2, 60.2 ft/sec; ③: 0, 80.2 ft/sec.

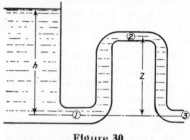

Figure 30

50. If water discharges in a stream $\frac{1}{2}$ inch in diameter from a faucet, with a speed of 30 ft/sec, what is the gauge pressure in the 1-in diameter pipe which the faucet terminates?   Neglect losses.

51. When the units lb, ft, slug, and sec are used, show that each term in (8) comes out in lb/ft^2 ($=$ ft·lb/ft^3), and each term in (9) and (10) in ft/sec.

52. Describe the spin a pitcher should give to a baseball if it is to curve to the right. Justify your answer by a diagram of the streamlines and application of Bernoulli's law.

53. The air-speed of a plane is measured by a Pitot-static tube (Fig. 31) of the type one can see protruding from the wings or fuselage. Show that if the differential manometer reads $(P_1 - P)$, the air-speed is $v = \sqrt{2(P_1 - P)/\rho}$, where ρ is the air density at the altitude of the plane.

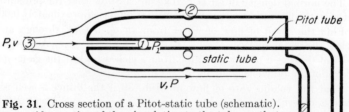

Fig. 31. Cross section of a Pitot-static tube (schematic). If we consider motion of the air relative to the tube, so that Bernoulli's law is applicable, the free-stream pressure and velocity, in front at ③, are P and v. In the Pitot tube (which is connected to the right side of the differential manometer), at ① the velocity is reduced to zero and the full ram pressure P_1 is developed. In the static tube, connected to the left side of the manometer, the entry holes are set far enough back so that the velocity and pressure outside the holes have the free-stream values. The pressure inside the static tube, like the pressure at a surface inside a boundary layer, will also be the free-stream pressure.

54. If a plane is flying at 300 knots at an altitude of 10,000 ft, where the air density is 0.9 kg/m³, determine the differential pressure indicated by its Pitot-static tube (Fig. 31) in mm of mercury.

55. The air-speed indicator of a plane is a differential manometer connected to a Pitot-static tube (Fig. 31). The dial however is not calibrated to read pressures, but to read knots under the assumption that the air has a standard sea-level density. The dial is said to read 'indicated air speed'; to get true air-speed, the reading must be corrected to the true density of the air at the pressure and temperature of the plane's altitude. If an air-speed indicator is calibrated for an air density of 1.40 kg/m³ and the plane flies at altitude 33,000 ft, where the air density has one-third this value, what is the true air speed when the indicated air speed is 220 knots?   Ans: 381 knots

56. A viscosimeter of the two-cylinder type described on p. 152 has the annular space filled with oil whose viscosity is being measured. The length of the cylinders is 6 in, their mean radius 3 in, the thickness of the annular space 0.1 in. The inner cylinder is fixed. It is found that a torque of 0.008 ft·lb is required to rotate the outer cylinder at 30 rev/min. Determine the viscosity of the oil and its ratio to that of water.

CHAPTER 7

MOMENTUM AND IMPULSE;
DYNAMICAL SYSTEMS

In this chapter we shall treat briefly certain problems involving collisions between bodies. In problems of this kind it is difficult if not impossible to determine the instantaneous values of the forces involved or even the exact time intervals during which the forces act. Therefore, it is impossible to write numerical equations for Newton's second principle in the form we have used thus far. However, even though we cannot give definite values for force or acceleration, it is still possible to apply Newton's principles to these problems; we can do this conveniently by introducing the quantities *momentum* and *impulse*. We shall show how these quantities are used in the solution of impact and collision problems.

The *principle of conservation of momentum* will be discussed and applied to a few simple problems. We shall also state and prove certain important theorems regarding the motion of *systems* of particles and of rigid bodies.

Before plunging into formal definitions and details, it might be well to discuss the general ideas involved in the definitions of momentum and impulse in a simple case. Consider a golf ball being driven from a tee. A large force acts on the ball during a short interval of time Δt, accelerating the ball from rest to a final velocity v. The magnitude of the force and the time interval Δt are difficult to determine, but the quantity $\bar{F} \Delta t$, where $\bar{F}$ is the average force acting during the time Δt, has a value that is readily computed. From Newton's second principle, $F = ma$, we infer that $\bar{F} = m\bar{a}$, and hence that $\bar{F} = mv/\Delta t$, from the definition of average acceleration. Therefore,

$$\bar{F} \Delta t = mv.$$

This equation is so useful in problems involving impacts and collisions that the quantities occurring are given special names. The product mv is called the *momentum* of the golf ball. The product $\bar{F} \Delta t$ is called the *impulse* required to change the momentum of the ball from zero to its final value mv. In collision processes, experimental measurements can

160

in general give us information on change of momentum and hence on impulse, but cannot give instantaneous values of the force or acceleration.

1. MOMENTUM

CERTAIN PROPERTIES of moving bodies depend directly on the product of the mass of the body and its velocity. For example, it is readily shown that the constant force required to bring a moving body to rest within a given time interval is proportional to the product, *mass times velocity.* We use the term *momentum* for this quantity.

> The **momentum p** of a particle is a vector defined as the product of its mass m and its velocity v: $p = mv$.

Since mass is a scalar quantity and velocity is a vector quantity, *momentum is a vector quantity.* It is measured in units that are the product of a mass unit by a velocity unit, for example, in kg·m/sec or slug·ft/sec. From the definition given above, it is evident that the momentum of a particle changes whenever either the mass or the velocity changes. As we have already indicated, the mass of a given particle may be regarded as constant except for particles having enormous velocities, comparable with the speed of light. Hence, in all cases of interest to us at present, we may attribute any change in the momentum of a particle to a change in its velocity, and write, for the rate of change of momentum,

$$dp/dt = m \, dv/dt = ma.$$

But by Newton's second principle, $F = ma,$ and therefore we may write

$$F = dp/dt. \quad \begin{Bmatrix} F \text{ in nt} \\ p \text{ in kg·m/sec} \\ t \text{ in sec} \end{Bmatrix} \text{ or } \begin{Bmatrix} F \text{ in lb} \\ p \text{ in slug·ft/sec} \\ t \text{ in sec} \end{Bmatrix} \quad (1)$$

This equation is actually a restatement of Newton's second principle in terms of momentum:

The time rate of change of the momentum of a particle is equal to the resultant external force acting on the particle and is in the direction of the resultant force.

From equation (1), we may write the change in momentum in time dt as

$$dp = F \, dt. \quad (2)$$

If $\bar{F}$ is the *average* force acting over a time interval Δt, it will produce change in momentum Δp given by

$$\Delta p = \bar{F} \, \Delta t. \quad (3)$$

2. IMPULSE

LET US NOW consider a process of the type occurring when a golf ball is struck with a golf club. (We shall treat the golf ball as a 'particle' and neglect rotational effects.)   The club is actually in contact with the ball only for a very short interval of time.   During this short time interval a very large force is exerted on the golf ball; this force varies with time in a complex manner that cannot in general be determined.   During the time the force acts, the golf ball and club undergo considerable deformation; the details of the process cannot be described completely even from the data obtained by modern high-speed photographic methods.   Forces of the kind exerted on the golf ball are called *impulsive forces*.

Let us assume that the graph in Fig. 1(a) shows the magnitude of the actual force exerted on the golf ball as a function of time and that this

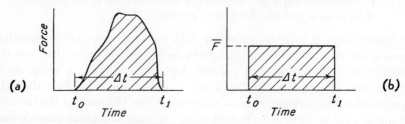

Fig. 1. An impulsive force.

force has a constant direction.   By equation (3), we see that the magnitude of the change in momentum in the time interval $\Delta t = t_1 - t_0$ during which the force acts is given by

$$\Delta p = \bar{F}\,\Delta t. \tag{4}$$

By definition, the time-average force $\bar{F}$ is such that $\bar{F}\,\Delta t$ is the area under the force curve.   The value of $\bar{F}$ is shown in Fig. 1(b), where the rectangle in Fig. 1(b) is drawn so as to have the same area as the cross-hatched area under the curve of Fig. 1(a).

Hence the impulsive force causes a change in momentum of magnitude equal to the area under the force curve of Fig. 1(a).   This area $\bar{F}\,\Delta t$ is called the *impulse*.

> The **impulse** is a vector defined as the time average of the force multiplied by the time interval during which the force acts.

Equation (3) states that

> *When an impulsive force acts on a particle, the change in momentum of the particle is equal to the impulse.*

The impulse is a vector quantity having the direction of the average force $\bar{F}$.   It is measured in units of force×time, either nt·sec or lb·sec.   These are seen to be the same as the units in which momentum is measured, in accordance with the identities

$$1 \text{ nt·sec} \equiv 1 \text{ kg·m/sec}, \quad \text{and} \quad 1 \text{ lb·sec} \equiv 1 \text{ slug·ft/sec},$$

which follow from equations (5), p. 83, and (10), p. 87.

In Fig. 1 and equation (4), we assumed that the impulsive force F had constant direction but varying magnitude during the time interval Δt. It is possible that the direction may vary also; in this case the averaging required to get $\bar{F}$ involves averaging separately the three components of F, but (3) and the above definition of impulse remain valid.

3. PRINCIPLE OF CONSERVATION OF MOMENTUM

Now LET US consider a collision between two particles, such as those of masses m_1 and m_2 shown in Fig. 2. Let us assume that during a collision these two particles exert forces on each other but that no other forces from outside this two-body system act on either particle. At any instant, F_1 is the force exerted on particle 1 by particle 2 and F_2 is the equal and opposite force exerted on particle 2 by particle 1. We may now write the change in momentum that particle 1 suffers during the collision as

$$\Delta p_1 = \bar{F}_1 \, \Delta t, \qquad (5)$$

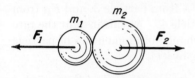

Fig. 2. Interaction between two particles in collision.

where Δt is the time interval during which the impulsive forces act. Similarly, the change in momentum of particle 2 is

$$\Delta p_2 = \bar{F}_2 \, \Delta t.$$

At each instant $F_2 = -F_1$, hence $\bar{F}_2 = -\bar{F}_1$. Therefore

$$\Delta p_2 = -\Delta p_1. \qquad (6)$$

Now let us consider the two particles as constituting a 'system' and define the *total momentum of the system* as

$$P = p_1 + p_2.$$

The total change ΔP occurring in the *momentum of the system* as a result of *internal forces* acting within the system, that is, the forces exerted by the two particles on each other during the collision, is

$$\Delta P = \Delta p_1 + \Delta p_2 = 0,$$

by (6). This equation expresses the important result that the total momentum of the system is not changed by the action of *internal* forces, a result known as the *principle of conservation of momentum*.

Example. *A man weighing* 200 lb *and a boy weighing* 80 lb *are on skates at rest facing each other. The man gives the boy a push that sends the boy backward at* 15 mi/hr. *What happens to the man?*

The forces between the man and the boy are *internal* to the system. Hence total momentum is conserved. It is initially zero; hence after the 'collision' the boy and man move off with momenta of equal magnitude but opposite direction:

$$m_{\text{Boy}} \, v_{\text{Boy}} = m_{\text{Man}} \, v_{\text{Man}}.$$

We can use any units we please in this equation if we use the same units on both sides. Mass is proportional to weight, so we can substitute weight in lb and speed in mi/hr to get

$$80 \ (15 \text{ mi/hr}) = 200 \ v_{\text{Man}}.$$

Hence $v_{\text{Man}} = 6$ mi/hr in the backward direction.

The principle of conservation of momentum is perfectly general and can be derived for a system containing any number of particles by an extension of the method we have already used for two particles.

Consider the four particles shown in Fig. 3. At a given instant, we assume that the particles are acting on each other with any system of forces whatsoever, arising either from collisions or from any type of action at a distance, provided only that Newton's third principle is satisfied. *No other forces* act on the particles.

At a particular instant, particle 1 experiences force F_{21} from particle 2, F_{31} from particle 3, and F_{41} from particle 4. At this instant the rate of change of momentum of particle 1 is, by (1),

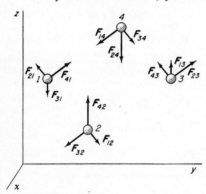

$$dp_1/dt = F_{21} + F_{31} + F_{41}. \quad (7a)$$

Employing a similar notation, we may write the rate of change of momentum of the other particles as

$$dp_2/dt = F_{12} + F_{32} + F_{42}, \quad (7b)$$

$$dp_3/dt = F_{13} + F_{23} + F_{43}, \quad (7c)$$

$$dp_4/dt = F_{14} + F_{24} + F_{34}. \quad (7d)$$

Fig. 3. A four-particle system.

The total momentum of the system is defined as

$$P = p_1 + p_2 + p_3 + p_4. \quad (8)$$

The rate of change of total momentum dP/dt is the vector sum of (7a), (7b), (7c), and (7d). Because of Newton's third principle, $F_{12} = -F_{21}$, $F_{13} = -F_{31}$, and so on, and we find that this vector sum vanishes:

$$dP/dt = 0. \quad (9)$$

The total momentum of the system of particles does not change with time, and hence P is a constant vector, unchanged by any type of interactions between the particles, so long as the system does not experience forces from bodies outside the system. The same type of derivation will clearly yield equation (9) no matter how many particles there may be in the system.

Equation (9) turns out to be much more important than one might suspect from the above simple derivation. For example, the system of particles might be all the atoms in a rigid body; equation (9) and others that we shall derive in this chapter will turn out to be fundamental to our later study of the dynamics of rigid bodies.   Before discussing this equation further we shall define certain useful concepts:

A dynamical system is a well-defined collection of matter.

The system may be composed of particles, of rigid bodies, of fluids, or any combination, but by *well-defined* we mean that we have specified exactly which material substance is considered as part of the dynamical system; all other matter in the universe is *external* to the dynamical system.

> The **total momentum of a dynamical system** is the vector sum of the momenta of all the individual particles or atoms in the system, as in (8).
>
> **Internal forces** are forces that the particles or atoms of a dynamical system exert *on each other*.
>
> **External forces** are forces exerted on particles in a dynamical system by particles external to the system.

With these definitions we can express equation (9), generalized so that P is the total momentum of a dynamical system, as the principle of conservation of momentum.   It will be recalled that equation (9) was derived on the assumption that only forces of the type that we have called internal forces are acting.

PRINCIPLE OF CONSERVATION OF MOMENTUM: *The total momentum of a dynamical system remains constant unless the system is acted on by external forces.*

This is one of the most important general principles of physics and is true without exception since it is derived directly from Newton's principles. It even remains true in the modern quantum and relativistic modifications of dynamics that we have mentioned earlier.

We shall now derive an important relation regarding the total momentum of a dynamical system:

The total momentum of a dynamical system is the same as the momentum of a single particle, of mass equal to the total mass, located at the center of gravity of the system and moving with the center of gravity.

If the particles of our system have masses $m_1, m_2, \cdots$, with total mass $m = m_1 + m_2 + \cdots$, the X-coordinate X_C of the center of gravity is defined (see p. 34) by

$$mgX_C = m_1 g X_1 + m_2 g X_2 + \cdots,$$

or

$$mX_C = m_1 X_1 + m_2 X_2 + \cdots. \tag{10a}$$

Similarly,

$$mY_C = m_1 Y_1 + m_2 Y_2 + \cdots, \tag{10b}$$

$$mZ_C = m_1 Z_1 + m_2 Z_2 + \cdots, \tag{10c}$$

Because of these relations, the *center of gravity* is also called the *center of mass*.

    Center of mass is a term synonymous with *center of gravity*.

If we differentiate (10a) with respect to t, we obtain the equation

$$mv_{cx} = m_1 v_{1x} + m_2 v_{2x} + \cdots,$$

where v_{cx} is the X-component of velocity of the center of mass. There are two similar equations for mv_{cY} and mv_{cZ}. The three equations together express the vector equation

$$m\boldsymbol{v}_c = m_1\boldsymbol{v}_1 + m_2\boldsymbol{v}_2 + \cdots.$$

The right side is the total momentum of the system; the left side is the momentum of a particle of mass equal to the total mass moving with the velocity of the center of mass. This proves the relation stated on p. 165.

4. EFFECT OF EXTERNAL FORCES ON A DYNAMICAL SYSTEM

We shall first consider the motion of a system of particles such as those of Fig. 3, interacting with each other in any way but acted on in addition by the external force of gravity. To equation (7a) we must add, on the right, the force $m_1\boldsymbol{g}$ of gravity. To (7b) we must add $m_2\boldsymbol{g}$, and so on. When these equations are added we no longer obtain the result (9), but rather

$$d\boldsymbol{P}/dt = m_1\boldsymbol{g} + m_2\boldsymbol{g} + \cdots = m\boldsymbol{g}.$$

But since, by the theorem we have just proved, $\boldsymbol{P} = m\boldsymbol{v}_c$, where $\boldsymbol{v}_c$ is the velocity of the center of mass, we see that $d\boldsymbol{P}/dt = m\boldsymbol{a}_c$, where $\boldsymbol{a}_c$ is the acceleration of the center of mass. Hence, $m\boldsymbol{a}_c = m\boldsymbol{g}$, or

$$\boldsymbol{a}_c = \boldsymbol{g}. \tag{11}$$

We have thus proved that

Irrespective of the internal forces that may act between the particles or bodies considered as constituting a dynamical system, the center of gravity moves, under the force of gravity, like a single particle, in a parabolic trajectory with downward acceleration $\boldsymbol{g}$.

One type of dynamical system is a rigid body. The internal forces are the forces that hold the different particles in rigid connection. The above result shows that when a rigid body (for example, a chair) is thrown or projected, the *center of gravity* moves in a parabolic trajectory like a single particle.

An interesting application of the above theorem concerns the trajectory of an exploding shell, neglecting air resistance. The first part of the trajectory has the familiar parabolic form shown in Fig. 4. At point X the shell explodes and shell fragments are blown out in all directions.

However, the forces of the explosion are *internal* forces, so the center of gravity of the shell fragments must complete the usual parabolic trajectory. In fact, after a projectile has been launched, it is impossible to modify the trajectory of the projectile's center of gravity by the action of any forces acting between particles *within* the projectile.

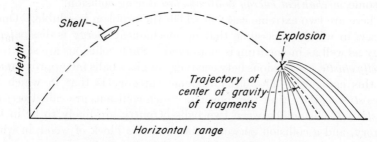

Fig. 4. Trajectory of an explosive shell, neglecting air resistance and the momentum of the high-explosive chemical.

We now state an extremely important relation which is a generalization of the above result. The student can readily prove the following theorem by the methods used in the previous derivation.

Irrespective of the internal forces which may act between the particles or bodies considered as constituting a dynamical system, the center of mass of the system moves like a single particle with acceleration F/m, where F is the resultant of all external forces acting on all the particles of the system, and m is the total mass of the system.

We shall need the above theorem in particular when we study the motion of a rigid body in Chap. 10. When the dynamical system is a single rigid body, the above theorem remains true whether or not the rigid body is rotating or is set into rotation by the external forces. Whether or not rotation is involved,

The center of mass of a rigid body moves like a single particle with acceleration F/m, where F is the resultant of all external forces acting on the body and m is the mass of the body.

This relation enables us to give a complete description of the *translational motion* of the rigid body (see definition of translation on p. 50). It is to be particularly noted that the forces that are added vectorially to obtain the resultant F need not be concurrent—they can act in any manner on various points of the body.

5. ELASTIC COLLISIONS

THE PROBLEM of the collisions of bodies is a difficult one because the conservation-of-momentum principle is the only rigorous principle applicable to the problem, and this principle alone is insufficient to determine the motion after collision from the motion before. The reason for this inadequacy is that an undetermined amount of energy may be converted into heat by deformation of the bodies during the collision, without violating conservation of momentum. *Momentum is always conserved*, but some *mechanical energy is always lost* during collision.

There are two extreme cases in which the problem is soluble. One is the case in which we assume that no mechanical energy is dissipated— energy as well as momentum is conserved. Such collisions are said to be *perfectly elastic*. Collisions between ivory or glass balls fall approximately into this category. The other extreme category is that in which the bodies *stick together* after the collision. Such collisions are called *perfectly inelastic*. Collisions between two balls of putty are likely to be in this category, and a collision between a bullet and a block of wood, in which the bullet remains embedded in the wood, certainly is.

We shall first consider perfectly elastic collisions between two 'particles' in which the velocities both before and after collision are along the same straight line. To visualize such a collision, consider two smooth nonrotating spheres colliding exactly 'head-on' when they are moving horizontally through the air. The instant after they separate they will be moving along the same straight line, still without rotation.

Fig. 5. Direct impact.

Such a collision is represented in Fig. 5, in which the masses of the bodies are m_1 and m_2, the velocity components before collision are u_1 and u_2, and those after collision are v_1 and v_2. These velocity components and the corresponding momentum components are taken as positive when directed to the right. Necessarily, in the configuration of Fig. 5, $u_1 > u_2$ if the bodies are to collide, and $v_2 > v_1$ if the bodies are to separate.

The total linear momentum of the system is unaltered by the impact, hence

$$m_1u_1 + m_2u_2 = m_1v_1 + m_2v_2. \tag{12}$$

Since we have assumed that the collision is perfectly elastic, we may write another equation for the conservation of energy during the collision process:

K.E. before impact = K.E. after impact

$$\tfrac{1}{2} m_1u_1^2 + \tfrac{1}{2} m_2u_2^2 = \tfrac{1}{2} m_1v_1^2 + \tfrac{1}{2} m_2v_2^2. \tag{13}$$

Rearranging this equation, we may write

$$m_1\,(u_1^2-v_1^2)=m_2\,(v_2^2-u_2^2),$$

or $\qquad\qquad m_1\,(u_1+v_1)(u_1-v_1)=m_2\,(v_2+u_2)(v_2-u_2).$ (13′)

By rearranging equation (12), we may also write

$$m_1\,(u_1-v_1)=m_2\,(v_2-u_2).$$ (12′)

By dividing (13′) by (12′), we get

$$u_1+v_1=v_2+u_2,$$

or $\qquad\qquad u_1-u_2=v_2-v_1.$ (14)

This result indicates that, in an elastic collision in which the motion is confined to one dimension, *the relative velocity of approach before collision is equal to the relative velocity of separation after collision.*

Equations (12) and (14) are the simplest pair to use in determining the velocity components v_1 and v_2 after collision from the velocity components u_1 and u_2 before collision.

Several special cases are of interest. For example, if $m_1=m_2$, equations (12) and (14) take the forms

$$u_1+u_2=v_1+v_2$$

and $\qquad\qquad u_1-u_2=v_2-v_1.$

By adding and subtracting these two equations we can obtain the relations

$$u_1=v_2 \quad \text{and} \quad u_2=v_1.$$ (15)

Equations (15) show that in direct, or 'head-on,' collision of two particles having equal masses, the particles *interchange* velocities during impact.

We shall now consider cases in which the body of mass m_2 is originally at rest. Since $u_2=0$, equations (12) and (14) become

$$m_1u_1=m_1v_1+m_2v_2$$

and $\qquad\qquad u_1=v_2-v_1.$

These two equations are readily solved for v_1 and v_2 in terms of u_1, with the result

$$v_1=\frac{m_1-m_2}{m_1+m_2}\,u_1, \qquad v_2=\frac{2m_1}{m_1+m_2}\,u_1.$$ (16)

We note from these equations that if $m_2\gg m_1$, $v_1\approx -u_1$ and v_2 is very small. In an elastic collision, where a particle strikes a much more massive particle at rest, the velocity of the light particle is approximately reversed and that of the massive particle is nearly unchanged. The extreme example is that of an elastic collision in which a particle strikes a smooth 'fixed' plane perpendicularly. By a fixed plane we mean one rigidly attached to the earth, so the mass factor associated with the plane is the whole mass of the earth. In this case the particle rebounds with exactly reversed velocity, as in Fig. 6.

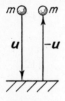

Now, we add a brief word about *imperfectly elastic collisions*, in which some of the original kinetic energy is dissipated as heat, and hence (13) and (14) are not valid. Newton concluded that in general (14) should be replaced by

Figure 6

$$v_2 - v_1 = e\,(u_1 - u_2), \tag{17}$$

where e is a factor, less than unity, that is approximately constant for a given pair of materials. The constant e is called the *coefficient of restitution*, and varies from 0 for materials that stick together to about 0.95 for glass against glass. If the value of e is known, (12) and (17) determine v_1 and v_2 from u_1 and u_2.

> **Example.** *A golf ball dropped from a height of* 1 meter *onto a concrete floor rebounds to a height of* 80 cm. *What is the coefficient of restitution between the ball and the floor?*
>
> In (17), let subscript 1 refer to the floor so that we can set $u_1 = v_1 = 0$. Let u_2 and v_2 represent the *upward* velocity of the ball before and after the collision. Then
> $$v_2 = -eu_2.$$
> Since the speed of a particle falling from height h is $\sqrt{2gh}$, we can write this last equation in the form
> $$\sqrt{h} = e\,\sqrt{H},$$
> where h is the height of rebound, H that of initial fall. Then
> $$e = \sqrt{h/H} = \sqrt{80/100} = 0.894.$$

6. PERFECTLY INELASTIC COLLISIONS

Let us now consider perfectly inelastic collisions, in which the two bodies have the same velocity after the collision. Collisions of this type are ordinarily accompanied by pronounced deformation of one or both of the colliding bodies. An inelastic collision may be visualized by imagining direct impact between two balls of putty. The two balls remain in contact after collision and therefore have a common final velocity v. This final velocity can be determined directly from the relation for conservation of momentum:

$$m_1 u_1 + m_2 u_2 = (m_1 + m_2)\,v. \tag{18}$$

When a stream of water impinges on a fixed flat plate, the impact practically follows the laws of perfectly inelastic collision. The stream spreads out during impact and the water flows along the surface of the plate as indicated at the top of Fig. 7. We can find the force F exerted by such a jet of water on the plate.   In time Δt, let mass Δm of water strike the plate.   Before collision this water had X-component of momentum $\Delta m\, u$.   After collision its X-component of momentum is zero.   Therefore in the collision its X-component of momentum is *decreased* by Δp

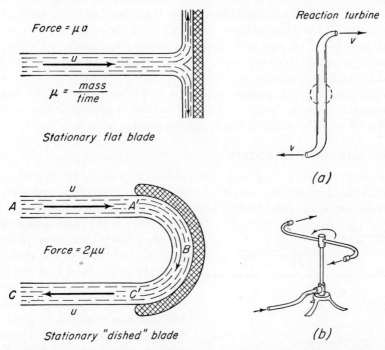

Force = μu

$\mu = \dfrac{mass}{time}$

Stationary flat blade

Reaction turbine

v

(a)

u

A　　　　A'

Force = $2\mu u$　　　B

C　　　C'

u

Stationary "dished" blade

(b)

Fig. 7. Stream of water striking turbine blades. In the discussion, the blades are considered as fixed in position.

Fig. **8.** Simple   reaction turbine.

$=\Delta m\, u$.   According to (3), this means that the plate must exert an average force to the left

$$F = \Delta p/\Delta t = u\,\Delta m/\Delta t.$$

But $\Delta m/\Delta t$ is the *mass of water striking the plate per unit time;* call this μ. Then

$$F = \mu u.$$

The force is constant and hence equal to its average; therefore F is the force exerted to the left by the plate on the water, or, by Newton's third law, F is *the force exerted to the right by the water jet on the plate.*

Engineers sometimes call this force an *impulse force.* The force applied in this way is employed in the *impulse turbine,* a water wheel operated by means of a high-speed water jet. The efficiency of such a turbine can be increased somewhat, as in the Pelton wheel, by 'dishing' the blades as shown at the bottom of Fig. 7. The direction of the water stream is changed when it strikes the curved surface of the dish, and if there is no friction it leaves the dish in direction $C'C$ with a velocity equal in magnitude to the velocity of the incident jet. The total force exerted on the dish is therefore given by $2u\mu$, since the change in velocity is $2u$. Engineers sometimes think of the total force as being made up of two parts: (1) the impulse force produced while the initial velocity to the right is reduced to zero and (2) the reaction force produced while the water is given a velocity toward the left. Such reaction forces are utilized in reaction turbines, of which the rotating sprinkler for lawns is a familiar example. A turbine of this type is shown in Fig. 8. Water flowing out from the center inside the turbine is ejected in the manner indicated, and the reaction force sets the turbine arms into rotation.

7. ACCELERATION OF ROCKETS

For extremely long-range projectiles, rockets have proved more practicable than missiles propelled from guns. A rocket is propelled by reaction forces supplied from a high-speed jet of gas ejected toward the

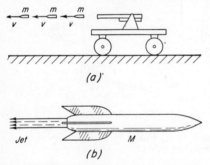

(a)

(b)

Fig. 9. Acceleration of bodies by reaction forces.

rear in much the same manner that reaction forces are used to set a reaction turbine in motion. In order to understand how the reaction is used, consider the sketch shown in Fig. 9(a), which shows a machine gun mounted on a car and firing a stream of bullets of mass m with a muzzle velocity v. Each bullet receives momentum mv as it leaves the gun. Hence, if n bullets are fired per second from the gun, they receive momentum $\Delta p = n\ mv$.

From (3), with $\Delta t = 1$ sec, we see that the average force exerted by the gun on these bullets is $F = n\ mv$. The magnitude of the reaction force acting on the gun is equal and opposite. Hence,

reaction = change of momentum of projectiles per sec = $n\ mv$.

This reaction force accelerates the gun and the car on which the gun is mounted.

An accelerating force is applied to the rocket in a similar manner, as indicated in the sketch in Fig. 9(b). In this case, we shall denote the jet velocity *relative to the rocket* by v and shall denote the constant rate of discharge (mass/sec) of hot gases by μ. Hence, the change of momentum per second of the material passing from the rocket into the jet is given by μv, and the magnitude of the reaction force which accelerates the rocket is given by the equation (derived exactly as in the case of the machine gun)

$$F = \mu v. \quad \begin{cases} F \text{ in lb} \\ \mu \text{ in slug/sec} \\ v \text{ in ft/sec} \end{cases} \quad \text{or} \quad \begin{cases} F \text{ in nv} \\ \mu \text{ in kg/sec} \\ v \text{ in m/sec} \end{cases} \quad (19)$$

This reaction force is called the *thrust*.

The true rocket is a reaction-propelled missile that carries all the materials from which the propulsion jet is formed, whereas the jet engine ordinarily used on manned aircraft carries only fuel and depends upon atmospheric oxygen to support combustion. The basic principles of propulsion are essentially the same for jet planes and for rockets. A true rocket operates best in the absence of an atmosphere.

Because of the occurrence in (19) of the factor v, the jet velocity, it is important to eject the jet at as high a speed as possible. In the German V-2 rocket, which burned alcohol in liquid oxygen to furnish the propelling gas, the jet velocity was of the order of 6000 ft/sec.

Example. *A rocket weighing 40 tons rises vertically from rest. It ejects gas at 6440 ft/sec at the rate of 1000 lb-mass/sec for 40 sec before the fuel is exhausted. Determine its initial upward acceleration and its acceleration at the end of 20 and 40 sec.*

From (19) we see that the upward force is constant, with the value

$$F = \mu v = \left(\frac{1000}{32.2} \frac{\text{slug}}{\text{sec}} \right) \left(6440 \frac{\text{ft}}{\text{sec}} \right) = 200,000 \text{ lb}.$$

This force is opposed by the weight of the rocket, which is 80,000 lb initially, 60,000 lb after 20 sec, and 40,000 lb after 40 sec. Hence the net upward force is

$$F(t=0) = 120,000 \text{ lb}; \quad F(t=20 \text{ sec}) = 140,000 \text{ lb}; \quad F(t=40 \text{ sec}) = 160,000 \text{ lb}.$$

The ratio of the net upward force to the force of gravity (the weight of the rocket) is hence

$$\frac{120,000}{80,000} = 1.5; \quad \frac{140,000}{60,000} = 2.33; \quad \frac{160,000}{40,000} = 4$$

at $t=0$, 20 sec, and 40 sec. The accelerations of the rocket are therefore

$$1.5 \, g; \quad 2.33 \, g; \quad 4 \, g$$

at these three times, where g is the acceleration of gravity.

PROBLEMS

1. A certain 11-kg body is subjected to a set of external forces. If the resultant force acting on the body is 55 nt downward, what is the time rate of change of the momentum of the body?   Ans: 55 kg·m/sec² downward.

2. If the body in Prob. 1 is initially at rest, what is its momentum after the resultant force of 55 nt has acted for 10 sec? What is its velocity at the end of this 10-sec interval?

3. A croquet ball with a mass of 400 g, initially at rest, is struck with a mallet and acquires a velocity of 4 m/sec. What is the magnitude of the change

in the momentum of the ball?   What impulse is associated with the force exerted by the mallet?   If the mallet is in contact with the ball for 0.1 sec, what is the magnitude of the average force exerted on the ball?

Ans: 1.6 kg·m/sec; 1.6 nt·sec; 16 nt.

4. A $\frac{1}{10}$-slug ball, initially at rest, acquires a velocity of magnitude 10 ft/sec when it is struck by a club.   What is the magnitude of the change in the momentum of the ball?   What impulse is associated with the force exerted by the club? If the club makes contact with the ball for 0.02 sec, what is the magnitude of the average force exerted on the ball?

5. A 500-g steel ball is dropped vertically on a concrete sidewalk.   It strikes the concrete normally at a velocity of 30 m/sec and rebounds with an initial upward velocity of 20 m/sec.   What is the impulse of the forces acting on the ball during this collision?   If the ball was in contact with the sidewalk for 0.01 sec, what average force did it exert against the walk?

Ans: 25 nt·sec upward; 2500 nt downward.

6. A $\frac{1}{2}$-slug lead ball is dropped from a height of 81 ft into a mud bank, where it comes to rest in 0.5 sec.   What average force was exerted on the ball in bringing it to rest?

7. A man weighing 200 lb stands in a boat weighing 300 lb at rest on the surface of a lake.   If the man dives from the boat with an initial horizontal velocity of 6 ft/sec eastward, what will be the initial horizontal velocity of the boat?   Neglect momentum given to the water.   Ans: 4 ft/sec westward.

8. In a marshalling yard, a freight car weighing 50 tons and traveling at 5 ft/sec overtakes one weighing 30 tons and traveling at 3 ft/sec.   They couple and move off together.   Find their speed and the loss of energy in the collision.

9. A projectile weighing 10 lb is fired horizontally from a gun weighing 4000 lb.   If the muzzle velocity of the projectile is 1200 ft/sec, what is the initial recoil velocity of the gun?   Ans: 3 ft/sec.

10. If a projectile weighing 200 lb were fired horizontally from the gun in Prob. 9 with a muzzle velocity of 1200 ft/sec, what would be the recoil velocity of the gun?

11. A railroad gondola car weighing 20 tons moves freely along a horizontal railroad track at a velocity of 30 ft/sec when 15 tons of snow fall vertically into the car from a snow bank overhanging the track.   What is the final velocity of the car?   Ans: 17.1 ft/sec.

12. If a bundle of 15-kg mass is dropped vertically onto a 7.5-kg sled traveling across the ice at 12 m/sec, what is the effect on the speed of the sled?

13. Prove the theorem on p. 167 which states that the center of mass of a dynamical system moves like a simple particle with acceleration F/m, where F is the resultant of the external forces and m is the total mass of the system.

14. Show that the theorem on p. 166, which states that the center of gravity of a dynamical system moves under the influence of gravity with downward acceleration g, is a particular case of the theorem referred to in Prob. 13.   Hence prove the theorem regarding motion under gravity from the more general theorem.

Note: In the following problems assume that all collisions are head-on and that there is no rotational motion.   In Probs. 15–24 assume that the collisions are *elastic* so that energy is conserved.

15. A ball A weighing 20 lb and moving at a velocity of 20 ft/sec in the $+X$-direction strikes a ball B weighing 1 lb that is initially at rest.   Find the

velocity, momentum, and kinetic energy of each ball after collision.   Ans:
A: 18.1 ft/sec, 11.2 slug·ft/sec, 102 ft·lb; B: 38.1 ft/sec, 1.18 slug·ft/sec, 22.6 ft·lb.

16. A 14-kg ball A traveling at a velocity of 10 m/sec in the $+X$-direction
strikes a 1-kg ball B initially at rest.   Find the velocity, momentum, and kinetic
energy of each ball after collision.

17. A 2-kg ball A moving with a velocity of 12 m/sec eastward strikes ball B
of mass 2 kg initially at rest.   Find the velocity, momentum, and kinetic energy
of each ball after the collision.

Ans: A: 0, 0, 0; B: 12 m/sec eastward, 24 kg·m/sec eastward, 144 joules.

18. A 2-kg ball A moving with a velocity of 12 m/sec eastward makes a
head-on collision with another 2-kg ball B moving with a velocity of 12 m/sec
westward.   Find the velocity of each ball after impact.

19. A 2-kg ball A moving with a velocity of 10 m/sec westward strikes a
20-kg ball B that is moving at 5 m/sec eastward.   Find the velocity of each
ball after the collision.   Ans: A: 17.3 m/sec eastward; B: 2.27 m/sec eastward.

20. A ball A weighing 2 lb and moving with a velocity of 30 ft/sec eastward
strikes a ball B weighing 2 lb and moving with a velocity of 70 ft/sec westward.
Find the final velocities of the two balls.

21. What percentage of its kinetic energy is transferred to the stationary
particle when a moving particle strikes a stationary particle of 100 times its mass?
of equal mass? of $\frac{1}{100}$ its mass?   Ans: 3.92%; 100%; 3.92%.

22. What percentage of its kinetic energy is transferred to the stationary
particle when a moving particle strikes a stationary particle of 10 times its mass?
of equal mass? of $\frac{1}{10}$ its mass?

23. Show that when a moving particle collides with a stationary particle
that is either k times as massive, or $1/k$ times as massive, it transfers to the
stationary particle the fraction $4k/(1+k)^2$ of its kinetic energy.

24. Show that when a very heavy particle strikes a very light stationary
particle, the light particle goes off with twice the velocity of the heavy particle.

25. A casehardened steel ball is dropped from a height of 16.1 ft onto a casehardened steel plate.   If the coefficient of restitution is 0.90, how high will the
ball rise on the first bounce after striking the surface?   Ans: 13.0 ft.

26. To what vertical height will the ball in Prob. 25 rise on the second bounce?
the third bounce? the nth bounce?

27. Solve Prob. 25 for a lead ball striking a lead surface if the coefficient of
restitution is 0.20.   Ans: 0.64 ft.

28. Show that if a sphere is dropped from height h onto a horizontal surface
of the same material, it rebounds to a height e^2h, where e is the coefficient of
restitution.

29. A 20-g lead bullet moving horizontally at a speed of 400 m/sec strikes
a 6-kg block of wood resting on a horizontal sheet of ice.   The bullet penetrates
the surface of the block, and the two bodies move off together along the surface
of the ice.   What is the magnitude of their common velocity after the collision?
How many joules of energy are changed into heat in the collision?

Ans: 1.33 m/sec; 1590 joules.

30. A bullet weighing 0.01 lb is fired horizontally into a wooden block weighing 5 lb that is at rest on a horizontal surface with coefficient of friction 0.25.
The embedded bullet causes the block to move 5 ft.   What was the speed of
the bullet?

31. A stream of water strikes a wall as shown at the top of Fig. 7. Find the force exerted on the wall when 10 ft³ of water strike the wall each minute and the stream velocity u is 40 ft/sec. Find the force if the stream were directed against a stationary dished blade in the manner shown at the bottom of Fig. 7.

Ans: 12.9 lb; 25.8 lb.

32. A garden hose lying on a concrete pavement is straight except for a small section near the nozzle. This section curves so that the nozzle points exactly at right angles to the main part of the hose. If water flows from the nozzle at a rate of 0.05 ft³/sec and a speed of 30 ft/sec, find the reaction force.

33. A man with an automatic rifle, weighing all-told 180 lb, fires a clip of 16 shells in 2 seconds. The man is on ice skates and moves backward without friction. Determine the average force on the man during the 2-sec interval and his speed at the end of this interval if each bullet weighs 0.03 lb and has a muzzle velocity of 3000 ft/sec.

Ans: 22.4 lb, 8 ft/sec.

34. If the stream of water mentioned in Prob. 31 were directed against the dished blades of a turbine, approximately what power is developed by the turbine if the speed of the water (with respect to the ground) is 10 ft/sec in the opposite direction from that at impact when it leaves the turbine, and the turbine blades are moving at 12 ft/sec at the point of water impact?

35. A 1-slug shell is fired from a gun. If the length of the barrel is 16 ft and the muzzle velocity of the shell is 1200 ft/sec, what is the average force (averaged with respect to distance) exerted on the projectile during its passage down the gun barrel?

Ans: 45,000 lb.

36. What average force would be required to give the projectile in Prob. 35 a muzzle velocity of 3000 ft/sec? 4000 ft/sec?

37. The V-2 rocket had about 250,000 lb thrust, and a jet velocity of about 6000 ft/sec. What weight of gas per second must be exhausted in the jet to achieve this thrust?

Ans: 1340 lb/sec.

38. A rocket of total mass M carries mass m of propellant that is ejected with speed v. Show that in the rough approximation in which the decrease in mass of the rocket as the propellant is expelled is neglected, this mass of propellant will accelerate the rocket from rest to a speed $V = vm/M$. (Assume the rocket to be in free space where there is no air resistance or gravity.) Show that the actual rocket will acquire a speed greater than this.

39. A jet engine is in a plane traveling at 600 ft/sec. The engine takes in 2500 ft³ of air having a mass of 5 slugs each second. The incoming air has of course the speed 600 ft/sec relative to the plane. This air is used to burn 0.2 slug of fuel each second, the energy being used to compress the products of combustion and eject them at the rear of the plane at 1200 ft/sec relative to the plane. What is the thrust of this jet engine and the horsepower it is delivering?

Ans: 3240 lb, 3540 hp.

40. If, by more efficient design, the exhaust velocity of the jet engine in Prob. 39 is increased to 2400 ft/sec, nothing else being changed, what will be the thrust and the horsepower?

41. A rigid body is lying at rest on a smooth horizontal plane, for example on a sheet of ice. The body is struck a horizontal blow at any point; the blow has impulse $\bar{F}\,\Delta t$. Show that after the blow the center of mass of the body moves at constant velocity $v = \bar{F}\,\Delta t/m$, where m is the mass of the body.

42. A stick of mass 6 kg lies on a smooth sheet of ice. A stone of mass 1.2 kg sliding along the ice at 8 m/sec hits the stick perpendicularly at some point and rebounds at 2 m/sec. Describe the subsequent motion of the center of mass of the stick.

43. Show that if two rigid bodies of masses m_1 and m_2 collide, the velocities of their centers of mass being u_1 and u_2 before the collision, then the velocities v_1 and v_2 of their centers of mass after the collision must satisfy the vectorial relation

$$m_1v_1 + m_2v_2 = m_1u_1 + m_2u_2,$$

irrespective of whatever rotational motion the bodies may have before and after the collision.

44. Two stones, sliding on a smooth horizontal sheet of ice, collide. Before the collision, the first stone, of mass 3 kg, has translational velocity 4 m/sec northward; the second stone, of mass 5 kg, has translational velocity 6 m/sec eastward. After the collision, the first stone moves off at 7 m/sec eastward. What is the velocity of the second stone after the collision?

45. Show that when a very light particle makes a (head-on) elastic collision with a very heavy object moving toward it, it rebounds with its own speed *plus* twice the speed of the moving object, and hence gains kinetic energy. When it makes such a collision with an object moving away from it, how does it rebound and does it gain or lose energy? Consider these questions in two ways: first by employing (12) and (14); then by using a coordinate system moving with the heavy object and employing the Newtonian principle of relativity. The most important application of these results is in the case of gas molecules striking the face of a moving piston in a cylinder. They do work and lose energy if the piston is moving away (gas expanding); the piston does work on the gas if it is moving toward the colliding molecules and the gas is being compressed.

46. A person leans over an elevator shaft and drops a light ball on the roof of an elevator moving upward at 10 ft/sec at the instant that the elevator is 40 ft below. Assuming that the ball rebounds elastically, to what height does it rise? Use a coordinate system moving with the elevator and the Newtonian principle of relativity.

CHAPTER 8

ELASTICITY AND STRENGTH OF MATERIALS

IN OUR TREATMENT of mechanics thus far, bodies have been assumed to be rigid, strings to be inextensible, and liquids to be incompressible. These assumptions are not strictly valid in any real physical situation, but can in many cases be justified when deformations are small or when the effects of the deformations are unimportant to the main problem being considered. For example, if a body is to be supported by means of wires of large diameter, the wires may experience only slight elongations that can be ignored in the computation of the forces to be expected in the system. If, however, the body is to be supported by fine wires, the wires may be elongated so much that the geometry of the system, and therefore the forces involved, may be quite different from what would be expected on the assumption that the wires are inextensible. In an extreme case the supporting wires might even break. The same considerations apply to beams and other structural members. Since the engineer must deal with real rather than with ideal materials in designing structures and machines, it is important that the elastic properties and strengths of materials be taken into consideration. In the present chapter, we shall consider some of these properties of materials.

1. HOOKE'S LAW; ELASTIC POTENTIAL ENERGY

EVERYONE has observed the bending of a piece of wood such as a diving board when a load is added; when the load is removed, the board regains its original shape. Likewise, a helical spring increases in length when a small load is added but regains its original length when the load is removed. These observed effects are examples of the *elasticity* of matter.

> An **elastic body** is one that experiences a change in volume or shape when the deforming forces act upon it but resumes its original size or shape when the deforming forces cease to act.

Recovery of the original configuration after application of forces is practically perfect for many kinds of materials, provided the distorting forces are not too great. If the distorting forces are too great, the *elastic limit* is exceeded and the recovery of the original configuration is incomplete.   In this case, the body is said to have acquired a *permanent set* or permanent deformation.   For example, if too heavy a load is supported by a helical spring, the spring may be permanently stretched.   The limiting load that can be supported by a spring without permanent deformation depends upon the size of the wire used, the way in which the spring is wound, and the material of which the wire is made.   For springs of the same shape and wire size, a spring made of lead wire would be permanently deformed by a much smaller load than that required to produce permanent deformation of a spring made of steel wire.   As we shall see later, the term *elastic limit* can be defined in such a way that it has a definite value for every *material.*   If the distorting forces acting on a body are made sufficiently great, the material will *rupture.*

Materials for which the elastic limit is extremely small are called *inelastic materials;* for example, dough, putty, and lead solder are inelastic materials, since bodies composed of these materials are permanently deformed when acted upon by relatively small forces.   Steel is a highly elastic material, since relatively enormous forces are required to produce permanent distortion of bodies composed of steel.

Nearly three centuries ago, the English experimental physicist Robert Hooke (1635–1703) discovered an important relationship:

HOOKE'S LAW: *The deformation of an elastic body is directly proportional to the magnitude of the applied force, provided the elastic limit is not exceeded.*

This law is valid for most metals and other structural materials, but *is not valid for rubber-like materials.*   It plays a fundamental role in the theory of elasticity.

The correctness of Hooke's law in a special case can be verified by adding weights to a helical spring in the manner indicated in Fig. 1. Before weight w is added, the length of the spring is l_0. The added weight of magnitude w produces elongation denoted by Y.

At the observed elongation, the spring exerts an upward restoring force F on the suspended body; this force is equal in magnitude and opposite in direction to the weight of the body, since the suspended

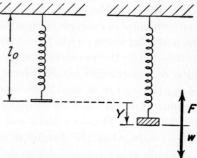

Fig. 1. The force of the weight on the spring is w. The equal and opposite reaction of the spring on the weight is the elastic force F.

body is in equilibrium.   We shall call this force F the *elastic force,* since it is exerted by the elastic spring by virtue of its deformation.

By adding different weights and noting the elongation, we obtain data that can be plotted in the manner shown in Fig. 2. The resulting straight-line relationship indicates that the observed elongation Y is proportional to the deforming force w. As the elongation Y is a measure of the deformation, we see that Hooke's law is verified for the spring in question; the relationships between the deforming force w, the elastic force F, and the elongation Y can be written

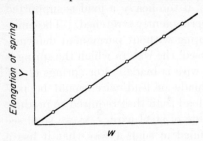

Fig. 2. The deformation Y in Fig. 1 is proportional to the applied force w.

$$w = KY, \qquad F = -KY, \quad (1)$$

where K is called the *force constant* of the spring.

The **force constant** of a spring is the force per unit displacement.

The force constant is measured in units like lb/ft or nt/m depending upon the units in which F and Y are measured. Its magnitude is a measure of the 'stiffness' of the spring. The negative sign in (1) is used to indicate that the vertical component of the elastic force has a sign opposite to that of the displacement Y, which in this case is taken as *positive downward*. Thus, if the displacement is downward as indicated in Fig. 1, the elastic force F is directed upward. If an upward external force acted in such a manner as to produce a negative elongation (compression) of the spring in Fig. 1, the elastic force F exerted by the spring would act downward and be regarded as positive.

We can now compute the potential energy stored in a stretched or compressed spring. We have already defined elastic potential energy on p. 106. In the elastic case, changes in potential energy are associated with changes in configuration of the elastic body. It is only these *changes* in potential energy that have physical significance. However, if we are interested in the potential energy when the body is distorted by application of a particular external force or torque, it is convenient to take the potential energy as zero in the configuration the body has when this particular external force or torque is removed, other external forces being unchanged. Thus we shall call the potential energy of the spring of Fig. 1 zero when the weight w is removed and the spring has length l_0, although other forces (of gravity and the supporting beam) still act; if these other forces could be removed the spring would have a still different length. With this understanding of the meaning of the configuration of zero potential energy, we may redefine *elastic potential energy* as follows:

> The **elastic potential energy** of a deformed body is the *negative* of the work done *by the elastic forces* when the body changes from the configuration defined as that of zero potential energy to the deformed configuration.

We see that the above definition is consistent with the general definition of energy given on p. 105, because the elastic potential energy as
defined above equals the work that could be done *by the elastic forces* as
the body returns from its deformed configuration to the configuration of
zero potential energy.   This is the same as the work done *by* the external forces that are required to effect the deformation, provided these
forces are increased *gradually* from zero to their final value.   The external
forces must be increased slowly so that the deformation will take place
slowly and the elastic body will acquire no appreciable kinetic energy.
If the deformation takes place rapidly the work of the external forces will
have to supply not only the elastic potential energy but the kinetic energy
associated with the particles in the elastic body.

As the spring of Fig. 1 changes from the condition of zero potential
energy on the left to the deformed condition on the right, the elastic force
F changes linearly from 0 to $-KY$.   Its average value, averaged with
respect to distance, is $-\frac{1}{2}KY$.   Therefore it does work $(-\frac{1}{2}KY)Y =$
$-\frac{1}{2}KY^2$ during the displacement Y.   The negative of this is, by definition, the potential energy

$$\text{P.E.} = \tfrac{1}{2}KY^2. \tag{2}$$

We note that this potential energy is the work that the elastic force F
would *do* as the spring returned to the configuration of zero potential
energy.   We note that it is also the work that the external force w would
have to do in order to effect the deformation, provided w were increased
gradually so that at each stage of elongation it were equal and opposite
to F.

Thus, the elastic potential energy of the spring is directly proportional
to the force constant and to the square of the elongation.   The potential
energy is seen to have the same value
for a compression as for an extension
of the same magnitude, since in either
case the same work must be done
against the elastic force to effect the
deformation.

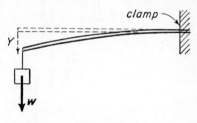

Hooke's law can also be easily
verified for many other simple cases.
In Fig. 3 a thin piece of steel such as

Figure 3

a hack-saw blade is clamped at one end and deformed by suspending
weights w from the free end.   Experiment shows that within the elastic
limit the distortion Y is proportional to the magnitude w.

Figure 4 shows a wire clamped at the upper end.   To the lower end is
attached a disk to which external forces F_{Ext} can be applied in such a manner as to exert a torque $L_{\text{Ext}} = 2F_{\text{Ext}}R$ which tends to twist the wire.   The
angle of twist can be taken as a measure of the deformation produced in

the wire.   Experiment shows that the deformation θ is directly proportional to the applied torque.   In a manner similar to that used for the helical spring, we may write

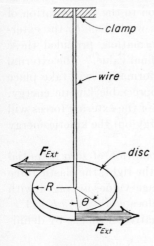

clamp

wire

F_{Ext}

disc

R

θ

F_{Ext}

Figure 4

$$L_{Ext} = C\theta. \qquad (3a)$$

The elastic reaction of the wire will exert an equal and opposite torque

$$L = -C\theta. \qquad (3b)$$

By an argument similar to that given previously, we find the expression

$$P.E. = \tfrac{1}{2} C\theta^2 \qquad (4)$$

for the elastic potential energy stored in the twisted wire.   The proportionality constant C in these equations is called the *torsion constant* of the wire.   It is measured in torque units per unit angular displacement, for example, nt·m/rad or lb·ft/rad.

The **torsion constant** of a wire or rod is the torque required per radian of twist.

Whereas Hooke's law holds well for most bodies composed of metal, wood, glass, and many other common materials, there are some elastic

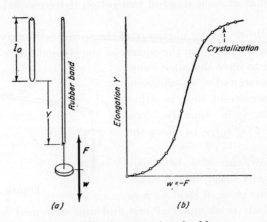

l_0

Rubber band

Y

F

w

Elongation Y

Crystallization

$w = -F$

(a)   (b)

Fig. 5. Elastic properties of rubber.

materials for which it does not hold at all.   Rubber is such a material. If we take a rubber band of initial length l_0 and deform the band by suspending weights w from the lower end in the manner indicated in Fig. 5(a), a plot of the resulting elongations Y has the form shown in Fig. 5(b).

The curve shown in this figure bears little resemblance to the straight line to be expected on the basis of Hooke's law. *Elastic* elongations of five or six times the original length can easily be obtained with a rubber band, whereas materials like metal, wood, and glass can only be stretched *elastically* a small fraction of their original length before the elastic limit is reached. Hence it is not surprising that these two types of materials have quite different relations between force and elongation. When subjected to large deformations, the structure of rubber undergoes marked changes, and crystallization sets in at a point marked on the curve in Fig. 5(b). This point determines the elastic limit beyond which a permanent set is acquired.

2. LONGITUDINAL STRESS AND STRAIN: GENERALIZATION OF HOOKE'S LAW

In our discussion of the original form of Hooke's law, we have described experiments that can easily be performed by stretching or compressing helical springs, bending thin strips of metal, or twisting wires. These simple experiments serve to verify Hooke's law for these particular *bodies* but do not add very much to our knowledge of the elastic properties of the *materials* of which the bodies are composed. For example, we were able to write equation (3) for a twisted wire, but the torsion constant C occurring in the equation applies only to the particular piece of wire used in the experiment. If we twisted another wire of the same material with different cross-sectional area and length, we should not know how to predict the deformation that would be produced by a given torque. Similarly, if we used only the simple form of Hooke's law, we should have to determine the elastic constants of each individual structural member before a building, a bridge, or a machine could be properly designed. Fortunately, it is possible to generalize Hooke's law in such a way as to make it possible to determine elastic constants for *materials*. The elastic constants of *bodies* such as structural members can then be calculated in terms of the elastic constants of the *materials* and the geometrical shapes and sizes of the bodies. This generalization of Hooke's law is therefore a much more valuable tool than the original simple law. In the following paragraphs, we shall discuss the concepts of *stress* and *strain*, in terms of which the general form of Hooke's law is stated.

Stress is related to the *force* causing deformation; *strain* is related to the *amount of deformation*. In order to understand the ideas involved, let us consider Fig. 6, which shows a long elastic rod of initial length l_0 and cross-sectional area A. If forces F are applied to the ends of the rod, the rod experiences an elongation e and we can say that the rod has undergone a *longitudinal strain*.

> **Longitudinal strain** of a wire or rod under tension or compression is defined as the increase in length per unit length.

In Fig. 6 the longitudinal *strain* σ is the ratio of the elongation e to the initial length l_0:

$$\sigma = e/l_0. \hspace{4cm} \text{(strain)}$$

The strain is accompanied by *internal forces* between adjacent parts of the rod. If the cross section of the rod at any point such as M in Fig. 6 be considered as a dividing plane, the material to the left of M exerts a force of magnitude F toward the left on the material to the right of M, whereas the material to the right exerts a force of magnitude F toward the right on the material to the left of M. These forces must have

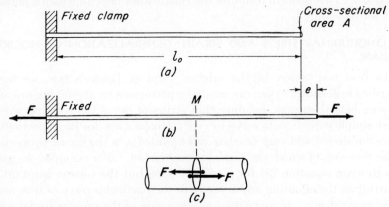

Fig. 6. Longitudinal stress is F/A. Longitudinal strain is e/l_0.

the same magnitude as the external applied forces, since each part of the rod is separately in static equilibrium. When such forces exist in the interior of a body, the body is said to be under *stress*.

> **Longitudinal stress** of a wire or rod under tension or compression is defined as the ratio of the internal force to the area across which it acts.

In the case of the uniform rod shown in Fig. 6, the longitudinal *stress S* is the same at all cross sections and equal in magnitude to the external force F divided by the cross-sectional area:

$$S = F/A. \hspace{4cm} \text{(stress)}$$

By performing experiments on rods of different sizes but composed of the same material, we find that the longitudinal stress S is proportional to the longitudinal strain σ, the proportionality constant being independent of the size of the rod. Thus we may write

$$S = E_Y \, \sigma,$$

where the proportionality constant E_Y is called *Young's modulus** or the *modulus of elasticity in tension*, and is a *constant* for a given *material*.

* Named for Thomas Young, English experimental physicist (1773–1829).

Thus we see that for any size rod or wire,

$$\frac{F}{A} = E_Y \frac{e}{l_0} \tag{5}$$

in the notation of Fig. 6.   Since e and l_0 are measured in the same length units, E_Y has dimensions of force/area, such as lb/ft^2, lb/in^2, or nt/m^2.

> **Young's modulus** is the ratio of stress to strain in the case of a rod or wire under tension or compression.

Thus, by introducing the quantities stress and strain we have been able to generalize Hooke's law in the case of stretched rods or wires to the statement:

Stress is proportional to strain, the proportionality constant depending only on the material and not on the particular body.

If we know Young's modulus for a given material and the length l_0 and cross-sectional area A of a given rod, the generalized form of Hooke's law given in equation (5) enables us to determine the elongation or deformation e produced by the application of an external force F.   The values of Young's modulus for several materials are given in Table I.   The same value of the modulus applies to compression of a stiff rod as for tension of a rod or wire of the same material.

Example.   *A steel piano wire will withstand a tensile stress of $100,000$ lb/in^2 and still obey Hooke's law since the elastic limit is about $120,000$ lb/in^2.   How much does a 100-in length of wire stretch when this stress is applied?   If the wire is $\frac{1}{25}$ inch in diameter, how much load must be applied to give this stress?*

From Table I, E_Y for steel is 29×10^6 lb/in^2.   We substitute this value and $F/A = 10^5$ lb/in^2 in (5) to get the strain

$$\frac{e}{l_0} = \frac{F/A}{E_Y} = \frac{10^5 \text{ lb/in}^2}{29 \times 10^6 \text{ lb/in}^2} = 3.4 \times 10^{-3} = 0.0034.$$

From this, we find that

$$e = 0.0034 \; l_0 = 0.0034 \times 100 \text{ in} = 0.34 \text{ in.}$$

The 100-in length of wire stretches by about $\frac{1}{3}$ in.

The area of a circle of diameter $\frac{1}{25}$ in $= 0.04$ in is $A = \pi(0.02)^2 = 12.5 \times 10^{-4}$ in^2.   Hence

$$F = (10^5 \text{ lb/in}^2) \times A = (10^5 \text{ lb/in}^2) \times 12.5 \times 10^{-4} \text{ in}^2 = 125 \text{ lb.}$$

This is the force required to stretch the wire by 0.34 in.

We shall now define the terms *isotropic* and *anisotropic*, which we shall have frequent occasion to use in the remainder of our study.   Isotropic, from the Greek, means 'the same in every direction,' anisotropic, of course, 'not the same in every direction.'

An **isotropic solid material** is one whose physical properties are independent of direction, an **anisotropic solid material,** one whose physical properties vary with direction.

Wood is the most familiar example of an anisotropic solid material—it has a grain and a structure that makes its physical properties quite different in the three principal directions. A ball or cube of wood would have different compressive properties in the different directions of applying the compressive stress; these properties could only be expressed by giving three different Young's moduli, not a single value. In our previous discussion we introduced only a single value of Young's modulus for a material—this discussion clearly applies only to isotropic materials.

TABLE I

TYPICAL ELASTIC CONSTANTS*

Material	Young's modulus E_Y		Shear modulus E_S	
	lb/in²	nt/m²	lb/in²	nt/m²
Aluminum.........	10×10^6	6.9×10^{10}	3.8×10^6	2.6×10^{10}
Brass.............	13×10^6	9.0×10^{10}	5.1×10^6	3.5×10^{10}
Copper............	16×10^6	11×10^{10}	6.0×10^6	4.1×10^{10}
Nickel............	30×10^6	21×10^{10}	11×10^6	7.6×10^{10}
Steel.............	29×10^6	20×10^{10}	11×10^6	7.6×10^{10}
Tungsten..........	$51 \cdot \times 10^6$	35×10^{10}	21×10^6	14×10^{10}
Glass.............	7.8×10^6	5.4×10^{10}	3.3×10^6	2.3×10^{10}

Material	Bulk modulus E_B		
	lb/in²	lb/ft²	nt/m²
Brass.............	15×10^6	22×10^8	10×10^{10}
Copper...........	20×10^6	29×10^8	14×10^{10}
Steel.............	25×10^6	36×10^8	17×10^{10}
Glass.............	5.2×10^6	7.5×10^8	3.6×10^{10}
Ethyl ether........	0.9×10^5	1.3×10^7	0.6×10^9
Ethyl alcohol.......	1.6×10^5	2.3×10^7	1.1×10^9
Water.............	3.1×10^5	4.5×10^7	2.1×10^9
Mercury...........	40×10^5	58×10^7	28×10^9

* These are typical values to be used in problem work. The actual values for different samples of the same solid depend upon the previous history of the solid; for example, by heat-treatment and mechanical 'working' one can vary the elastic constants of copper by as much as 12 per cent. The elastic constants for steel, brass, and glass vary widely with the exact composition and treatment of these materials.

Discussion of the elastic behavior of anisotropic materials is much more complex than for isotropic materials; in this chapter we shall confine our attention to isotropic materials.

Single crystals are (with certain exceptions such as rock salt and diamond) anisotropic. They have different elastic, optical, and electrical properties in different directions. Metals are in general composed of large numbers of individual crystals but, while each individual crystal is anisotropic, so many individual crystals are jammed together with random orientations in a piece of metal that the metal as a whole ordinarily behaves isotropically. The elastic constants given in Table I are for such ordinary multicrystalline metals. A broken piece of cast iron usually furnishes a surface on which the individual crystals are large enough to be visible to the eye.

3. VOLUME ELASTICITY: BULK MODULUS

WE HAVE SEEN how the problem of longitudinal extension or compression can be treated satisfactorily by the application of a generalized form of Hooke's law. The generalization that *stress is proportional to strain* can be applied to problems other than those involving longitudinal deformations, although of course different definitions of stress and strain must be used to suit the different types of deformation.

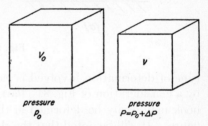

Let us next consider the problem of bulk or volume elasticity. Figure 7 shows a body that has volume V_0 when subjected to a uniform external hydrostatic pressure P_0, and also

Fig. 7. Volume elasticity: a decrease in volume results from an increase in pressure.

shows the same body with smaller volume V when the pressure is increased to $P = P_0 + \Delta P$. It is found that for isotropic materials, the change in volume takes place without change in the shape of the body; the cube remains a cube.

In the case of bulk compression, **volume stress** is defined as the pressure increase ΔP; **volume strain** is defined as the *decrease* in volume per unit volume, or $(V_0 - V)/V_0 = -\Delta V/V_0$.

Again it is found experimentally that stress is proportional to strain:

$$\Delta P = E_B \,(-\Delta V/V_0), \qquad (6)$$

where the proportionality constant E_B is a characteristic of the material called the *bulk modulus*. The bulk modulus has the dimensions of pressure, that is, force/area.

The **bulk modulus** is the ratio of stress to strain in the case of volume compression.

Values of the bulk modulus for several materials are listed in Table I.

Equation (6) enables us to compute the change ΔV in the volume of a body when the pressure increases by a given amount ΔP, provided we know the initial volume of the body and the bulk modulus. The change in volume will be negative if the change in pressure is positive.

Since no question of rigidity is involved in volume elasticity, equation (6) applies to liquids as well as to solids. The volume elasticity of gases will be considered in Chap. 15.

4. ELASTICITY OF SHAPE: SHEAR MODULUS

THE THIRD TYPE of elasticity we shall consider is one in which the *shape* of a body is changed without change in the *volume* of the body. The

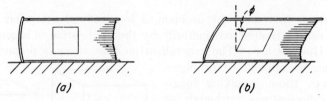

Fig. 8. Shear.

type of deformation involved is called a *shear*, which can be understood by a consideration of Fig. 8. Part (a) shows a book lying on a table; the book may easily be deformed in the manner indicated in part (b) of the figure. It will be noted that the shape of the book has been altered without change in the volume of the book; consequently, the deformation is a *shear*. A comparison of parts (a) and (b) of Fig. 8 shows that a rectangular element of surface area becomes a parallelogram when shear occurs. The angle ϕ in the figure is called the *angle of shear*.

A book is an anisotropic body that is relatively inelastic to deformation of the type indicated in Fig. 8. In order to understand how a shear is produced in an isotropic body, let us consider the volume element shown in Fig. 9; this element of volume has been taken from the interior of a body experiencing a shear. The forces F_1 are exerted on the element in the directions tangential to the faces of area A_1, and the forces F_2 are exerted in directions tangential to the faces of area A_2; these forces are exerted by the material outside the volume element on the material inside. The resultant force and the resultant torque on the material in the volume are zero; this must be so, since the material is not experiencing linear or angular acceleration. When the surface forces F_1 and F_2 act in the manner indicated, the face of area A_3, which was a rectangle in the undeformed body, becomes a parallelogram.

Shearing strain is defined as the shear angle ϕ shown in Fig. 9, in radians.

Over the elastic range, the shear angle ϕ is always a very small angle; it is greatly exaggerated in Fig. 9.

Shearing stress is defined as the tangential force per unit area, F_1/A_1 or F_2/A_2 in Fig. 9. The condition for rotational equilibrium shows that these two ratios are always equal.

Demonstration that $F_1/A_1 = F_2/A_2$ is left to the student; in equation (7) below we shall call this ratio just F/A, or S.

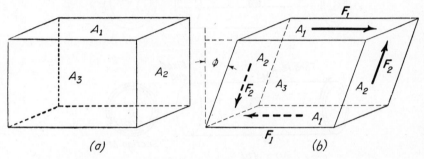

Fig. 9. Shearing stress and strain within a material medium: (a) unstressed parallelopiped, (b) the same parallelopiped under shearing stress.

It is found experimentally that shearing stress is proportional to shearing strain:

$$S = F/A = E_s\,\phi \qquad\qquad (7)$$

with a proportionality constant E_s, called the *shear modulus* or *modulus of rigidity*, that depends only on the type of material of which the body is composed. The shear modulus has dimensions of force/area.

The **shear modulus** is the ratio of stress to strain when shearing forces act on an isotropic body.

Values of the shear modulus for several materials are given in Table I.

To see how the shear modulus may be determined experimentally, consider a thin-walled hollow cylinder that is twisted about its geometrical axis by clamping one end of the cylinder in a fixed position and applying a torque to the free end; this operation results in a uniform shear. A thin-walled cylinder before deformation is shown in Fig. 10(a); a small 'square' surface element is cross-hatched and a long 'rectangular' surface element is shown by the dashed lines passing along the cylinder surface from end to end. When the cylinder is twisted as shown in part (b) of the figure, the small 'square' becomes a 'rhombus' and the 'rectangle' becomes a 'parallelogram' of the indicated shape; therefore, the material experiences a pure shear. Now let us find expressions for strain and stress from the labeled diagram in Fig. 10(c).   The strain can be expressed as the shear angle ϕ.   However, the shear angle ϕ is not as easy to measure as θ, the angle of rotation of the twisted end.   In the elastic range ϕ is small, and we can write

$$\text{shearing strain} = \phi = r\theta/l, \tag{8}$$

where l is the length of the cylinder.   The torque L must appear across any section such as MM, since the part of the cylinder to the left of MM

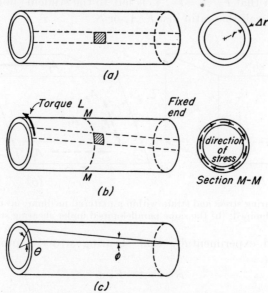

(a)

Torque L
M

Fixed end

direction of stress

M

Section M-M

(b)

θ ϕ

(c)

Fig. 10. Shear resulting from twist of a thin-walled cylinder of length l, radius r, and wall-thickness Δr.

is in rotational equilibrium.   If we call the shearing stress S at section MM, this stress acts across a total cross-sectional area $2\pi r \, \Delta r$, so that it exerts torque $L = (2\pi r \, \Delta r) \, S \cdot r$.   Hence,

$$\text{shearing stress} = S = L/2\pi r^2 \, \Delta r. \tag{9}$$

The ratio of shearing stress (9) to shearing strain (8) is by (7) the shear modulus.   Hence we have

$$E_s = \frac{L/2\pi r^2 \, \Delta r}{r\theta/l}, \quad \text{or} \quad E_s = \frac{Ll}{2\pi r^3 \theta \, \Delta r}. \tag{10}$$

Equation (10) enables us to determine the shear modulus E_s for a material from measurements of the rotation θ produced by applying a torque L to a thin-walled cylinder of the material.   If the modulus E_s is known, equation (10) can be used to predict the rotation θ produced by the application of a torque L to the end of a thin-walled tube.   A similar equation can be derived for a twisted *solid* rod or wire of radius r and length l.   This equation is

$$E_s = 2Ll/\pi r^4\theta, \tag{11}$$

where θ is the twist angle for torque L.*   In making actual measurements, the torque $L = w \cdot R$ is frequently applied by hanging weights w on a wheel of radius R clamped to the free end of the section of rod or tube being studied, in the manner indicated in Fig. 11.

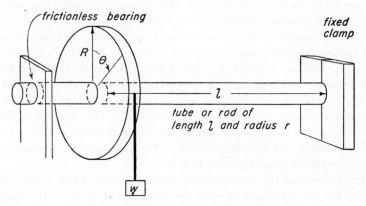

Fig. 11. Measurement of torsion constant.

The ratio L/θ, the torque required per radian of twist, gives the *torsion constant* of the tube or rod.   This constant can be computed from (10) or (11).   We note from (8) that even if ϕ is very small, θ can be large if l/r is large so that θ can be an easily measured angle.

The force constant of a *helical spring* can be computed once we know the torsion constant of the wire from which it is made.   We do not give the details here, but merely point out that when a spring elongates, the wire of which it is formed does not stretch, it merely *twists*.   Any small section of the wire behaves exactly like a piece of wire in torsion, and hence the torsion constant governs its elastic behavior.

Example.   *The elastic limit for shearing stress of a particular steel is 40,000 lb/in². An automobile drive shaft made of this steel has 2-in diameter and 0.1-in thickness. How much torque can a 6-ft shaft of this tubing transmit without acquiring a permanent set? What will be the angle of twist and the angle of shear for this shaft at the elastic limit?*

From (9), the torque, when the shearing stress is 40,000 lb/in², is

$$L = 2\pi r^2 \, \Delta r \, S = 2\pi \, (1 \text{ in})^2 \, (0.1 \text{ in})(40{,}000 \text{ lb/in}^2) = 25{,}100 \text{ lb·in}.$$

---

* This relation is derived by dividing the rod up into cylindrical shells of radius ρ and thickness $d\rho$.   According to (10), the torque dL required to twist such an element through angle θ is $dL = (2\pi\theta E_s/l)\rho^3 \, d\rho$.   Integration of this expression from $\rho = 0$ to r gives (11).

Using the shear modulus of steel in Table I, we find the shear angle ϕ from (7):

$$\phi = S/E_S = (40,000 \text{ lb/in}^2)/(11 \times 10^6 \text{ lb/in}^2) = 3.64 \times 10^{-3} \text{ rad} = 0°.208.$$

The angle of twist θ is obtained from (8):

$$\theta = (l/r)\phi = (6/\tfrac{1}{12})\ 3.64 \times 10^{-3} \text{ rad} = 0.262 \text{ rad} = 15°.0.$$

5. RELATIONS AMONG ELASTIC CONSTANTS

We have thus far introduced three elastic moduli: Young's modulus, the bulk modulus, and the shear modulus. Of all the elastic moduli that can be defined for an isotropic elastic material, only two are independent. All elastic moduli can be expressed in terms of any two of them. For example, if we choose the bulk modulus E_B and shear modulus E_S as the independent ones, it can be shown that Young's modulus E_Y can be expressed as $E_Y = 9E_B E_S/(3E_B + E_S)$. Actually, the stretching of a wire involves a change in both shape and volume of the wire, and consequently both volume elasticity and shape elasticity are involved. As the length increases, the diameter d decreases. *The ratio of the relative lateral contraction $\Delta d/d$ to the relative longitudinal extension $\Delta l/l$ is called Poisson's ratio ρ.* It is dimensionless. For most metals, Poisson's ratio has a value in the neighborhood of 0.3.

The problem of the experimental determination of the elastic moduli is easiest for Young's modulus and the shear modulus, since the measurements involved consist of determining the elongation produced by a known longitudinal force acting on a wire of known length and cross-sectional area for Young's modulus and determining the rotation produced by a known torque acting on a rod of known dimensions for the shear modulus. The direct determination of the bulk modulus is considerably more difficult. The values for the bulk modulus E_B and for Poisson's ratio ρ may be determined from E_Y and E_S by means of the relations $E_B = \tfrac{1}{3} E_S E_Y/(3E_S - E_Y)$ and $\rho = (E_Y/2E_S) - 1$. These relations do not hold for single crystals of material; single crystals have different elastic properties in different directions and require more than two independent constants to describe their elastic behavior. The relations do, however, hold for crystalline materials that are composed of a large number of small crystals oriented at random, as in the usual case for the solid metals of engineering practice. They also hold for amorphous materials such as glass.

The only elastic modulus applicable to a liquid or gas is the bulk modulus, since a fluid in equilibrium will not withstand any tangential stress.

6 ELASTIC LIMIT AND ULTIMATE STRENGTH OF MATERIALS

Now let us consider the behavior of elastic materials, obeying Hooke's law, when subjected to large tensile stresses that carry the material beyond its elastic limit. To determine this behavior a specimen such as shown in the insert to Fig. 12 is machined from a bar of the material and screwed into the jaws of a tensile-testing machine. This machine is so arranged as to stretch the bar gradually (that is, gradually *increase the strain*) and to measure the force F required to give any desired value of strain.

Fig. 12 illustrates the behavior of a specimen of medium steel as an example. The quantities plotted are e/l_0, where e is the elongation of a section of constant area between two marks originally a distance l_0 apart, and F/A_0, where A_0 is the *original* cross-sectional area. F/A_0 is called the *apparent stress* because after the bar has been subjected to a large

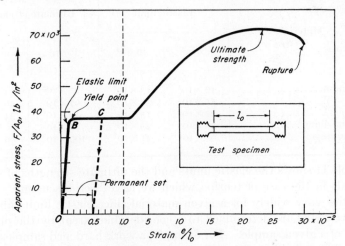

Fig. 12. Typical stress-strain diagram for medium steel in tension. Note the change in scale of strain by a factor of 10 at the broken line.

strain its area is considerably reduced so the true stress F/A would be larger than F/A_0.

In Fig. 12, the curve between O and B is a straight line, showing that stress is proportional to strain for small strains, in accordance with Hooke's law. The elastic limit is reached at B; after stresses greater than that for point B have been attained, the bar no longer regains its original length when the distorting forces are removed. If the tension is removed at C, the strain retraces the broken curve and the bar is left with a permanent set. The value of the stress at point B is called the *elastic limit* for the material. As the stress is increased beyond the elastic limit, the *yield point* is soon reached. At the yield point, a large increase in strain occurs with almost no increase in stress; in fact, when the yield point is reached, the bar appears to flow like an extremely viscous liquid. As the strain is further increased, the stress changes as in Fig. 12 until rupture occurs. The *ultimate tensile strength* is the highest point of the curve of Fig. 12, the maximum apparent stress that the material can withstand. The ultimate strength is frequently slightly higher than the stress at rupture, and may be much above the yield point, as in steel.

Certain *brittle* materials such as glass and phosphor-bronze rupture at the elastic limit. For such materials no permanent set can be produced. The ultimate strength and the elastic limit are equal. Materials that *yield*, in the manner of medium steel, are said to be *ductile*. They can be drawn into wire through dies, whereas brittle materials cannot.

TABLE II

TYPICAL ELASTIC LIMITS AND ULTIMATE STRENGTHS FOR MATERIALS IN TENSION

Material	Elastic limit		Ultimate strength	
	lb/in²	nt/m²	lb/in²	nt/m²
Aluminum...............	19×10^3	13×10^7	21×10^3	14×10^7
Brass...................	55×10^3	38×10^7	67×10^3	46×10^7
Copper..................	22×10^3	15×10^7	49×10^3	34×10^7
Steel, medium...........	36×10^3	25×10^7	72×10^3	50×10^7
Steel, spring............	60×10^3	41×10^7	100×10^3	69×10^7

Table II shows the elastic limits and the ultimate strengths of several materials in the case of tension which we have been discussing. These properties vary widely for a given material since elastic limits and ultimate strengths are determined to a considerable extent by the previous history of a given sample. For example, a work-hardened sample and an annealed sample have very different properties in the case of copper and steel.

PROBLEMS

1. When a body weighing 2 lb is attached to the end of a spring hanging vertically, the spring is stretched 0.5 in. What is the force constant of this spring?
Ans: 48 lb/ft.

2. When a 2-kg block is attached to the end of a spring hanging vertically, the spring experiences an elongation of 5 cm. Find the force constant of this spring in nt/m.

3. Assuming that the spring in Prob. 1 obeys Hooke's law, find the elongations produced when a body weighing 32 lb is suspended from the end of the spring.
Ans: 8 in.

4. Assuming that the spring in Prob. 2 obeys Hooke's law, find the elongation produced (a) when a 5-kg block is suspended from the end of the spring and (b) when a force of 50 nt is applied to the end of the spring.

5. What is the potential energy of the stretched spring mentioned in Prob. 3 when it supports the 32-lb weight? when it supports a 64-lb weight?
Ans: 10.7 ft·lb; 42.7 ft·lb.

6. What is the potential energy of the stretched spring for each case mentioned in Prob. 4? Express this energy in joules.

7. The end of a long wire hanging vertically and clamped at the upper end is twisted through an angle of 30° when a torque of 3 lb·ft is applied to the free end. What is the torsion constant for this wire? What torque is exerted by the clamp on the upper end of the wire? What is the potential energy of this twisted wire?

Ans: $18/\pi$ lb·ft/rad; 3 lb·ft; 0.785 ft·lb.

8. One end of a long brass rod is clamped tightly so as to prevent rotation. When a torque of 9 nt·m is applied to the free end, the free end experiences a rotation of 5°. What is the torsion constant of this rod? What is the potential energy of the twisted rod?

9. A projectile weighing 10 lb is fired horizontally from a gun weighing 4000 lb at a muzzle velocity of 1200 ft/sec. The initial recoil energy of the gun is all transformed into potential energy of a spring. What must be the force constant of the spring if the recoil is to be limited to 2 ft?   Ans: 280 lb/ft.

10. A railroad car weighing 40 tons rolls at 5 ft/sec into a 'bumper' at the end of a track. The kinetic energy of the car is all transformed into potential energy in a coil spring in the bumper. What must be the force constant of the spring in tons/inch if the motion of the spring is to be restricted to 3 in?

11. A mass of 10 kg is supported by a steel wire 8.0 m in length and 1.0 mm in diameter. What is the resulting elongation?   Ans: 5.09 mm.

12. A mass of 8 kg is supported by a copper wire of length 8 m and diameter 2 mm. What is the resulting elongation?

13. A 2-ton weight is supported by a steel rod 10 ft long and 1.0 inch in diameter. What is the resulting elongation?   Ans: 0.0213 in.

14. An elevator cage weighs 8500 lb and is supported by two steel cables 60 ft long. If each of the cables has an effective cross-sectional area of 1 in², what elongation is produced by the elevator cage? What additional elongation does each cable experience when the cage has an upward acceleration of 8 ft/sec²?

15. A brass rod is 1 ft long and has a cross-sectional area of 1.5 in². What compressional force must be applied at the ends of this rod in order to produce a decrease of 0.01 inch in the length of the rod?   Ans: 16,200 lb.

16. What compressional stress is involved when the length of a steel rod 10 ft long is decreased by 0.01 in?

17. When an elastic rod is stretched, work is done against the elastic forces and the rod acquires elastic potential energy. Show that the potential energy per unit volume can be expressed as $\frac{1}{2}\sigma S = \frac{1}{2}E_Y\sigma^2 = \frac{1}{2}S^2/E_Y$, where σ is the longitudinal strain, S is the longitudinal stress, and E_Y is Young's modulus for the material of which the rod is composed. What units should be used for S, E_Y, and the potential energy per unit volume in the MKS and British systems?

18. Considering a vertical wire carrying a weight as a spring, express the force constant of the spring in terms of the dimensions of the wire and Young's modulus.

19. What increase in pressure is required to decrease the volume of a cubic meter of water by 0.01 per cent?   Ans: 2.1×10^5 nt/m².

20. What increase in pressure is required to decrease the volume of a cubic meter of ether by 0.1 per cent?

21. Show that so long as the volume change in (6) is small compared to the original volume, we can write

$$\Delta P = E_B \, \Delta\rho/\rho_0,$$

where ρ_0 is the original density and $\Delta\rho$ the increase in density.

22. At what depth below the surface of a lake is the density of water 0.1 per cent greater than that of surface water at the same temperature?

23. Find the ratio of density of water at a point 500 ft below the surface of a lake to the density of water at the surface.   (Neglect temperature differences.)
Ans: 1.000699.

24. What pressure would be required to increase the density of brass by 0.1 per cent? the density of glass by 0.1 per cent? the density of ether by 0.1 per cent?

25. What pressure would be required to increase the density of steel by 0.1 per cent? the density of copper by 0.1 per cent? the density of water by 0.1 per cent?   Ans: 1.7×10^8 nt/m²; 1.4×10^8 nt/m²; 2.1×10^6 nt/m².

26. When equal and opposite forces of magnitude F_1 are applied to the top and bottom faces of a parallelopiped as in Fig. 9, show that to maintain rotational equilibrium forces must be applied to the right and left faces of such magnitude F_2 that the stresses F_2/A_2 and F_1/A_1 are equal.   Show that this statement is true for arbitrary magnitude of the angle ϕ, although only small angles are involved in elastic shear.

27. A copper tube 2.0 cm in radius is 4.1 m in length and has a wall thickness of 1 mm.   One end of this tube is firmly clamped and a torque tending to twist the tube is applied to the other end.   What is the torsion constant for this tube? What angular displacement is produced by a torque of 32 nt·m?
Ans: 503 nt·m/rad; 0.0636 rad.

28. Find the torsion constants of steel and brass tubes having the same dimensions as the copper tube described in Prob. 27.

29. Find the torsion constant of a solid steel wire $\frac{1}{8}$ inch in diameter and 4 ft long.   Ans: 5.5 lb·in/rad.

30. What torque is required to twist the wire of Prob. 29 through $\frac{1}{4}$ rev?

31. What is the largest mass that can be supported by a medium steel wire 2 mm in diameter? by a copper wire 2 mm in diameter?   Ans: 160 kg; 110 kg.

32. What is the greatest mass that can be supported by a brass wire 2 mm in diameter? by an aluminum rod 2 mm in diameter?

33. What is the maximum tensile force that can be supported by a medium steel structural member with a cross-sectional area of 4 in²?   Ans: 288,000 lb.

34. What is the maximum tensile force that can be supported by a brass structural member with a cross-sectional area of 2 in²?

35. Show that the slope of the line OB on Fig. 12 is in agreement (to the one-significant-figure accuracy with which this slope can be read) with the value of E_Y given in Table I.

36. In Prob. 33, what is the maximum tensile force that can be applied without a resultant permanent set when the tension is removed?

37. Medium steel requires a stress of 50,000 lb/in² for rupture in shear. Determine the force required to punch a 1-in diameter hole in a steel plate $\frac{1}{4}$-in thick by means of a punch and die.   Ans: 39,200 lb.

38. Explain the action of metal shears.

CHAPTER 9

ROTATIONAL MOTION

IN EARLIER CHAPTERS we have pointed out that any motion of a rigid body can be described as a combination of *translation* and *rotation* (see definitions, p. 50). So far, we have discussed the kinematics and dynamics of translational motion in considerable detail, but we have not discussed rotational motion.

In the present chapter we shall study the elementary kinematics and dynamics of the rotational motion of a rigid body mounted on a fixed axis. A rigid body is essentially a collection of particles constrained by forces that keep the particles in place in the body. Since the dynamical behavior of the rigid body can be deduced from the dynamical behavior of the particles of which it is composed, it was desirable first to study the dynamics of particles.

More general motions of a rigid body, involving both translation and rotation, will be considered in the following chapter.

1. KINEMATICS OF PURE ROTATION: ANGULAR DISPLACEMENT, VELOCITY, AND ACCELERATION

Pure rotation is the rotation of a rigid body about a fixed axis.

Let us consider Fig. 1, which shows the cross section of a rigid body that can rotate about a fixed axis through O perpendicular to the plane of the diagram. The body might be a wheel with the axis through O at its center, or the body might be a cam, balance weight, or pendulum not centered at O. All points on the axis remain stationary during rotation, while all other points in the body move in circles with centers located on the axis. The position of every point in a body having this type of motion can be determined in terms of the angular position of any reference radius OA of the body relative to some fixed direction OX. In other words, the angle between OA and OX can be used in determining the positions of all points in a rotating rigid body, since the *relative* positions of the points in the body do not change.

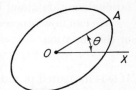

Fig. 1. Angular displacement. O is a fixed axis perpendicular to the paper; OX is a fixed direction in space; OA is a radial line 'painted' on the rigid body.

The angle between OX and OA can be used to describe the *orientation* of the rigid body as a whole.   If OA initially coincides with OX and later has turned through angle θ, we can think of θ as the *angular displacement* of the body.

> **Angular displacement** of a rigid body in pure rotation is defined as the angle through which any radius of the body turns; it is usually taken as positive for a counterclockwise rotation and negative for a clockwise rotation.

Now that we have defined angular displacement θ, we may proceed at once to the formal definition of angular velocity ω by means of the equation

$$\omega = d\theta/dt. \tag{1}$$

If θ is measured in radians and t in seconds, ω is expressed in radians per second (rad/sec).

> The **angular velocity** of a rigid body in pure rotation is the time rate of change of its angular displacement; it is usually taken as positive for a counterclockwise sense of rotation and negative for a clockwise sense.

The above treatment of angular velocity about a fixed axis is analogous to the treatment of torque about a fixed axis given in Chap. 1.   Actually, like torque, angular velocity is a vector quantity represented by a vector directed along the axis.   We shall discuss the vectorial properties of angular velocity later.

When the angular velocity is constant, the angular displacement of the body in t sec is given by

$$\theta = \omega t. \tag{2}$$

This equation is analogous to the equation $X = v_x t$ which gives the X-coordinate of a particle moving with constant velocity v_x in translational motion along the X-axis.

We can now proceed to a definition of angular acceleration α by means of the equation

$$\alpha = d\omega/dt.$$

If ω is measured in radians per second and time in seconds, angular acceleration α will be expressed in radians per second per second (rad/sec^2).

> **Angular acceleration** of a rigid body in pure rotation is defined as the time rate of change of angular velocity.

From the relation $$d\omega = \alpha\, dt,$$

we see that positive angular acceleration produces a positive change in angular velocity.   If the body is rotating counterclockwise and has a positive angular acceleration, its speed of rotation is increasing; if it is rotating clockwise and has a positive angular acceleration, positive increments are being added to its negative angular velocity, and the body is slowing down.

We may now write equations describing the motion of a body experiencing *constant angular acceleration* α. If the angular velocity of the body is ω_0 at time $t=0$, its angular velocity ω at the end of t sec can be written as $\omega = \omega_0 + \Delta\omega$, where $\Delta\omega$ is the change in angular velocity during the t-sec interval. Since for constant angular acceleration $\Delta\omega = \alpha t$, this expression for ω becomes

$$\omega = \omega_0 + \alpha t. \tag{3}$$

In order to find the angular displacement θ experienced by the body during the t-sec interval, we write

$$\theta = \bar{\omega}t, \tag{4}$$

where $\bar{\omega}$ is the average angular velocity. Just as in the case of uniformly accelerated rectilinear motion, we may express $\bar{\omega}$ in the form

$$\bar{\omega} = \tfrac{1}{2}(\omega_0 + \omega), \tag{5}$$

where ω is the final velocity given by equation (3). Substitution of (3) in (5) leads to $\bar{\omega} = \omega_0 + \tfrac{1}{2}\alpha t$, and substitution of this value in (4) gives

$$\theta = \omega_0 t + \tfrac{1}{2}\alpha t^2 \tag{6}$$

for the magnitude of the angular displacement during the t-sec interval.

By elimination of t from equations (3) and (6), we obtain the relation

$$\omega^2 = \omega_0^2 + 2\alpha\theta. \tag{7}$$

Example. *A motor-driven grinding wheel starts from rest and receives a constant counterclockwise angular acceleration of 3 rad/sec² for 12 sec. Determine its angular velocity at the end of this period and the angle through which it has turned.*

From (3), the angular velocity of the wheel at the end of 12 sec is $+36$ rad/sec. The average angular velocity of the wheel during the first 12 sec is $+18$ rad/sec, as given by (5). The total angular displacement of the wheel can be obtained from (4):

$$\theta = (18 \text{ rad/sec})(12 \text{ sec}) = 216 \text{ rad},$$

or from (6): $\theta = \tfrac{1}{2}(3 \text{ rad/sec}^2)(12 \text{ sec})^2 = 216 \text{ rad}.$

Since there are 2π radians in one complete revolution, the wheel turns through $216/2\pi = 34.4$ revolutions during the first 12 sec of motion.

We note that there is an exact correspondence between rotational motion about a fixed axis and translational motion along a straight line (the X-axis) if we associate θ with X, ω with v_x, and α with a_x. The relations we have found between θ, ω, and α are exactly the same as the relations we found in Chap. 3 between X, v_x, and a_x. As we go into the dynamics of rotational motion about a fixed axis and enlarge this list of associated quantities, we shall find essentially that we shall not need to remember any new analytical relations if we remember the analytical relations governing translational motion along a straight line and the fairly obvious system of correspondence between rotational and translational quantities.

2. THE MOTION OF A POINT IN A RIGID BODY IN PURE ROTATION

THE ANGULAR displacement, angular velocity, and angular acceleration of a rigid body rotating about an axis are characteristic of the motion of the rigid body *as a whole*. Let us now consider the relations between these quantities and the displacement, velocity, and acceleration of a single point in the rotating body. Every point in a body in pure rotation moves in a circle whose center is on the axis of rotation. Let the broken circle in Fig. 2 represent the path of a point P in a body rotating about an axis through O. The point is at distance r from the axis of rotation. When the radius OP makes angle θ radians with a fixed reference line OX, the arc length from P measured counterclockwise from the reference line will be the length S in Fig. 2, where

$$S = r\theta. \qquad (8)$$

If θ is given as a function of t, this relation will determine S as a function of t. Since r is a constant, we can differentiate the relation (8) with respect to t to obtain

$$dS/dt = r\, d\theta/dt.$$

But dS/dt is the magnitude of the velocity of the point P along its circular path, which we denote by v, and $d\theta/dt$ is the angular velocity ω, so

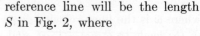

Figure 2

$$v = r\omega. \qquad (9)$$

The value of v obtained from this relation gives both the speed and the sense of motion of P along the arc, since v comes out positive for counterclockwise rotation (ω positive) and negative for clockwise rotation (ω negative). For a given angular velocity, the speed varies directly as the distance r from the axis, as we would expect.

We now differentiate equation (9) with respect to t. This gives

$$dv/dt = r\, d\omega/dt.$$

The expression dv/dt is *not* the acceleration of P since the velocity is continuously changing direction; it is the rate of change of speed rather than the rate of change of velocity.   But it is, as remarked at the end of Chap. 3, one component of the acceleration of P: the component *tangent* to the circular path of P, which we shall denote by a_T.   Since $d\omega/dt$ is the angular acceleration α, the above relation becomes

$$a_T = r\alpha. \qquad (10a)$$

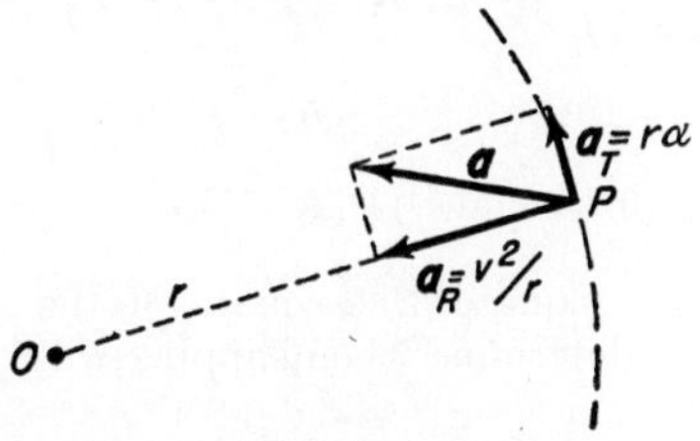

The radial component of the acceleration of P, directed toward the center, is, as in Chap. 3,

$$a_R = v^2/r; \qquad (10b)$$

Fig. 3. Radial and tangential acceleration components. The tangential component has the direction indicated if α is positive; the opposite direction if α is negative.

this relation obtains whether or not the speed v is constant.   From (9), we get the useful alternative expressions

$$a_R = v\omega = \omega^2 r.$$

The proofs of relations (10) for the case of motion in a circle at varying speed are similar to, but more complex than, the proof of (10b) given in Chap. 3 for motion in a circle at constant speed.   We omit these proofs.

A point P at radius r from the axis of a rigid body in pure rotation with angular velocity ω and angular acceleration α has speed $r\omega$, centripetal acceleration v^2/r, tangential acceleration $r\alpha$.   The velocity vector is tangent to the circular path of P and points counterclockwise if ω is positive, clockwise if ω is negative; similarly the tangential component of acceleration points counterclockwise or clockwise according to whether α is positive or negative (see Fig. 3).

This completes the kinematical description of the motion of P in terms of the angular motion of the rotating body of which P is a point. The position S of P, measured along the arc, its speed v, and the components of its acceleration a are given by

$$S = r\theta; \quad v = r\omega; \quad a_T = r\alpha, \quad a_R = v^2/r = v\omega = \omega^2 r. \qquad (11)$$

These relations hold only when the angular unit in θ, ω, α is the radian. In checking the dimensions of these equations, note that the radian is a dimensionless quantity defined as the ratio of two lengths (arc/radius) measured in the same length units.

Example. *A 'fun-house' contains a circular horizontal rotating table that starts from rest and accelerates at the uniform rate of 0.4 rad/sec². A person sits on the table at a distance of 3 ft from the axis. If the coefficient of static friction is 0.15, how long after the table starts to rotate does the person start to slide?*

The person will slide when the force required to accelerate him in his circular motion is greater than the maximum force of static friction, 0.15 mg. Equating this to ma_{Max}, we see that sliding starts at

$$a_{Max} = 0.15\,g = 0.15\,(32.2 \text{ ft/sec}^2) = 4.83 \text{ ft/sec}^2.$$

The tangential component of the acceleration of the person is constant at

$$a_T = r\alpha = (3 \text{ ft})(0.4 \text{ rad/sec}^2) = 1.2 \text{ ft/sec}^2.$$

Since the angular velocity at time t is

$$\omega = \alpha t = (0.4 \text{ rad/sec}^2)\, t,$$

the radial component of acceleration is

$$a_R = \omega^2 r = (3 \text{ ft})(0.16/\text{sec}^4)\, t^2 = (0.48 \text{ ft/sec}^4)\, t^2.$$

The resultant acceleration is $a = \sqrt{a_R^2 + a_T^2}$. Equate the square of the resultant acceleration to the square of a_{Max} to determine when slipping will occur:

$$a_T^2 + a_R^2 = a_{\text{Max}}^2$$
$$(1.2)^2 + (0.48)^2\, (t^4/\text{sec}^4) = (4.83)^2,$$

from which $t^4 = 95.0 \text{ sec}^4,$ $t = 3.12 \text{ sec}.$

The person will start to slip 3.12 sec after the platform starts turning.

3. WORK, POWER, AND KINETIC ENERGY IN PURE ROTATION

IF WE WERE to follow the same order in which we discussed the motion of a particle, we should proceed next to apply Newton's second principle to derive the dynamic relation between the torque ($L = FR$ in Fig. 4) applied to a rigid body in pure rotation, and the angular acceleration of the body. Actually, a direct derivation of this relation is analytically difficult because of the complex set of internal forces that hold the body rigid, and the complex changes that must occur in these forces when the individual particles are accelerated. However, it turns out to be comparatively easy to derive expressions for work, power, and kinetic energy in the case of rotational motion, and then to apply the powerful principle of conservation of energy (equating work done to increase in kinetic energy) to derive the relation between torque and angular acceleration. Hence we consider work, power, and kinetic energy before considering direct dynamical relationships.

Consider a wheel on which a constant torque is acting, for example the system of Fig. 4 in which a constant force F exerts a constant torque $L = FR$. If the string in Fig. 4 moves a distance S, work $W = FS$ is done by the force F. During this motion, the wheel turns through an angle $\theta = S/R$. We desire to express the work in terms of torque and angle instead of force and distance. We can do this by substituting $F = L/R$ and $S = R\theta$ in the expression $W = FS$ to obtain

$$W = L\theta. \qquad \left\{ \begin{array}{l} W \text{ in joules} \\ L \text{ in m·nt} \\ \theta \text{ in rad} \end{array} \right\} \text{ or } \left\{ \begin{array}{l} W \text{ in ft·lb} \\ L \text{ in lb·ft} \\ \theta \text{ in rad} \end{array} \right\} \quad (12)$$

Work is the product of torque by angular displacement if the torque is constant.

If the torque is not constant, we can see that, since $dW = F\,dS$, the element of work done by the torque L in the small angular displacement $d\theta$ is given by

$$dW = L\,d\theta.$$

If we divide this last equation through by the element of time dt during which the angular displacement $d\theta$ takes place, we obtain

$$dW/dt = L\,d\theta/dt.$$

In this equation, dW/dt is the rate at which the torque L does work, that is, the *power;* and $d\theta/dt$ is the angular velocity ω.   Hence the power

$$P = L\omega. \qquad \begin{Bmatrix} P \text{ in watts} \\ L \text{ in m·nt} \\ \omega \text{ in rad/sec} \end{Bmatrix} \text{ or } \begin{Bmatrix} P \text{ in ft·lb/sec} \\ L \text{ in lb·ft} \\ \omega \text{ in rad/sec} \end{Bmatrix} \quad (13)$$

Power is the product of torque by angular velocity.

Now let us consider the kinetic energy of a body in pure rotation. That a rotating body has energy by virtue of its motion is apparent if we

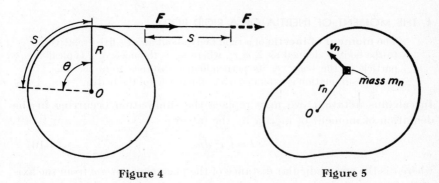

Figure 4   Figure 5

try to stop a large flywheel by applying a brake shoe.   The brake shoe becomes very hot as the rotational kinetic energy is transformed into heat.   It is also well known that considerable work must be done to set a massive wheel into rotation even when frictional effects are negligible.

The kinetic energy of a rotating body is the sum of the kinetic energies of the particles of which it is composed.   To obtain an expression for the kinetic energy let us consider the body in Fig. 5, which is rotating at angular velocity ω about a stationary axis through O.   Consider a typical particle of mass m_n at radius r_n.   The kinetic energy of this particle is $\frac{1}{2}\,m_n v_n^2$, where v_n is the speed of the particle in its circular path of radius r_n.   Since $v_n = r_n\omega$, we may write the kinetic energy of the particle in the form $\frac{1}{2}\,m_n r_n^2 \omega^2$.   Therefore, the total kinetic energy of the body is the sum

$$\text{K.E.} = \Sigma \, \tfrac{1}{2}\,m_n r_n^2\,\omega^2.$$

Since the angular velocity ω of all particles in the body is the same, we can factor out $\frac{1}{2} \omega^2$ and write

$$\text{K.E.} = \frac{1}{2} \left[\Sigma \ m_n r_n^2 \right] \omega^2.$$

This equation is analogous to the equation $\text{K.E.} = \frac{1}{2} mv^2$ for the kinetic energy of translation of a particle. Just as m is said to be a measure of the *inertia* of the particle, the quantity in square brackets is called the *moment of inertia* of the rigid body about the axis through O. Moment of inertia is ordinarily denoted by the letter I. Thus

$$I = \Sigma \ m_n r_n^2. \tag{14}$$

Therefore, we may write

$$\text{K.E.} = \frac{1}{2} I \omega^2 \quad \left\{ \begin{matrix} \text{K.E. in joules} \\ I \text{ in kg·m}^2 \\ \omega \text{ in rad/sec} \end{matrix} \right\} \text{ or } \left\{ \begin{matrix} \text{K.E. in ft·lb} \\ I \text{ in slug·ft}^2 \\ \omega \text{ in rad/sec} \end{matrix} \right\} \tag{15}$$

for a body of moment of inertia I rotating with angular velocity ω. We shall return to applications of this formula after we have discussed the moment of inertia of a rigid body.

4. THE MOMENT OF INERTIA OF A RIGID BODY

The **moment of inertia** of a rigid body about an axis fixed relative to the body is defined as $\Sigma \ m_n r_n^2$, where m_n is the mass of a typical particle of the body, r_n its perpendicular distance from the axis, and the summation is extended over all particles of the body.

In calculus notation, we may replace the summation occurring in the definition of moment of inertia by the integral

$$I = \int r^2 \, dm, \tag{16}$$

where r is the perpendicular distance of the mass element dm from the axis of rotation, and the integral is taken over all mass elements in the body. This integration can be performed readily for most regular solids. Since such integrations are treated in elementary calculus texts, we shall merely list in Fig. 6 the moments of inertia for several regular solids about axes through their centers of mass.

From the values given in Fig. 6 and from (14) and (16), it can be seen that the moment of inertia of a body depends upon two factors: (a) *the total mass of the body* and (b) *the distribution of the mass about the axis*. The second factor is determined by the *size* and *shape* of the body. For any body it is always possible to find a radial distance from any given axis at which the whole mass of the body could be concentrated into a single particle that would have the same moment of inertia as the body about that axis. This radial distance is called the *radius of gyration* of the body about the given axis and is usually denoted by k. Thus, if the total mass m of the body were located in a particle at this distance k from the axis, the moment of inertia I would be mk^2. Since, by definition of k, this is equal to the actual moment of inertia, we have

$$I = mk^2, \quad \text{or} \quad k = \sqrt{I/m}. \tag{17}$$

> The **radius of gyration** of a body about a given axis is the distance from that axis at which the whole mass of the body could be concentrated without alteration of the moment of inertia.

The radius of gyration k is a measure of the size-and-shape factor in the moment of inertia. The rotational inertia of an irregularly shaped wheel,

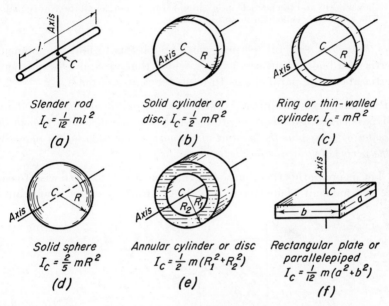

Fig. 6. Moments of inertia of various rigid bodies of mass m about axes through their centers of mass.

such as a flywheel, is frequently specified by giving its mass and its radius of gyration.

Example. *Determine the radius of gyration of a slender rod of mass m and length l about a transverse axis through its center of mass.*

The value of the moment of inertia of this body about the axis in question is given in Fig. 6 as $\frac{1}{12} ml^2$. Hence from (17),

$$\tfrac{1}{12} ml^2 = mk^2 \quad \text{and} \quad k = \sqrt{\tfrac{1}{12}}\, l = 0.289\, l.$$

Thus, so far as rotation about the axis in question is concerned, we could replace the rod by a ring of radius k or a point mass at distance k from the axis as in Fig. 7.

The moments of inertia given in Fig. 6 are for rotation about axes passing through the centers of mass of the objects shown. The *parallel-*

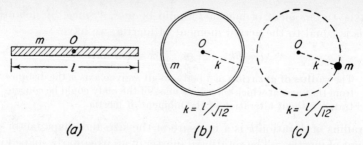

Fig. 7. The slender rod in (a) has the same moment of inertia as the ring shown in (b) and the particle in (c) provided the masses of all three are equal. The radius k is called the *radius of gyration*.

axis theorem is a useful relation which enables us to find the moment of inertia of a body about *any* axis, provided that we know the moment of inertia about the parallel axis through the center of mass:

PARALLEL-AXIS THEOREM: *The moment of inertia of a body about any axis is equal to its moment of inertia about a parallel axis through the center of mass plus the product of the mass of the body by the square of the perpendicular distance between the two axes.*

Let us prove this theorem by making use of Fig. 8. We wish to calculate the moment of inertia of a body of arbitrary shape about an axis

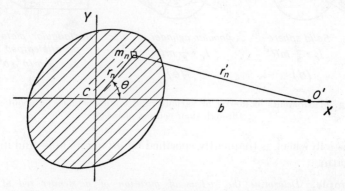

Fig. 8. The moment of inertia I' about the axis of rotation O' is given by
$$I' = I_C + mb^2.$$

perpendicular to the plane of the figure and passing through O'. We have taken the origin C of our coordinate system at the center of mass of the body. Consider a particle of mass m_n. The distance of this particle from axis O' is r'_n and hence the moment of inertia I'_n of this particle about axis O' is

$$I'_n = m_n r'^2_n.$$

By the law of cosines, $r_n'^2 = r_n^2 + b^2 - 2br_n \cos\theta$.

Furthermore, $r_n \cos\theta = X_n$.

where X_n is the X-coordinate of the typical particle. Hence,

$$I_n' = m_n r_n^2 + m_n b^2 - 2m_n b X_n.$$

Since the moment of inertia I' of the body about axis O' is given by

$$I' = \Sigma \, I_n',$$

we have $\qquad I' = \Sigma \, m_n r_n^2 + b^2 \, \Sigma \, m_n - 2b \, \Sigma \, m_n X_n.$

The first term, $\Sigma \, m_n r_n^2$, is simply I_c, the moment of inertia of the body about an axis perpendicular to the plane of the diagram and passing through C, the center of mass. In the second term, $\Sigma \, m_n = m$, the total mass of the body. The third term is zero, since, by definition of the center of mass, $(\Sigma \, m_n X_n)/m$ is the X-coordinate of the center of mass, which is zero in Fig. 8 [see equation (10a), p. 165]. Therefore, $\Sigma \, m_n X_n = 0$. Hence,

$$I' = I_c + mb^2, \tag{18}$$

where I_c is the moment of inertia of the body about the parallel axis through the center of mass, m is the mass of the body, and b is the perpendicular distance of the axis through O' from the axis through C. Thus, *the parallel-axis theorem* is proved.

Example. *Determine the moment of inertia of the solid cylinder of Fig. 6(b) about an axis parallel to that shown, but passing through the periphery of the cylinder.*

Substitute $I_c = \frac{1}{2} mR^2$, $b = R$, in (18) to obtain $I' = \frac{3}{2} mR^2$.

Example. *Determine the moment of inertia of the rod of Fig. 6(a) about a transverse axis at one end of the rod.*

Substitute $I_c = \frac{1}{12} ml^2$, $b = \frac{1}{2} l$, in (18) to obtain

$$I' = \frac{1}{12} ml^2 + \frac{1}{4} ml^2 = \frac{1}{3} ml^2.$$

It must be emphasized that (18) holds only when I_c is the moment of inertia about an axis *through the center of mass*, since we have used the 'balancing' property of the center of mass explicitly in the derivation.

5. APPLICATION OF THE PRINCIPLE OF CONSERVATION OF ENERGY

THE PRINCIPLE of conservation of energy is very useful in solving problems involving rotational motion. We shall illustrate its use in the following examples:

Example. *Consider the frictionless arrangement shown in Fig. 9, in which a weight, suspended from a cord wrapped around a hub, is released and allowed to descend, thereby setting a large wheel into rotation about a fixed axis O. Determine the linear velocity v of the suspended body and the angular velocity ω of the wheel after the suspended body has descended a distance h.*

We note that the final kinetic energy of the system will be equal to the decrease in the potential energy of the weight:

$$\tfrac{1}{2}\,I\omega^2 + \tfrac{1}{2}\,m_1 v^2 = wh.$$

In evaluating the final kinetic energy, it is convenient to use the relation $v = r\omega$ between the downward linear velocity v of the weight, the angular velocity ω of the wheel, and the radius r of the hub. Substituting this value for v, we obtain

$$\tfrac{1}{2}\,m_2 k^2\omega^2 + \tfrac{1}{2}\,m_1 r^2\omega^2 = wh.$$

This gives

$$\omega^2 = \frac{2wh}{m_2 k^2 + m_1 r^2},$$

from which ω and $v = r\omega$ can be computed.

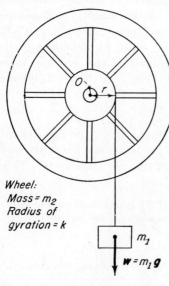

Wheel:
Mass = m_2
Radius of
gyration = k

m_1

$w = m_1 g$

Figure 9

Example. *If $w = 16.1$ lb, $r = 4$ in, $m_2 = 2$ slugs, and $k = 15$ in in Fig. 9, what angular and linear velocities are acquired when the weight falls from rest through $h = 6$ ft?*

By substitution of the values $w = 16.1$ lb, $h = 6$ ft, $m_2 = 2$ slugs, $k = \tfrac{5}{4}$ ft, $m_1 = \tfrac{1}{2}$ slug, and $r = \tfrac{1}{3}$ ft in the last equation of the preceding example, we obtain

$$\omega^2 = \frac{2 \times 16.1 \text{ lb·6 ft}}{2 \text{ slug·}2\tfrac{5}{16} \text{ ft}^2 + \tfrac{1}{2} \text{ slug·}\tfrac{1}{9} \text{ ft}^2}$$

$$= 60.7\,\frac{\text{lb}}{\text{slug·ft}}.$$

To interpret this last expression, we remember that $1 \text{ lb} = 1 \text{ slug·ft/sec}^2$, in accordance with Newton's second principle. If we make this substitution we find $\omega^2 = 60.7/\text{sec}^2$, which we can write more intelligibly as $60.7 \text{ rad}^2/\text{sec}^2$, since the radian is a dimensionless unit. The square root of this value gives

$$\omega = 7.79 \text{ rad/sec.}$$

The final downward velocity of the weight is therefore

$$v = r\omega = \tfrac{1}{3} \text{ ft·}7.79 \text{ rad/sec} = 2.60 \text{ ft/sec.}$$

6. DYNAMICS OF PURE ROTATION

IN BEGINNING our discussion of the dynamics of rotational motion, let us recall that in Chap. 1 we introduced *torque L* as the measure of the tendency of force to produce changes in rotational motion. When a body undergoes a change in rotational motion, it experiences an angular acceleration. We should like to find a relation between torque L and angular acceleration α that is analogous to the Newtonian relation $F = ma$, which governs translational motion.

We may *derive* a relation between L and α by applying Newton's laws to a simple example of rotational motion such as that given in Fig. 10, which shows a particle of mass m that is constrained to move in a circular path of radius R about an axis through O. We might approximate this situation by attaching a small steel ball of mass m to one end of a slender wooden rod of negligible mass and attaching the other end of the wooden rod to a bearing that is free to rotate about a vertical axis so that the ball moves in a horizontal circle. Or, m might be a particle resting on a frictionless horizontal table and attached by a string of length R to a point O on the table. Now let us apply a tangential force of magnitude F_T to the particle of mass m. The particle will then experience a tangential acceleration of magnitude a_T given by Newton's second principle,

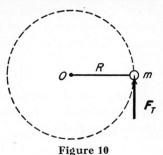

Figure 10

$$F_T = ma_T,$$

since F_T is the only force component tangent to the circle.

By use of equation (10a) we may write

$$F_T = mR\alpha, \tag{19}$$

where α is the angular acceleration of the particle about the axis through O in rad/sec². This equation states that α is proportional to the magnitude of the tangential force. The moment L of this force about the axis through O is $F_T R$. Hence, by multiplying both sides of (13) by R, we obtain

$$L = [mR^2]\,\alpha = I\alpha, \tag{20}$$

which gives us our desired relationship between L and α for this simple case.

We note immediately the similarity between equation (20), $L = I\alpha$, and the equation $F = ma$ for Newton's second principle. The role of *torque* L in rotational motion is analogous to the role of *force* F in translational motion; the role of angular acceleration α is analogous to that of linear acceleration a; and the role of moment of inertia I is analogous to that of mass m.

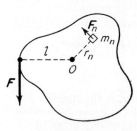

Figure 11

Now let us consider a rigid body of any shape mounted so that it can rotate about an axis through O as in Fig. 11. The body can be considered as divided up into small pieces, of which the nth typical piece, of mass m_n, is shown in the figure. If the rigid body is to have angular acceleration α, this typical piece must have acting on it a resultant tangential force given by (19) as $F_n = m_n r_n \alpha$, corresponding to a torque about O of $L_n = [m_n r_n^2]\,\alpha$. The torque required to cause the angular acceleration must be supplied by some external force F, with lever arm l, giving torque $L = Fl$. We shall show from the principle of conservation of energy that *the total external torque needed to give the rigid body the angular acceleration α is just the sum over the pieces of the body of the torques $L_n = [m_n r_n^2]\,\alpha$.* Thus,

$$L = \Sigma\, L_n = \Sigma\, [m_n r_n^2]\, \alpha = I\alpha. \tag{21}$$

A rigorous demonstration of (21) can be obtained by equating the power furnished by the torque L to the rate of change of kinetic energy of the rotating body:

$$P = (d/dt)(\text{K.E.}).$$

Substitution of (13) for power and (15) for kinetic energy gives

$$L\omega = (d/dt)(\tfrac{1}{2}\, I\omega^2)$$
$$= I\omega\, d\omega/dt = I\omega\alpha$$

or $\qquad\qquad L = I\alpha. \qquad \left\{ \begin{array}{l} L \text{ in nt·m} \\ I \text{ in kg·m}^2 \\ \alpha \text{ in rad/sec}^2 \end{array} \right\}$ or $\left\{ \begin{array}{l} L \text{ in lb·ft} \\ I \text{ in slug·ft}^2 \\ \alpha \text{ in rad/sec}^2 \end{array} \right\}$ (22)

If more than one force acts on the rotating body, it is easily seen that L in (22) should be the *resultant* torque. This equation, $L = I\alpha$, is the rotational analogue of Newton's second principle, $F = ma$.

Example. *Go back to Fig. 9 and the example on pp. 207–208 and derive the expression for the angular velocity of the wheel after the suspended body has fallen a distance h from the dynamical equations $L = I\alpha$ and $F = ma$.*

We note that the resultant downward force on the suspended body is $(w - T)$, where T is the tension in the cord, and that the resultant clockwise torque acting on the wheel is $L = Tr$. If a is the linear acceleration of the suspended body, we may write the equation of motion as

$$w - T = m_1 a \qquad \text{or} \qquad w - T = m_1 r\alpha, \tag{i}$$

since the acceleration a equals the tangential acceleration of a point on the wheel at radius r, which, by (10a), is $r\alpha$. For the wheel,

$$L = I\alpha \qquad \text{or} \qquad Tr = I\alpha = m_2 k^2 \alpha. \tag{ii}$$

Elimination of T from the equations on the right in (i) and (ii) gives

$$\alpha = \frac{wr}{m_1 r^2 + m_2 k^2}.$$

While the weight falls a distance h, the wheel turns through the angle $\theta = h/r$. Equation (7) shows that a wheel starting from rest, having angular acceleration α, and turning through angle θ acquires angular velocity given by

$$\omega^2 = 2\alpha\theta = 2\,\frac{wr}{m_1 r^2 + m_2 k^2}\,\frac{h}{r} = \frac{2wh}{m_1 r^2 + m_2 k^2}.$$

This is the same result that we derived earlier, and somewhat more simply, from the principle of conservation of energy.

We can now discuss further the close analogy between the physical quantities and relations involved in rotational motion about a fixed axis and those involved in translational motion along a straight line.   Table I

TABLE I

QUANTITIES AND RELATIONS USED IN DESCRIBING RECTILINEAR MOTION
AND THEIR ROTATIONAL ANALOGUES

Quantity or relation	Rectilinear motion	Rotational motion
Displacement..........	S (linear)	θ (angular)
Velocity..............	$v = dS/dt$ (linear)	$\omega = d\theta/dt$ (angular)
Acceleration..........	$a = dv/dt$ (linear)	$\alpha = d\omega/dt$ (angular)
Inertia...............	m (mass)	I (moment of inertia)
Force, torque.........	F (force)	L (torque)
Newton's principle.....	$F = ma$	$L = I\alpha$
Element of work.......	$F\,dS$	$L\,d\theta$
Kinetic energy.........	$\frac{1}{2}\,mv^2$	$\frac{1}{2}\,I\omega^2$
Power.................	Fv	$L\omega$
Momentum............	mv (linear)	$I\omega$ (angular)
Impulse..............	$\overline{F}\,\Delta t$ (linear)	$\overline{L}\,\Delta t$ (angular)

gives a summary of the more important analogies.   Study of this table should prove useful.   The last two angular quantities in this table will be introduced in the next chapter.

PROBLEMS

1. What angular displacement in radians is experienced by the minute hand of a clock during a 15-min interval?   What is the angular displacement of the hour hand during this interval?   Ans: $\frac{1}{2}\pi$ rad, $\frac{1}{24}\pi$ rad, clockwise.

2. What angular displacement is experienced by the second hand of a watch during 1 hr?   What are the angular velocities, in revolutions per hour, in revolutions per minute, and in radians per second, of the second hand, the minute hand, and the hour hand of a watch?

3. A grinding wheel is mounted on the shaft of a motor that makes 1800 rev/min when turning at full speed.   The wheel attains full speed 15 sec after the switch is closed.   What is the magnitude of the average angular acceleration experienced by the wheel?   Assuming constant acceleration, find the magnitude of the average angular velocity and the angular displacement of the wheel during this 15-sec interval.   Ans: 4π rad/sec², 30π rad/sec, 450π rad.

4. If the switch is turned off after the wheel in Prob. 3 has attained full speed, the wheel comes to rest after 3 min.   Find the magnitude of the average angular deceleration of the wheel.   Assuming constant deceleration, find the magnitude of the average angular velocity of the wheel and the angular displacement experienced during this 3-min interval.

5. A flywheel initially at rest experiences constant angular acceleration.   In 9 sec this flywheel is observed to turn through an angle of 450 radians.   What is the average angular velocity of the wheel?   What is the final angular velocity of the wheel?   What is the angular acceleration of the wheel?

Ans: 50 rad/sec; 100 rad/sec; 11.1 rad/sec².

6. Starting from rest and experiencing constant angular acceleration, a flywheel makes 4000 revolutions in $1\frac{1}{2}$ min. Find its angular acceleration.

7. A flywheel experiencing constant angular acceleration makes 10 rev in 4 sec. If the angular velocity of the wheel at the end of this 4-sec interval is 20 rad/sec, find the initial angular velocity and the angular acceleration of the wheel.   Ans: 11.4 rad/sec; 2.15 rad/sec².

8. A flywheel experiencing constant angular acceleration makes 12 rev counterclockwise in 5 sec. If the angular velocity of the wheel at the beginning of this 5-sec interval is 4 rad/sec clockwise, find the angular acceleration and the final angular velocity of the wheel.

9. At what times between noon and 1 p.m. is the angle between the minute hand and the hour hand of a clock equal to 1 radian? Ans: 12:10.4 and 12:55.0.

10. At what times between six and seven o'clock is the angle between the minute hand and the hour hand of a clock equal to 1 rad?

11. A grinding wheel 12 inches in diameter is mounted on the shaft of a motor, which makes 1800 rev/min. Find the magnitude of the velocity of a point on the rim of the wheel.   Ans: $30\,\pi$ ft/sec.

12. A flywheel 5 ft in diameter is rotating at a speed of 450 rev/min. Find the magnitude of the velocity of a point on the rim of the flywheel.

13. Find the centripetal acceleration of a point on the rim of the grinding wheel in Prob. 11. Express this acceleration in terms of g_0, the standard gravitational acceleration.   Ans: 17,800 ft/sec²; 552 g_0.

14. Find the centripetal acceleration in ft/sec² of a point on the rim of the flywheel mentioned in Prob. 12. Express this in terms of g_0, the standard gravitational acceleration.

15. A flywheel 4 ft in diameter experiences an angular acceleration of 5 rad/sec². Find the tangential acceleration of a point on the rim of this flywheel.   Ans: 10 ft/sec².

16. A grinding wheel 10 inches in diameter experiences an angular acceleration of 3 rad/sec². Find the tangential acceleration of a point on the rim of the wheel.

17. In an arrangement similar to that shown in Fig. 12, the weight w has a constant downward acceleration of 1.5 ft/sec² and the radius of the cylinder is 2 ft. If the weight starts from rest, find the tangential velocity and acceleration of a point such as P ten seconds after motion has begun. What is the angular acceleration of the cylinder at this time? the angular velocity? the radial acceleration of point P?   Ans: 15 ft/sec; 1.5 ft/sec²; 0.75 rad/sec²; 7.5 rad/sec; 112.5 ft/sec².

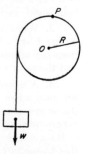

Figure 12

18. Referring to Prob. 17, find the tangential velocity and the tangential and radial components of the acceleration of point P at 2, 4, and 6 sec after motion has started. What can be concluded concerning the time variations of the radial and tangential components of the acceleration of points on the rim?

19. A particle of mass 2 kg rests without slipping on a horizontal turntable at a distance of 40 cm from the vertical axis of rotation. Draw a diagram showing the magnitudes and directions of all forces acting on the particle when the turntable is rotating at 4 rad/sec and accelerating at 3 rad/sec². What is the magnitude of the force of friction and the angle it makes with the radius?   Ans: 13.0 nt; 10°.6.

20. A string is wound around the rim of a cylindrical grindstone of mass 2 slugs. By pulling on the end of the string, a man exerts a constant tangential force of 3 lb. If the radius of the grindstone is 8 in, find the magnitude of the torque applied to the grindstone. If its bearings are frictionless, find the magnitude of the angular acceleration of the grindstone and its angular velocity 6 sec after it starts from rest.

21. A resultant torque of 6 nt·m applied to a 5-kg wheel gives the wheel an angular acceleration of 2 rad/sec². Find the moment of inertia of the wheel and its radius of gyration. Ans: 3 kg·m²; 77.5 cm.

22. In Prob. 21, what are the values of ω and θ at time t after the wheel starts from rest? Show that the work done by the torque during this time t equals the increase in kinetic energy of the wheel.

23. What torque must be applied to a 2-slug solid cylinder 18 inches in diameter in order to produce an angular acceleration of 3 rad/sec² about its own axis? about an axis parallel to the axis of the cylinder but passing through the rim of the cylinder? Ans: 1.69 lb·ft; 5.06 lb·ft.

24. Answer the questions in Prob. 23 for a sphere of the same mass and diameter as the cylinder.

25. In the arrangement shown in Fig. 12, the mass of the cylinder is 12 kg. the radius of the cylinder is 50 cm, and the suspended body weighs 9.81 nt, Find the downward acceleration of the body, the angular acceleration of the cylinder, and the tension in the string.
Ans: 1.40 m/sec²; 2.80 rad/sec²; 8.40 nt.

26. Solve Prob. 25 for a case in which the mass of the suspended body is 2.5 kg.

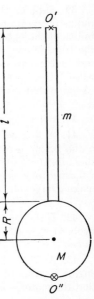

27. A clock pendulum consists of a long slender rod of mass m and length l and a flat disk of mass M and radius R as shown in Fig. 13. Show that the moment of inertia of this pendulum about an axis through O' is given by the expression $I' = \frac{1}{3} ml^2 + \frac{3}{2} MR^2 + 2MlR + Ml^2$.

28. Find an expression for the moment of inertia of the pendulum in Prob. 27 when the disk is replaced by a sphere of radius R and mass M. What would be the moment of inertia of this pendulum about an axis through O''?

29. A 10-lb weight is joined to a 5-lb weight by a string that passes over a pulley weighing 3 lb. The pulley is in the shape of a solid cylinder of 3-in radius. If there is no friction at the bearings and no slipping of the string on the cylinder, find the acceleration of the masses and the tensions in the two parts of the string.
Ans: 9.76 ft/sec²; 6.97, 6.52 lb.

Figure 13

30. A 10-kg mass is joined to a 5-kg mass by a string that passes over a pulley of mass 7 kg, radius 14 cm, and radius of gyration 11 cm. If there is no friction at the bearings and no slipping of the string, find the acceleration of the masses and the tensions in the two parts of the string.

31. A cylindrical grinding wheel that weighs 32.2 lb is rotating at an angular velocity of 80 rad/sec. The diameter of the wheel is 18 inches. What is the kinetic energy of this wheel? Ans: 900 ft·lb.

32. In Fig. 4, compute the angular acceleration of the wheel from $L = I\alpha$, and from this, the angular velocity of the wheel after the force has acted through distance S, if the wheel starts from vest.   Verify that the kinetic energy of the wheel equals the work done by the force.

33. A 2-slug flywheel has a radius of gyration of 18 in.   What is the angular velocity of this flywheel when its rotational kinetic energy is equal to that of a shell weighing 4 lb and moving at a velocity of 1000 ft/sec?   Ans: 166 rad/sec.

34. What angular velocity does the flywheel in Prob. 33 have when its kinetic energy is equal to that of a 2-ton automobile moving at a speed of 30 mi/hr?

35. A solid cylinder similar to that shown in Fig. 4 is set in motion by the method shown in the figure.   The weight of this cylinder is 16.1 lb and its radius is 6 in.   If the force acting on the cord is 20 lb, find the angular velocity of the cylinder when the cord has experienced a 10-ft displacement.   Ans: 80 rad/sec.

36. Find the angular velocity of the cylinder described in Prob. 35 when a cord exerting a force of 15 lb undergoes a 5-ft displacement.

37. A man shuts off the motor operating the grinding wheel mentioned in Prob. 31 and the wheel comes to rest after making 300 revolutions.   What torque (assumed constant) is exerted by the frictional forces acting on the wheel?
Ans: 0.478 lb·ft.

38. What constant total frictional torque must be applied to the wheels of an automobile traveling at 60 mi/hr in order to bring it to rest in 150 ft?   The tires are 22 inches in outside diameter.

39. Suppose that the mass of the wheel shown in Fig. 9 is 12 kg and that its radius of gyration is 120 cm.   The mass of the suspended body is 3 kg and the radius of the hub is 40 cm.   Find the rotational kinetic energy of the wheel and the translational kinetic energy of the suspended body if the body starts from rest and moves down a distance of 5 m.   What is the angular velocity of the wheel? the linear velocity of the suspended body? the tension in the cord? (Assume that friction is negligible.)
Ans: 143 joules, 3.97 joules; 4.07 rad/sec; 1.63 m/sec; 28.6 nt.

40. Solve Prob. 39 for a case in which the mass of the suspended body is 15 kg.

41. A flywheel of mass 12 kg and radius of gyration 1.2 m, with a hub of radius 0.4 m, is rotating at a speed of 15 rev/sec when a brake shoe is applied to the hub, the coefficient of friction between shoe and hub being 0.3.   How large a normal force is exerted on the hub by the shoe if the wheel comes to rest after making 50 revolutions?   What becomes of the initial kinetic energy of the wheel?
Ans: 2,040 nt.

42. If the force applied by the brake shoe to the hub of the wheel described in Prob. 41 were 100 nt, how many revolutions would the wheel make before coming to rest?

43. A Prony brake is a water-cooled brake used for loading a motor or an engine in tests of its power output.   The brake is so arranged that the torque that the motor is exerting on the brake can be measured by means of a lever arm and a scale.

(a) Draw a sketch showing a suitable arrangement for making this torque measurement.

(b) The torque exerted by an electric motor turning at 2000 rev/min is measured as 60 lb·ft.   What horsepower is being delivered by the motor?

(c) The electrical input to this motor is measured by electrical instruments as 19.2 kw.   What is the efficiency of the motor?   Ans: (b) 22.8 hp; (c) 88.5%.

44. A rope brake is used to load a motor in a test of its power output.   The motor is equipped with a flanged water-cooled pulley, and 1½ turns of rope are taken around the pulley.   The two ends of the rope are brought vertically down to the floor where they are attached to spring balances.   A suitable arrangement is provided to tighten the rope in order to load the motor.

(a) Draw a sketch of this arrangement.

(b) If the centers of the two vertical ropes are 18 inches apart and the tensions are 125 and 325 lb when the motor is turning at 480 rev/min, what horsepower is being delivered by the motor?

(c) If the electrical input to the motor is measured by electrical instruments as 12.2 kw, what is the efficiency of the motor?

45. A flywheel whose moment of inertia is 150 kg·m² will come to rest in 300 sec from an angular velocity of 600 rev/min owing to the constant frictional torque of the bearings.   How much power must be expended against this frictional torque to maintain the speed at 600 rev/min?   Ans: 1.97 kw.

46. If the frictional torque on the wheel of a gyroscope (moment of inertia 2200 g·cm²) is so small that it requires a power of only 9 milliwatts to keep it running at 6000 rev/min, how long will the wheel run before coming to rest after the supply of power is cut off, the frictional torque being assumed constant?

47. In the example on pp. 191–192, what is the maximum horsepower that can be transmitted when the drive shaft is turning at 3000 rev/min if the elastic limit is not to be exceeded?

48. Compute the torque transmitted by the drive shaft of an automobile engine when the power output is 70 hp and the drive shaft is turning at 2500 rev/min.

49. A uniform rod of length 3 ft, weighing 7 lb, is free to rotate in a vertical plane about a fixed horizontal axis at one end.   If the rod is released from rest when it is standing straight up from the pivot, what is its angular velocity when it passes through the straight-down position? when it is horizontal?

Ans: 8.02 rad/sec; 5.67 rad/sec.

50. When the rod of Prob. 49 hangs straight down at rest, it is struck a blow that gives the lower end an initial horizontal velocity of 18 ft/sec.   How high does the rod swing before coming to rest?

51. A flywheel rotating freely on a horizontal shaft is lopsided, its center of mass being 5 mm from the axis of rotation.   The flywheel has 10 kg mass and 6 cm radius of gyration (relative to the axis of rotation).   If friction is neglected, and the speed of the flywheel is 20 rad/sec when the center of mass is directly above the axis, what is the speed when the center of mass is directly below the axis?   Ans: 21.3 rad/sec.

52. A trapeze artist is swinging in a vertical circle on a rigid trapeze.   If his angular velocity is 2 rad/sec at the top of the swing, what is his angular velocity at the bottom of the swing?   Take the center of mass as 12 ft from the axis of rotation, and the radius of gyration as 13 ft.

53. A 12-slug wheel is rotating at constant angular velocity of 180 rev/min about a fixed vertical axis.   Its radius of gyration about this axis is 2 ft.   The rim of the wheel is slightly thicker on one side than the other so that the center of mass of the wheel and axle is 1 in from the axis of rotation.   Determine the magnitude and direction of the horizontal force that must be exerted by the bearings.   Ans: 355 lb.

54. In Prob. 51, determine the vertical force exerted by the bearings in each of the two positions of the wheel mentioned in the last sentence.

CHAPTER 10

MECHANICS OF RIGID BODIES

IN THIS CHAPTER, we shall first consider a type of motion of rigid bodies that involves both translation and rotation, called *two-dimensional motion*. In this type of motion, the axis of rotation has a fixed direction but not necessarily a fixed position in space. One of the important applications is to the case of rolling wheels.

Angular momentum and *angular impulse* will then be defined, and the *principle of conservation of angular momentum* stated.

A brief discussion of *gyroscopic motion*, a type of rotational motion in which the axis of rotation does not have a fixed direction in space, will conclude the chapter.

1. TWO-DIMENSIONAL MOTION

WE SHALL NOW consider the two-dimensional motion of a rigid body that is not constrained to rotate about a *fixed* axis. The kinematical and dynamical description of this important type of motion is not difficult.

> In **two-dimensional motion,** each particle of the body moves in a plane, parallel to the XY-plane of Fig. 1, for example. Each particle has X- and Y-components of velocity but no Z component.

A rolling wheel meets this requirement; so does a disc thrown into the air and spinning about its axis like the familiar 'yo-yo'; so does a rigid body sliding on a plane surface.

The motion can be described as a translation of the center of mass C plus a rotation about an axis through the center of mass and perpendicular to the XY-plane, as indicated in Fig. 1. If the center of mass has coordinates X_C, Y_C, which are functions of time, the translational velocity has components

$$v_X = dX_C/dt, \qquad v_Y = dY_C/dt,$$

while the translational acceleration has components

$$a_X = dv_X/dt, \qquad a_Y = dv_Y/dt.$$

216

A line that is painted on the body, such as CA in Fig. 1, makes an angle θ with the X-direction.   The angle θ will in general vary with time.   The angular velocity of the body as a function of time is defined by

$$\omega = d\theta/dt,$$

while the angular acceleration is defined by

$$\alpha = d\omega/dt.$$

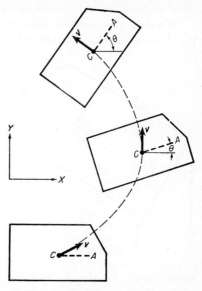

These definitions of ω and α are simple generalizations of those given earlier for the case of pure rotation.

Specification of $X(t)$, $Y(t)$, and $\theta(t)$ makes possible a complete kinematical description of the translational and rotational motion in this case.

The *dynamical* behavior of bodies in two-dimensional motion is determined by two laws that are derived directly from Newton's principles. The first, which governs the translational motion (even in the case of three-dimensional motion) is the law stated on p. 167:

Fig. 1. Two-dimensional motion. C is the center of mass; the line CA is painted on the body.

> *The resultant of all the forces acting equals the mass times the acceleration of the center of mass.*

The second law governs the rotational motion about the center of mass. This law, which is a generalization of the formula $L = I\alpha$ to the case where the center of mass is moving, is proved in more advanced texts:

> *In two-dimensional motion, the resultant torque about the center of mass equals the moment of inertia about an axis through the center of mass times the angular acceleration.*

In applying these laws, we must use one of the systems of units, already described, in terms of which the equations $F = ma$ and $L = I\alpha$ are valid.

One of the simplest applications of these dynamical laws is to the case of a shape such as that of Fig. 1 cut out of a body and thrown into the air with the initial velocity of its center of mass in the XY-plane and its initial angular velocity about an axis perpendicular to the XY-plane. (Or we might imagine similarly throwing a wheel, a disc, or a hoop into the air.)   Air resistance neglected, the only external force acting is the force of gravity; hence the center of mass moves in a parabola like a projected particle.   Since the forces of gravity have no net torque about the center of mass, which is the point at which the body would balance, there is no angular acceleration and the body continues to rotate at constant angular velocity equal to its initial angular velocity.

We shall now consider the energy of a body in two-dimensional motion. By the relation that we derived on p. 118, the *potential energy* of the body is the same as that of a particle located at a center of mass and containing all the mass of the body. In order to compute the *kinetic energy* of the body we shall have to consider in more detail the motion of the individual particles of the body.

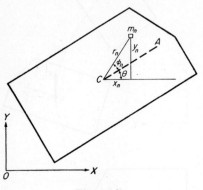

Figure 2

Consider a representative particle of the body of Fig. 1. As indicated in Fig. 2, let this particle have mass m_n and be at fixed distance r_n from the center of mass C, where the radius r_n makes fixed angle ϕ_n with the line CA. At the particular instant shown, let the X- and Y-coordinates of the particle relative to the center of mass C, be x_n, y_n. The X- and Y-coordinates of the particle relative to the fixed origin of coordinates O will then be

$$X_n = X_C + x_n = X_C + r_n \cos(\theta + \phi_n),$$
$$Y_n = Y_C + y_n = Y_C + r_n \sin(\theta + \phi_n).$$

The components of the velocity of the particle will be obtained by differentiating X_n and Y_n with respect to time. In this differentiation, the only terms on the right that change with time are X_C, Y_C, and θ, where $dX_C/dt = v_X$, $dY_C/dt = v_Y$, $d\theta/dt = \omega$. Hence we obtain

$$dX_n/dt = v_X - r_n \sin(\theta + \phi_n)\ \omega = v_X - y_n\omega,$$
$$dY_n/dt = v_Y + r_n \cos(\theta + \phi_n)\ \omega = v_Y + x_n\omega.$$

The kinetic energy of the particle is $\frac{1}{2}\ m_n$ times the sum of the squares of these velocity components, and the kinetic energy of the whole body is obtained by summing over the particles:

$$\text{K.E.} = \Sigma\ \tfrac{1}{2}\ m_n\ [(dX_n/dt)^2 + (dY_n/dt)^2]$$
$$= \Sigma\ \tfrac{1}{2}\ m_n(v_X^2 + v_Y^2) + \Sigma\ \tfrac{1}{2}\ m_n(x_n^2 + y_n^2)\omega^2 - \Sigma\ m_n v_X y_n\omega + \Sigma\ m_n v_Y x_n\omega.$$

The first term in the last line is just $\frac{1}{2}\ mv^2$, where m is the total mass of the body and v is the speed of the center of mass. The second term is $\frac{1}{2}\ \omega^2\ \Sigma\ m_n r_n^2 = \frac{1}{2}\ I_C\ \omega^2$, where I_C is the moment of inertia about the center of mass. The fourth term can be written as $v_Y\omega\ \Sigma\ m_n x_n$, where the summation is seen to vanish because of the balancing property of the center of mass; similarly the third term vanishes.   Thus

$$\text{K.E.} = \tfrac{1}{2}\,mv^2 + \tfrac{1}{2}\,I_c\,\omega^2. \tag{1}$$

The first term is called the *translational kinetic energy*, the second the *rotational kinetic energy*.

> *The kinetic energy of a body in two-dimensional motion equals the kinetic energy of a particle containing the whole mass and moving with the center of mass plus the rotational kinetic energy computed as if the body were in pure rotation about the center of mass.*

2. ROLLING BODIES

ONE OF THE interesting cases of two-dimensional motion is that of bodies that roll on a surface without slipping.   We shall confine our attention to the rolling of circular bodies such as wheels, cylinders, and spheres, in which the center of mass is at the center of the circle.

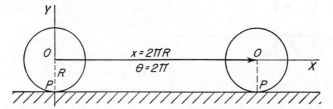

Fig. 3. When the rolling wheel turns through an angle of 2π rad, the center O experiences a displacement $2\pi R$ in the X-direction.

The condition that the body roll without slipping imposes a definite kinematical relationship between the linear motion and the angular motion of the body.   Figure 3 shows a cross section of a wheel rolling along a surface (not necessarily horizontal).   Let the initial position of the axis through the center O pass through the origin of the coordinate system as shown.   If the wheel rotates in a clockwise direction until one complete clockwise rotation has taken place, the center experiences a displacement $2\pi R$ in the positive X-direction; that is, the wheel must make one complete revolution in the time that its center advances a distance equal to the circumference of the wheel.   Thus, when the clockwise angular displacement θ is 2π, the linear displacement of the center in the X-direction is $2\pi R$.   Hence, for the rolling wheel, we see that

$$X = R\theta. \tag{2}$$

Taking the derivative of both sides of this equation with respect to time, we obtain

$$dX/dt = R\,d\theta/dt, \quad \text{or} \quad v = R\omega, \tag{3}$$

where v is the X-component of the velocity of the center of the wheel and

ω is the angular velocity. Taking the time derivative of both sides of (3), we obtain

$$dv/dt = R\, d\omega/dt \quad \text{or} \quad a = R\alpha \qquad (4)$$

where a is the X-component of the acceleration of the center and α is the angular acceleration. Note that θ, ω, and α are *positive in a clockwise sense* in these equations, rather than in the usual counterclockwise sense. This change of convention is useful for problems of rolling bodies.

The application of the dynamical laws for two-dimensional motion to the case of rolling bodies will be illustrated by the following examples.

Example. *Find the translational acceleration that results when a force F acts through the center of mass of the solid cylinder of radius R shown in Fig. 4, and find the force of friction $\mathfrak{F}$.*

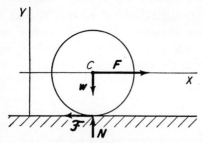

Fig. 4. A solid cylinder that rolls without slipping. The resultant of F and $\mathfrak{F}$ causes a linear acceleration of the center of mass C. The moment of the frictional force $\mathfrak{F}$, about C, causes an angular acceleration.

We first note that $w = N$, since the center of mass has no acceleration in the Y-direction. The equation of motion of the center of mass in the X-direction is

$$F - \mathfrak{F} = ma; \qquad (i)$$

the clockwise torque about the center determines the angular acceleration:

$$\mathfrak{F}R = I_C\, \alpha, \qquad (ii)$$

where I_C is the moment of inertia about the center of mass. Remembering that $I_C = \tfrac{1}{2}\, mR^2$ for a solid cylinder, and that $\alpha = a/R$, we may rewrite (ii) in the form

$$\mathfrak{F}R = (\tfrac{1}{2}\, mR^2)(a/R), \quad \text{or} \quad \mathfrak{F} = \tfrac{1}{2}\, ma.$$

Adding this equation to (i) and solving the resulting equation for a, we obtain

$$a = \tfrac{2}{3}\, F/m.$$

The rolling cylinder accelerates two-thirds as fast as a particle having the same applied force. The angular acceleration is

$$\alpha = a/R = \tfrac{2}{3}\, F/mR.$$

The force of friction is $\qquad \mathfrak{F} = \tfrac{1}{2}\, ma = \tfrac{1}{3}\, F.$

Example. *Using the results of the previous example show that if the cylinder starts from rest and moves a distance S to the right, the work done by F equals the increase in kinetic energy.*

We note that no work is done against the force of friction $\mathfrak{F}$ since there is no sliding—no relative motion of the surfaces. $\mathfrak{F}$ is of the nature of a force of static friction.*

---

* In the ideal case of a rolling body, no energy is lost because of friction. In the real case, some energy is lost—a wheel rolling on a horizontal surface will gradually slow up, but much less rapidly than a sliding body—because there is some *distortion* of the surfaces; the contact is not a pure line contact and the force system is not precisely as we have described it. By observation of the deceleration of a body rolling

The work done by F is $\qquad W = FS.$

The translational velocity acquired is given by $v^2 = 2aS = \frac{4}{3} FS/m$; hence the translational kinetic energy is

$$\text{K.E.}_T = \tfrac{1}{2} mv^2 = \tfrac{2}{3} FS.$$

By (3), $\omega = v/R$; hence $\omega^2 = v^2/R^2 = \frac{4}{3} FS/mR^2.$ The rotational kinetic energy is thus

$$\text{K.E.}_R = \tfrac{1}{2} I_C \,\omega^2 = \tfrac{1}{2} (\tfrac{1}{2} mR^2)(\tfrac{4}{3} FS/mR^2) = \tfrac{1}{3} FS.$$

The total kinetic energy

$$\text{K.E.} = \text{K.E.}_T + \text{K.E.}_R = FS = W,$$

as was to be shown.

Example. *Consider a solid cylinder that starts from rest and rolls without slipping down the inclined plane of Fig. 5. Determine the acceleration of the center, the force of friction, the minimum coefficient of static friction, and the velocity at the bottom of the plane.*

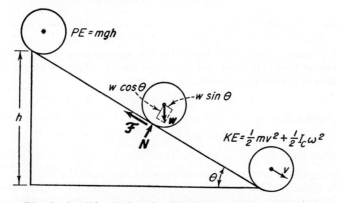

Fig. 5. A solid cylinder of radius R rolls without slipping.

The forces acting on the cylinder will be the force $w = mg$ of gravity, the normal reaction N of the plane, and whatever frictional force $\mathfrak{F}$ is required to prevent slipping. The forces normal to the plane will balance, since there is no acceleration of the center of mass in this direction. Therefore

$$N = mg \cos\theta. \tag{i}$$

The net force down the plane will produce an acceleration a of the center of mass:

$$mg \sin\theta - \mathfrak{F} = ma. \tag{ii}$$

The clockwise torque about the center of mass will equal the moment of inertia times the clockwise angular acceleration:

$$\mathfrak{F}R = I_C\, \alpha. \tag{iii}$$

on a horizontal surface it is possible to determine the small force $\mathfrak{F}_R$ attributable to such 'rolling friction.' It is found that $\mathfrak{F}_R$ is proportional to the normal force N since by Hooke's law the distortion of the surfaces is proportional to N. Hence a 'coefficient of rolling friction' can be defined such that $\mathfrak{F}_R = \mu_R N$; this coefficient is usually much smaller than μ_K or μ_S.

As before, $\alpha = a/R$ and $I_C = \frac{1}{2} mR^2$, so (iii) gives $\mathcal{F} = \frac{1}{2} ma$. When this value is substituted in (ii), we find that

$$a = \frac{2}{3} g \sin\theta,$$

which is a constant acceleration two-thirds as great as the acceleration of a particle *sliding* down a *smooth* plane of the same inclination. We also find that

$$\mathcal{F} = \frac{1}{3} mg \sin\theta,$$

so that we need a coefficient of *static* friction of at least

$$\mathcal{F}/N = \frac{1}{3} \tan\theta$$

to prevent slipping.

We can obtain the velocity of the cylinder at the bottom from the kinematical laws of uniform acceleration. The center of mass moves a slant distance $S = h/\sin\theta$ with acceleration $a = \frac{2}{3} g \sin\theta$. It therefore acquires velocity given by

$$v^2 = 2aS = \frac{4}{3} gS \sin\theta = \frac{4}{3} gh,$$

or
$$v = 2 \sqrt{\tfrac{1}{3} gh}.$$

Example. *Compute the speed v of the solid cylinder in Fig. 5 and the previous example from considerations of conservation of energy.*

The cylinder at rest at the top of the hill has potential energy mgh. At the bottom of the hill this has been converted into translational kinetic energy $\frac{1}{2} mv^2$ plus rotational kinetic energy $\frac{1}{2} I_C \omega^2$:

$$mgh = \frac{1}{2} mv^2 + \frac{1}{2} I_C \omega^2.$$

Remembering that $I_C = \frac{1}{2} mR^2$ and $\omega = v/R$, we rewrite this equation as

$$mgh = \frac{1}{2} mv^2 + \frac{1}{4} mv^2 = \frac{3}{4} mv^2,$$

which gives the value
$$v = 2 \sqrt{\tfrac{1}{3} gh}$$

for the magnitude of the final translational velocity of the center of mass. It will be noted that the principle of conservation of energy is a powerful tool that has enabled us to solve this problem with much less work than is involved in the direct applicaton of the laws of motion in the preceding example.

Now, let us consider the instantaneous velocity of various points on a wheel rolling in the X-direction as in Fig. 3. We can regard the rolling as a combination of *translation* and *rotation about the central axis through O*. If we consider *translation only*, all points in the wheel have the same velocity v as the center; this is shown in Fig. 6(a). If we consider *rotation only*, the center is at rest, whereas point P at the top of the wheel has X-velocity $+R\omega$ and point O' at the bottom of the wheel has X-velocity $-R\omega$; these are indicated in Fig. 6(b). Combining these X-components of velocity, we have

$$\text{for point } P: \quad v_X = v + R\omega = 2v,$$
$$\text{for point } O: \quad v_X = v \qquad = v,$$
$$\text{for point } O': \quad v_X = v - R\omega = 0,$$

since $R\omega = v$. These results are shown schematically in Fig. 6(c).

We note that the point that at any instant is at the bottom of the wheel is at rest. This must be so because this point is in contact with, and not slipping on, a surface at rest. Since the wheel is a rigid body, the velocities given in Fig. 6(c) are sufficient to determine that at any instant the whole velocity pattern is one of pure rotation about the point

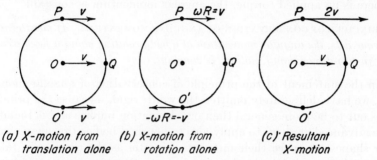

(a) X-motion from   (b) X-motion from   (c) Resultant
  translation alone   rotation alone   X-motion

Fig. 6. A rolling wheel. The combined effects of translation and rotation about an axis through O give the same result as a pure rotation with the same angular velocity about O'.

of contact with angular velocity v/R, the same as the angular velocity in the rotation about O.

3. ANGULAR MOMENTUM

THE ROTATIONAL quantity that is analogous to linear momentum $p = mv$ is called *angular momentum* and is denoted by

$$H = I\omega. \qquad (5)$$

The equation $L = I\alpha$ can be restated in terms of angular momentum. For a rigid body $dH = I\,d\omega$, and we may write

$$L = I\alpha = I\,d\omega/dt,$$

or $\qquad\qquad L = dH/dt.$ $\left\{\begin{matrix} L \text{ in m·nt} \\ H \text{ in kg·m}^2/\text{sec} \\ t \text{ in sec} \end{matrix}\right\}$ or $\left\{\begin{matrix} L \text{ in lb·ft} \\ H \text{ in slug·ft}^2/\text{sec} \\ t \text{ in sec} \end{matrix}\right\}$ (6)

We have studied two cases for which the equation $L = I\alpha$ is valid—the cases of pure rotation and of two-dimensional motion of rigid bodies. Equation (6) is valid in either of these cases. In the case of *pure rotation,* the torque in (6) and the moment of inertia in (5) must be taken *about the fixed axis of rotation;* in the case of *two-dimensional motion* these quantities must be taken *about the center of mass.* We shall assume these conventions as understood in the following statements of a definition, a law, and a principle.

> **Angular momentum** of a rigid body in pure rotation or in two-dimensioual motion is defined as moment of inertia times angular velocity.

Equation (6) states that

The time rate of change of the angular momentum of a rigid body in pure rotation or in two-dimensional motion is equal to the resultant externally applied torque.

If there is no applied torque, the angular momentum is constant:

PRINCIPLE OF CONSERVATION OF ANGULAR MOMENTUM: *If no external torque acts, the angular momentum of a body rotating about a fixed axis, or in two-dimensional motion, is constant.*

In the statement of the principle of conservation of angular momentum, we have deliberately omitted the word 'rigid,' because the principle turns out to be more general than our derivation implies and is found by more advanced analysis to apply also to nonrigid bodies that may change their shape and hence their moment of inertia as the rotation is taking place. If a rotating body changes shape so that the moment of inertia changes from I to I', the angular velocity will change from ω to ω' in such a way that the angular momentum is unchanged:

$$H = H', \qquad \text{therefore} \qquad I\omega = I'\omega'. \tag{7}$$

As examples of the application of this relation to the case of rotation about a fixed axis, consider the case of a man standing on a small rotating platform, or a toe dancer spinning on one toe, or a spinning skater. If the person extends his arms so that his moment of inertia about the vertical axis of rotation increases, his angular velocity of rotation will decrease, while if he presses his arms close into his body to decrease his moment of inertia, his angular velocity will increase. The observed effects can be striking, especially if the man has weights in his hands, because of the large effect of the r^2 factor in the moment of inertia.

As an application to two-dimensional motion, consider a tumbler or a diver; these athletes essentially execute a two-dimensional motion in a vertical plane. When the diver desires a high angular velocity of tumble, he curls up into a ball to minimize his moment of inertia; just before hitting the water he straightens out and his angular velocity decreases greatly.

4. ANGULAR IMPULSE

IF A RIGID body is given a blow with impulse $\bar{F}\,\Delta t$, the body changes momentum by $m\,\Delta v = \bar{F}\,\Delta t$, as we have seen in Chap. 7. This is the translational momentum and Δv is the change in velocity of the center of mass.

When given a blow, the rigid body in general also changes angular momentum. Consider, for example, a stick lying on a smooth horizontal sheet of ice as in Fig. 7. A horizontal blow with average force $\bar{F}$

that has lever arm l about a vertical axis through the center of mass exerts average torque $\bar{L} = \bar{F}l$.   Now, since $L = I_c\,\alpha$, $\bar{L} = I_c\,\bar{\alpha} = I_c\,\Delta\omega/\Delta t$. Hence

$$\bar{L}\,\Delta t = I_c\,\Delta\omega, \qquad\qquad (8)$$

where I_c is the moment of inertia about the center of mass and the torque is about the center of mass.   The right side of (8) is the change in angular momentum; the left side is defined as *angular impulse.*

> The **angular impulse,** when a rigid body is acted on by torque, is defined as the time average of the torque multiplied by the time interval during which the torque acts.

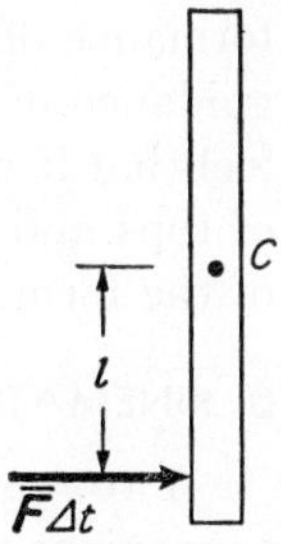

Equation (8) is written for general two-dimensional motion of a rigid body.   If the body is mounted on a fixed axis O (case of pure rotation), the similar equation $\bar{L}\,\Delta t = I_o\,\Delta\omega$ holds with torques and moment of inertia taken about the fixed axis.   These equations state that

Angular impulse equals change of angular momentum.

This relation is exactly analogous to the similar relation that applies to translational motion.

Figure 7

> **Example.**   *The stick of Fig. 7 has mass* $\frac{1}{3}$ *slug and length* 4 ft; *it is initially at rest on a smooth horizontal plane and is struck by an impulsive force of impulse* 3 lb·sec *at a distance* $l = 1\frac{1}{2}$ ft *from the center.   Determine the subsequent motion.*
>
> The center of mass acquires velocity
>
> $$v = \Delta v = \frac{\bar{F}\,\Delta t}{m} = \frac{3 \text{ lb·sec}}{\frac{1}{3} \text{ slug}} = 9 \text{ ft/sec},$$
>
> in the direction of the impulse, which is to the right in Fig. 7.   After the impulse, no horizontal forces act on the stick so the center of mass continues to move in a straight line with this velocity.
>
> The angular impulse $\bar{L}\,\Delta t$ is the impulse $\bar{F}\,\Delta t$ times the lever arm, or $(3 \text{ lb·sec})(\frac{3}{2} \text{ ft}) = \frac{9}{2}$ lb·sec·ft.   The moment of inertia about the center of mass is $I_C = \frac{1}{12}\cdot\frac{1}{3}$ slug·$(4 \text{ ft})^2 = \frac{4}{9}$ slug·ft².   Hence by (8) the stick acquires angular velocity
>
> $$\omega = \Delta\omega = \frac{\frac{9}{2} \text{ lb·sec·ft}}{\frac{4}{9} \text{ slug·ft}^2} = 8\frac{1}{8} \text{ rad/sec},$$
>
> or 1.61 rev/sec.   The stick continues to revolve at this angular velocity as the center of mass moves to the right in a straight line.

5. GYROSCOPIC MOTION

So FAR we have discussed rotational motion only in the case where there is a fixed axis or where the motion takes place in two dimensions.

The general problem of rotational motion in three dimensions is extremely complex and far beyond the mathematical level of this text. However, there is one case for which a comparatively simple discussion can be given; this is the case of a top or gyroscope spinning *very rapidly* about its symmetry axis.

Within recent years, gyroscopes have been developed for the performance of very important functions in connection with the control and guidance of airplanes, ships, weapons, and missiles. For this reason we feel that it will be worth while to give a brief introduction to the behavior of tops and gyroscopes, making no attempt to give rigorous derivations of the formulas used.

6. KINEMATICS OF GYROSCOPIC MOTION

A TOP or gyroscope can rotate independently about three axes. It is convenient to take these as the nonorthogonal axes shown in Figs. 8 and 9. In the familiar top (Fig. 8), the *spin axis* is the axis of symmetry around

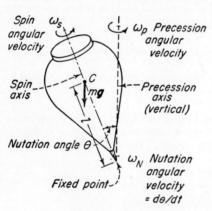

Fig. 8. Top.

which the top spins with *spin angular velocity* ω_S. The *precession axis* is the vertical axis. As the spin axis moves around the vertical axis in a cone of semiangle θ, the top is said to *precess* with a certain *precession angular velocity* ω_P. If the angle θ, called the *nutation angle*, changes so that the spin axis *nods* toward and away from the vertical, the top is said to undergo *nutation*. $d\theta/dt$ is called the *nutation angular velocity* ω_N. The *nutation axis* is a horizontal axis perpendicular to the plane containing the spin axis and the precession axis. The point at the end of the top is supposed to be a fixed point in this discussion; with this restriction, any conceivable motion of the top can be considered as compounded of spin, precession, and nutation.

If we now look at the freely mounted gyroscope of Fig. 9, we can understand the system of three gimbals if we note that rotation in the bearings of each of the three gimbals corresponds precisely to one of the three modes of motion of the top discussed above. Thus the gyro wheel rotates in the bearings of the innermost gimbal at the spin angular velocity ω_S; this gimbal rotates in the bearings of the next at the nutational angular velocity ω_N; and this gimbal rotates in the bearings of the outermost fixed gimbal at the precession angular velocity ω_P.

Although the precession axis is drawn vertical in Fig. 9 to correspond to Fig. 8, the gyro of Fig. 9 is supposed to be a *free* gyro, which means that

it is perfectly balanced so that gravity can exert no torques whatsoever; consequently, which way is up is immaterial, and there is no significance to taking the precession axis vertical rather than in some other direction. The center of gravity of the gyro wheel in Fig. 9 is supposed to be at its exact center of symmetry, and each of the gimbals is supposed to be perfectly balanced in frictionless bearings.

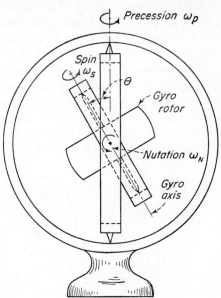

Fig. 9. Gyroscope in three-gimbal mounting.

We now note one important point which a little careful study of Fig. 9 will convince us is true, namely, that for any position of the outer fixed gimbal in Fig. 9, the gyro axis is capable of taking on any direction in space whatsoever by proper rotation of the two inner gimbals in the precessional and nutational bearings.

7. DYNAMICS OF GYROSCOPIC MOTION

THE TOP or gyroscope can have, in addition to its spin angular velocity ω_S, angular velocities of precession and nutation ω_P and ω_N. It turns out that these angular velocities can be considered as vectors directed along the respective axes and can be added vectorially. Angular momentum H is of the nature of moment of inertia times angular velocity and is a vector. But since the moments of inertia associated with the different angular velocities are different, the expression for the angular-momentum vector in the general case is complex. However, *in the case where the spin angular velocity is very large compared to the other angular velocities, the angular-momentum vector H will to a good approximation be directed along the spin axis and will have magnitude $I\omega_S$, where I is the moment of inertia about the spin axis.* The direction of the vector H is related to the sense of turning by the right-hand rule which we have already discussed on p. 20 in connection with torque. This direction is illustrated in Fig. 10.

If L is the torque acting on the top (about the fixed point), or on the gyro rotor (about the center of gravity), the equation of motion is the vector equation

$$dH/dt = L, \tag{9}$$

which says that, in the time dt, the change in the angular momentum vector H has magnitude $L\,dt$ and direction the same as the direction of the torque vector. This equation is the vectorial generalization of (6), in which the axis of rotation has a fixed direction in space so that only one component of the vectors L and H is involved.

The torque vector is a vector along the particular axis through the fixed point around which the torque tends to cause rotation and is taken with sense given by the right-hand rule. If at the particular instant for which Figs. 8 and 11 are drawn, the axis of the top lies in the YZ-plane, the torque of gravity tends to cause rotation about the X-axis and hence is a vector pointing along the X-axis, of magnitude $mgl\,\sin\theta$.

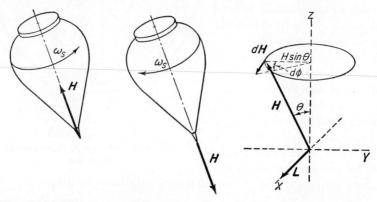

Fig. 10. Relation between direction of angu-   **Fig. 11.** Rate of precession
lar momentum vector and sense of spin.   of the top shown in Fig. 8.

Now let us derive the formula for the angular velocity of precession of the familiar rapidly spinning top. Let the top be spinning in the sense of Fig. 8, so that the angular momentum is a vector along the axis in the direction shown in Fig. 11. Equation (9) shows that dH is parallel to the X-axis, which means that it is perpendicular to H and directed tangent to the circle of radius $H\sin\theta$ shown in Fig. 11. H changes only in direction, not in magnitude. Furthermore, as the end of H moves around the circle of Fig. 11, the torque L changes direction continuously so that the direction of dH remains continuously perpendicular to that of H.

Since $dH = L\,dt = mgl\,\sin\theta\,dt$, in time dt the end of H turns through angle $d\phi = dH/H\sin\theta = mgl\sin\theta\,dt/H\sin\theta = mgl\,dt/H = mgl\,dt/I\omega_s$. Since $d\phi/dt$ is the precession angular velocity ω_P, this gives

$$\omega_P = mgl/I\omega_s \qquad (10)$$

for the rate of precession. This formula is only valid provided that ω_P comes out small compared to ω_s so that the assumption that the angular momentum vector is directed along the spin axis is justified. The precession angular velocity (10) increases in proportion to the torque of gravity, and decreases in proportion to the angular momentum; consequently, the faster a given top spins, the less its precession angular velocity. It will be noted that the precession velocity is independent of the angle θ between the axis of the top and the vertical.

The above discussion shows why the torque of gravity does not make a top tip over. So long as the spin angular velocity does not decrease because of friction, the torque of gravity can add increments $d\mathbf{H}$ of angular momentum *only* in the direction indicated in Fig. 11 and such increments do not tend to change θ. The situation is analogous to the action of centripetal force on a body moving in a circular path. The centripetal force adds increments of velocity that continuously change the direction of the velocity, but not its magnitude. The fact that the torque of gravity does not cause a top to tip over is exactly analogous to the fact that the gravitational pull of the sun on the earth does not cause the earth to fall into the sun.

8. APPLICATIONS OF GYROSCOPES

THE IMPORTANT property of the free gyroscope in Fig. 9 is that it is impossible by means of gravity, or by means of torques applied to the outer gimbal, to exert any torque whatsoever on the gyro wheel. Consequently, the angular-momentum vector remains fixed in magnitude and direction in space. No matter what motion may be given to the frame of the outer gimbal, the direction in space of the gyro axis will not vary.

Such universally mounted gyros are useful for maintaining a fixed direction of reference in a body which may be undergoing changes in direction. The axis of the steering gyro of a torpedo is initially given the desired direction of motion of the torpedo, and the gyro serves to steer the torpedo in this direction. An essentially free gyro, known as the *directional gyro*, is used in the automatic pilot of an airplane to maintain constant direction of flight. Other gyroscopes are used in the rate-of-turn indicator and the artificial horizon in aircraft.

Foucault first used a free gyroscope to demonstrate the rotation of the earth, making use of the fact that the axis of a free gyroscope maintains constant direction *in space*.

There are many applications of gyroscopes that employ a two-gimbal mounting, so that torques can be applied to the gyro wheel about some axes and not about others. Perhaps the most important application of such a gyro is in connection with the shipboard *gyrocompass*. In the gyrocompass, the gyro axis is constrained

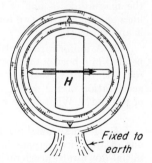

Fig. 12. Principle of the gyrocompass. The angular momentum $\mathbf{H}$ is constrained to remain in the horizontal plane. Torques arising from the rotation of the earth cause $\mathbf{H}$ to change direction until it points north.

to remain horizontal, as indicated in Fig. 12. Analysis of the torques on this gyro wheel, which is fixed to the rotating earth, shows that the angular-momentum vector turns and points to the north.

Gyroscopic principles are involved in the explanation of why a rapidly rolling wheel does not tip over; how it is possible to balance a bicycle or motorcycle; how the spin of a rifle bullet prevents it from tumbling under the action of the forces of the air; and why the axis of the earth maintains a practically fixed direction in space, undergoing only a very slow precession because of the torque exerted by the gravitational attraction of the moon and the sun on the equatorial bulge of the earth (the precession of the equinoxes).

PROBLEMS

1. A 200-g meter stick lies at rest on the smooth surface of a table. Two horizontal transverse forces of equal magnitude and opposite direction are applied to the stick. The magnitude of each force is 0.3 nt. Find the magnitude of the angular acceleration of the stick (a) when one force acts at the 0-cm mark and the other at the 20-cm mark, (b) when one of the forces acts at the 40-cm mark and the other at the 60-cm mark, and (c) when one of the forces acts at the 60-cm mark and the other at the 80-cm mark. Find the linear acceleration of the center of mass for each of the above cases.

Ans: 3.6 rad/sec^2, 0 m/sec^2, in every case.

2. Two applied forces, equal in magnitude but opposite in direction, are said to constitute a *couple*. In the case of plane motion, show that when a couple is applied to a body at rest as in the example of Prob. 1 above:

(a) it tends to induce pure rotation about the center of mass;

(b) the moment of the couple about the center of mass equals the product of the magnitude of one of the forces by the perpendicular distance between the lines of action of the two forces, and is otherwise independent of where the couple is applied to the body.

3. A uniform rod is 10 ft long and has a mass of 3 slugs. This rod is suspended in a horizontal position by two vertical wires attached to the ends of the rod. If the wire at one end suddenly breaks, what is the initial downward acceleration of the center of gravity? What is the initial angular acceleration of the rod? What is the initial tension in the other wire?

Ans: 24.1 ft/sec^2; 4.83 rad/sec^2; 24.1 lb.

4. If a man weighing 129 lb were hanging by one hand at a point 2 ft from one of the wires supporting the rod mentioned in Prob. 3, what would be his initial downward acceleration if the wire closer to him were to break suddenly? if the wire at the other end were to break suddenly?

5. An automobile is equipped with wheels of diameter 2 ft. At a certain time this automobile is moving without skidding at a velocity of 30 mi/hr eastward. Find the instantaneous linear velocity of a point at the top of one of the wheels (a) with respect to the car and (b) with respect to the road. Find the instantaneous linear velocity of a point at the bottom of one of the wheels (c) with respect to the car and (d) with respect to the road.

Ans: (a) 44 ft/sec, eastward; (b) 88 ft/sec, eastward; (c) 44 ft/sec, westward; (d) 0.

6. In Fig. 6, compute the velocity of the point on the leading edge of the rim at the same height as the center of the wheel by adding vectorially the velocities arising from translation alone and from rotation alone. Show that the resultant velocity corresponds to that arising from pure rotation about the point of contact O' with angular velocity ω.

7. A lawn roller consists of a large solid cylinder 2 ft in diameter with a handle attached at the axle. The mass of the roller is 4 slugs. By pulling on the handle a boy exerts a horizontal force of 50 lb in the manner indicated in Fig. 4. Find the linear acceleration of the center of mass and the angular acceleration of the cylinder. Ans: 8.33 ft/sec²; 8.33 rad/sec².

8. A boy exerts a force of 4 lb on a metal hoop 3 ft in diameter. The mass of the hoop is ½ slug. If the force is horizontal and its line of action is 1 ft above the sidewalk, find the acceleration of the center of mass of the hoop.

9. The coefficient of static friction between the ground and the lawn roller described in Prob. 7 is 0.4. What is the largest horizontal acceleration that can be imparted to the center of mass without causing the roller to slide? What horizontal force must be applied in the manner shown in Fig. 4 in order to produce this acceleration? Ans: 25.8 ft/sec²; 155 lb.

10. A spool of thread has rim diameter 4 cm, but the thread unwinds from a layer 2 cm in diameter. The radius of gyration is 1 cm. The spool is placed with its axis horizontal on a horizontal surface, with the end of the thread leading out from the *under* side of the spool. The thread end is held horizontally and pulled in a direction perpendicular to the spool axis. Show that if the rims of the spool do not slip, the thread will wind itself up! Determine the relation between the acceleration of the spool, the tension in the thread, and the mass of the spool.

11. A solid sphere of 1-ft radius and 40-lb weight rolls without slipping down a plane inclined at an angle of 30° to the horizontal. Find the linear acceleration of the center of this sphere. Solve the same problem for a sphere of radius 2 ft and weight 250 lb. Ans: 11.5 ft/sec²; 11.5 ft/sec².

12. A hoop 3.5 ft in diameter and weight 27.2 lb rolls without slipping down a plane inclined at an angle of 30° to the horizontal. Find the linear acceleration of the center of this hoop.

13. A solid cylinder of diameter 2 ft and mass 1 slug rolls down an inclined plane. The initial position of the cylinder was 20 ft vertically above its final position at the foot of the slope. What is the final total kinetic energy of the cylinder at the foot of the inclined plane? How much kinetic energy is associated with translational motion and how much kinetic energy is associated with rotational motion? Ans: 644 ft·lb; 429 ft·lb; 215 ft·lb

14. Solve Prob. 13 for a hollow cylinder (hoop) with mass and diameter equal to that of the solid cylinder.

15. Derive an expression for the final translational velocity of the center of a hollow cylinder (hoop) that has rolled without slipping down an inclined plane from an initial height h. Ans: $v = \sqrt{gh}$.

16. Derive an expression for the final translational velocity of the center of mass of a solid cylinder that has rolled without slipping down an inclined plane from an initial height h. Make a similar derivation for a solid sphere and for a wheel of radius of gyration k. Show that the equation for the wheel also applies to the other bodies considered when the proper values of k are used.

17. A 'yo-yo' has the string wrapped around a reduced section of radius 0.5 cm, but the radius of gyration is 3 cm. The string is held in the hand and the yo-yo with its axis horizontal is allowed to unwind the string as it falls vertically. What fraction of the kinetic energy it acquires is rotational? Ans: $^{36}\!/_{37}$.

18. A man stands on a small platform that is rotating about a vertical axis at a speed of 1 rev/sec in frictionless bearings; his arms are outstretched and he holds weights in each hand.   With his hands in this position, the total moment of inertia of the man and the platform is 6 kg·m². If by drawing in the weights the man decreases the moment of inertia to 2 kg·m², what is the magnitude of the resulting rotational velocity of the platform?

19. A man stands at the edge of a high-diving platform, extends his arms straight over his head, and allows himself to fall forward.   His feet lose contact with the end of the board when he makes an angle of 30° with the horizontal. What is his angular velocity at the moment that his feet lose contact?   Assume for purposes of computation that the man in this position is dynamically equivalent to a uniform stick 6 ft long and that his initial fall is equivalent to the fall of this stick pivoted at the bottom end.   Ans: 2.84 rad/sec.

20. The man in Prob. 19, who is dynamically equivalent to a stick 6 ft long when leaving the diving board at 2.84 rad/sec, curls up and becomes dynamically equivalent to a solid cylinder 2½ ft in diameter.   What is then his angular velocity of tumble?

21. A straight rod 6 ft long having mass 1 slug is bent at right angles at its center and laid flat on a horizontal surface.   What is the moment of inertia of this bent rod about a vertical axis through its center of mass?   Ans: 1⅝ slug·ft².

22. The bent rod of Prob. 21 is lying at rest on a smooth horizontal sheet of ice.   One end of the rod is struck with a hammer (on the very end, parallel to the length of this half of the rod) with sufficient force to set the rod into rotation at 3 rad/sec.   What translational velocity is acquired by the rod?

23. In a children's playground is a small merry-go-round of radius 4 ft, mass 4 slugs, and radius of gyration 3 ft.   A child of mass 3 slugs runs at 15 ft/sec tangent to the rim of the merry-go-round when it is stationary and jumps on. What is the angular velocity acquired by the merry-go-round if friction is negligible?   Ans: 1⁵⁄₇ rad/sec.

24. If the merry-go-round of Prob. 23 was turning toward the child when he jumps on, and his impulse exactly stops the merry-go-round, what was its angular velocity?

25. A particle slides down a friction-less track forming the loop-the-loop in Fig. 13.   The center of mass of the particle initially descends the vertical distance h, then rises the distance D as it traverses the circular loop.   Determine the minimum height h required in terms of the diameter D so that the particle will remain in contact at the top of the loop. (To work this problem, assume that the loop exerts such a normal force

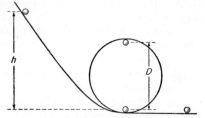

Fig. 13. Loop-the-loop.

on the particle that it does remain in contact.   If the required normal force turns out to be a force of attraction at the top of the loop, in the absence of this force the particle would have left the loop before reaching the top.   The limiting case is when the normal force is exactly zero at the top.)   Ans: $h = $⁵⁄₄ D.

26. Solve Prob. 25 for the case where a sphere of diameter small compared to D rolls without slipping around the loop-the-loop.   Repeat for a solid cylinder and a thin hoop.

27. A top of moment of inertia 0.0175 slug·in² is spinning at 25 rev/sec at an angle $\theta = 20°$. The top weighs 14 oz and has its center of gravity 1.5 in from its point. The spin is clockwise as seen from above. What is the angular velocity of precession of the top axis, and is it clockwise or counterclockwise as viewed from above?   Ans: 0.913 rev/sec; clockwise.

28. A top of moment of inertia 8000 g·cm² is spinning at 18 rev/sec at an angle $\theta = 30°$. The top has 900 g mass and has its center of mass 5 cm from its point. The spin is counterclockwise as seen from above. What is the angular velocity of precession of the top axis, and is it clockwise or counterclockwise as viewed from above?

29. A suitcase, with a rapidly turning gyro rotor mounted with its axis fixed horizontally parallel to the long dimension of the suitcase, is carefully handed to a porter.

(a) When the porter, in turning, attempts to turn the suitcase about a vertical axis, how does the suitcase actually move?

(b) When the porter attempts to swing the suitcase about a transverse horizontal axis, how does the suitcase actually move?

In the above show by means of vector diagrams the relation between the directions of the gyro-spin-velocity vector, the torque vector, and the vector that expresses the angular velocity acquired by the suitcase.

30. In Fig. 12, let the plane of the paper be a vertical E–W plane at the earth's equator, and look at the figure from the south. Show that the rotation of the earth occasions a torque on the gyro wheel that tends to make H swing toward the north, into the paper. Show that when H has swung to the north, there is no further tendency for the direction of H to change, so that the gyro is in equilibrium with H pointing north.

CHAPTER 11

PERIODIC MOTION

IN THIS CHAPTER we shall consider some types of motion in which the resultant force or torque acting on a body varies periodically. These types include the motion of a particle at constant speed in a circular path and the vibratory motion of a particle about an equilibrium position when the restoring force is proportional to the displacement. Vibratory motion results when a body hanging from a spring is pulled downward and then released; other common examples of this type of motion are the vibrations of strings and air columns of musical instruments, the vibrations of bridges and buildings, and the oscillation of the balance wheel of a watch or of the pendulum of a clock.

Motion in a circle at constant speed and vibratory motion are both *periodic* motions:

> A **periodic motion** is one in which the motion of a body is identically repeated in each of a succession of equal time intervals.

For example, a particle moving at constant speed in a circle traverses the same path over and over again with the same velocities; a pendulum repeats its to-and-fro motion again and again.

> A **cycle** is one complete execution of a periodic motion.

> The **period** of a periodic motion is the time T required for the completion of a cycle.

> The **frequency** of a periodic motion is the number f of cycles completed per unit time.

From their definitions, it is readily seen that the period T of a periodic motion is the reciprocal of the frequency f:

$$T = 1/f, \qquad f = 1/T. \tag{1}$$

For example, if the rotational *frequency* of a motor shaft is 30 cycles/sec (30 rev/sec), the *period* of the rotational motion is $\frac{1}{30}$ sec.

The principles we shall learn in studying periodic motion in this chapter will have applications not only in mechanics but also in the study of sound, light, and electricity. Sound waves, light waves, radio waves, and alternating currents are all periodic phenomena.

234

1. MOTION IN A CIRCLE AT CONSTANT SPEED

WE HAVE already shown that a particle moving at constant speed v in a circular path must be acted upon by a resultant force that is *centripetal*. The *magnitude* of this force is constant, but the *direction* of the force changes continuously and is always at right angles to the path.

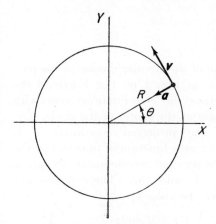

Consider the particle shown in Fig. 1. The angular displacement θ of the particle from its initial position $\theta_0 = 0$ at $t = 0$ is given by the relation

$$\theta = \omega t \qquad (2)$$

in radians, where $\omega = v/R$ in rad/sec. We may also write θ in terms of the frequency f in rev/sec. Since $\omega = 2\pi f$,

$$\theta = 2\pi f t. \qquad (2')$$

Knowing θ and R, we may write the rectangular coordinates of the particle as a function of time as

Fig. 1. Circular motion.

$$X = R\, \cos\theta, \qquad Y = R\, \sin\theta,$$

or
$$X = R\, \cos 2\pi f t, \qquad Y = R\, \sin 2\pi f t. \qquad (3)$$

If we wish to obtain the rectangular components of the velocity of the particle, we may differentiate X and Y in (3) with respect to time t. This differentiation gives

$$v_X = dX/dt = -2\pi f R\, \sin 2\pi f t, \qquad v_Y = dY/dt = 2\pi f R\, \cos 2\pi f t. \qquad (4)$$

This result is reasonable, since the magnitude of the maximum value of either v_X or v_Y is just the constant tangential speed $v = \omega R = 2\pi f R$, and we verify that $v_X^2 + v_Y^2 = (2\pi f R)^2 = v^2$. The correctness of the signs in (4) can be verified by computing the instantaneous velocity vectors for the particle in Fig. 1 for various values of $\theta = 2\pi f t$, such as 0, $\frac{1}{4}\pi$, $\frac{1}{2}\pi$, $\cdots$.

In order to determine the rectangular components of the acceleration, we may differentiate v_X and v_Y in (4) with respect to time t. This gives

$$a_X = dv_X/dt = -4\pi^2 f^2 R\, \cos 2\pi f t, \qquad a_Y = dv_Y/dt = -4\pi^2 f^2 R\, \sin 2\pi f t. \qquad (5)$$

These are the rectangular components of the *centripetal acceleration*, whose magnitude is

$$a = v^2/R = \omega^2 R = 4\pi^2 f^2 R.$$

The correctness of the signs in (5) can be verified by computing the centripetal acceleration vectors in Fig. 1 for various values of θ.

Equations (2), (3), (4), and (5) give a complete *kinematical* description of the motion of a particle at constant speed v in a circular path of radius R. The centripetal force required to produce the centripetal acceleration has components $F_X = ma_X$, $F_Y = ma_Y$, and magnitude

$$F = ma = m(v^2/R) = m(4\pi^2 f^2 R),$$

where m is the mass of the particle.

2. SIMPLE HARMONIC MOTION

Now LET US consider the projection of the circular motion of the particle in Fig. 1 on the Y-axis of the rectangular coordinate system with origin at the center of the circle.

The projected coordinate Y is given as a function of time by (3); the velocity and acceleration are given by (4) and (5). These projections have the values

$$\left. \begin{array}{l} Y = R \sin 2\pi ft, \\ v_Y = 2\pi fR \cos 2\pi ft, \\ a_Y = -4\pi^2 f^2 R \sin 2\pi ft. \end{array} \right\} \quad (6)$$

The projected motion can be represented by the sketch in Fig. 2, which shows the position Y, velocity v_Y, and acceleration a_Y for one complete cycle of the motion.

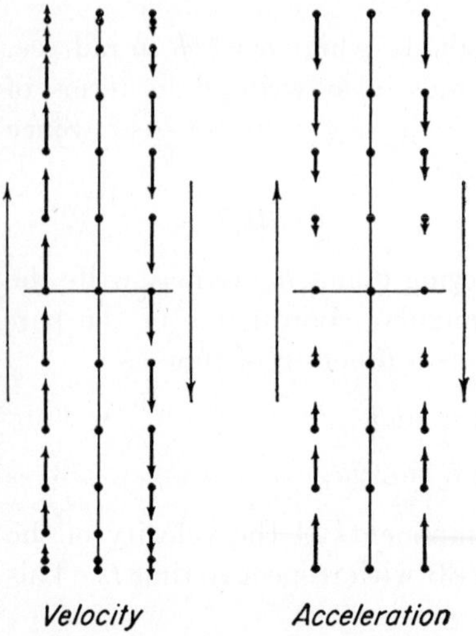

Fig. 2. Projections on the Y-axis of the position, velocity, and acceleration of the particle of Fig. 1 at successive intervals of $\frac{1}{24}$ rev. A particle that actually moves up and down the Y-axis in just this way executes simple harmonic motion.

Now let us consider a particle that actually *moves along the Y-axis* in the manner of (6) and Fig. 2. We can think of Y as giving the *displacement* of the particle from its initial position $Y = 0$. From (6), we note that

$$a_Y = -(4\pi^2 f^2) Y. \quad (7)$$

Since $4\pi^2 f^2$ is a constant, the acceleration is proportional to the displacement Y from the origin but opposite in direction, alternating in sign as Y alternates in sign. Rectilinear motion of the type given by (6) and (7) is called *simple harmonic motion*.

Simple harmonic motion is a rectilinear motion in which the magnitude of the acceleration is proportional to the magnitude of the displacement of the particle from an origin, and the direction of the acceleration is always opposite to that of the displacement.

In order for a particle to execute simple harmonic motion, it must experience a *restoring force* that is proportional to the displacement but opposite in direction, so that the restoring force always gives the particle an acceleration toward the origin. Since the origin is the position of zero force, it is called the *equilibrium position*. According to (6), the particle makes equal excursions on the two sides of its equilibrium position.

Elastic forces obeying Hooke's law have the character that gives rise to simple harmonic motion. For example, suppose that we have a steel ball of mass m supported by a Hooke's-law spring as shown in Fig. 3. At the equilibrium position of the ball, the downward pull of gravity and the upward pull exerted by the spring are equal and opposite. If we pull the ball downward a distance A *below* its equilibrium position, we do work on the ball and increase its potential energy. If we then release the ball, the spring pulls it back to its equilibrium position, and the potential energy is changed into kinetic energy. The ball continues to move upward until it is at a distance A *above* its equilibrium position and then starts downward again. In the absence of frictional effects, the ball continues to move up and down about its

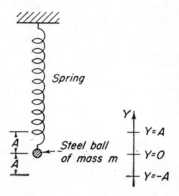

Fig. 3. A steel ball supported by a spring will execute simple harmonic motion if moved away from its equilibrium position and then released.

equilibrium position; the motion is *oscillatory* or *vibratory*. Energy relations will be considered in the next section. Here we shall consider the forces involved.

At the equilibrium position, which we call $Y=0$, the upward force of the spring on the ball will be just equal and opposite to the downward force of gravity on the ball, and the net force on the ball will be zero. If now the ball is pulled *down* an arbitrary distance b (to $Y=-b$), the upward force of the spring will be *increased* by Kb, where K is the spring constant. Since the force of gravity is unchanged, the net force on the ball will be upward and of magnitude Kb. This net force is the *restoring force*. If we take the restoring force F as positive upward (that is, in the $+Y$-direction), we can write $F=Kb$ when the ball is at $Y=-b$, or, in terms of Y,

$$F = -KY. \tag{8}$$

Let us see that this same formula gives the restoring force for positive values of Y. Suppose that the ball is *above* its equilibrium position at $Y=c$. Then the upward force of the spring on the ball will be *less* than the force at the equilibrium position by an amount Kc, and the force of gravity will be unchanged; therefore, the net force will be downward, toward the equilibrium position. Since a downward force is taken as negative, we must write the restoring force in this case as $F = -Kc = -KY$, as in (8).

Hence, the system of Fig. 3 has a *restoring* force proportional to the displacement from equilibrium, and gives rise to simple harmonic motion.

As another example of an elastic system that gives rise to simple harmonic motion, consider the mass of Fig. 4, which slides on a frictionless horizontal plane and is attached to two *stretched* springs of spring constants K_1 and K_2. We call the equilibrium position $Y = 0$. At the equilibrium position, the force exerted to the right by the right-hand spring will be just equal and opposite to the force exerted to the left by

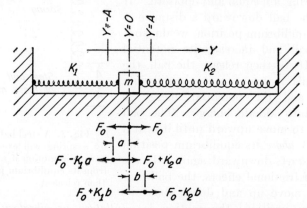

Fig. 4. A mass sliding on a frictionless horizontal plane between two stretched springs. (If one does not like the idea of a frictionless plane, he can visualize a cart with small wheels of negligible rotational inertia.)

the left-hand spring. The magnitudes of these forces are denoted by F_0 in Fig. 4.

If this body is moved to the left of the equilibrium position, to $Y = -a$, the force of the right-hand spring to the right is *increased* by $K_2 a$; that of the left-hand spring is *decreased* by $K_1 a$. The result (see diagram below Fig. 4) is a net force to the right (*restoring force*) $F = (K_1 + K_2)a$. If we let $K = K_1 + K_2$, the restoring force is $F = Ka$ or

$$F = -KY. \qquad (9)$$

Again, if the body is to the right of the equilibrium position, at $Y = b$, we see by a similar argument that (9) gives the correct restoring force. K is called the *effective force constant* in this case.

In general, when a body is acted on by *elastic* forces in such a way that it has a definite equilibrium position, and restoring forces come into play when it is displaced from the equilibrium position, the restoring force will be given by a relation such as (8) or (9), with an effective force constant K related to the elastic constants of the system. The restoring force will give the body an acceleration toward the equilibrium position when it is displaced from it. By Newton's second principle, if we can neglect the mass of the springs in comparison with the mass m of the body,

$$F = m \, d^2Y/dt^2 = -KY,$$

or

$$a_Y = d^2Y/dt^2 = -(K/m)Y. \tag{10}$$

This is exactly the form of relation between a_Y and Y that occurs in equation (7)—the acceleration is proportional to the displacement Y but opposite in direction. Hence the particle executes simple harmonic motion of the type (6):

$$Y = A \sin 2\pi ft. \tag{11}$$

The frequency f of the motion is immediately obtained by comparison of (7) and (10). It is such that

$$4\pi^2 f^2 = K/m,$$

or

$$f = \frac{1}{2\pi} \sqrt{\frac{K}{m}} \cdot \quad \left\{ \begin{matrix} f \text{ in cycles/sec} \\ K \text{ in nt/m} \\ m \text{ in kg} \end{matrix} \right\} \text{ or } \left\{ \begin{matrix} f \text{ in cycles/sec} \\ K \text{ in lb/ft} \\ m \text{ in slugs} \end{matrix} \right\} \tag{12}$$

This equation gives us the *frequency* f of a simple harmonic motion that takes place under the action of a resultant force of type (8). The *period* is given by

$$T = 1/f = 2\pi \sqrt{m/K}. \tag{13}$$

It should be noted that by a complete oscillation or *cycle* of a particle executing simple harmonic motion we mean a complete 'round trip' of the particle; thus, if the particle in Fig. 3 has an initial displacement $Y = -A$, a complete oscillation includes the upward motion through the origin to $+A$ and back to the original displacement $-A$.

In the motion of equation (11), A is called the *amplitude* of the motion.

> The **amplitude** of a simple harmonic motion is the magnitude of the maximum displacement of the particle from its equilibrium position.

It will be noted that in the case of simple harmonic motion of a body acted on by an elastic restoring force of the type we have been considering, *the frequency and period are entirely independent of the amplitude of the motion.* To make this seem reasonable, we note from (11) that the velocity $v_Y = dY/dt = 2\pi fA \cos 2\pi ft$, where f is the constant of the system given by (12). This velocity, as a function of t, is directly proportional to the amplitude A. Hence if the amplitude is doubled, the velocity is doubled, and the particle travels twice as far at twice the speed, taking the same periodic time per cycle.

Equation (11) represents the case in which Y is 0 and v_Y is positive when $t=0$. Other initial conditions can be obtained by shifting the origin of t. The equations

$$Y = A\ \sin(2\pi ft \pm \tfrac{1}{2}\pi) = \pm A\ \cos 2\pi ft \qquad (14)$$

represent the motions in which $Y = \pm A$ at $t=0$. The most general equation satisfying (10) is obtained by adding an arbitrary constant ϕ (called the *phase angle*) to the argument of the sine in (11):

$$Y = A\ \sin(2\pi ft + \phi). \qquad (15)$$

Different values of ϕ merely correspond to different initial positions of the particle (at $t=0$) executing the *same* simple harmonic motion.

Example. *A spiral spring 3 m long hangs from the ceiling. When a mass of 1 kg is suspended from the spring, the spring lengthens by 40 cm in the equilibrium configuration. The mass is then pulled down an additional 10 cm and released. Determine the characteristics of the subsequent motion, neglecting the mass of the spring.*

t (sec)	$4.95\,t$ sec^{-1} (rad)	Equiv. degrees	Y (cm)	v_Y (cm/sec)	a_Y (cm/sec²)
0	0	0	−10	0	+245
0.1	0.495	28°4	−8.80	+23.6	+216
0.2	0.990	56°7	−5.49	+41.4	+135
0.3	1.485	85°1	−0.85	+49.3	+21
0.4	1.980	113°4	+3.97	+45.4	−97
0.5	2.475	141°8	+7.86	+30.6	−193
0.6	2.970	170°2	+9.85	+8.4	−241
0.7	3.465	198°5	+9.48	−15.7	−232
0.8	3.960	226°9	+6.83	−36.1	−167
0.9	4.455	255°2	+2.55	−47.9	−62
1.0	4.950	283°6	−2.35	−48.1	+58
1.1	5.445	312°0	−6.69	−36.8	+164
1.2	6.940	340°3	−9.42	−16.7	+231
1.3	7.435	368°7	−9.88	+7.5	+242

The weight of the 1-kg mass at standard gravity is 9.81 nt. Since this weight lengthens the spring 0.4 m, the force constant is

$$K = (9.81\ \text{nt})/(0.4\ \text{m}) = 24.5\ \text{nt/m}.$$

The period of the simple harmonic motion is given by (13):

$$T = 2\pi\ \sqrt{(1\ \text{kg})/(24.5\ \text{nt/m})} = (2\pi/4.95)\ \text{sec} = 1.27\ \text{sec},$$

while the frequency is

$$f = 1/T = (1/1.27 \text{ sec}) = 0.787 \text{ cycle/sec.}$$

We can use (14) with the minus sign to determine the position Y measured in cm from the equilibrium position, if we insert $A = 10$ cm, $2\pi f = 4.95 \text{ sec}^{-1}$. This substitution gives

$$Y = -10 \cos(4.95\, t \text{ sec}^{-1}) \text{ cm.}$$

Since the period is 1.27 sec, we compute the fourth column of the accompanying table by inserting the values $t = 0, 0.1 \text{ sec}, \cdots, 1.3 \text{ sec}$ in this relation to cover the motion during the first period. These values of Y are plotted in Fig. 5.

Differentiation of the preceding equation gives

$$v_Y = dY/dt = (49.5 \text{ sec}^{-1}) \sin(4.95\, t \text{ sec}^{-1}) \text{ cm}$$
$$= 49.5 \sin(4.95\, t \text{ sec}^{-1}) \text{ cm/sec.}$$

A second differentiation gives

$$a_Y = dv_Y/dt = 245 \cos(4.95\, t \text{ sec}^{-1}) \text{ cm/sec}^2.$$

Values of v_Y and a_Y are tabulated and plotted along with those of Y.

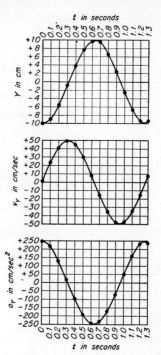

Figure 5

3. ENERGY RELATIONSHIPS IN SIMPLE HARMONIC MOTION

Now LET US consider the energy relationships involved in the simple harmonic motion of the particle in Fig. 3 or Fig. 4. To give the body its initial displacement, we must do *work* against the restoring force. As a result of the performance of this work, the system acquires potential energy. When the body is released, this initial potential energy is converted into kinetic energy as the body moves back to its equilibrium position; as a result of its momentum at the equilibrium position, the body moves past the equilibrium position and its kinetic energy is converted into potential energy as work is done against the restoring force. Hence, the energy of the system is alternately all in the form of potential energy when the displacement is a maximum and all in the form of kinetic energy as the body passes through its equilibrium position. However, if there are no frictional effects, *the mechanical energy* (kinetic plus potential) *is at all times constant and is equal to the initial work done on the system.* Let us now see how this fact can be used in determining the velocity of the particle at various points in the path traversed.

The total external work we should have to do against the restoring force to give the body a displacement Y represents the potential energy. Since the restoring force (8) or (9) is exactly of the form considered on

p. 180, we can use the result (2), p. 181, and write

$$\text{P.E.} = \tfrac{1}{2}\,KY^2. \tag{16}$$

If the body is given an initial displacement A and is released from rest,

$$\left.\begin{aligned} \text{initial potential energy} &= \tfrac{1}{2}KA^2,\\ \text{initial kinetic energy} &= 0. \end{aligned}\right\} \tag{17}$$

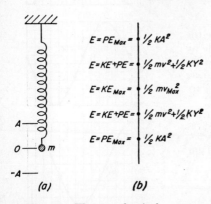

$$E = PE_{Max} = \tfrac{1}{2}\,KA^2$$

$$E = KE + PE = \tfrac{1}{2}\,mv^2 + \tfrac{1}{2}\,KY^2$$

$$E = KE_{Max} = \tfrac{1}{2}\,mv_{Max}^2$$

$$E = KE + PE = \tfrac{1}{2}\,mv^2 + \tfrac{1}{2}\,KY^2$$

$$E = PE_{Max} = \tfrac{1}{2}\,KA^2$$

(a)   (b)

Fig. 6. The mechanical energy associated with simple harmonic motion alternates between being all kinetic and all potential. Part (b) shows the range from $-A$ to $+A$ on an enlarged scale, and the expressions for K.E. and P.E. at various points in the motion.

This initial potential energy is equal to the total energy E of the system, and at all times after the body has been released the sum of the potential energy and kinetic energy of the system is equal to this total energy E:

$$\text{P.E.} + \text{K.E.} = E = \tfrac{1}{2}\,KA^2. \tag{18}$$

The kinetic energy of the system is $\tfrac{1}{2}\,mv_Y^2$, provided the mass of the springs is negligible. Hence, when the body has displacement Y, (18) becomes

$$\tfrac{1}{2}\,KY^2 + \tfrac{1}{2}\,mv_Y^2 = \tfrac{1}{2}\,KA^2. \tag{19}$$

The shift of the energy from potential to kinetic and back is illustrated in Fig. 6. In order to obtain the magnitude of the velocity, we may solve equation (19) for v_Y; thus,

$$v_Y^2 = (K/m)(A^2 - Y^2), \tag{20}$$

and
$$v_Y = \pm\,\sqrt{K/m}\,\sqrt{A^2 - Y^2}. \tag{20'}$$

This equation gives the velocity component v_Y as a function of the position Y. When $Y = 0$, the velocity has its maximum value $v_{\text{Max}} = \pm\,\sqrt{K/m}\;A$, in agreement with the value obtained by differentiation of (11). This formula for v_{Max} gives $\tfrac{1}{2}\,mv_{\text{Max}}^2 = \tfrac{1}{2}\,KA^2$, which expresses the fact that the value of the energy at the equilibrium position, when it is all kinetic, equals the value at the maximum excursion, when it is all potential.

One other point should be mentioned concerning mechanical energy associated with a particle of mass m executing simple harmonic motion. Since the total energy $E = \tfrac{1}{2}\,KA^2$, we see that

The total energy is directly proportional to the square of the amplitude.

Example. *For the oscillating weight whose motion is described in the example on pp. 240–241, determine the maximum kinetic and potential energies, the total energy, and the velocity as a function of position.*

The maximum kinetic energy is

$$\tfrac{1}{2}\,mv^2_{\text{Max}} = \tfrac{1}{2}\,(1\ \text{kg})(0.495\ \text{m/sec})^2$$
$$= 0.122\ \text{joule.}$$

The maximum potential energy is

$$\tfrac{1}{2}\,KA^2 = \tfrac{1}{2}\,(24.5\ \text{nt/m})(0.1\ \text{m})^2$$
$$= 0.122\ \text{joule.}$$

The total energy has the same value, 0.122 joule. From (20), we see that

$$v^2_Y + (K/m)Y^2 = (K/m)A^2,$$

or $v^2_Y + (24.5\ \text{sec}^{-2})Y^2 = (24.5\ \text{sec}^{-2})A^2.$

This is the equation of the ellipse plotted in Fig. 7. The scales of Y and v_Y in this plot are chosen so as to make the ellipse a circle.

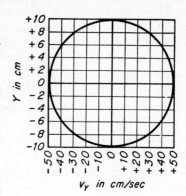

Figure 7

4. ANGULAR SIMPLE HARMONIC MOTION; TORSIONAL OSCILLATION

As MIGHT BE expected, there is a rotational analogue to the simple harmonic motion of a particle. Consider a body such as the disk shown in Fig. 8. The body is suspended by a vertical wire that obeys Hooke's law for torsional deformations. If the body is rotated through an angle θ from its equilibrium position, the wire exerts a *restoring* torque proportional to θ which we can write (see p. 182) in the form

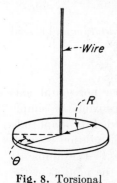

$$L = -C\theta. \tag{21}$$

The restoring torque produces an angular acceleration $\alpha = d^2\theta/dt^2$ of the body, given by the relation

$$L = I\alpha = -C\theta, \tag{22}$$

where I is the moment of inertia of the body. Hence,

Fig. 8. Torsional oscillation.

$$\alpha = d^2\theta/dt^2 = -(C/I)\theta. \tag{23}$$

The mathematical form of (23) is identical with that of equation (10). Hence the solution to the problem of the motion when the body is released from rest at angle Θ from equilibrium will be analogous to (14):

$$\left.\begin{aligned}
\theta &= \Theta\cos 2\pi ft, \\
\omega &= d\theta/dt = -2\pi f\Theta\sin 2\pi ft, \\
\alpha &= d\omega/dt = -4\pi^2 f^2\Theta\cos 2\pi ft = -(4\pi^2 f^2)\ \theta.
\end{aligned}\right\} \tag{24}$$

Comparison with (23) shows that the frequency f is given by the relation $4\pi^2 f^2 = C/I$; hence

$$f = \frac{1}{2\pi}\sqrt{\frac{C}{I}}. \quad \begin{Bmatrix} f\ \text{in cycles/sec} \\ C\ \text{in lb·ft/rad} \\ I\ \text{in slug·ft}^2 \end{Bmatrix} \text{ or } \begin{Bmatrix} f\ \text{in cycles/sec} \\ C\ \text{in nt·m/rad} \\ I\ \text{in kg·m}^2 \end{Bmatrix} \tag{25}$$

These equations are like those for linear simple harmonic motion, except that all quantities involved in translational motion have been replaced by their rotational analogues; the motion is called *rotational* or *angular simple harmonic motion*. The maximum angle Θ is called the *amplitude* of the angular simple harmonic motion.

We can readily write down the energy relationships for a body executing angular simple harmonic motion. The external work done on the system in giving the body its initial angular displacement Θ is equal to $\frac{1}{2} C\Theta^2$; this is the value of the initial potential energy of the system and therefore the value of the total mechanical energy E of the system. If the body is released and permitted to oscillate about its equilibrium position, the mechanical energy E of the system remains constant, provided there are no frictional effects. At any angle θ in the subsequent motion the potential energy is $\frac{1}{2} C\theta^2$ and the kinetic energy is $\frac{1}{2} I\omega^2$; therefore, we may write

$$\text{P.E.} + \text{K.E.} = E,$$

or
$$\tfrac{1}{2} C\theta^2 + \tfrac{1}{2} I\omega^2 = \tfrac{1}{2} C\Theta^2.$$

From this equation, we obtain an expression analogous to (20'):

$$\omega = \pm \sqrt{C/I} \ \sqrt{\Theta^2 - \theta^2}. \tag{26}$$

The system of Fig. 8 is frequently called a *torsion pendulum* and is said to execute *torsional oscillations*.

5. THE MOTION OF A PENDULUM

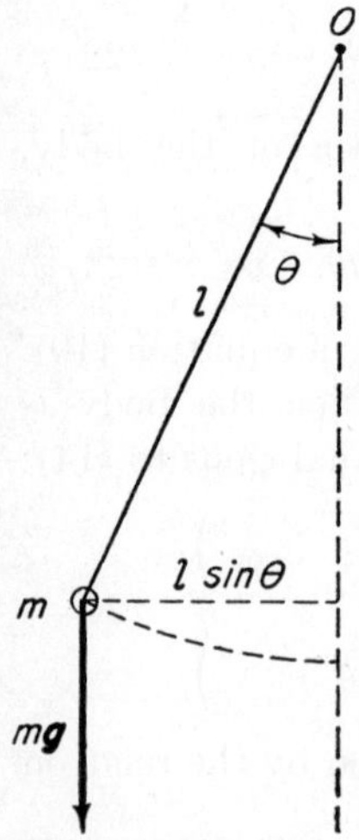

Fig. 9. The simple pendulum.

THE ROTATIONAL motion of a pendulum about a horizontal axis through its point of support approximates simple harmonic motion very closely, provided the amplitude of oscillation about the equilibrium position is small compared to one radian. As the first example of pendulum motion, let us consider the motion of the *simple pendulum* shown in Fig. 9, which consists of a particle of mass m, called the *bob*, supported by a light wire or thread of length l and negligible mass. A simple pendulum is an idealization in which the whole mass is considered as concentrated at a point.

We can consider the motion as the rotational oscillation of a rigid body about a horizontal axis through O, the fixed point of support. The equilibrium position of the pendulum is the position in which the center of gravity of the bob is immediately below the point of support O. If the pendulum has an angular displacement θ from the equilibrium position as shown in Fig. 9, the force of gravity exerts a torque about the axis through O that tends to restore the pendulum to the equilibrium position. The magnitude of this torque is $mgl \sin\theta$. For small angular displacements, $\sin\theta$ may be replaced by θ itself measured in radians. Hence, for small values of θ, we may write

$$L = -mgl\theta, \tag{27}$$

where the negative sign is used because the torque is counterclockwise when θ is clockwise, and vice versa. This torque gives the pendulum an angular acceleration α given by the relation

$$L = I\alpha = -mgl\theta$$

or
$$\alpha = d^2\theta/dt^2 = -(mgl/I)\theta, \tag{28}$$

where I, the moment of inertia about the axis through O, is $I = ml^2$.

Equation (28) is identical in form with equation (23). Therefore, we conclude that the angular motion of the pendulum is similar to that of the body in Fig. 8. The frequency f of the simple pendulum, for *small* angular oscillations, is given by (25), with C replaced by mgl, as

$$f = \frac{1}{2\pi}\sqrt{\frac{mgl}{ml^2}} = \frac{1}{2\pi}\sqrt{\frac{g}{l}}. \tag{29}$$

Using this value for the frequency, we may use equations (24) to determine the angular displacement θ, angular velocity ω, and the angular acceleration α of the pendulum. By multiplying these quantities by l, we may determine the arc length from the equilibrium position, linear velocity, and tangential acceleration of the bob as functions of time. The frequency of a simple pendulum is seen by (29) to be independent of its mass.

A rigid pendulum, such as the familiar clock pendulum, is called a *physical pendulum*. A physical pendulum executes rotational simple harmonic motion like a simple pendulum, provided the amplitude of the motion is small, and we can readily derive a general expression for its frequency of oscillation.

The drawing in Fig. 10 represents a body pivoted about a horizontal axis perpendicular to the drawing and passing through point O located

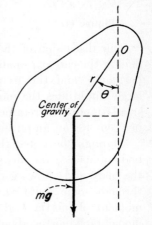

Fig. 10. The physical pendulum.

at a distance r from the center of gravity of the body. The equilibrium position of the body is the position in which the center of gravity is directly below the axis through O. If the body has an angular displacement θ from this equilibrium position, the restoring torque has the value

$$L = -mgr \sin\theta,$$

or, for small displacements,

$$L = -mgr\theta.$$

The body therefore has angular acceleration $d^2\theta/dt^2$ given by

$$I \, d^2\theta/dt^2 = -mgr\theta$$

or

$$d^2\theta/dt^2 = -(mgr/I)\theta,$$

where I is the moment of inertia of the body about the axis through O. This equation is similar to equation (28), and hence the frequency and period of oscillation are given by

$$f = \frac{1}{2\pi}\sqrt{\frac{mgr}{I}}, \qquad T = 2\pi\sqrt{\frac{I}{mgr}}. \qquad (30)$$

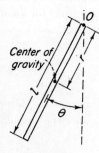

Figure 11.

Example. *Find the frequency of oscillation of a meter stick pivoted at one end as in Fig. 11.*

Let l be the total length of the stick; then $r = \frac{1}{2}\,l$ and $I = \frac{1}{3}\,ml^2$. Hence, the oscillation frequency is given by

$$f = \frac{1}{2\pi}\sqrt{\frac{\frac{1}{2}mgl}{\frac{1}{3}ml^2}} = \frac{1}{2\pi}\sqrt{\frac{3g}{2l}}.$$

Taking $g = 9.81$ m/sec^2, $l = 1$ m, we obtain

$$f = \frac{1}{2\pi}\sqrt{\frac{3 \times 9.81 \text{ m/sec}^2}{2 \times 1 \text{ m}}} = 0.610 \text{ cycle/sec.}$$

Our discussion of the motion of pendulums has been an approximate one for the case of 'small amplitudes.' In this case the motion is simple-harmonic, and the frequency is independent of the amplitude. For large amplitudes the motion is periodic but not simple-harmonic. The small-amplitude treatment gives the frequency correctly to within one per cent for an amplitude as large as 20° (on each side of the vertical).

It might be noted that if g is known, the moment of inertia I of a body of mass m and any shape whatever can be determined by suspending the body and allowing the body to swing as a pendulum about an axis through some point O. By noting the frequency of oscillation, the moment of inertia I about the axis can be obtained from (30). The moment of inertia about a parallel axis through the center of gravity can then be determined by the parallel-axis theorem given on p. 206.

Because of the occurrence of g in (30), this formula can be used to determine the acceleration of gravity by measuring the frequency of a pendulum of accurately known dimensions. The pendulum method furnishes one of the most accurate values of g obtainable.

6. EQUILIBRIUM OF A DYNAMICAL SYSTEM

The dynamical system consisting of the pendulum of Fig. 10 and the earth is in stable equilibrium when the pendulum is at angle $\theta = 0$, which is its position of *minimum* potential energy.   When it is in this position, the pendulum-earth system will not tend by itself to change its configuration, and any stray external forces that might tend to change the configuration would have to do work to increase the potential energy, and when such stray forces were removed, the internal forces would tend to return the pendulum to the position of minimum potential energy.

Exactly similar statements can be made about the weight-spring system of Fig. 4, even though the potential energy is here of elastic, rather than gravitational, nature.

Generalization of the above arguments to other types of systems involving any type of potential energy leads to the following important physical principle:

> *A dynamical system is in stable equilibrium when it is at rest in a configuration of minimum potential energy.*

We shall have occasion to apply this principle to the configurations of liquids in Chap. 16, where we shall introduce a 'surface potential energy' arising from the forces between the liquid molecules.   This principle will explain why liquid droplets are spherical, and why the meniscus of a liquid assumes its characteristic shape.

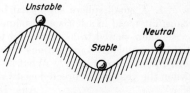

Figure 12

To conclude this discussion, we might define the terms: *stable, neutral,* and *unstable* equilibrium, illustrated in Fig. 12.

> A dynamical system at rest is in **stable equilibrium** when any small change in configuration resulting from forces external to the system *increases* the potential energy of the system, and the resulting internal forces tend to return the system to its original configuration.

An example is the pendulum of Fig. 10 at $\theta = 0$, or a cone resting on its base.   The external force might result from a breeze or from jarring of the supports.

> A dynamical system at rest is in **unstable equilibrium** when any small change in configuration resulting from forces external to the system *decreases* the potential energy of the system, and the resulting internal forces tend to move the system far from its original configuration.

An example is the pendulum of Fig. 10 at $\theta = 180°$.   At this position it is in equilibrium—there is no torque—but any small disturbance from this position will result in torques internal to the pendulum-earth system that tend to send it toppling toward $\theta = 0$. Another example of a system in unstable equilibrium is a cone *balanced on its point*.

A dynamical system at rest is in **neutral equilibrium** when any small change in configuration resulting from forces external to the system *does not change* the potential energy of the system, and no net internal force results.

A wheel mounted on a frictionless horizontal axle exactly through its center of gravity is one example of neutral equilibrium; a sphere resting on a perfectly flat horizontal plane is another; so is a circular cone *resting on its side*.

We see that configurations of *stable*, *neutral*, and *unstable* equilibria correspond to configurations of *minimum*, *constant*, and *maximum* potential energy, respectively.

PROBLEMS

Note: Consider the masses of springs as negligible and the amplitude of oscillation of pendulums as small compared to 1 rad, unless otherwise instructed.

1. A small sphere supported by a metal rod is set into circular motion at constant speed in a horizontal plane. The motion of the sphere is counterclockwise when viewed from above and the radius of the circular path is 2 ft. If the sphere completes 3 revolutions every 2 sec, what is its tangential velocity? its centripetal acceleration? What is the direction of its centripetal acceleration when the velocity is directed eastward? when the velocity is directed northward?

Ans: 18.9 ft/sec; 178 ft/sec²; northward; westward.

2. If the sphere in Prob. 1 is directly *east* of the center of its path at time $t = 0$, write expressions for the northward components of (a) its displacement from the center, (b) its tangential velocity, and (c) its centripetal acceleration, as functions of time in seconds. (Use a coordinate system like that in Fig. 1.)

3. If the sphere in Prob. 2 weighs 2 lb, what is the magnitude of the centripetal force acting on the sphere? Write an expression for the northward component of the centripetal force as a function of time.

Ans: 5.53 lb; $F_Y = -5.53 \sin(9.42 \text{ sec}^{-1} t)$ lb.

4. A centripetal force of 20 nt acts on a 500-g body moving in a circular path 80 cm in radius. Find the rotational frequency of the body in its motion about the center of the circle. (Treat the body as a point mass.)

5. A force of 10 lb produces an elongation of 0.25 in when applied to a certain coil spring. What is the force constant of this spring? If a block weighing 8.05 lb supported by this spring is displaced 3 in downward from its equilibrium position and then released, the block executes simple harmonic motion. What is the frequency of this motion? the period? the amplitude?

Ans: 480 lb/ft; 6.98 cycles/sec; 0.143 sec; 0.25 ft.

6. When a body of 2-kg mass is suspended from a spring, the spring experiences an elongation of 4 cm. What is the force constant of this spring? If the body is displaced 2 cm upward from its equilibrium position and then released, the body executes simple harmonic motion. Find the amplitude, frequency, and period of the motion.

7. Write equations for the upward displacement Y, the velocity v_Y, and the acceleration a_Y as a function of time for the body described in Prob. 5.
Ans: $Y = -0.25 \cos(43.8\,t\ \mathrm{sec}^{-1})$ ft; $v_Y = 11.0 \sin(43.8\,t\ \mathrm{sec}^{-1})$ ft/sec;
$$a_Y = 480 \cos(43.8\,t\ \mathrm{sec}^{-1})\ \mathrm{ft/sec^2}.$$

8. Write equations for the displacement, velocity, and acceleration as functions of time for the body described in Prob. 6.

9. The masses of bodies can be compared by observing their frequencies of oscillation when supported by a spring. A body of mass 1.000 kg is supported by a spring; when this body is set into motion about its equilibrium position, the frequency is found to be 0.543 cycle/sec. When the first body is removed and a second body of unknown mass is supported by the same spring and set into motion, the frequency is found to be 1.214 cycles/sec. What is the mass of the second body? Ans: 0.200 kg·

10. If a third body of unknown mass supported from the spring mentioned in Prob. 9 has an oscillation frequency of 0.531 cycle/sec, what is the mass of the body? What is the force constant of the spring?

11. In Fig. 4, if the block weighs 50 lb and the springs have force constants of 6 lb/in and 9 lb/in, determine the period of oscillation. Ans: 0.584 sec.

12. In Fig. 4, if the mass is 50 kg and the springs have force constants of 60 nt/cm and 90 nt/cm, determine the period of oscillation.

13. Show that the expression on the right of (12) has the dimensions of sec^{-1} and that that on the right of (13) has dimensions of sec. Do this for the case in which K and m are expressed in MKS units and also for the case in which they are expressed in British gravitational units.

14. Show by differentiation that expressions (11), (14), and (15) all satisfy the differential equation (10) when f is given by (12).

15. A body of mass 0.5 slug is supported by a spring with force constant 120 lb/ft. If the body is executing simple harmonic motion with an amplitude of 1 in, what is the mechanical energy associated with the motion? When is the potential energy a maximum? When is the kinetic energy a maximum?
Ans: 0.417 ft·lb.

16. What is the frequency of the harmonic motion executed by the body described in Prob. 15? What is the maximum velocity of the body? What is the kinetic energy of the body when it is 0.5 in from its equilibrium position? What is the potential energy of the system when the body has a displacement of 0.5 in?

17. A 2-kg body supported by a spring executes simple harmonic motion at a frequency of 3 cycles/sec with an amplitude of 4 cm. What is the maximum kinetic energy of the body? What is the maximum potential energy of the system? What is the force constant of the spring?
Ans: 0.568 joule; 0.568 joule; 710 nt/m.

18. How much additional energy would have to be imparted to the system described in Prob. 17 in order to increase the amplitude of the oscillation to 8 cm? What would be the maximum velocity of the suspended body oscillating with an amplitude of 8 cm? What would be the displacement of the body when the potential energy and the kinetic energy of the system are equal?

19. A 500-g body is supported by a spring having a force constant of 150 nt/m. What maximum external force must be applied to the body in order to give it a displacement of 6 cm? How much work must be done in order to produce this displacement? If the body were released, what would be the frequency of the resulting motion? What is the velocity of the body when it is 3 cm from its equilibrium position? Ans: 9.00 nt; 0.270 joule; 2.76 cycles/sec; ±0.900 m/sec.

20. A body weighing 16.1 lb is suspended from a spring with force constant 100 lb/ft. By pushing this body, a man gives it a velocity of 4 ft/sec when it passes through its equilibrium position. What is the kinetic energy of the body at its equilibrium position? What will be the amplitude of the body's oscillatory motion about its equilibrium position? At what position will its velocity be 2 ft/sec?

21. The disk in Fig. 8 has mass 0.5 slug and radius 6 in. When an external torque of $L = 2$ lb·ft is applied, the disk turns through an angle $\theta = 30°$. What is the torsion constant of the wire? If the external torque is removed, the disk oscillates about its equilibrium position. What is the frequency of the oscillation? What is the total mechanical energy associated with the oscillatory motion? Ans: 3.82 lb·ft/rad; 1.25 cycles/sec; 0.524 ft·lb.

22. A slender uniform rod of mass 0.5 slug and length 4 ft is attached perpendicular to the same wire as in Prob. 21. The point of attachment is at the mid-point of the rod. What is the frequency of oscillation of the rod? If the amplitude of the oscillation is 30°, what is the maximum angular velocity of the rod?

23. A 1-kg solid sphere of radius 10 cm is attached to the end of a wire. If the sphere is twisted from its equilibrium position and then released, torsional oscillations result. If the frequency of the oscillatory motion is 1.5 cycles/sec, what is the torsion constant of the wire? Ans: 0.355 nt·m/rad.

24. A large wheel of mass 4 kg is attached to the end of the wire mentioned in Prob. 23, the wire coinciding with the axis of the wheel. When the wheel is twisted from its equilibrium orientation and released, it oscillates with a period of 5 sec. What is the moment of inertia of the wheel? its radius of gyration?

25. A wire with a torsion constant of 0.20 nt·m/rad supports a solid disk of mass 4 kg and radius 50 cm as shown in Fig. 8. One joule of work is done in twisting the disk from its equilibrium orientation; it is then released and permitted to oscillate. Find the amplitude of the oscillation and the maximum angular velocity of the disk. Ans: 3.16 rad; 2.00 rad/sec.

26. Find the values of the kinetic and potential energies and the angular velocity of the system described in Prob. 25 when the angular displacement is (a) 1 rad, and (b) 2 rad.

27. The balance wheel of a watch is supposed to have a period of 1 sec when it oscillates as a torsion pendulum. If the balance wheel has mass 1.5 g and radius of gyration 3 mm, what must be the torsion constant of the hairspring? Ans: 5.33×10^{-7} nt·m/rad.

28. A simple pendulum consists of a small bob of mass 100 g at the end of a thread 120 cm long. What is the moment of inertia of this pendulum about an axis passing through the point of suspension of the thread? What is the frequency of oscillation of the pendulum?

29. A 'seconds pendulum,' which beats seconds, has a period of 2 sec. What should be the length of such a simple pendulum at a place where the gravitational acceleration is 9.81 m/sec²? Ans: 0.994 m.

30. What would be the precise length (to four significant figures) of a simple seconds pendulum at a sea-level station at the equator? at 40° N. lat.? at the North Pole? (See Table I, p. 64.)

31. A flat circular disk of 2-ft diameter is pivoted for rotation about a horizontal axis perpendicular to the face of the disk and passing through the periphery of the disk.   Find the frequency of oscillation of the resulting pendulum.   What is the length of the simple pendulum of the same period?   Ans: 0.521 cycle/sec; 3.00 ft.

32. The disk mentioned in Prob. 31 is pivoted for rotation about a certain horizontal axis perpendicular to the face of the disk.   If the period of oscillation of the disk about this axis is 4 sec, what is the distance of this axis from the center of the disk?

33. What is the period of a pendulum formed by pivoting a meter stick so that it is free to rotate about a horizontal axis passing through the 100-cm mark? through the 75-cm mark? through the 60-cm mark?

Ans: 1.64 sec; 1.53 sec; 1.94 sec.

34. Show that the three periods in Prob. 33 are in the ratio $\sqrt{40}:\sqrt{35}:\sqrt{56}$ exactly.

35. If a stick of length l is mounted so as to rotate about a horizontal axis perpendicular to the stick and a distance r from the center, show that the period has a *minimum* value when $r = l/\sqrt{12} = 0.289\ l$.

36. A bicycle wheel has diameter 26 in and weighs 7 lb.   When hung by its rim across a horizontal knife-edge 12.5 in from the center, it executes small vibrations with a period of 1.53 sec.   What is its radius of gyration (with respect to the center of the wheel)?

37. To determine the moment of inertia of a flywheel weighing 100 lb, it is hung with the inside of its rim over a horizontal knife-edge, and found to oscillate at 0.6 cycle/sec.   If the knife-edge is 11 in from the center of the flywheel, determine the radius of gyration about the axis through the center of the wheel.

Ans: 1.11 ft.

38. Show that if a thin circular hoop is hung over a knife-edge, it oscillates with the same frequency as a simple pendulum of length equal to the diameter of the hoop.

39. A one-meter bar is pivoted at the 60-cm mark in an evacuated enclosure. If it makes 1860 (small) oscillations in one hour, what is the value of g?

Ans: 9.84 m/sec².

40. If the meter bar of Prob. 39 at another location makes 3710 (small) oscillations in two hours, what is the value of g?

41. What is the maximum tension in the string when a simple pendulum of mass 100 g supported by a string 120 cm long is oscillating with an amplitude of 0.2 rad on each side of the vertical?   Ans: 1.020 nt.

42. Show that the maximum tension in the string of the simple pendulum of Fig. 9, when the amplitude Θ is small, is $mg(1+\Theta^2)$.

43. The simple pendulum of Fig. 9 executes periodic motion of amplitude Θ, less than 90° but not necessarily small compared to 1 rad.   Show that the tangential acceleration at the end of the swing ($\theta = \Theta$) is $g \sin\Theta$.   Show that the value of α in the small-amplitude approximation would give $g\Theta$.   What is the ratio of the approximate to the exact values at $\Theta = 60°$? 30°? 15°?

Ans: 1.21; 1.05; 1.01.

44. In Prob. 43, show that the square of the maximum speed of the bob is $v^2 = 2gl(1 - \cos\Theta)$.   Show that the small amplitude approximation would give $v^2 = gl\Theta^2$.   What is the ratio of the approximate to the exact value of the maximum speed for $\Theta = 60°$? 30°? 15°?

45. If the lower end of the oscillating stick of Fig. 11 has speed v when $\theta = 0$, show that the upward lift of the pivot at this point of the swing is $mg + \frac{1}{2}\ mv^2/l$. State carefully the reasoning involved in all steps of the solution of this problem.

46. Show that for small oscillations the physical pendulum of Fig. 10 has the same period as a simple pendulum of length k^2/r, where k is the radius of gyration about axis O.

47. Show that at any angle θ, not necessarily small, the physical pendulum and the simple pendulum of Prob. 46 will have the same angular acceleration; hence that they will move in synchronism and have the same period for any amplitude Θ, large or small.

48. The bob of a simple pendulum is supported by a flexible thread of length l. When the bob hangs straight down it is given an initial speed v_0 by a horizontal impulse. The bob is carried past $\theta = 90°$ and above the point of support. The string ceases to be taut and the bob leaves its circular path when the string makes (acute) angle ϕ with the upward vertical. Show that $v_0 = \sqrt{gl\,(2+3\cos\phi)}$. Verify separately the correctness of this equation for the special cases $\phi = 0$ and $\phi = 90°$.

49. The ballistic pendulum of Fig. 13 is a cubical block of wood suspended at the corners by four parallel strings in such a way that if the block is given a horizontal impulse, it will move in pure translation, without rotation. If the strings are 4 ft long, the block has mass $\frac{3}{2}$ slug, and a bullet of mass 0.003 slug fired into the block from the right causes the pendulum to swing to $\theta = 15°$, what was the speed of the bullet?   Ans: 1480 ft/sec.

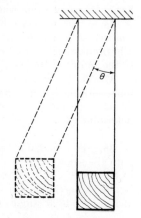

Fig. 13. Ballistic pendulum.

50. Using the crude but phenomenologically realistic model of a solid illustrated in Fig. 1, p. 257, show that Young's modulus would be given by $E_Y = N^{2/3}K\lambda$, where N is the number of atoms per m³, K is the force constant of each spring, and λ is the distance between atoms (the length of the spring).

51. From optical studies there is evidence that the vibration frequencies of atoms in solids are of the order of 10^{13}/sec. Assume that this is the frequency of vibration to right and left of a single copper atom in Fig. 1, p. 257, when all other atoms are at rest. Compute the force constant of an individual spring. Use the fact that 64 g of Cu atoms (one mole) contain 6×10^{23} atoms (Avogadro's number).   Ans: 210 nt/m.

52. From the results of the two problems above, compute the order of magnitude of Young's modulus for copper and compare with the value given in Table I, p. 186.

53. Repeat the computation of Probs. 51 and 52 for the case of aluminum, using the same vibration frequency.

PART II
HEAT

CHAPTER 12

TEMPERATURE; THERMAL EXPANSION

WITH THIS CHAPTER we begin our study of the branch of physics known as *heat*, which deals with certain phenomena that cannot be described completely in terms of the theories presented earlier under the heading of mechanics.

It is the aim of physics to develop a single consistent body of theory that is sufficiently general to permit a complete description of physical phenomena in terms of *fundamental physical quantities*, the number of such fundamental quantities being kept as small as possible. Thus, the whole of mechanics can be described in terms of *length, mass,* and *time*. For these quantities we chose quite arbitrary units—the kilogram, meter, and second. It was appropriate to take length, mass, and time as fundamental quantities because these quantities cannot be defined in terms of a simpler set of physical quantities, or in terms of each other. We then proceeded to define other useful quantities, such as *force, momentum, energy, acceleration,* and *density,* in terms of the three fundamental quantities that we had selected. Quantities defined *in terms* of the fundamental quantities are called *derived quantities*. We could have chosen a different set of quantities as fundamental—for example, force, length, and time—; the important thing is that just *three* such quantities are required.

No difficulty was encountered in defining *all* the quantities needed for the description of mechanical phenomena in terms of just the three fundamental quantities: length, mass, and time. However, in describing *thermal* phenomena we find that we need one quantity that cannot be thus defined. This quantity is *temperature*. Until the middle of the last century still another quantity—the *quantity of heat* contained in a body—was regarded as fundamental. Then, as we shall discuss in Sec. 1, the work of Rumford and Joule showed that heat is simply a form of mechanical energy associated with random motions of atoms and molecules, so that quantity of heat can be expressed in mechanical energy units. However, as will be pointed out in Sec. 2, *temperature* is a physical quantity of a type distinctly different from *quantity of heat*, and we still have to introduce temperature as a new *fundamental quantity*. Our

255

definition of temperature will consist of a description of the *operations* that must be performed in its measurement.

1. HEAT IS MECHANICAL ENERGY OF RANDOM MOTION ON A MICROSCOPIC SCALE

LITTLE PROGRESS was made in the understanding of phenomena involving heat until the truth of the statement contained in the title of this section was realized.

During the eighteenth and early nineteenth centuries, heat was generally regarded as an elastic fluid, which supposedly pervaded all matter, for which the name *caloric* was adopted. It was supposed that the transfer of heat from a hot body to a cool body consisted of a flow of caloric from the hot to the cool body. The hot body lost caloric and became cooler; the cool body gained caloric and became warmer.

The absurdity of this notion of heat as a kind of substance was strikingly pointed out by Count Rumford* in 1789 in connection with the large amount of heat developed by friction when cannon-boring machinery was operated with a blunt boring tool. Little happened except that an enormous amount of heat was created. Rumford concluded that the source of heat generated by friction appeared to be inexhaustible, so that the heat could not possibly be a kind of substance but must somehow be associated with 'motion.'

Nevertheless, the equivalence of heat and mechanical energy was not firmly established until 1843, when James Prescott Joule showed experimentally that there is a definite proportionality between mechanical work done (in ft·lb) and the heat developed (in thermal units, BTU) when work is done against friction. From Joule's work it was recognized that the thermal units (cal, BTU), which we shall define later, were just units of energy like the mechanical units (joule, ft·lb), and were definite numerical multiples of these mechanical units. Thus, thermal phenomena were related to dynamics and the study of the relations between the two subjects, called *thermodynamics*, made rapid progress in the last half of the nineteenth century with the work of Clausius, Kelvin, Maxwell, Helmholtz, Gibbs, Boltzmann, and many others.

Let us try to visualize in more detail the meaning of the title of this section. It will be simplest to think first of a solid body whose atoms are held in a regular array by elastic forces of an electrical origin. These forces behave exactly as if the atoms of the solid were connected to each other by spiral springs, as in Fig. 1. What is your first impression when you look at this figure? That it resembles a bedspring? Well, a bedspring is a good model to visualize. Or does it appear that if you gave the

---

* Count Rumford (1753–1814), born Benjamin Thompson in North Woburn, Mass., performed his celebrated experiments in Munich while in charge of the Bavarian arsenal. He was a loyalist at the time of the American Revolution.

array of Fig. 1 a little push you could set it into vibration like a bowl of jelly? Well, you can. Of course these springs are relatively stiff and there are a tremendous number of them, about 10^{23} per cm^3, so you would have to push pretty hard to get much effect. But a hammer blow on the solid of which Fig. 1 is a piece would definitely set it into vibration. The mechanical energy of the hammer, which apparently disappears when the hammer strikes the solid, does not actually disappear; it goes into energy of vibration of the atoms of the solid and the atoms of the hammer face. This vibration is on a scale too small and too fast to be seen or photographed. The amplitude of vibration is of the order of 10^{-9} cm, the frequency of the order of 10^{13} per second. But we can *feel* the vibration. If we touch the solid with out finger tips, some of the vibration energy is transmitted to the atoms of our nerve endings, and the solid feels *hot*. Yes, *this energy of vibration is heat.*

Before going further we must take the opportunity to explain two useful scientific adjectives that we shall have frequent occasion to use, namely, *macroscopic* and *microscopic*. The motion of the hammer is called *macroscopic* because it can be seen and photographed. The kinetic energy of motion of the hammer is called *macroscopic mechanical energy*, or just *mechanical energy*, because it can be computed from the measured velocity of a body of *macroscopic size*, containing a tremendous number of atoms all moving together in a manner that can be seen and photographed. Any body that can be seen and photographed, even though it may be necessary to use a microscope, is called *macroscopic*. The word *microscopic* as used in physics is reserved for phenomena that take place on a scale much too small to be detected by any mechanical measuring instrument and too small to be seen by the best microscope, a scale in fact of the order of atomic sizes. *Random mechanical motion on a microscopic scale*, such as the vibration of the atoms of Fig. 1, *manifests itself as heat* and needs for its detection types of measuring instruments and sense organs different from those employed for detection of macroscopic motion—so entirely different that the fact that heat and macroscopic motion both involve mechanical energy of the same fundamental type was not generally recognized until 1843.

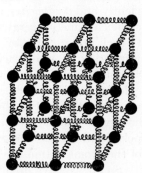

Fig. 1. The forces between atoms in a solid are like those that would be exerted by a set of springs.

Now let us return for a moment to our bedspring analogy. There is one serious discrepancy in the analogy between the vibrations of the bedspring and those of the atoms in Fig. 1. The macroscopic motion of a bedspring gradually subsides, not because the mechanical energy disappears, but because (owing to friction) it is converted from macroscopic into microscopic mechanical energy—that is, into heat. The motion of the atoms of Fig. 1, however, will not subside but will go on indefinitely unless the energy is given to some other body; it cannot be converted into heat because it *is* heat. The 'springs' of Fig. 1 are not ordinary springs with internal friction—they are electrical springs with no property analogous to friction.

The process of adding heat to a solid consists in transferring to it more and more energy, which appears in the solid as energy of atomic vibration. As a result of this increase in energy, the solid feels hotter to the touch, and we say that the *temperature* of the solid has been raised. If the temperature is raised sufficiently, the vibrations become so violent that the solid *melts* and becomes a *liquid*. In the liquid phase the molecules are still held close together by large forces, so that the liquid remains compact and of definite volume, but the molecules have sufficient energy of motion to overcome the forces tending to hold them in a definite spatial arrangement and are able to move around rather freely so long as they remain close to each other. Raise the temperature of the liquid sufficiently and it *vaporizes* and becomes a *gas*. The molecules have acquired sufficient kinetic energy to overcome the forces tending to hold them close to each other. One by one they jump clear of the liquid surface and go wandering off into space at high speed, so that the gas will eventually completely fill a container of any size in which it is confined. The molecules of a gas are ordinarily so far apart that they exert negligible forces on each other. The thermal energy of a gas then consists of kinetic energy of random translational motion plus, in the case of diatomic and polyatomic gases, energy of rotation of the molecules and of vibration of the atoms within the individual molecules.

So far we have used the word *heat* in its popular non-technical sense. The word is used this way in the title PART II, HEAT of this portion of the book, and in the heading of this section. However, since the nature of thermal phenomena has become clearly understood, the word *heat* has taken on a more restricted technical meaning to which we should adhere. We shall begin our technical definitions by correcting the title of this section and thereby defining *thermal energy:*

> **Thermal energy** is mechanical potential and kinetic energy of random motion on a microscopic scale.

The term *heat* has the following restricted technical meaning:

> **Heat** is thermal energy in the process of being added to, or removed from, a given material substance, or in the process of being transferred from one portion of material substance to another.

The measurement of *quantities* of heat will be considered in Chap. 12.

We note that *heat* and *thermal energy* bear the same relation to each other as *work* and *mechanical energy*. *Heat* and *work* represent energy in transition.   A review of mechanical principles shows that work is macroscopic mechanical energy in the process of being added to or removed from a material substance.

2. TEMPERATURE

THE SENSATIONS of 'hotness' and 'coldness' of a given body are determined by what is called its *temperature*.   Add heat to a body and its temperature ordinarily rises.   Remove heat from a body (that is, let it give thermal energy to some other body) and its temperature ordinarily goes down.   For a *given* body, the quantity of thermal energy determines the temperature, but the relation between thermal energy (per unit of volume or of mass) and temperature is different for every different substance.   *The temperature of a body is not, fundamentally, a measure of its thermal energy but, rather, is a measure of its ability to transfer heat to other bodies.*

To clarify this idea, consider a block of copper and a beaker of water. When the block of copper is placed in the beaker of water, one of three things will happen:

(a) The copper will cool down and the water will warm up, indicating transfer of heat from copper to water.

(b) Neither will cool down or warm up, indicating no transfer of heat.

(c) The copper will warm up and the water will cool down, indicating transfer of heat from water to copper.

(Until we have discussed *thermometers*, we can assume that we use our crude cutaneous senses, by feeling the copper and water, to determine whether these have warmed up or cooled down.)

By *definition*, we say that before the block of copper was placed in the water, the following conditions prevailed:

In case (a), *the copper was at a higher temperature than the water.*
In case (b), *the copper and the water were at the same temperature.*
In case (c), *the copper was at a lower temperature than the water.*

In case (b), we shall find that the actual microscopic mechanical-energy contents of the copper and of the water (per unit mass, per unit volume, per molecule, or however we wish to specify them) are quite different; but at the surface of contact, the motions of the water and copper molecules are such that *on the average no energy is transferred from one substance to the other.*   The copper and the water in this case have the same temperature.

> Two bodies have the **same temperature** if, when placed in contact, no heat flows from one to the other.   Body A is at **higher temperature** than body B if, when they are placed in contact, heat flows from A to B.

A group of objects and substances within a well-insulated enclosure, such as a pot of hot coffee, a bucket of ice, and the furniture, walls, and air in a thermally insulated closed room, will transfer heat in such a way that eventually they will all come to the same temperature. At this stage *thermal equilibrium* is said to be established, and no rearrangement of the objects can result in further transfer of heat.

If the body of Fig. 1 is at room temperature, we do not have to hit it with a hammer to set the atoms into vibration. They must already be in fairly violent vibration, since they are capable of giving up a good deal of heat to a colder body, say a block of ice, with which the body might be placed in contact. Hitting the body with the hammer just *adds* thermal energy and sets the atoms into *more violent* vibration. All matter possesses a certain amount of thermal energy.

As temperature scales are set up, there is no theoretical upper limit to temperature; one can go on increasing the thermal energy, and hence the temperature, of a substance indefinitely. On the other hand, *there is a definite lower limit to temperature.* Starting with a body at room temperature, one cannot go on taking thermal energy away from it indefinitely. When it has given up all the thermal energy it is capable of giving up, it has become as cold as it can get, and is said to be at the *absolute zero of temperature.*

> **Absolute zero** is the temperature of a body that is no longer capable of giving up any thermal energy.

That this is the same temperature for all bodies follows logically from our definitions of 'same temperature' and 'higher temperature.'

It has been established experimentally that on the ordinary Centigrade and Fahrenheit temperature scales,

$$\text{absolute zero} = -273.16° \text{ C} = -459.69° \text{ F}. \qquad (1)$$

In the laboratory it has been possible to reach temperatures within a few thousandths of a degree of absolute zero. The method of determining the value (1) will be discussed in Chap. 17.

3. TEMPERATURE SCALES

TEMPERATURE is determined by measurement of some mechanical, electrical, or optical quantity whose value has a one-to-one correlation with temperature. Usually the temperature of a substance is not determined by a measurement made on the substance directly, but by measurement on an instrument called a *thermometer* that is brought into thermal equilibrium with the substance and hence acquires the same temperature.

Thermometers based on the expansion of a liquid were invented early in the seventeenth century. At first they had completely arbitrary scales, so that each thermometer gave readings peculiar unto itself. The desirability of standardizing the readings was recognized late in the seventeenth century, and our present scales were devised during the first half of the eighteenth century.

In defining a temperature scale, two conveniently reproducible temperatures called the *fixed points* are used.

> The **lower fixed point** (the **ice-point**) is the temperature of a mixture of pure ice and water exposed to the air at standard atmospheric pressure.

> The **upper fixed point** (the **steam-point**) is the temperature of steam from pure water boiling at standard atmospheric pressure.

The temperature scale used in all scientific work and in common use in many countries is the *Centigrade scale*, in which the fixed points are taken as 0° C and 100° C; hence the name of the scale.*

The common Fahrenheit scale was devised in 1714 by Gabriel Daniel Fahrenheit, scientist and scientific instrument manufacturer in Danzig and Amsterdam. On this scale the fixed points are 32° F and 212° F. Fahrenheit arrived at these curious figures by taking 0° as the temperature of a freezing mixture of ice and salt in his laboratory (actually a temperature as low as −9° F may be obtained with the proper mixture of ice and salt), and choosing 96°, for some unexplained reason, to represent the temperature of the human body (his scale missed this value by 2.6°, but this discrepancy can be attributed to experimental inaccuracy).

A third scale, still in common use in Scandinavian countries and parts of Germany, was devised about 1731 by a Frenchman, René Antoine de Réaumur, who called the fixed points 0° and 80°. We shall not be further concerned with the Réaumur scale.

The original thermometers were of the type still in common use; they make use of the volumetric thermal expansion of liquid mercury from a reservoir into an evacuated glass capillary tube of uniform bore. The positions of the end of the liquid column in the capillary tube at the temperatures of the fixed points are determined and marked. The distance between the marks is divided into 100 equal spaces for the Centigrade scale, or 180 for the Fahrenheit scale, to give the individual degrees. Above and below the fixed points the scale may be extended by marking off degrees of the same size. This calibration is illustrated in Fig. 2.

The method of interpolating and extrapolating the scale relative to the fixed points, depending as it does on the expansion properties of a particular substance, mercury, lacks fundamental significance. Also, it is impossible to extend the scale in this way below the freezing point and

---

* In 1948, the Ninth General Conference on Weights and Measures decided that the Centigrade scale should be called the *Celsius scale*, in honor of Anders Celsius (1701–1744), a Swedish astronomer who was one of the first proponents of this scale. The name *Celsius* has not yet come into general use in English-speaking countries, although it has been used on the continent of Europe for some time.

above the boiling point of mercury. These difficulties were resolved by Lord Kelvin, who devised a *thermodynamic scale of temperature* that is independent of the physical properties of any particular substance. This is the fundamental scale internationally adopted for thermometer calibrations. The mercury thermometer, calibrated as above, gives readings very close to those of the thermodynamic scale, and hence the calibration we have described furnishes a satisfactory definition of temperature in the ordinary range pending a more detailed consideration of the thermodynamic scale in Chap. 17.

Because there are 100 Centigrade degrees (C deg) and 180 Fahrenheit degrees (F deg) between the ice-point and the steam-point, we see that

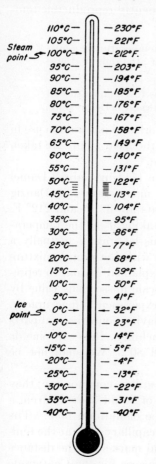

Fig. 2. Centigrade and Fahrenheit temperature scales.

$$100 \text{ C deg} = 180 \text{ F deg},$$

so

$$1 \text{ C deg} = \tfrac{9}{5} \text{ F deg}, \Bigg\} \quad (2)$$

and

$$1 \text{ F deg} = \tfrac{5}{9} \text{ C deg.}$$

Note that because of the way temperature scales are set up we must distinguish in notation between a temperature and a temperature difference. We write *temperatures* as °, C, or F; thus,

$$0° \text{ C} = 32° \text{ F},$$
$$5° \text{ C} = 41° \text{ F}.$$

The difference between two temperatures is not a temperature but a temperature interval. It would be nonsense to conclude, by subtracting the first of the equations immediately above from the second, that $5° \text{ C} = 9° \text{ F}$, when we have already noted that $5° \text{ C} = 41° \text{ F}$, but we can properly conclude that

$$5 \text{ C deg} = 9 \text{ F deg.}$$

This is an equation that relates the *sizes* of Centigrade and Fahrenheit degrees rather than relating actual temperatures. We write *temperature intervals* as C deg or F deg, and these symbols can be handled like ordinary units by using the relations in (2).

We now turn to the problem of converting temperatures from one scale to the other. Rather than trying to remember a formula for this, it is best to remember the fixed points of each scale, and hence the relative size of the degrees, and to use the scheme of the following illustrative examples:

Example. *What is the Centigrade temperature corresponding to 68° F?*

We start by noting that

$$68° \text{ F} = 36 \text{ F deg above the ice-point,}$$

which, from (2),　　$= 36 \times \frac{5}{9}$ C deg above the ice-point

$$= 20 \text{ C deg above the ice-point} = 20° \text{ C.}$$

Example. *What is the Fahrenheit temperature corresponding to* $-273.16°$ C *(the most accurately determined value of absolute zero)?*

We note that

$$-273.16° \text{ C} = 273.16 \text{ C deg below the ice-point}$$

$$= 273.16 \times \frac{9}{5} \text{ F deg below the ice-point}$$

$$= 491.69 \text{ F deg below the ice-point,}$$

which, since the ice-point is $+32°$ F,

$$= -459.69° \text{ F.}$$

For much of the theory of heat, it is necessary to express temperatures on an *absolute scale*, in which temperatures are measured from absolute zero. There are two absolute scales in use, one in which temperatures are measured in degrees of Centigrade size, the other in which Fahrenheit-size degrees are used.

The absolute scale in which temperatures are measured from absolute zero in Centigrade-size degrees is always used in scientific work, and is known as the *Kelvin scale*. Since absolute zero is $-273°$ C,* a temperature may be expressed in ° K by adding 273 to the value in ° C. Thus,

$$\text{absolute zero} = 0° \text{ K,} \qquad 10° \text{ C} = 283° \text{ K,}$$

$$0° \text{ C} = 273° \text{ K,} \qquad -10° \text{ C} = 263° \text{ K,} \quad \text{etc.}$$

Temperature differences on the Kelvin scale are the same as on the Centigrade scale and are measured in units that can be called either C deg or K deg.

The absolute scale employing Fahrenheit-size degrees is in frequent use in engineering practice and is known as the *Rankine scale*. Since absolute zero is $-460°$ F,* a temperature may be expressed in ° R by adding 460 to the value in ° F.

Any property of matter that varies with temperature in a measurable way can be made the basis of a thermometer. The various properties that are used for thermometric purposes are:

(a) Expansion of a liquid.
(b) Expansion of a solid (see next section).
(c) Variation of pressure or volume of a gas (see Chap. 15).

---

* For ordinary purposes this round number is sufficiently accurate.

(d) Variation of electrical resistance (see Chap. 29).
(e) Thermoelectricity (see Chap. 31).
(f) Variation of quantity of radiated energy (see Chap. 14).
(g) Variation of color of radiated light (see Chap. 37).
(h) Variation of vapor pressure (see Chap. 16).

4. THERMAL EXPANSION OF SOLIDS

LET US LOOK again at Fig. 1 and attempt to visualize the atoms in
violent thermal agitation. Since the average amplitude of vibration of
the molecules increases with temperature, it seems reasonable that the
average distance between the atoms should increase with temperature,
and hence that the over-all size of the solid should increase with temperature—such a thermal expansion is observed. The increase in dimensions
of a solid with increasing temperature is small. The order of magnitude
is easy to remember: *a meter length of solid lengthens by about 1 millimeter
for a temperature rise of 100 Centigrade degrees.*

Thermal expansion is of sufficient magnitude, however, to be an
important factor in many engineering and practical problems. Thermal
expansion makes necessary the provision of expansion joints in buildings,
bridges, and steam pipes, and provision for temperature compensation of
pendulums of clocks and balance wheels of watches; it makes possible the
shrink-fitting of steel tires on wheels and of collars on shafts; and it results
in the breakage of ordinary glass when heat is irregularly applied.

The change in any linear dimension of a solid, such as the length,
width, height, radius, or distance between two marks, is known as the
linear expansion. We shall denote the length in question by l; the
increase in length that arises from an increase in temperature of ΔT
we shall denote by Δl. The quantities ΔT and Δl are considered to be
positive for increases and negative for decreases. Thus, $\Delta T = +10$ C deg
means a temperature rise of 10 C deg; this might be accompanied by an
increase of length represented by $\Delta l = +0.15$ mm.

Experiment shows that the change in length, Δl, is proportional* to
the change in temperature, ΔT. It is of course also proportional to the
length l itself, so we can write

$$\Delta l = \alpha \, l \, \Delta T, \tag{3}$$

where α is called the *coefficient of linear expansion.* This coefficient has
different values for different materials. Since we can write

$$\alpha = \frac{\Delta l}{l \, \Delta T}, \tag{4}$$

The **coefficient of linear expansion** of a solid is the change in
length per unit length per degree change in temperature.

---

* This statement is sufficiently accurate for ordinary purposes. Careful tabula-
tions of physical constants give a power series in ΔT of which (3) is the first term, and
the other terms are negligible unless ΔT is very large.

The dimensions of α are deg^{-1}; its value does not depend on the particular unit of length used, but does depend on the size of unit used to measure ΔT.   Thus, if a meter bar lengthens 1 mm for a temperature increase of 100 C deg, we have, from (4),

$$\alpha = \frac{10^{-3} \text{ m}}{1 \text{ m} \times 100 \text{ C deg}} = \frac{10^{-5}}{\text{C deg}}. \tag{5}$$

Since, from (2), 1 C deg $= \frac{9}{5}$ F deg, this same coefficient of linear expansion is

$$\alpha = \frac{10^{-5}}{\text{C deg}} = \frac{10^{-5}}{\frac{9}{5} \text{ F deg}} = \frac{\frac{5}{9} \times 10^{-5}}{\text{F deg}}.$$

Since the F deg is only $\frac{5}{9}$ as large as the C deg, the solid expands only $\frac{5}{9}$ as much per F deg as per C deg.

For most purposes, α can be considered to be a constant for a given solid material, independent of the particular temperature at which the temperature change takes place, although accurate measurements do show a slight variation of α with temperature.   We shall ignore such variations and assume that if a meter bar lengthens 10^{-5} m when the temperature goes from $0°$ C to $1°$ C, it will also lengthen by 10^{-5} m when the temperature goes from $100°$ C to $101°$ C.   Furthermore, to the accuracy with which most expansion coefficients are known for commercial materials (two significant figures), it does not matter whether the l in (3) and (4) is taken to be the length at the initial temperature or at the final temperature, since these differ only by the quantity Δl, which is very small compared to l itself.

Values of the coefficient of linear expansion of various commercial materials are given in Table I.

TABLE I

TYPICAL COEFFICIENTS OF LINEAR EXPANSION OF COMMERCIAL MATERIALS
NEAR ROOM TEMPERATURE (PER C DEG)

Aluminum	24 $\times 10^{-6}$	Magnesium	26 $\times 10^{-6}$
Bakelite	28	Nickel	13
Brass or bronze	19	Oak (across fiber)	54
Brick	9	Oak (parallel to fiber)	5
Copper	17	Pine (across fiber)	34
Glass (ordinary)	9	Pine (parallel to fiber)	5
Glass (Pyrex)	3	Platinum	8.9
Gold	14	Quartz (fused)	0.4
Granite	8	Silver	19
Ice	51	Solder	25
Invar (Ni 36%, Fe 64%)	0.9	Steel	12
Iron (cast)	11	Tin	20
Lead	29	Tungsten	4.3

When an isotropic solid expands thermally, the distance between every two points increases in the ratio α per degree temperature rise, just as in the case of a photographic enlargement except that the solid is three-dimensional. For example, the size of a hole in the solid *enlarges* in the same ratio as an external dimension. That the hole enlarges, rather than shrinks as students have been known to state, should be clear from the analogy with the photographic enlargement which is illustrated in Fig. 3. Every line drawn on the solid, whether straight or curved, lengthens in the ratio α per degree temperature rise. For example, if C is the circumference of a circle, $\Delta C = \alpha\, C\, \Delta T$.*

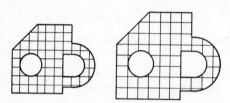
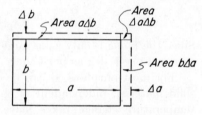

Fig. 3. The thermal expansion of a solid is like a photographic enlargement.

Fig. 4. Thermal increase in area. The sizes of Δa and Δb are highly exaggerated.

Let us now consider what happens to the *area* of a figure drawn on the surface of an isotropic solid, or to the area of a sheet of solid. We consider first the change in area of a rectangle (Fig. 4) of sides a and b, area $A = ab$. When the temperature increases by ΔT, a lengthens by $\Delta a = \alpha\, a\, \Delta T$, b lengthens by $\Delta b = \alpha\, b\, \Delta T$, and the area increases by

$$\Delta A = a\, \Delta b + b\, \Delta a + \Delta a\, \Delta b,$$

as may be seen algebraically from the equation $A + \Delta A = (a + \Delta a)(b + \Delta b)$, or geometrically from Fig. 4. On substituting the values of Δa and Δb in the equation above, we find

$$\Delta A = a\alpha b\, \Delta T + b\alpha a\, \Delta T + \alpha^2 ab\, (\Delta T)^2 = \alpha\, ab\, \Delta T\, (2 + \alpha\, \Delta T).$$

Now we see from Table I that $\alpha \sim 10^{-5}$/C deg; so even if ΔT is as large as 1000 C deg, $\alpha\, \Delta T \sim 10^{-2}$, which is negligible in comparison with 2. Therefore, we can drop the $\alpha\, \Delta T$ term in this equation and write $\Delta A = 2\alpha\, ab\, \Delta T$, or

$$\Delta A = 2\alpha\, A\, \Delta T. \qquad (6)$$

What we have neglected is the area $\Delta a\, \Delta b$ of the small rectangle in Fig. 4 in comparison with the area of the two strips $a\, \Delta b$ and $b\, \Delta a$. In equation (6), 2α expresses the change in area per unit area per degree.

---

* It should be noted that we are considering *isotropic* solids. Anisotropic solids such as wood have different linear expansion coefficients for different directions, as noted in Table I for oak and pine. Noncubic single crystals may have a different value of α for each crystal axis.

The **coefficient of area expansion** of a solid is the change in area per unit area per degree change in temperature.

The coefficient of area expansion of an isotropic solid is twice the coefficient of linear expansion.

If we consider that (6) applies to an infinitesimal rectangle and then use calculus methods, we can easily see that formula (6) will give the change in area for a surface with a boundary of any shape and that it will apply equally well to plane and curved surfaces. For example, it will give the change in surface area of a sphere or in the surface area of a hole in a solid.

An exactly similar computation involving similar approximations shows that the change in volume of a solid of volume V is given by

$$\Delta V = 3\alpha \, V \, \Delta T. \tag{7}$$

Here, 3α expresses the change in volume per unit volume per degree.

The **coefficient of volume expansion** of a solid or liquid is the change in volume per unit volume per degree change in temperature.

The coefficient of volume expansion of an isotropic solid is three times the coefficient of linear expansion.

The difference in expansion coefficient of different metals, usually brass $(\alpha = 19 \times 10^{-6}/\text{C deg})$ and steel $(\alpha = 12 \times 10^{-6}/\text{C deg})$, is utilized in thermometry and more particularly in the common *thermostat* by welding strips of these materials together to form a *bimetallic strip*. As illustrated in Fig. 5, if the strip is straight at a certain temperature, it will bend one way at higher temperatures, the other way at lower temperatures, because the brass has a greater tendency than steel to lengthen or shorten with temperature change. Bimetallic strips are also used in the rim

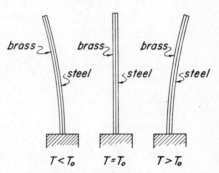

Fig. 5. Principle of the bimetallic thermometer or thermostat element. In the thermostat, the motion of the strip opens or closes electrical contacts.

of the balance wheel of a watch to vary the moment of inertia in such a way as to keep the period of the balance wheel constant as the temperature changes.

5. THERMAL EXPANSION OF LIQUIDS

In the case of a *fluid* (a liquid or a gas) we are not concerned with linear or area expansion because the *shape* of a fluid is not well defined;

only the *volume* of a fluid is of significance. The ways in which liquids and gases respond to changes in temperature or pressure are quite different. Gases respond strongly, whereas the change of volume of liquids with changes in temperature or pressure is very small, only slightly greater than that of solids. Gases will be considered in detail in Chap. 15.

Experiment shows that for liquids it is possible to define a coefficient of volume expansion of the same type as we defined for a solid. In the case of a solid we denoted the coefficient of volume expansion in (7) by 3α, since it was directly related to the coefficient of linear expansion. In the case of a liquid we have no coefficient of linear expansion, so we shall denote the *coefficient of volume expansion* by β, writing

$$\Delta V = \beta \, V \, \Delta T. \qquad (8)$$

For most liquids the value of β is relatively independent of the temperature at which the temperature change ΔT takes place. Typical values of β are given in Table II; it is seen that these values are in general of the order of 10 times as great as the coefficient of volume expansion 3α for a solid. The behavior of water is distinctly anomalous, and will be considered separately.

TABLE II

COEFFICIENTS OF VOLUME EXPANSION OF LIQUIDS NEAR ROOM
TEMPERATURE

Liquid	β	Density at 20° C
Alcohol, ethyl..............	112 $\times 10^{-5}$/C deg	791 kg/m^3
Alcohol, methyl............	120	792
Benzene...................	124	877
Carbon tetrachloride.......	124	1,595
Ether, ethyl..............	166	714
Glycerin..................	51	1,261
Mercury..................	18.2	13,546
Turpentine...............	97	873

One is frequently concerned with the change of density of a liquid, since density is a well-defined property that can readily be measured by a hydrometer. The density is defined by the equation

$$\rho = m/V, \qquad (9)$$

where m is the mass of liquid that occupies a volume V. In this equation both ρ and V depend on temperature. If we differentiate with respect to temperature, we find

$$\frac{d\rho}{dT} = -\frac{m}{V^2}\frac{dV}{dT} = -\frac{\rho}{V}\frac{dV}{dT},$$

or

$$\frac{1}{\rho}\frac{d\rho}{dT} = -\frac{1}{V}\frac{dV}{dT}.$$

To the approximation in which (8) is valid, these differentials can be replaced by finite changes, and we can write

$$\frac{1}{\rho}\frac{\Delta\rho}{\Delta T} = -\frac{1}{V}\frac{\Delta V}{\Delta T} = -\beta.$$

Hence, $$\Delta\rho = -\beta\,\rho\,\Delta T. \qquad (10)$$

The minus sign expresses the fact that since volumes increase with increasing temperature, densities decrease with increasing temperature. From (10), changes in density can be computed from the coefficients of volume expansion given in Table II.

The use of an equation such as (8) or (10) implies that the change in volume or density is so small that it does not matter whether the volume or density inserted on the right is the value at temperature T or that at $T+\Delta T$. This condition is not satisfied over so large a temperature range for volumetric expansion of liquids as it is for solids. When this condition is not satisfied, one must consult detailed data on density as a function of temperature, given in handbooks and physical tables.

Example. *Two thermometers made of ordinary glass have exactly the same shape and size and contain, at 0° C, identical volumes of methyl alcohol and mercury respectively. Compare the intervals between the degree marks on the two thermometers.*

When the temperature rises one degree, the volume of the glass container increases by an amount proportional to the coefficient of volume expansion of glass; the volume of the liquid increases by an amount proportional to the coefficient of volume expansion of the liquid. Only insofar as the coefficient for the liquid is greater than that for the glass, so that new volume needs to be occupied, will the liquid rise in the stem. It is easy to see that for the two geometrically identical thermometers in question the amount of rise per degree will be proportional to the *difference* between the volume expansion of the liquid and that of the glass; that is, proportional to the difference in coefficients of volume expansion. Hence if we denote the intervals between the degree marks by l_{Alcohol} and l_{Mercury} respectively,

$$\frac{l_{\text{Alcohol}}}{l_{\text{Mercury}}} = \frac{\beta_{\text{Alcohol}} - 3\,\alpha_{\text{Glass}}}{\beta_{\text{Mercury}} - 3\,\alpha_{\text{Glass}}} = \frac{120\times10^{-5} - 2.7\times10^{-5}}{18.2\times10^{-5} - 2.7\times10^{-5}} = \frac{117}{15.5} = 7.61.$$

The alcohol-in-glass thermometer will have degree intervals 7.6 times as large as those of the mercury-in-glass thermometer.

Anomalous behavior of water. The density of water does not decrease at all regularly with temperature according to an equation like (10). Rather, the density of water increases slightly from 0° C to 4° C, where it has its maximum value of 1000 kg/m³ or 1.0000 g/cm³;* then the density

---

* It is to this value of *unit* maximum density of water, in g/cm³, that the relative sizes of the kilogram and meter were originally supposed to correspond. Accurate measurements show that the international standards of mass and length correspond to this value to within 3 parts in 100,000; the maximum density of water is actually 0.999973 g/cm³ at 3.98° C (see inset to Fig. 6).

decreases, at first slowly and later more rapidly. The density of liquid water is plotted against temperature in Fig. 6. *Between 0° C and 4° C, water contracts as the temperature rises.* Such a contraction with increasing temperature is extremely exceptional among known liquids. Salt solutions, such as sea water, behave in the same way for a few degrees above the freezing point. This behavior is critical to the manner in

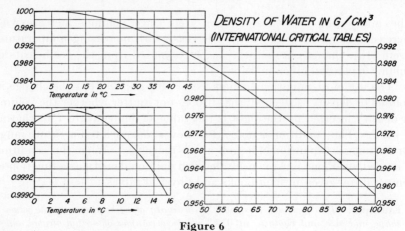

Figure 6

which lakes and the polar ocean freeze from the top down rather than from the bottom up.

PROBLEMS

1. What is normal human body temperature, 98.6° F, on the Centigrade scale? the Kelvin scale? the Rankine scale?   Ans: 37.0° C, 310.2° K, 558.4° R.

2. What is pasteurization temperature, 165° F, on the Centigrade scale? the Kelvin scale? the Rankine scale?

3. What is the melting point of silver, 960.5° C, on the Fahrenheit scale? the Kelvin scale? the Rankine scale?   Ans: 1761° F, 1233° K, 2221° R.

4. What is the melting point of gold, 1063° C, on the Fahrenheit scale? the Kelvin scale? the Rankine scale?

5. At what temperature will the reading of a Fahrenheit thermometer be exactly double that of a Centigrade thermometer?   Ans: 320° F.

6. At what temperature will the reading of a Centigrade thermometer be the same as that of a Fahrenheit thermometer?

7. What is the difference between 20° C and 32° F in C deg? in F deg?
                           Ans: 20 C deg, 36 F deg.

8. What is the difference between 350° F and 10° C in C deg? in F deg?

9. A metal rod 120 cm long increases in length by 1.48 mm when heated from 0° C to 96° C. What is the coefficient of linear expansion of this metal in (C deg)$^{-1}$? in (F deg)$^{-1}$?   Ans: 12.8×10^{-6}/C deg; 7.1×10^{-6}/F deg.

10. A glass rod 120 cm long increases its length by 0.72 mm when heated from 0° C to 75° C. What is the coefficient of linear expansion of this glass in (C deg)$^{-1}$? in (F deg)$^{-1}$?

11. If steel railroad rails are placed when the temperature is 35° F, how much gap must be left between each standard 39-ft rail section and the next if the rails should just touch when the temperature rises to 120° F?   Ans: 0.27 in.

12. How many inches provision for expansion and contraction must be provided for a 400-ft steel bridge section to allow for temperature extremes of −20° F and +110° F?

13. A locomotive wheel is 48 inches in diameter. A steel tire, with diameter 0.020 inch undersize at 20° C is to be shrunk on. To what temperature must it be heated to make the diameter 0.020 inch oversize?   Ans: 89.5° C.

14. A blacksmith wants to fit a steel tire on a wooden wheel 36 inches in diameter. He makes the tire 0.1 inch undersize in diameter at 20° C. To what temperature must he heat the tire before it can just be slipped over the wheel?

15. Shrink fits are frequently made by cooling the male part in solid carbon dioxide, which has a temperature of −78.5° C. How many ten-thousandths of an inch oversize can a steel shaft be made at 30° C and still fit a 1-in hole if it is first cooled with CO_2?   Ans: 13.

16. A clock with an uncompensated brass pendulum is adjusted at 70° F. How many seconds will the clock gain or lose per day at 100° F?

17. If a steel tape is accurate at 20° C and is used to measure off a mile at 20° F, how many feet should be read on the tape to get a true mile?

Ans: 5281.7 ft.

18. If a steel tape is accurate at 20° C and is used to measure off a mile at 100° F, how many feet should be read on the tape to get a true mile?

19. A hollow spherical electrode used in a high-voltage machine is made of aluminum. If the electrode has a diameter of exactly 1 m at 0° C, find the increase in diameter, surface area, and volume when heated by allowing steam at 100° C and 1 atm pressure to enter the sphere.

Ans: 2.40×10^{-3} m, 1.51×10^{-2} m^2, 3.77×10^{-3} m^3.

20. A cylindrical steel drum has a volume of exactly 80 gallons when filled with steam at 100° C. What is the volume of this drum at 20° C? If the length of the drum is exactly twice its diameter, how much does the surface area of the drum change when the temperature drops from the steam point to 20° C?

21. A quantity of mercury occupies 150 cm^3 at 20° C. What is its change in volume when cooled to 0° C?   Ans: −0.546 cm^3.

22. A narrow-necked brass bottle is just filled with 116 cm^3 of ethyl alcohol at 0° C. How many cm^3 spill over when the bottle is brought to a room temperature of 19° C?

23. A narrow-necked bottle of ordinary glass is just filled with mercury at 20° C. The volume of mercury is then 80.0 cm^3. How many cm^3 spill over when the bottle is placed in steam at 100° C?   Ans: 0.99 cm^3.

24. Derive a general formula that gives the volume of a liquid that spills over in problems such as 22 and 23 in terms of β for the liquid, α for the container, and the temperature rise.

25. A thermometer is made of a capillary tube of ordinary glass of 0.0100 mm^2 cross section at 0° C. At 0° C, there is 0.600 cm^3 of mercury in the reservoir and capillary up to the 0° mark. How far does the mercury move up the tube at 15° C?   Ans: 14.0 cm.

26. A thermometer is made of a capillary tube of ordinary glass of 0.0150 mm^2 cross section at 0° C. At 0° C there is 0.400 cm^3 of methyl alcohol in the reservoir and capillary up to the 0° mark. How far does the fluid move up the tube at 5° C?

27. A brass cube 4 cm on an edge at 0° C is weighed in water at 0° C and at 50° C. Find the difference in the weights.   Ans: 5.75×10^{-3} nt.

28. What pressure in atmospheres is required to keep water from expanding when it is heated from 4° C to 100° C?

29. A steel bar 1 in² in cross section and 18 in long is inserted with no clearance between two fixed supports when the temperature is 0° C. If the bar is heated to 70° C, what force does the bar exert on each support?   Ans: 24,400 lb.

30. A steel surveyor's tape is accurate at 70° F. With what tension in lb/in² would it have to be stretched at 40° F in order to read correctly?

31. In modern practice, railroad rails are sometimes butt-welded into a continuous length. If rails are laid and welded in the summer at 90° F, what is the tensile stress in the winter at −20° F? If the ultimate strength is 72,000 lb/in², what is the factor of safety with respect to rupture?   Ans: 21,300 lb/in²; 3.4.

32. A bimetal strip to be used in a thermostat is made by fastening a strip of steel to a strip of brass by closely spaced rivets. Each strip is 1 cm thick and 20 cm long at 0° C. Compute the approximate radius of curvature of the bimetal strip when its temperature is 100° C. If one end of the bimetal strip is fixed, what is the movement of the free end when the temperature is raised from 0° C to 100° C?

33. A steel tank is filled with turpentine when the temperature is 15° F, at which temperature its volume is 80 gal. How much liquid will overflow when the temperature is 105° F?   Ans: 3.74 gal.

34. An entrepeneur buys 2000 gal of benzene when the temperature is −15° F and sells the benzene the following summer when the temperature is 95° F. Assuming no loss by evaporation, find how many gallons he has for sale.

NOTE: When atmospheric or other pressures are expressed in mm or inches of mercury, what is meant is the height of mercury column, at the 0° C density of 13,595.0 kg/m³ and under the pull of standard gravity, that will balance the pressure being measured. A barometer reading must therefore be corrected for both temperature of mercury and for local gravity (latitude and altitude of location). It is easy to show that the correction from local acceleration of gravity, g_{Local}, to standard gravity, g_0, is made by multiplying the barometric height by g_{Local}/g_0. From Table I p. 64, we see that at sea level this correction can amount to as much as 8 parts in 3000 or 2 mm in 760 mm. In the following three problems we assume that the barometer is located where the pull of gravity is standard, and we shall consider the correction for temperature.

35. Show that when the temperature of a liquid in a barometer changes by ΔT, the pressure remaining constant, the height h changes by

$$\Delta h = \beta \, h \, \Delta T, \tag{11}$$

where β is the coefficient of volume expansion. *Suggestion:* since the pressure is $h\rho g$ in appropriate units, write $(h+\Delta h)(\rho+\Delta\rho)g = h\rho g$ and solve for Δh by the methods we have been using.

36. When the Weather Bureau gives a barometric height of 29.54 in, what would be the height in inches of a mercury barometer at 25° C?

37. The mercury in a barometer stands at a height of 759.6 mm in a room at 20° C. What would be the mercury height at 0° C?   Ans: 756.8 mm.

NOTE: In the next two problems equation (11) can be used, because the height of each column is a measure of the same pressure difference, that between point P and the atmosphere. Apparatus based on the principle of Fig. 7 furnishes the most accurate measurement of coefficients of volume expansion of liquids.

38. In Fig. 7, if the water bath on the left is at 10° C, that on the right at 25° C, $h = 153$ cm, and $\Delta h = 1.43$ cm, determine the coefficient of volume expansion of the liquid in the U-tube.

39. In Fig. 7, the U-tube is filled with a liquid whose volumetric expansion is to be determined. The water bath on the left is kept at 0° C by melting ice. The bath on the right is at a temperature of 15.0° C, h is 116 cm, and Δh is observed as 1.50 cm. Determine β. Ans: 86×10^{-5}/C deg.

40. The temperature of a block of aluminum is raised 100 F deg. How much must the hydrostatic pressure be increased in order to prevent expansion of the block?

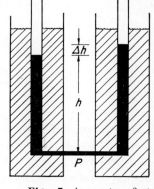

Fig. 7. Apparatus first used by Dulong and Petit in 1816.

41. Prove that the change in moment of inertia, I, of a solid object is given by $\Delta I = 2\alpha I \, \Delta T$.

42. Prove (using the result of Prob. 41) that the change in period, t, of any physical pendulum is given by $\Delta t = \frac{1}{2}\alpha t \, \Delta T$.

43. Show that if a thread of liquid of length l is contained in a capillary tube of uniform bore and the temperature of tube and liquid is raised by ΔT, then the increase in length of the thread will be $\Delta l = (\beta - 2\alpha) l \, \Delta T$, where α refers to the material of the tube. What will be the *apparent* change in length as measured by graduations on the tube?

44. Show that the coefficient of volume expansion of an isotropic solid is 3α. By similar methods, find the cubical expansion coefficients for oak and pine wood from the data given in Table I. If an anisotropic solid has linear coefficients α_1, α_2, and α_3 for three mutually perpendicular directions in the solid, what is the cubical expansion coefficient for the solid?

45. Determine the relative lengths of the 0° C–2° C, 2° C–4° C, 4° C–6° C, 6° C–8° C, and 8° C–10° C graduations of a water-in-ordinary-glass thermometer.

46. Discuss the way in which the pendulum of an accurate clock is 'compensated' by attaching tubes containing mercury to the bottom of the pendulum.

47. The steel hairspring of a watch has a torsion constant that decreases with increasing temperature, while the moment of inertia of the wheel increases. Show that both of these effects can be 'compensated' by making the rim of the balance wheel from a bimetallic strip and splitting the rim at two points.

48. The volume of the hot-water heating system of a house is equivalent to that of 12,000 ft of 1-in inside diameter steel pipe. How much room must be allowed for expansion in the reservoir (see Fig. 3, p. 292) if the system is filled at 40° F and is heated to 180° F?

CHAPTER 13

CALORIMETRY

CALORIMETRY refers to the laboratory science of making measurements of quantities of heat—that is, of quantities of thermal energy added to or removed from a quantity of matter. Under this heading we shall not discuss details of laboratory techniques but rather the principles underlying calorimetric methods and the calorimetric determination of the thermal constants of matter.

We start with definitions of the 'thermal' units that were developed for the study of heat exchange before the nature of heat was clearly understood. These thermal units are actually energy units and have definite sizes in terms of the mechanical energy units we have already studied, but so long as attention is confined to the exchange of heat between different bodies, with no introduction of mechanical or electrical energy, the relation of the thermal energy units to the mechanical energy units does not enter the considerations.

Everything we shall study in this chapter is based on the equation

loss of heat by hot bodies = gain of heat by cold bodies,

which applies when bodies at various temperatures are placed in juxta-position and come to thermal equilibrium in a properly insulated enclo-sure, called a *calorimeter*. Thermal units were invented and this equation was applied in the days when heat was considered a kind of substance (caloric), and indeed it is seen that this equation is consistent with con-servation of quantity of a substance. Only with the study of interchange of energy between thermal and other forms was it recognized that heat is not a substance but mechanical energy of a particular form, and hence that this equation expresses the principle of conservation of energy.

Much of the modern calorimetric work is done by electrical methods, and the most accurate values of the thermal constants are so obtained. In these methods, heating is done electrically, and the quantities of energy furnished are measured by electrical means. The way in which such electrical measurements are made will be studied in Part V of this text.

1. THE THERMAL UNITS OF ENERGY

COMMON USAGE based on the historical course of development of the subject makes it necessary to introduce new units for the measurement of quantities of thermal energy.   It is unfortunate that we may not merely measure quantities of heat in joules or ft·lb, but it is necessary to establish access to the large body of experimental data expressed in thermal units.   We shall be able to change freely from thermal units to ordinary mechanical units by means of conversion factors where this is desirable.

The common metric thermal unit of energy is the *calorie* (cal):

> The **calorie** is the amount of energy required to raise the temperature of one gram of water from 14.5° C to 15.5° C.

The *kilocalorie* (kcal) is 1000 calories, and is thus the energy required to raise the temperature of one kilogram of water from 14.5° C to 15.5° C.*

The only other heat unit in use in the United States is the *British thermal unit* (BTU).   This unit is the amount of energy required to raise the temperature of one pound-mass of water by one Fahrenheit degree centered around 15° C = 59° F:

> The **British thermal unit** (BTU) is the amount of energy required to raise the temperature of one pound-mass of water from 58.5° F to 59.5° F.

To relate the BTU and the cal, we use the experimental fact that for small temperature intervals the heat required to raise the temperature of water is proportional to the temperature interval.   Thus, since 1 C deg = $\frac{9}{5}$ F deg,

> $\frac{9}{5}$ BTU will raise the temperature of 1 pound-mass, or 453.6 g, of water from 14.5° C to 15.5° C.

> 1 BTU will raise the temperature of $\frac{5}{9} \times 453.6$ g = 252.0 g of water from 14.5° C to 15.5° C.

But it requires 252.0 cal to do just this, so

$$1 \text{ BTU} = 252.0 \text{ cal.} \tag{1}$$

Joule determined the relation between the BTU and the ft·lb by measuring the temperature rise of water stirred by rotating paddles turned at a measured angular velocity with a measured torque.   Such experiments show that

$$1 \text{ cal} = 4.186 \text{ joules;} \quad 1 \text{ BTU} = 778 \text{ ft·lb.} \tag{2}$$

2. SPECIFIC HEAT

> The **specific heat** of a substance is the quantity of heat required to increase the temperature of unit mass of the substance one degree.

---

* This is the usage among physical scientists.   We note, however, that physiologists in discussing food metabolism use the term *calorie* for what we call the kilocalorie.   Popular cookbook tables that say that there are "120 calories in one wedge of angel cake" or "250 calories in two codfish balls" are really referring to the approximate number of *kilo*calories of heat developed when one wedge of angel cake or two codfish balls are burned (in a bomb calorimeter, in pure oxygen, after thorough drying).

The specific heat is expressed in the metric system in cal/g·C deg (or in kcal/kg·C deg). In the British system it is always the pound-mass that is used as the unit mass in defining specific heat, rather than the slug. While we were careful in Part I on Mechanics to reserve the abbreviation lb for the force unit, it should cause no confusion if we now adopt the customary loose practice of using the same abbreviation for the quite different unit of mass. Thus the unit of specific heat in the British system is the BTU/lb·F deg, but the student must keep in mind that the lb in the denominator stands for pound-mass and not for pound-force, as it does for example in equation (2).

Since

$$\frac{1 \text{ BTU}}{1 \text{ lb} \times 1 \text{ F deg}} = \frac{252.0 \text{ cal}}{453.6 \text{ g} \times 5/9 \text{ C deg}} = 1 \frac{\text{cal}}{\text{g·C deg}} = 1 \frac{\text{kcal}}{\text{kg·C deg}}, \quad (3)$$

the numerical value of the specific heat is the same in any of these sets of units. We notice that the cal and BTU were defined in such a way that the specific heat of water would be exactly one unit in either system. It takes 1 cal to raise the temperature of 1 g of water 1 C deg, and 1 BTU to raise the temperature of 1 lb of water 1 F deg. Since the specific heat of water is one unit in either system of units and since the specific heat of any other substance must bear a constant ratio to that of water, independent of the system of units, the specific heat of any substance must have the same numerical value in both systems, as demonstrated by (3).

Specific heat is ordinarily denoted by the symbol c.

While the specific heat of a substance varies slightly with the temperature at which the temperature change takes place, it will be adequate for our present discussion to assume that specific heat is a constant independent of temperature. Then we can determine the heat (customarily

TABLE I

SPECIFIC HEATS OF SOLIDS AND LIQUIDS
(In cal/g·C deg or BTU/lb·F deg)

Metallic solids		Nonmetallic solids		Liquids	
Aluminum	0.212	Ice	0.48	Water	1.00
Brass	0.090	Clay	0.22	Ethyl alcohol	0.58
Copper	0.094	Coal	0.3	Gasoline	0.5
Gold	0.031	Concrete	0.16	Mercury	0.033
Iron and steel	0.11	Glass	0.12–0.20	Mineral oil	0.5
Lead	0.031	Limestone	0.22	Methyl alcohol	0.60
Platinum	0.032	Marble	0.21	Olive oil	0.47
Silver	0.056	Paraffin	0.69	Petroleum	0.51
Tin	0.055	Rubber	0.48	Sea water	0.93
Zinc	0.094	Wood	0.3–0.7	Turpentine	0.41

denoted by Q) necessary to raise the temperature of a mass m of a substance by ΔT degrees by multiplying the specific heat c (which is the heat added per unit mass per degree) by m and by ΔT.   Hence,

$$Q = c \, m \, \Delta T. \tag{4}$$

In this equation, if m is in lb and ΔT in F deg, Q will be in BTU; if m is in g and ΔT in C deg, Q will be in cal; c will have the same *numerical* value in each case.

Values of the specific heat of various solids and liquids are given in Table I; the specific heats of gases will be considered in Chap. 15.   It will be noted that water has the highest specific heat of any of the common substances listed in Table I.   The slight variation of the specific heat of water with temperature is plotted in Fig. 1.

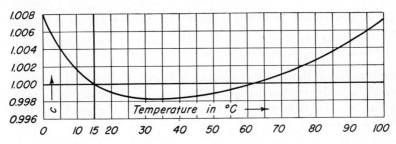

Fig.   1. Specific heat of liquid water, in cal/g·C deg or BTU/lb·F deg, as a function of temperature. These values were determined by measuring the electrical energy required to heat the water one degree at various temperatures. Source of data: N. E. Dorsey, *Properties of Ordinary Water Substance*, p. 258 (Reinhold, New York, 1940).

Specific heats of many substances can be determined by the method of mixtures.   A discussion of this method will illustrate the principle on which all calorimetric computations are made, namely,

loss of heat by hot bodies = gain of heat by cold bodies.   (5)

A calorimeter is a vessel that is well jacketed (thermally insulated) to prevent heat flow to or from the surroundings.   Since such heat flow cannot be entirely eliminated, elaborate methods are used in accurate work to estimate, and correct for, the actual heat transfer to the surroundings.   We shall not discuss these methods here.   The following example will illustrate a typical calorimetric determination of the specific heat c_{Cu} of copper.   In working this example, it is assumed that the calorimeter is perfectly insulated.

Example.   *A copper calorimeter of 250-g mass contains 400 g of water. Calorimeter and water are initially at room temperature of 20.0° C as measured by a thermometer in the water.   A block of copper of 1-kg mass is heated to 100° C by placing it in the steam from water boiling at normal atmospheric* *pressure. It is then removed from the steam and quickly placed in the water of the calorimeter. The copper block cools, the water and the calorimeter become warmer, and the final temperature, as read on the thermometer, is found to be 34.5° C. From these data determine the specific heat c_{Cu} of Cu.*

The fundamental equation (5) becomes

$$\left\{ \begin{array}{l} \text{heat lost by} \\ \text{copper block} \end{array} \right\} = \left\{ \begin{array}{l} \text{heat gained} \\ \text{by water} \end{array} \right\} + \left\{ \begin{array}{l} \text{heat gained by cop-} \\ \text{per calorimeter} \end{array} \right\}.$$

The value of each of these terms is given by (4) as $mc\,\Delta T$ (in cal). Substituting the known values of m, c, and ΔT, we have

$$1000\ \text{g} \cdot c_{Cu} \cdot 65.5\ \text{C deg} = 400 \cdot 1 \cdot 14.5\ \text{cal} + 250\ \text{g} \cdot c_{Cu} \cdot 14.5\ \text{C deg},$$

whence $c_{Cu} = 0.094\ \text{cal/g} \cdot \text{C deg.}$

In the above substitution, 14.5 C deg is the temperature increase of the calorimeter ($34.5 - 20.0 = 14.5$), and 65.5 C deg is the temperature decrease of the copper block ($100.0 - 34.5 = 65.5$).

It is convenient to define a quantity called the *heat capacity:*

> The **heat capacity** of a body is the quantity of heat required to raise the temperature of the body by one degree.

Heat capacity is measured in units such as BTU/F deg, cal/C deg. For a composite body containing masses m_1, m_2, $\cdots$, of materials of specific heats c_1, c_2, $\cdots$, it is seen that the heat capacity is given by the expression $m_1 c_1 + m_2 c_2 + \cdots$.

3. LATENT HEATS OF FUSION AND OF VAPORIZATION

IF WE START with a piece of ice at $-20°$ C, we must add heat to it (0.48 cal/g·C deg according to Table I) in order to raise its temperature to $0°$ C. At this point further addition of heat causes some of the ice to melt. *During the melting process no temperature rise takes place.* For each 80 cal of heat added, one gram of ice melts. Only after sufficient heat has been added to melt *all* the ice does any temperature rise of the water take place. The value, 80 cal/g, is known as the *latent heat of fusion** of ice.

> The **latent heat of fusion** of a substance is the heat that must be added to unit mass of the solid at its melting point to change it to liquid at the same temperature and pressure.

If we put a pan of water on the stove and turn on the gas, the temperature of the water rises fairly rapidly to its boiling point of $100°$ C (at normal pressure). After this temperature has been reached, we must continue to supply heat for a very much longer time if we want to evaporate all the water. Supplying heat at a constant rate causes the water to evaporate at a constant rate. *During the process of evaporation no tem-*

---

* The term *latent* is used here to indicate that the addition of this heat does not result in any change in temperature, so that its addition is not apparent in the reading of a thermometer. *Fusion* is the scientific synonym for *melting.*

perature rise takes place; a thermometer in the steam and one in the water will each read 100° C continuously.   But we have to add 540 cal to evaporate each gram of water.   This value, 540 cal/g, is known as the *latent heat of vaporization* of water.

> The **latent heat of vaporization** of a substance is the heat that must be added to unit mass of the liquid at its boiling point to change it to vapor at the same temperature and pressure.

The boiling point of a liquid varies with pressure, and the latent heat of vaporization varies also.   Furthermore, evaporation of a liquid takes place also at temperatures below its boiling point and a latent heat is involved in this process.   The melting point of a solid varies only very slightly with pressure.   These matters will be treated in Chap. 16.   For the present we shall confine ourselves to processes taking place at normal atmospheric pressure.

Either of the two latent heats can be expressed in cal/g or BTU/lb. The relation between these units is given by

$$1 \frac{\text{BTU}}{\text{lb}} = \frac{252.0 \text{ cal}}{453.6 \text{ g}} = \tfrac{5}{9} \frac{\text{cal}}{\text{g}}, \qquad\qquad \Biggr\} \quad (6)$$

and
$$1 \text{ cal/g} = \tfrac{9}{5} \text{ BTU/lb}.$$

Hence, the latent heat of fusion of water is

$$80 \text{ cal/g} = 80 \times \tfrac{9}{5} \text{ BTU/lb} = 144 \text{ BTU/lb},$$

and the latent heat of vaporization of water is

$$540 \text{ cal/g} = 970 \text{ BTU/lb}.$$

The reason why a factor $\tfrac{9}{5}$ occurs in converting latent heats from metric to English units even though no such factor occurs in specific heats can be seen from the following argument: It takes 1 cal to raise the temperature of 1 g of water 1 C deg, 1 BTU to raise the temperature of 1 lb of water 1 F deg.   But the BTU does not raise the temperature of the pound by as much as the cal raises the temperature of the gram because 1 F deg is smaller than 1 C deg; the BTU has only $\tfrac{5}{9}$ the physical effect on the lb that the cal has on the g.   To raise the temperature of 1 g of water from its freezing to its boiling point requires 100 cal, whereas to raise the temperature of 1 lb of water from its freezing to its boiling point requires 180 BTU.   It takes 180 BTU to have the *same physical effect* on a pound-mass as 100 cal have on a gram.   Hence, it takes 144 BTU to have the same effect on a pound-mass as 80 cal has on a gram—for example, in melting ice.

In calorimetric problems involving melting, freezing, vaporization, or condensation, one must include the latent heats among the quantities of

TABLE II

TEMPERATURE AND LATENT HEATS OF FUSION AND VAPORIZATION
AT NORMAL PRESSURE

Substance	Melting point (°C)	Latent heat of fusion (cal/g)	Boiling point (°C)	Latent heat of vaporization (cal/g)
Water.............	0	79.70	100	539.2
Ammonia.........	−75	108.0	−34	327.1
Helium...........	−272	......	−269	5.97
Hydrogen........	−259	15.0	−253	106.7
Methane.........	−182	14.5	−161	138
Nitrogen.........	−210	6.2	−196	47.8
Oxygen..........	−219	3.3	−183	51
Ethyl alcohol.....	−115	24.9	78	204.3
Methyl alcohol...	−98	22.0	65	262.8
Aluminum........	660	93.0	2056	2000
Copper..........	1083	50.6	2595	1760
Gold.............	1063	16.1	2966	446
Iron.............	1539	65	2740	1620
Lead.............	327	6.3	1744	222
Mercury.........	−39	2.7	357	71
Platinum.........	1774	27.1	4407	640
Silver...........	960	24.3	2212	552
Tin.............	232	14.4	2270	650
Tungsten........	3400	44	5927	1180
Zinc............	419	24.1	907	362

heat lost or gained.   Table II gives the melting and boiling points and the corresponding latent heats for various substances.   The latent heats given for water in Table II represent the most accurate determinations; the rounded-off values in the text above are sufficiently accurate for use in the problems in this book.

Example. *How many grams of ice at 0° C must be added to 500 g of water at 100° C in a 200-g aluminum calorimeter in order to cool the calorimeter and its contents to 25° C?*

We denote the unknown mass of ice by m and use the basic calorimetry principle (5).   The ice gains heat: (80 cal/g) $m = 80\ m$ cal/g are required to melt the ice and (1 cal/g·C deg)(m)(25 C deg) $= 25\ m$ cal/g are required to raise the temperature of the water resulting from the melted ice to the final temperature of 25° C.   The hot water loses (1 cal/g·C deg)(500 g)(75 C deg) $= 37,500$ cal in cooling from 100° C to 25° C, while the aluminum calorimeter loses (0.212 cal/g·C deg)(200 g)(75 C deg) $= 3180$ cal.   Equating heat gain to heat loss gives

$$80\ m\ \text{cal/g} + 25\ m\ \text{cal/g} = 37,500\ \text{cal} + 3180\ \text{cal},$$
$$105\ m = 40,680\ \text{g},$$
$$m = 387\ \text{g},$$

the required mass of ice.

4. HEAT OF COMBUSTION

WHEN A chemical reaction takes place, it is ordinarily either *exothermic*, meaning that it gives out heat, or *endothermic*, meaning that it takes in heat.   A certain amount of chemical binding energy is changed into thermal energy, or vice versa.   The amount of this energy, per unit quantity of material reacting, is known as the *heat of reaction*.

The principal chemical reaction that is used for heating purposes is the process of combination with oxygen—burning or *combustion*.   In this case the heat of reaction is known as *heat of combustion* and is specified in cal/g, or BTU/lb.   The mass in the denominator refers to the mass of material burned but does not include the mass of the oxygen that enters

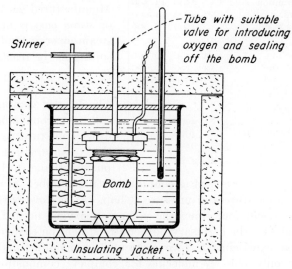

Fig. 2. Bomb calorimeter (schematic).

the reaction.   Thus, the statement that the heat of combustion of anthracite is 8000 cal/g means that one gram of anthracite, when it reacts completely with whatever mass of oxygen is necessary to ensure complete combustion, gives out 8000 cal of heat.

Heats of combustion are ordinarily measured in a *bomb calorimeter*. The 'bomb' (Fig. 2) is a massive gun-metal cylinder, fitted with a gas-tight screwed cover, and capable of withstanding the high pressures of the gaseous combustion products.   In this calorimeter a measured mass of material burns in an atmosphere of pure oxygen under pressure so that complete combustion is assured.   The ignition is by an electric current through a fine wire, and the combustion takes place with explosive violence.   The heat of combustion is determined by the final temperature rise of the water and of the calorimeter and its contents, after thermal equilibrium is reached.

Table III gives the heats of combustion of various solid and liquid fuels. The relations (6) connect the metric and British units, for the same reason as in the case of latent heats. Heats of combustion of gaseous fuels are ordinarily given in BTU per ft³ of gas, the volume being measured at 1 atm and 0° C. Typical values for gaseous fuels are

Manufactured gas
500–550 BTU/ft³

Natural gas
1000–1100 BTU/ft³

TABLE III

TYPICAL VALUES OF HEAT OF COMBUSTION

SUBSTANCE	cal/g	BTU/lb
Solid fuels		
Anthracite.........	8000	14,400
Bituminous coal...	7500	13,500
Coke.............	6000	11,000
Pine wood........	4500	8,000
Liquid fuels		
Gasoline..........	11,400	20,500
Kerosene.........	11,200	20,000
Diesel oil........	10,500	19,000
Alcohol..........	6,400	11,500
Foodstuffs		
Proteins..........	4000	7,200
Carbohydrates....	4000	7,200
Fats.............	9500	17,000

Manufactured gas (called *coal gas* or *steam gas*) is made by blowing steam over incandescent coal, resulting in the reaction

$$C + H_2O \rightarrow CO + H_2.$$

The heat of combustion of the resulting carbon monoxide and hydrogen mixture is only about half that of natural gas, which is almost pure methane (CH_4). Since equal volumes of different gases contain the same numbers of molecules at the same temperature and pressure (Chap. 15), a stove burning natural gas requires about four times the volume of oxygen needed for one burning artificial gas (the necessary burner adjustment on changeover has been a common experience). Two molecules of manufactured gas ($CO + H_2$) require only one O_2 molecule for complete combustion, whereas two molecules of CH_4 require four molecules of O_2.

Example. *If all the heat produced were used effectively, how many ft³ of natural gas would be required to heat 8 lb (approximately one gallon) of water in a 2 lb aluminum saucepan from 72° F to the boiling point?*

We note that (1 BTU/lb·F deg)(8 lb)[(212−72) F deg] = 1120 BTU are required to heat the water and (0.212 BTU/lb·F deg)(2 lb)[(212−72) F deg] = 59.4 BTU to heat the saucepan. Thus, the total quantity of heat needed is 1120 BTU + 59 BTU = 1179 BTU. If the heat of combustion of natural gas is 1000 BTU/ft³, then we see that (1179 BTU)/(1000 BTU/ft³) = 1.179 ft³ are required.

PROBLEMS

1. The mechanical output of an electric motor is ½ hp. This is 70 per cent of the electric power input, the balance of the input being 'lost' as heat. How many BTU of heat are developed per minute?   Ans: 9.09.

2. The electrical input to a motor is ¾ kw, of which 90 per cent is delivered as useful mechanical work, the balance being wasted as heat. At what rate in cal/sec is heat being liberated?

3. How many cal are required to raise the temperature of 8 g of iron from 35° C to 44° C? from 35° F to 44° F?   Ans: 7.9 cal; 4.4 cal.

4. How many BTU are required to raise the temperature of 15 kg of copper from 25° F to 43° F? from 25° C to 43° C?

5. A copper calorimeter of 63-g mass contains 79.5 g of a liquid at 18° C. Into this is placed a 120-g block of copper at 100° C. The final temperature is 39.0° C. What is the specific heat of the liquid?   Ans: 0.338 cal/g·C deg.

6. A copper calorimeter of mass 40 g contains 106 g of water at 15° C. A 100-g nugget of gold at a temperature of 99° C is placed in the calorimeter. The final temperature is found to be 17.6° C. What value does this experiment give for the specific heat of gold?

7. A 1.5-kg platinum ball is removed from an oven and placed in a copper calorimeter of 0.5-kg mass containing 1.6 kg of water. The temperature of the water rises from 20.0 to 25.8° C. What was the temperature of the oven?

Ans: 225° C.

8. A blacksmith throws a red-hot horseshoe weighing 2 lb, at a temperature of 1900° F, into a pail containing 40 lb of water at 70° F. If all the heat goes into warming the water, what is its temperature rise?

9. At what rate will ice be melted by a 200-watt electric heater submerged in a mixture of ice and water?   Ans: 36.0 g/min.

10. At what rate will water at 100° C be evaporated by a 1-kw electric heater if all the energy supplied goes into latent heat?

11. A 200-g copper calorimeter contains 300 g of water at 20° C. How much steam at 100° C must be added to raise the temperature of the water to 65° C?

Ans: 25.0 g.

12. A 1-kg copper ball is heated in a steam bath at 100° C and is then placed on a large cake of ice at 0° C. How much ice will be melted?

13. If a total of 30 kg of molten lead at 327° C is dropped into 4 liters of water initially at 20° C, how much water is evaporated, assuming no heat loss?

Ans: 148 g.

14. If 10 kg of steam at 120° C is passed into a vessel containing 50 kg of ice at −20° C, what will be the temperature of the mixture when it has reached equilibrium? Assume no heat loss, and take the specific heat of steam as 0.5 cal/g·C deg.

15. An electric motor is loaded by means of a Prony brake until it is delivering 20 hp. The Prony brake initially contains 15 lb of water at 72° F. Assume that the whole 20 hp delivered by the motor goes into heating the water. How many pounds of water are boiled away during the first 10 minutes of operation of the motor?   Ans: 6.58 lb.

16. A 500-watt electric heater is immersed in 3.5 lb of water at 62° F contained in a 1.2-lb aluminum vessel. Neglecting loss of heat and the heat capacity of the electric heater, how long will it take to heat the water to boiling and boil off 0.25 lb?

17. A continuous-flow steam generator takes in 1 liter of water per minute at 10° C and changes it to steam at 100° C. How many kilowatts of electrical power are necessary to furnish the required heat?   Ans: 43.9.

18. Bismuth melts at 271° C. Its specific heat is 0.032 cal/g·C deg. To determine its latent heat of fusion, 2 kg of molten bismuth at its melting point are dropped into a 1-kg copper calorimeter containing 3 kg of water at 15° C. The temperature rises to 22.1° C. What is the latent heat of fusion of bismuth?

19. To determine the latent heat of fusion of water, 1 lb of ice at 32° F is dropped into 5 lb of water in a 1-lb copper calorimeter at 100° F. The final temperature is observed as 64° F. What value does this experiment give for the latent heat of fusion of water?　　　　　　Ans: 151 btu/lb.

20. How much heat must be added to 20 g of ice at −15° C in order to convert the ice to steam at 100° C? How much heat must be added to 10 lb of snow at 0° F in order to change it to steam at 212° F?

21. When delivering 100 hp, a Diesel engine burns 1 lb of oil per minute. Find the over-all efficiency of the engine.　　　　　　Ans: 22.3%.

22. Compare the costs of heating with bituminous coal at $9.00 per ton, natural gas at 65 cents per 1000 ft³, and electricity at 1.5 cents per kwh.

23. In a determination of the heat of combustion of gasoline, 6 grams of gasoline are burned in a bomb calorimeter containing 2 kg of water and 7.5 kg of steel. The resulting rise in temperature is observed to be 24 C deg. What value does this give for the heat of combustion?　　　　Ans: 11,300 cal/g.

24. At what price per kwh would the cost of heating with electricity be the same as the cost of heating with anthracite at $18 per ton if the reasonable assumptions are made that all the electrical energy but only 50 per cent of the heat of combustion of the anthracite is delivered as useful heat?

25. A mixing faucet is supplied with cold water at 45° F and hot water at 135° F. The cold-water tap is first adjusted for a flow of 0.5 gal/min. The hot-water tap is then adjusted to give a total flow of 1.3 gal/min through the faucet. What is the temperature of the resulting warm water?　　　Ans: 100° F.

26. Five pounds of snow at 20° F are placed in a pan on a 1-kw hot plate. What is the minimum time required to produce boiling water?

27. How many gallons of kerosene would be equivalent in heating value to 1 ton of bituminous coal? How long would a 1500-watt electric heater have to be operated in order to produce an amount of heat equivalent to that obtained from the combustion of 1 ton of bituminous coal?　　　Ans: 203 gal; 5260 hr.

28. How much heat must be added to a 200-g block of aluminum initially at 20° C in order to increase the volume of the block by one per cent? If an equal quantity of heat were added to 200 g of mercury initially at 20° C, what would happen?

29. A 'flow calorimeter' is used to measure the specific heat of a liquid by having a stream of the liquid pass through the calorimeter at a measured rate. While the liquid is inside the calorimeter, heat is added at a known rate, usually by an electric heating element. From the resulting temperature difference between the input and the output points in the stream, the specific heat of the liquid can be obtained. In a certain flow calorimeter equipped with a 200-watt heating element, it was found that with a flow rate of 500 cm³/min for a liquid of density 0.9 g/cm³, a steady-state difference of 12 C deg existed between the liquid temperatures at output and input points. Calculate the specific heat of the liquid.　　　　　　Ans: 0.53 cal/g·C deg.

30. If water flows through the continuous-flow calorimeter described in Prob. 29 at a rate of 300 cm³/min, what will be the steady-state temperature difference between input and output?

31. A 2-lb block of ice at 32° F is placed in a bucket capable of holding 8 lb of water. Water is added until the bucket will hold no more with the block of ice floating freely, and it is found that half the ice melts. Neglecting the heat capacity of the bucket and thermal losses, find the initial temperature of the water.

Will the bucket overflow or the water level drop as the ice melts?   In answering this question, neglect the small thermal expansions.   Ans: 56.0° F.

32. Compare the quantity of ice fresh from the freezer of a refrigerator at 0° F with the quantity of ice that has been allowed to warm up to 32° F, that is required to cool a given volume of beverage to 32° F.

33. An industrial process requires that 3000 gal of water per hour be heated from 40° F to 150° F. To do this, steam at atmospheric pressure is passed from a boiler into a copper coil immersed in the water. The steam condenses in the coil and is returned to the boiler as water at 160° F. How many pounds of steam are required each hour?   Ans: 2680 lb.

34. A lead bullet moving at 800 ft/sec strikes a log and comes to rest. If half the initial kinetic energy of the bullet goes into heating the bullet, how much will the temperature of the bullet rise?

35. Water moving at a speed of 20 ft/sec approaches the brink of a waterfall 200 ft high.   After passing over the fall the water comes to rest in a pool at the base of the waterfall.   If all the mechanical energy of the water at the top of the fall is dissipated, how much does the temperature of the water rise when the water comes to rest, if all the heat produced goes into heating the water?
Ans: 0.265 F deg.

36. If the stirring element of a blender or mixer has 200 w of mechanical power input, what is the rate of temperature rise of the fluid in the blender if its heat capacity equals that of 1 lb of water?

37. The electric utilities of the U. S. produce an average of 1 kwh of electrical energy per pound of bituminous coal; the best producers obtain 1 kwh for ¾ lb of coal.   What are the average and the best over-all efficiencies of this production of electrical energy?   Ans: 25.4 %; 33.8 %.

CHAPTER 14

HEAT TRANSFER

IN THIS CHAPTER we consider rather briefly the methods by which thermal energy is transferred from one body to another or from one material medium to another. The computation of heat transfer in practical cases is frequently very complex and mathematically difficult; we confine ourselves here to an introductory discussion of fundamental principles and to simple examples of technical importance. Further discussion of heat transfer by *radiation* will be taken up in Chap. 37.

1. METHODS OF HEAT TRANSFER

THERE ARE three distinct methods by which thermal energy is transferred from one point to another when temperature differences exist:

Conduction is a process of heat transfer within a material medium, in which thermal energy is passed from molecule to neighboring molecule in the course of the purely thermal motions, no mass motion of the medium being involved.

Convection is the process of transfer of heat from one place to another by the actual mass motion of heated liquid or gas from the one place to the other.

Radiation is the transfer of thermal energy by means of electromagnetic waves, no material medium playing an essential role in the process of transmission.

Wherever two different portions of material media have different temperatures, heat will be transferred from the hot portion to the cool, so that the temperature tends to become equalized. By two portions of material media we can mean various things, such as the hot sun and the cool earth, the hot oven and the cool roast, the hot radiator and the cool furniture, the hot air in a room and the cold air outside in winter, or the hot inside portion of the wall of a house and the cold outside portion.

Radiation involves emission, transmission, and absorption of electromagnetic energy (*radiant energy*) in a form exactly analogous to light, as will be explained in more detail in Chap. 37. All bodies at temperatures above absolute zero are continuously radiating energy, at a rate proportional to the fourth power of the absolute temperature, but depending

286

also on surface condition, bodies with dull surfaces radiating at a higher rate than those with polished surfaces. Like light, radiant energy is transmitted *best* through a vacuum, but fairly well through a gaseous medium and through *transparent* liquids and solids. Radiation is the process involved in the transmission of heat from the sun through the vacuum of outer space to the earth. Within a *non-transparent solid* medium, heat can be transferred from point to point only by conduction. Where there is a material medium available to transmit the heat and where temperatures are low (less than 200° C), radiation is usually of little importance in comparison with conduction and convection. In liquid and gaseous media, convection by means of circulating currents of fluid is ordinarily the most important process of heat transfer.

In any given problem in heat transfer, two or three of these processes may be active simultaneously. The total heat transferred will be obtained by adding the amounts transferred by the different processes. It is convenient to consider the different processes one at a time.

2. LAWS OF HEAT CONDUCTION

Suppose that we have a slab of solid material (Fig. 1) in which there is a *temperature gradient*, by which we mean a space rate of change of

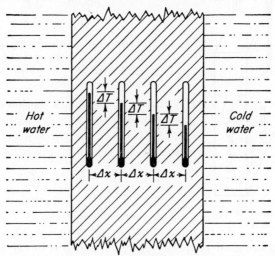

Fig. 1. The rate of heat flow is proportional to the temperature gradient $\Delta T / \Delta x$.

temperature from one point to another in the material. A temperature gradient is set up in Fig. 1 because one side of the slab is in contact with hot water, the other with cold water. It is found experimentally that inside the slab there is a *uniform* space rate of change of temperature, that is, a constant temperature gradient. This uniformity is indicated schematically by the thermometer readings in Fig. 1. The temperature gradient is defined as the derivative dT/dx, in C deg/cm for example. Under steady conditions thermometers at equal distances Δx will show equal temperature differences ΔT, so that the value of dT/dx is the same as $\Delta T/\Delta x$.

The temperature gradient in Fig. 1 is associated with a heat flow through the solid slab, from left to right (from the region of higher temperature to the region of lower temperature). The heat flow per unit time per unit area can be measured by calorimetric methods. The area referred to here is the area of surface of the slab in a plane normal to the paper in Fig. 1—the area of surface in contact with the hot water, for example. If we let dQ/dt denote the *rate of heat flow* through the slab in cal/sec, BTU/sec, BTU/min, or any other appropriate unit, then the heat flow per unit time per unit area will be $(dQ/dt)/A$, where A is the area.

It is found experimentally that the rate of heat flow per unit area is proportional to the temperature gradient $\Delta T/\Delta x$. The proportionality constant is a characteristic of the slab material called the *thermal conductivity*, or *coefficient of heat conduction*, and is denoted by the symbol k. Analytically,

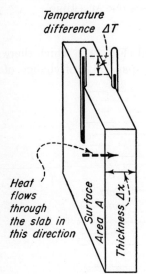

Temperature difference ΔT

Heat flows through the slab in this direction

Surface Area A

Thickness Δx

$$\frac{dQ/dt}{A} = k\,\frac{\Delta T}{\Delta x}. \qquad (1)$$

The **thermal conductivity** of a material substance is the *rate* of heat flow *by conduction* per unit area per unit-temperature gradient.

If, as in Fig. 2, we have a section of slab of area A and thickness Δx, with temperature difference ΔT between the two faces of the slab, the rate of heat flow will be given by

$$\frac{dQ}{dt} = kA\,\frac{\Delta T}{\Delta x}. \qquad (2)$$

Fig. 2. Definition of the symbols in equation (2).

The thermal conductivity k has the same dimensions as $(dQ/dt)\,\Delta x/A\,\Delta T$. Various systems of units are used in specifying k. If dQ/dt is in cal/sec, Δx in cm, A in cm^2, and ΔT in C deg, the unit of k is the cal/sec·cm·C deg. In British engineering units, the thermal conductivity of structural and insulating materials is usually specified with dQ/dt in BTU/hr, Δx in inches, A in ft^2, and ΔT in F deg. In this case k is in BTU·in/hr·ft^2·F deg. Conversion of k from one system of units to another can be done in the usual way by using the conversion factors for each unit. Thus,

$$1\,\frac{\text{BTU·in}}{\text{hr·ft}^2\text{·F deg}} = \frac{(252\text{ cal})(2.54\text{ cm})}{(3600\text{ sec})(929\text{ cm}^2)(0.556\text{ C deg})} = \frac{1}{2900}\,\frac{\text{cal}}{\text{sec·cm·C deg}}.$$

In the British engineering units specified above, the numerical values of the thermal conductivities of nonmetallic structural and insulating materials are not far from unity.   Thus, the typical thermal conductivity of concrete is 12 BTU·in/hr·ft²·F deg, and that of most insulating materials (fiber blanket, glass wool, mineral wool, or corkboard) is about 0.25 BTU·in/hr·ft²·F deg.   In cal/sec·cm·C deg the numerical value of k would be smaller than these by a factor of 2900.

Metals have much larger coefficients of heat conduction than non-metals, greater by a factor of 100 or more.   The thermal conductivity of metals is closely related to the electrical conductivity, since both heat and electricity are transferred in metals principally by the agency of free electrons (see Chap. 27).   There is an almost constant ratio between the coefficients of heat conduction and the coefficients of electrical conductivity for different metals, a fact that is known as the *Wiedemann-Franz law*.   The thermal conductivity of a metal varies with temperature in the same way as does the electrical conductivity (see Chap. 29); here we shall be content with using an average value satisfactory for temperatures in the neighborhood of room temperature (20° C).   The best electrical conductors, and also the best heat conductors, are silver, copper, and gold, in that order.   Silver has a thermal conductivity of approximately 1.0 cal/sec·cm·C deg = 2900 BTU·in/hr·ft²·F deg.

Table I gives typical values of thermal conductivity of various materials in both the systems of units we have discussed.   It will be noticed that the thermal conductivities of fluids are very low.   In general the heat transferred by conduction in liquids and gases is negligible compared with that transferred by convection.

If air is confined in very small spaces so that it cannot circulate, as in the pores of corkboard or wool clothing, convective processes are inhibited; and since conduction is also low, we have a poor heat transmitter called a *heat insulator*.   Such an insulator is said to contain 'dead-air' spaces, meaning that the air cannot circulate readily so that it cannot readily transmit heat by convection.

In determining the amount of heat conducted through a wall or a window, it is not correct to give the outer surface the outdoor temperature and the inner surface the indoor temperature.   On a winter day when the room temperature is 60° F, the inner surface of a pane of single window glass may be below 32° F, as witnessed by the familiar frosting of the inside of windows in cold climates.   Similarly, the outer surface of the glass may be well above the outdoor temperature; for example, it may be 0° F when it is −20° F out-of-doors.   Only part of the temperature drop occurs through the glass, the rest occurs through the layers of air close to the glass inside and outside.   In applying (2) to conduction through the glass, one must use the actual temperature difference between the inner and outer surfaces as ΔT; the difficulty of determining this actual tem-

TABLE I

TYPICAL VALUES OF THE THERMAL CONDUCTIVITY k NEAR 20° C

Substance	cal / sec·cm·C deg	BTU·in / hr·ft²·F deg
Metals		
Silver..........................	1.01	2930
Copper..........................	0.92	2680
Gold..........................	0.70	2030
Brass..........................	0.26	750
Steel..........................	0.11	320
Cast iron..........................	0.11	320
Aluminum..........................	0.48	1390
Mercury, liquid....................	0.015	44
Nonmetallic solids		
Brick, common....................	1.7×10^{-3}	5.0
Concrete..........................	4.1×10^{-3}	12.0
Wood (across grain)...............	0.3×10^{-3}	0.9
Glass..........................	1.4×10^{-3}	4.0
Enamel..........................	2.0×10^{-3}	6.0
Hollow and porous materials		
Hollow tile, 4 in thick...............	....	4.0*
Concrete block, 8 in thick..........	....	8.0*
Cinder block, 8 in thick............	....	5.0*
Fiber-blanket insulation.........	0.09×10^{-3}	0.27
Glass wool or mineral wool..........	0.09×10^{-3}	0.27
Sawdust..........................	0.14×10^{-3}	0.41
Corkboard..........................	0.10×10^{-3}	0.30
Liquids		
Water..........................	1.43×10^{-3}	4.15
Ethyl alcohol......................	0.42×10^{-3}	1.23
Gases		
Air..........................	0.056×10^{-3}	0.16
Hydrogen......................	0.400×10^{-3}	1.16

* These are effective coefficients applicable only to a wall of thickness mentioned, since the material is not homogeneous. For an extensive listing of building materials see Eshbach, *Handbook of Engineering Fundamentals*, 2d ed., p. 13–39 (Wiley, 1952).

perature difference makes the practical engineering computation of heat losses subject to a good many semi-empirical rules.

For a discussion of practical details of the apparatus used for the measurement of thermal conductivity, the reader is referred to specialized books on the subject of heat. The conductivity of a solid is usually determined by measuring the rate at which heat enters or leaves a rod or slab. This is equal to the rate at which heat flows through the rod or slab. If the heat is supplied by circulating hot water, the temperature drop and rate of flow of the water determine the amount of heat entering the solid.   If the heat is extracted by means of cold water, the amount of heat leaving can be similarly determined.   The temperature gradient is usually computed from the readings of thermocouples (see Chap. 31) buried in the material in the manner indicated by the thermometers of Fig. 1.   In the measurement of thermal conductivity of a liquid or gas, the sample is in the form of a horizontal sheet which is heated from above and cooled from below so that no heat is transferred by convection.

Example.   *A typical household electric refrigerator is equivalent to a box of corkboard 3 in thick and of 50 ft² area.   During a period when the door is not opened, assume that the interior wall has the average temperature 40° F and the exterior wall 80° F.   If the refrigerator motor is to run only 20% of the time during such a period, at what rate in* BTU/hr *must heat be extracted from the interior while the motor is running?*

To find the average rate of heat flow from the room into the refrigerator, we use (2) with the mixed British system of units we have described, taking the value of k for corkboard from Table I:

$$\frac{dQ}{dt} = kA\frac{\Delta T}{\Delta x} = 0.30 \; \frac{\text{BTU·in}}{\text{hr·ft}^2\text{·F deg}} \times 50 \; \text{ft}^2 \; \frac{40 \; \text{F deg}}{3 \; \text{in}} = 200 \; \frac{\text{BTU}}{\text{hr}}.$$

If the refrigerator motor is to run only one-fifth of the time when the door is unopened and no warm food is introduced, heat must be extracted at five times this rate while the motor is running, or at the rate of 1000 BTU/hr.

3. CONVECTION AND RADIATION; NEWTON'S LAW OF COOLING

AT ORDINARY temperatures, the principal method of heat transfer in liquids and gases is *convection*.   Liquids and gases are comparatively poor heat *conductors*, as will be seen from Table I; and unless temperatures are high, radiation does not play an important role.   The mechanism by which heat is transferred from a hot-water or steam 'radiator' to the air, walls, and objects in a room is almost entirely convection.   The term 'radiator' is a misnomer.   One reason for the inefficiency of the open fireplace is that it depends almost entirely on radiation for heat transfer to the room.   While the temperature difference between the fire (and adjacent firebrick) and the room is much larger than in the case of a radiator, a large proportion of the heat is lost by *convection* up the chimney to the out-of-doors.   One gets much more effective heating from the same fire burning in a stove, where heat can be transferred to the room by convection.

The process of heating a room by a radiator can be described as follows: The air molecules that collide with the radiator leave with more energy than they had before impact because the radiator is at higher temperature than the air.   This process raises the temperature of a thin layer of air in immediate contact with the hot radiator, and the density of this air layer decreases.   The hydrostatic balance in the room is thus upset.   Archimedean buoyant forces come into play to cause the rarefied hot air to rise to the top of the room.   Similarly, when room air comes into contact with the cooler outside walls of the room, the room air transfers heat to these walls; its temperature decreases, and it becomes more dense than the surrounding air.   Again Archimedean forces come into play to cause this cooled air to sink to the floor.   Thus a temperature gradient is set up, with warmer air near the ceiling, cooler air near the floor.   The temperature gradient is maintained by a continuous circulation in which cool floor air is heated by the radiator and rises, while warm ceiling air is cooled by the walls and sinks.   It is this circulation that effects the heat transfer from the radiator to the cool room walls and maintains an average air temperature in the room that is somewhere between that of the hot radiator and that of the cool walls and window glass.

The same process of natural convection is depended on to effect the circulation of hot water from furnace to radiator in older installations.

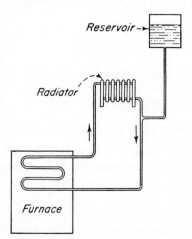

Reservoir→

Radiator

Furnace

Fig. 3. Convective circulation of heat from furnace to radiator. (A reservoir or a pressure tank partly filled with air must be provided to allow for the net expansion or contraction of the water in the system.)

This process is illustrated schematically in Fig. 3.   The water in the furnace coils is heated and expands somewhat. This expansion upsets the hydrostatic balance in the piping of Fig. 3.   The lighter water which has been heated rises, the denser water which has been cooled by loss of heat in the radiator sinks, and thus a circulation is set up.   This circulation depends on the fact that the two connections to the furnace coils are made at different heights.   If both connections were made at the same height, the circulation would not be efficiently set up. The circulation is aided, for the same reason, if the circulating water enters the radiator at the top and leaves at the bottom.   In recent heating installations, a pump is used to increase the rate of circulation.   The heat is still transferred by convection—mass motion of material.

In this case, or in the case of use of a fan in hot-air circulation, the transfer is said to be by *forced* convection, as distinguished from *natural* or *free* convection.

The laws governing the rate of heat transfer by convection are very complex because complex fluid-dynamic phenomena are involved.   One law which was discovered empirically by Newton relates to the rate of cooling (or warming) of a given body when it is at a temperature different from that of the surrounding air:

NEWTON'S LAW OF COOLING: *The rate of heat transfer to the surrounding air is proportional to the difference in temperature between the body and the air.*

This law is found to agree with observed behavior very well when the heat-transfer process is predominantly convective, even though a certain amount of the heat may be transferred by conduction and radiation.

If the rate of heat loss is proportional to the difference $T - T_{Am}$ between the temperature T of the body and the temperature T_{Am} of the surrounding air (called the *ambient temperature*), the rate of decrease of temperature of the body $(-dT/dt)$ will also be proportional to $T - T_{Am}$. The temperature of a body 100 deg above the ambient temperature will start to fall rapidly, but when the body has cooled to 50 deg above its surroundings, its temperature will be falling only half as fast, since by Newton's law of cooling, heat will be removed from the body only half as fast. If the temperature of the body is 50 deg *below* ambient, its temperature will *rise* at the same rate as it will *fall* if the temperature of the body is 50 deg *above* ambient.

If two containers at the same temperature are externally identical but have different heat capacities, the temperature of the one of greater heat capacity will drop less rapidly than that of the other since the rate of heat transfer will be the same, but more heat must be transferred per degree change of temperature.

Example. *When a 25-watt lamp bulb is placed inside a closed metal can, the temperature of the can rises until it is 100 F deg above that of the surrounding air. To what would the temperature of the can rise if the bulb were changed to one of 50 watts?*

The power generated in the lamp bulb can only be dissipated by transfer from the can to the surrounding air. Hence the rate of this heat transfer, expressed in watts, just equals the wattage of the bulb. According to Newton's law of cooling, if the rate of heat transfer is to be doubled, the temperature difference must be doubled. Hence for the 50-watt bulb, the can would have to reach a temperature 200 F deg above that of the surrounding air before heat would be transferred as fast as it is generated.

4. THERMAL RADIATION

As WE have noted before, all materials at temperatures above absolute zero are continually emitting radiation. As the temperature of a solid is increased, the energy radiated from the solid increases rapidly and there is also a variation in the character of the emitted radiation, which is at first apparent only to the sense of feeling, then becomes visible to the eye. The nature of this variation in character will be discussed quantitatively when we consider the subject of electromagnetic radiation; here we shall discuss the total quantity of radiated energy and its variation with temperature.

We have noted that the amount of radiant energy emitted by a solid depends on the character of the surface of the solid.   In beginning the discussion of radiation, it is helpful to define an 'ideal radiator' or 'perfect radiator.'   It is impossible, from a consideration of *emission* only, to decide what an ideal radiator should be.   By comparing the rates of radiation of energy from different surfaces of the same area and at the same temperature, we could select the surface from which the emission was greatest and define this as the ideal radiator, but we should have no assurance that there might not be some other surface of equal area that would give greater emission at the same temperature.   The fact that

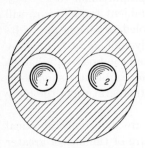

there is an upper limit to the rate at which energy can be emitted as radiation from a given body at a given temperature can be deduced only by considering the inverse process, absorption.

Let us consider the solid object shown in Fig. 4, which is maintained at a uniform temperature T throughout.   Within this solid there are two evacuated cavities containing opaque bodies 1 and 2 of the same size.   The bodies 1 and 2 may be made of quite different materials; for example, 1 may be of metal with a mirror surface, and 2 may be made of wood.   It is found by experiment that as a result of radia-

Fig. 4. Two spherical bodies of the same size but of different materials placed within spherical cavities.

tive interchanges of heat, the temperatures of bodies 1 and 2 eventually become equal to the temperature T of the enclosing walls and remain at that temperature.

In order to be able to study the processes taking place at the surface of each body after equilibrium is reached, let us assume that the inner walls of the cavities are perfectly absorbing* (this condition can be closely approximated in practice by coating these inner walls with lampblack). Then the only radiation reaching bodies 1 and 2 is that *radiated* by the inner walls of the cavities; these cavity walls do not reflect any radiation and return it to the bodies.   Under these circumstances, the radiant energy incident per second on unit area of each body will be the same; call it E, in watts/m². Of the incident radiation E, a certain fraction will be reflected and the remainder will be absorbed.   As indicated in Fig. 5, let ρ denote the fraction of the incident radiation that is reflected and α denote the fraction that is absorbed; ρ is called the *reflection factor* and α the *absorption factor*.   These quantities are dimensionless and their sum is unity for the surface of any opaque body: $\alpha + \rho = 1$.   The

---

* This assumption simplifies the discussion considerably, since it makes it unnecessary for us to consider multiple reflections.   It is a convenient simplifying assumption but not a necessary one.

product $\rho_1 E$ gives the radiation reflected from unit area of body 1 and $\rho_2 E$ the radiation reflected from unit area of body 2, in watts/m². Similarly, $\alpha_1 E$ and $\alpha_2 E$ give the radiation absorbed per unit area of bodies 1 and 2, respectively, in watts/m².

In the absence of other processes, the absorbed energy would produce an increase in the temperatures of the two bodies. However, experiment shows that the temperatures of the two bodies remain equal to the temperature of their surroundings. This result is understandable if we remember that bodies 1 and 2 are also emitting radiation. Let the rate of radiation be W_1, in watts/m², for body 1 and W_2, in watts/m², for body 2; W_1 and W_2 are called the *emissive powers* of the surfaces.

> The **emissive power** of a surface is the rate of emission of radiant energy from unit area of the surface. The emissive power depends on the physical character of the surface and on its temperature.

Now, if the temperatures of the bodies in Figs. 4 and 5 are to remain constant, as much energy must be lost per second by emission as is gained by absorption and we may write

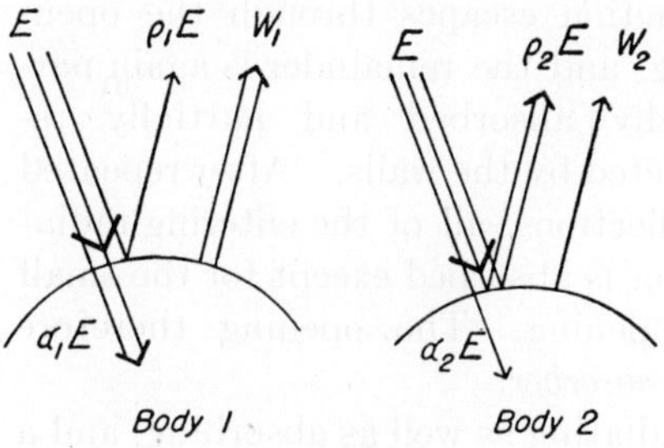

Body 1　　　　　　Body 2

Figure 5

rate of absorption = rate of emission

$$\alpha_1 E = W_1, \qquad \alpha_2 E = W_2.$$

Dividing the first equation by the second, we find that

$$\frac{\alpha_1}{\alpha_2} = \frac{W_1}{W_2}, \quad \text{or} \quad \frac{W_1}{\alpha_1} = \frac{W_2}{\alpha_2}. \qquad (3)$$

Equation (3) gives

KIRCHHOFF'S LAW OF RADIATION: *The ratio of the emissive powers (rates of radiation) of any two surfaces at the same temperature is equal to the ratio of the absorption factors of the two surfaces.*

Qualitatively, we can say that '*good radiators are good absorbers.*'

Now we return to the problem of defining a perfect radiator. As we have already noted, there is no *a priori* way in which we could immediately set an upper limit on the emissive power W. However, it is evident that there *is* a maximum value of the absorption factor α; since no surface can absorb *more* than *all* of the incident radiation, the maximum value α can have is unity. In view of equation (3), we may say that a surface having the maximum emissive power is one that has the maximum absorption factor and is therefore one that absorbs all radiation incident upon it; such a surface is *black* to radiation of all wavelengths. Therefore, we may define a perfect radiator as follows:

> A **perfect radiator** is a body that absorbs all incident radiation and is therefore called a **black body**. A perfect radiator is a perfect absorber.

Such a body would appear black unless its temperature were high enough for the body to be self-luminous.

No material surface absorbs *all* of the radiation incident upon it; even lampblack reflects about one per cent of the incident radiation. In

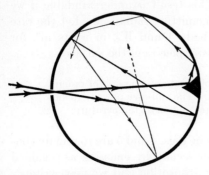

practice, a perfect black surface can be most closely approximated by a very small opening in the wall of a large cavity such as the one shown schematically in Fig. 6; radiation may enter or leave the cavity through the opening. Of the radiation entering through the opening, a part is absorbed by the interior walls of the cavity and a part is reflected. Of the part reflected, only a small fraction escapes through the opening, and the remainder is again partially absorbed and partially reflected by the walls. After repeated reflections, all of the entering radiation is absorbed except for the small

Fig. 6. A small hole in the wall of an enclosure, showing complete absorption of two representative rays. If the cavity walls are rough or dull, reflection from the cavity walls is largely diffuse and the projection on the wall opposite the opening is not necessary.

portion that escapes through the opening. The opening therefore approximates a *black surface* or *perfect absorber*.

The inside walls of the cavity are radiating as well as absorbing, and a part of this radiation escapes through the opening. It can be shown that if the walls are at a uniform temperature T, the radiation that escapes is almost identical with that which would be emitted by a perfect radiator at temperature T. The hole closely approximates in all respects the surface of a black body emitting so-called *black-body radiation*.

The total radiation emitted from the surface of a body increases rapidly as the temperature of the surface is increased. The quantitative relationship between emissive power and surface temperature of an ideal radiator or black body is called the *Stefan-Boltzman law* and has the form

$$W_0 = \sigma T^4, \qquad \text{(black body)} \quad (4)$$

where W_0 is the emissive power of a black body at absolute temperature T. The rate of radiation increases as the *fourth power* of the absolute temperature. The proportionality constant σ has the value 5.669×10^{-8} watt/m^2·(K deg)^4.

The total radiation from many surfaces that are definitely not black is also very nearly proportional to the fourth power of the absolute temperature. This is true of surfaces composed of platinum, iron, tungsten, carbon, and many other materials. In every case, however, the proportionality constant is less than that for an ideal-radiator surface. In fact, if the absorption factor α of a body is independent of its temperature, we see from (3) that its emissive power is

$$W = \alpha W_0 = \alpha \sigma T^4.$$

These matters will be discussed further in Chap. 37 after we have studied the physical characteristics of electromagnetic radiation.

Example. *A small hole in the wall of an electric furnace used for refining steel behaves to engineering accuracy as a perfect black body. The energy emerging from such a hole can be measured by means of a radiation pyrometer. If the hole has an area of 1 cm², and it is desired to maintain the molten steel at 1650° C, at what value of energy radiation should the electrical controls be set?*

In (4) we substitute $T = (1650+273)° \text{K} = 1923° \text{K}$. Then

$$W_0 = \sigma T^4 = 5.67 \times 10^{-8} \frac{\text{w}}{\text{m}^2 \, (\text{K deg})^4} (1923 \text{ K deg})^4$$

$$= 5.67 \times 10^{-8} \times 1.37 \times 10^{13} \text{ w/m}^2 = 7.77 \times 10^5 \text{ w/m}^2 = 77.7 \text{ w/cm}^2,$$

which gives **77.7 watts** as the desired rate of radiation from the 1 cm² hole.

PROBLEMS

1. How much heat is conducted in 24 hr through a pane of glass 15 ft² in area and $\frac{3}{16}$ in thick if the surface temperatures are 60° F and 10° F?

Ans: 384,000 BTU.

2. How much heat is conducted in 24 hr through a solid concrete building wall 8 in thick and 400 ft² in area if the surface temperatures are 60° F and 30° F?

3. A domestic refrigerator has a wall area of 52 ft² and is insulated with corkboard 3 in thick. The room temperature is 75° F, the inside temperature is 40° F, and it may be assumed that the temperature drop all occurs through the corkboard. Twenty pounds of food at room temperature, with average specific heat 0.9 BTU/lb·F deg, are placed in the refrigerator and cooled to the inside temperature in one hour. How much heat must be extracted during this hour by the cooling coils in the refrigerator? How many pounds of ice would have to melt (from ice at 32° F to water at 32 °F) to extract this same heat?

Ans: 812 BTU; 5.64.

4. A certain freezing-plant building is 50 ft long, 25 ft wide, and 20 ft high. Walls and roof are insulated with corkboard 1 ft thick. Let the inside temperature of the corkboard average 0° F and the outside temperature average 50° F over a 24-hr period. The heat conduction through the floor is negligible. Let 12 tons of produce of average specific heat and latent heat the same as water and ice be placed in the plant at 65° F to be frozen to 0° F during this period. What must be the 'tonnage' of the refrigerating machine required for this plant, if a 'one-ton' refrigerating machine will extract in one day as much heat as one ton of ice at 32° F melting to water at 32° F? (This is the unit actually used in rating refrigerating machines.)

5. A partition between two parts of a pressure vessel is made of sheet steel $\frac{1}{2}$ in thick. What thickness of (a) copper, (b) brass, and (c) aluminum sheet would be equivalent to the steel sheet so far as conductive transfer of heat is concerned? Ans: 4.18, 1.18, 2.18 in.

6. What thicknesses of (a) wood, (b) solid concrete, and (c) cast iron have the same insulating value as $\frac{1}{2}$ in of corkboard?

7. If a body cools at the rate of 0.8 F deg/sec when it is 40 F deg above its surroundings, how fast does it cool when it is 30 F deg above its surroundings? Use Newton's law of cooling. Ans: 0.6 F deg/sec.

8. If a body cools at the rate of 5 C deg/sec when it is at a temperature of 40° C and ambient temperature is 20° C, how fast does it warm up when it is at 20° C and the ambient temperature is 25° C?

9. The wall of a freezing plant is composed of 1 ft of corkboard inside 8 in of solid concrete. If the temperature of the inner wall of the corkboard is 0° F and that of the outer wall of the concrete is 65° F, find the temperature of the corkboard-concrete interface and the heat flow in BTU/ft²·hr. Ans: 63.9° F; 1.60 BTU/ft²·hr.

10. A large cast-iron steam pipe $\frac{1}{4}$ in thick is covered with 1 in of asbestos insulation of conductivity 0.27 BTU·in/hr·ft²·F deg. If the temperature of the inner wall of the pipe is 230° F and that of the outer wall of the asbestos is 80° F, find the temperature of the iron-asbestos interface and the heat loss per square foot per hour.

11. Under ideal combustion conditions, how much coal with heat of combustion 14,000 BTU/lb must be burned per month (30 days) to heat a building with wall area 1500 ft² of hollow clay tile 4 in thick, roof area 500 ft² of built-up material 2 in thick, of effective conductivity 2.0 BTU·in/hr·ft²·F deg, and window area 300 ft² of glass $\frac{1}{8}$ in thick, if it is assumed that inside surfaces are at 60° F, outside surfaces at 30° F? Ans: 8.95 tons.

12. From Newton's law of cooling, one may write for a hot body at temperature T

$$dT/dt = -K\,(T - T_{Am}),$$

where K is a constant for the body in question. Show by integration that the temperature of the body at any time t is given by the expression

$$T = T_{Am} + (T_0 - T_{Am})e^{-Kt},$$

where T_0 is the temperature of the hot body at $t=0$.

13. A hot block of iron cools from 700° C to 600° C in 4 min when the ambient temperature is 20° C. How long is required for this body to cool from 600° C to 500° C? from 500° C to 400° C? from 400° C to 300° C? Assume that Newton's law of cooling applies (see Prob. 12). Ans: 4.79, 5.86, 7.65 min.

14. The specific heat of a liquid can be determined by the 'method of cooling.' The scheme involved is the following: A certain mass of water m_W is placed in a closed container of mass m_C composed of a metal of specific heat c_C and heated to temperature T_1. A mass m_L of the liquid of unknown specific heat c_L is placed in an identical container and heated to temperature T_1. The containers are allowed to cool to some lower temperature T_2 and the times t_W and t_L required for the cooling processes for the containers of water and liquid are then noted. From Newton's law of cooling derive the relation

$$\frac{m_L \cdot c_L + m_C \cdot c_C}{m_W \cdot c_W + m_C \cdot c_C} = \frac{t_L}{t_W}, \quad \text{and hence} \quad c_L = \frac{m_W c_W t_L + m_C c_C (t_L - t_W)}{m_L t_W}.$$

15. A 200-g sample of water at 80° C is placed in a small covered copper vessel. In 15 min the temperature of the water has dropped to 60° C. The water is then removed from the vessel, and a 300-g sample of olive oil at 80° C is placed in the container. Neglecting the heat capacity of the container, find how long it will take the olive oil to cool to 60° C. (See Prob. 14.)

Ans: 10.6 min.

16. What temperature gradient exists in an aluminum rod 2 cm in diameter if it transmits 12 cal/sec along the length of the rod?

17. A cubical thin-walled metal box measuring 3 ft on an edge contains 50 lb of ice at 32° F. The interior of the box is to be maintained at 32° F in a room whose temperature is 92° F. How thick a layer of corkboard should be attached to the outer walls of the box in order to make the ice last two days?

Ans: 6.48 in.

18. A one-room building without windows measures 15 ft × 20 ft × 8 ft, and is covered with a 4-in layer of glass-wool insulation. The inside walls of the room are to be maintained at 70° F when the outside wall temperature is 30° F. How much heat must be supplied to the room each hour in order to maintain the desired temperature? If this heat is to be supplied by an electric heater, what should be the power rating of the heater? Neglect heat loss through the floor.

19. A layer of ice on a pond is 1 cm thick. When the upper surface of the ice is at 5° F and the temperature of the water just below the ice is 32° F, at what rate does the ice become thicker? (The thermal conductivity of ice is 5×10^{-3} cal/cm·sec·C deg.)

Ans: 0.061 cm/min.

20. A sphere of iron is 5 cm in diameter. At a certain temperature, the sphere loses thermal energy by radiation and convective cooling at a rate of 100 watts. At what rate is its temperature decreasing?

21. A 240-g sample of water at 40° C is placed in a thin-walled copper container. When the vessel is placed in a room where the temperature is 20° C, the temperature of the water drops initially at the rate of ⅓ C deg per minute. At what rate is heat being removed from the container? (Neglect the thermal energy lost by the copper container.) If 100 g of crushed ice at 0° C were placed in the container, how long would it take all the ice to melt?

Ans: 80 cal/min; 100 min.

22. What is the emissive power of a black body in watts/m² at temperatures of 27° C, 327° C, and 727° C?

23. Radiant energy is incident on a certain opaque body at the rate of 30 watts/m². The surface absorbs 20 watts/m². (a) What is the reflection factor of the surface? (b) What is the absorption factor? (c) If the body is in thermal equilibrium with its surroundings and can exchange energy with its surroundings only by radiation, what is the emissive power of the body?

Ans: 0.333; 0.667; 20 watts/m².

24. Radiant energy is incident on the surface of a black body at the rate of 50 watts/m². (a) At what rate is radiant energy reflected from each unit area of the surface? (b) At what rate is radiant energy absorbed by each unit area of the surface? (c) If the black body is in radiative equilibrium with its surroundings, what is its emissive power?

25. What would be the emissive power of a black body at the same temperature as the opaque body described in Prob. 23? Ans: 30 watts/m².

26. The emissive power of the surface of a certain opaque body is 45 watts/m². The emissive power of a black body at the same temperature is 50 watts/m². What is the absorption factor for the surface of the opaque body?

27. A silver surface has a reflection factor of 0.97 at 727° C. What is the emissive power of this surface at this temperature? What is the ratio of the emissive power of a silver surface at this temperature to that of a black body at the same temperature? (This ratio is called the *emissivity* of the surface.)

Ans: 1700 w/m²; 0.03.

28. A radiation pyrometer is used to measure the amount of radiation emerging from a hole of area 1 cm² in the wall of a furnace. If 115 watts emerge, what is the temperature of the interior of the furnace?

29. From measurements of solar radiation received on the earth, it is concluded that the sun radiates at the rate of 6250 watts per square centimeter of its surface area. Assuming that the sun is a perfect black body (such a gaseous mass has close to zero reflection for incident radiation), compute its surface temperature. Ans: 5760° K.

30. Two very large plane plates face each other with a small distance of separation so that we can consider that all radiation emitted by one plate strikes the other. The two plates are at the *same temperature;* plate 1 has absorption factor ½, plate 2 has absorption factor ⅓. Each m² of plate 1 radiates at the rate ½ W_0, each m² of plate 2 at the rate ⅓ W_0. Show that of the power ½ W_0 radiated by plate 1, a total of ¼ W_0 is eventually absorbed by plate 2 while ¼ W_0 is reabsorbed by plate 1. Of the power ⅓ W_0 radiated by plate 2, a total of ¼ W_0 is absorbed by plate 1, while 1/12 W_0 is reabsorbed by plate 2. Hence verify that the rate of absorption of each plate equals its rate of emission and that the temperature equilibrium is maintained in the radiation process in spite of the difference in emissive powers.

31. Consider again the two plates of Prob. 30, and let plate 1 be maintained at temperature T and radiate at the rate ½ W_0. Let the temperature of plate 2 be maintained at $\sqrt{2}\,T$ so that it radiates twice as much energy as it would at temperature T, namely at the rate ⅔ W_0. Determine, in terms of W_0, the rate of heat transfer from plate 2 to plate 1. Ans: ¼ W_0.

32. Show that as the surface of a lake is cooled in the fall and winter, convective processes will tend to mix the water and keep it at constant temperature throughout until the temperature drops to 4° C, and that thereafter the surface cooling will not result in further mixing, but will result in the formation of ice. Water transfers heat readily by convection but poorly by conduction. Hence show that the tendency for the main body of the water to cool further by conduction can readily be overcome by the heat supplied by the warm earth at the bottom, which can be distributed by convection.

33. What diameter should a tungsten lamp filament, with absorption factor 0.33, have in order that it will come to a temperature of 3000° K when it is radiating 5 watts per cm length? Ans: 0.105 mm.

34. Why is a Dewar flask or Thermos bottle (a) made double-walled? (b) evacuated? (c) silvered?

35. In the example on p. 293, let T be the temperature of the can *above* the ambient temperature, which is taken as $T=0$. Let C be the heat capacity of the can (see p. 278) in joules/deg. Neglect the small heat capacity of the bulb. Let the rate of heat transfer in watts be given by Newton's law of cooling in the form BT, where B is a constant measured in watts/deg. If the bulb of power P, in watts, is turned on at time $t=0$, when $T=0$, write the differential equation that governs the rise of temperature of the can. Verify that this differential equation has the solution

$$T = (P/B)(1 - e^{-t/\tau}), \quad \text{where} \quad \tau = C/B.$$

Sketch this curve for a numerical example for which you supply your own constants, and show that τ represents a *time-constant* that gives the time required for the fraction $(1 - e^{-1})$ of the total temperature rise.

CHAPTER 15

PROPERTIES OF GASES

THE LAWS that govern the behavior of most of the common gases under ordinary conditions are remarkably simple. They are called the *ideal-gas laws*. These laws are obeyed extremely closely by such gases as air, oxygen, nitrogen, hydrogen, and helium under all conditions except those of extremely low temperature or extremely high pressure. They are very closely obeyed, too, by carbon dioxide under ordinary conditions of temperature and pressure. However *solid* CO_2 can exist at *normal* pressure but at the low temperature of $-80°$ C; and *liquid* CO_2 can exist in tanks at *normal* temperature but at the high pressure of about 65 atmospheres. Clearly, under these conditions the CO_2 is not behaving like an ideal gas. It turns out that *the vapor of any substance behaves like an ideal gas if the pressure is sufficiently low and the temperature sufficiently high*. If the temperature is decreased, or the pressure raised, to a value near to that required for condensation to a liquid, then significant departures from the ideal-gas laws are observed.

The ideal-gas laws furnish such a good approximation to the behavior of most gases under most conditions encountered in scientific and engineering work that it will be profitable to devote this chapter to a study of *the ideal gas*. In the succeeding two chapters we shall discuss cases of departure of gases from ideal behavior. We shall not continue to repeat the word *ideal* in this chapter because to ordinary engineering accuracy most gases of interest *are* ideal under most conditions.

1. THE GAS LAWS

THE DENSITY of a gas depends on only three variables: the pressure, the temperature, and of course the kind of gas. There are three experimental laws, known as Boyle's law, Charles' law, and Avogadro's law, which give the dependence of the density on these three variables.

Boyle's experiments demonstrated

BOYLE'S LAW: *If the temperature of a given kind of gas is held constant, its density is directly proportional to the absolute pressure.*

If the pressure on a given sample of gas is doubled, its volume becomes one-half, and hence its density is doubled; and so on.

The experiments of Charles and Gay-Lussac demonstrated

CHARLES' LAW: *If the pressure on a given kind of gas is held constant, its density is inversely proportional to its absolute temperature.*

Thus, if a given sample of gas at atmospheric pressure is heated from 0° C to 273° C (from 273° K to 546° K), its absolute temperature doubles, its volume doubles, and its density becomes one-half.

In 1811 Avogadro proposed an hypothesis now called *Avogadro's law,* whose validity was not proved until the kinetic theory was developed in the period following 1850:

AVOGADRO'S LAW: *At the same temperature and pressure, different kinds of gases have densities proportional to their molecular masses.*

This law implies that equal volumes of different gases at the same temperature and pressure contain the same numbers of molecules—since if they contain the same numbers of molecules they will have masses and hence densities proportional to the average masses of the individual molecules, that is, proportional to the molecular masses.*

If we let ρ stand for the density, P for the absolute pressure, T for the absolute temperature, and M for the molecular mass (*the molecular mass is to be considered as dimensionless; it is 16 times the ratio of the average mass of a molecule of the gas to the mass of a single O^{16} atom†*), we can combine the above three laws into a single law which says that

$$\rho \propto PM/T.$$

In this proportionality, the proportionality constant must be a universal constant since we have taken into account all factors influencing the density of a gas.   Hence if we write

$$\rho = \frac{1}{R}\frac{PM}{T},$$

$$\begin{pmatrix}\text{general}\\\text{gas law}\end{pmatrix} \quad (1)$$

---

* The reader is presumed to have learned about molecular mass, moles (frequently called gram-molecules), Avogadro's number, and similar concepts from previous work in chemistry.   Hence, these ideas are introduced very informally in this chapter.   However, a complete and accurate set of definitions of these quantities is given in italics in the following text.

† Natural oxygen contains atoms of three different masses, called *isotopes* $O^{16}, O^{17},$ *and* O^{18}.   The ratios of the masses of these isotopes are $16.0000 : 17.0045 : 18.0049$, and their relative abundances are in the ratios $2500 : 1 : 5$.   We shall employ the *physical scale* of atomic and molecular masses, in which the atomic mass of the predominant isotope O^{16} is taken as 16 exactly.   This makes the molecular mass of natural O_2 come out as 32.0087.   The difference between this value and the value of exactly 32 that is assigned on the *chemical scale* is unimportant for most applications of the gas laws.

The molecular mass of a gas must be defined in terms of the *average* mass of the molecules because even a 'pure' gas such as H_2 contains isotopes of different masses.

A list of atomic masses will be found in Sec. 4 of the Appendix.

as is customary, the constant R must be a universal constant independent of the kind of gas considered. Equation (1) is called *the general gas law*, and R is called the *universal gas constant*.

Since density is mass per unit volume, if a mass m of gas occupies volume V, we have $\rho = m/V$. If we substitute this in (1), we obtain

$$\frac{m}{V} = \frac{1}{R}\frac{PM}{T}, \qquad (2)$$

or

$$PV = \frac{m}{M} RT. \qquad \left(\begin{array}{c}\text{general}\\\text{gas law}\end{array}\right) \quad (3)$$

This convenient form of the gas law enables us to compute the volume occupied by a mass m of any kind of gas under any pressure and temperature; or the mass of gas contained in volume V under any conditions of pressure and temperature; or the pressure of mass m of gas in volume V at temperature T. We can also write (2) in the form

$$\frac{PV}{T} = \frac{Rm}{M}. \qquad (4)$$

The right side of this equation is constant so long as we consider a given mass of a certain gas. Hence, *for a given mass of the same gas under two different conditions,*

$$\frac{P_1 V_1}{T_1} = \frac{P_2 V_2}{T_2}. \qquad (5)$$

We can use equation (2) to compute the value of R. It is observed that *one mole of any gas at normal temperature and pressure* occupies a volume of 22,421 cm³.* We shall translate this statement into MKS units and substitute in (2). The volume in question is

$$V = 22{,}421 \times 10^{-6} \text{ m}^3.$$

Normal temperature is $T = 273.16°$ K,

as we have stated on p. 260. Normal pressure is the pressure exerted by a column of mercury exactly 0.76 m high when it is at 0° C and under standard gravity. This corresponds (cf. p. 138) to

$$P = 1.0132 \times 10^5 \text{ nt/m}^2.$$

A mole of gas is, by definition, M grams *of the gas, or* $10^{-3} M$ kg *of the gas;* hence

$$m = 10^{-3} M \text{ kg}.$$

---

* 'Normal temperature and pressure' are defined as 0° C and 1 atm. We shall abbreviate this frequently recurring expression as NTP.

Solving equation (2) for R and substituting these values, we obtain

$$R = \frac{VPM}{Tm} = \frac{22,421 \times 10^{-6} \text{ m}^3 \times 1.0132 \times 10^5 \text{ nt·m}^{-2} \times M}{273.16 \text{ K deg} \times 10^{-3} \text{ } M \text{ kg}}$$

$$= 8317 \text{ nt·m/kg·K deg,}$$

or

$$\boxed{R = 8317 \text{ joule/kg·K deg} = 8317 \text{ m}^2/\text{sec}^2\text{·K deg,}} \qquad (6)$$

since the nt·m is a joule, and since the nt is a kg·m/sec². This is the value of R to be used in (1), (2), (3), and (4) when all other quantities are expressed in MKS units.

We now state one other important experimental law that applies when we have a mixture of gases:

DALTON'S LAW OF PARTIAL PRESSURES: *If several types of gas are put into the same container, the total pressure exerted is the sum of the partial pressures that each type of gas would exert if it alone occupied the container.*

For example, if a mass m_X of a gas of molecular mass M_X is in a container of volume V at temperature T, it would exert pressure

$$P_X = \frac{m_X}{M_X} \frac{RT}{V}, \qquad (7)$$

by (3). A mass m_Y of a gas of molecular mass M_Y alone in this container would exert pressure

$$P_Y = \frac{m_Y}{M_Y} \frac{RT}{V}. \qquad (8)$$

Dalton's law asserts that if the two gases are both placed in this container, the total pressure will be

$$P = P_X + P_Y, \qquad (9)$$

where P_X and P_Y are known as *partial pressures*.

Comparison of (7) with (8) shows that *the partial pressures of the different types of gas are proportional to the numbers of molecules of each type in the container.*

In normal *dry air*, 78.09 per cent of the molecules are N_2, 20.95 per cent are O_2, 0.93 per cent are A (argon), and the other 0.03 per cent are CO_2, Ne, Kr, Xe, He, and H_2. This composition gives an average molecular mass of 28.97. *For all ordinary purposes, dry air behaves like an ideal gas of molecular mass 29.0.* At NTP, 1 mole (29.0 g) of dry air would occupy 22.4 liters, so dry air would have the density

$$\rho = \frac{m}{V} = \frac{0.0290 \text{ kg}}{0.0224 \text{ m}^3} = 1.293 \frac{\text{kg}}{\text{m}^3}. \qquad (10)$$

It is noted that the density of air at NTP is a little over $\frac{1}{1000}$ the density of water, which is 1000 kg/m³.

All the relations of this section remain true in the British gravitational system of units commonly used by mechanical and aeronautical engineers. In this system we express m in slugs, V in ft³, ρ in slug/ft³, P in lb/ft², T in Rankine deg, R in ft·lb/slug·R deg. There is no alteration of molecular mass M, since this is dimensionless.

If the units in (6) are changed to the British system, the universal gas constant has the value

$$R = 49{,}690 \text{ ft·lb/slug·R deg} = 49{,}690 \text{ ft}^2/\text{sec}^2\text{·R deg.} \quad (11)$$

It is this value of R that must be used in the equations of this section when British units are employed.

Example. *What is the density of helium gas in a tank at a pressure of 120 atm and a temperature of 27° C?*

We shall solve this problem in two ways: first by direct substitution in (1); second by using the well-known volume (22.4 liters) of a mole at NTP.

For substitution in (1) in MKS units, we use $P = 120$ atm $= 120$ $(1.013 \times 10^5$ nt/m²$) = 1.216 \times 10^7$ nt/m²; $M = 4.004$ from Sec. 4 of the Appendix; $T = (273 + 27)$ K deg $= 300$ K deg; R as given by (6); to find

$$\rho = \frac{(1.216 \times 10^7 \text{ nt/m}^2) \times 4.004}{(8317 \text{ nt·m/kg· K deg})(300 \text{ K deg})} = 19.5 \text{ kg/m}^3.$$

As the second method of solution we start with the fact that at NTP one mole of any gas occupies 22.42 liters. Hence at NTP, 4.004 g $= 4.004 \times 10^{-3}$ kg of helium occupies 22,420 cm³ $= 22.42 \times 10^{-3}$ m³. If on the right side of (5) we insert the volume of 1 mole of helium at NTP, we can find on the left side the volume V_1 of 1 mole at $P_1 = 120$ atm and $T_1 = 300°$ K. Pressures can be left directly in atm, which is one of the advantages of this scheme. Substitution in (5) gives

$$\frac{120 \times V_1}{300} = \frac{1 \times 22.42 \times 10^{-3} \text{ m}^3}{273}$$

or $\qquad V_1 = (22.42 \times 10^{-3} \text{ m}^3)\,(^{300}\!\!\!/_{273})(\frac{1}{120}) = 20.5 \times 10^{-5} \text{ m}^3.$

The density of the mole of helium is then

$$\rho = \frac{m}{V_1} = \frac{4.004 \times 10^{-3} \text{ kg}}{20.5 \times 10^{-5} \text{ m}^3} = 19.5 \text{ kg/m}^3,$$

which agrees with the previous result.

2. EXTERNAL WORK; THERMAL ENERGY

IF A GAS expands by pushing apart the walls of its container, as in the case of the expansion of the gas in a balloon or in the cylinder of Fig. 1 when the piston moves to the right, the gas does mechanical work on the walls of the vessel. This work is called the *external work* done *by* the gas. In the case of Fig. 1, the external work done by the gas is the product of the distance the piston moves to the right by the average force exerted by the gas on the piston because of the gas pressure. If the piston moves to the *left* in Fig. 1, external work is done *on* the gas; in this case the external work done *by* the gas is considered as a negative quantity.

We shall now discuss the relations between *heat added* to a gas, *external work* done by the gas, and changes in the *thermal energy* of a gas.

> The **thermal energy** of a gas is the total microscopic mechanical energy of the molecules, including all the energy of the thermal motion—kinetic energy of translation and rotation, and kinetic and potential energy of vibration of the individual molecules—as well as any potential energy that may result from forces between the different molecules of the gas.*

If one adds *heat* to a gas, this heat all goes into increasing the thermal energy of the gas, *provided that* the gas does no external work while the

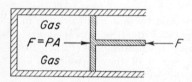

heat is being added. But if the gas pushes back the walls of the container and hence does external work while the heat is being added, conservation of energy requires that some of the added heat be used to supply the energy needed for this external work. This is the case, for example, if the pressure on the gas is kept constant while heat is being added. In Fig. 1, if the net force F which pushes on the piston from the right is kept constant, the pressure of the gas will remain

Fig. 1. External work done by a gas. The force F acting on the right side of the piston is the resultant of the force exerted by the pressure of the external atmosphere and any force that may be applied directly to the piston.

constant since the piston is in static equilibrium. If heat is added under these conditions, the gas will expand and do external work; part of the added heat goes into increasing the internal thermal energy and part into doing external work.

From the above arguments we conclude that conservation of energy requires the following energy balance:

(heat added to a gas) = (increase in thermal energy)
+ (external work done by the gas). (12)

This fundamental relation expresses the *first principle of thermodynamics* as applied to gases. It is noted that each of the three terms in equation (12) may be either positive or negative. Heat removed from the gas is considered a negative amount of heat added. A decrease in thermal energy is a negative increase. External work done *on* the gas when the gas contracts is expressed as negative external work done *by* the gas.

The thermal energy per unit mass of gas, for example the number of joules/kg, cal/g, or BTU/lb, we shall call the *specific thermal energy* and denote by e. Since the state of a gas is completely determined when

---

* The thermal energy is sometimes called the *internal energy* of the gas.

temperature, pressure, and the kind of gas are specified, the specific thermal energy can depend only on these three quantities.

> The **specific thermal energy** of a gas is the thermal energy per unit mass of the gas.

Everything that has been said in this section so far holds rigorously for real gases. We now state an important experimental law that is found to hold *extremely closely* for all real gases for which the general gas law is closely obeyed, and which is assumed to hold *exactly* for our ideal gas. This experimental law is that

> *The specific thermal energy of a gas depends only on the kind of gas and the temperature; it is independent of the pressure.*

This means that there is no variation of specific thermal energy of a given kind of gas with variations in pressure, and consequent variations in density, so long as the temperature does not change. It means that the thermal energy of a given mass of a given kind of gas is known once the temperature is given, no matter what the pressure or volume may be.

The simplest demonstration of this law is by means of Joule's free-expansion experiment, which employs the apparatus shown in Fig. 2. Two copper vessels are connected by a pipe fitted with a stopcock. Initially one vessel is filled with a gas and the other vessel is evacuated. The two vessels are then immersed in a carefully insulated water calorimeter and allowed to come into thermal equilibrium with the water. After thermal equilibrium has been established, the stopcock is opened and the gas is allowed to rush from the full vessel into the empty one. After thermal equilibrium has been estab-

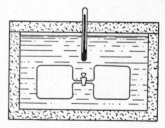

Fig. 2. Joule's free-expansion experiment (schematic).

lished again throughout the system, it is found experimentally that *the temperature of the water has not changed.* Since the gas is in thermal equilibrium with the water both before and after the expansion, *the temperature of the gas has not changed.* Since the temperature of the water does not change, no heat is gained or lost by the water, so *no heat has been added to or removed from the gas.*

The rest of the argument consists in applying the first principle of thermodynamics (12) to the over-all effects of this expansion process. As noted above, the experimental result indicates that *no heat is added* to the gas. It is also clear that *no external work is done* by the gas, because the walls of the vessel do not move. Hence, according to (12), *the thermal energy of the gas does not change.* We have noted above that *the temperature of the gas does not change.* So here we have the same mass of gas at two quite different states of pressure, volume, and density but at the, same temperature, and have demonstrated experimentally that the thermal energy in these two states is the same.

It is by this argument that one derives from Joule's experiment the conclusion that the specific thermal energy is independent of gas density if the temperature is constant, and completely determined by kind of gas and temperature.

3. SPECIFIC HEAT OF A GAS AT CONSTANT VOLUME

IF WE PLACE a sample of gas in a container of fixed volume and add heat, all the heat added goes into increasing the thermal energy of the gas. (This statement is true only if the volume of the gas is held constant.)

> The **specific heat at constant volume** is the amount of heat that must be added to a unit mass of gas to increase its temperature by one degree when the volume is held constant.

This specific heat at constant volume is denoted by c_V; like the specific heats for solids and liquids which were defined in Chap. 13, it has the same numerical value in cal/g·C deg and in BTU/lb·F deg. The amount of heat that must be added to a mass m of gas to increase its temperature ΔT degrees at constant volume is thus

$$Q = mc_V \, \Delta T. \tag{13}$$

Since this heat all goes into thermal energy, c_V is a measure of the increase in thermal energy when unit mass is heated one degree. The increase in specific thermal energy is thus given by multiplying the specific heat at constant volume by the change in temperature:

$$\boxed{\Delta e = c_V \, \Delta T.} \tag{14}$$

This equation is of particular importance because *it gives the increase in specific thermal energy that is associated with a temperature rise ΔT whether or not the volume changes while the temperature is rising.* This statement follows from the conclusion based on Joule's free-expansion experiment that the change in thermal energy is dependent purely on the change in temperature. Thus, by a measure of the specific heat at constant volume, where we know that all the heat goes into thermal energy, we can determine the coefficient of ΔT in the expression for the change in thermal energy for any type of process. For a mass m of gas, the change in thermal energy will always be

$$m \, \Delta e = mc_V \, \Delta T. \tag{15}$$

4. WORK DONE BY AN EXPANDING GAS; SPECIFIC HEAT AT CONSTANT PRESSURE

IF THE GAS in the cylinder of Fig. 3 is at pressure P, it exerts a force F on the piston equal to PA, where A is the area of the piston. We imagine the piston to be frictionless but still gastight.   Then, for equilibrium, a resultant force F, equal and opposite to that exerted by the gas, must be exerted externally on the piston.

By varying the external force, or by adding or subtracting heat, we can cause the gas to expand or contract. We shall now derive a general equation for the work done by the gas when it expands from volume V_1 to volume V_2.

In Fig. 3, if the piston moves to the right a distance dX, the work that the gas does on the piston is

$$dW = F\ dX = PA\ dX.$$

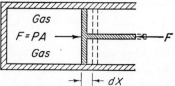

Fig. 3. Work done by a gas in expanding. The force F acting on the right side of the piston is the resultant of the force exerted by the pressure of the external atmosphere and any force that may be applied directly to the piston.

But $A\ dX$ is the increase of volume of the gas when the piston of area A moves to the right a distance dX.   We write $A\ dX = dV$ and obtain

$$dW = P\ dV.$$

It can be readily shown that this relation gives the work done whenever a gas exerting a pressure P increases its volume by dV, whether the volume changes in the geometrical configuration of Fig. 3 or in any other geometrical configuration, such as, for example, the expansion of the gas in a balloon or of a quantity of air in a house which must push aside the outdoor atmosphere as it expands through the openings to the outdoors when it is heated.

If, then, a quantity of gas expands from volume V_1 to volume V_2, the external work done by the gas is

$$W = \int_{V_1}^{V_2} P\ dV. \tag{16}$$

This relation holds no matter how the pressure may vary as the volume changes, but in order to evaluate the integral we must know the pressure P as a function of the volume V.

An especially simple case is that of an *expansion at constant pressure*, in which P is constant and can be taken outside the integral sign.   In this case we have

$$W = P \int_{V_1}^{V_2} dV = P\ (V_2 - V_1). \tag{17}$$

We are now in a position to compute the amount of heat that must be added to a gas to increase its temperature from T_1 to T_2 *when the pressure is kept constant*.   Let the mass of gas be m.   Then its volume at T_1 will be, by (3),

$$V_1 = (Rm/PM)T_1,$$

and that at T_2 will be　　$V_2 = (Rm/PM)T_2.$

During the process of adding heat, the volume will increase by

$$V_2 - V_1 = (Rm/PM)(T_2 - T_1).$$

Hence, according to (17), the gas will do external work of amount

$$W = (Rm/M)(T_2 - T_1).$$

The heat that must be added to the gas is, according to (12), the sum of the increase in thermal energy and the external work done by the gas. According to (15), the increase in thermal energy is

$$mc_V \ (T_2 - T_1),$$

so the total heat that must be added is

$$Q = mc_V \ (T_2 - T_1) + (Rm/M)(T_2 - T_1). \tag{18}$$

The **specific heat at constant pressure** is the amount of heat that must be added per unit mass per degree increase in temperature when a gas is heated and the pressure is kept constant.

This specific heat at constant pressure is denoted by c_P; thus to increase the temperature of a mass m of gas by ΔT degrees at constant pressure, we must add heat

$$Q = mc_P \ \Delta T. \tag{19}$$

From equation (18), we can compute the value of the specific heat at constant pressure as

$$c_P = \frac{Q}{m \ \Delta T} = \frac{Q}{m(T_2 - T_1)} = c_V + \frac{R}{M}.$$

The specific heat at constant pressure is greater than the specific heat at constant volume: in heating a gas at constant pressure we must not only add heat to supply the increase in thermal energy that is associated with the temperature rise but also must add heat to supply the energy for doing external work in the expansion.

In the equation $\qquad c_P = c_V + R/M, \tag{20}$

we must use the same units in all three terms. If we use R in mechanical energy units, joules/kg·K deg or ft·lb/slug·R deg, we must express c_P and c_V in the same units. It is frequently more convenient to use c_P and c_V in thermal units, cal/g·C deg or BTU/lb·F deg, and to change R to these thermal units. If the value of R given by (6) is converted to thermal units by using the relation 1 cal = 4.186 joules, it becomes

$$R = 1.987 \ \text{cal/g·C deg} = 1.987 \ \text{BTU/lb·F deg}. \tag{21}$$

It is convenient to remember that R is numerically very close to 2 in these thermal units.

We shall now discuss the magnitudes of c_V and c_P. First we note that since c_V is a measure of the rate of increase of thermal energy with increase of temperature, and since the thermal energy is independent of pressure and depends only on the temperature of the gas, c_V must be *independent of pressure*. Since, for a given gas, the difference between c_P and c_V is a constant, c_P must also be *independent of pressure*.

Over a very wide range of temperature from values close to the boiling point of the liquid up to at least $500°$ C, c_V and c_P are independent of temperature for monatomic and many diatomic gases and have values given by remarkably simple formulas that are explained by the kinetic theory of gases.

For a monatomic gas, c_V has the value $\frac{3}{2}R/M$; hence, from (20), c_P has the value $\frac{5}{2}R/M$. Thus,

for He, $c_V = \frac{3}{2}(1.987$ cal/g·C deg)/(4.00) $= 0.745$ cal/g·C deg,

for Ne, $c_V = \frac{3}{2}(1.987$ cal/g·C deg)/(20.19)$= 0.148$ cal/g·C deg,

for Hg vapor, $c_V = \frac{3}{2}(1.987$ cal/g·C deg)/(200.7)$= 0.015$ cal/g·C deg.

These values are in complete agreement with experiment.

For a light diatomic gas, c_V has the value $\frac{5}{2}R/M$, c_P the value $\frac{7}{2}R/M$. Thus,

for H_2, $c_V = \frac{5}{2}(1.987$ cal/g·C deg)/(2.017)$= 2.463$ cal/g·C deg,

for N_2 or CO, $c_V = \frac{5}{2}(1.987$ cal/g·C deg)/(28.0) $= 0.178$ cal/g·C deg.

for O_2, $c_V = \frac{5}{2}(1.987$ cal/g·C deg)/(32.0) $= 0.155$ cal/g·C deg,

These values are also in complete agreement with experiment.

The specific heat of H_2 gas is the highest of all known specific heats. For heavy diatomic gases such as Cl_2 and Br_2, the specific heats are slightly greater than those given by the above expressions, and for these gases, as well as for polyatomic gases, the specific heats increase with increasing temperature.

Specific heats of gases are rather difficult to measure directly, because the mass of gas and hence the quantity of heat involved are necessarily small. Continuous flow methods are applicable to the determination of the specific heat at constant pressure. The ratio c_P/c_V may be accurately determined by indirect methods involving measurement of temperature change in an adiabatic expansion or compression (see Chap. 17) or the measurement of the speed of sound in the gas (see Chap. 19). This ratio alone is sufficient to determine both c_P and c_V if the gas is assumed ideal so that relation (20) is satisfied.

Example. *The air in a room of 150 m^3 volume is heated from $0°$ C to $20°$ C when the atmospheric pressure out-of-doors is 1 atm. Assuming normal venting to the atmosphere, determine approximately the net amount of heat that must be added. Assuming that the air is at 1 atm initially and that the room is hermetically sealed, determine the net heat that must be added.*

The term 'net heat' is used here because, of the heat that might initially be added to the air, the major part is abstracted to heat the walls of the room or leaks out by conduction through the walls, window glass, etc.

Since over 99 % of the molecules of air are *diatomic* N_2 and O_2, air behaves, for practical purposes, like a perfect *diatomic* light gas of molecular mass 29.0 and density 1.29 kg/m³ at NTP as given by (10). Hence for air,

$$c_V = \tfrac{5}{2}\,R/29.0 = \tfrac{5}{2}(1.99 \text{ kcal/kg·C deg})/29.0 = 0.172 \text{ kcal/kg·C deg},$$
$$c_P = \tfrac{7}{2}\,R/29.0 = \tfrac{7}{2}(1.99 \text{ kcal/kg·C deg})/29.0 = 0.240 \text{ kcal/kg·C deg}.$$

The gas is originally at NTP and has mass $(150 \text{ m}^3)(1.29 \text{ kg/m}^3) = 194$ kg. Since the density of the gas is inversely proportional to the absolute temperature the mass of the gas in the room at 20° C is $(194 \text{ kg})(^{273}\!/_{293}) = 181$ kg if the pressure remains at 1 atm. The mass of gas that is being heated continuously decreases. We can get the approximate answer requested by computing the heat required to raise the temperature of the *average* mass, 187.5 kg, from 0° C to 20° C:

$$mc_P\,\Delta T = (187.5 \text{ kg})(0.240 \text{ kcal/kg·C deg})(20 \text{ C deg}) = 900 \text{ kcal}.$$

If the room were hermetically sealed, the whole 194 kg would be heated 20 C deg at constant volume and the net heat required would be

$$mc_V\,\Delta T = (194 \text{ kg})(0.172 \text{ kcal/kg·C deg})(20 \text{ C deg}) = 667 \text{ kcal}.$$

5. THE KINETIC THEORY OF GASES

DURING the latter half of the nineteenth century, it was realized by Maxwell, Boltzmann,* and others that the extreme simplicity of the experimental behavior of gases which we have sketched so far in this chapter implied an extreme simplicity in the structure of gases on a molecular scale. Only by making a very simple picture of an ideal gas can one expect to derive such very simple laws. This picture and the derivation of the experimental laws from it constitute the subject matter of the *kinetic theory of gases.*

In order to derive results that are consistent with the fact that the specific thermal energy of a gas depends on temperature alone, it is necessary to assume that the molecules of a gas are essentially *free particles*, that is, that most of the time they are acted on by no forces. They do, however, make collisions with each other and with the walls of the vessel, and during these collisions very large forces act to change the direction of the molecular motion. Between collisions the molecules move in straight lines in random directions at very high speeds.†

---

* JAMES CLERK MAXWELL (1831–1879), Scottish theoretical physicist, most famous for his development of the mathematical theory of electricity and magnetism and the electromagnetic theory of light; LUDWIG BOLTZMANN (1844–1906), German theoretical physicist.

† The effect of the force of gravity on the paths is insignificant. The molecules are on the average traveling so fast (with speeds of the order of 1 mi/sec) that the curvature of path introduced by gravity has a negligible effect over the ordinary distance between collisions, and the molecules may be assumed to move in straight lines between collisions.

The following picture is convenient and accurate: The molecules of a monatomic gas behave as if they were hard rigid spheres with diameters of the order of 10^{-8} cm. At NTP there are 2.7×10^{19} of them per cm³. They are on the average about 30 diameters apart. They rush about madly in truly random directions at speeds of the order of 1 mi/sec, making collisions each time they have gone about 1000 diameters along a given path. The molecules of a monatomic gas have no energy of rotation— only energy of translation. The molecules of a diatomic gas behave like rigid dumbbells moving in the same frantic manner except that now rotational energy may be interchanged at each collision. Of course the molecules are not really hard spheres or dumbbells, but the intramolecular forces hold the electrons and nuclei so firmly in position that the molecules behave during collisions as if they were such rigid bodies.

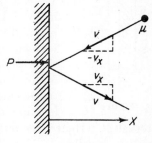

Figure 4

The pressure of the gas on the walls of the container arises from the collisions of the molecules with the walls. In Fig. 4, P represents the average force that a unit area of the wall exerts on the gas molecules, which is equal and opposite to the average force the gas molecules exert on a unit area of the wall (the gas pressure). In accordance with the discussion of Chap. 7, the force P of the wall equals the total change of X-component of momentum of all molecules colliding with unit area of the wall in unit time. Since the number of collisions is enormous ($\sim 10^{14}$ per cm² per sec at NTP), the force P appears as a steady pressure.

When an individual molecule of mass μ (we have used m for mass of gas, M for molecular mass, so we shall use μ for the mass of an individual molecule) that has X-component of velocity $-v_x$ collides with the wall and rebounds with reversed X-component of velocity, as in Fig. 4, the X-component of momentum before the collision is $-\mu v_x$, after the collision it is $+\mu v_x$, so the change in X-component of momentum is $2\mu v_x$. We have assumed the collision to be elastic, that is, that the molecule does not lose kinetic energy in the collision. This assumption will hold true on the average if the gas is not gaining or losing energy.

Now let us compute the pressure of a gas with N molecules, each of mass μ, per unit volume. (If the gas has molecules of different masses, and even pure gases do because of the occurrence of isotopes, this computation will give the partial pressure of the molecules of mass μ, and the total pressure will be the sum of the partial pressures.) The principal purpose of this computation is to show that the temperature is proportional to the average kinetic energy of the molecules. We shall also get a measure of the speed with which the molecules must be traveling. To take account of the different values of v_x that will occur (Fig. 4), let us split the N molecules per unit volume up into groups according to their X-component of velocity at a particular time. Let us say that there are N_j molecules per unit volume with X-component either $+v_{xj}$ or $-v_{xj}$, that is, ½ N_j with $+v_{xj}$ and ½ N_j with $-v_{xj}$.

We shall compute the partial pressure of these molecules and then sum over j to include molecules of all values of v_x. *This partial pressure will be given by the product of the number of collisions per unit area per second of these molecules by the change $2\mu v_{xj}$ in X-component of momentum per collision.* How many of these molecules collide per second? In the

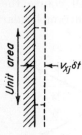

Figure 5

volume $v_{xj}\,\delta t$ of Fig. 5 there will be $N_j v_{xj}\,\delta t$ molecules. Of these, half will be moving to the left, half to the right. We can take the time δt sufficiently small so that all the molecules in this volume that are moving to the left may be validly assumed to reach the wall and collide with it without colliding with any other molecule. Since in time δt a molecule moves a distance $v_{xj}\,\delta t$ in the X-direction, we see that just half of the molecules contained in the sheet of thickness $v_{xj}\,\delta t$ at any given instant strike the wall during the succeeding time interval δt. Hence, the number of molecules striking unit area of the wall in time δt will be ½ $N_j v_{xj}\,\delta t$, so the number of molecules striking unit area in unit time will be ½ $N_j v_{xj}$.

Consequently, if we refer to the statement in italics in the previous paragraph, we see that the partial pressure will be ½ $N_j v_{xj} \times 2\,\mu v_{xj}$ $= N_j \mu v_{xj}^2$. To get the total pressure of the N molecules per unit volume, we must sum this expression over j. Since this expression is $\mu \times$ (number of molecules of a given X-velocity) $\times$ (square of X-velocity), the sum will be $\mu \times$ (total number of molecules) $\times$ (*average* square of X-velocity). That is,

$$P = N\mu \overline{v_x^2}. \tag{22}$$

If v is the magnitude of the velocity of a molecule, $v^2 = v_x^2 + v_Y^2 + v_z^2$. If we average over all the molecules, we obtain $\overline{v^2} = \overline{v_X^2} + \overline{v_Y^2} + \overline{v_z^2}$. But since no direction is preferred over any other in a truly random motion, we must have

$$\overline{v_X^2} = \overline{v_Y^2} = \overline{v_Z^2}.$$

Hence, $\overline{v^2} = 3\,\overline{v_X^2}$,   or $\overline{v_X^2} = ⅓\,\overline{v^2}$.

So, from (22), $P = ⅓\, N\mu \overline{v^2}.$ $\tag{23}$

Now $N\mu$, the product of the number of molecules per unit volume by the mass of a single molecule, is just the density ρ. So we can write

$$P = ⅓\, \rho \overline{v^2}. \tag{24}$$

This theory shows that the pressure is proportional to the density and the mean square speed. Now experiment, equation (1), gives

$$P = (R/M)\,\rho T. \tag{25}$$

Thus experiment shows that the partial pressure is proportional to the density and the temperature. For a given kind of molecule, the mean square speed must, then, be a measure of the absolute temperature.

To secure agreement between our kinetic theory and experiment, we can equate (24) and (25) to obtain

$$\overline{v^2} = 3RT/M \tag{26}$$

for the mean square speed of molecules of molecular mass M at absolute temperature T. This equation shows that the mean square speed is proportional to the temperature, but for different kinds of molecules at the same temperature is inversely proportional to the molecular mass.

Light molecules with low M move faster than heavy molecules with high M at the same temperature. This is true whether the molecules are mixed in the same container or are in different containers. Actually, we shall show that

Molecules of different masses at the same temperature have the same average translational kinetic energy, and this energy is directly proportional to the temperature.

If we denote the translational kinetic energy of a molecule by $E = \frac{1}{2}\,\mu v^2$, then the average value of E is

$$\bar{E} = \frac{1}{2}\,\mu\overline{v^2} = \frac{3}{2}\,(\mu/M)\,RT. \tag{27}$$

The right side of (27) is independent of the kind of molecule because the molecular mass M is by definition proportional to the mass μ. This proves the statement in italics above.

Example. *Determine the root-mean-square speed of* H_2 *molecules of* $M = 2.017$ *at* $T = 0°$ C.

We find from (26) that

$$\overline{v^2} = 3 \times 8317\;\frac{m^2}{sec^2\cdot K\;deg} \times \frac{273\;K\;deg}{2.017} = 3{,}380{,}000\;\frac{m^2}{sec^2}.$$

The root-mean-square speed is thus $\sqrt{\overline{v^2}} = 1840$ m/sec,

or 1.14 mi/sec. For higher temperatures this value would be greater, for heavier molecules it would be less, in accordance with (26).

The root-mean-square speed is not exactly the same as the mean or average speed $\bar{v}$ of the molecules because the process of squaring all speeds, averaging, and then taking the square root will give a slightly larger answer than that obtained by averaging the speeds themselves. Maxwell, by a more detailed analysis of the motion of a collection of molecules having the simple mechanical properties we have described, determined that the speed distribution, which is called the *Maxwellian distribution*, is of the form plotted in Fig. 6. There has been ample experimental check that the molecular speeds are actually distributed in this fashion.

The mean or average speed turns out to be 0.921 times the root-mean-square speed. So, for H_2 at 0° C, the mean speed $\bar{v}$ is 0.921×1840 m/sec $= 1690$ m/sec $= 1.05$ mi/sec. The molecules are by no means all moving at this speed, but are distributed over a wide range of speeds as indicated in Fig. 6. Only 1 in 10,000 of the molecules has a speed over $3\bar{v}$; there

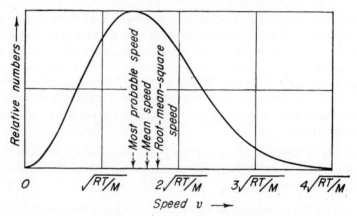

Fig. 6. The Maxwellian distribution. The relative numbers of molecules having speeds in unit speed range at various values of speed are proportional to the ordinates of this curve.

is, however, a definite but very small probability that a molecule may have a very much greater speed.

6. BROWNIAN MOTION

IN A MIXTURE of gases, kinetic theory gives to the molecules of different types the same average translational kinetic energy. Each gas behaves in every respect as if the other gas were not present at all, except that if two gases at different temperatures are mixed, energy is quickly interchanged in the collisions between molecules so that the two kinds of gases come to the same temperature, and hence the same average translational energy.

An interesting application of the kinetic theory occurs in connection with *Brownian motion*. In 1827 an English botanist, Robert Brown, pointed out that very fine particles of dust, smoke, or pollen contained in air (or in a liquid) seem to execute very irregular motions when observed in a high-power microscope. The correct explanation of these random motions which almost make the particles seem to be alive as they per-

petually dart hither and thither, was not given until much later.   The
motion is explained by the kinetic theory of gases.   The particle of dust
behaves as if it were just a very large molecule.   In air it has the same
average translational kinetic energy as the gas molecules.   It is repeatedly interchanging energy with the air molecules that collide with it, and
in the course of time has velocities ranging over the whole of the Maxwellian distribution with relative probabilities given by the curve of
Fig. 6.   But unlike the air molecules, the particle is large enough to be
watched in a microscope and its average velocity is comparatively slow.
Hence, details of the kinetic theory predictions are subject to direct
experimental check by observation of the Brownian motion of small particles, and have been accurately confirmed in a number of careful experimental investigations.

*Brownian motion furnishes the most direct and convincing check of the
validity of the kinetic theory.*

PROBLEMS

NOTE: Pressure is *absolute* unless otherwise specified.   Pressures in cm refer
to cm of mercury unless otherwise specified.   Use the values $273°$ K $=0°$ C;
$460°$ R $=0°$ F.

1. If 1 liter of a certain gas at 76 cm and $0°$ C has a mass of 1.87 g, what
would be the mass of a liter of the same gas at 60 cm and $47°$ C?   Ans: 1.26 g.

2. If air has a density of 1.29 kg/m³ at sea level when the
pressure is 76 cm and the temperature is $0°$ C, what will be its
density at 30,000 ft altitude where the pressure is 20 cm and the
temperature $-50°$ C?

3. The measured volume of a quantity of hydrogen collected
over mercury as in Fig. 7 is 700 cm³ when the temperature is
$23°$ C and the mercury stands $h=5$ cm above the reservoir.   The
barometer reads 72 cm.   What is the volume of H_2 at NTP, and
what is its mass?   Ans: 569 cm³; 0.0512 g.

4. A flask containing 1 liter of hydrogen gas at 2 atm pressure
is connected to a flask containing ½ liter of argon gas at 1 atm
pressure and the two gases are allowed to mix.   The temperature
remains constant throughout the process.   What is the resulting
pressure?

5. An air flask used for charging torpedoes holds 25 ft³ of air
at 3000 lb/in² and $75°$ F.   How many ft³ of air is this at NTP and
what is its mass in pounds?   Ans: 4690; 378 lb.

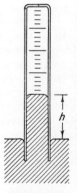

Figure 7

6. A tank holds 2 ft³ of oxygen at a pressure of 30 atm and a temperature
of $70°$ F.   After some oxygen is withdrawn, the pressure is 6 atm and the temperature $60°$ F.   How many pounds of oxygen were withdrawn?

7. A carelessly made barometer has some air trapped above the mercury.
The mercury stands at 73.2 cm when the air space is 10 cm long.   When the
barometer tube is pushed down into the reservoir so that the air space is only
5 cm long, the mercury stands at 71.6 cm.   What is the true barometric reading?
                              Ans: 74.8 cm.

NOTE: A schematic diagram of a constant-volume gas thermometer is shown in Fig. 8. The volume of gas in the bulb is kept constant by raising or lowering the mercury reservoir so that the mercury in the right-hand tube always stands at the etched mark. This type of thermometer gives very accurate temperature measurements over a wide range in terms of the simple law that pressure is proportional to temperature if volume is constant. For accurate work, corrections which we shall ignore are applied for the thermal expansion of the bulb, for the part of the gas that is in the narrow stem and is not at the same temperature as the rest, and for the change in density of mercury in the manometer with change in room temperature.

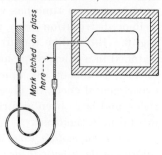

Fig. 8. Constant-volume gas thermometer (prototype).

8. In an experiment with a constant-volume gas thermometer the mercury level in the reservoir is 7.8 cm below the etched mark when the bulb is in melting ice; it is 17.2 cm above the etched mark when the bulb is in steam from boiling water. The barometer reads 76.0 cm. From these data and the definitions of the fixed points of the centigrade thermometer, determine the value of the absolute zero of temperature on the centigrade scale.

9. Hydrogen behaves like a perfect gas down to liquid-air temperatures. If a constant-volume hydrogen thermometer (see Fig. 8) has mercury level in the reservoir 28.5 cm above the etched mark when the temperature of the bulb is $0°$ C, 41.4 cm below the etched mark when the bulb is immersed in boiling liquid oxygen, and 46.4 cm below the etched mark when the bulb is immersed in boiling liquid nitrogen, and if the barometer reads 76.0 cm, determine the boiling points of oxygen and nitrogen.   Ans: $-183°$ C; $-196°$ C.

10. The airtight bag of a radiosonde balloon is partially inflated with 100 m^3 of He at the ground under conditions of NTP. What is the maximum load (mass of bag plus suspended gear) that can be lifted?

11. As the balloon of Prob. 10 rises, the helium expands to fill the bag more and more completely. If the bag is not yet filled out taut at a height of 10 km where the pressure is 20 cm and the temperature is $-55°$ C, what is the maximum mass that can be supported at this altitude?   Ans: 111 kg.

12. A vessel contains 39.9 g of argon (A) and 4.032 g of hydrogen (H_2) under a total pressure of 76 cm. Find the partial pressures of the argon and the hydrogen and the volume of the vessel.

13. A vessel contains 16.03 g of methane (CH_4) and 42.03 g of nitrogen (N_2). The total pressure is 200 cm, the temperature $100°$ C. Find the partial pressures of the methane and of the nitrogen and the volume of the vessel.
          Ans: 80 cm; 120 cm; 29.1 liters.

14. A bottle is partly filled with water at $0°$ C and corked. The bottle is then placed in a freezer and the water frozen at $0°$ C. The cork will blow if the gauge pressure exceeds $\frac{1}{8}$ atm. What is the maximum fraction of the volume that can be filled with water without the cork blowing? (Ignore the negligible change in volume of the bottle or the ice resulting from increase in pressure.)

15. Two glass bulbs, of volumes 400 cm^3 and 200 cm^3, are connected by a capillary tube. This container is sealed when it contains dry air at $20°$ C and 76 cm. The larger bulb is then immersed in steam at $100°$ C, the smaller in ice water at $0°$ C. Neglecting thermal expansion of the glass, find the resulting pressure.   Ans: 86.2 cm.

16. A diving bell contains 125 ft^3 of air at normal pressure when it is at the surface of the water. After it has been lowered to a depth of 150 ft, what are the pressure and volume of the air in it? What volume of additional air, measured at normal pressure, must be pumped in to again fill the bell? Neglect temperature change and water-vapor content.

17. Krypton is a monatomic rare gas. Compute its specific heat at constant pressure and its specific heat at constant volume. Compare with the observed value: $c_P/c_V = 1.67$. Ans: 0.060, 0.036 cal/g·C deg.

18. Xenon is a monatomic rare gas. Compute its specific heat at constant pressure and its specific heat at constant volume. Compare with the observed value: $c_P/c_V = 1.67$.

19. Compute the specific heat of O_2 gas at constant volume; at constant pressure. Compare with the observed values: $c_P = 0.217$ cal/g·C deg; $c_P/c_V = 1.40$. Ans: 0.155, 0.217 cal/g·C deg.

20. Compute the specific heat of F_2 gas at constant volume; at constant pressure. Compare with the observed value: $c_P = 0.182$ cal/g·C deg.

21. How much heat must be added to 0.2 kg of H_2 gas to raise its temperature from $-100°$ C to $25°$ C at constant pressure? What is the increase in thermal energy? How much external work is done? How much heat would be needed to accomplish the same temperature rise at constant volume?
Ans: 86.2, 61.6, 24.6, 61.6 kcal.

22. How much heat must be added to 0.3 kg of air to raise its temperature from $20°$ C to $110°$ C at constant pressure? What is the increase of thermal energy? How much external work is done by the gas? How much heat would be needed to accomplish the same temperature rise at constant volume?

23. In the manufacture of lead pipes, the solid lead is forced continuously through an annular die by applying a pressure of 14,000 nt/cm^2. Given that the specific heat of lead is 0.0313 and its density is 11.4 g/cm^3, how much will the temperature of the lead rise in passing through the die if it is assumed that all work goes into heating the lead?

24. Eight liters of O_2 at $0°$ C and 2 atm pressure is heated to $273°$ C at constant pressure.
(a) Use (17) to determine the external work in joules done by the gas.
(b) Use the value of c_V in joules/kg·K deg to determine the increase in thermal energy.
(c) Use the corresponding value of c_P to determine the heat added.
(d) Verify that the first principle of thermodynamics (12) is satisfied.

25. Six liters of H_2 gas at NTP is heated to $100°$ C at constant pressure. Make the same computations as in (a) through (d) of Prob. 24.
Ans: (a) 223 joules; (b) 556 joules; (c) 779 joules.

26. The entire thermal energy of a monatomic gas is translational kinetic energy. From (27), show that for a monatomic gas $c_V = \frac{3}{2} R/M$, as stated on p. 311.

27. Calculate the average translational kinetic energy of an argon atom at $25°$ C. At what Centigrade temperature does the average energy have half this value? Ans: 6.18×10^{-21} joule; $-124°$ C.

28. Calculate the average translational kinetic energy of a molecule of benzene vapor (C_6H_6) at a temperature of $25°$ C; at a temperature of $100°$ C.

29. Calculate the root-mean-square speed and the mean speed of argon atoms of atomic mass 40.0 at $25°$ C. Ans: 432, 397 m/sec.

30. Calculate the root-mean-square speed and the mean speed of benzene-vapor molecules of molecular mass 78.0 at 100° C.

31. Calculate the total kinetic energy of translation of all the molecules in 1 liter of an ideal gas at 25° C and 2 atm pressure.   Ans: 304 joules or 72.6 cal.

NOTE: In the following two problems you will need to use the fact that there are 6.025×10^{23} molecules in one mole (*Avogadro's number*) to determine the 'molecular masses.'

32. Calculate the root-mean-square speed of oil droplets of diameter 2 microns and density 0.9 g/cm^3 in their Brownian motion in air at NTP.

33. Calculate the root-mean-square speed of smoke particles of mass 5×10^{-17} kg in their Brownian motion in air at NTP.   Ans: 1.50 cm/sec.

34. A hand pump with a cylinder 12 in long is used to pump air into a tire. Assuming the temperature of the air to remain constant, find how far the piston must be moved before air can enter the tire if the gauge pressure of the air in the tire is 20 lb/in^2 at the beginning of the stroke and the atmospheric pressure is standard.

35. Considering the volume of an automobile tire to be 30 liters, find what volume of air at standard atmospheric pressure and 20° C must be pumped into the tire to increase the gauge pressure reading from 20 lb/in^2 to 30 lb/in^2. Assume the temperature of all the air in the tire to be raised from 20° C to 25° C in the process.   Ans: 18.7 liters.

36. A heavy piston is placed in the top of an upright cylinder of air at 27° C and normal atmospheric pressure.   The piston compresses the air isothermally and comes to rest between the top and bottom of the cylinder.   If the piston weighs 40 lb and is 4 inches in diameter, to what temperature must the air in the cylinder be heated in order to raise the piston to its initial position at the top of the cylinder?   (Assume that friction and leakage are negligible.)

37. Prove that the external work done by a gas in expanding from pressure P_0 and volume V_0 to pressure P_1 and volume V_1 *isothermally* (at constant temperature) is

$$W = P_0 V_0 \log_e(V_1/V_0) = (m/M)RT \log_e(V_1/V_0).$$

How much heat must be added to the gas during this expansion?   Ans: W.

38. An air bubble at the bottom of a swimming pool 10 m deep has a radius of 2 mm.   Calculate the radius of the bubble just as it reaches the surface of the pool if the temperature of the water is 20° C and the barometer stands at 750 mm.

39. An air sample at NTP is placed in a closed steel container.   If the container and air are heated to 100° C, what is the increase in pressure inside the container?   If a similar container were completely filled with mercury at 0° C and sealed, what would be the increase in pressure inside the container if the temperature were raised to 100° C?   (Assume that the container expands only because of the temperature increase.)   Ans: 0.37 atm; 398 atm.

40. What volume will be occupied by 5 g of methane gas (CH_4) at a pressure of 2 atm when the temperature is 27° C?   How much work would be done in compressing this gas isothermally to one-half its initial volume?   How much heat must be removed from the gas during compression?

41. Two grams of hydrogen and 3 g of carbon dioxide are introduced into an evacuated 3-liter cylinder.   Find the pressure inside the cylinder if the temperature is 52° C.   Ans: 9.5 atm.

42. There are 6.03×10^{23} molecules in a mole of any gas. The best 'vacuum' yet obtained in the laboratory is 10^{-11} mm of mercury. How many molecules are there in each cm^3 of this 'vacuum' at normal temperature?

43. An air sample initially at $20°$ C and normal atmospheric pressure occupies a volume of 1 ft². If it is heated at constant pressure until its volume is 1.5 ft³ and is then heated at constant volume until its absolute pressure is 1.5 atm, what is the final temperature of the air? Ans: $387°$ C.

44. If one makes the crude assumption that the temperature of the air does not vary as one ascends vertically, the variation of pressure with altitude h is given by the formula

$$P = P_0 e^{-gMh/RT}$$

where P_0 is the pressure at sea level where $h=0$, M is the molecular mass of the atmosphere, and T and g are assumed constant. Verify this equation by showing that the decrease in pressure $-dP$ when h is increased by dh equals the weight $\rho g\, dh$ of a unit column of air of thickness dh.

45. Prove that for an ideal gas or mixture of gases,

$PV = \frac{2}{3}$ (total translational kinetic energy of the molecules).

46. Show that if we use the notation $\gamma = c_P/c_V$, then

$$c_V = \frac{R/M}{\gamma - 1}, \quad \text{and} \quad c_P = \frac{\gamma R/M}{\gamma - 1}.$$

47. A liter of nitrogen at normal atmospheric pressure is compressed isothermally to a volume of 500 cm^3. Find (a) the resulting absolute pressure, (b) the work done on the gas, (c) the amount of heat that must be extracted from the gas, and (d) the change in thermal energy of the gas.

Ans: (a) 2 atm, (b) 70.2 joules, (c) 70.2 joules, (d) 0.

48. Show that one would compute the correct pressure of a gas on the walls of a cubical box whose edges are oriented in the X-, Y-, and Z-directions by assuming that one-third of the molecules are moving back and forth parallel to the X-axis, one-third parallel to the Y-axis, and one-third parallel to the Z-axis, all molecules having speed $\sqrt{\overline{v^2}}$ as given by (26).

49. In the formula $dW = P\, dV$ for the work done by a gas, we can use the kinetic theory value for P only if the gas is continuously in thermal equilibrium, which means, in Fig. 3, that the speed of the piston must be very small compared to the average speed of the gas molecules, so that the energy loss of those particular molecules that hit the piston can be considered as continuously redistributed among all the molecules of the gas. (It is conceivable that, in Fig. 3, the piston could be pulled to the right so fast that the gas would be 'left behind'; certainly kinetic theory would not apply in this case.) Consider the model of the preceding problem in which one-third of the molecules are moving right or left in Fig. 3, with speed $v = \sqrt{\overline{v^2}}$. Let the piston be moving to the right with speed v_P, where $v_P \ll v$. Using the Newtonian principle of relativity, show that the loss of kinetic energy of each molecule hitting the piston (assuming perfectly elastic collisions) is $2\mu v v_P$, and hence that the total loss of energy per second per unit area of piston is just $P v_P$, which is the power developed per unit area.

CHAPTER 16

SOLIDS, LIQUIDS, AND GASES

IN THIS CHAPTER we shall discuss the three *phases* of matter—solid, liquid, and gaseous—and the conditions that govern transitions from one to the other. We shall confine our attention to the case of pure substances, such as H_2O or CO_2, or of pure substances in the presence of a foreign gas, such as water vapor in air. We shall further restrict our attention to substances that are *crystalline* in the solid phase. All the substances whose melting and boiling points were given in Table II on p. 280 fall into this category. The solid is either a *single* crystal or a collection of crystals of various sizes, shapes, and orientations, and there is a definite melting temperature at which a sharp transition from solid to liquid phase occurs. This restriction eliminates from consideration waxlike and glasslike substances in which the solid is not crystalline but *amorphous*, with the molecules arranged in random positions as in a liquid rather than in a regular array as in a crystal. Such amorphous substances do not make a sharp transition from solid to liquid at a definite temperature. Instead, they make a gradual transition over a range of temperatures, with the solid first softening and turning into a thick viscous liquid. The reader is undoubtedly familiar with the great difference between the gradual softening of wax or glass and the sharp transition from hard ice to liquid water.

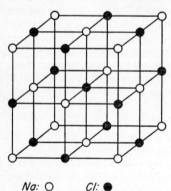

Na: ○   Cl: ●

Fig. 1. Structure of NaCl.

1. FUSION; FREEZING

IN A crystalline solid, the atoms are arranged in a regular array. For example, in common salt (NaCl), the Na and Cl atoms (actually Na^+ and Cl^- ions) are arranged at the corners of cubes as in Fig. 1. As a result of this cubic atomic arrangement, most of the individual crystals of table salt are perfect cubes, as can be readily observed with a little magnification. In ice, the atoms are arranged in a more complex pattern with hexagonal symmetry, giving rise to the beautiful hexagonal patterns of snow crystals shown in Fig. 2.

The atoms or ions in a crystal are held together by electric and magnetic forces which act exactly like a collection of little springs (see Fig. 1, p. 257).   The atoms have definite *equilibrium positions* but are capable of *oscillating or vibrating* about these positions.   The internal thermal energy of a solid consists principally of the energy of such vibrations. The average energy and amplitude of vibration increase with the increase in temperature as heat is added to a solid until, at a certain definite temperature (0° C for ice), molecular groups at the surface of the solid that happen to have unusually high energy move completely away from their equilibrium positions and enter the *liquid phase*.

Fig. 2. Photographs of snow crystals. [*From Thomas A. Blair, Weather Elements, Prentice-Hall.*]

In the liquid phase, the molecules no longer have definite equilibrium positions, although the attractive forces between molecules are still sufficiently large to prevent the molecules from getting very far apart.   In fact, the distance between neighboring molecules in the liquid is comparable with the distance between neighboring molecules in the solid, but the molecules have sufficient translational kinetic energy to keep sliding around past each other like the particles in a barrel of flour when stirred by the hands.   *The molecules of the liquid have a greater average energy than the molecules of the solid at the same temperature (the melting temperature).*

The temperature of a solid cannot be raised above the temperature of fusion (melting).   After the solid has reached this temperature, all added heat goes into melting more solid, the added heat supplying the energy difference between the liquid and the solid.   The temperature will not again commence to rise until *all* of the solid has been melted.

There is thus only one temperature, the temperature of fusion, at which solid and liquid can coexist in thermal equilibrium.   Above this temperature the substance is necessarily all liquid; below this temperature it is necessarily all solid.*   When solid and liquid coexist at the fusion

* More accurately, below the fusion temperature the substance is *all* solid if there is *any* solid.   It is possible to *supercool* a liquid below the fusion temperature.   Very pure dust-free water has been cooled as low as −40° C without freezing.   Apparently the difficulty in freezing lies in the formation of the first crystalline nucleus on which

temperature and no heat is added, there is equilibrium between the number of particularly energetic molecules that leave their positions on the surface of the solid and pass into the liquid state and the number of particularly slow molecules that recrystallize from the liquid onto the solid. If heat is added, more molecules pass into the liquid; if heat is taken away, more molecules pass from liquid to solid.

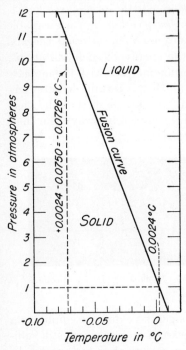

The fusion temperature depends slightly on pressure; for example, the fusion temperature of water *decreases* 0.00750 C deg for each atmosphere increase in pressure. Thus we have not a definite fusion temperature but a *fusion curve* on a PT-diagram, such as that shown for water in Fig. 3. It is seen that we can make ice melt not only by increasing the temperature but also by increasing the pressure. Because ice shrinks upon melting, it seems reasonable that increased pressure should tend to make it melt, since this results in a smaller volume. In fact, all substances that shrink on melting (the only known pure substances are water, gallium, and bismuth) have fusion curves that slant to the left like that of Fig. 3, so that increased pressure tends to make them melt. On the other hand, most substances expand on melting and have fusion curves that slant to the right, so that increased pressure tends to make them freeze.

Fig. 3. Fusion curve for pure air-free H_2O. It should be noted that the melting point of pure *air-free* water is not 0° C, but 0.0024° C, at 1 atm. It is the melting point of ice in contact with water saturated with air by being open to the atmosphere that is exactly 0° on the Centigrade scale at 1 atm pressure.

The extremely low friction encountered in skating can be attributed to this tendency for ice to melt under pressure. The sharp blades of the skates make contact only over a very small area, where the pressure is truly enormous. (For example, the weight of a 150-lb man applied to an area of 1 mm² gives a pressure of 150 lb/$\frac{1}{6000}$ in² = 15×6000 lb/in² = 6000 atmospheres.) This pressure causes incipient melting of the ice in this region so that we really skate on a film of water. This theory is supported by the fact that on an extremely cold day, say at −20° F, when

---

condensation can take place. If a tiny ice crystal is dropped into supercooled water, freezing of a large mass takes place suddenly. There is no similar difficulty in the process of melting, and superheating a solid is impossible.

the temperature of the surface of the ice is also very low, the ice seems less slippery and skating not so good.

The latent heat of fusion is the heat that must be added to change unit mass of the substance from solid to liquid *with no change in pressure or temperature*, that is, *at a particular point on the fusion curve.* The value of the latent heat of fusion varies somewhat from point to point on the fusion curve.

2. VAPORIZATION; CONDENSATION

CONSIDER the vessel of Fig. 4, which contains only H_2O, liquid and vapor. The vessel is at a definite temperature T and we are interested in the factors that determine the absolute pressure P.

A molecule in the interior of the liquid experiences, on the average, no resultant force from the other liquid molecules, since it has, on the average, equal numbers of molecules on all sides. It will have an average translational kinetic energy that depends on the temperature and which within wide limits is independent of the pressure in the liquid. But a molecule that approaches the surface of the liquid experiences, as indicated in Fig. 5, a large resultant force directed back into the liquid. The existence of this force is

Fig. 4. A vessel of constant volume containing only water and water vapor.

manifested in the phenomenon of *surface tension.* The surface molecules are continually being pulled back into the liquid and new ones are coming out to take their places. One can think of a molecule that approaches

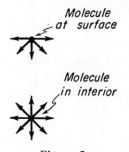

Figure 5

the surface from inside as 'hitting' the surface and 'bouncing' back, because as soon as it gets to within a few molecular layers of the surface it begins to experience a force tending to retard its outward motion and to pull it back into the fluid—it experiences an acceleration component into the fluid that decreases its outward component of velocity to zero and then reverses this velocity component.

But the velocity distribution among the fluid molecules will be such that there are some that approach the surface so fast that in spite of the retarding forces they escape through the surface and enter the vapor. These molecules 'evaporate' or 'vaporize.' *The number of molecules that have sufficient kinetic energy to evaporate (per second per unit area of fluid surface) increases rapidly as the temperature of the liquid is raised and depends only on the temperature of the liquid.*

On the other hand, *every vapor molecule that strikes the liquid surface enters the liquid, since it immediately experiences large forces pulling it into the liquid. At any given vapor temperature, the number of molecules per*

second striking unit area of a surface is proportional to the vapor pressure.
This statement is true whether or not the vapor behaves like a perfect gas.

If we start with liquid in the vessel of Fig. 4 and a vacuum in the space
above it, the liquid will start evaporating at a rate determined entirely by
the liquid temperature. The vapor pressure will increase until there are
as many molecules in the vapor striking the liquid surface and condensing
as there are molecules evaporating from the surface of the liquid. When
this condition is reached there is no further increase in vapor pressure.
The rate of evaporation depends only on the temperature; the vapor
pressure is proportional to the rate of condensation; since these two rates
must be equal, we see that, *in Fig. 4, the vapor pressure is determined by the
temperature.*

TABLE I
PRESSURE OF SATURATED WATER VAPOR

Temp. (° C)	Pressure (mm Hg)	Temp. (° C)	Pressure (mm Hg)	Temp. (° C)	Pressure (atm)
−60	0.008	12	10.52	100	1
−40	0.097	14	11.99	110	1.414
−20	0.776	16	13.63	120	1.959
−10	1.950	18	15.48	140	3.566
0.0100	4.579	20	17.53	150	4.697
2	5.29	25	23.76	200	15.35
4	6.10	30	31.82	250	39.26
6	7.01	50	92.52	300	84.79
8	8.04	70	233.7	350	163.2
10	9.21	90	525.9	374.15	218.4

The vapor pressure as a function of temperature is readily measured
by an apparatus similar to that shown in Fig. 4. In the case of water
this pressure is given by the curve of Fig. 6 and the data of Table I.

Now let us consider the cylinder of Fig. 7, which contains only H_2O.
Let us assume that we maintain the pressure constant, say at ½ atm
(38 cm of Hg) absolute. If we start with ice at a temperature below 0° C
and add heat, the H_2O will remain solid until we reach +0.0061° C
(Fig. 3). At this temperature the ice will change to liquid water as we
add sufficient heat to cause fusion. After all the ice has melted, the temperature of the liquid will rise as we continue to add heat. Not until we
reach the temperature of 81.6° C given by the curve of Fig. 6 will any
vapor be formed. For, suppose that at some lower temperature, say
72° C, an incipient bubble of vapor were formed. The vapor in this
bubble would have to be at a pressure of ½ atm if it were to be formed at
all. But water at 72° has a surface rate of evaporation which equals the
rate of condensation of vapor at a pressure of ⅓ atm and is much less

than the rate of condensation of vapor at ½ atm. So the vapor in the bubble would condense much faster than the liquid would evaporate into the vapor bubble, and the incipient bubble would collapse immediately.

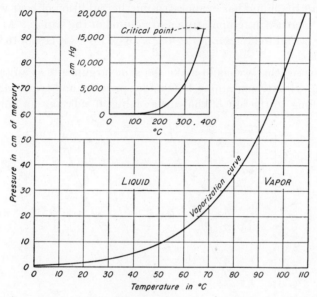

Fig. 6. Vaporization curve for water. This curve gives the conditions under which liquid and vapor can coexist, and hence gives the pressure of vapor saturated as in Fig. 4. No vapor can exist (in stable fashion) to the left of this curve; no liquid to the right. Vapor to the right of this curve is called *superheated steam*. This is also the boiling-point curve.

Not until we reach a temperature of 81.6° C will the liquid evaporate from a surface fast enough to maintain a bubble of vapor at ½ atm pressure. At this temperature liquid and vapor can coexist in equilibrium. If we add heat to the liquid so that the liquid exceeds this temperature ever so slightly, the liquid will evaporate faster than the vapor (at ½ atm) condenses, and the vapor bubbles will grow. The liquid will be topped by a layer of vapor. The rate of change of liquid to vapor will be governed purely by the rate at which heat is added since the latent heat

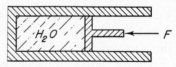

Fig. 7. A cylinder *filled* with H_2O (or other pure substance).

of vaporization must be furnished by the added heat.   Since it is only the most energetic liquid molecules that can evaporate, every molecule that evaporates in excess of those that condense results in a decrease in the average energy per liquid molecule which must be made up by the addition of heat if the temperature of the liquid is not to fall.

If the *pressure* exerted by the piston in Fig. 7 is kept constant, no temperature rise above 81.6° C will take place until *all* the liquid has evaporated. During this evaporation process the volume of course increases enormously and the piston of Fig. 7 must be imagined to move about 200 ft to the right on the scale of this figure.

After all the liquid has evaporated, further addition of heat will result in further increase in temperature and volume of the vapor.   At 81.6° C, this vapor is said to be *saturated steam;* above 81.6° C it is said to be *superheated steam.*

We now see that we could make the same arguments at any pressure, and that a cylinder containing H_2O under pressure and temperature conditions falling to the left of the curve of Fig. 6 will contain only liquid.

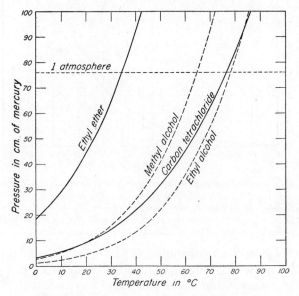

Fig. 8. Vaporization curves for various liquids.

To the right of this curve it will contain only vapor.   Only for values of P and T falling *on* the vaporization curve can liquid and vapor coexist; at these values of P and T the vapor is said to be *saturated.*

Of the latent heat of vaporization, most goes into the increased thermal energy of the vapor, but an appreciable amount goes into mechanical work in pushing back the piston to increase the volume.   At a pressure of 1 atm (1.013×10^5 nt/m²) and a temperature of 100° C, the latent heat $L = 539.2$ kcal/kg; the vapor has specific volume of 1.673 m³/kg; the liquid has specific volume of 0.001 m³/kg.   The change in volume per kg is $\Delta V = 1.672$ m³/kg, and the external work done per kg is

$$P \, \Delta V = (1.013 \times 10^5 \text{ nt/m}^2)(1.672 \text{ m}^3/\text{kg}) = 1.694 \times 10^5 \text{ joules/kg},$$

or, since 1 kcal = 4186 joules, $P \, \Delta V = 40.5$ kcal/kg.

Hence, since $L = \Delta e + P\,\Delta V$, where Δe is the increase in specific thermal energy,

$$\Delta e = (539.2 - 40.5)\ \text{kcal/kg} = 498.7\ \text{kcal/kg}.$$

Of the latent heat, 7.5 per cent goes into doing external mechanical work, 92.5 per cent into the increase in thermal energy of the vapor as compared with the liquid.

Exactly similar considerations apply to the vaporization of any pure liquid. Vaporization curves for other familiar liquids are given in Fig. 8.

3. SUBLIMATION; THE TRIPLE POINT

A COMPARISON of the fusion curve of Fig. 3 and the vaporization curve of Fig. 6, both for water, shows that these curves intersect. The point of intersection is at

$$P = 4.579\ \text{mm}, \qquad T = 0.0100°\ \text{C}. \tag{1}$$

Since solid and liquid can coexist along the fusion curve, and since liquid and vapor can coexist along the vaporization curve, the point of intersection of these curves must give a value of P and T at which solid, liquid,

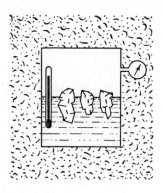
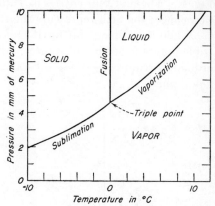

Fig. 9. The triple point.   **Fig. 10.** Triple-point diagram for water.

and vapor can all three coexist. This point (1) is therefore called the *triple point* for water.

It is easy to determine the triple point of water, and in practice this point is reproducible to within 0.0001 C deg. Take a thermally insulated vessel containing only ice and liquid water. Then increase the volume somewhat to make space for vapor, as in Fig. 9. Evaporation will take place—some slight adjustment of the quantity of ice and that of liquid water will occur in arriving at thermal equilibrium, and the system will settle down at the temperature and pressure of the triple point. *There is only one temperature and one pressure at which solid, liquid, and vapor phases can coexist in stable equilibrium.*

What is the phase of the substance at pressures below that of the triple point? It is seen (Fig. 10) that the fusion and vaporization curves intersect in such a way that no liquid can exist at lower pressures. But both solid and vapor can exist. Below the pressure of the triple point we have a third curve, called the *sublimation curve*, which represents conditions for equilibrium between solid and vapor. This curve is shown for water in Fig. 10. The diagram of Fig. 10, which shows all three curves and the triple point, is commonly called the *triple-point diagram*. The sublimation curve is not a direct continuation of the vaporization curve. It has a slightly different slope at the triple point.

Sublimation represents a direct evaporation of molecules from a crystalline solid into the vapor phase. At the low pressures and temperatures occurring on the sublimation curve, solid and vapor can coexist, with equilibrium between the rate of sublimation and the rate of condensation. There is a latent heat of sublimation which is exactly analogous to the other latent heats we have considered. The phenomena that would take place if a piece of ice at $-10°$ C were placed in an insulated evacuated enclosure are similar to those that were discussed in connection with Fig. 4. The first four entries of Table I represent points on the sublimation curve; the fifth represents the triple point.

While the triple point for H_2O lies well below ordinary pressures, the triple points for some substances, notably CO_2 and iodine, lie well above ordinary pressures, so these substances are not commonly observed in the *liquid* phase.

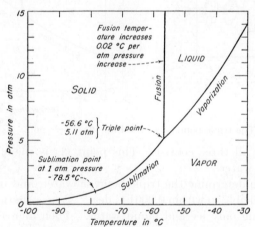

Fig. 11. Triple-point diagram for CO_2.

The triple-point diagram for CO_2 is shown in Fig. 11. The triple point is at $-56.6°$ C and 5.11 atm. We are acquainted with solid CO_2 in equilibrium with its vapor at 1 atm pressure and a temperature of $-78.5°$ C, and with its sublimation. The latent heat of sublimation is

137.9 cal/g at 1 atm pressure.   We are also acquainted with liquid CO_2 in tanks; this liquid is at room temperature but must be at a pressure above 56.5 atm or it could not exist as a liquid at 20° C.

4. THE CRITICAL POINT

FIGURE 6 shows the vaporization curve for water *ending* at a temperature of 374.15° C and a pressure of 218.4 atm.   The end of the vaporization curve is called the *critical point*.   As we follow up the vaporization curve, the difference in density between liquid and vapor becomes less and less, and the latent heat of vaporization less and less, until both vanish at the critical point.   For other substances the vaporization curve ends similarly at a critical point.   Values of pressure, temperature, and specific volume at the critical points of various substances are tabulated in Table II.

TABLE II

CRITICAL CONSTANTS

Substance	Critical Temperature (° C)	Critical Pressure (atm)	Critical Volume (cm³/g)
Water.............	374.15	218.4	3.1
Carbon dioxide......	31.1	72.9	2.15
Oxygen............	−119	50	2.33
Argon............	−122	48	1.88
Nitrogen...........	−147	33.5	3.21
Neon.............	−229	27	2.07
Hydrogen..........	−240	13	3.23
Helium............	−268	2.3	14.5

Above the critical pressure, no liquid-vapor phase transition occurs for any temperature.   Above the critical temperature, no liquid-vapor phase transition occurs for any pressure.   Above the critical pressure only two phases occur, instead of the usual three.   These are the crystalline solid phase and the *amorphous* phase.   As the temperature is raised with the pressure above critical, the amorphous phase changes *continuously* from a state which behaves much like a liquid to a state which behaves like a perfect gas, as we shall see in the next section.   Similarly, above the critical temperature only *one* phase, the amorphous phase, exists.

We now see that we can make a *continuous* change from liquid (say water at 20° C and 1 atm) to vapor (say steam at 110° C and 1 atm) by so altering the pressure and temperature that we go *around the end* of the vaporization curve.   This possibility emphasizes the fact that there is no *fundamental* difference between a liquid and a vapor, whereas each of these differs fundamentally from a crystalline solid, in that its structure is amorphous rather than crystalline, with a random rather than a regular molecular arrangement.

Gases for which a phase transition cannot be observed when the pressure is increased at room temperature, because their critical temperature lies below room temperature, are sometimes called *permanent* gases. All except the first two substances of Table II are of this type.

5. REAL GASES

REAL GASES do not obey the ideal gas law perfectly. This discrepancy is best illustrated by plotting *isothermals* on a $P\rho$-diagram as we do in

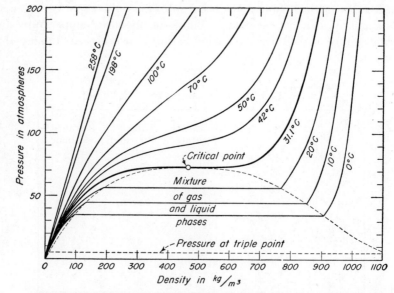

Fig. 12. Isothermals for CO_2, including the critical isothermal at 31.1° C, and showing the region in which vapor and liquid coexist. At the bottom of this region, below the 5-atm pressure of the triple point indicated by the horizontal broken line, is a region in which vapor and solid coexist.

Fig. 12 for CO_2 and Fig. 13 for dry air. These are curves in which density is plotted against pressure at a constant temperature. These isothermals show the increase of density with increase of pressure as we move up a vertical line in the triple-point diagram. At a temperature above the critical temperature, the density increases along a smooth curve as the pressure is increased. At a temperature below the critical temperature, the density increases smoothly until the vaporization (or sublimation) pressure is reached; then the density increases by a finite amount with no change in pressure as liquefaction (or solidification) takes place. Then the density of the liquid again increases smoothly with temperature. The process of liquefaction occurs along a horizontal portion of the isothermal, on which liquid and vapor coexist. As we move to the right along this horizontal portion, the density of the vapor and that of the liquid remains constant, but the fraction of the substance that is liquid increases from 0 to 100 per cent.

On such a $P\rho$-diagram, the isothermals for an ideal gas of molecular weight M are straight lines passing through the origin, of slope

$$\frac{P}{\rho} = \frac{RT}{M} = \left(0.08206 \ \frac{\text{atm}\cdot\text{m}^3}{\text{kg}\cdot\text{K deg}}\right)\frac{T}{M}, \tag{2}$$

when P is in atmospheres, ρ in kg/m^3, and T in ° K.

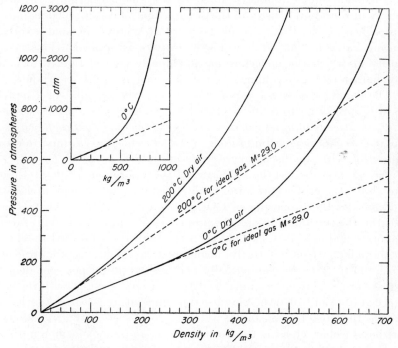

Fig. 13. Isothermals at 0° C and 200° C for dry air.

*The isothermals for a real gas always start out from the origin with the slope given by (2); the vapor of every substance behaves like an ideal gas if the pressure is sufficiently low.**

Departures from the ideal-gas law arise from forces between the molecules of a gas. These forces are of two types: (1) strong repulsive forces when the molecules come very close together, these forces giving the molecules a more or less well-defined size and making them appear to

---

* It is to be noted that if the temperature is very high, the gas molecules may be partially dissociated into atoms so that the average molecular mass to be inserted in (2) is less than the molecular mass at ordinary temperatures. Dissociation of the O_2 and N_2 atoms of air begins to be of significance at a temperature of about 2500° C.

bounce when they collide; and (2) weaker attractive forces of somewhat longer range which are the cause of the cohesion of liquids and solids. These forces are usually called *Van der Waals' forces*, after the man who first determined the character of the intermolecular forces required to account for observed departures from the ideal gas law.

The attractive forces cause the density to be greater than the ideal density and result in the curves of Fig. 12 swinging to the right of the ideal curve. Even the dry-air curves of Fig. 13 at first swing slightly to the right of the ideal curves, but only by a small fraction of one per cent.

The short-range repulsive force causes the isothermals to swing sharply upward as a density of the order of that of water (1000 kg/m³) is approached. The density seems to refuse to increase beyond a certain limiting value no matter how much pressure is applied. This is the density at which the molecules are apparently packed tightly together and characteristics of volume elasticity become like those of a liquid.

The behavior of water vapor closely approximates that of a perfect gas at all pressures up to its saturation pressure. *For temperatures below 60° C, the density of water vapor never differs from the ideal density by more than 0.5 per cent, even at saturation.* This statement is of importance in connection with the discussion of humidity in Sec. 7.

We can now discuss the properties of the amorphous state, at a pressure above the critical pressure, in more detail. Let us look at Fig. 12 and consider the properties of CO_2 at 100 atm pressure. At 0° C and 100 atm, the substance has all the properties of a liquid. It will start to evaporate and split into two phases if the pressure is lowered to 35 atm isothermally. It is relatively incompressible; doubling the pressure (from 100 to 200 atm) isothermally only results in a 4 per cent density increase or a 4 per cent volume decrease. If now we start with the substance at 0° C and 100 atm and raise the temperature *isobarically* (that is, keeping the pressure constant), we move to the left in Fig. 12 along a horizontal isobar, crossing the isothermals in continuous fashion until we reach a temperature of, say 258° C. At 258° C and 100 atm the substance behaves exactly like a perfect gas, obeying the ideal gas law very accurately. At this temperature, doubling the pressure isothermally doubles the density or halves the volume. Lowering the pressure isothermally does not result in any phase change. The transition from a substance that is 'obviously' a liquid to one that is 'obviously' a gas has, however, been continuous as we raised the temperature isobarically, and there is no good criterion for deciding where we should stop calling the substance a liquid and start calling it a gas.

6. BOILING

So FAR in this chapter we have confined our attention to a single pure substance in an enclosure. It is important to consider the case in which there is a foreign permanent gas such as air above the surface of a liquid.

Let us start by considering the heating of water in an open vessel. If the barometer reads 76 cm, the pressure on the surface of the water is 76 cm and the pressure within the water is the same except for a slight addition arising from the weight of the water. When the temperature of the water is below 100° C, evaporation takes place only from the surface of the water, and some of the heat added to the water goes into latent heat in this evaporation. The evaporation takes place only at the free surface, since an incipient steam bubble within the water would be unable to support a pressure of 76 cm and would collapse. The amount of evaporation can be restricted by restricting the surface area.

If heat is added at a sufficient rate, the temperature of the water will increase to 100° C. At this temperature, for the first time, steam bubbles can form and grow within the body of the water, because now the vapor pressure within the bubble equals the hydrostatic pressure of the atmosphere. *Ebullition (boiling)* will begin and continue until all the water has boiled away, with no further increase in temperature.

From this type of argument we see that the vaporization curve of Fig. 6 gives the boiling point of water in an open vessel as a function of atmospheric pressure applied to the surface. If the applied pressure is reduced, the boiling temperature goes down. The curves of Fig. 8 similarly give the boiling temperatures of other liquids at various pressures.

Example. *In the vacuum distillation process of drying a pharmaceutical product, it is desirable to have the water boil off at a temperature of not over 50° C in order not to damage the product. What absolute pressure must be maintained in the distillation chamber?*

According to Table I, water will boil at 50° C if the pressure is reduced to 9.25 cm of Hg; hence the vacuum pumps must maintain this pressure or lower.

7. MIXTURES OF GASES AND VAPORS; HYGROMETRY

LET us now return to Fig. 4, p. 325, and suppose that the space above the liquid water contains air or some other permanent gas as well as water vapor. Most permanent gases are only slightly soluble in liquid water, so that only a comparatively few of the gas molecules will enter the water and be dissolved in it. Unlike water-vapor molecules, most of the air or gas molecules that strike the liquid surface will bounce off as if it were a solid surface.

The water seems to ignore the presence of the air. The rate of evaporation is still determined purely by the temperature of the water and is independent of the pressure of the air. The rate of condensation is the same function of the partial pressure of the water vapor and the temperature as if the air were not present. Hence, *in equilibrium the partial*

pressure of the water vapor is given by the vaporization curve of Fig. 6.
The total pressure in the space above the liquid water will be the sum of
the partial pressure of the air, which is given by the general gas law in
terms of the temperature, volume, and mass of air, and of the partial
pressure of the water vapor, which is given by the vaporization curve.

Similar considerations apply to the case of any permanent gas confined in the space above any liquid in which the gas is not very soluble.
In the case of a permanent gas confined with a solid such as ice or CO_2
at a temperature below that of the triple point, the vapor pressure will be
given by the sublimation curve.

The case we have discussed is that in which the air or other gas is
saturated with the vapor of the liquid.   Another important case is that in
which there is no liquid present but only vapor, which may have less
partial pressure than the saturation vapor pressure.   A vapor cannot
have *greater* partial pressure than the saturation pressure corresponding
to the temperature of the vapor because then condensation of the vapor
to liquid or solid would take place.*   Thus, the water vapor in the atmosphere can have any partial pressure up to that of saturation.   If the
partial pressure exceeds that of saturation, condensation occurs, and
formation of clouds, fog, dew, or frost results.

The term *humidity* is used to describe the water-vapor content of the
atmosphere.

> The **absolute humidity** is the mass of water vapor per unit volume
> of atmosphere.

> The **relative humidity** is the ratio of the partial pressure of water
> vapor in the atmosphere to the partial pressure that would cause
> saturation at the temperature of the atmosphere.

The relative humidity is also, to a close approximation, the ratio of the
actual density of water vapor to the saturation density at the same temperature, since water vapor below 60° C obeys the ideal gas law very
closely, as we have pointed out in Sec. 5.

The measurement of humidity is called *hygrometry*.   Absolute humidity is measured by drawing a known volume of air through a drying agent
and measuring the increase in weight of the drying agent.   Relative
humidity is most accurately measured by determining the *dew point*.
In the dew-point apparatus, a polished metal surface is slowly cooled,
and the temperature is noted at which dew first begins to cloud the surface.   In this experiment, the atmosphere is cooled locally in the vicinity
of the metal surface.   Since the atmosphere in the region near the metal
surface is in pressure equilibrium with the balance of the atmosphere, the

---

* Dust particles and electric charges serve as 'condensation nuclei' on which
droplets of liquid or small ice crystals form.   They will also form on solid surfaces.
If few condensation nuclei are present, supersaturation may exist for a short period.

partial pressures of air and water vapor in this region will be the same as in the remainder of the atmosphere near the station where the measurement is being made.   But when the temperature of the air near the metal surface drops so that the partial pressure of the water vapor equals the saturation pressure, liquid water will begin to condense on the metal surface.

> The **dew point** is that temperature at which water vapor begins to condense, and hence that temperature at which the partial pressure of the water vapor present in the atmosphere equals the saturation pressure.

Since the saturation pressure at the dew point is the actual pressure of water vapor in the atmosphere, we see from the definition of relative humidity that

$$\left\{\begin{array}{l}\text{relative}\\\text{humidity}\end{array}\right\} = \frac{\text{saturation pressure at dew point}}{\text{saturation pressure at actual atmospheric temperature}}. \quad (3)$$

Another method of measuring humidity is by means of wet- and dry-bulb thermometers.   If the bulb of a thermometer is covered with a wet cloth, evaporation of the water will lower the temperature reading.   The rate of evaporation, and hence the change in temperature reading, will depend on the relative humidity.   The wet-bulb thermometer will give a reading somewhere between the actual temperature (the dry-bulb thermometer reading) and the dew point.   The wet-bulb reading cannot be below the dew point.   Such a situation would result in condensation on, rather than evaporation from, the wet bulb, and hence in a heating, rather than a cooling effect.   Within this possible range, the actual temperature to which the wet bulb comes depends somewhat on the air velocity past the wet bulb.   Handbooks contain tables that give the relative humidity as a function of dry- and wet-bulb readings for a standard air velocity of 15 ft/sec.

Weather observers usually use a form of wet- and dry-bulb hygrometer called a *sling psychrometer*, in which the thermometers are whirled rapidly about the hand in order to establish the necessary air current past the wet bulb.

A less accurate form of hygrometer depends on the fact that human hair expands in length in approximate proportion to relative humidity. The change in length of a single hair mounted under tension may be read on a dial calibrated to give relative humidity.

The behavior of a wet-bulb thermometer has a direct relation to the dependence of human comfort on humidity, since the body is cooled by evaporation of perspiration.   The higher the relative humidity, the warmer a heated room 'feels.'   It has been experimentally determined that a room at 70° F and 100 per cent relative humidity feels about as warm as one at 75° F and 50 per cent relative humidity or one at 80° F and 10 per cent relative humidity.   For comfort and health, a relative humidity between 30 per cent and 70 per cent is usually recommended.

Example. *In the winter, an air-conditioning system takes in outside air at 4° C and 65 per cent relative humidity and changes it to 25° C and 50 per cent relative humidity.   It does so by first heating the air part way, then saturating it with water vapor by means of a spray, then heating the air again to the desired final temperature.   What should be the temperature of the air after it leaves the spray saturated with water vapor?*

From Table I on p. 326, we see that the saturation pressure of water vapor at 25° C is 23.76 mm of Hg.   Fifty per cent relative humidity corresponds to 0.50×23.76 mm = 11.88 mm water-vapor pressure.   Saturated air has this water-vapor pressure at 13.8° C.   Hence the air leaving the spray must be at 13.8° C.

8. SURFACE PHENOMENA OF LIQUIDS

Let us now return to the subject of *surface tension* mentioned in Sec. 2.   As indicated in Fig. 5, a molecule in a liquid is subjected to attractive forces from its neighbors.   For molecules well inside the liquid, while these forces will fluctuate because of thermal agitation, they will average out to zero so that the molecule can move about in the liquid without doing any net work against these forces.   However, a molecule near the surface of a liquid is subjected to a resultant force directed back into the liquid.   A molecule at the surface can thus be considered as having potential energy greater than that of a molecule in the interior by the work that has been done against this force in bringing the molecule from the interior of the liquid to the surface.   A liquid thus has a *surface potential energy* proportional to its surface area.   To increase the surface area requires work equal to the increase in surface energy as more molecules are brought from interior to surface positions.   The surface tends, like a stretched membrane, to assume a shape of minimum area, because this shape is the shape having minimum potential energy, the condition for stable equilibrium (see p. 247).   Thus, a water droplet in the air assumes a spherical form, since a sphere has a minimum surface area for a given volume.   In fact, the surface of a liquid behaves in all respects like a membrane stretched with constant tension per unit width.

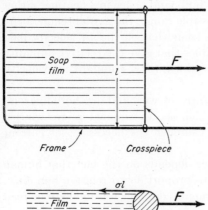

Fig. 14. Surface tension.

The behavior of a liquid surface can be demonstrated by means of the wire frame equipped with a sliding crosspiece shown in Fig. 14.   The wire frame is dipped into a soap solution and a film is formed as shown. Since the surface of the film tends to become a minimum, it tends to pull the crosspiece to the left in the figure.   In order to keep the crosspiece at rest, it is necessary to exert a force F to the right.

Now let us stretch the film by moving the crosspiece a distance δX to the right.   This requires work $F \, \delta X$, while the increase in surface area of the soap film is $2 \, l \, \delta X$, the factor 2 appearing because there are two surfaces.

> The **surface tension** of a liquid is defined as the surface potential energy per unit area of surface, which is the same as the work done per unit increase in surface area.

Thus, for the soap film, the *surface tension* σ is given by

$$\sigma = (F \, \delta X)/(2 \, l \, \delta X) = F/2l. \tag{4}$$

Thus
$$F = 2 \, l \, \sigma. \tag{5}$$

The meaning of the last equation is easily visualized from the lower sketch in Fig. 14, which shows the forces exerted on the crosspiece.   Each surface of the soap film exerts a force on the wire crosspiece; the sum of these forces exerted on the wire by liquid surfaces is just balanced by the force F.   Careful experiment shows that force F is indeed proportional to l, as indicated in (5).   The surface tension σ thus can be considered as *force per unit width* as well as *work per unit area;* it can be measured in joules/m² or in nt/m, which are actually identical units. It is like the tension in a stretched membrane such as a drumhead.

Since the surface tension of extremely thin soap films (thickness can be readily determined by *optical* methods involving interference) has

TABLE III

VALUES OF SURFACE TENSION σ

Liquid	Temperature	σ (joules/m² or nt/m)
Acetone.......	20° C	0.0237
Benzene.......	20	0.0289
Carbon Tetrachloride.....	20	0.0268
Ethyl Alcohol..	20	0.0223
Mercury.......	20	0.465
Water.........	0	0.0730
	25	0.0720
	50	0.0680

the same value as that of thicker films, one is led to the experimental conclusion that *the surface energy is contained in a layer just a few molecular distances thick.*

Because of surface tension the pressure P inside a liquid droplet is greater than the pressure P_0 outside.   The spherical droplet in Fig. 15 is separated into two equal portions by the imaginary vertical plane.   Consider the forces acting on the left-hand hemisphere.   This hemisphere is subject to two forces directed toward the right: $P_0 \cdot \pi r^2$, the resultant of the forces arising from the external pressure P_0; and $\sigma \cdot 2\pi r$, the resultant force arising from surface tension at the periphery of the shaded plane.

In order for the left-hand hemisphere to be in equilibrium, these two

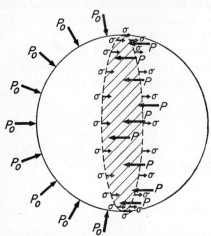

forces must be balanced by the resultant force arising from internal pressure at the shaded plane: $P \cdot \pi r^2$, where P is the internal pressure. Thus, the equilibrium condition is

$$P \cdot \pi r^2 = P_0 \cdot \pi r^2 + \sigma \cdot 2\pi r,$$

or $$P = P_0 + 2\sigma/r. \qquad (6)$$

The pressure within a spherical droplet is greater than the external pressure by $2\sigma/r$. This pressure difference can become very large for small values of r.

Similar considerations show that the pressure in a gas bubble in a liquid is also $2\sigma/r$ greater than the pressure in the surrounding liquid,

Fig. 15. Forces acting on the left half of a spherical droplet of radius r. P_0 is the external pressure, P the internal pressure, and σ the surface tension.

while the pressure in a *hollow* spherical bubble such as a soap bubble is $4\sigma/r$ greater than that outside because surface tension acts on both the inside and outside surfaces of the film. This latter relation furnishes one method of measurement of surface tension, as illustrated in the following example.

Example. *A soap bubble 2 cm in diameter is formed on a pipe attached to a water manometer, as in Fig. 16. The differential pressure is observed as 1.20 mm of water. What is the surface tension of the soap solution?*

Since the density of water is $\rho = 1000$ kg/m³, the pressure difference $\rho g h$ is
$(1000 \text{ kg/m}^3)(9.81 \text{ m/sec}^2)(1.20 \times 10^{-3} \text{ m})$
$= 11.8 \text{ nt/m}^2$

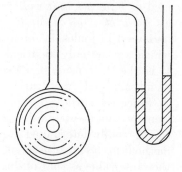

We equate this to $4\sigma/r$ to determine σ:
$$4\sigma/r = 4\sigma/(0.01 \text{ m}) = 11.8 \text{ nt/m}^2,$$
from which $\sigma = 0.029$ nt/m.

Figure 16

Let us now look at the energy relationships involved when a liquid is in contact with a solid surface. For a liquid that *does not tend to adhere to* or 'wet' a solid surface, the force of attraction of the molecules of the liquid at the interface toward the molecules of the solid (the *adhesive* force) is less than the force tending to draw them back into the liquid (the *cohesive* force). Thus they still have a *positive* potential energy which we denote by γ for a unit area of the interface. The value of γ, the *interface potential energy per unit area*, will be less than the surface tension σ if there is some force of attraction between the liquid and solid molecules. If there is no force of attraction γ will be equal to σ. If there is a force of repulsion between the liquid and solid molecules, γ can even be greater than σ.

The opposite case occurs with liquids that *adhere to* or 'wet' the solid surface. Here the liquid molecules at the interface are attracted by the solid more strongly than they are attracted back into the liquid. They thus have a *negative* potential energy with respect to molecules in the interior and *the interface potential energy per unit area, γ, is negative.*

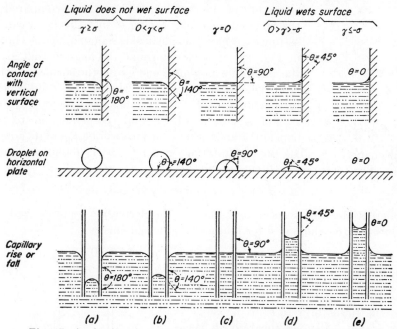

Fig. 17. Angle of contact. For mercury on clean glass, $\theta = 140°$ as in (b); for water on clean steel, $\theta = 90°$ as in (c); for water on clean glass, $\theta = 0°$ as in (e).

A critical limiting case is $\gamma = 0$; here the force of attraction toward the solid, acting on the liquid molecules at the interface, equals the force tending to draw them back into the liquid. They acquire no change in potential energy in moving from the interior of the liquid to the solid surface.

Whether the interface energy γ is positive, zero, or negative, and its size in relation to σ, has an important effect on the shape of a liquid droplet on a solid surface, on the capillary rise or fall, and on the angle of contact between a liquid and a vertical solid surface. This dependence is illustrated in Fig. 17.

The 'angle of contact' θ in Fig. 17 depends on the ratio of γ to σ. To see why this is so, consider the top row of sketches in Fig. 17. In the center, for $\gamma = 0$, any movement of the liquid surface up or down at the solid would increase the area of liquid surface and hence the potential energy, so the minimum potential energy occurs at $\theta = 90°$. But when γ is positive, the total potential energy is decreased by baring some of the interface at the expense of a slight increase in liquid surface, as at the left; while when γ is negative, the total potential energy is decreased by wetting more of the surface, as at the right.

To derive the relation between θ, γ, and σ, consider the layer of fluid of thickness s against the vertical plate at the top of Fig. 17. This thick-

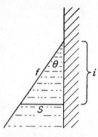

ness s is taken as small compared to the radius of curvature of the liquid surface but large compared to the range of molecular forces, so that this layer can be assumed to have the idealized triangular shape shown in Fig. 18. Let us determine the angle θ that gives the minimum potential energy for the surfaces of this fluid, since this will govern whether the fluid creeps further up the interface (smaller θ) or the opposite.

Figure 18

For a unit depth of fluid (perpendicular to the paper) the area of fluid surface will be f, and its potential energy σf. The area of interface will be i, with potential energy γi. The total potential energy will be

$$e = \sigma f + \gamma i = \sigma s/\sin\theta + \gamma s/\tan\theta.$$

Differentiate with respect to θ and set the derivative equal to zero to determine the value of θ for minimum potential energy:

$$de/d\theta = -\sigma s \cos\theta/\sin^2\theta - \gamma s/\sin^2\theta = 0.$$

This gives $$\cos\theta = -\gamma/\sigma, \qquad (7)$$

and this result is seen to correspond to the diagrams in Fig. 17 for the various ratios of γ to σ in the range $-\sigma \leq \gamma \leq \sigma$. Beyond this range θ has the extreme value 0° or 180° as indicated.

We can now discuss the important phenomenon of *capillarity*—the tendency of a liquid to rise in a small tube that it wets, or to be depressed in a small tube that it does not wet. *If the tube is sufficiently small*, the surface of the fluid in the tube (the *meniscus*) can be assumed spherical, since this is the surface of minimum area. From Fig. 19, we see that the radius of

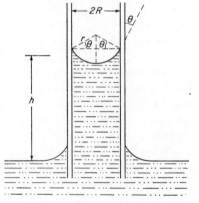

Figure 19

curvature of this spherical surface is $r = R/\cos\theta$, where R is the radius of the tube and θ the angle of contact. By an argument similar to that used in deriving (6), the pressure in the fluid just below the meniscus is less than the atmospheric pressure just above the meniscus by the amount of $2\,\sigma/r$. But this decrease of pressure just equals the weight of a unit column of the fluid lifted. We denote the mean height of rise by h. Thus

$$2\,\sigma/r = 2\sigma\,\cos\theta/R = \rho gh,$$

or
$$h = 2\sigma\,\cos\theta/\rho gR.$$

The height of capillary rise is thus inversely proportional to the radius of the tube. The very fine capillaries in plants and trees lead to the rise of sap to great heights. The capillaries between soil particles lead to the rise and evaporation of groundwater. If the soil is cultivated so that the particles have less intimate contact, this rise is inhibited.

Interface phenomena are important to many practical problems. As indicated at the right of Fig. 17, a drop of water on *clean* glass will spread indefinitely until it becomes a monomolecular layer; but any traces of oil on the glass will interrupt this spreading. Oil will spread in the same way on water. *Lubricants* must spread if they are to be effective.

The rate of solution of powders is influenced by interface phenomena. If the liquid wets the powder particles, it will penetrate between them and facilitate solution. If it does not wet the particles, the particles will coagulate into masses difficult to dissolve. The striking difference in rate of solution of various brands of soluble coffee, particularly in cold water, is an illustration of these differences.

In the same connection, the rate of flow of a liquid through a porous medium, even though it may be flowing under gravity or under the action of a pressure differential, is greatly influenced by interface phenomena. Capillarity will *aid* the flow in cases (d) and (e) of Fig. 17, but will oppose and retard the flow in cases (a) and (b). Considerations of such phenomena are of inportance to the petroleum engineer, since they influence the rate of flow of petroleum through porous oil-bearing strata.

Figure 20   Figure 21

Surface tension is of great industrial importance in the *flotation process* of separation of mineral ores, utilized to the extent of about $\frac{1}{4}$ million tons per day. The ore is finely ground and then agitated in a solution that wets the undesired minerals and does not wet the desired ones. Even though they are denser than water, the unwetted particles are 'floated' by surface tension as indicated in Fig. 20, and thus separated from the wetted particles, which sink to the bottom.

Detergent action involves a preferential spreading in which one liquid (the detergent) displaces another (oil or grease) on the surface of a solid because of its strong attraction toward the surface (Fig. 21).

PROBLEMS

NOTE: The saturated vapor pressure of mercury is very low at ordinary temperatures (0.0001 cm at 20° C, 0.028 cm at 100° C).]

1. Compute an accurate height in meters at which a water barometer will stand when the temperature is 30° C, the pressure 1 standard atmosphere, and the acceleration of gravity normal.   Ans: 9.941 m.

2. A mercury barometer reads 754 mm.   A drop of water is then introduced at the bottom of the mercury column and rises to the surface of the mercury. After evaporation has taken place, a small amount of liquid water remains.   By how many mm is the mercury column depressed if the temperature is 30° C?

3. If it is desired to have water boil at 70° C, what pressure should be maintained in a vacuum cooker? ·   Ans: 23.4 cm of Hg.

4. If it is desired to have water in a pressure cooker boil at 110° C when the ordinary boiling point is 100° C (the change of 10 C deg about doubles the cooking speed), to what gauge pressure in lb/in² should the valve be set?

5. If it is desired to have water in a pressure cooker boil at 110° C in a mountain location where the ordinary boiling point is only 90° C, to what gauge pressure in lb/in² should the valve be set?   Ans: 10.6 lb/in².

6. (a) A large vacuum pump continuously exhausts the vapor from a thermally insulated vessel containing water.   Why does the water cool down and freeze?   (b) If you had an ample supply of liquid oxygen at its boiling point under 1 atm pressure, how would you proceed to make solid oxygen? (This procedure has been used to solidify all gases except He.)

7. The measured volume of a quantity of hydrogen collected over water is 490 cm³, the temperature being 20° C and the barometer reading 750 mm.   The volume is measured with the water level the same inside and outside the hydrogen bottle.   Calculate the volume of dry hydrogen at NTP.   Ans: 440 cm³.

8. A sample of oxygen collected over water at 18° C occupies a volume of 804 cm³ when the water level is the same inside and outside the bottle.   Find the volume of dry oxygen at NTP if the barometer reads 749.5 mm at the time of collection.

9. A flask is partly filled with warm water at 70° C.   The air above the water is allowed to become saturated and then the flask is tightly corked.   If the barometer reads 770 mm at the time of corking, what will be the pressure in the flask the next day when it is at temperature 30° C and the barometer has dropped to 730 mm?   Ans: 506 mm.

10. A vessel containing air and water vapor is sealed at 100° C with the total pressure 76.0 cm, partial pressure of water vapor 16.7 cm.   It is then allowed to cool.   Compute the total pressure in the vessel at 70° C and at 30° C.

11. What is the dew point when the temperature is 30° C and the relative humidity 45 per cent?   Ans: 16.8° C.

PROBLEMS 345

12. On a winter day the outdoor temperature is $-10°$ C, and because of the snow the relative humidity is 100 per cent. Unless moisture is added to the air, the partial pressure of water vapor will be the same inside a house at 20° C. What will be the relative humidity in the house?

13. If the outdoor temperature is 15° C and the relative humidity 75 per cent, what will be the relative humidity inside a room at 25° C if no moisture is added to the inside air?   Ans: 40.4%.

14. (a) If a man enters a room at 25° C from an outdoor temperature of 18° C and his glasses steam up, what is a minimum value of the relative humidity in the room? (b) At what relative humidity in a room at 25° C will ice-water glasses collect a coating of moisture?

15. A vessel of 1 liter volume contains 1 g of H_2O at 100° C. What fraction of the gram is liquid?   Ans: $673/1672$.

16. A boiler of 0.5 m³ volume contains 100 kg of H_2O at 200° C. How many kg of steam are in the boiler?

17. At the triple point, the specific volumes of liquid water, ice, and steam are 1, 1.09, and 206,300 cm³/g. The pressure is 4.58 mm. The latent heat of fusion is 79.7 kcal/kg; the latent heat of vaporization is 597.4 kcal/kg. From these data determine the differences in specific thermal energy of water and ice and of steam and water at the triple point, and determine the latent heat of sublimation at the triple point. Show that if heat is added to a vessel of constant volume containing ice, liquid water, and steam, almost all the heat is used to melt ice to form liquid and very little of the heat goes into the formation of more vapor.   Ans: 79.7, 567.2, 677.1 kcal/kg.

18. At 1 atm pressure and the sublimation temperature, solid CO_2 has a density of 1.53 g/cm³. Using the vapor density given by the ideal gas law, find the percentage of the latent heat of sublimation that goes into increase in thermal energy and the percentage that goes into external work.
                                                                          Ans: 93.6%; 6.4%.

19. An air-conditioning unit works in the summertime by cooling the air below the desired temperature to condense out excess water vapor, and then reheating the air. If outside air is taken in at 95° F and 65 per cent relative humidity, and delivered at 74° F and 45 per cent relative humidity, to what temperature must it be cooled to lower the water-vapor content to the desired value?   Ans: 51° F.

20. In the air-conditioning installation described in Prob. 19, if air is taken in at 100° F and 30 per cent relative humidity, and delivered at 70° F and 60 per cent relative humidity, to what temperature must it first be cooled to lower the water-vapor content to the desired value?

21. Find the relative humidity on a day when the temperature is 30° C and the dewpoint is 18° C.   Ans: 48.6%.

22. On a certain day the temperature is 25° C, the relative humidity is 60 per cent, and the barometer reads 75 cm of mercury. What portion of the atmospheric pressure is due to dry air?

23. What is the total force exerted by the steam on the end of a cylindrical boiler 3 ft in diameter if the temperature of the water inside is 120° C?
                                                                          Ans: 29,300 lb.

24. The skating edge of an ice skate has an area of 4 mm². If a skater weighing 180 lb rests his entire weight on a single skate, calculate the lowering of the melting point of the ice immediately beneath the cutting edge by assuming that the melting point varies linearly with pressure over the required range. Discuss the effect of this variation in melting point on the friction between skate and ice.

25. Give an expression for the ratio of the density of air saturated with water vapor at 20° C to that of dry air at 20° C, the pressure being 760 mm in both cases.   Ans: $[17.5(18.0/29.0)+742.5]/760$.

26. Repeat Prob. 25 for air saturated with both water vapor and carbon tetrachloride.

27. What is the *maximum* value that could be obtained for the melting point of ice?   How would it be obtained?

28. A water spray is used in an air conditioning system that changes one cubic meter per second of dry air at 4° C to air at 25° C and 50 per cent relative humidity.   How many kilograms of water are needed per hour?

29. How high will water at 25° C rise in a glass capillary tube of internal diameter 0.8 mm?   Find the depression of mercury in a glass capillary with 0.5-mm internal diameter at 20° C, if the angle of contact for mercury in glass is 140°.   Ans: 1.83 cm; 0.885 cm.

30. What size of air bubble in water at 25° C has internal pressure 1 atm greater than the pressure of the surrounding water?

31. Show that the height of rise of the liquid film between two parallel plates with their lower edges immersed in a liquid is $h = 2\,\sigma\cos\theta/a\rho g$, where a is the distance between the plates.

32. By means of an 'atomizer,' 1 cm³ of water at 20° C is dispersed as a fine spray.   If the droplets are of uniform size, 10 microns in diameter, how much surface energy has to be supplied in producing the spray?

33. Two mercury droplets, each having a radius of 1 mm, coalesce to form a single droplet.   What is the ratio of the surface potential energy of the coalesced droplets to the original surface potential energy?   Ans: $\sqrt[3]{2}:1$.

34. What is the freezing point of a cloud droplet 10 microns in diameter? of a droplet 1 micron in diameter?   Clouds are observed unfrozen even at temperatures below 0° F; what are the various factors that influence whether or not the droplets freeze?

35. Two soap bubbles are connected by means of a glass tube as shown in Fig. 22.   At the moment the connection is effected, bubble A has a diameter of 1 inch

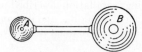

Figure 22

and bubble B has a diameter of 3 inches.   What happens after the connection is established?

CHAPTER 17

THERMODYNAMICS

IN THIS CHAPTER we give a very brief introduction to a dicipline called *thermodynamics*, which was developed during the nineteenth century by Carnot, Joule, Kelvin, Clausius, Gibbs, Rankine, and many others. This discipline is capable of drawing a surprisingly large body of important conclusions and formulas as logical deductions from just two simple postulates known as the first and second principles of thermodynamics. The first principle is merely a statement of the conservation of energy for processes involving interchanges of mechanical and thermal energy. The second principle asserts the inability of any heat engine to derive mechanical energy from thermal energy unless substances at two *different* temperatures are available and utilized, the hotter substance giving up heat and the cooler substance absorbing heat. These postulates are accepted because no conclusions at variance with experience have yet been deduced from them. The conclusions that can be drawn from these simple postulates are fundamental to many branches of physics and chemistry as well as to power, refrigeration, and aeronautical engineering. In this chapter we confine our attention to certain simple applications in the fields of power and refrigeration, and describe briefly the operation of the steam engine. We also discuss the manner in which the absolute thermodynamic temperature scale is set up.

1. THE FIRST PRINCIPLE OF THERMODYNAMICS

As WE have already noted, the first principle of thermodynamics is a statement of the principle of conservation of energy when both mechanical and thermal forms of energy are taken into account. In dynamics we do not have a rigorous principle of conservation of energy. Macroscopic mechanical energy (kinetic plus potential) is conserved only when no heat is generated. But if we include thermal energy, the principle of conservation of energy is much more general, and the sum of the mechanical energy and the thermal energy of an isolated system is conserved provided only that there are no electrical, chemical, or nuclear phenomena occurring which involve forms of energy other than mechanical and

347

thermal. With this restriction taken as understood, the *first principle of thermodynamics* can be stated in the following form:

FIRST PRINCIPLE OF THERMODYNAMICS: *When mechanical energy disappears, an equivalent quantity of thermal energy appears; and when thermal energy disappears, an equivalent quantity of mechanical energy appears; the equivalence being expressed by the relations*

$$1 \text{ cal} = 4.186 \text{ joules}; \qquad 1 \text{ BTU} = 778 \text{ ft·lb}.$$

Thus, when a bullet is fired into a fixed block of wood and embeds itself there, it loses all its mechanical kinetic energy, but an equivalent quantity of heat appears in the bullet and the block. When a coasting automobile is brought to rest, the mechanical kinetic energy of the car and its passengers appears as heat in the brakes and bearings and at the road surface. Reciprocally, when steam in a cylinder expands and does mechanical work, the work done is accompanied by an equivalent decrease in the thermal energy of the steam.

In the useful processes for converting heat into work or work into heat, there is always a working substance (for example steam or the gaseous products of combustion of gasoline in the case of an engine, ammonia or Freon in the case of a refrigerator). The working substance undergoes certain changes of pressure, volume, and temperature, accompanied by certain changes in thermal energy. In this case the first principle of thermodynamics gives a relation similar to that discussed on p. 306:

$$\begin{Bmatrix} \text{heat added to} \\ \text{substance} \end{Bmatrix} + \begin{Bmatrix} \text{mechanical work} \\ \text{done on substance} \end{Bmatrix} = \begin{Bmatrix} \text{increase in thermal} \\ \text{energy of substance} \end{Bmatrix}. \quad (1)$$

This relation presupposes that changes in *macroscopic* mechanical kinetic and potential energy of the substance are of negligible importance, as is the case in actual engines and refrigerators.

2. ADIABATIC EXPANSION AND COMPRESSION

CONSIDER a substance (which might be a gas or might be partly liquid

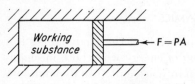

Fig. 1. A working substance in a cylinder with non-conducting walls and a non-conducting piston.

and partly vapor) in the cylinder of Fig. 1. The cylinder and the face of the piston are assumed to be perfectly insulated thermally so that *no heat can enter or leave the working substance.* The substance is at pressure P, which requires that a certain force $F = PA$ be applied to the piston.

If the force F is gradually increased, the working substance will be gradually compressed. At each stage it will be compressed to such a volume that its pressure just balances the force of the piston. Work will be done on the substance by the piston. Since no heat enters or leaves the substance, this work will go entirely into increasing the thermal energy of the substance, as we see from (1).   This increase will result in a gradual increase in temperature of the substance.   Here *gradual* denotes that the work is done sufficiently slowly to give the energy added by the work (in the first instance at the face of the piston) ample time to distribute itself throughout the whole of the substance so that at each instant the working substance can be considered to be in thermal equilibrium, with no more than an infinitesimal temperature gradient needed to carry the heat from the part of the substance near the face of the piston to the balance of the substance.   A compression carried out under the above ideal conditions is said to be *adiabatic*.

The reverse process, in which the force on the piston is gradually decreased, so that the substance gradually expands, doing work, and hence decreases in thermal energy and temperature, is called an *adiabatic expansion*.   In an adiabatic expansion the work done by the gas exactly equals the decrease in thermal energy.

The adiabatic expansion is to be contrasted with the free expansion discussed on p. 307, in which the substance, an ideal gas, does no work and suffers no change in thermal energy.   One could in principle approximate a free expansion by drawing the piston back so fast that the gas is 'left behind.'   The gas then exerts no force and does no work.   Hence the insistence, in defining an adiabatic process, that equilibrium conditions exist continuously, so that at each instant the substance exerts a pressure on the piston corresponding to its equilibrium pressure at a given temperature and volume.

> An **adiabatic process** is one that takes place with no addition or removal of heat, and with sufficient slowness so that the substance can be considered to be continuously in thermal and mechanical equilibrium.

No entirely adiabatic process occurs in practice, but the expansion of steam in the cylinder of a steam engine, of the hot gases in an internal-combustion engine, and the compression of the air in a Diesel engine or in an air compressor are all approximately adiabatic.   These processes take place rapidly enough that only a small amount of heat has time to enter or leave the substance from the cylinder walls, and yet slowly enough so that thermal and mechanical equilibrium is approximately maintained throughout the gas in the cylinder.   An *ideal* engine or refrigerator would employ processes that are exactly adiabatic.   Study of such ideal devices sets important theoretical limits to the capabilities of real engines and refrigerators.

The laws governing adiabatic processes in an ideal gas are not difficult to derive.   Let a mass m of gas expand adiabatically from volume V_1 with pressure P_1, temperature T_1, and density ρ_1, to a greater volume V_2, with pressure P_2, temperature T_2, and density ρ_2, as in Fig. 2.   Since no heat is added, the work done by the gas equals its decrease in thermal energy. But by (15), p. 308, the decrease in thermal energy is $mc_V(T_1-T_2)$. So in the *adiabatic expansion* of Fig. 2,

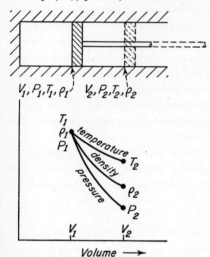

$$\text{work done by gas} = mc_V(T_1-T_2) \quad (2)$$

Similarly, in the reverse *adiabatic compression*, with notation also as in Fig. 2,

$$\text{work done on gas} = mc_V(T_1-T_2). \quad (3)$$

Equations (2) and (3) give the mechanical work done in an adiabatic process in terms of the temperature change. But we do not yet know how to relate the temperature change to the volume change. We can determine the relation between the temperature change and the volume change by considering an infinitesimal step in the expansion process. When the volume changes

Fig. 2. Adiabatic expansion or compression of an ideal gas.

from V to $V+dV$, the gas does work $P\,dV$. At the same time let the temperature change from T to $T+dT$. Then the increase in thermal energy of the gas is $mc_V\,dT$. Since dT is negative if dV is positive, it is better to say that the decrease in thermal energy is $-mc_V\,dT$. Since the work done by the gas equals the decrease in thermal energy, we have

$$P\,dV = -mc_V\,dT. \quad (4)$$

The minus sign is associated with the fact that dT/dV is negative as indicated in Fig. 2.

Now in (4) we can substitute the value of P given by the general gas law (3), p. 303:

$$P = \frac{R}{M}\,m\,\frac{T}{V},$$

and the value of c_V given by Prob. 46, p. 321:

$$c_V = \frac{R}{M}\,\frac{1}{\gamma-1},$$

where γ is the ratio c_P/c_V. When we make these substitutions in (4) and cancel common factors, we obtain

$$\frac{T}{V}\,dV = -\frac{dT}{\gamma-1},$$

which can be written as

$$dT + (\gamma - 1)TV^{-1}\, dV = 0.$$

If we multiply this equation through by $V^{\gamma-1}$, we obtain

$$V^{\gamma-1}\, dT + (\gamma - 1)TV^{\gamma-2}\, dV = 0. \tag{5}$$

The left side of this equation is just the differential $d(TV^{\gamma-1})$, so

$$d(TV^{\gamma-1}) = 0. \tag{6}$$

This result means that the change in the product $TV^{\gamma-1}$ is zero in every step in the adiabatic expansion, so this product remains constant throughout the process:

$$TV^{\gamma-1} = \text{const} \tag{7}$$

in an adiabatic process. [Although we have discussed an adiabatic expansion explicitly, the compression is exactly the reverse process, and (4) and (7) are equally valid for an adiabatic compression.] In particular, the product in (7) has the same value at the beginning and the end of the process, so

$$T_2 V_2{}^{\gamma-1} = T_1 V_1{}^{\gamma-1} \tag{8}$$

in the notation of Fig. 2. This is the equation we need to find T_2 if T_1, V_1, and V_2 are given, so that we can compute the work from (2) or (3) if the volume change is given.

By combining (8) with the general gas law in the form (5), p. 303, we can get equations relating pressure and volume, or pressure and temperature, in an adiabatic expansion:

$$P_2 V_2{}^\gamma = P_1 V_1{}^\gamma, \tag{9}$$

$$\frac{P_2}{T_2{}^{\gamma/(\gamma-1)}} = \frac{P_1}{T_1{}^{\gamma/(\gamma-1)}}. \tag{10}$$

The proof of (9) and (10) is left as an exercise.

Example. *Air is introduced into the cylinder of a diesel engine at a temperature of 27° C. What is the temperature of the air after it has been compressed to $\frac{1}{24}$ of its initial volume?*

We employ (8) and remember that absolute temperatures are involved. Hence $T_1 = 300°$ K, and we may write

$$T_2\,(\tfrac{1}{24} V_1)^{(1.41-1)} = (300°\ \text{K})\,V_1{}^{(1.41-1)},$$

$$T_2 = (300°\ \text{K})(24)^{0.41},$$

since for air $\gamma = 1.41$. To evaluate $(24)^{0.41}$, we take the logarithm of 24, multiply by 0.41, and look up the antilog of the product. The result is 3.68, and hence $T_2 = (300°\ \text{K})(3.68) = 1104°$ K, or 831° C.

In an adiabatic expansion, the pressure drops more rapidly with volume than it does in an isothermal expansion, since in the adiabatic case not only does the volume increase but also the temperature decreases, both of which factors contribute to a pressure drop. This point, which

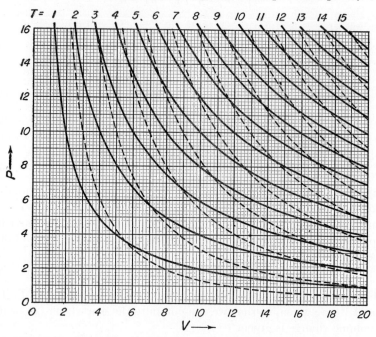

Fig. 3. Isothermals (solid lines) and adiabatics (broken lines) on a PV-diagram for an ideal gas with $\gamma = 1.67$. The units in which P, V, T are measured will vary with the quantity and kind of gas and must be chosen so that the general gas law is satisfied.

is important for later discussion in this chapter, is illustrated in Fig. 3, which shows a family of PV-curves satisfying the isothermal equation

$$PV = \text{const}, \qquad \text{(isothermal)} \quad (11)$$

and also a family of steeper curves satisfying the adiabatic equation

$$PV^{1.67} = \text{const}, \qquad \text{(adiabatic)} \quad (12)$$

for the case $\gamma = 1.67$ appropriate to an ideal monatomic gas.

Example. *A sample of helium in a cylinder equipped with a movable piston has a volume of 20 liters when the pressure is 1 atm. An external force on the piston compresses the gas adiabatically to one-fifth of its initial volume. What is the pressure of the gas after compression?*

Since the initial pressure and volume are given, it is convenient to use (9) in finding the final pressure. The units to be used are arbitrary provided the same units are used on each side of the equation; hence we set $P_1 = 1$ atm, $V_1 = 20$ liters, $V_2 = 4$ liters, and solve for P_2 in atmospheres. Thus, our equation is

$$(1\text{ atm})(20\text{ liters})^{1.67} = P_2 \,(4\text{ liters})^{1.67},$$

since $\gamma = 1.67$ for helium.   This gives

$$P_2 = 5^{1.67} \text{ atm.}$$

Using logarithms, or the log-log slide rule, we find that $5^{1.67} = 14.7$, and hence $P_2 = 14.7$ atm.   Note that $V = 20$, $P = 1$ and $V = 4$, $P = 14.7$ are two points on one of the broken curves in Fig. 3.

3. AN IDEAL HEAT ENGINE EMPLOYING THE CARNOT CYCLE

WE SHALL now discuss a highly idealized heat engine known as the Carnot engine.*   This discussion will show how it is possible to obtain mechanical work from heat by using a working substance that is carried through a cyclic process.   The Carnot cycle is of fundamental importance because it gives an expression for engine efficiency which, as will be shown in Sec. 5, furnishes a theoretical limit to the efficiency that a real heat engine can have.

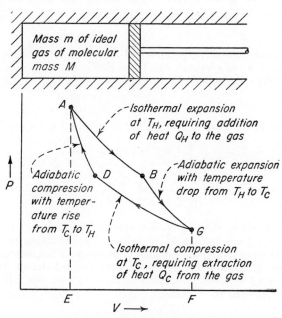

Fig. 4. The Carnot cycle.

In the Carnot engine, the working substance is an ideal gas contained in a cylinder equipped with a piston.   By suitable manipulations, the gas is made to follow around a closed curve on the PV-diagram.   The curve is a quadrilateral made up of pieces of two isothermals and two adiabatics from Fig. 3.   Such a cycle is drawn schematically in Fig. 4.

We imagine that we have two large reservoirs with which the gas in the cylinder can somehow be put into thermal communication.   We have

* Devised by Sadi Carnot, French engineer, in 1824, in connection with a study of methods for improvement of the efficiency of the steam engine.

a hot reservoir at temperature T_H from which heat can be supplied to the gas, and a cold reservoir at temperature T_C to which the gas can give up heat. We start with the gas at point A, with volume V_A, pressure P_A, and temperature T_H. The four steps in the cycle are then executed as follows:

$A \rightarrow B$:

The gas is placed in thermal communication with the hot reservoir. It expands slowly from volume V_A to volume V_B, remaining in thermal equilibrium with the reservoir, so that the gas maintains constant temperature T_H. In this isothermal expansion the work done by the gas is that given by Prob. 37 on p. 320, namely.

$$(m/M)RT_H \log_e(V_B/V_A).$$

Since the temperature, and hence the thermal energy, of the gas does not change in going from A to B, the heat supplied by the reservoir must exactly equal the work done. *We call the heat supplied by the hot reservoir Q_H.* Then

$$Q_H = (m/M)RT_H \log_e(V_B/V_A). \tag{13}$$

$B \rightarrow G$:

The gas is next thermally insulated and is allowed to continue its expansion adiabatically until its temperature has fallen to T_C, the temperature of the cold reservoir. In this expansion the work done by the gas is, from (2),

$$mc_V(T_H - T_C). \tag{14}$$

The ratio of the final volume V_G to the initial volume V_B is given by (8) as

$$T_C V_G{}^{\gamma-1} = T_H V_B{}^{\gamma-1},$$

or

$$\frac{V_G}{V_B} = \left[\frac{T_H}{T_C}\right]^{\frac{1}{\gamma-1}}. \tag{15}$$

$G \rightarrow D$:

The gas is placed in thermal communication with the cold reservoir. It is compressed slowly from volume V_G to volume V_D, remaining in thermal equilibrium with the reservoir so the gas maintains constant temperature T_C. Since the temperature, and hence the thermal energy, does not change, the work done on the gas must all be given up as heat to the cold reservoir. *We call the heat given to the cold reservoir Q_C.* Then

$$Q_C = (m/M)RT_C \log_e(V_G/V_D). \tag{16}$$

The volume V_D to which the isothermal compression is carried is chosen to be that volume lying on the adiabatic through A. This volume will be given by the relation

$$\frac{V_D}{V_A} = \left[\frac{T_H}{T_C}\right]^{\frac{1}{\gamma-1}}. \tag{17}$$

$D \rightarrow A$:

The gas is again insulated and compressed adiabatically back to its initial condition at A. The work done *on* the gas in this compression is

$$mc_V(T_H - T_C). \tag{18}$$

We can see from an examination of Fig. 4 that in going once around the whole cycle the gas must have done a net amount of work. Since $\int P\,dV$ equals the area under the curve on a PV-diagram, the work done *by* the gas in expanding from A to B to G equals the area $ABGFEA$, and the work done *on* the gas during the compression from G to D to A equals the smaller area $ADGFEA$. The *net* work done *by* the gas equals the difference between these areas, the area of the quadrilateral $ABGDA$.

This net work per cycle is given by

$$(13)+(14)-(16)-(18)=Q_H-Q_C \tag{19}$$

Since the net work is positive, it must be that $Q_H>Q_C$. If we compare (15) and (17) we see that

$$\frac{V_G}{V_B}=\frac{V_D}{V_A}, \quad \text{and hence} \quad \frac{V_G}{V_D}=\frac{V_B}{V_A}.$$

Therefore the logarithms in (13) and (16) are equal, and we see from these equations that

$$\boxed{\frac{Q_H}{Q_C}=\frac{T_H}{T_C}.} \tag{20}$$

Hence $Q_H>Q_C$, since $T_H>T_C$ by assumption. That the net work per cycle is Q_H-Q_C follows directly from the first principle of thermodynamics, since in going once around the cycle we have added heat Q_H-Q_C to the gas. Since the gas ends with the same thermal energy as at the start, this heat must all have gone into doing external work.

> The **efficiency** of the Carnot engine is defined as the ratio of the net work done per cycle to the heat supplied by the hot body per cycle.

We can readily compute the efficiency of the Carnot engine from the relation above:

$$\boxed{\left(\begin{array}{c}\text{Carnot}\\ \text{efficiency}\end{array}\right)=\frac{Q_H-Q_C}{Q_H}=1-\frac{Q_C}{Q_H}=1-\frac{T_C}{T_H}=\frac{T_H-T_C}{T_H}.} \tag{21}$$

This efficiency depends only on the ratio T_H/T_C of the absolute temperature of the hot reservoir from which heat is extracted to the absolute temperature of the cold reservoir to which heat is given. The efficiency is zero at $T_H/T_C=1$, and increases as T_H/T_C increases. It is 0.5 at $T_H/T_C=2$, 0.75 at $T_HT_C=4$, and so on.

4. AN IDEAL REFRIGERATOR EMPLOYING THF CARNOT CYCLE

WE CAN run the heat engine of Fig. 4 'backwards,' meaning that we go around the cycle in the counterclockwise direction rather than in the clockwise, reversing all the arrowheads in Fig. 4. We can start at C with an adiabatic *compression* to B; then an isothermal compression to A, during which heat is *given to* the *hot* reservoir; then an adiabatic expansion to D; and finally an isothermal expansion back to C, during which heat is *taken from* the *cold* reservoir. The machine is now acting as a *refrigerator*, taking heat from a cold body and giving it to a hot body.

The magnitudes of Q_H, the heat given to the hot body, and Q_C, the heat taken from the cold body, are the same as computed in Sec. 3. Furthermore, the net work done in the cycle is again the area $ABCDA$, but now this is net work done *on* the gas, since more work is done on the gas during the compression than is done by the gas during the expansion. This net work is $Q_H - Q_C$.

To extract an amount Q_C of heat from the cold body, we must do mechanical work of amount $Q_H - Q_C$. The sum, $Q_C + (Q_H - Q_C) = Q_H$, of the heat extracted from the cold body and the mechanical work done must be added to the hot body as heat. To accomplish the extraction of Q_C units of heat requires mechanical work equal to

$$W = Q_H - Q_C = \left(\frac{Q_H}{Q_C} - 1\right) Q_C = \left(\frac{T_H}{T_C} - 1\right) Q_C = \frac{T_H - T_C}{T_C} Q_C. \quad (22)$$

The greater the temperature ratio T_H/T_C, the more the work required to effect the transfer of a given quantity of heat from the cold to the hot body.

Example. *On p. 291, we worked out an example in which it was found that a refrigerating system would have to transfer* 1000 BTU/hr *from the interior of a refrigerator at* 40° F *to the exterior air at* 80° F. *If this were an ideal Carnot refrigerator, how much work (in BTU's) would have to be done by the engine per hour and what would be its required horsepower?*

We get the power from (22) by substituting $T_H = 80°$ F $= 540°$ R, $T_C = 40°$ F $= 500°$ R, $Q_2 = 1000$ BTU/hr, as

$$P = \left(\frac{40°}{500°}\right) \left(1000 \frac{\text{BTU}}{\text{hr}}\right) = 80 \frac{\text{BTU}}{\text{hr}}.$$

Since 1 BTU/hr $= 3.93 \times 10^{-4}$ hp (see table in Sec. 8 of the Appendix), this represents only

$$80 \times 3.93 \times 10^{-4} \text{ hp} = 0.0314 \text{ hp}.$$

5. THE SECOND PRINCIPLE OF THERMODYNAMICS

THE FIRST principle of thermodynamics places no restrictions on our ability to change thermal energy into mechanical energy; it merely tells how much mechanical energy will appear if thermal energy disappears.

Experience, however, tells us that whereas it is very easy to turn mechanical energy completely into thermal energy (as in friction), there are severe restrictions on our ability to effect the reverse transformation. In particular, the oceans of the world are filled with water at 4° C that contains an enormous amount of thermal energy; yet experience teaches us that it is impossible to devise a machine that will change this energy into mechanical energy. The only way we seem to be able to turn thermal energy into mechanical energy is to have bodies at two *different* temperatures available and to introduce between them some kind of machine that interferes to a certain extent with the natural tendency of heat to flow from the hot body to the cold body and manages to turn some, *but only some*, of the heat flowing from the hot to the cold body into work. We shall show that the Carnot efficiency (21) gives the maximum fraction of the heat that can be turned into work.

No one has ever devised a way of changing any of the *completely random* motion of the molecules of a material medium in thermal equilibrium into the *coordinated* or *mass* motion that represents macroscopic mechanical energy, in such a way that the only resulting effect is the cooling (decrease in *microscopic* mechanical energy) of the material medium; the second principle of thermodynamics asserts that it is *impossible* to do so.

The *second principle of thermodynamics* is an inference from experience that embodies the above ideas, for example, that of the nonutilizability of the heat of the oceans. From this simple principle a great many detailed conclusions can be drawn, all of which are in agreement with experiment. This agreement gives us complete confidence in the universal applicability of the principle. The second principle states:

SECOND PRINCIPLE OF THERMODYNAMICS: *It is impossible even in principle to construct an engine that will deliver mechanical work derived purely from the cooling of a single heat reservoir, no heat being given out to a reservoir at lower temperature.*

From this principle we can proceed to derive a number of important laws relating to engines and refrigerators:

All reversible engines have the same efficiency when they operate between reservoirs at the same two temperatures.

A reversible engine is one which, like the Carnot engine, will work equally well as a refrigerator, running through a cycle that accomplishes *exactly* the reverse of the engine cycle. All reversible engines are idealized concepts in that truly isothermal and truly adiabatic processes never occur, and friction is never entirely absent. An engine that works exactly like the Carnot engine but employs a real imperfect gas would still be reversible. The gas may even liquefy and evaporate during the cycle, as does the working substance in actual refrigerating cycles. One can imagine using isothermals like those of CO_2 in Fig. 12, p. 332 (replotted on a PV-diagram), and corresponding highly distorted adiabatics. Such a cycle would still be entirely reversible so long as the steps in the cycle were truly isothermal or adiabatic.

The above law is proved as follows: Suppose that we have two reversible engines A and B, of efficiencies α and β.   As an engine, A takes heat Q_H from the hot reservoir, delivers mechanical energy αQ_H, and gives heat

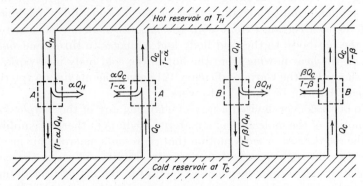

Fig. 5. Energy transformations effected by reversible engines. Left to right: A as engine; reversed A as refrigerator; B as engine; reversed B as refrigerator. The arrows at the center represent mechanical output of the engine or input to the refrigerator.

$Q_C = (1 - \alpha)Q_H$ to the cold reservoir.   Note that $Q_H = Q_C/(1-\alpha)$.   As a refrigerator, A takes $(1-\alpha)Q_H = Q_C$ from the cold body, is supplied with mechanical energy $\alpha Q_H = \alpha Q_C/(1-\alpha)$, and delivers $Q_H = Q_C/(1-\alpha)$ to the hot body. B does similarly, with efficiency β.   These relations are illustrated in Fig. 5 in terms of the heat taken from the hot body in the case of the engine and the heat taken from the cold body in the case of the refrigerator.

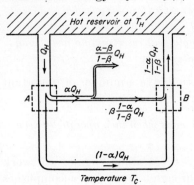

Fig. 6. If $\alpha > \beta$, we could use A to drive B as a refrigerator and get net work $(\alpha - \beta)/(1 - \beta)$ for each unit of heat that A took in. The symbolism in the above diagram is the same as in Fig. 5, and the quantities of energy can be verified by comparison with Fig. 5.

Now assume that A is more efficient than B, that is, that $\alpha > \beta$.   Then, as indicated in Fig. 6, we can use A as an engine to drive B as a refrigerator. The heat given out by A at the low temperature will be the heat input to B. A will be able to drive B and still furnish *additional* mechanical energy. The combination would be a self-acting engine that takes thermal energy from a single reservoir and changes it into work, in contradiction to the second principle.   Therefore A is *not* more

efficient than B.   Similarly, we prove that B is *not* more efficient than A; therefore, A and B must have the same efficiency.   Therefore *every reversible engine has the Carnot efficiency* (21), since it has the same efficiency as the Carnot reversible engine which employs an ideal gas.

   No actual engine can have a greater efficiency than a reversible engine working between the same two temperatures.

An actual engine is nonreversible. It always has friction losses that cause nonreversible transformations of mechanical energy into heat, departures from thermal equilibrium that cause nonreversible transfers of heat, loss of thermal energy by conduction to colder bodies, etc.

   Let A, Fig. 6, be an actual engine of efficiency α; B a reversible engine of efficiency β.   Then if $\alpha > \beta$, we can use part of the mechanical output of A to drive B as a refrigerator to return all the heat given out by A to the hot body and still have some mechanical output from A left over. This result is in violation of the second principle.   Therefore, A is *not* more efficient than B.   In this case we cannot turn the argument around, since A is not reversible.   We conclude that *no actual engine can be more efficient than an ideal reversible engine, which has the Carnot efficiency* (21).

   We shall postpone discussion of this law until we consider actual engines in Sec. 6.

   For any refrigerator to take Q_C units of heat from a cold body at T_C and transfer it to a hot body at T_H, at least $W = Q_C(T_H - T_C)/T_C$ units of mechanical work must be done on the working substance of the refrigerator.

The mechanical work mentioned in this law is the value (22) required by a Carnot cycle, or, from arguments similar to those earlier in this section, by any reversible cycle.

   Let us suppose that we use the heat output at temperature T_H of the refrigerator of Fig. 7 as the input to an ideal engine, which has the maximum possible efficiency $(T_H - T_C)/T_H$.   Then the situation depicted in principle in Fig. 7, in which the ideal engine drives the refrigerator and still has mechanical energy left over, *is in violation of the second principle*, since this result would represent generation of mechanical energy purely by extraction of heat from the cold reservoir.

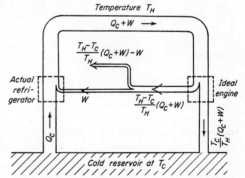

Fig. 7. The above system violates the second principle if it is self-acting and a net amount of work is delivered.

   In Fig. 7, let the refrigerator take heat Q_C from the cold reservoir. Let work W be required to drive the refrigerator, so that by energy conservation, heat $Q_C + W$ is given out at T_H.   Let this be the input to the ideal engine. Since the efficiency of the ideal engine is $(T_H - T_C)/T_H$, the ideal engine does $[(T_H - T_C)/T_H](Q_C + W)$ units of work, returning the remainder of the heat to the cold reservoir. The situation depicted in Fig. 7, in which this amount of work is greater than W, is in violation of the second law, so this quantity of work must be less than or equal to W:

$$\frac{T_H - T_C}{T_H}(Q_C + W) \leqq W,$$

or
$$WT_H \geqq (T_H - T_C)(Q_C + W),$$

$$WT_H \geqq (T_H - T_C)Q_C + WT_H - WT_C.$$

If we subtract WT_H and add WT_C on both sides of this inequality, we obtain

$$WT_C \geqq (T_H - T_C)Q_C,$$

or
$$W \geqq \frac{T_H - T_C}{T_C}Q_C, \qquad (23)$$

which demonstrates the law. We shall discuss this law when we consider refrigerators in Sec. 7.

6. THE STEAM ENGINE

A SIMPLE steam power plant is represented schematically in Fig. 8. Water is heated and evaporated in a boiler, usually at a pressure well above atmospheric and hence at a temperature well above 100° C. The

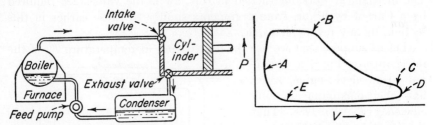

Fig. 8. A simple steam power plant. The circulating-water system that extracts the latent heat in the condenser is not shown.

Fig. 9. Typical indicator diagram showing conditions in a steam-engine cylinder.

pressure is controlled by a feed pump which feeds in water as needed to maintain the pressure. The temperature is the vaporization temperature at the fixed pressure. We consider the simplest case, in which the steam is not superheated after it has been formed. The steam enters the cylinder through an intake valve and is exhausted to a condenser through an exhaust valve. The condenser is pumped free from air so that the pressure in the condenser is close to the low vapor pressure at the temperature of the water that circulates through the condenser to condense the steam.

The conditions *in the cylinder* of the engine are shown by the *indicator diagram* of Fig. 9. On this diagram the actual pressure in the cylinder is plotted as a function of the varying volume of the cylinder. The closed curve on the indicator diagram is traversed clockwise once during each cycle. The net mechanical work done per cycle of the engine, in ft·lb, is seen to be just the area of the closed curve on the indicator diagram in $(lb/ft^2)\cdot ft^3$. This plot is called an indicator diagram because a steam-engine cylinder can be readily equipped with a card that moves back and forth with the piston, and on which a recording pressure gauge connected to the cylinder will write the diagram automatically. This is the simplest way of determining the actual mechanical power developed by the engine.

In Fig. 9, the intake valve is opened at A, and steam from the boiler is admitted during the first part of the stroke until the intake valve is closed at B. During the major portion of this part of the stroke the pressure is essentially constant at boiler pressure. From B to C, both valves are closed and the steam undergoes an essentially adiabatic expansion with resultant drop in pressure and temperature. Since the steam was saturated on admission, some of the steam condenses in the cylinder during this expansion. The exhaust valve is opened at C a short time before the end of the expansion stroke at D, and the pressure rapidly drops to the condenser pressure, which is maintained during the return stroke until the exhaust valve is closed at E. From E to A the remaining steam is compressed to cushion somewhat the sudden pressure rise occurring when the intake valve is opened at A.

One must not make the mistake of considering the indicator diagram of Fig. 9 as analogous to the Carnot-cycle diagram of Fig. 4. Figure 9 plots conditions in the cylinder for a variable quantity of working substance as steam enters and leaves. The diagram that is analogous to Fig. 4 is the Rankine diagram of Fig. 10, in which one takes a pound of H_2O and follows this same material around the closed circuit of Fig. 8—from water to steam in the boiler, to the cylinder, to the condenser, and back to water in the boiler.

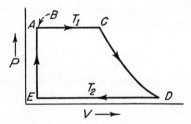

Fig. 10. Rankine diagram for a pound of H_2O passing once around the circuit of the power plant of Fig. 8.

At A on the Rankine diagram, the substance is in the form of water which has just been pumped into the boiler but is still at condenser temperature T_2. Between A and B the water has been heated to the boiling point T_1. B to C represents the volume increase (actually enormous in comparison with that shown schematically on Fig. 10) on evaporation. This is an isothermal process in which heat is added at T_1. At the condition C the gas enters the cylinder and accomplishes the first part of the work cycle in the cylinder before the intake valve is closed. *CD* represents the approximately adiabatic expansion from T_1 to T_2, partly in the cylinder and partly through the exhaust valve into the condenser; this last part is inherently irreversible. *DE* represents the volume decrease accompanying complete condensation to water, with latent heat given up at temperature T_2. Finally, *EA* represents the pressure increase on the liquid when it is pumped back into the boiler.

A great deal can be learned from a detailed analysis of the diagram of Fig. 10 and its implications, but this we must leave for a specialized course in the thermodynamics of heat engines. We shall merely consider the theoretical limit to the efficiency of the steam engine. Let heat Q_1 be added to our pound of H_2O. This heat is added in the boiler, partly at temperatures between T_2 and T_1 as the water is heated from *A* to *B*, mostly at T_1 as the water is evaporated. In principle, all this heat could have been derived from a body at temperature T_1. Heat is given up to the cooling water in the condenser at T_2. Our actual engine cannot be more efficient than an ideal reversible engine acting between a reservoir at T_1 and one at T_2. So of the heat added to the water in the boiler, at most only a fraction

$$\frac{T_1-T_2}{T_1} \quad \left(\begin{array}{l}T_1=\text{boiler temperature}\\T_2=\text{condenser temperature}\end{array}\right) \quad (24)$$

can be converted into work. If we define the *thermal efficiency* of our steam cycle as the ratio: (work done)/(heat added to the water in the boiler), then *expression (24) furnishes a theoretical upper limit to this thermal efficiency.* The value (24) is called the *Carnot efficiency.*

For example, if $T_1=350°$ F$=810°$ R and $T_2=100°$ F$=560°$ R, the Carnot efficiency is

$$\text{Carnot efficiency}=\frac{T_1-T_2}{T_1}=\frac{250}{810}=31\%.$$

The thermal efficiency of an actual engine of 250-hp rating operating between these temperatures might be given by:

$$\text{thermal efficiency}=\frac{\text{work done}}{\text{heat added to water}}=23\%;$$

whereas the over-all efficiency, which takes into account waste in heat value of the fuel in heating the water, might be given by

$$\text{over-all efficiency}=\frac{\text{work done}}{\text{heat value of fuel burned}}=17\%.$$

Since the Carnot efficiency furnishes an upper limit, no changes in this steam plant could bring the efficiency above 31 per cent unless T_1 and T_2 were changed. The advantage of using a high steam temperature and a low condenser temperature is immediately apparent.

Example. *An idealized four-stroke internal combustion engine can be considered to operate as in the diagram of Fig. 11. The air, fuel mixture at volume V_2, and temperature T_2 is compressed adiabatically to V_1, T_3 during stroke 1. An explosion then occurs that raises the temperature to T_1 without change in volume. The products of combustion expand adiabatically to V_2, T_4 during stroke 2. The exhaust valve then opens and the return to V_2, T_2 is made during strokes 3 and 4, the first of which pushes the exhaust gases from the cylinder while the second draws in new air, fuel mixture. Determine the efficiency of this idealized engine in terms of the compression ratio $R = V_2/V_1$, and show that this efficiency is less than that of a Carnot engine operating between temperatures T_1 and T_2. Assume that the air, fuel mixture and the products of combustion both have the same specific heat as air, which is the predominant component.*

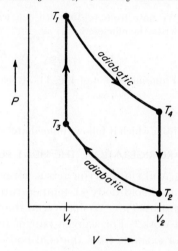

Figure 11

From (8) we find that

$$T_3 V_1{}^{\gamma-1} = T_2 V_2{}^{\gamma-1}$$

or $\qquad T_3 = T_2 (V_2/V_1)^{\gamma-1} = T_2 R^{\gamma-1}.$ (i)

Similarly $\qquad T_1 = T_4 (V_2/V_1)^{\gamma-1} = T_4 R^{\gamma-1}.$ (ii)

The heat that is added during the explosion raises the temperature of mass m of gas from T_3 to T_1 at constant volume. Hence

$$\text{heat added} = mc_V (T_1 - T_3).$$

The work done by the gas during the adiabatic expansion is given by (2) as

$$\text{work done by gas} = mc_V (T_1 - T_4).$$

Similarly, (3) gives the work done on the gas during the adiabatic compression:

$$\text{work done on gas} = mc_V (T_3 - T_2).$$

Hence the net work done during the cycle (the area of the closed figure) is

$$\text{net work done} = mc_V [(T_1 - T_3) - (T_4 - T_2)].$$

The efficiency is the ratio of the net work done to the heat added:

$$\text{efficiency} = E = \frac{\text{net work done}}{\text{heat added}} = 1 - \frac{T_4 - T_2}{T_1 - T_3}.$$

By subtracting (i) from (ii), we find

$$(T_1 - T_3) = (T_4 - T_2) R^{\gamma-1}$$

hence $\qquad E = 1 - \dfrac{1}{R^{\gamma-1}}.$ (iii)

The larger the compression ratio R, the closer to unity is the efficiency. Gasoline engines are restricted to a compression ratio of about 8 because of the tendency of the fuel mixture to predetonate (knock) if its temperature is raised too high on the compression stroke. For $R = 8$ and $\gamma = 1.4$, $R^{\gamma-1} = 2.3$ and $E = 57$ per cent for the ideal cycle.

The efficiency of a Carnot cycle operating between T_1 and T_2 would be

$$E_{\text{Carnot}} = \frac{T_1 - T_2}{T_1} = 1 - \frac{T_2}{T_1}.$$

We note from (i) that we can write $R^{\gamma-1} = T_3/T_2$, and hence that we can write the efficiency (iii) as

$$E = 1 - \frac{T_2}{T_3}.$$

From inspection of Fig. 11 we see that

$$\frac{T_2}{T_3} > \frac{T_2}{T_1},$$

from which it follows immediately that $E < E_{\text{Carnot}}$, as we were asked to prove.

7. REFRIGERATION, THE HEAT PUMP

A REFRIGERATOR acts as a reversed heat engine in that it extracts heat from a cold body at temperature T_C and gives it to a hot body at temperature T_H. We have seen that to effect this transfer requires mechanical work. For a given pair of temperatures, the more heat the refrigerator extracts from the cold body per unit of work done, the better is the refrigerator, since the cost of operation is principally the cost of supplying the work by means of an electric motor or other type of engine. Hence, we define a performance coefficient as

$$\text{performance coefficient} = \frac{\text{heat extracted}}{\text{work done}} = \frac{Q_C}{W}. \qquad (25)$$

The argument of Sec. 5 proves that *the performance coefficient of an actual refrigerator is always less than that of a reversible refrigerator,* which is, from (22),

$$\text{Carnot performance coefficient} = \frac{T_C}{T_H - T_C} = \frac{1}{(T_H/T_C) - 1}. \qquad (26)$$

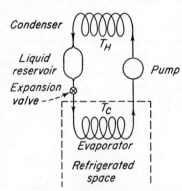

Fig. 12. Refrigeration system (schematic). Heat is extracted at the low temperature T_C and given up at the high temperature T_H.

The Carnot performance coefficient depends only on the ratio T_H/T_C; it is very large when T_H/T_C is close to 1; it is greater than unity when T_H/T_C is less than 2, less than unity when T_H/T_C is greater than 2.

The refrigeration cycle actually used is a vapor cycle, employing a gas that is easily condensed by pressure. Ammonia (NH_3), sulphur dioxide (SO_2), and Freon (CCl_2F_2) are most commonly used. Figure 12 shows a schematic diagram of the equipment. The pump keeps the pressure in the evaporator low and that in the condenser high. The working substance evaporates at low temperature, taking in heat, and condenses at high temperature, giving out heat. The work referred to in (25) is that done by the pump.

The name *refrigerator* implies an apparatus whose purpose is to *cool;* but the *same* apparatus can be used as a *heater*—when so used it is called a *heat pump*. The heat pump extracts heat from a cold body (the earth or underground water) and furnishes it to a warmer body (the air in a house or building). To accomplish this heat transfer, mechanical energy must be used, but the mechanical energy can be small compared to the amount of heat transferred, provided the temperature differences involved are low.

Example. *Suppose that an ample supply of underground water is available at 50° F to circulate past the evaporator, and it is desired to heat air, circulating past the condenser, to 80° F to use in heating a house. To accomplish the heat transfer, suppose that the refrigerant is operated at 40° F in the evaporator and at 110° F in the condenser. Suppose that the mechanical power is furnished electrically and that the installation will give an over-all performance coefficient of half the Carnot performance coefficient. Compare the cost of using this heat pump with that of direct electrical heating.*

The Carnot performance coefficient for a refrigerator operating between 40° F and 110° F is

$$\frac{460+40}{110-40} = \frac{500}{70} = 7.1.$$

We have introduced the term *over-all* performance coefficient; by this we mean the ratio of heat extracted to electrical energy supplied to the motor to account for the fact that a motor is not 100 per cent efficient in converting electrical energy to work. With an over-all performance coefficient of half the Carnot coefficient, or 3.5, the heat extracted from the underground water will be 3.5 times the total electrical energy used. The heat given to the house will be 4.5 times the total electrical energy used. As compared with house heating by direct expenditure of electrical energy in an electric heater, we have gained a factor of 4.5 in heat, $3.5/4.5 = 78$ per cent of the heat coming from the cold underground water.

On the basis of performance similar to that in the above example, heating by electrical energy begins to compete economically with heating by combustion of fuel, and heat pumps are beginning to be installed in increasing numbers for house heating. Although an ample supply of underground water is desirable, installations have been made in which the evaporator tubing has been buried in such a way as to thread through a large volume of earth, the heat being extracted directly from the earth.

8. LIQUEFACTION OF GASES

GASES that can be liquefied by pressure alone at normal temperature, that is, those whose critical temperature lies well above normal temperature, can easily be obtained in liquid form at their boiling point at normal atmospheric pressure.   For example, suppose we want to obtain a quantity of liquid ammonia in an open flask at $-33.5°$ C, its boiling point at 1 atm pressure.   We start with gaseous ammonia and compress it to about 10 atm pressure, at which point it will liquefy at room temperature.   We extract the heat of compression and the latent heat by means of circulating water or circulating air until we have liquid ammonia at 10 atm pressure and room temperature.   If we then release the pressure, with the liquid in a thermally insulated vessel, the liquid will first evaporate rapidly; but since the latent heat of evaporation must come from the liquid itself, the liquid will also cool rapidly so that soon we shall be left with a large fraction of the liquid at $-33.5°$ C.   This liquid can be kept for a long time in a double-walled flask.

This procedure will not work for a permanent gas whose critical temperature is below room temperature because the gas cannot be liquefied by pressure at room temperature, and hence no latent heat can be made available for cooling.

A permanent gas (oxygen) was first liquefied in 1877 by a Swiss physicist, Raoul Pictet, who used a vapor refrigeration cycle similar to the one we have described in the previous section except that the cycle was in two stages.   The high-temperature stage employed SO_2, and the evaporator in the SO_2 cycle drew its heat from the condenser in a lower temperature CO_2 cycle.   The evaporator in the CO_2 cycle cooled the oxygen gas to its liquefaction temperature.   All gases except hydrogen and helium have been liquefied by such multistage vapor refrigeration cycles.

Another process of liquefaction, the *Claude process* widely used for liquefaction of air, employs essentially an adiabatic expansion for cooling. In principle, by letting a gas expand and do work, the temperature can be lowered as much as we please.

Finally, the *Linde process* has been most successful in liquefying gases such as hydrogen and helium, and is also widely used for liquefaction of air.   This process, whose theory we shall not attempt to discuss rigorously, depends on the fact that actual gases are not perfect and do suffer some temperature change on *free expansion*.   Although, as we have noted on p. 307, a perfect gas would not suffer a temperature change on free expansion because its thermal energy depends on temperature alone, the thermal energy of a real gas depends somewhat on pressure as well as on temperature; and at temperatures not too far above the critical, the temperature suffers a substantial *decrease* on free expansion through a pressure range of several hundred atmospheres.   The Linde apparatus is like the Claude apparatus, except that a free expansion through a valve is substituted for an adiabatic expansion in an expansion engine to effect the cooling.   By precooling hydrogen with liquid air before expansion, hydrogen is readily liquefied; and by precooling helium with liquid hydrogen before expansion, helium is readily liquefied.

9. THE ABSOLUTE THERMODYNAMIC TEMPERATURE SCALE

So FAR we have been very loose about our definition of temperature. We are now prepared to define a temperature scale of fundamental significance that does not depend on the properties of any particular substance. This scale was defined by the English physicist William Thomson (Lord Kelvin) about 1850, and is called *the absolute thermodynamic temperature scale.*

We have defined an *ideal* gas as one that rigorously obeys the relation

$$T = PM/R\rho. \tag{27}$$

If we had an ideal gas, this equation would serve as an excellent definition of temperature. The thermodynamic scale is essentially an ideal-gas scale. But we do not have an ideal gas. However, we shall see that the laws we have derived from the second principle of thermodynamics will enable us to determine ideal-gas temperatures from the behavior of *actual substances.*

We have seen that for a Carnot cycle employing an ideal gas, the ratio of heat exchanged with the hot body to heat exchanged with the cold body is

$$\frac{Q_H}{Q_C} = \frac{T_H}{T_C}. \tag{28}$$

We have *proved* from the second principle that (28) holds also for *any* reversible cycle employing an *actual* substance. Hence (28), for any reversible cycle working on adiabatics and isothermals, is taken as the *definition* of temperature ratio. We still need to specify the temperature *difference* between two fixed points to define the size of the units on our scale. The temperature *difference* between the *steam-point* and the *ice-point* is taken as 100 K deg or 180 R deg.

Suppose that we have a quantity of actual substance—say a gas—and that we have studied its properties in detail, employing an arbitrary temperature scale, such as the scale depending on the expansion of mercury which we have discussed earlier. In particular, we know the pressure and volume as a function of our arbitrary temperature, and we know c_P and c_V (say in joules/kg per arbitrary degree) for every pressure and temperature. It turns out that this information gives us enough data to draw adiabatics and isothermals on a PV-diagram as in Fig. 13. It also gives us enough data to *compute* the heat that would have to be added in an isothermal expansion or removed in an isothermal compression at any temperature on our arbitrary scale.

If the ice-point isothermal has temperature T_{IP} on the Kelvin scale, the size of the units is fixed so that the steam-point isothermal will have temperature $T_{\mathrm{SP}} = T_{\mathrm{IP}} + 100$. Then if we consider a cycle (cross-hatched in Fig. 13) operating between the ice-point and the steam-point and make the computations of Q_{SP} and Q_{IP} mentioned above, we can write

$$\frac{T_{IP}+100}{T_{IP}} = \frac{Q_{SP}}{Q_{IP}},$$

from which we can compute the absolute value of T_{IP}, the ice-point temperature on the Kelvin scale.

The second principle of thermodynamics guarantees that we shall get the same value for T_{IP} no matter what substance we use. It is in this way, by

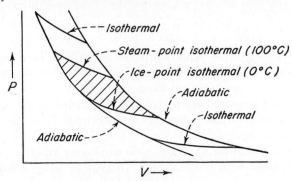

Fig. 13. Isothermals and adiabatics for a real substance (schematic).

careful measurement of the properties of real gases, that the experimental value

$$T_{IP} = 273.16° \pm 0.01° \text{ K}$$

has been determined. The absolute thermodynamic temperature at any other arbitrary fixed temperature point can be similarly determined by computations employing a cycle reaching to an isothermal at that temperature, as indicated in Fig. 13.

Although these ideas are simple in principle, the fixing of the absolute temperature scale has required a formidable amount of experimental work on the accurate determination of the properties of real substances, particularly of hydrogen and helium.

It is possible to set up a thermodynamic scale of temperature with only *one* fixed point by assigning to this fixed point a definite *absolute* temperature. Such a scale, which is now under international consideration, was proposed by Kelvin and Joule in 1854 and independently by Giauque in 1939. On the scale currently proposed, the triple point of H_2O is assigned a temperature of 273.170° K. This value is chosen so that the resulting scale will have degrees of the same size as the Centigrade scale and will agree with the present Kelvin scale to engineering accuracy. The new temperature scale will have certain advantages in high precision thermometry. Note that if the *absolute* temperature of one point is fixed, equation (28) determines in principle the absolute temperature of any other point on the scale.

PROBLEMS

1. An automobile of 3,000-lb mass, traveling at 30 mi/hr, is brought to rest by the action of its brakes. Assuming that all the energy is converted into heat in the brakes, which have a mass of 60 lb and a specific heat of 0.12 BTU/lb·F deg, what will be the rise in temperature of the brakes?   Ans: 16.1 F deg.

2. A lead bullet at 20° C is fired into sand at a speed of 450 m/sec. Assuming that 50 per cent of the heat generated is distributed uniformly in the lead of the bullet, what will be the temperature rise of the lead? (Take the specific heat as 0.030 cal/g, the melting point as 327° C, the latent heat of fusion as 6.0 cal/g.)

3. During launching, a yacht of 600-ton mass slides down inclined ways through a vertical distance of 9 ft before striking the water. If the yacht is then moving at 16 ft/sec, how many BTU of heat were developed by friction on the ways?   Ans: 7720 BTU.

4. A locomotive exerts a drawbar pull of 30,000 lb on a 400-ton train when it is going up an incline of 1° slope at a constant speed of 45 mi/hr. How many BTU per second are generated in the wheels and bearings of the cars of the train?

5. The electrical input to an electric motor is 750 kw, of which 85 per cent is delivered as useful mechanical work, the remainder being wasted as heat. Compute the mechanical horsepower output and the rate of heat generation.
          Ans: 855 hp; 26.9 kcal/sec.

6. The mechanical input to an electric generator is 500 hp, of which 95 per cent is delivered as electrical energy, the balance being wasted as heat. Determine the electrical output in kilowatts and the rate of heat generation.

7. The air in the cylinder of a Diesel engine is at 30° C and 1 atm before compression. It is compressed to $\frac{1}{18}$ of its original volume. Find the final temperature and pressure of the air if the compression is adiabatic and $\gamma = 1.4$.
          Ans: 691° C; 57.3 atm.

8. The air in the cylinder of a Diesel engine is at a temperature of 200° F and a pressure of 18 lb/in² at the beginning of compression. It is compressed to $\frac{1}{12}$ of its original volume. Find the temperature and pressure of the air at the end of the adiabatic compression. Take $\gamma = 1.4$.

9. Find the work necessary to compress 22.4 liters of helium at NTP adiabatically to one-quarter of this volume.   Ans: 5180 joules.

10. Derive equations (9) and (10).

NOTE: In a *Wilson cloud chamber* (Fig. 14), air that is saturated with water vapor is rapidly expanded adiabatically to about 20 per cent greater volume   After the expansion the water vapor is at a partial pressure above that of saturation at the reduced temperature and begins to condense. The air is said to be *supersaturated*. The water vapor condenses on electrically charged ions and on dust particles, which serve as condensation nuclei. Electrically charged ions are particularly effective as condensation nuclei. Hence, if a high-speed charged particle passes through the chamber close to

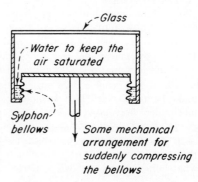

Fig. 14. Schematic drawing of one type of Wilson cloud chamber.

the time of the expansion, leaving behind a trail of ionized air molecules, this trail will be shown up as a track of fog droplets which can be photographed. Such a photograph is reproduced near the end of Chap. 32. The following problem illustrates the principle of operation.

11. If air saturated with water vapor at 30° C and a total pressure of 1 atm is expanded adiabatically to 20 per cent greater volume, find the partial pressure of the water vapor in the supersaturated air just after the expansion, and compare with the pressure of saturated vapor. In computing the temperature after the expansion, neglect the difference between γ for water vapor and that for air and assume that the whole gas has $\gamma = 1.4$. This method will introduce little error because the water vapor, which has a slightly lower γ, constitutes only a small fraction of the whole gas. Ans: 24.6 mm as compared with 8.4 mm for saturation.

12. In Fig. 3, there are two adiabatics crossing both curves $T=3$ and $T=2$; there is one adiabatic crossing both $T=6$ and $T=4$. By reading the values of P and V at these points of intersection as accurately as you can, determine three values of the pressure ratio P_2/P_1 and the volume ratio V_2/V_1 that result in a temperature rise $T_2/T_1 = \frac{3}{2}$ in an adiabatic compression. Compare these ratios with the values computed from (8) and (10) for $\gamma = \frac{5}{3}$ and this temperature ratio.

13. Compute the efficiency of a Carnot engine operating with reservoir temperatures of 150° C and 30° C. Ans: 28.4%.

14. Compute the efficiency of a Carnot engine operating with reservoir temperatures of 250° C and 30° C.

15. If the Carnot engine of Fig. 4 contains 10 kg of gas of $M=29$ and $\gamma=1.4$, and if $P_A=10$ atm, $P_B=5$ atm, $T_H=273°$ C, and $T_C=0°$ C, make a table showing in joules (a) the heat added *to* the gas, (b) the work done *by* the gas, and (c) the *increase* in thermal energy, in each of the four steps of the cycle and for the whole cycle.

Ans:	$A{\to}B$	$B{\to}G$	$G{\to}D$	$D{\to}A$	*Whole Cycle*
(a)	1,086,000	0	−543,000	0	543,000
(b)	1,086,000	1,960,000	−543,000	−1,960,000	543,000
(c)	0	−1,960,000	0	1,960,000	0

16. If the Carnot engine of Fig. 4 contains 2 kg of gas of $M=4$ and $\gamma=1.67$, and if $P_A=12$ atm, $P_B=8$ atm, $T_H=400°$ C, and $T_C=20°$ C, make a table showing in joules for each step of the cycle and for the whole cycle: (a) the heat added *to* the gas, (b) the work done *by* the gas, (c) the *increase* in thermal energy.

17. To extract 1 joule of heat from a body at 0° C and give it to a body at 100° C, how many joules of mechanical energy are required by a Carnot refrigerator, and how many joules are given to the hot body? Ans: 0.366; 1.366.

18. To extract 1 kcal of heat from a body at −100° C and give it to a body at 100° C, how many kcal of mechanical energy are required by a Carnot refrigerator, and how many kcal are given to the hot body?

19. If a Carnot refrigerator extracts enough heat from water at 32° F to make 1 ton of ice at 32° F per hour, giving this heat to the air at 90° F, how many mechanical horsepower are required to drive the refrigerator? Ans: 13.3.

20. If a Carnot refrigerator which extracts heat from a cold-storage plant at −20° F and gives it to the atmosphere at 100° F has 100 'ton' capacity (meaning that the amount of heat extracted in 24 hr is the latent heat of 100 tons of ice), what horsepower is needed to drive the refrigerator?

NOTE: The next two problems are in British units. Take the specific heat of liquid water as 1 BTU/lb·F deg over the whole range required. The following table will give the required vaporization temperatures and latent heats:

P (lb/in²)	1.0	2.0	100	165
T (° F)	102	126	328	366
L (BTU/lb)	1035	1022	888	857

21. A steam engine which exhausts to a condenser at a pressure of 2.0 lb/in² receives steam at 100 lb/in² absolute pressure. The steam consumption is 14 lb per indicated horsepower-hour. What is the thermal efficiency of the engine? What is the Carnot efficiency? Ans: 16.7%; 25.6%.

22. Steam is supplied to an engine at 165 lb/in² absolute. The condenser pressure is 1.0 lb/in² absolute. The steam consumption is 10 lb per indicated horsepower-hour. What is the thermal efficiency? What is the Carnot efficiency?

23. If the area of the indicator diagram for the cylinder of Fig. 8 is 50 (lb/in²)·ft³ and the engine operates at 400 cycles/min, what horsepower does it develop? Ans: 87.3 hp.

24. If the area of the indicator diagram on each side of a double-acting cylinder is 40 (lb/in²)·ft³, at what speed must the engine run to develop 90 hp? (A *double-acting* cylinder is closed on both ends and steam is admitted alternately on the two sides of the piston.)

25. How many pounds of ice can be frozen per hour by a refrigerating machine working between 0° F and 100° F if it has 50 per cent of the performance coefficient of a Carnot machine working between these same limits and is driven by a ¼-hp motor? The ice is frozen to a temperature of 15° F from water initially at 60° F. Ans: 8.14.

26. How many horsepower are required to freeze 100 tons per day of ice at 15° F from water initially at 60° F by a refrigerating machine working between 0° F and 90° F which has 70 per cent of the performance coefficient of a Carnot machine working between these same limits?

27. Compare the cost of heating a house by coal of 14,000 BTU/lb at $15.00 per ton, with 60 per cent over-all combustion efficiency, and by electricity at 1.5 cents per kilowatt-hour if a heat pump of over-all performance coefficient of 3.5 is used. Ans: 11,200 BTU/cent for coal; 10,200 BTU/cent for the heat pump.

28. A sample of CO_2 in a cylinder with a movable piston is heated by a burner. If 60 cal of heat are added to the gas and the gas expands against an external pressure of 1 atm from an initial volume of 1 liter to a final volume of 1.6 liters, what is the change in the thermal energy of the gas?

29. A gas is heated by a burner. If the gas receives 2 BTU and expands from 0.7 ft³ to 1.0 ft³ against an external pressure of 2 atm, what is the increase in thermal energy of the gas? Ans: 0.37 BTU.

30. If we have a reservoir at absolute zero, is it possible to have a 100 per cent efficient Carnot engine? By means of a Carnot refrigerator, how much work must be done in order to maintain a reservoir at absolute zero?

31. A heat engine employs a piston with area A, which makes N power strokes per second in a cylinder of length l. If P is the average pressure during the power stroke, show that the developed power is given by the product $PlAN$.

32. A diesel engine can operate with a compression ratio higher than that of an ordinary gasoline engine because the fuel is not injected until the air in the cylinder has been compressed, so predetonation cannot occur. The compression raises the air temperature sufficiently so that the fuel is spontaneously ignited.

Compare the efficiency of a diesel engine of compression ratio 16 with that of a gasoline engine of compression ratio 8, assuming that both follow the ideal indicator diagram of Fig. 11.

33. A certain heat engine uses a diatomic gas as a 'working substance.' The gas has an initial volume of 1 ft^3 at a pressure of 2 atm. The gas is heated and expands at constant pressure to 2 ft^3. It is then cooled, the pressure dropping to 1 atm without change in volume. The gas is next cooled further in such a way that its volume decreases to 1 ft^3, the pressure remaining 1 atm. The gas is finally heated at constant volume until the pressure is again 2 atm. Plot this cycle on a PV-diagram. (a) How much work is done by the engine during one cycle? (b) At what point of the cycle is the thermal energy of the gas greatest? (c) How many complete cycles would this engine make each second if its output is 4 horsepower? Ans: (a) 2116 ft·lb; (c) 1.04.

34. Steam is supplied to a large turbine at a temperature of 900° F and is exhausted at 500° F for use with a lower-pressure heat engine. What is the Carnot efficiency of the turbine? If the lower-pressure heat engine exhausts the steam into the atmosphere at 100° F, what is its Carnot efficiency? Compare the work that would be obtained from these two engines, assumed ideal, with that from a single ideal engine operating between 900° F and 100° F.

35. A certain heat engine has a power output of 4 hp. This heat engine receives saturated steam from a boiler in which the absolute pressure is 39.3 atm, and exhausts into a condenser at 50° C. What is the Carnot efficiency of this heat engine? If the overall efficiency of this engine is 10%, how much bituminous coal is used each hour in heating the boiler? Ans: 38.2%; 7.54 lb

36. A gasoline engine consumes 600 lb of gasoline while operating at 124 hp during a test run of 8 hr. What weight of fuel does the engine use per horsepower hour? How many gallons of gasoline are consumed per horsepower hour? What is the overall efficiency of the engine? (Density of gasoline is 42 lb/ft^3.)

37. A certain airplane engine develops a torque of 1212 lb·ft when operating a propeller at 2600 rev/min. What is the horsepower developed by the engine? If the overall efficiency of this engine is 20 per cent, how many gallons of gasoline are burned per hour? Ans: 600 hp; 66.2.

38. Energy from the sun reaches the top of the earth's atmosphere at a rate of approximately 1.98 cal/cm^2·min. Neglecting atmospheric absorption, calculate the rate at which heat is supplied to a solar engine employing a paraboloidal mirror 3 m in diameter. Discuss various ways in which such a solar engine might be constructed. If this solar engine has a Carnot efficiency of 20 per cent, what is the maximum power output that might be expected?

39. By using a refrigerator employing a Carnot cycle, we wish to remove heat from various cold reservoirs and give the heat to a reservoir at 27° C. How much work must be done in removing 1 joule of thermal energy from a reservoir at 0° C? at −73° C? at −173° C? at −223° C? Ans: 0.0989, 0.500, 2.00, 5.00 joules.

Part III

WAVE MOTION AND SOUND

CHAPTER 18

WAVE MOTION

THE UNDERLYING concept in the use of the term *wave* in physical science is embodied in the following general definition:

> A **wave** involves some physical quantity that is a function of both position and time and that (a) changes in magnitude more or less regularly with time at a given location and (b) at a fixed time changes in magnitude from place to place in a more or less regular manner.

To draw an example from familiar usage, in the case of a 'cold wave moving eastward across the country,' (a) the temperature at Chicago may be high on one day, fall to a low value the next day when the 'crest' of the cold wave reaches the city, and rise to a high value the following day when the crest has passed; (b) on the day the crest of the cold wave is in Chicago, the temperature may be high at Denver, lower in Iowa, very low in Chicago, slightly higher in Cleveland, and high in New York. In this case, the quantity that is changing is temperature and the pattern of its variation *with time* at the Chicago location shows striking similarity to its variation *with geographical position* at any one time.

Water waves furnish another familiar example: (a) at any *fixed position* the surface of the water (or a fisherman's bobber) moves up and down periodically with the passage of time, while (b) at any given *instant* the height of the surface of the water approximates a periodic function of position.

Waves can furnish a mechanism for transmission of energy without physical transfer of material. For example, energy is transferred from a bell to the ears of a distant listener by a *mechanical wave motion* in the air; there is no transfer of material from the bell to the listener but only a transfer of energy by waves consisting of pressure variations in the intervening medium. In the chapter following this one we shall concern ourselves with a discussion of such *sound waves*. In later chapters dealing with *light* and *radio transmission*, we shall discuss *electromagnetic waves;* although these electromagnetic waves are not mechanical waves like sound waves, the basic ideas that we shall introduce in the present chapter are useful in the treatment of all types of wave motion, including electromagnetic waves.

In the present chapter, we shall first consider in detail the transmission of mechanical waves along a stretched string or wire. After we have derived the equations describing this simple type of wave motion, we shall treat more complicated types by analogy but shall not attempt detailed analyses.

1. MECHANICAL WAVES

IN ORDER for mechanical wave motion to occur, it is necessary to have a *source* that produces a displacement or *disturbance* of some kind and an *elastic medium* through which the disturbance can be transmitted. An elastic medium behaves as if it were a succession of adjoining particles with each particle occupying an equilibrium position; if one of the particles is displaced from its equilibrium position, this particle is immediately subjected to a restoring force as a result of attraction or repulsion by neighboring particles, which, in turn, are subjected to reaction forces exerted by the original particle. If one of the particles in a medium is given a sudden displacement by the *source*, this particle exerts forces on its immediate neighbors, which experience displacements; these immediately neighboring particles exert forces on *their* neighbors, which also undergo displacements, and so on. In

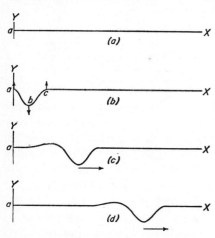

Fig. 1. Production and transmission of a transverse displacement (trough) in a stretched string.

this way, the initial disturbance at the source causes a displacement 'wave' to travel into the surrounding medium. As a result of the inertia of the particles, the displacements of all the particles do not take place instantaneously; the displacements of the particles far removed from the source occur later than the displacements of particles close to the source.

Let us first consider the motion of a wave along a stretched string. In Fig. 1, part (a) shows a long string with its two ends attached to rigid supports. In part (b), a portion of the string is distorted in the indicated manner by pulling downward at point *b* while points *a* and *c* are held at their initial positions; this distorted portion of the string is called a *trough*. If the string is suddenly released at points *b* and *c*, the displaced portion is pulled back to its equilibrium position as a result of the elastic properties of the string; but as a result of this action on the part of the string near *b*, the parts of the string immediately to the right are pulled downward and the trough moves to the right at a definite speed as shown in parts (c) and (d) of the figure. A *crest*, or upward displacement, would travel along the string in Fig. 1 at the same speed as that of the trough. The passage of a *crest* or a *trough* along a stretched string is an example of a *transverse* wave motion.

> In a **transverse wave** the displacements of the particles of the medium are perpendicular to the direction of propagation of the wave.

Another type of wave, which can occur in a stretched spring, is illustrated in Fig. 2.   Part (a) of the figure shows a long coil spring with one end supported at point a; the support at the other end is not shown.   If the spring is distorted in the manner indicated in Fig. 2(b) so that the

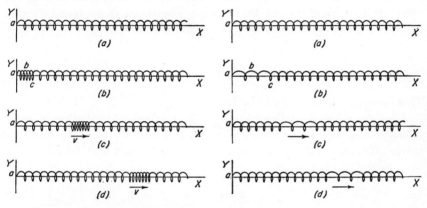

Fig. 2. Production and transmission of a 'condensation' along a helical spring.

Fig. 3. Production and transmission of a 'rarefaction' along a helical spring.

coils of the spring are more closely spaced around point b than in other parts of the spring, the region in the vicinity of b is called a *condensation*. If the external forces producing the distortion are removed, the elastic restoring forces accelerate particles near b toward their equilibrium positions.   When this acceleration occurs, the coils toward the right of the original condensation position are pushed closer together, and the condensation moves toward the right as shown in Figs. 2(c) and 2(d).

Similarly, a *rarefaction*, in which the coils are initially pulled farther apart as in Fig. 3, will move to the right along the spring in the manner shown.   Figures 2 and 3 illustrate *longitudinal* wave motion.

> In a **longitudinal wave** the displacements of the particles of the medium are parallel to the direction of propagation of the wave.

The coils of the spring in Figs. 2 and 3 do not move up and down but only to the right and left, in directions parallel to the X-direction of propagation.   Contrast with the transverse wave of Fig. 1, where the particles move up and down.

The waves of Figs. 1, 2, and 3 are propagated to the right at certain speeds. The speed with which a wave moves through an elastic medium depends on the rapidity with which a distorted portion of the medium sets adjacent portions in motion. This rapidity depends in direct fashion on the forces that are brought to bear by a distortion, in inverse fashion on the inertia of the material that must be moved. In general, formulas for wave speed are of the form

$$\text{wave speed} = \sqrt{\frac{\text{elastic force factor}}{\text{inertia factor}}}. \tag{1}$$

The elastic force that tends to restore the shape of a stretched string is measured by the *tension* (F) in the string; the inertia is measured by the *mass per unit length* (μ) of the string. The speed of propagation of a transverse wave of small amplitude along a string is given by

$$v = \sqrt{\frac{F}{\mu}}. \qquad \left(\begin{array}{c}\text{transverse} \\ \text{wave in string}\end{array}\right) \quad (2)$$

This formula will be derived in Sec. 3.

The elastic force tending to restore the original configuration of a distorted spring depends on the force constant K and the total length l of the spring; the inertia again depends on μ, the mass per unit length. The formula for wave speed is

$$v = \sqrt{\frac{Kl}{\mu}}. \qquad \left(\begin{array}{c}\text{longitudinal} \\ \text{wave in spring}\end{array}\right) \quad (3)$$

These equations give v in m/sec if F is in nt, K in nt/m, l in m, and μ in kg/m; v in ft/sec if F is in lb, K in lb/ft, l in ft, and μ in slug/ft.

Example. *Formula (3) for the speed of a longitudinal wave in a spring indicates at first glance a dependence on the length l of the spring. Now it is physically clear that the speed of a longitudinal wave along a spring can depend only on how the spring is constructed and not on its over-all length since a pulse started as in Fig. 2 must travel with a speed governed by local conditions and not by where the right end of the spring might happen to be. Compute the speed of travel of a wave on a spring 4 ft long with $K = 1$ lb/ft and $\mu = \frac{1}{9}$ slug/ft. Then compute the speed of travel on the same spring cut in half so it is only 2 ft long, and verify that the speeds are the same.*

Direct substitution in (3) gives

$$v = \sqrt{(1 \text{ lb/ft})(4 \text{ ft})/(\tfrac{1}{9} \text{ slug/ft})} = 6 \text{ ft/sec}$$

for the speed in the case of the original spring. The original spring would stretch 1 ft under application of a stretching force of 1 lb. Each half of this spring would experience the same stretching force of 1 lb, but would stretch only $\frac{1}{2}$ ft. Hence when the spring is cut to 2-ft length, its force constant changes to $K = (1 \text{ lb})/(\tfrac{1}{2} \text{ ft}) = 2$ lb/ft. In (3), K doubles if l is halved, the product Kl and hence the wave speed being independent of length.

2. SINUSOIDAL WAVE MOTION

In the type of wave we have discussed thus far, a single nonrepeated disturbance, called a *pulse*, is initiated at the source and then travels away from the source through the medium. Another important type of wave motion is the *regular wave train* or *continuous wave*. In this type of wave, a regular succession of pulses is initiated at the source and transmitted through the medium. Thus, if a floating block of wood is pushed up and down regularly on a water surface, a regular train of waves will be propagated outward.

The simplest type of regular wave train is a sinusoidal wave motion, which is illustrated in Fig. 4. Part (a) of this figure shows one end of a

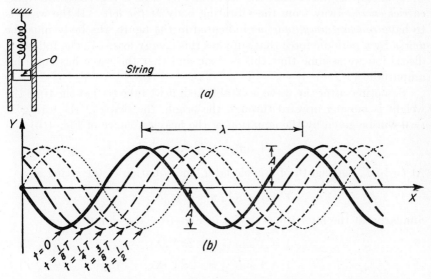

Fig. 4. Production and propagation of a sinusoidal transverse wave train in a long string. Part (b) shows the motion of the string during one half cycle of oscillation of O, from $Y = 0$ to $+A$ and back to 0.

long string attached to a weight supported by a spring. The weight is arranged so that it can move freely in the vertical 'ways' of the frame shown. If the weight is pulled downward a distance A and then released, the weight will move in the vertical direction with simple harmonic motion of a certain frequency f. Since the end of the string is attached to the weight, the oscillating weight acts as a source of a sinusoidal transverse wave that travels to the right along the string in the manner indicated by the curves of Fig. 4(b). These curves show successive 'snapshots' of the shape of the string during one half-cycle, after the motion has been well established. *The distance between adjacent crests or adjacent troughs in such a wave is called the wavelength;* in the figure the wavelength is denoted by λ. Each time the particle O attached to the weight makes a complete oscillation, the wave moves a distance λ in the X-direction. Hence the wave speed is

$$v = \lambda/T, \tag{4a}$$

where T is the period of oscillation. In terms of the frequency $f = 1/T$, the wave speed can be written as

$$v = f\lambda. \tag{4b}$$

The relations (4a) and (4b) are important general relations, between wave speed, wavelength, and frequency or period, that hold for sinusoidal wave motion of *any type.*

It should be noted that the wave of Fig. 4, as it moves to the right, carries *energy* away from the vibrating body at the left. If the wave is to have *constant amplitude*, as indicated in the figure, the body must be *driven* by a periodic force that supplies this energy loss. In the following discussion we assume that this is done and that the wave has constant amplitude A.

Sometime after the wave is established, if we take $t=0$ at the time the weight is moving upward through the origin, the shape of the string at $t=0$ will be given by the equation of the heaviest curve of Fig. 4(b):

$$Y = A \sin(-2\pi X/\lambda). \tag{$t=0$}$$

At $t = \frac{1}{8} T$, one-eighth of a cycle later, the equation of the string is

$$Y = A \sin(\tfrac{1}{4}\pi - 2\pi X/\lambda). \tag{$t = \frac{1}{8} T$}$$

Similarly, at the later times shown in Fig. 4(b), the equations are

$$Y = A \sin(\tfrac{1}{2}\pi - 2\pi X/\lambda), \tag{$t = \frac{1}{4} T$}$$

$$Y = A \sin(\tfrac{3}{4}\pi - 2\pi X/\lambda), \tag{$t = \frac{3}{8} T$}$$

$$Y = A \sin(\pi - 2\pi X/\lambda). \tag{$t = \frac{1}{2} T$}$$

From these, we can write the equation for Y as a function of X and t. Note that for the point O at $X=0$,

$$Y = A \sin 2\pi t/T. \tag{$X = 0$}$$

This dependence on t at $X=0$ and the above equations for dependence on X at fixed t are consistent if we write

$$Y = A \sin(2\pi t/T - 2\pi X/\lambda). \tag{5a}$$

If in this expression we substitute $T = 1/f$ and $\lambda = v/f$, we obtain the convenient form

$$Y = A \sin 2\pi f(t - X/v). \tag{5b}$$

This is the equation for a sinusoidal transverse wave traveling in the positive X-direction with amplitude A. From this equation, the Y-coordinate of a particle at any point X can be calculated at any time t, provided we know the amplitude A of the wave, the frequency f of the source, and the speed of propagation v of the wave.

For a wave traveling toward the left, a similar argument gives the equation

$$Y = A \sin 2\pi f(t + X/v) \qquad (6)$$

for a sinusoidal transverse wave traveling in the negative X-direction.

Sinusoidal longitudinal waves in a long coil spring can be produced by the arrangement shown in Fig. 5. One end of the spring is attached to a steel ball supported at the end of a hacksaw blade; the other end of the hacksaw blade is held in a clamp as indicated. If the ball is given a

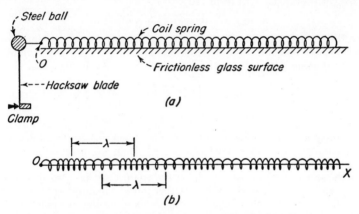

Fig. 5. Production and transmission of a sinusoidal longitudinal wave train in a long coil spring. The wave is moving to the right.

small displacement A to one side and then released, it will execute simple harmonic motion of frequency f and as a result of this motion will set up a sinusoidal longitudinal wave train in the spring. The appearance of the spring at a certain time after the wave train had been started is given in Fig. 5(b); *the wavelength λ is the distance between adjacent condensations or adjacent rarefactions*, as indicated in the figure. Again we must assume that a driving force supplies the energy carried away by the wave, if the wave is to have constant amplitude.

In order to write the equation for the longitudinal wave traveling in the X-direction, we note that all the particles in the spring execute simple harmonic motions about their equilibrium positions and that these motions are parallel to the X-axis. Since the amplitude of the oscillation of the steel ball is A, this is also the amplitude of oscillation of point O at the end of the spring and, if there is no friction, of all other points in the spring. The motion of the particle whose equilibrium position is X in Fig. 5 is exactly like the motion of the corresponding particle in Fig. 4, *except that the motions in Fig. 5 are right and left rather than up and down.*

If we let x denote the *displacement from the equilibrium position*, then by analogy with (5), this displacement is given as a function of time by

$$x = A \ \sin 2\pi f(t - X/v), \tag{7}$$

where X is the coordinate of the equilibrium position of the particle. This is the equation for *a longitudinal wave traveling in the $+X$-direction*. For *a longitudinal wave traveling in the $-X$-direction*, the equation is

$$x = A \ \sin 2\pi f(t + X/v). \tag{8}$$

Example. *In Fig. 5, if the wave speed is 6 ft/sec and if the steel ball vibrates through a total distance of 0.1 ft at 1.5 cycles/sec; what is the wavelength of the longitudinal traveling wave? Write the equation for the wave.*

We get the wavelength from (4b):

$$\lambda = v/f = (6 \text{ ft/sec})/(1.5/\text{sec}) = 4 \text{ ft}.$$

Since the wave is traveling to the right, the displacement x at time t of the particle whose equilibrium position is X is given by (7). For the amplitude A we must use *half* the total distance the ball moves, or $A = 0.05$ ft. Hence

$$x = (0.05 \text{ ft}) \ \sin\left[2\pi \ \frac{1.5}{\text{sec}} \left(t - \frac{X}{6 \text{ ft/sec}} \right) \right]$$

$$= (0.05 \text{ ft}) \ \sin 3\pi (t \ \sec^{-1} - \tfrac{1}{6} X \ \text{ft}^{-1}).$$

The argument of the sine is seen to become dimensionless (as all arguments of trigonometric functions must always be) when we insert a *time t* and a *distance X*, for example $t = 3$ sec and $X = 5$ ft.

In the above equation, a 'particle' at the origin $X = 0$ has zero displacement at $t = 0$ and is moving to the right. Other initial conditions would be represented by including a phase angle in the argument of the sine much as in the case discussed on p. 240.

3. DERIVATION OF THE SPEED OF A TRANSVERSE WAVE ON A STRING

WE SHALL now write the differential equation satisfied by a simple sinusoidal transverse wave and use this equation in deriving an expression for the speed of a transverse wave on a string.

To obtain the desired differential equation, let us first write an expression for the second derivative of Y with respect to t when X is constant* in (5b):

$$Y = A \ \sin 2\pi f(t - X/v)$$

$$\partial Y/\partial t = 2\pi f A \ \cos 2\pi f(t - X/v)$$

$$\partial^2 Y/\partial t^2 = -4\pi^2 f^2 A \ \sin 2\pi f(t - X/v)$$

or
$$\partial^2 Y/\partial t^2 = -4\pi^2 f^2 Y. \tag{9}$$

---

* The symbols $\partial/\partial t$ and $\partial^2/\partial t^2$ denote differentiation with respect to t when X is held constant; similarly $\partial/\partial X$ and $\partial^2/\partial X^2$ denote differentiation with respect to X at a constant value of t. $\partial Y/\partial t$ and $\partial^2 Y/\partial t^2$ are the velocity and acceleration of the particle of the string at X, in its up and down motion. $\partial Y/\partial X$ and $\partial^2 Y/\partial X^2$ are the slope and second derivative of the curve contained in a snapshot of the string at instant t.

Similarly, we may take derivatives of Y with respect to X when t is constant; thus,

$$\partial Y/\partial X = -(2\pi f/v)A \, \cos 2\pi f(t-X/v)$$

$$\partial^2 Y/\partial X^2 = -(4\pi^2 f^2/v^2)A \, \sin 2\pi f(t-X/v)$$

or $\qquad\qquad \partial^2 Y/\partial X^2 = -(4\pi^2 f^2/v^2)Y.$ $\qquad\qquad\qquad$ (10)

By combining (9) and (10) we obtain the differential equation

$$\frac{\partial^2 Y}{\partial X^2} = \frac{1}{v^2}\frac{\partial^2 Y}{\partial t^2}, \qquad\qquad (11)$$

which applies to a transverse wave traveling in either the $+X$- or $-X$-direction; proof that (11) applies to waves traveling in the $-X$-direction is left as a problem.

Although we derived equation (11) for a sinusoidal wave, it will be noted that neither frequency f nor wavelength λ appears in the equation. The equation actually applies to *any type* of transverse wave traveling in a direction parallel to the X-axis.

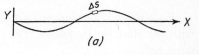

(a)

Let us now drive an expression for the speed of a transverse wave in a string *when the amplitude of the motion is small.* Consider the element of length ΔS in Fig. 6, which gives the configuration of the string at a certain instant. The tension F acts on the ends of the element as shown in the enlarged drawing of part (b). The Y-component of the

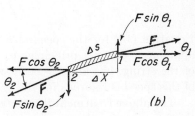

(b)

Figure 6

resultant force on this element of length has the value

$$\Sigma \, F_Y = F \, \sin\theta_1 - F \, \sin\theta_2 = F(\sin\theta_1 - \sin\theta_2).$$

If the amplitude of motion is small, the angles θ_1 and θ_2 will be small in comparison with one radian, and we can set

$$\sin\theta_1 = \tan\theta_1 \quad \text{and} \quad \sin\theta_2 = \tan\theta_2.$$

However, the magnitude of $\tan\theta_1$ is simply the slope of the curve at point 1 and $\tan\theta_2$ is the slope at point 2. Thus, denoting the slopes at points 1 and 2 by $[\partial Y/\partial X]_1$ and $[\partial Y/\partial X]_2$, respectively, we may write

$$\Sigma \, F_Y = F([\partial Y/\partial X]_1 - [\partial Y/\partial X]_2).$$

When ΔX is small (infinitesimal), we have, by definition,

$$\partial^2 Y/\partial X^2 = [(\partial Y/\partial X)_1 - (\partial Y/\partial X)_2]/\Delta X,$$

where ΔX is the projection of ΔS on the X-axis.   Hence we obtain

$$\Sigma\, F_Y = F\ (\partial^2 Y/\partial X^2)\ \Delta X$$

for the Y-component of the resultant force.

   With this force, the Y-component of acceleration $\partial^2 Y/\partial t^2$ of the center of mass of the element can be obtained from Newton's second principle:

$$\Sigma\, F_Y = \mu\ \Delta S\ \partial^2 Y/\partial t^2,$$

where $\mu\ \Delta S$ is the mass of the element.   We now let point 1 approach point 2 so that ΔS becomes infinitesimal.   Then ΔX approaches $\Delta S\ \cos\theta_2$. But $\cos\theta_2 = 1 - \tfrac12\theta_2^2 + \cdots$, and we must assume θ_2 sufficiently small so that we can set $\cos\theta_2 = 1$ and $\Delta X = \Delta S$.   Then

$$\Sigma\, F_Y = F(\partial^2 Y/\partial X^2)\ \Delta S = \mu\ \Delta S\ \partial^2 Y/\partial t^2,$$

or
$$\frac{\partial^2 Y}{\partial X^2} = \frac{\mu}{F}\frac{\partial^2 Y}{\partial t^2}. \qquad (12)$$

   Equation (12) becomes identical with (11) if we identify the term F/μ with v^2; that is, to make (11) consistent with Newton's principle we must set

$$v = \sqrt{F/\mu}. \qquad (13)$$

   Equation (13) for the speed of a transverse wave in a string, derived by applying Newton's principles to the motion of an infinitesimal element of the string, has already been stated in Sec. 1.   The above derivation of this speed is rigorous for the case of waves of *small amplitude*.

   The above treatment illustrates the type of argument used in deriving the formulas for the speeds of the various types of waves considered in this and the following chapter.   Since these derivations are slightly above the general mathematical level of this text, we shall omit the proofs of the formulas for speeds of waves of other types.

4. INTERFERENCE PHENOMENA; THE SUPERPOSITION PRINCIPLE

   THUS FAR, we have considered the passage of a *single* wave disturbance —a pulse or a continuous wave train—through a medium.   However, it is possible for two or more waves to pass through a medium simultaneously.   Let us now consider the effects when *two* transverse wave trains pass simultaneously along a stretched string.   In this case, the resultant lateral displacement Y of a point in the string is simply the sum of the displacements the point would have if each wave train traveled along the string by itself.   If the first wave train alone would produce displacement Y_1, and if the second wave train alone would produce displacement Y_2, the resultant displacement is given by

$$Y = Y_1 + Y_2. \qquad (14)$$

In other words, *the effects of the two waves superpose,* and equation (14) gives a statement of this *superposition principle.*

Mathematically the superposition principle obtains because the differential equation (11) is *linear* and *homogeneous* (contains the first power of Y in each term); hence if $Y_1(X, t)$ and $Y_2(X, t)$ satisfy the equation, so does $Y = Y_1 + Y_2$. Physically we may state the principle as follows:

SUPERPOSITION PRINCIPLE: *When two or more waves move simultaneously through a region of space, each wave proceeds independently, as if the other were not present. The resulting 'displacement' at any point and time is the vector sum of the 'displacements' of the individual waves. This principle holds for mechanical waves on strings, springs, and liquid surfaces, and for sound waves in gases, liquids, and solids, provided the displacements are not too great. It holds rigorously for light waves and electromagnetic waves of any intensity, in which case 'displacement' refers to electric intensity.*

When two waves traveling in the same direction are superposed, the shape of the string at any instant can be determined by the method illustrated in Fig. 7. At a particular instant, the displacements Y_1 arising from the first wave are given by the light solid curve and the displacements Y_2 arising from the second wave are given by the broken curve. The resultant displacements are given by the heavy curve, which is obtained by adding the displacements Y_1 and Y_2 for every point along the string. Since the speeds of the two wave trains in the string are

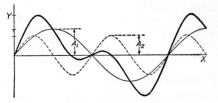

Fig. 7. Superposition of two waves moving in the $+X$-direction. In this example, $Y_1 = A_1 \sin 2\pi f_1(t - X/v)$ (light curve), $Y_2 = A_2 \sin 2\pi f_2(t - X/v)$ (broken curve), and $A_2 = \frac{3}{4} A_1$, $f_2 = 2f_1$.

the same, waves with the shape given by the heavy curve will travel along the string with the same speed as that of the component waves.

One important case involves the passage of two wave trains of the *same frequency*, both traveling in the $+X$-direction. Let the equations of the two wave trains be given by

$$Y_1 = A_1 \sin 2\pi f(t - X/v), \qquad Y_2 = A_2 \sin[2\pi f(t - X/v) + \phi], \quad (15)$$

where ϕ represents the phase difference between the waves.

In the case $\phi = 0$, the resulting wave train has the form

$$Y = (A_1 + A_2) \sin 2\pi f(t - X/v).$$

In this case in which the two wave trains are exactly in phase, the resulting wave train is similar to the component waves and has an amplitude equal to the sum of the amplitudes of the component waves; the resulting configuration at a given time is given by Fig. 8(a).   The two waves are said to 'interfere constructively.'

In the case $\phi=\pi$ in (15), the two component waves produce displace-

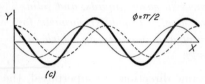

ments in opposite directions since

$$\sin[2\pi f(t-X/v)+\pi]$$
$$= -\sin2\pi f(t-X/v).$$

Hence, by (14), the resultant displacement is

$$Y=(A_1-A_2)\sin2\pi f(t-X/v).$$

The two waves are said to 'interfere destructively.' A complete cancellation of the two component waves is obtained if $A_1=A_2$; this case is illustrated in Fig. 8(b).   An observer would see no wave at all.

Fig. 8. Interference of two sinusoidal waves of the same amplitude and the same frequency, *traveling in the same direction,* for three values of phase difference. The two waves are represented by the light solid and broken curves, the resultant by the heavy curve.

A case intermediate between the two we have discussed is illustrated in Fig. 8(c).   In this case, $\phi=\frac{1}{2}\pi$ and $A_1=A_2$.

Now let us consider the important case of two sinusoidal transverse wave trains of *equal* amplitude and the same frequency *traveling in opposite directions* along a string.   This is a case frequently met in practice, as we shall see in the next section.   Let the first wave, traveling toward the right in Fig. 9(a), be described by the equation

$$Y_1=A\,\sin2\pi f(t-X/v),$$

and the second wave, traveling toward the *left* in Fig. 9(b), by

$$Y_2=A\,\sin2\pi f(t+X/v).$$

Then, from (14), the combination of these two waves is given by

$$Y=A\,\sin2\pi f(t-X/v)+A\,\sin2\pi f(t+X/v). \tag{16}$$

Recalling the relations for sums and differences of angles:

$$\sin(a+b)=\sin a\,\cos b+\cos a\,\sin b, \quad \sin(a-b)=\sin a\,\cos b-\cos a\,\sin b,$$

we may write equation (16) in the forms

$$Y=[2A\,\cos2\pi fX/v]\sin2\pi ft, \qquad Y=[2A\,\cos2\pi X/\lambda]\sin2\pi ft. \tag{17}$$

The wave pattern given by (17) is called a *standing wave;* the motion associated with this type of wave is illustrated in Fig. 9(c), (d), (e), (f), for four positions of the component traveling waves, at times $t=0$, $\frac{1}{4} T$, $\frac{1}{2} T$, and $\frac{3}{4} T$, where $T=1/f$. The particles in the standing wave (17) execute simple harmonic motion of frequency f about their equilibrium positions. However, the amplitude of their motion (which is given by $2A \cos 2\pi X/\lambda$) is not the same for all points along the string as in the case of a traveling wave, but varies from a maximum value of $2A$ at the points $X=0$, $\frac{1}{2}\lambda$, λ, $\frac{3}{2}\lambda$, $\cdots$, at which $\cos 2\pi X/\lambda = \pm 1$, to zero at the points $X=\frac{1}{4}\lambda$, $\frac{3}{4}\lambda$, $\frac{5}{4}\lambda$, $\frac{7}{4}\lambda$, $\cdots$, at which $\cos 2\pi X/\lambda = 0$.

For the standing wave pattern shown in Fig. 9, the motions of all particles in the region between $X=0$ and $X=\frac{1}{4}\lambda$ are exactly in time phase with one another and with the motion of particles in the region between $X=\frac{3}{4}\lambda$ and $X=\frac{5}{4}\lambda$, but are π radians out of phase with the motion of particles in the region between $X=\frac{1}{4}\lambda$ and $X=\frac{3}{4}\lambda$ and in the region between $X=\frac{5}{4}\lambda$ and $X=\frac{7}{4}\lambda$. This phase relationship is illustrated schematically in Fig. 10, which indicates that when particles in a length of the string equal to one-half wavelength are going *up*, the particles in the immediately neighboring parts of the string are going *down*.

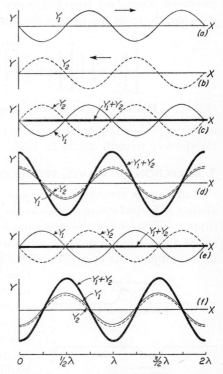

Fig. 9. A standing wave is produced when two waves of the same frequency travel *in opposite directions*. The traveling waves Y_1 and Y_2 are shown in (a) and (b) at $t=0$. The resultant wave Y_1+Y_2 is shown, at four times during a complete cycle, in (c), (d), (e), and (f).

It will be noted from Fig. 9 that at certain points in the string the particles never leave their equilibrium positions. These points, denoted by N in Fig. 11, are called *nodes*. The points midway between the nodes are points at which the amplitude of vibration is a maximum. These points are called *antinodes* or *loops* and are denoted by L in Fig. 11. It should be noted that the wavelength λ of the component *traveling* waves which produce the standing wave is equal to the distance between *alternate* nodes or between *alternate* antinodes in the standing

Fig. 10. Velocities of particles in a standing wave.

wave; that is, *twice* the distance between *adjacent* nodes or *adjacent* antinodes.

A standing wave may be regarded as a *stationary interference pattern* produced when two traveling wave trains of the same amplitude and wavelength, traveling in opposite directions, *interfere.* If two traveling

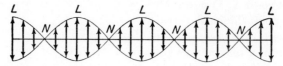

Fig. 11. A standing wave pattern, showing nodes and loops.

waves of different wavelength are traversing a medium, no *stationary* interference pattern can be formed.

5. REFLECTION OF WAVES; PRODUCTION OF STANDING WAVES

LET US NOW consider what happens when a transverse pulse advancing along a stretched string arrives at the end of the string attached to a *rigid* support. The end of the string must remain at rest. The arriving pulse exerts a force on the support, and the reaction force exerted on the string by the support sets up a reflected pulse with its displacement in the direc-

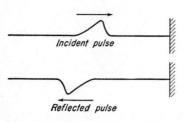

Fig. 12. Reflection of a transverse-wave pulse at a rigid wall.

tion opposite to that of the original pulse. The result is shown schematically in Fig. 12. It will be noted that in reflection the *shape* of the pulse remains unchanged; in Fig. 12 the leading portion of the incident pulse and the leading portion of the reflected pulse are both steep. However, in the incident pulse the particles of the string are displaced *upward* whereas in the reflected pulse the particles suffer *downward* displacements; in other words, an incident *crest* is reflected as a *trough.* Similarly, an incident *trough* would be reflected as a *crest.*

Just as transverse pulses are reflected at the ends of a string, so also will continuous transverse wave trains be reflected. When a continuous train of sinusoidal waves arrives at a fixed end of a stretched wire or string, a continuous train of reflected sinusoidal waves appears at the end and travels in the opposite direction. Thus, we have *two wave trains of the same wavelength traveling in opposite directions;* as we showed in the preceding section, this is the condition necessary for the production of a standing wave. It should be noted, however, that in the case of a stretched string there are *two* fixed ends; neither end of such a string can move, and therefore *the fixed ends of the string must appear as nodes in any standing-wave pattern that may be formed.* This statement implies that only for certain definite wavelengths will a standing-wave pattern be formed in a given string; some of the possible wave patterns are shown in Fig. 13. The wavelength λ is equal to twice the distance between adjacent nodes; for the standing-wave patterns shown in the diagrams of Fig. 13, the wavelengths are

(a): $\lambda_1=2l=2l/1,$ (c): $\lambda_3=\tfrac{2}{3}\,l=2l/3,$ (e): $\lambda_5=\tfrac{2}{5}\,l=2l/5.$

(b): $\lambda_2=\ l=2l/2,$ (d): $\lambda_4=\tfrac{1}{2}\,l=2l/4,$

Thus, the allowed values for the wavelengths that permit a standing wave to be produced in a string of length l are given by the general equation

$$\lambda=2l/n, \qquad (n=1,2,3,\cdots) \quad (18)$$

where n can be any positive integer. The corresponding frequencies of vibration, given by (4a) as

$$f=v/\lambda=n(v/2l), \qquad (19)$$

will give the frequencies of the sound emitted by the vibrating string, as we shall discuss in the next chapter.

The standing wave patterns of Fig. 13 are called the *normal modes of oscillation* of the string. The simplest pattern shown in (a) gives the *fundamental mode of oscillation;* the other patterns represent *higher modes of oscillation.* In the case of a string in which the frequency of the fundamental mode is sufficiently low, it is not difficult to excite the fundamental or one of the higher modes by applying alternating forces by hand near the end of the string at one of the frequencies given by (19). If one applies the alternating forces at a frequency different from that of one of the normal modes, one does not obtain a 'regular' motion, but rather a very erratic, irregular motion.

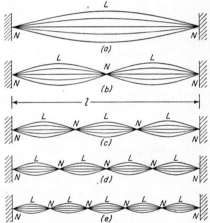

Fig. 13. Standing wave patterns in a stretched string.

Example. *A steel piano wire 1 meter long has a mass of 20 grams and is stretched with a force of 800 newtons. What are the frequencies of its fundamental mode of oscillation and of the next three higher modes?*

The velocity of a transverse wave on this wire is given by (2) as

$$v=\sqrt{F/\mu}=\sqrt{(800\text{ nt})/(0.02\text{ kg/m})}=200\text{ m/sec}.$$

The wavelength of the fundamental mode is $2l=2$ m, hence the frequency is

$$f=v/\lambda=(200\text{ m/sec})/(2\text{ m})=100\text{ cycles/sec}.$$

According to (19) the frequencies of the higher modes are 2, 3, 4, $\cdots$ times this, or

$$200, 300, 400, \cdots \text{ cycles/sec.}$$

PROBLEMS

1. A string exactly 1 m long and with a mass of 5.0 g is under a tension of 10 nt. What is the speed of a transverse wave in this string?   Ans: 44.7 m/sec.

2. What would be the speed of a transverse wave in the string mentioned in Prob. 1 if it were under a tension of 30 nt?

3. A rope is 12 m in length. Experiment shows that a transverse wave passes from one end of the rope to the other in 1.5 sec when the rope is under a tension of 20 nt. What is the total mass of the rope?   Ans: 3.75 kg.

4. What should be the tension in the rope mentioned in Prob. 3 in order for transverse waves to move along the rope at a speed of 24 m/sec?

5. A cord 36 ft long weighs 0.5 lb. If tensile forces of magnitude 25 lb are applied to the ends of this cord, with what speed will transverse waves move along the cord?   Ans: 241 ft/sec.

6. What is the magnitude of the stretching forces that must be applied to the ends of the cord in Prob. 5 in order for transverse waves to move along the cord at a speed of 300 ft/sec? at 100 ft/sec?

7. Verify that the expressions on the right of (2) and (3) actually represent the same unit as the speed on the left in the two unit systems used in the text.

8. The speed of *longitudinal* waves in a slender rod is given by $v = \sqrt{E_Y/\rho}$, where E_Y is Young's modulus and ρ is the density of the material of the rod. In what units should Young's modulus and density be expressed in order to obtain speed in m/sec? in ft/sec? Find the speed of longitudinal waves in a steel rod, in a copper rod, and in an aluminum rod.

9. A fisherman sitting on a dock observes that his float makes ten complete oscillations in 4 sec and that the distance between crests of the waves is 2 ft. What is the speed of the waves?   Ans: 5 ft/sec.

10. A fisherman in an anchored boat observes that the crest of a wave passes him every 2 sec, and that it takes 4 sec for the crest to move the 40-ft length of the boat. What is the wavelength of the waves?

11. (a) Plot $Y = 3 \sin 2\pi[(60 \text{ sec}^{-1})t - (\tfrac{1}{2} \text{ m}^{-1})X]$ m against X at $t=0$ and at $t = \tfrac{1}{480}$ sec. From your plots determine amplitude, wavelength, and speed. (Make the plots neatly and explain your reasoning carefully.)

(b) Plot the same function against t at $X=0$, and determine the time of vibration. Verify that in this case $\lambda = vT$.

12. Repeat Prob. 11 for the case $Y = 3 \sin 2\pi[(60 \text{ sec}^{-1})t + (\tfrac{1}{2} \text{ m}^{-1})X]$ m. What is the essential difference between this case and that of Prob. 11?

13. The speed of transverse waves in a certain string is 50 ft/sec. This string is excited at one end by a device like that shown in Fig. 4. If the oscillation frequency of the body attached to the end of the string is 5 cycles/sec, what is the wavelength of the waves in the string?   Ans: 10 ft.

14. If the tension in the string in Prob. 13 were doubled, what would be the speed of transverse waves in the string? What would be the wavelength of the waves produced when one end of the string is subjected to transverse displacements at a frequency of 5 cycles/sec? of 12 cycles/sec?

15. Sinusoidal transverse waves of frequency 8.0 cycles/sec are passing along a string. The distance between a crest and the adjacent troughs is 4.5 ft. What is the wavelength? What is the speed of the wave?   Ans: 9.0 ft; 72 ft/sec.

16. If the tension in the string in Prob. 15 were doubled, what would be the speed of transverse waves? What would be the wavelength for frequency 8.0 cycles/sec? What would be the distance from a crest to the following trough?

17. A sinusoidal wave train is moving along a string. The equation giving the displacement Y of a point at coordinate X has the following form:

$$Y = 0.12 \sin 16\pi[t \sec^{-1} - X/(50 \text{ m})] \text{ m}.$$

Find the following quantities: (a) the amplitude of the wave motion, (b) the frequency of the wave motion, (c) the speed of the wave motion, and (d) the wavelength. (e) In which direction is the wave moving?
Ans: (a) 12 cm; (b) 8 cycles/sec; (c) 50 m/sec; (d) 6.25 m; (e) +X-direction.

18. Repeat Prob. 17 for a wave motion given by the equation

$$Y = 0.08 \sin 20\pi[t \sec^{-1} + X/(45 \text{ m})] \text{ m}.$$

19. Sinusoidal longitudinal waves are sent out in a coil spring, from a vibrating source at one end of the spring as in Fig. 5. The frequency of vibration of the source is 20 cycles/sec. The distance between successive condensations in the spring is 30 cm. Find the speed of a condensation as it moves along the spring. The maximum longitudinal displacement of a particle in the spring is 4 cm. Write an equation for this wave motion for waves moving in the +X-direction if the source is at $X=0$ and the displacement at the source is zero when $t=0$.
Ans: 6.00 m/sec; $x = 0.04 \sin 40\pi[t \sec^{-1} - X/(6 \text{ m})]$ m.

20. A source vibrating at a frequency of 12 cycles/sec produces longitudinal waves of amplitude 0.04 m in a coil spring. The speed of propagation of longitudinal waves in the spring is 20 m/sec. Write an equation describing this motion.

21. Start with equation (6) for a wave traveling in the −X-direction and derive equation (11).

22. From the equation for a sinusoidal transverse wave in a string, derive an expression for the *maximum* velocity of a particle in the string. How does the maximum velocity depend upon wave amplitude? upon wave frequency?

23. Two transverse waves of equal amplitude and wavelength are traveling in opposite directions along a string. If the equations of the two waves are

$$Y_1 = 2 \sin 2\pi(t \sec^{-1} - \tfrac{1}{4} X \text{ m}^{-1}) \text{ m} \quad \text{and} \quad Y_2 = 2 \sin 2\pi(t \sec^{-1} + \tfrac{1}{4} X \text{ m}^{-1}) \text{ m},$$

compute and plot the shape of the string in the region between $X=0$ and $X=4$ m at the times $t=0$, $\tfrac{1}{4}$, $\tfrac{1}{2}$, $\tfrac{3}{4}$, and 1 sec.

24. The distance between a node and the adjacent antinodes in a standing wave is 50 cm. What is the wavelength of the component waves?

25. The distance between adjacent nodes in a standing wave is 2 ft. What is the wavelength of the component waves?   Ans: 4 ft.

26. Write the equation of a standing wave of wavelength 1.5 m and frequency 15 cycles/sec.

27. What is the longest wavelength of traveling waves that can produce a standing wave in a string 10 ft long?   Ans: 20 ft.

28. Find the five longest wavelengths of traveling waves that can produce standing waves in a string 24 inches long.

29. Two waves, each of wavelength 5 ft, travel in opposite directions in a stretched string 20 ft long. How many loops are formed? Excluding the nodes at the *fixed* ends of the string, how many nodes appear in the string?

Ans: 8 loops; 7 nodes.

30. A standing wave is set up in a string 10 ft long. There are 7 loops in the standing wave. What is the wavelength of the waves producing the pattern?

31. A flexible copper wire 1 mm in diameter and 10 m long has its ends attached to rigid supports. (a) What is the speed of longitudinal waves in this wire (see Prob. 8)? (b) At what tension would transverse waves have the same speed as longitudinal waves? (c) Is this possible?

Ans: (a) 3520 m/sec; (b) 86,500 nt.

32. A string 10 m long has a mass of 50 g and is stretched between rigid supports, the tension in the string being 10 nt. If this string is plucked near one support, how long a time will be required for the resulting pulse to travel to the far end of the string, experience reflection, and travel back to its point of origin? How long is required for a complete round trip of a pulse initiated anywhere in the string? Considering multiple reflections, find the number of 'round trips' a pulse would make each second.

33. Equation (10) shows that the particles in a string through which a sinusoidal transverse wave is passing oscillate about their equilibrium positions with simple harmonic motion. The mechanical energy of each particle is the sum of its potential and kinetic energies and is always equal to the *maximum* value of its kinetic energy. Using the result of Prob. 22 for the maximum velocity and computing the mechanical energy of a 'particle' of mass $\mu \Delta X$, show that the energy W *per unit length* of the string is given by $W = 2\pi^2 \mu f^2 A^2$.

34. Consider the transverse wave

$$Y = A \sin 2\pi f(t - X/v),$$

traveling *to the right* along a string. Consider a typical point of the string, located at $X = X_0$. Let the tension be F, and assume that the angle of the string with the X-axis is always small. (a) Show that the Y-component of force exerted *by* the string to the left of X_0 *on* the string to the right of X_0 is

$$F_Y = -F \ (\partial Y/\partial X)_{X=X_0} = 2\pi f \mu A \ \cos 2\pi f(t - X_0/v).$$

(b) Show that the work done by the force component in (a) during one second is

$$\int_0^1 F_Y \ (\partial Y/\partial t)_{X=X_0} \ dt = 2\pi^2 \mu f^2 A^2 \ v.$$

Since this represents work done *by* the string to the left of X_0 *on* the string to the right, it represents power transmitted *to the right* along the string.

35. Comparing the results of Probs. 33 and 34, show that the whole mechanical energy of the string is propagated along the string with the wave velocity v. This result, and the fact that power is proportional to A^2 and f^2, apply to longitudinal mechanical waves as well as to transverse.

CHAPTER 19

SOUND

THE TERM *sound* has two distinct uses. The physiologist or psychologist uses the word *sound* in connection with the sense of hearing and the auditory sensations produced by certain types of disturbances in the air.

> In physics the term **sound** is used to denote the disturbances themselves rather than the sensations produced; in other words, to denote the *waves* in the air or other elastic material media that are capable of producing the sensation of hearing.

The frequencies of audible waves lie between about 20 cycles/sec and 20,000 cycles/sec, but the term *sound* is used by physicists to include disturbances having frequencies outside the range to which the normal human ear responds. Waves of frequency below the audible range are termed *infrasonic;* those of frequency above audible frequencies are called *ultrasonic.* Ultrasonic waves are beginning to have increasing practical importance for such uses as the detection of flaws in the interior of solid bodies, the production of stable emulsions of normally immiscible liquids, the coagulation of aerosols, and the destruction of micro-organisms. The echo time of a short pulse of underwater ultrasonic waves is used in the 'fathometer' to measure water depth and in 'sonar' (the underwater-sound analog of 'radar') to measure the direction and range of such underwater objects as submarines.

The physicist in his description of audible sound waves does attempt to correlate their psychological effects with the physical properties of the waves themselves; thus, as we shall show, the psychological characteristics of sound—*pitch, loudness,* and *quality*—can be correlated with physical properties—*frequency, intensity,* and *waveform*—of the sound waves.

In order for sound waves to be produced, there must be a *source* that initiates a mechanical disturbance and an *elastic medium* through which the disturbance can be transmitted. The source may be a vibrating solid, such as the stretched strings of a piano or violin or the walls of a bell; it may be an oscillating air column as in a trumpet or organ pipe. The medium involved most frequently is air; the frequency of the sound wave in the medium is of course the same as the frequency of vibration of the sound source. A simple experiment will show the necessity of an elastic material medium to transmit the sound from the source to the ear. If an ordinary electric doorbell is suspended by fine wires inside a bell jar in such a way that it does not make contact with the walls of the jar, the sound of the ringing bell can be heard when air is inside the bell jar. However, if the air is removed from the bell jar by a vacuum pump, the sound can no longer be heard. This result indicates that a material medium such as air is necessary for the transmission of the sound from the bell. That sound waves can be transmitted by solids as well as by air can be shown by tilting the evacuated bell jar so that the bell touches the wall of the jar; as soon as contact is made between the bell and the wall, the sound can be heard again. That sound waves can also be transmitted by liquids can easily be shown by ringing a bell beneath the surface of oil or water in a large beaker.

In this chapter, we shall discuss the production and transmission of sound waves and some of the characteristic effects produced by sound.

1. PRODUCTION OF SOUND BY VIBRATING SOLIDS

WE SHALL first discuss the various ways in which a solid body can vibrate; these ways in which a body can vibrate are called the 'normal modes of oscillation' of the body. The possible modes depend upon the shape of the body, the density of the body, the elastic properties of the body, and on the *boundary conditions* imposed at the boundary of the body by restraints produced or imposed by other bodies or other media in contact with the body in question.

We have already discussed the vibration of a stretched string that has both ends fixed by connection to rigid supports. With these boundary conditions, there are certain normal modes of oscillation which correspond to the standing wave patterns shown in Fig. 13, p. 389. If we impart energy to the stretched string by plucking it or by stroking it properly with a violin bow, the string vibrates in one or more of the modes shown in this figure. As the string vibrates, energy is transfered to the surrounding air in the form of sound waves; as the energy is transferred to the air, the vibration of the string itself gradually dies out.

The frequencies of the sound waves produced in the air are the same as those of the string, since the string is the source of the sound waves. The frequencies of the normal modes of vibration of the string are given by (19), p. 389, as

$$f_n = \frac{nv}{2l} = \frac{n\sqrt{F/\mu}}{2l}, \qquad (n = 1, 2, 3, \cdots) \quad (1)$$

where F is the tension, μ the mass per unit length, and l the length of the string. The lowest possible frequency corresponds to $n = 1$; this is the frequency of the fundamental mode of vibration of the string and is called the *fundamental frequency*.   The frequencies of the higher modes of vibration corresponding to $n = 2, 3, \cdots$ are called *overtones*.

Equation (1) shows that for a string we may express the frequencies of all modes of oscillation in terms of the fundamental frequency f_1 by the simple relation

$$f_n = nf_1. \qquad (n = 1, 2, 3, \cdots) \quad (2)$$

The frequencies of the higher modes of oscillation of the string are all integral multiples of the fundamental frequency; a set of frequencies bearing this type of relationship are called *harmonics*.   The fundamental frequency, for which $n = 1$, is called the *first harmonic;* the frequency for which $n = 2$ is called the *second harmonic;* and so on.

For *any* vibrating body, *the lowest frequency is called the fundamental frequency;* the first frequency higher than the fundamental is called the *first overtone;* the second higher frequency is called the *second overtone;* and so on.   *The overtones are not always simple integral multiples of the fundamental.*   When, as in the case of a drum or a bell, they are not integral multiples of the fundamental they are called *nonharmonic overtones*.

When the overtones *are* integral multiples of the fundamental, they are said to form a harmonic sequence.   For a vibrating string, all harmonics are present, and we may write

$$\text{fundamental} = \text{first harmonic}: \quad f_1 = \quad f_1,$$
$$\text{first overtone} = \text{second harmonic}: \quad f_2 = 2\,f_1,$$
$$\text{second overtone} = \text{third harmonic}: \quad f_3 = 3\,f_1,$$
$$\cdots \qquad\qquad \cdots \qquad\qquad \cdots$$
$$(n-1)\text{th overtone} = n\text{th harmonic}: \quad f_n = n\,f_1.$$

Thus, the first harmonic for the string is the fundamental frequency itself and the overtones give all the multiples of the first harmonic.   Although in the case of a string *all* harmonics are possible, this is not necessarily the case for vibrating bodies even though the overtones be harmonics.   For some types of organ pipes and clamped bars the odd harmonics are present and all even harmonics are absent.

If a string is plucked at any point selected at random, several modes of oscillation are usually excited simultaneously.   However, by employing the proper procedure, we may excite *particular* modes of oscillation.   Thus, if the string is plucked gently at its mid-point, the fundamental mode will be excited.   If one plucks the string at a point one-quarter of its length from the end while gently touching the mid-point, the first overtone will be excited.   Similarly, by plucking the string at a point one-sixth of its length from the end and gently touching the string at a point one-third of the way from the end, one can excite the second overtone.

We have been considering only the modes of oscillation of a string or flexible wire in which *transverse* motions occur.   However, there are also corresponding longitudinal modes of vibration of a wire or rod clamped at the ends.   For the longitudinal vibrations also, the ends must be nodes, so the normal modes will again be given by Fig. 13, p. 389, if we imagine these drawings to represent magnitudes of longitudinal, rather than transverse, displacements.   The permitted wavelengths of longitudinal waves will again be given by (18), p. 389.

The speed of a longitudinal wave in a wire or rod is given by a formula like (1), p. 378, in which the elastic force factor is Young's modulus E_Y and the inertia factor is the density ρ of the material.   Thus

$$v_L = \sqrt{\frac{E_Y}{\rho}}. \qquad \genfrac{(}{)}{0pt}{}{\text{longitudinal}}{\text{wave in rod}} \quad (3)$$

The frequencies for the various modes of longitudinal vibration can be written in terms of the speed v_L in the form

$$f_n = \frac{v_L}{\lambda_n} = \frac{n v_L}{2l} = \frac{n \sqrt{E_Y/\rho}}{2l}. \qquad (4)$$

The frequencies of longitudinal waves in a wire will usually be much higher than those of transverse waves because the longitudinal wave speed is usually very high.   In musical instruments such as the violin or piano, only the transverse oscillations are desired.   In playing the violin, a novice usually manages to excite longitudinal vibrations by moving the bow lengthwise along the string; the resulting sound is an objectionable shrill squeak.

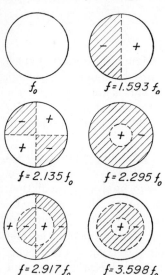

Fig. 1. Modes of oscillation of a circular membrane.

As an example of a vibrating body whose overtones are *not* harmonics of the fundamental, let us now consider qualitatively the circular membrane used on a drum.   The boundary condition is simple; the periphery of the membrane is fixed by clamps so that it cannot move.   If some part of the drumhead is given a blow, a wave pulse travels outward from the point receiving the blow and is reflected at the fixed periphery of the membrane; in this way a standing wave pattern is set up.

Some of the possible standing wave patterns or normal modes of vibration are shown in Fig. 1, which shows the *nodal lines* as broken lines across the membrane.   At these lines and at the periphery there is no motion; at points approximately midway between the nodal lines, displacements of maximum amplitude occur.   In the simplest mode of oscillation, the center of the membrane is an antinode and the periphery is a nodal line; this mode of oscillation has the lowest frequency, the fundamental f_0.   For the mode giving the first overtone, shown at the upper right in Fig. 1, the motion of the part of the membrane to the right of the nodal line is 180° out of phase with the motion of the part of the membrane to the left of the nodal line; that is, when the part of the membrane to the right is moving toward the reader, the part to the left is moving away from the reader.   It is easy to visualize the motion shown in the other parts of Fig. 1 by remembering that the motions of parts of the membrane on opposite sides of a nodal line are out of phase by 180°.

The frequencies of the various normal modes of oscillation are given in the figure in terms of the fundamental frequency denoted by f_0.   The frequencies of the overtones are *not* integral multiples of the fundamental f_0; that is, the overtones are *not* harmonics.   The characteristic frequencies may be determined experimentally by subjecting the membrane to vibrations of known frequencies by placing a loudspeaker directly above the horizontal membrane and exciting the loudspeaker by means of an audio-frequency oscillator whose frequency can be varied slowly. The drumhead will be set into vibration of large amplitude when the frequency of the sound waves from the loudspeaker coincides with the frequency of some mode of oscillation of the membrane; and if the drumhead is covered with a thin layer of fine powder such as chalk dust, the powder will move about over the drumhead and accumulate along the nodal lines. By noting the pattern of nodal lines and by noting the frequency at which the pattern occurs, one can determine the resonance frequencies for each of the modes of oscillation shown in Fig. 1.

The restoring forces in a flexible drumhead result from the tension of the stretched membrane.   A metal plate has modes of vibration similar to those of a stretched membrane.   In this case the restoring forces appear as a result of bending stresses in the plate.   Vibrations of membranes and plates are of importance to the engineer concerned with the design of diaphragms for loudspeakers, telephones, and microphones.

We could discuss other types of solid bodies, such as bells, cymbals, and the transversely vibrating bars of the xylophone, which are common sources of sound.   In most such solid bodies there are many possible modes of oscillation and the sound waves produced usually have components of many different frequencies.

Of the various vibrating solids we have mentioned thus far, the drumhead and the bell are most effective in the direct production of sound waves of *large amplitude*.   Their large surface areas account for their great effectiveness.   If a given amount of energy is imparted to a drumhead, this energy is quickly imparted to the surrounding air by the large, flat surfaces of the vibrating membrane.   However, if an equal amount of

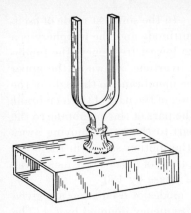

Fig. 2. Tuning fork mounted on a wooden box, which acts as an 'acoustic amplifier.'

energy is imparted to a stretched string, this energy is imparted very slowly to the surrounding air because the surface area of the string is small; hence, vibration of the string persists for a long time. In order to make a vibrating string or tuning fork more effecting in setting up sound waves in the air, the string can be 'coupled' mechanically to a body of large area or volume which is effective in imparting vibrational energy to the surrounding air. The sounding board of a piano, the case of a violin, and the sound box (Fig. 2) of a tuning fork are familiar examples.

2. SPEED OF SOUND IN SOLIDS, LIQUIDS, AND GASES

WE HAVE given in equation (3) the speed of a longitudinal wave in a *rod*. This formula is valid only for rods small in diameter in comparison with the wavelength because the diametral contractions and expansions that accompany changes in length (Poisson's ratio, p. 192) introduce additional complications if the rod is not small compared to the wavelength. In the case of an *extended* solid, the speed of longitudinal waves is not given by (3) but by

$$v_L = \sqrt{\frac{E_B + \tfrac{4}{3}E_S}{\rho}}, \qquad \left(\begin{matrix}\text{longitudinal} \\ \text{wave in solid}\end{matrix}\right) \quad (5)$$

which involves the bulk modulus and the shear modulus.

In the case of a *transverse* wave in an extended solid, the shear modulus alone determines the speed, which is given by

$$v_T = \sqrt{\frac{E_S}{\rho}}. \qquad \left(\begin{matrix}\text{transverse} \\ \text{wave in solid}\end{matrix}\right) \quad (6)$$

Comparison of (5) and (6) shows that the speed of the longitudinal wave in an extended solid is always much greater than that of the transverse wave. The difference in arrival time of these two types of wave is used in seismology to estimate the distance of an earthquake from the observing station.

A fluid cannot sustain a shear ($E_S = 0$), so no transverse wave can be transmitted and the speed of a longitudinal wave is given by

$$v = \sqrt{E_B/\rho}. \qquad \text{(wave in fluid)} \quad (7)$$

Compressions and rarefactions taking place at audio frequencies must be regarded as *adiabatic* rather than isothermal; hence the E_B to be used in the above formulas is the adiabatic bulk modulus. The distinction is unimportant in the case of solids and liquids, which are relatively incompressible and whose properties vary little with small changes in temperature.   The speeds of sound in solids and liquids vary only slowly with temperature.   Typical experimental values for longitudinal waves in thin solid rods and in liquids are given in Tables I and II.

<table>
<tr><td colspan="3">TABLE I
Measured Speeds of Sound
in Solid Rods
(From Smithsonian Physical Tables)</td></tr>
</table>

Material	Speed of sound	
	(m/sec)	(ft/sec)
Aluminum........	5104	16,750
Copper..........	3560	11,680
Iron............	5130	16,830
Lead...........	1322	4,340
Nickel..........	4973	16,320
Glass (typical)....	5550	18,050
Vulcanized rubber.	54	177

TABLE II
Measured Speeds of Sound
in Liquids
(From *Smithsonian Physical Tables*)

Material	Speed of sound	
	(m/sec)	(ft/sec)
Alcohol, methyl...	1143	3750
Carbon bisulfide...	1060	3477
Ether...........	1032	3386
Mercury.........	1407	4614
Turpentine........	1326	4351
Water..........	1461	4794
Sea water........	1500	4922

Now we turn to the important problem of calculating the speed of sound in gases.   Sir Isaac Newton first derived the expression (7) for the speed of sound in a gas but he made the mistake of using the isothermal bulk modulus; careful measurement revealed that the Newtonian expression gave too low a value.   Over a century later, in 1816, Laplace obtained the correct expression when he showed that gas compressions taking place at audio frequencies must be regarded as adiabatic.   The correct expression for the speed of sound in a gas is

$$\text{speed} = \sqrt{\frac{\text{adiabatic bulk modulus}}{\text{density}}}. \tag{8}$$

We recall that the bulk modulus is defined as the ratio of stress to strain, where the stress is the pressure variation dP and the accompanying strain is the change in volume per unit volume $-dV/V$.   Hence

$$E_B = dP/(-dV/V) = -V\,dP/dV. \tag{9}$$

The equation governing an adiabatic process in an ideal gas is (p. 351)

$$PV^\gamma = \text{const},$$

where γ is the ratio of the specific heat at constant pressure to the specific heat at constant volume.   By differentiation of this equation we obtain

$$\gamma P V^{\gamma-1}\,dV + V^\gamma\,dP = 0,$$

or
$$\gamma P = -V\,dP/dV. \tag{10}$$

Comparison of (10) with (9) shows that for an adiabatic process,

$$E_B = \gamma P. \qquad (11)$$

Hence, the Laplace expression for the speed of sound in a gas is

$$v = \sqrt{\gamma P/\rho}. \qquad \text{(wave in gas)} \quad (12)$$

Experiment shows that the expression given in (12) is correct.

Consideration of (12) reveals the interesting fact that at a given temperature, *the speed of sound in a gas is independent of the pressure.* From the general gas law, we recall that the density ρ is directly proportional to the pressure P. Thus, if we place air in a tank at an absolute pressure of 8 atm, the density of the gas is 8 times its density at atmospheric pressure; hence P/ρ and therefore the speed of sound in the air inside the tank is the same as in air at atmospheric pressure, provided the temperature is the same. This independence of pressure is experimentally verified at all pressures at which a gas obeys the ideal gas laws.

Now let us consider the effect of temperature variations on the speed of sound. From our discussion of the general gas law, we recall that

$$P/\rho = RT/M,$$

where R is the universal gas constant, T the absolute temperature, and M is the molecular mass of the gas. Substitution in (12) then gives

$$v = \sqrt{\gamma RT/M}. \qquad \text{(wave in gas)} \quad (13)$$

Hence *the speed of sound in a given kind of gas depends* only *on the temperature.* The speed is directly proportional to the square root of the absolute temperature and may be calculated for any gas from formula (13), which is in complete agreement with experiment within the accuracy with which gases behave ideally. The measured temperature dependence in air is given in Table III; this follows the law (with T in ° K):

$$v = 331\sqrt{T/273°} \text{ m/sec.}$$

TABLE III

MEASURED SPEED OF SOUND IN AIR
(From *Smithsonian Physical Tables*)

Temp. (C)	Speed	
	(m/sec)	(ft/sec)
0°	331.36	1087.1
20°	344	1129
100°	366	1201
500°	553	1814
1000°	700	2297

In contrast to air, hydrogen has a low molecular weight and the high sound speed of 1270 m/sec at 0° C.

Owing to its relatively low value, the speed of propagation of sound in air can be readily determined by direct measurement of the time required for sound to traverse a given distance. Everyone has had the experience of 'seeing a noise made' and then waiting patiently for the sound to arrive—lightning is a common example—and has heard the sound of a jet plane coming from where the plane was and not at all from where it is.

Indirect laboratory methods of determining the speeds of sound in gases will be discussed later.

Example. *Determine the speed of sound in hydrogen gas at 0° C.*

We shall do this problem in two ways: first by comparing with the speed in air, assumed as known; second, by direct substitution in (13).

The speed in air is 331 m/sec at 0° C. Air and hydrogen are both diatomic, so they have the same γ in (13). The speed of sound differs only because of the much lower molecular weight of hydrogen, and is inversely proportional to the square root of the molecular weight. Thus

$$\frac{v_{\text{Hydrogen}}}{v_{\text{Air}}} = \sqrt{\frac{M_{\text{Air}}}{M_{\text{Hydrogen}}}} = \sqrt{\frac{29.0}{2.017}} = \sqrt{14.4} = 3.79,$$

and $v_{\text{Hydrogen}} = 3.79 \times 331 \text{ m/sec} = 1250 \text{ m/sec}.$

We get the same answer by direct substitution in (13):

$$v_{\text{Hydrogen}} = \sqrt{1.40 \ (8317 \text{ m}^2/\text{sec}^2 \cdot \text{K deg})(273 \text{ K deg})/2.017}$$
$$= \sqrt{1.58 \times 10^6 \text{ m}^2/\text{sec}^2} = 1260 \text{ m/sec}.$$

3. PRODUCTION OF SOUND BY VIBRATING AIR COLUMNS

WE CAN best approach the subject of the vibrations of an air column by considering a column closed at both ends, as in Fig. 3(a). The air in

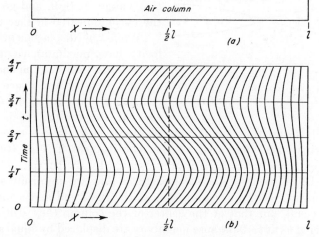

Fig. 3. Fundamental mode of oscillation of an air column closed at both ends.

this column can be set into longitudinal vibration of large amplitude by a small diaphragm vibrating with *very small amplitude* at exactly the resonant frequency, if the diaphragm is placed at an appropriate position inside the closed column.

The normal mode of oscillation of the air in this column is one in which the air rushes back and forth from left to right.   There is no motion of the air at the closed ends, and a maximum amplitude of oscillation at the center.   The displacement is governed by the equation for a longitudinal standing wave,

$$x = A \sin(\pi X/l) \sin(2\pi t/T).$$

This expression is like (17), p. 386, with $\lambda = 2l$, amplitude A instead of $2A$, and a phase shift from cos to sin to secure nodes at $X = 0$ and $X = l$.

In Fig. 3(b), the positions of various particles of air are plotted as a function of time.   At $t = 0$, these particles are in their equilibrium positions and are uniformly spaced along the column.   At $\tfrac{1}{4}T$, they have maximum displacement to the right; at $\tfrac{2}{4}T$, no displacement; at $\tfrac{3}{4}T$, maximum displacement to the left; again at $\tfrac{4}{4}T$, no displacement.   The values of this displacement x as a function of X, at these various times,

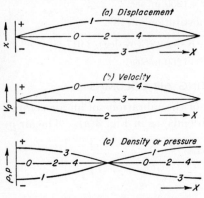

are indicated by the curves 0, 1, 2, 3, 4 of Fig. 4(a), which is the usual way of representing this standing wave.

The velocities of the various air particles are determined by the slopes (from the vertical) of the curves of Fig. 3(b). The particle velocities have their maximum positive values at $t = 0$, and go through the cycle indicated in Fig. 4(b).

While the displacement and velocity have maximum values at the center, and nodes at the ends of the column, density and hence pressure changes are largest at the ends and zero at the center. It is easy to

Fig. 4. Variation of displacement, particle velocity, and density or pressure along the column of Fig. 3. Curves *0, 1, 2, 3, 4,* refer to successive times $t = 0, \tfrac{1}{4}T, \tfrac{2}{4}T, \tfrac{3}{4}T, \tfrac{4}{4}T$.

show analytically that the density change is proportional to $-\partial x/\partial X$, the negative space derivative of the displacement in Fig. 4(a); hence density and pressure changes are represented by the curves of Fig. 4(c). In Fig. 3(b) we see that the set of particles that are uniformly spaced at $t = 0$ suffer, at $t = \tfrac{1}{4}T$, a compression at the right end and a rarefaction at the left end, but that at the center of the column they still have the same spacing as at $t = 0$ because neighbors are displaced by equal amounts.

The oscillation of Fig. 4 represents a standing wave in which the wavelength is $\lambda = 2l$; the frequency would be determined by $f = v/\lambda = v/2l$, where v is the speed of sound in air.   This is the fundamental mode of oscillation of the air column of Fig. 3.   Higher modes would have additional displacement nodes between the ends of the column, exactly as in the case of a stretched string.

Air columns that are employed in musical instruments are not closed at both ends; they are *open* at one or both ends in order to obtain more effective transmission of the vibrations of the column into the atmosphere as sound waves and to facilitate excitation of the oscillations.

If the column of Fig. 3(a) were cut in half at $X = \frac{1}{2} l$ and the right half removed, the left half would continue to have the fundamental mode of oscillation illustrated by the left halves of Figs. 3 and 4.   The reason for this is that the center of the column is a *pressure node* at which the pressure remains at atmospheric.   Hence removing half the tube will not change conditions in the other half since the center of the tube does not depart from atmospheric pressure.   The only effect will be that air will now rush into and out of the tube from the atmosphere, as is needed for transmission of some of the energy of vibration as a sound wave.

The normal modes of oscillation of air columns or organ pipes are determined by the rules that

A closed end is a pressure antinode or a displacement node.

An open end is a pressure node or a displacement antinode.

Organ pipes are of two types: *closed* (one end closed and one open) and *open* (both ends open).   The normal modes of vibration of these two types are illustrated in Fig. 5, in which the curves represent maximum

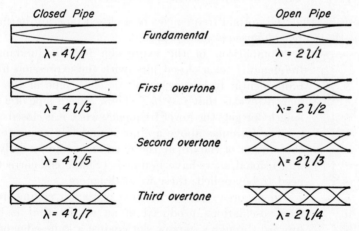

Fig. 5. Normal modes of oscillation of organ pipes. The curves represent maximum displacements.

displacements, as in Fig. 4(a).   The wavelengths of the sound waves to which the pipes are resonant are given in terms of the length l of the pipe; one can easily verify the correctness of the values given in Fig. 5 by recalling that the wavelength in the standing wave pattern is equal to the distance between *alternate* nodes or *alternate* antinodes, that is, to four times the distance between a node and the adjacent antinode.

Remembering that the speed of the waves in the pipe is just the speed v of sound in the air, we can write down the frequencies for the various modes of oscillation from the relation $f = v/\lambda$. From Fig. 5 we see that for an open pipe $\lambda = 2l/n$, where n is an integer. Thus, the resonance frequencies of an *open* organ pipe can be written as

$$f = nv/2l. \qquad (n = 1, 2, 3, \cdots) \qquad (14)$$

If we denote the fundamental frequency of the open pipe by f_o, we may rewrite (14) in the form

$$f = nf_o, \quad \text{where} \quad f_o = v/2l.$$

We note (a) that the normal frequencies of an open organ pipe are harmonics and (b) that *all harmonics are present*, since n takes on all integral values.

The case of a *closed* organ pipe is somewhat different. From Fig. 5 we see that $\lambda = 4l/n'$, where n' can assume only *odd-integral* values. Hence the resonance frequencies are given by the expression

$$f = n'v/4l. \qquad (n' = 1, 3, 5, \cdots) \qquad (15)$$

If we denote the fundamental frequency of the closed pipe by f_c we may write (15) in the form

$$f = n'f_c, \quad \text{where} \quad f_c = v/4l.$$

We note (a) that the normal frequencies of a closed pipe are harmonics but (b) that *only odd harmonics are produced*.

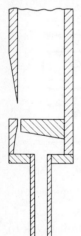

Comparison of the expression for the fundamental frequency f_c of a closed pipe with the expression for the fundamental frequency f_o of an open pipe of the same length reveals that $f_o = 2f_c$. Thus, with a pipe of a given length one gets the lower frequency when it is closed.

The formulas above are not completely accurate since the motion of the air at the open end is not strictly one-dimensional, as we have assumed. Small 'end corrections' need to be applied; these we shall ignore.

In an organ pipe, vibration of the air column results from oscillations produced in an air jet that is blown upward through a narrow slot against a knife-edge or 'lip' forming a part of the pipe wall as shown in Fig. 6. The jet of air from the slot is deflected alternately into and out of the pipe at the knife-edge. This alternation occurs at the resonance frequency of the pipe, being controlled by air alternately entering and leaving the pipe as the air in the pipe near this end moves alternately up and down at resonance frequency. The air pressure and the distance from the slot to the knife-edge should be properly adjusted in order to produce the funda-

Fig. 6.
Lower end of an organ pipe.

mental; usually the fundamental and many of the overtones are excited simultaneously. If the pressure of the air supplied to the lower part of the tube is too great, the fundamental may not be appreciably excited although many overtones will be produced. It should be noted that the lower end of an organ pipe is a region of maximum vibration, and therefore this end of the pipe should be regarded as *open*.

The knife-edge or lip of a *flue* organ pipe, like that shown in Fig. 6, is a rigid solid which does not vibrate. Certain other wind instruments contain a thin metal or wooden plate called a *reed*. The reed itself is caused to vibrate by the air stream. The reed may be mounted so that it vibrates freely or in such a way that it alternately opens and closes an air passage. The reed produces vibrations in the air column. Metal reeds are used in reed organ pipes and harmonicas; wooden reeds are employed in clarinets, oboes, and bassoons. The reed principle is also used in brass wind instruments; in this case the lips of the player act as double reeds. Sounds produced by reeds are modified by the pipe or horn resonator used; in the clarinet and similar instruments the effective length of the pipe is varied by opening and closing small openings in the side.

The human voice organ may be regarded as a double-reed pipe instrument. The double reed is formed by the vocal cords; the oral and nasal cavities act as resonators.

Measurement of the resonance frequency of air columns furnishes a means of determining the speed of sound in a gas, since the length of column and the frequency determine this speed. If a tuning fork is held near the open end of a tube closed at the other end by a movable rigid disk, it is easy to determine the lengths of tube for which a standing wave pattern is set up, since the observer hears a much louder sound at these lengths. The tube resonates with the tuning fork and increases the sound transmission to the atmosphere. The frequency of oscillation of the tuning fork can be accurately measured by means of a stroboscope. When a tuning fork is mounted on a sound box (Fig. 2), the 'acoustic amplification' is most effective if the length of the air column in the sound box is chosen so that one of its natural modes of oscillation has the frequency of the tuning fork.

Example. *To determine the speed of sound in hydrogen gas at 20° C, a long glass tube is filled with hydrogen at this temperature. One end of the tube is rigidly closed; the other end is closed by a stiff metal diaphragm driven by a loudspeaker. A small amount of light powder has been dusted into the tube. When a standing wave is set up in the tube, the powder is swept away from the displacement (velocity) antinodes by the motion of the gas, and collects sharply at the nodes, where there is no motion. Hence the distance between the nodes can be measured. Such a tube is called a Kundt's tube. One of the higher normal modes of oscillation gives nodes 10.5 cm apart when the frequency is 6200 cycles/sec. What value does this give for the sound speed?*

Since the wavelength is *twice* the distance between nodes in a standing wave, the wavelength is $\lambda = 2 \times 10.5$ cm $= 21.0$ cm $= 0.210$ m.   Hence

$$v = \lambda f = 0.210 \text{ m} \times 6200/\text{sec} = 1300 \text{ m/sec}.$$

4. PSYCHOLOGICAL EFFECTS OF SOUND WAVES

Now LET us turn to the question of the relationship between the psychological effects of sound waves and the physical properties of the sound waves.   In terms of effects on the listener, we usually characterize sound by properties called *loudness*, *pitch*, and *quality*.

The meaning of the term *loudness* is well known from common usage. The loudness of a sound is intimately connected with the *intensity* of the sound wave.   Like all traveling waves, a sound wave involves the transmission of energy or power in the direction of propagation.   The intensity is defined in terms of this power:

> The **intensity** of a sound wave is the energy transferred per unit time through unit area normal to the direction of propagation. It is commonly measured in watts/m².

For a pure tone of given frequency there is a one-to-one correspondence between *loudness* and *intensity*, but in general the relationship between the loudness of a sound and its intensity is not simple.   Loudness cannot be measured in physical terms, since it depends on the ear and judgment of the individual observer.   It is relatively easy for two or more observers to agree that two sounds are equally loud, but different observers will not agree that one sound is 'twice as loud' as another. The difficulties of comparing the loudness of two sounds is greatest if the two sounds differ greatly in frequency.

The intensities of sounds that can be heard by the ear vary over an enormous range.   A sound that is so loud that it is almost painful may have an intensity as much as 10^{12} times that of a sound that is barely audible.   In view of this wide range of intensities, it is convenient to use a logarithmic scale in defining an *intensity level* for use in comparison of sound intensities:

> The **difference in intensity level** of two sound waves, of intensities I and I_0, is measured in a unit called the decibel* (db), and is defined as $10 \log_{10}(I/I_0)$ db.

This logarithmic type of intensity-level scale corresponds roughly with the behavior of the ear.   For example, the level of a sound of any intensity must be raised by about 3 db (a *factor* of 2 in intensity) before the ear perceives a very noticeable change in loudness.

If we take the intensity of the minimum detectable sound as I_0, the

---

* The bel, the unit used to specify $\log_{10}(I/I_0)$, was named in honor of Alexander Graham Bell (1847–1922), the inventor of the telephone.   The smaller unit, the decibel, is more convenient for most work.

intensity I of a sound at the point of painfulness will be approximately $10^{12} I_0$, as mentioned above. Thus, the intensity level of this almost painful sound would be $10 \log_{10}(10^{12} I_0/I_0)$ db $= 120$ db above the threshold of audibility.

In certain types of acoustical-engineering work, it is desirable to select some standard reference intensity I_0 as the threshold of audibility and to specify the intensity level of any other sound of intensity I in terms of this reference level. By international agreement an intensity of 10^{-12} watt/m² has been selected as a *standard threshold of audibility* and is used as the value of I_0. If the hearing threshold is taken as 10^{-12} watt/m², it is noted that the pain threshold, 120 db higher, corresponds to power transmission of 1 watt/m². This convention is used in Table IV, which is based on a survey made by the New York City Noise Abatement Commission.

TABLE IV

TYPICAL VALUES OF INTENSITY LEVEL ABOVE THRESHOLD

Sound	Intensity level
Painful	120 db
Riveting	95
Elevated train	90
Busy street traffic	70
Conversation in home . . .	65
'Quiet' radio in home . . .	40
Whisper	20
Rustle of leaves	10
Hearing threshold	0

Now let us consider the characteristic of sound known as *pitch*. Pitch is designated by musicians by letters corresponding to the keys on the piano. Except for extremely loud sounds, there is a one-to-one correspondence between pitch and frequency, the higher the pitch, the higher the frequency. In going *up* the scale one octave, we double the frequency; thus, the A notes on the piano have the following frequencies: 27.5, 55, 110, 220, 440, 880, 1760, and 3520 cycles/sec. Audible sounds range in frequency from about 20 cycles/sec for sounds of the very lowest pitch to about 20,000 cycles/sec for sounds of highest pitch; the exact limits of the audible range vary from individual to individual. The most important frequency range for speech lies between 100 and 1000 cycles/sec; a telephone transmission system can operate satisfactorily even if it transmits only the frequencies in this range.

Now let us consider the third sound characteristic: *quality*. The meaning of the term *quality* or *timbre* can be illustrated by sounding middle C successively on a flute, on a pipe organ, and on a violin. If these instruments are properly tuned, the fundamental frequencies of the three notes is the same, but we should have little difficulty in distinguishing between the sounds produced by the three instruments. The property of the three sounds which makes it possible for us to tell them apart is called *quality*. *The quality of a musical sound is determined by the relative intensities of the overtones present.* Thus, although the fundamental frequency of the note sounded by the three instruments mentioned above is the same, the note from each instrument has a different and distinctive pattern of overtone intensities which gives the note its distinctive *quality*.   Hence, we may define sound quality as the psychological effect produced by the relative intensities of the overtones present in a sound.

In a good tuning fork only one mode of oscillation is excited, and hence the fork vibrates at only one frequency.   The sound waves that are set up are therefore simple harmonic waves, that is, sinusoidal waves of a single frequency.   A simple tone like that from a tuning fork is not particularly interesting.   An interesting musical tone usually contains many overtones and these overtones are largely harmonics.

Recalling our discussion of the superposition principle in Chap. 18, we see that quality is related to the *wave-shape* of the sound waves produced by a given source.   If the source is a tuning fork, the waves will be sinusoidal waves of a single frequency; but if the source is vibrating simultaneously in several modes of different frequency, the wave produced will consist of the superposition of several sinusoidal waves with different frequencies and different amplitudes, and the resultant waveform will be complex.   Thus, we see that our earlier statement that the quality of a sound depends on the number, frequencies, and relative intensities of the overtones is equivalent to the statement that *sound quality is determined by waveform*.   The radically different characteristic waveforms of the different vowel sounds can be readily demonstrated on an oscilloscope connected to a microphone.

A *noise*, in contrast to a musical sound, has a waveform with no semblance of regularity of any kind; the waveform consists of a series of random displacements.

5. RESPONSE OF THE EAR TO SOUND WAVES*

THE EAR consists of three major portions called the outer ear, the middle ear, and the inner ear (Fig. 7).   Sound waves enter the outer ear, travel down the ear canal, and strike a thin membrane called the eardrum, which forms the boundary between the outer ear and an airspace called the middle ear.   In the middle ear, a mechanism consisting of three small bones called the hammer, the anvil, and the stirrup transmit vibrations from the eardrum to the oval window.   The oval window is a membrane that transmits vibrations to the inner ear, which is filled with a liquid.   In the cochlear spiral, which is a tube about 3.5 cm long and 1 or 2 mm in diameter, are the terminals of the auditory nerve.   There are approximately 30,000 nerve terminals in the cochlea, and different frequencies have their greatest effects on nerve terminals located at different

---

* Much of the material in this section is taken from an excellent review article by Harvey Fletcher of the Bell Telephone Laboratories, which appeared in the REVIEWS OF MODERN PHYSICS for January, 1940.   An interesting discussion of the physics of the human ear is given in an article by Francis M. Wiener in PHYSICS TODAY for December, 1949.

positions along the spiral. Sound signals are 'received' by these terminals, and are transmitted electrochemically to the brain. The vestibular apparatus shown in Fig. 7 is not associated with hearing. It consists of three fluid-filled semicircular canals in three orthogonal planes, and controls the sense of balance or equilibrium.

In earlier sections we have given approximate values for the limits of the intensities and frequencies of sound waves that can be heard by the 'normal' human ear. Actually, the ear is not a detector equally sensitive to all frequencies in the audio range. Extensive studies on the subject of the range of audibility have been made by the United States Public Health Service and the Bell Telephone Laboratories. Some of the

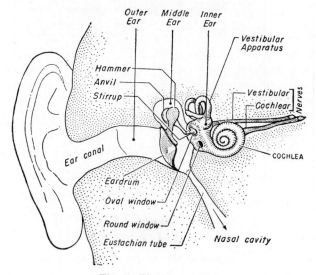

Fig. 7. The human ear.

results of these studies are summarized in the graph shown in Fig. 8. The curves show plots of sound intensity as a function of frequency. Three different ordinate scales are shown: the first gives absolute intensities in watts/m², the second gives the intensity level in db above the standard reference level of 10^{-12} watts/m², and the third gives the amplitude of pressure variation produced by the sound wave. The uppermost curve shows at various frequencies the intensity of the sound that is loud enough to be almost painful; sounds of this intensity can be felt as cutaneous sensations as well as heard. The height of this curve is almost constant at a level of 120 db above the standard reference level; this curve does not show extremely wide variations for various individuals. The lower curves represent the thresholds of hearing for various fractions of the group studied. Thus, 99 per cent of the individuals studied could hear sounds with lower intensities than those shown by the curve labeled

99 per cent, 95 per cent could hear sounds with intensities less than those given by the next lower curve labeled 95 per cent, and so on. The lowest curve shows that 1 per cent of the group could hear sounds of intensity nearly 10 db below the standard reference level in the region between 2000 and 4000 cycles/sec, the region in which the average ear is most sensitive. At the limits of the audible region, the curves all approach the threshold of feeling or pain.

It should be emphasized once more that the curves shown in Fig. 8 give the results of a study of a large *group* of individuals. For a single individual the curve showing the hearing threshold may not resemble any of the curves in the figure. It is possible for an individual to have acute

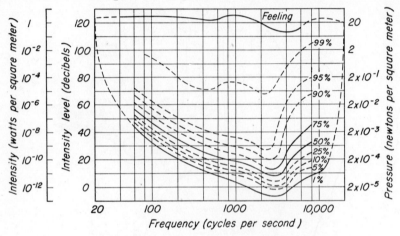

Fig. 8. Percentage of individuals who can hear sounds of various intensities.

hearing for some frequencies in the range of normal audibility and to be quite deaf to other frequencies.

The *extraordinary* sensitivity of the ear should be noted. At the point where the lowest curve of Fig. 8 crosses the 0-decibel line at $f = 1500$ cycles/sec, the pressure amplitude is 2×10^{-10} atm, and it can be calculated that the displacement amplitude in the sound wave is only 5×10^{-10} cm, which is about $\frac{1}{100}$ of the distance *between the molecules* in the eardrum. The corresponding maximum particle velocity in the sound wave is only 5×10^{-6} cm/sec, which is superposed on a random motion of the air molecules in their thermal motion that averages 50,000 cm/sec in speed.

6. INTERFERENCE OF SOUND WAVES

WE SHALL first discuss interference effects that occur when two sound waves of the same frequency arrive at the same point. The two waves can either come from the same source along different paths, or can come from different sources.

The first case involves the propagation of waves from a *single* source along *different paths* to a common point, where interference can be produced. This can be demonstrated by the arrangement shown in Fig. 9. A source of sound such as the diaphragm of a speaker is inserted at position S at the end of a tube. The diaphragm is set into oscillation by means of an audio-oscillator unit so that sound waves of a constant frequency are sent out in the air inside the tube. These waves travel to the opening O along two paths A and B. Path A has a constant length but the length of path B can be varied by means of the 'trombone' arrangement shown in the figure.

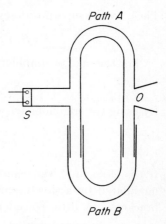

If the two paths are of *equal* length, the waves arrive exactly in phase at the opening O and sound will be heard by the auditor. If the length of path B is now varied slowly, the intensity of the sound wave decreases to a minimum when the difference between paths B and A is one-half wavelength. As the length of path B is increased still further, the intensity of the sound increases to a maximum when the difference between path A and B is equal to a whole wavelength. Further elongation of path B leads to successive minima and maxima of intensity of the sound heard. These observations can be

Fig. 9. Schematic diagram of apparatus for demonstrating interference between sound waves.

summarized in terms of l_A and l_B, the lengths of paths A and B, respectively, in the following way:

Intensity maxima occur when $l_B - l_A = n\,\lambda.$ $(n = 0, 1, 2, \cdots)$

Intensity minima occur when $l_B - l_A = (n + \tfrac{1}{2})\,\lambda.$ $(n = 0, 1, 2, \cdots)$

The observed effects are readily explained on the basis of the superposition principle. When the path difference is an integral number of wavelengths, the waves arriving at O are effectively *in phase* and reinforcement occurs. When the path lengths differ by an odd number of half wavelengths—that is, by $(n + \tfrac{1}{2})\,\lambda$—the waves arriving at O are 180° out of phase and destructive interference occurs. This apparatus furnishes a convenient method of measuring the wavelength of sound and hence of determining the speed of sound provided a sound source of known frequency is employed.

If two wave trains of slightly *different frequency* traverse a medium, a stationary interference pattern will not be formed. However, if their frequencies are nearly equal, two sets of waves can interfere in such a way as to produce a sound with pulsating intensity at a given point; these pulsations in intensity are known as *beats*. From the superposition principle it is easy to see the reason for the production of beats. Let the magnitude of the displacement produced at a given point by one wave be given by

$$S_1 = A \sin 2\pi f t \tag{16}$$

and the magnitude of the displacement produced by the second wave be

$$S_2 = A' \sin 2\pi f' t. \tag{17}$$

Then, by the superposition principle, the resultant displacement is

$$S = S_1 + S_2 = A \sin 2\pi f t + A' \sin 2\pi f' t.$$

For the sake of simplicity, let us consider a case in which $A = A'$; then

$$S = A \ (\sin 2\pi f t + \sin 2\pi f' t).$$

By using the trigonometric relation for the sum of two sines, we can write

$$S = \left[2A \ \cos 2\pi \left(\frac{f - f'}{2} \right) t \right] \sin 2\pi \left(\frac{f + f'}{2} \right) t. \tag{18}$$

If f is close to f', this can be regarded as a wave of frequency $\frac{1}{2}(f+f')$ modulated by a slowly varying amplitude given by the term in square brackets. A little consideration will reveal that the *magnitude* of this

|←——————————————— *1 second* ———————————————→|

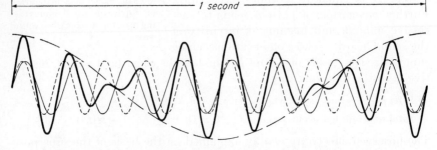

Fig. 10. Beats. The light solid curve is (16) with $f = 8$ cycles/sec; the light broken curve is (17) with $f' = 10$ cycles/sec; we have taken $A = A'$. The heavy curve is the sum (18); the long-dash curve is the term in (18) in square brackets.

amplitude attains a maximum value $f - f'$ times per second. Thus, an observer will hear $f - f'$ *beats* per second. Figure 10 illustrates the case of superposition of frequencies 8 and 10 cycles/sec, and the heavy curve representing the sum reaches maximum amplitude 2 times per second. If a tuning fork with a frequency of 256 cycles/sec and one with a frequency of 260 cycles/sec are sounded simultaneously, an observer will hear four beats each second of sound of frequency 258 cycles/sec. By counting beats it is possible to determine accurately the frequency difference between two sounds of nearly equal frequency.

When the difference between the frequencies of two sounds is more than 10 or 15 cycles/sec, the beats become difficult to distinguish. However, when the difference is great enough to correspond to an audible frequency, one may hear a *difference tone*. For example, if two intense sound waves having frequencies of 10,000 cycles/sec and 8500 cycles/sec reach the observer, he may hear a difference tone of 1500 cycles/sec. It is also sometimes possible to hear *summation tones;* for example, if waves of proper amplitude and with frequencies of 400 cycles/sec and 700 cycles/sec reach the ear, it is possible to hear a tone with a frequency of 1100 cycles/sec.

There are three other physical phenomena connected with the behavior of sound waves that should be mentioned, namely *reflection*, *refraction*, and *diffraction*. Since these phenomena are shared by light waves and are much more important in the case of light, we shall treat them in detail later in Part IV. Reflection gives rise to *echoes;* refraction changes the path of sound waves when they pass through a medium in which the wave speed varies with position and gives rise, for example, to anomalous sound transmission over lakes; diffraction gives sound waves the ability to 'bend around corners.'

Example. *In the natural diatonic musical scale, middle C and G have frequencies 256 and 384 cycles/sec, in the ratio 2 to 3. Pianos are tuned to a scale of equal temperament in which C and G are 256 and 386 cycles/sec. A piano-tuner systematically beats harmonics of notes against each other in order to adjust frequencies exactly. What should he hear when he beats middle G against low C?*

Low *C*, one octave below middle *C*, has half the frequency, or 128 cycles/sec. Its third harmonic has three times this frequency, or 384 cycles/sec. If the piano is properly tuned to equal temperament, this should give two beats per second against the middle *G* of 386 cycles/sec.

7. DOPPLER EFFECT

When a source of sound is moving with respect to an observer or an observer is moving with respect to the source, the pitch of the sound heard by the observer is different from the pitch heard when the source and observer are both at rest. Casual observation by a man on a station platform shows that the pitch of a locomotive whistle is *higher* when the locomotive is approaching the station than when the locomotive is standing still; the pitch is *lower* when the locomotive is moving away from the observer than when the locomotive is standing still. The effect is very noticeable when an express train is moving at high speed past the station platform of a local stop. Careful measurement shows that the pitch does not depend simply upon the relative velocity of source and observer but also depends to some extent on whether the source or the observer is moving with respect to the air or other medium in which the sound travels. The change in frequency caused by the motion of the source or the observer is called the *Doppler effect*.   We shall first consider the case of a moving source and a stationary observer, then the case of a stationary source and a moving observer, then the case in which both are moving.

Moving source and stationary observer.   When the source is moving, the motion causes a change in *wavelength* of the sound in air.   In order to

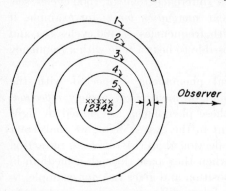

see how this change comes about, let v be the speed of sound in air, λ_s the wavelength in air when the source is at rest, and f_s the actual frequency of the source.   If the source is traveling toward the right at speed v_s, the successive condensations produced by the source will have positions like those shown in Fig. 11.   Each successive condensation is closer to the preceding condensation moving toward the right than it would be for a stationary source.   The wavelength λ of the sound

Fig. 11. Doppler effect: positions of successive condensations from a source moving toward the right with speed v_s.

propagated to the right is less than the normal wavelength λ_s by the distance the source moves in one period T_s, that is, $\lambda = \lambda_s - v_s T_s = \lambda_s - v_s \lambda_s / v$, since $T_s = \lambda_s / v$.   Thus

$$\lambda/\lambda_s = (v - v_s)/v. \tag{19}$$

Since the speed of transmission of sound through the stationary air is unaltered by the motion of the source, the waves moving to the right will have a frequency f given by

$$f = v/\lambda \quad \text{rather than by} \quad f_s = v/\lambda_s. \tag{20}$$

This frequency of the sound waves in the air is higher than the frequency of the source.   In order to find the frequency f of the sound waves in terms of the frequency of the source, we note that $f/f_s = \lambda_s/\lambda$ and hence that

$$f = f_s \, v/(v - v_s). \tag{21}$$

This is the frequency that would be heard by a stationary observer at the right of Fig. 11, whom the source is *approaching* with speed v_s.   In this case the frequency heard by the observer would be

$$f_o = f_s \, v/(v - v_s). \tag{22}$$

The wavelength of the sound proceeding to the left in Fig. 11 would be longer than the wavelength in the case of a stationary source.   Equation (22) still applies to this case if we consider that v_s, the speed of approach, has a negative value; that is, if we regard a speed of recession as a negative speed of approach.

Moving observer and stationary source. With a stationary source, the wavelength of the sound is the same in all directions, but the moving observer encounters more waves per unit time as he *approaches* the source. The effect observed is therefore a direct change in frequency. Using v_o to denote the *speed of approach* of the observer in moving toward the source, f the frequency of sound in the air, and f_o the frequency heard by the observer, we may write

$$f_o/f = (v+v_o)/v,$$

since the number of waves received per second is proportional to the speed of the waves relative to the observer. Hence, for an observer moving with respect to the source the observed frequency f_o is given by

$$f_o = f\,(v+v_o)/v, \tag{23}$$

where v_o is the speed of approach of the observer. If the source is stationary, $f = f_s$, the frequency of the source, and

$$f_o = f_s\,(v+v_o)/v. \tag{24}$$

If the observer is moving away from the source, v_o assumes a negative value, and the frequency f_o is less than it would be if source and observer were both stationary.

Moving source and moving observer. With the source and observer both in motion, we can combine the results obtained in equations (21) and (23). In (23) we must substitute for f, not the frequency of the source, but the frequency in the air given by (21). This substitution gives the following expression for the frequency of the sound heard by the observer:

$$f_o = f_s\,(v+v_o)/(v-v_s). \tag{25}$$

In this equation, v_o and v_s are positive when they represent speeds of approach, negative when they represent speeds of recession.

We have derived (25) for the case in which source and observer are moving along the line connecting them. In the more general case it can be shown that (25) is valid when v_s is the *component* of source velocity directed *toward* the observer, and v_o is the *component* of observer velocity directed *toward* the source.

Example. *Sound of frequency 1000 cycles/sec from a stationary source is reflected from an object approaching the source at 31 m/sec, back to a stationary observer located at the source, on a day when the air is at 0° C. Determine the frequency heard by the observer. (While this situation may be of only academic interest in the case of sound, the corresponding phenomenon for radio waves is the basis of the modern 'radar' method of measuring speeds of moving automobiles and planes, as we shall discuss on p. 434.)*

The moving reflector receives the frequency $f_R = f_S (v+v_R)/v$ given by (24) with the reflector velocity v_R substituted for v_o. This is the frequency reflected by the reflector, which now acts as a moving source, so the observer receives a frequency given by (22) as

$$f_o = f_R v/(v-v_R) = f_S (v+v_R)/(v-v_R). \tag{26}$$

The velocity of the moving reflector enters *twice* into the Doppler-frequency formula. The reflector acts like a moving observer in receiving the sound and then like a moving source in re-emitting it.

Substituting $f_S = 1000/\text{sec}$, $v = 331$ m/sec, $v_R = 31$ m/sec in (26), we find

$$f_o = 1000 \text{ sec}^{-1} (362/300) = 1210 \text{ cycles/sec}$$

for the frequency heard by the observer.

8. SOUND ABSORPTION; ARCHITECTURE ACOUSTICS

STUDY OF the absorption of sound waves by the walls, furniture, and persons in a room, begun by Sabine at Harvard University in 1895, have proved to be of extreme value to the architect in providing optimum acoustical properties in rooms of various kinds. These 'optimum' properties vary; they are different for classrooms, concert halls, reading rooms, broadcast studios, and auditoriums. However, by suitable choice of wall shapes and wall materials, the architect can meet specific acoustic requirements.

Waves traveling in certain types of media are damped out or absorbed as a result of 'frictional' effects of various kinds. For sound waves in air these frictional losses are very small, but absorption is very great in certain other media such as felt and some types of fiberboard. The chief quantity of practical interest in connection with these absorbing materials is not the fraction of energy lost per unit path length within the material but the effectiveness of the material in *not* reflecting sound waves that are incident at the surface of the material.

To illustrate this point, let us consider a unidirectional sound wave striking a wall. Of the energy reaching the wall, part will be reflected, part will be transmitted through the wall, and part will be absorbed in the wall material. The acoustical engineer is usually concerned only with the energy *reflected* and regards all energy not reflected as being absorbed; he thus lumps energy transmitted through the wall and energy actually 'absorbed' in the wall material as 'absorbed,' since it is removed from the room in which he makes his measurements. If the intensity of the sound wave striking the wall is I, an '*absorption*' *coefficient* α for the wall material is defined in such a way that αI is 'absorbed' and the intensity of the reflected wave is $(1-\alpha) I$. The factor α is a number ranging from zero for a hypothetical perfectly reflecting surface to unity for an open window, which from the point of view of the acoustical engineer is a perfect 'absorber.'

It is difficult to determine the absorption coefficient by the method suggested by its definition, since the sound will suffer multiple reflections from the walls of the room in which the measurement is made. Absorption coefficients for various materials are usually determined in terms of the acoustical properties of a test room in which the material in question serves as wall and floor covering, by measurement of rate of decay of sound level after a source is turned off.

By experiment Sabine discovered that when a source begins to send out sound waves at a constant rate into a large room the sound level in the room rises to a certain constant intensity I_0. Then, when the source is turned off (at $t=0$), the intensity of the sound in the room decreases or 'decays' exponentially in a manner described by the relation

$$I = I_0 e^{-Bt}, \tag{27}$$

where B is a constant depending on the characteristics of the room and its wall materials. By recording I as a function of time t, the value of B can be determined.

In order to determine the absorption coefficient of the wall and floor material from the measured value of the decay constant B, we may reason as follows: The initial intensity I_0 of sound at the instant the source is cut off is decreased by a factor of $(1-\alpha)$ for one reflection, to the value $(1-\alpha) I_0$. After two reflections the intensity is $(1-\alpha)^2 I_0$, and so on. If there are n reflections per unit time, the intensity I at the end of time t after the source is shut off is given by

$$I = (1-\alpha)^{nt} I_0. \tag{28}$$

Equating the expressions for I given in (27) and (28), we obtain

$$(1-\alpha)^{nt} I_0 = I_0 e^{-Bt} \quad \text{or} \quad (1-\alpha)^{nt} = e^{-Bt}.$$

Taking the natural logarithm of both sides of this equation, we obtain

$$nt \log_e(1-\alpha) = -Bt \quad \text{or} \quad n \log_e(1-\alpha) = -B, \tag{29}$$

which would give us a value of α in terms of the measured value of B if we knew the value of n, the number of reflections per unit time. After considering rooms of different sizes and shapes, Sabine concluded that one could assume that the sound waves on the average travel a distance $4V/A$ between successive reflections, where V is the volume of the room and A the total wall area of the room. On this assumption, the number n of reflections per unit time is given by $n = vA/4V$, where v is the speed of sound in air. By making measurements of decay constant in rooms with various types of walls, Sabine and later workers have determined the typical absorption coefficients listed in Table V for various materials. Absorption coefficients vary somewhat with sound frequency. The method just described is capable of measuring absorption coefficients as a function of frequency.

One of the major problems facing the acoustical engineer and architect is the design of rooms and auditoriums having proper acoustical properties. Sabine introduced a quantity, the time of reverberation T, in terms of which the acoustical properties of a room are judged.

> The **time of reverberation** is defined as the time for a sound to decrease to one-millionth of its steady-state intensity I_0 after the source is stopped, that is, to drop by 60 db.

As a result of numerous experimental studies, Sabine was able to select optimum values for the reverberation in rooms of different sizes. For speech, the optimum reverberation times vary from about 0.8 sec in a room with a volume of 1000 ft³ to about 2.0 sec in a room with a volume of 1,000,000 ft³. For music, optimum reverberation times are somewhat greater than for speech. A broadcasting studio should be very 'dead'; that is, the reverberation time should be as short as possible. From a knowledge of absorption coefficients, one can do a great deal to control

TABLE V

ABSORPTION COEFFICIENTS FOR VARIOUS BUILDING MATERIALS
(For sound of frequency 512 cycles/sec)

Cork tile.	0.08	Wood flooring.	0.03
Hair felt.	0.42	Wood paneling.	0.06
Heavy draperies.	0.50	Plaster.	0.03
Brick wall.	0.02	Fiberglas board 1 inch thick.	0.65
Clay tile.	0.03	Figerglas board 2 inches thick.	0.99
Concrete.	0.02	Acoustex wall material 1 inch thick	0.81
Glass.	0.03	Acoustic Celotex 1 inch thick.	0.58

reverberation times by using appropriate wall materials. As a result of the studies of Sabine and others, it is now possible to design auditoriums scientifically, whereas previously the design was largely a hit-or-miss proposition to the architect, and if the acoustical properties of the completed auditorium were bad, little could be done except to add wall hangings of various types.

Example. *Consider an auditorium* $50 \times 50 \times 30$ *ft, in which it is desired to have a reverberation time of* 1.5 *sec. Assuming the same absorption factor for all surfaces, what should this factor be?*

The volume V is 75,000 ft³, while the surface area A of the four walls, floor, and ceiling is 11,000 ft². Sabine's formula gives the number of reflections per second as

$$n = vA/4V = (1100 \text{ ft/sec})(11,000 \text{ ft}^2)/4(75,000 \text{ ft}^3) = 40/\text{sec},$$

in round numbers.

If the intensity is to fall to one-millionth in a reverberation time of 1.5 sec, we must have, according to (27)

$$e^{-Bt} = e^{-1.5B \text{ sec}} = 10^{-6}.$$

Take logarithms to the base e:

$$-1.5B \sec = -6 \log_e 10 = -6 \ (2.30),$$

from which $-B = -9.20/\sec.$

We then find, from (29),

$$\log_e(1-\alpha) = -B/n = -0.23,$$
$$1-\alpha = e^{-0.23} = 0.79,$$
$$\alpha = 0.21,$$

as the desired effective average absorption coefficient.

PROBLEMS

1. A wire 5 ft long under 25 lb tension has a fundamental frequency of 512 cycles/sec when transverse oscillations are excited. What is the mass of the wire?   Ans: 4.77×10^{-6} slug.

2. What is the frequency of the fundamental transverse mode of oscillation of a steel wire of mass 25 g and length 2.0 m when the tension in the wire is 5 nt? What are the frequencies of the first three overtones?

3. A copper wire 0.1 cm in diameter is 4.0 m in length. Find the speeds of transverse and longitudinal waves in this wire when a tensile force of 12 nt is applied to each end. Find the frequency of the fundamental transverse and longitudinal modes of oscillation of this wire. ($E_Y = 11 \times 10^{10}$ nt/m² and $\rho = 8900$ kg/m³ for Cu.) Ans: 41.4 m/sec, 3520 m/sec; 5.18 cycles/sec, 440 cycles/sec.

4. Solve Prob. 3 for a steel wire with the same dimensions and tension as the copper wire. ($E_Y = 20 \times 10^{10}$ nt/m² and $\rho = 7800$ kg/m³ for steel.)

5. String B has twice the length, twice the diameter, twice the tension, and twice the density (g/cm³) of string A. What overtone of B agrees in frequency with the fundamental of A?   Ans: third.

6. A certain string is tuned to give middle C—256 cycles/sec, when under a 50-lb tension. How much should the tension be increased in order to produce high C—512 cycles/sec?

7. An observer sees the flash of a gun and hears the report 4.5 sec later. What is the distance between the observer and the gun if the temperature is 20° C?   Ans: 5080 ft.

8. A man sees the 'steam' from a locomotive whistle 2 sec before he hears the sound. What is the distance from the man to the locomotive if the temperature is 20° C?

9. An observer sees the flash of an explosion on the opposite shore of a lake. If the lake is exactly 1 mi wide, how long will it be before he hears the sound reaching him through the air? If the observer uses a hydrophone to receive the sound transmitted through the water, how long after the explosion does he receive the sound? Air and water are at 15° C.   Ans: 4.73 sec; 1.12 sec.

10. If a charge of dynamite is set off on a railroad track, how long does it take the sound to travel through the steel rails to an observer exactly 5 mi away? How long after receiving the sound signal transmitted by the rails will the observer receive the sound signal transmitted through the air? Use (3) to compute the speed in the rails. Take air temperature as 20° C.

11. A sound of 612 vibrations/sec takes 0.744 sec to travel vertically from a point 200 m under water to a point 200 m in the air above the surface of the water. The speed in air is 330 m/sec. From these data alone calculate (a) the wavelength of this sound in air, (b) the wavelength of this sound in water.

Ans: (a) 0.539 m; (b) 2.37 m.

12. An observer drops a stone down a well, and notes with a stopwatch that 16 sec elapse from the time he lets the stone fall until he *hears the sound* of its striking at the bottom. How deep is the well if the temperature of the air in it is 10° C?

13. A dynamite blast is set off on the surface of a lake. A swimmer near the shore receives two shock waves—one through the water and one through the air at 68° F. Four seconds elapse between the times of arrival of the two waves. How far was the swimmer from the explosion? Ans: 5900 ft.

14. A ship is in a dense fog in a Norwegian fiord, which is one mile wide. In order to find his location in the channel, the captain fires a gun and hears the first echo after 3 sec. (a) How far is the ship from the center of the fiord? (b) How long after the gun was fired did the second echo arrive? Use 1050 ft/sec as the speed of the sound.

15. Calculate the speed of sound in water ($E_B = 2.1 \times 10^9$ nt/m²) and compare your result with that given in Table II. Ans: 1450 m/sec.

16. Compare the wavelength of sound waves of frequency 512 cycles/sec when the waves are traveling in water with the wavelength of the same sound in air.

17. The observed value of γ for oxygen is 1.40. Using this value, find the speed of sound in oxygen at 0° C. Ans: 315 m/sec.

18. The observed value of γ for helium is 1.67. Using this value, find the speed of sound in helium at 0° C.

19. Newton's formula for speed of sound was $v = \sqrt{P/\rho}$, derived on the erroneous assumption that the process of transmission of sound was isothermal. Show that this is the formula that would be obtained from (7) on the isothermal assumption.

20. What are the wavelengths in air, hydrogen, and carbon dioxide at 20° C of sounds of frequencies 20,000, 2000, 200, and 20 vibrations/sec?

21. On a day when the speed of sound in air is 1080 ft/sec, what are the frequencies of the fundamental and first three overtones of an organ pipe 16 ft long when the tube is operated as a *closed* pipe? Ans: 16.9, 50.6, 84.4, 118/sec.

22. Solve Prob. 21 for the case where the pipe is used as an *open* pipe.

23. What should be the length of a closed organ pipe if the fundamental frequency is to be 256 cycles/sec? What should be the length of an open organ pipe to give this fundamental frequency? Assume $v = 1080$ ft/sec.

Ans: 1.05 ft; 2.11 ft.

24. At a time when the speed of sound is 1080 ft/sec, the fundamental frequency of a closed organ pipe is 256 cycles/sec. What is the fundamental frequency of this pipe on a day when the speed of sound is 1112 ft/sec?

25. If a piano is tuned to match an organ on a warm summer afternoon, in which direction will it be out of tune in the cool of the evening?

26. What is the length of air column in a long, narrow sound box, closed at one end, whose fundamental frequency is resonant with a 256 cycle/sec tuning fork when the temperature is 20° C?

27. An open organ pipe at the front of a church is tuned to 264 cycles/sec at 20° C, and an open organ pipe in the echo organ at the rear is tuned to 528 cycles/

sec at 20° C.   On Sunday the rear of the church is at 25° C, the front at 20° C. How many beats occur between the fundamental of one pipe and the first over-tone of the other when they are sounded together?   Ans: 4.8/sec.

28. A certain note on a piano gives 4 beats per sec when sounded with a 256 cycle tuning fork and 8 beats per sec when sounded with a 260 cycle tuning fork.   What is the frequency of the note?

29. Pure tones of 1000, 1100, 1200, and 1300 cycles/sec are sounded together. To the auditor, a much lower-pitched note seems to predominate.   Explain this phenomenon and determine the frequency of the note.

30. A closed organ pipe has a fundamental frequency of 256 cycles/sec under normal conditions.   A practical joker fills the pipe with helium.   What is the fundamental frequency of the helium-filled pipe?

31. In the arrangement shown in Fig. 9, the vibrating diaphragm at S has a frequency of 1324 cycles/sec.   If the length of path A is fixed at 50 cm, for what lengths of path B will intensity maxima be observed?   For what lengths of path B will intensity minima be observed?   (Take 331 m/sec as the speed of sound in air.)   Ans: 50, 75, 100, 125, $\cdots$ cm; 62.5, 87.5, 112.5, $\cdots$ cm

32. If the arrangement in Fig. 9 were set in such a way that the difference in length of paths A and B is 40 cm, what are the five lowest frequencies of S capable of giving intensity maxima?

33. In arrangement similar to that in Fig. 9, paths A and B are each 2 m in length.   If path A is filled with air at 0° C and path B is filled with hydrogen at 0° C, what is the lowest frequency that will produce an intensity maximum?
                                                        Ans: 225 cycles/sec.

34. Referring to Prob. 33, find the next three higher frequencies that will produce intensity maxima.   Work Prob. 33 for a case in which path B is filled with chlorine gas.

35. The fundamental frequency of a certain locomotive whistle is 400 cycles/sec and the speed of the locomotive is 100 ft/sec.   On a day when the speed of sound in air is 1100 ft/sec, what will be the fundamental frequencies of the sounds heard by an observer on a station platform as the locomotive passes the station with its whistle blowing?   Ans: approach: 440 cycles/sec; at station: 400 cycles/sec; recession: 367 cycles/sec.

36. What frequencies would be heard by the observer in Prob. 35 if the speed of the locomotive were 120 mi/hr?

37. If the fundamental frequency of a bell at a railroad crossing is 400 cycles/sec, what frequencies will the engineer of a locomotive hear as the locomotive passes the crossing at 100 ft/sec if the speed of sound is 1100 ft/sec?   Ans: approach: 436 cycles/sec; at crossing: 400 cycles/sec; recession: 363 cycles/sec.

38. What sound frequencies would the engineer in Prob. 37 hear if the speed of his locomotive were 120 mi/hr.

39. Locomotive A is moving southward at a speed of 100 ft/sec while locomotive B is moving northward at a speed of 100 ft/sec.   If the whistle on locomotive A has a fundamental frequency of 256 cycles/sec, what will be the frequencies of the sounds heard by the engineer on locomotive B as the two locomotives pass each other?   Take the speed of sound as 1100 ft/sec.
Ans: approach: 307 cycles/sec; adjacent: 256 cycles/sec; recession: 213 cycles/sec.

40. Solve Prob. 39 for a case in which the speed of locomotive A is 120 ft/sec and the speed of locomotive B is 80 ft/sec; also for the case in which the speed of A is 80 ft/sec and that of B is 120 ft/sec.

41. Discuss the effects of wind velocity on the Doppler effect.

42. What is the apparent pitch of a whistle of 700 vibrations/sec (a) if source and observer are approaching each other, each moving with ⅛ the speed of sound? (b) if they are mutually receding, each at this same speed?

43. A man walks at 3 m/sec on a still day along the line between two fire stations. The fire whistles on the two stations sound simultaneously at a frequency of 500 vibrations/sec. Find the apparent frequency of each whistle and the number of beats per second. Take $v = 330$ m/sec. Ans: 495, 505, 9.06/sec.

44. A man approaching a stationary wall at speed v_M blows a whistle of frequency f_S. Find the frequency of the echo heard by the man.

45. By expanding the logarithm in (29) as a power series, show that for an absorption coefficient $\alpha \ll 1$, $B = n\alpha = vA\alpha/4V$ on Sabine's assumption. Also show that the reverberation time $T = 55.3 \ V/\alpha vA$, for small α.

46. Compute the reverberation time of a room $30 \times 30 \times 15$ ft if all surfaces are covered with acoustic material or rugs of $\alpha = 0.60$.

47. Show how formula (27) can be plotted on semilog paper in such a way that the slope of the curve gives the value of B. Make such a plot for the case $B = 9$/sec.

Part IV
LIGHT

CHAPTER 20

THE NATURE OF LIGHT AND ITS PROPAGATION

As WE HAVE NOTED in our study of heat, all objects are continually emitting and absorbing radiant energy. The thermal radiation from an object only slightly hotter than the human body is invisible but can be detected by the cutaneous senses. However, if the temperature of an object is above about 500° C, some of the emitted radiation is *visible*.

> **Light** is radiant energy that is capable of affecting the retina of the human eye.

Thermal excitation (as in the candle and the incandescent lamp) is not the only cause of light emission; other familiar sources involve electrical excitation (the neon sign), fluorescence (the fluorescent lamp), or chemiluminescence (the fire-fly), and, most recently, electroluminescence.

Objects that emit light are called *luminous* and are visible as a result of the emitted light. Nonluminous objects become visible only when they are *illuminated;* that is, when the light from a luminous object strikes them. In general, when light is incident on a material, some is *reflected*, some is *absorbed*, and some is *transmitted;* the ratios may vary with the *color* of the incident light. These effects determine the appearance of the material. Objects that transmit no light are said to be *opaque*. Materials like clear glass or air, which transmit light so well that a luminous object may be clearly seen through them, are called *transparent;* other materials such as frosted glass or paraffin, which transmit light but are not clear, are called *translucent*.

Many of our most frequent experiences with light involve *reflection* and *refraction*. We see our images in mirrors and other polished surfaces by means of light that has undergone *regular reflection;* nonluminous objects may be seen by means of light that has been *diffusely reflected* from their surfaces. We are also familiar with the change in direction of propagation of light as it passes from one medium to another. This change in direction, called *refraction*, causes a stick partially submerged in water to appear bent. Refraction of white light is usually accompanied by a splitting of the white light into its component spectral colors, as in the case of the rainbow; this phenomenon is called *dispersion*.

Three other phenomena not so frequently encountered are *interference*, *diffraction*, and *polarization*. The colors observed in thin layers of oil on water are due to the *interference* of light waves that are reflected from the upper and lower surfaces of the oil film. A person looking through a narrow slit at some distant light source sees a series of light and dark lines parallel to the sides of the slit. These light and dark lines are caused by *diffraction*. Light that has passed through Polaroid films has become *polarized*. The effects of *polarization* are such that the light transmitted by one Polaroid film is absorbed completely when intercepted by a second Polaroid film oriented at right angles to the first.

These various properties of light will be considered in the chapters that follow.

1. NATURE OF LIGHT

Sir Isaac Newton and others attempted to explain optical phenomena in terms of a theory that pictured light as streams of minute *particles* emitted by luminous objects. This theory failed to account satisfactorily for phenomena involving interference, diffraction, and polarization, and predicted an incorrect value for the speed of light in media such as glass and water. By 1850, Newton's particle theory had been completely abandoned in favor of a theory that treats light as a *wave motion*. The theoretical work of Maxwell in 1864 led to the conclusion that the waves must be *electromagnetic* in nature, since his computations of the properties that electromagnetic waves should have exactly duplicated the known properties of light waves, including a prediction of their *speed* that agreed exactly with observation.

The wave theory, in which the waves are *electromagnetic* in nature, is adequate to account for all phenomena involved in light transmission, and there is no reason to doubt its 'correctness' for describing the behavior of light while it is being transmitted from a source to the body that ultimately absorbs it. However, as we shall see in Chap. 37, light is emitted or absorbed in packets, called *quanta*, each having a definite energy and momentum. Hence, during emission and absorption, light has some of the properties of particles. But quanta bear little resemblance to material particles—we can best think of them as 'electromagnetic' particles. These 'quantum' properties of light were not even suspected until the year 1900.

Careful observation of interference and diffraction phenomena enables us to measure the wavelength of light waves accurately. The *wavelengths* vary from about 400 mμ* in the violet to about 700 mμ in the red (see Fig. 7, p. 430). To visualize these values, note that 1000 m$\mu = \frac{1}{1000}$ mm and

* 1 micron (μ) $= 10^{-6}$ meter; 1 millimicron (mμ) $= 10^{-9}$ meter $= 10^{-6}$ mm.

that visible light has a wavelength of about half this value, or about $\frac{1}{2000}$ mm. Study of polarization phenomena indicates that the waves are *transverse*. Observations of the effects of electric and magnetic fields on light sources and on the transmission of light through media confirm the conclusion that light waves are electromagnetic waves similar to radio waves except for differences in wavelength and frequency.

A luminous source may emit radiation of wavelengths both longer and shorter than those of visible radiation. These types of radiation are known as *infrared* and *ultraviolet*, respectively. Infrared, visible, and ultraviolet radiations are all portions of the *electromagnetic spectrum*, which includes radiation of all wavelengths from extremely long radio waves to extremely short X rays and the gamma rays from radioactive materials. The basic nature of all electromagnetic radiation is the same.

2. RECTILINEAR PROPAGATION

THAT LIGHT travels in straight lines in a uniform medium is a fact that is familiar to all of us. Since light consists of waves, we might expect light waves to bend around obstacles as sound waves do. Actually, light waves do bend around obstacles (the phenomenon of *diffraction*, Chap. 25), but the wavelength of light is so short compared to that of sound that by comparison the bending of light is extremely slight. For most practical purposes such as surveying and navigation, the assumption of rectilinear propagation is a sufficiently close approximation to permit highly accurate measurements of position. The direction or path of propagation of light may be represented by a straight line called a *ray*.

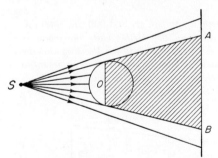 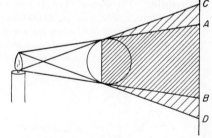

Fig. 1. Shadow cast by an opaque object illuminated by a point source of light.

Fig. 2. Shadow cast by an opaque object illuminated by an extended source.

One of the simplest consequences of the straight-line propagation of light is the production of shadows. Thus, the point source of light S in Fig. 1 will illuminate all parts of the screen above A and below B, but all points between A and B will be in darkness, since light from the source is stopped by the opaque body O. When a point source is involved, the boundary of the shadow is sharply defined and has the shape of the opaque body as seen from the source.

Most actual sources are too large to be approximated by points, so that the boundaries of shadows are not sharply defined. In Fig. 2 the parts of the screen between A and B are in complete shadow; the regions between C and A and between B and D are in partial shadow; the portions of the screen beyond C and D are fully illuminated. In a shadow of this type, the regions of complete and partial shadow are called the *umbra* and *penumbra*, respectively.

Rectilinear propagation is used directly in the so-called pinhole camera. This arrangement is illustrated in Fig. 3. An opaque screen

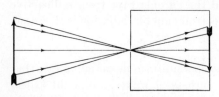

Fig. 3. The pinhole camera.

with a small hole in it is placed between a luminous or strongly illuminated object and a sheet of film. From every point on the object a ray of light passes through the small hole in the screen and falls on the film; rays from all points on the *object* pass through the hole and form an inverted *image* on the film in the manner indicated in the figure. If the opening is extremely small compared with the distance to the film, the image is sharp and well-defined but is rather dim. A pinhole camera can actually be used in photographic work if long exposure times are possible or if the object being photographed is very bright. One of the best pictures of the first atomic-bomb explosion was made with a pinhole camera of the type just described.

Example. *The diameters of the sun, earth, and moon are 864,000 mi, 8000 mi, and 2160 mi. The sun is 92,000,000 mi from the earth, while the moon is 236,000 mi. Show that when the earth is on the line between the sun and the moon, the diameter of the umbra of the earth's shadow is more than sufficient to completely envelop the moon, so that total eclipses of the moon are possible.*

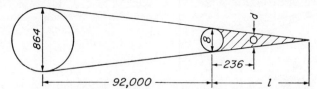

Fig. 4. Total eclipse of the moon (distances in thousands of miles).

The geometrical situation is shown in Fig. 4, with the umbra cross-hatched. The length l of the umbra is computed from

$$\frac{92000+l}{864} = \frac{l}{8}; \qquad l = 860$$

(all numbers represent thousands of miles). The moon is at a distance $860 - 236 = 624$ thousand miles from the apex of the cone. The diameter of the umbra at this distance is computed from

$$\frac{d}{624} = \frac{8}{860}; \qquad d = 5.80,$$

which is over twice the diameter, 2.16 thousand miles, of the moon.

3. VISION

AT THIS POINT we shall consider briefly some of the physical processes involved in vision.   If light proceeding from a luminous point enters the eye, the luminous point is the apex of a divergent beam, or cone of rays, the base of the cone being the pupil of the eye as shown in Fig. 5. Whenever such a cone of rays enters the eye, the eye 'sees' the luminous point.   Each point of a luminous source acts as such a point source.   Bodies that are not self-luminous are visible by light that falls upon them and is diffusely reflected in all directions.   Each point on the illuminated body then behaves like a luminous point source.

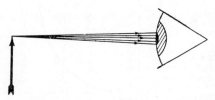

Fig. 5. Light rays entering the eye from a point on a luminous object.

The knowledge of our surroundings that is obtained from visual sensation depends on perception of relative brightness, of the apparent size and shape of objects, of their relative positions, and of their color.   Relative brightness and, to some extent, color are useful guides in judging distance. Probably the most valuable means of judging relative distance results from the fact that our two eyes give us slightly different pictures of any

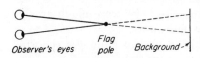

Fig. 6. Depth perception by means of binocular vision.

scene.   Thus, as indicated in Fig. 6, a near-by flagpole would be seen against a slightly different background of trees and buildings when viewed by each of our eyes.   These two pictures are transmitted to the brain, which interprets them in the light of earlier experiences as meaning that the flagpole is closer than the buildings or trees. This mechanism of depth perception is a process somewhat like the triangulation technique used in surveying, the 'base line' in the present case being the distance between the two eyes.

The sensitivity of the eye varies for different wavelengths.   Under conditions of moderate or strong illumination the eye is most sensitive to yellow-green light of wavelength 555 millimicrons.   The spectral sensitivity curve has a maximum at this wavelength and falls off rapidly for longer and shorter wavelengths, as in Fig. 7, which plots the *reciprocals* of the relative numbers of watts of radiant energy that must fall on the eye to give visual response at different wavelengths.   This curve is determined by using the flicker photometer, which will be discussed in Chap. 21. On Fig. 7 are also shown typical values of the wavelengths associated with the different colors.

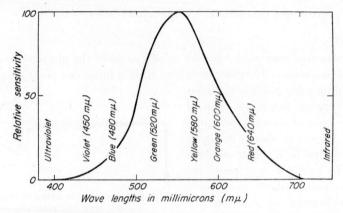

Fig. 7. Relative sensitivity of the human eye to light of various wavelengths.

4. SPEED OF LIGHT

THE *speed of light* is so great that early attempts at its measurement proved unsuccessful. Galileo conducted an experiment in which two observers stationed in towers some distance apart flashed signals at each other with lanterns. The second observer was supposed to flash a signal as soon as he received a light signal from the first observer. The experiment was inconclusive, and Galileo decided that the speed of light was too great for measurement by this method and that light transmission might indeed be instantaneous. In view of our present knowledge, it is easy to recognize that the reaction times of the observers were much greater than the time of transit of light between the towers.

The first successful determination of the speed of light was reported by the Danish astronomer Olaus Roemer in 1675, when he announced a calculation of the speed of light from observations of irregularities in the times between successive eclipses of the innermost moon of Jupiter by that planet. The general argument used by Roemer can be understood by a consideration of Fig. 8, which shows certain relative positions of Jupiter and the earth. For simplicity, we shall consider Jupiter at rest in its orbit, since its motion is slow compared with that of the earth and can easily be taken into account in actual calculations. The observed interval between successive eclipses of Jupiter's moon as it passes behind the planet is the same (about 42.5 hr) at times of the year when the earth is near positions A and C but the interval between successive eclipses is greater when the earth is near B, and less when the earth is near D. These variations are not due to irregularities in the motion of Jupiter's moon, but are caused by variations in the times required for light to travel from Jupiter to the earth.   Because the distance between Jupiter and the earth is increasing when the earth is at B, the time required for light to travel from Jupiter to the earth is increasing, and the measured interval between successive eclipses increases accordingly.   A similar line of reasoning accounts for the shorter eclipse intervals noted when the earth is at D.   This apparent change in frequency of the eclipses is analogous to the apparent change in frequency of sound in the Doppler effect.

From observations made when the earth was near A, Roemer predicted the exact time at which a certain eclipse should take place one-half year later when the earth was near C, making no allowance for the time required for light to traverse the distance AC, the diameter of the earth's orbit.   He found that the eclipse occurred later than the predicted time.

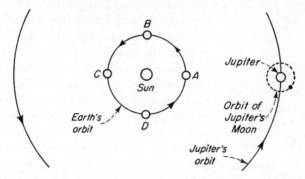

Fig. 8. Roemer's determination of the speed of light (schematic).

Roemer's measurements were not very accurate; recent measurements show the eclipses to be very nearly 1000 sec or $16\frac{2}{3}$ min late at C as compared with predictions made at A.   Roemer correctly concluded that this time represents the time required for light to traverse a distance equal to the diameter of the earth's orbit.   Since the diameter of the earth's orbit is 186,000,000 mi, this determination gives 186,000 mi/sec as the speed of light.

Roemer's conclusions, not credited at the time, were confirmed in 1727 by James Bradley, who employed a quite different astronomical method of determining the speed of light.   In observing the position of the fixed stars at different times of the year, Bradley found a small displacement in apparent position, always in the direction the earth was traveling at the time the observation was made.   This effect is due to the motion of the earth relative to the light coming from the star.   Let us look at light coming from a star in a direction perpendicular to the plane of the earth's orbit, from the standpoint of an observer who does not share the orbital motion; that is, an observer *at rest relative to the sun*.   If the earth and telescope were at rest, the telescope would have to be pointed in direction AB in Fig. 9.   Since the earth is moving with an orbital velocity v, the telescope must be tilted so as to point in direction CB.   This phenomenon is known as the *aberration of light*.   The effect is analogous to the backward slant of rain or snow as observed from a moving train.

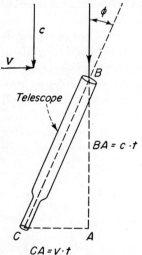

Fig. 9. Aberration of light. The light from a star is traveling vertically downward in this figure.

From the figure, it can be seen that while the light moves the distance BA, the telescope must move the distance CA.   If the speed of light is denoted by c, we see that $\tan\phi = CA/BA = v/c$.   The angle ϕ cannot be measured directly by an observer on the earth, but if he observes stars that are in a direction approximately perpendicular to the plane of the earth's orbit during the course of a year, so that the earth is first traveling one way and one-half year later the other way, these stars apparently describe a little orbit whose angular diameter can be accurately measured. The angle ϕ is found to be 20″.492; from this and the known value of approximately 18.5 mi/sec for the orbital speed of the earth, the speed of light is found to be 186,300 mi/sec. Bradley's method is more accurate than

Roemer's, but both have been surpassed in accuracy by direct terrestrial observations of the speed of light.

The first successful terrestrial measurement was made by A. H. L. Fizeau in 1849.   The principle of his method was the obvious one of sending out a brief flash of light and measuring the time for this light flash to travel to a distant mirror and return to the observer.   Fizeau's experiments were similar in principle to the later experiments described below; in Fizeau's work a rotating toothed wheel played a role similar to that of the rotating mirror in Fig. 10.

In 1850, J. B. L. Foucault used a rotating-mirror type of apparatus to measure the speed of light in water as well as in air; he found that the speed in water is less than the speed in air, a result which had been predicted on the wave theory of light, but which was in contradiction to Newton's particle theory.

The most accurate direct measurements of the speed of light were made by A. A. Michelson and his colleagues in the years following 1926 with apparatus similar to that of Foucault.   In the schematic diagram of Fig. 10, light from an arc passes through a slit S and is reflected from one face of the octagonal mirror R.   From this face the light passes to the small fixed plane mirrors b and C which reflect it to the large concave mirror M, of about 30-ft focal length and so placed that S is effectively at its focus (see Chap. 22).   Mirror M renders the beam parallel and sends it to a distant mirror, not shown, that reflects it back to M, after which the light retraces its path to lens L and the eye of the observer. Of course, suitable optical arrangements, not indicated in Fig. 10, are made so that the lens is above or below the source, not directly behind it.

Mirror M was located on Mount Wilson in California, and the distant mirror was located on Mount San Antonio, about 22 mi away. The inter-

vening distance D was measured by the United States Coast and Geodetic Survey as $35,385.5 \pm 0.3$ m; this is probably the most accurate survey ever made.

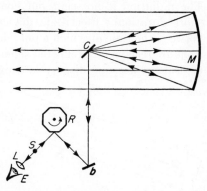

Fig. 10. Michelson's apparatus for the determination of the speed of light (geometry greatly distorted).

In this apparatus, when the rotating mirror R is at rest, the path traversed by the light is that shown in Fig. 10, and an image of the source slit is observed at cross hairs in the eyepiece L. As the mirror R begins to rotate, the final image at the cross hairs is displaced laterally. As the rotational speed is increased, the displacement becomes so large that no image is observed. Finally, a sufficient rotational speed is attained so that the mirror turns through one-eighth of a revolution during the transit time of the light. At this speed, an image is again observed at the cross hairs. If this rotational speed is measured, the speed of light c can be determined from the relation

$$c = \frac{\text{distance traveled by the light}}{\text{time required for mirror to turn } \frac{1}{8} \text{ rev}}.$$

As the rotational speed is further increased, the image again disappears and later reappears at the cross hairs at a rotational speed twice as great as previously, so that the mirror turns $\frac{1}{4}$ rev in the time taken by the light to traverse its path.

The results obtained in this experiment and later experiments by others give

$$c = 299,793 \pm 1 \text{ km/sec}$$

as the present best value of the speed of light in a vacuum. The speed in air is less by one part in 10,003. All types of electromagnetic radiation, from the shortest gamma rays and X rays to the longest radio waves, travel with this same speed. This same speed is computed from Maxwell's electromagnetic theory by using constants determined from electrical and magnetic measurements in which no electromagnetic radiation is involved!

One important application in which use is made of the knowledge of the speed of light occurs in *radar* (*radio direction and ranging*) systems. Short radio waves called *microwaves* are sent out from radiators backed by parabolic reflectors of the type shown schematically in Fig. 11(a). If this radiation strikes an object such as an airplane or a ship, some of the radiation is reflected to the parabolic reflector and detected by a receiver. The radiation is not sent out continuously but in pulses of extremely short duration. Electronic devices are used to indicate the interval between the time at which a pulse is sent out and the time at which reflections are received. Reflected signals are displayed on an oscilloscope. A typical oscilloscope display is shown in Fig. 11(b). The time between

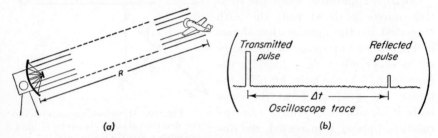

Fig. 11. Pulsed microwave radar system.

transmission of a pulse of radiation and reception of an 'echo' can be accurately determined. Since this radiation travels with the well-known speed c of light, this time measurement gives an accurate measurement of the range of the object causing the reflection.

Microwaves can also be used for measurement of the approach speed of an object by means of the *Doppler effect* on electromagnetic waves. In this case a continuous wave is sent out and the frequency shift Δf of the wave reflected by the moving object is measured. This frequency shift can be accurately measured electronically by measuring the beat frequency (exactly analogous to sound) when the transmitted wave and the reflected wave are superposed. An argument exactly analogous to that for Doppler effect in sound gives the expression

$$\Delta f = 2 \ (v/c) f \tag{1}$$

for this frequency increase, where v is the approach speed of the object.

Example. *A microwave radiator having wavelength exactly* 0.1 m *is used to measure the speed of an oncoming automobile. The observed frequency shift is* 380 *cycles/sec. What is the speed of the automobile?*

We note that the above frequency shift gives a beat that is precisely in the range of sound frequencies; hence it is very easy to measure its frequency accurately. The frequency of the microwaves is obtained from the relation

$$f = c/\lambda = (3.00 \times 10^8 \text{ m/sec})/(0.1 \text{ m}) = 3.00 \times 10^9 \text{ cycles/sec.}$$

The last equation in the text above then gives

$$v = \frac{1}{2} c \, \Delta f / f = \frac{1}{2} \, (3.00 \times 10^8 \text{ m/sec})(380/\text{sec})/(3.00 \times 10^9/\text{sec})$$
$$= 19.0 \text{ m/sec} = 42.5 \text{ mi/hr}$$

as the speed of approach of the automobile.

PROBLEMS

1. An incandescent lamp with small filament and clear bulb is suspended 3 ft above the center of a table top. If the area of the table top is 4 ft² and if the distance from the table top to the floor is 3 ft, what is the area of the shadow formed on the floor?   Ans: 16 ft².

2. Using the dimensions given in the example on p. 428, compute the approximate width, on the surface of the earth, of the path of partial solar eclipse. Show that with the moon at 236,000 miles, a total solar eclipse is not possible near January 1, when the sun is 91.2 million miles from the earth, but is possible near July 1 when the sun is at 94.6 million miles. (Note however that the moon's distance varies from 222 to 253 thousand miles.)

3. A pinhole camera is used to form an image of an object 2 ft tall located 10 ft in front of the pinhole. If the distance from the pinhole to the film is 5 in, what is the height of the image?   Ans: 1 in.

4. The diameter of the sun is 864,000 mi and that of the moon is 2160 mi. A 'pinhole camera,' consisting of a small hole in a window shade and a white card held 10 ft from the hole, is used to obtain an image of the sun at a time when the sun is at a distance of 92,900,000 mi from the earth and to obtain an image of the full moon at a time when the moon is 236,000 mi from the earth. Find the diameters of the images produced.

5. A vertical pin is located 40 cm in front of an observer. If the pupils of the observer's eyes are 6.0 cm apart, what angle is subtended at the pin by the observer's optical 'base line,' that is, by the distance between his eyes?   Ans: $8°6$.

6. A vertical wire is located 50 cm in front of an observer. If the pupils of this observer's eyes are 6.4 cm apart, what angle is subtended at the wire by the distance between his pupils?

7. Let us suppose that in Galileo's experiment the two observers were stationed in towers 6 mi apart. Using present knowledge of the value of the speed of light, calculate the time of transmission of a light signal from one tower to the other.   Ans: 32.2 μsec.

8. An observer sees lightning strike a tree on a hill 10 mi away. How long after the lightning has struck does the observer see the flash?

9. Roemer first gave 22 min for the time required for light to traverse a distance equal to the diameter of the earth's orbit. Using the more recent values of 92,900,000 mi as the mean radius of the earth's orbit and 186,300 mi/sec as the speed of light, calculate the time required for light to traverse the earth's orbit and find the per cent error in Roemer's determination of this time.

Ans: 997 sec or 16.6 min; 32%.

10. If the observed period of revolution of Jupiter's moon is 42.5 hr when the earth is at A or C in Fig. 8, how many seconds longer or shorter are the apparent periods when the earth is at B and D? Take the orbital speed of the earth as 18.5 mi/sec.

11. Using 92,900,000 mi as the radius of the earth's orbit, 1 year as the time for one revolution of the earth about the sun, and $20''49$ of arc as the aberration angle denoted by ϕ in Fig. 9, calculate the speed of light.   Ans: 186,000 mi/sec.

12. Aberration of light will occur as a result of the rotation of the earth on its axis. Taking 7900 mi as the diameter of the earth, calculate this aberration angle and compare with the value of $20''.49$ arising from orbital motion.

13. Taking 35,386 m as the distance between the stations on Mount Wilson and Mount San Antonio in Michelson's experiment, find the lowest rotational speed at which the image will again be observed at the cross hairs after the rotation of the mirror has begun.   Ans: 529 rev/sec.

14. During the years 1930–1933, Michelson's group made a direct measurement of the speed of light in vacuum by using an evacuated tube approximately 1 mi long. The rotating mirror had 32 faces and the light traveled back and forth between mirrors at the ends of the tube a total distance of 8 mi during the time of replacement of one of the 32 mirror faces by the next one. What is the value of the minimum rotational speed required for the image to be observed in the following mirror face?

15. A short pulse of radiation is sent out by a radar set such as that in Fig. 11, and a reflection is received 45 μsec later. How far away is the object that produced the reflection?   Ans: 4.19 mi.

16. A reflection of radiation from an airplane is noted by a radar operator 628 μsec after a pulse of radiation has been sent outward. What is the distance of the plane from the radar station?

17. Radar pulses have recently been reflected from the moon, which is 236,000 mi from the earth. What is the time interval before receipt of the echo in this case?   Ans: 2.54 sec

18. When we observe the sun, we see it at the position it had when the light left the sun. What is the angle between this position and its actual position at the moment of observation?

19. On a day when the speed of sound is 1080 ft/sec, a gun is fired 54 ft away from an observer. By the time the sound of the shot reaches the observer, how far has the light from the muzzle flash traveled?   Ans: 9320 mi.

20. A continuous microwave radiator having wavelength 22 cm is used to measure the speed of an approaching airplane at an airport. The Doppler frequency shift is observed as 720 cycles/sec. What is the approach speed of the plane?

21. Derive equation (1) for the microwave Doppler shift from the equation (26), p. 416, that applies in the case of sound, introducing the fact that v is very small compared to c.

22. A microwave frequency can be measured directly in terms of the unit of time, the second, by electronic techniques that have been developed for counting cycles (just as an electric clock counts the cycles of an alternating current). Show how reflection of microwaves from an object approaching at known speed thus gives another method of measuring the speed of light.

CHAPTER 21

ILLUMINATION AND PHOTOMETRY

OUR GREAT natural source of light is the sun. Man has developed many 'artificial' sources of light. These include, in order of development, the torch, the oil lamp, the candle, the gas lamp with mantle, the carbon arc lamp, the carbon-filament electric lamp, the tungsten-filament electric lamp, the luminous gas tube, the fluorescent lamp, and the electroluminescent display.

In the present chapter we shall discuss the methods of measuring *intensities of light sources* and of measuring *illumination*. We note that much of the radiation from light sources lies in the infrared and ultraviolet, invisible to the eye but readily detectable by photographic or electrical methods. In specifying the photometric quantities, *source intensity* and *illumination*, we are not interested in such radiation but only in radiation of *visible light* as it

affects the eye. In some respects this requirement makes photometry an *inexact* science, since measurements of photometric quantities necessarily depend on the physiological and psychological response of the eye. Such measurements are like measurements of the *loudness* of a sound, as distinguished from its *intensity*.

In this chapter we shall have frequent occasion to employ the concept of *solid angle*, which we have not introduced heretofore. A solid angle in *steradians* is defined in a manner similar to a

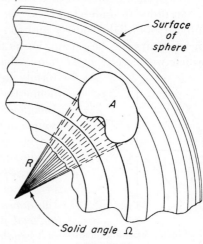

Figure 1

plane angle in *radians*. Consider a cone whose apex is at the center of a circumscribed sphere of radius R as in Fig. 1. Let the cone cut out an area A of the surface of the sphere. Since the area A is proportional to R^2, we can use the dimension-less ratio A/R^2 as a measure of the solid angle Ω of the cone in steradians, defining $\Omega = A/R^2$ in steradians.

> One **steradian** is the solid angle subtended at the center of a sphere by a portion of the surface of area equal to the square of the radius of the sphere.

The solid angle subtended *by the whole sphere* is the whole area $4\pi R^2$ divided by R^2, or 4π steradians. This is analogous to the plane angle subtended by a whole circle, which is 2π radians.

1. PHOTOMETRIC QUANTITIES: SOURCE INTENSITY, LIGHT FLUX, AND ILLUMINATION

LIGHT IS defined as radiant energy that is capable of affecting the retina of the eye. This definition suggests immediately that the intensity of a given source of light might be measured in terms of the number of joules of light radiated per second, and specified as radiated power in watts. This procedure would be desirable from many points of view, but unfortunately is not satisfactory since *we are interested only in the effect of the radiant energy on the eye,* and the eye is *not* equally sensitive to equal amounts of energy of different colors (see Fig. 7, p. 430). This fact forces us to use the eye itself as the basic detecting device. The usual method employed in determining the intensity of a light source consists of the visual comparison of the source with some arbitrarily chosen standard source by means of a device called a photometer. The intensity of the source is then expressed in terms of that of the standard source.

In order to understand the concepts involved in the measurement of intensities of light sources and to see how a consistent system of photometric units can be set up, let us first consider an idealized situation in which we have a *point source* that radiates *isotropically*, that is, uniformly in all directions. We shall arbitrarily define the *intensity* of this source as *one candle*. Imagine a sphere circumscribed about the point source in the manner indicated in Fig. 2. Light travels outward from the source and strikes the inside surface of the sphere. We need a unit in terms of which to measure the rate of flow or *flux* of visible radiation. The unit is called the *lumen* and we may define it by saying that *the total flux emitted by a source whose intensity is 1 candle is 4π lumens.* Since there are 4π steradians in the total solid angle surrounding a point source, this statement is equivalent to saying that *an isotropic point source of one-candle intensity radiates one lumen per steradian.*

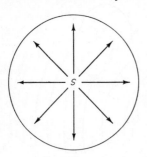

Fig. 2. Isotropic point source at the center of a hollow sphere.

Another light quantity we shall use frequently is *illumination*, which is defined as *light flux falling on unit area* of a surface and can properly be measured in *lumens/ft²* or *lumens/m²*. Thus, if the radius of the hollow sphere with a point source of 1 candle at its center is 1 ft, the illumination of the inner surface of the sphere is 4π lumens/4π ft² $= 1$ lumen/ft². *One lumen per square foot* is sometimes called a *foot-candle*, but this term is gradually becoming obsolete.

The light quantities we have introduced are denoted by the symbols indicated below:

Quantity	Symbol	Unit
Source intensity	I	candle
Light flux	F	lumen
Illumination	E	lumen/ft² or lumen/m²

From the discussion above, it can be seen that the total light flux F from an isotropic point source of intensity I, in candles, is given by

$$F = 4\pi I, \quad \text{in lumens.} \tag{1}$$

Similarly, the illumination E of the inner surface of a sphere of radius R by an isotropic point source of intensity I at the center of the sphere is given by the relation

$$E = \frac{F}{A} = \frac{4\pi I}{4\pi R^2} = \frac{I}{R^2}, \tag{2}$$

in lumens/ft² or lumens/m² according to whether R is in ft or m. We shall consider the actual choice of the candle in the following section. When we substitute a value of I in candles in (2), E comes out initially in candles/area rather than lumens/area. *Candle* and *lumen* are both units of light power.

2. REAL LIGHT SOURCES; THE CANDLE

THE ABOVE discussion serves to introduce the quantities *source intensity*, *light flux*, and *illumination* and to indicate the principles by which a system of photometric units can be set up. Actually, in practice *it is impossible to produce an isotropic point source*. A real source, such as a candle flame or an incandescent filament, can be considered as a *point* source, provided that measurements of illumination are made at a sufficiently great distance, but it cannot be treated as an isotropic source. We get around this difficulty by defining a particular direction from which a standard source is to be observed, and define its intensity in candles *when viewed from this direction*. The lumen is then defined in terms of the light flux per unit solid angle for a *small* solid angle *in this particular direction*.

Suppose, in Fig. 3, that the source were an isotropic point source of intensity I candles. In solid angle $\delta\Omega$, it would then emit $\delta F = I \, \delta\Omega$ lumens, since it emits one lumen per unit solid angle per candle. If now

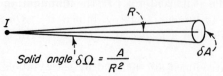

the source in Fig. 3 is a real source, the distance R large compared to the dimensions of the source, and the light flux δF passes through area δA subtending solid angle $\delta\Omega$ at the 'center' of the source, the candlepower of the

Fig. 3. Radiation in a given direction from a light source.

source, *as viewed in this particular direction*, is defined as

$$I = \delta F / \delta\Omega. \tag{3}$$

The *mean intensity* of the source is defined as

$$I_{\text{Mean}} = F_{\text{Total}}/4\pi, \tag{4}$$

where F_{Total} is the total light flux emitted in all directions, and 4π is the total solid angle in the sphere.

Now consider the *illumination* of the surface δA in Fig. 3 by the real source of intensity I in this particular direction. The illumination E is defined as the number of lumens striking the surface per unit area of surface. In this case,

$$E = \delta F / \delta A = \delta F / (R^2 \, \delta\Omega),$$

or, substituting from (3), we find that

$$E = I/R^2. \tag{5}$$

Hence, for R large compared with source dimensions, the illumination from a real source is given by the same inverse-square law (2) as for an isotropic source, except that I will vary with direction for a real source.

We shall now consider the definition of the standard candle. For many years, the so-called 'international candle' was defined as the source intensity of the flame of a spermaceti candle, burning at the rate of 120 grains per hour, when viewed in a horizontal plane. Such a candle was inconvenient to use in practical measurements, but the unit was long retained. Later, carefully calibrated incandescent lamps, viewed in a particular direction, were used as practical secondary standards in most national standards laboratories. A serious objection to the use of a candle or incandescent lamp as a standard source is that a source of this type is not accurately reproducible.

A new *accurately reproducible* standard source, developed by the U. S. National Bureau of Standards, was adopted by the International Committee on Weights and Measures in 1948. This standard source consists of a glowing cavity with temperature equal to that of solidifying platinum.

A schematic diagram of the cross section of the source is shown in Fig. 4. The platinum, contained in a thorium-oxide crucible and surrounded by powdered thorium oxide acting as an insulating material, is placed in an alternating magnetic field and heated by currents induced in the platinum itself. A sighting tube, also composed of thorium oxide and containing some powdered thorium oxide, extends into the molten platinum. Thorium oxide is chosen because it is a material that is very white and that is still solid at the melting point of platinum. When the radiation that comes out of this tube vertically is viewed, the source intensity is defined as 60 candles per square centimeter of opening when the platinum in cooling reaches its solidifying temperature. The circular opening at the end of the sighting tube is made small (approximately $\frac{1}{60}$ cm² in area) to approximate a point source. If the area of opening were exactly $\frac{1}{60}$ cm², the source intensity would be exactly 1 candle and give out 1 lumen/steradian in directions very near the vertical.

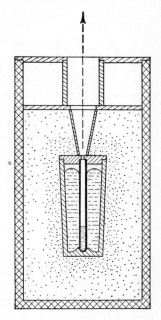

Fig. 4.
The standard light source.

In terms of the standard light source, *observed in directions very near the vertical at the temperature of solidifying platinum*, the units of source intensity and light flux are defined as follows:

> The **candle** is the source intensity per $\frac{1}{60}$ cm² of opening of the standard light source.
>
> The **lumen** is the flux per unit solid angle per $\frac{1}{60}$ cm² of opening of the standard light source.

The lumen is seen to be a unit that is basically of the nature of *power* (rather than of energy). At any particular wavelength, there is a definite relation between the lumen and the watt. Thus at the maximum sensitivity of the eye, at wavelength 555 mμ, 1 watt of radiant energy equals 621 lumens. At other wavelengths, the watt will be fewer lumens in proportion to the ordinates of Fig. 7, p. 430.

> The **over-all efficiency** of a light source is defined as the ratio of total light flux emitted to total power supplied to the source.

The theoretical maximum possible over-all efficiency of a source is seen to be 621 lumens/watt (and this source would give only yellow-green light). The over-all efficiencies of present-day lamps of about 2000 lumens output are 17 lumens/watt for a tungsten lamp and 58 lumens/watt for a fluorescent lamp, in terms of watts input of electrical power to the lamp.

> **Example.** *A 100-watt bulb is hung base up at the center of a sphere of 3-ft radius whose walls are blackened so that it may be assumed that they absorb all light. A 'light-meter' is used to measure the illumination at various points on the wall of the sphere. The illumination is 25 lumens/ft² at the bottom of the sphere, 18 lumens/ft² on a horizontal diameter, and 5 lumens/ft² at the top. The total light flux is determined to be 1900 lumens. What is the source intensity of the bulb when viewed from below, from the side, and from above? What is the mean intensity?*

From (5) we see that source intensity $I = ER^2$, where E is the illumination. Substitution of $E = 25$, 18, and 5 lumens/ft², and $R = 3$ ft gives

$$I = 225, \ 162, \ 45 \text{ candles}$$

for the intensity of the source viewed in the three specified directions. The mean intensity is determined from (4) as

$$I_{\text{Mean}} = 1900 \text{ lumens}/4\pi = 151 \text{ candles}.$$

3. ILLUMINATION

LET US NOW consider the illumination of a surface to which the light rays are not perpendicular. In Fig. 5, δA represents an element of area whose normal makes an angle θ with the rays of light reaching this element from source S. This element subtends the solid angle $\delta\Omega = \delta s/R^2$ at source S, where δs is the projection of δA on the plane perpendicular to R.

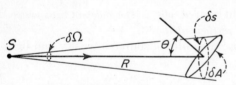

Since $\delta s = \cos\theta \ \delta A$,

$$\delta\Omega = \cos\theta \ \delta A/R^2.$$

Therefore, in view of equation (3), the flux δF through this element of area is given by

$$\delta F = I \ \delta\Omega = I \cos\theta \ \delta A/R^2.$$

Fig. 5. Light incident at an angle θ to the normal to a surface.

The illumination E of this area is by definition the flux per unit area, that is,

$$E = \delta F/\delta A = I \cos\theta/R^2. \tag{6}$$

When the surface is tilted by the angle θ shown in Fig. 5, the illumination is reduced to $\cos\theta$ times the illumination (5) for normal incidence.

In order to give some idea of illuminations frequently encountered, we might point out that on a clear day the illumination from direct sunlight is about 8000 lumens/ft² and the illumination from direct sunlight plus skylight is as great as 10,000 lumens/ft². On a 'dark' day illumination outdoors drops to 100 lumens/ft² or less. The full moon gives an illumination of 0.03 lumen/ft². Indoors one rarely encounters illumination of more than 20 lumens/ft². The following are *recommended values of illumination* for spaces of various types:

Classrooms	12 lumens/ft²	Laboratories	12 lumens/ft²
Club lounges	5	Library reading rooms	12
Drafting rooms	25	Offices	10
Hallways	3	Railway cars	8
Hotel lobbies	8	Sidewalks	0.5

In practical problems such as planning lighting installations or arranging for proper photographic exposure times it is often necessary to have a fairly accurate measurement of illumination. Instruments using photoelectric cells are sufficiently accurate for this purpose. These instruments are known as 'light meters.' In these meters, the light reaching the sensitive surface of a photoelectric cell produces an electric current which within definite limits is proportional to the light flux striking the sensitive surface. Although the sensitivity of the photoelectric cell for various colors cannot be adjusted to be exactly the same as the sensitivity of the eye, the light meter can be used to obtain approximate values of illumination.

Example. *The radiant energy of the sun is* 19.4 kcal/min *per square meter of area normal to the sun's rays at the distance of the earth. About half of this energy is in the visible wavelengths (see the* 6000-degree *curve of Fig. 5 of Chap. 37). Assuming that none of this energy is absorbed by the earth's atmosphere (actually about* 10 *per cent is so absorbed), compute the rate at which radiant energy falls on* 1 m² *of the earth's surface at latitude* 40° N *at noon on June* 21-22 *(the summer solstice) and at noon on December* 21-22 *(the winter solstice).*

The angle between the plane of the earth's equator and the plane of the ecliptic (the plane of the earth's orbit) is 23°.5 (the latitude of the tropic of Cancer). At noon at the summer solstice, the sun is at the zenith at the tropic of Cancer and hence is $40° - 23°.5 = 16°.5$ from the zenith at 40° N latitude. Considering δA as an area on the earth's surface in Fig. 5, the angle θ is then 16°.5, and the rate of receipt of radiation is

$$(19.4 \text{ kcal/min·m}^2) \cos 16°.5 = (19.4 \text{ kcal/min·m}^2)(0.959) = 18.6 \text{ kcal/min·m}^2.$$

On the other hand, at the winter solstice, the sun is directly overhead at the tropic of Capricorn, at 23°.5 S latitude, and the angle θ in Fig. 5 is $40° + 23°.5 = 63°.5$ for a point at 40° N. The rate of radiation receipt is

$$(19.4 \text{ kcal/min·m}^2) \cos 63°.5 = (19.4 \text{ kcal/min·m}^2)(0.446) = 8.65 \text{ kcal/min·m}^2.$$

That there should be a great difference between summer and winter temperatures at 40° N latitude is not surprising in view of these results.

4. PHOTOMETRY

THE MEASUREMENT of relative source intensity is called *photometry*, and the instruments used in this measurement are called *photometers*. The eye itself is incapable of directly comparing two luminous sources with accuracy, but it can determine with remarkable precision whether or not the illuminations of adjacent surfaces are equal. An illumination difference of one part in 150 can be detected. One of the simplest instruments used for comparing the intensities of sources by matching illuminations from the sources is the Bunsen grease-spot photometer shown schematically in Fig. 6. The essential part of this photometer is a flat screen of opaque white paper having a translucent grease spot at the center. The grease spot reflects less light and transmits more light than the balance of the paper. The screen is illuminated on its two sides by the light from the source S of known intensity and the source X of unknown intensity that are to be compared. The sources are so oriented that the illuminations are from the particular directions in which it is desired to compare the intensities.

If the illumination is more intense on one side of the screen, the grease spot will appear dark against its background from this side but

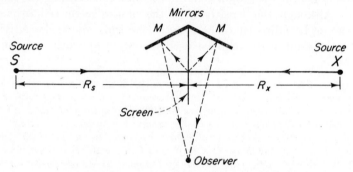

Fig. 6. Diagram of Bunsen's grease-spot photometer.

bright against its background if viewed from the side with weak illumination. The spot will very nearly disappear when the illumination is equal on the two sides; this condition can be realized by moving the screen to the proper position between the two sources. The mirrors M allow both sides of the screen to be seen at the same time; this feature is of considerable importance in matching the illuminations. If I_s and I_x are the intensities of the sources S and X, respectively, and the distances are R_s and R_x when the illuminations are equal, then

$$\frac{I_s}{R_s^2} = \frac{I_x}{R_x^2}, \quad \text{or} \quad I_x = I_s \frac{R_x^2}{R_s^2}. \tag{7}$$

The sharper the boundary between two areas, the more accurately the adjustment to equal illumination can be made. One of the best devices for obtaining a sharp boundary is in the Lummer-Brodhun photometer, which has a chalky white screen and an optical arrangement of prisms that enable the observer to view a circle of one side of the screen sharply superposed on an annular section of the other side. The two sides of the screen are again illuminated by the two sources being compared, and adjustment to equal illumination is made by varying the distances between the sources and the screen.

If the light from the sources being compared is not of the same *color*, no photometric balance can be attained with this type of photometer. One method of comparing light sources of different color makes use of the *flicker photometer*, in which the screen seen by the observer is illuminated alternately by light from the two sources. If the frequency of the alternation has the proper value, the color difference disappears, because of persistence of vision, before the brightness flicker becomes unobservable. After the frequency of alternation has been adjusted to the proper value, the source intensities are compared by noting source distances R_S and R_X at which the brightness flicker disappears. Another method of comparing sources of different color involves the use of photoelectric cells provided with optical filters; combinations of photoelectric cells and filters can be chosen so as to have a color response that reproduces that of the eye, as given in Fig. 7, p. 430. However, it is noted that this curve of color response was itself obtained by use of a flicker photometer.

PROBLEMS

1. An isotropic point source of light has a source intensity of 5 candles. (a) What is the total light flux from this source? (b) Calculate the illumination at a point on a surface 10 ft away from the source if the light strikes this surface perpendicularly.   Ans: 20π lumens; 0.05 lumen/ft².

2. An isotropic point source of light emits a flux of 320 lumens. (a) What is the source intensity? (b) Calculate the illumination of the inner surface of a sphere of 2-m radius if the point source is located at its center.

3. A certain light source emits only light of wavelength 555 mμ and radiates at the rate of 0.05 watt. What is the luminous flux?   Ans: 31.1 lumens.

4. A certain light source emits only green light of wavelength 555 mμ and has a total flux of 300 lumens. At what rate in watts is energy radiated in the form of visible radiation? By comparison it is found that a source of blue light also has a flux of 300 lumens. Does this second source emit energy more or less rapidly than the first source?

5. If the diameter of the opening in the standard light source (Fig. 4) is exactly 1.5 mm, compute the total source intensity of this opening when viewed along the axis of the sighting tube.   Ans: 1.06 candles.

6. What is the total light flux from an isotropic point source that has an intensity equal to that of the opening in the standard source when viewed from the prescribed direction? Use the data given in Prob. 5. Does the standard source have this total flux?

7. The light of the full moon, 240,000 mi from the earth, gives an illumination of 0.03 lumen/ft². (a) Neglecting absorption in the earth's atmosphere, determine the source intensity of the moon. (b) How far away from a 40-watt tungsten lamp of 35-candle intensity in the horizontal direction must a vertical screen be placed to have the same illumination as in full moonlight?
Ans: 4.8×10^{16} candles; 34 ft.

8. The light of the sun, 93,000,000 mi from the earth, gives a direct illumination of 8000 lumens/ft². (a) Neglecting absorption in the earth's atmosphere, determine the source intensity of the sun. (b) How far away from a 40-watt tungsten lamp of 35-candle intensity in the horizontal direction must a vertical screen be placed to have the same illumination as in sunlight?

9. A 150-candle light hangs at the geometrical center of a cubical room 20 ft on an edge.   Assuming the source to be isotropic and considering only the direct illumination, find: (a) the total number of lumens striking the floor; (b) the average illumination of the floor; (c) the maximum and minimum values of the illumination of the floor.

Ans: $100\,\pi$ lumens; 0.785 lumen/ft²; 1.50, 0.287 lumen/ft².

10. If a 16-candle lamp placed 2 ft above the surface of a table is switched on for 7 min, how many lumens fall on a square inch of table top directly below the lamp during the time the light is on?

11. A 100-watt tungsten filament has a flux of 1630 lumens.   What would be the intensity of an isotropic point source that has this total flux?

Ans: 130 candles.

12. If direct sunlight produces an illumination of 8000 lumens/ft² on a surface tilted so that the sun's rays are perpendicular to the surface, what is the corresponding illumination on level ground if the sun is 60° above the horizon?

13. On March 22 the noon sun at Quito, Ecuador, produces an illumination of 8000 lumens/ft² on level ground when the sun is directly overhead.   What is the illumination at this position from direct sunlight at 2 P.M.?   At 4 P.M.?   (Neglect atmospheric absorption.)   Ans: 6930 lumens/ft²; 4000 lumens/ft².

14. A suspended light source has an effective source intensity of 300 candles when viewed from below.   At what distance above a drafting table should this source be suspended in order to give the recommended illumination of 25 lumens/ft²?   At this distance, what would be the illumination in lumens/m² of the table surface immediately below this lamp?

15. A workbench 16 ft long is illuminated by three 300-candle lamps suspended at a height of 6 ft above the bench.   One of the lamps is located above the center of the bench and the other two are located above its ends.   What is the illumination immediately below the center lamp?   (Assume isotropic radiation from the lamps.)   Ans: 11.9 lumens/ft².

16. For the workbench described in Prob. 15, calculate the illumination immediately below one of the end lamps.

17. An incandescent lamp has a flux of 10 lumens/steradian in a certain direction.   What is the illumination on a surface 9 ft away and normal to the light beam in this direction?   What is the intensity of the source in this direction?

Ans: 0.123 lumen/ft²; 10 candles.

18. Referring to the example on p. 443, determine the rates of radiation receipt at 9 A.M. at 40° N latitude at the time of the winter and summer solstices. (You will need to use formulas of spherical trigonometry to determine the angles involved.)

19. In using a Bunsen grease-spot photometer, a standard 40-candle lamp is mounted at the zero mark on a 1-m optical bench and a lamp of unknown intensity is mounted at the 100-cm mark.   It is found that the two sides of the screen are equally illuminated when the screen is at the 70-cm mark.   What is the intensity of the lamp being tested?   Ans: 7.35 candles.

20. In a Bunsen grease-spot photometer, a lamp of unknown intensity is placed above the zero mark of a 2-m optical bench and a standard 150-candle lamp is placed above the 200-cm mark.   In order to have the two sides of the screen equally illuminated, the screen must be placed at the 120-cm mark. What is the source intensity of the lamp being tested?

21. A 50-candle standard lamp is placed 30 cm away from the diffusing screen of a Lummer-Brodhun photometer. At what distance from the screen should a 100-candle lamp be placed if both sides of the screen are to have equal illumination? Calculate the screen illumination.   Ans: 42.4 cm; 556 lumens/m².

22. A standard 100-candle lamp is placed 40 cm away from the diffusing screen of a Lummer-Brodhun photometer. A lamp of unknown source intensity must be placed 70 cm from the screen if both sides of the screen are to be illuminated equally. What is the source intensity of the test lamp? What screen illumination would the test lamp produce if it were located 50 cm away from the screen?

23. Using the response curve of the eye (Fig. 7 on p. 430), estimate the over-all efficiency of an ideal source of white light that radiates a uniform amount of energy in each mμ range between 400 and 700 mμ, and radiates no energy outside this range. This might be considered the goal in fluorescent-lamp design.

24. How many 10-watt tungsten lamps of over-all efficiency 7.8 lumens/watt would be required to produce total luminous flux approximately equal to the flux from a 1000-watt tungsten lamp of over-all efficiency 21.5 lumens/watt? Calculate the costs of producing a flux of 21,500 lumens for 8 hr by a single 1000-watt lamp and by the set of 10-watt tungsten lamps if electrical energy costs 6 cents per kilowatt·hour.

25. A certain room is illuminated by five 40-watt fluorescent lamps of over-all efficiency 58.0 lumens/watt. How many 200-watt tungsten lamps of over-all efficiency 18.3 lumens/watt would be required to produce an approximately equivalent light flux in the room? Compare the costs of illuminating the room by these two methods for a 10-hr day if electrical energy costs 6 cents per kilowatt hour.   Ans: 3; 12 cents, 36 cents.

CHAPTER 22

REFLECTION OF LIGHT

LIGHT TRAVELS in straight lines through a homogeneous isotropic transparent medium such as air. When a light beam strikes a boundary between two media, some or all of the light may be turned back into the first medium; some may pass into the second medium, usually with a change in the direction of propagation. The first effect is known as *reflection;* the second as *refraction.* In this and the following two chapters we shall treat these two phenomena by tracing light *rays.* Treatment of optical phenomena by tracing rays is called *geometrical optics;* this is the simplest approach to use in the treatment of lenses and mirrors and in discussing optical instruments. However, there are certain important phenomena that cannot be treated by the methods of geometrical optics but can only be explained in terms of the wave nature of light; these phenomena are treated in a later chapter called *Physical Optics.*

1. REFLECTION AT PLANE SURFACES

REFLECTION of light occurs in accordance with two experimental laws:

FIRST LAW OF REFLECTION: *The reflected ray lies in the plane containing the incident ray and the normal to the reflecting surface at the point of incidence.*

SECOND LAW OF REFLECTION: *The angle of incidence is equal to the angle of reflection. (The angle of incidence is the angle between the incident ray and the normal; the angle of reflection is the angle between the reflected ray and the normal.)*

In Fig. 1, ABC represents a plane reflecting surface perpendicular to the plane of the paper. The normal BN is in the plane of the paper. If an incident ray IB is in this plane, the first law states that the reflected ray BR is also in the plane of the paper. The second law states that the angle of incidence $i = \angle IBN$ is equal to the angle of reflection $r = \angle RBN$.

Reflection of light from a smooth polished surface is called *regular reflection* or *specular reflection.* Reflection from a rough or 'mat' surface like that of cement or newsprint occurs in many directions when a parallel beam of light is incident on the surface, as indicated in Fig. 2, although

448

the laws of regular reflection are obeyed by any single ray.   The incident beam of light is said to be *diffused* at the rough surface and reflection at

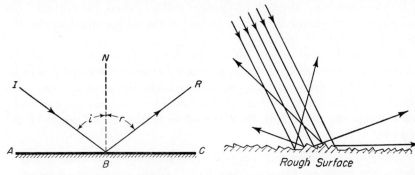

Fig. 1. Reflection of light.

Fig. 2. Diffuse reflection at a rough surface.

a rough surface is called *diffuse reflection.**   It is by diffuse reflection that we are able to see nonluminous bodies when light strikes them.   The

reflected rays from any small portion of a rough surface travel in so many different directions that the small area is visible to us in essentially the same manner as a similar small area on the surface of a luminous body.   On the other hand, we cannot really 'see' a perfect mirror.   Diffuse rather than regular reflection is required to make the surface of a body visible.

Let us next consider the reflection of light by a plane mirror when the light is emitted by a point source near the mirror.   Figure 3 shows three typical rays coming from the point source O (called the *object*) and making angles of incidence i_1, i_2, and i_3 at the reflecting surface of the mirror.   These rays will

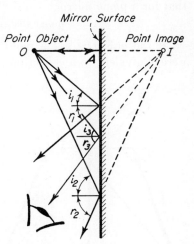

Fig. 3. Formation of a virtual image by a plane mirror.

be reflected from the mirror with angles of reflection $r_1 = i_1$, $r_2 = i_2$, and $r_3 = i_3$, respectively.   An additional ray normal to the mirror is shown

---

* The above discussion is not completely satisfactory, because of course all surfaces are rough on an atomic scale.   But the scale of atomic size is small in comparison with the wavelength of light.   The dividing line between regular and diffuse reflection is not sharp, but if the width of the hills in Fig. 2 is large compared with the wavelength of the light, the reflection is diffuse as in the figure.   On the other hand, if the width of the hills in Fig. 2 were small compared with the wavelength of the light, the reflection would be regular, as in Fig. 1.   Consequently, in order to make a good mirror, a glass or metal surface must be polished so that its irregularities are small in size compared with the wavelength of light.

reflected back along itself. It is a simple matter of geometry to show that all such reflected rays, when extended back of the mirror as shown by broken lines, pass through a common point I, along the normal from the object to the mirror at a distance behind the mirror equal to the distance of the object in front.

When an observer places his eye in the position indicated, all the reflected rays that enter his eye appear to come from the point I, and he apparently sees a luminous point source, called an *image*, at I. Since I is behind the mirror, and the rays that seem to come from I do not really pass through the point I at all, I is said to be the *virtual* image of the object O.

A plane mirror forms a virtual image of a point object, the image being behind the mirror on the normal from the object to the mirror, at a distance behind the mirror equal to that of the object in front.

If we call the distance from the object to the mirror the *object distance* and the distance from the image to the mirror the *image distance*, we conclude that for a plane mirror

image distance = object distance.

If the object is not a point object, it is possible to treat it as if it were equivalent to a collection of point sources as indicated in Fig. 4, in

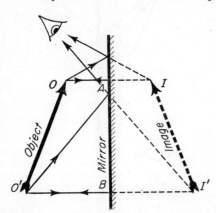

which rays from two points O and O' of the object are traced to the eye. Consideration of Fig. 4 shows that the eye sees a virtual image equal in size to the object, each point of the image being as far behind the mirror as the corresponding point of the object is in front. Since the arrows representing both object and image in the figure are pointing upward, we may also conclude that the image is *upright*. Thus, we may summarize our discussion of the plane mirror by saying that it *forms a virtual, upright image whose size is equal to that of*

Fig. 4. Formation of the image of an extended object.

the object, with image distance equal to object distance. These considerations apply whether the object is self-luminous or whether it is nonluminous with a diffusely reflecting surface which, when illuminated, reflects light rays in all directions.

2. REFLECTION BY CONCAVE SPHERICAL MIRRORS

A spherical mirror is a mirror whose surface can be obtained by cutting off a portion of a reflecting sphere. We shall consider mirrors that might be cut from a sphere by a plane in the manner indicated in Fig. 5. The line *PN* represents the cutting plane, and arc *PSN* the portion of the sphere to be used as the mirror. The distance *PN* is called the *linear aperture* of the mirror, the angle α the *angular aperture*. For reasons that we shall discuss later, the mirror must be only a small portion of the total spherical surface if it is to be of any value in optical instruments. In other words, the *angular aperture* α must be small. If the *inner* surface of the spherical segment *PSN* is the reflecting surface, the spherical mirror is said to be *concave;* if the *outer* surface is used as the reflecting surface, the mirror is said to be *convex*.

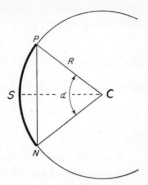

Fig. 5. Construction of a spherical mirror.

The *axis* of a spherical mirror is a line *CS* drawn from the center of the original sphere to the center of the mirror. A spherical mirror can be used to produce images of luminous or illuminated objects placed near its axis. In order to see how images are produced by a concave mirror, let

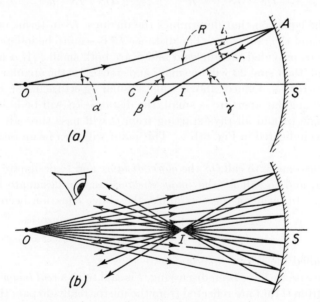

Fig. 6. Formation of a real image of a point object by a concave mirror.

us consider rays from a point object on the mirror axis as shown in Fig. 6. Let *OA* be a ray which strikes the mirror at point *A*; after reflection, this ray traverses the path *AI*, where *I* is on the mirror axis. The normal to the mirror surface at a point *A* can be constructed by drawing the radius *R* from the center of curvature *C*. The angle of reflection *r* will be equal to the angle of incidence i. Remembering that the exterior angle of a triangle is equal to the sum of the opposite interior angles, we may write for triangle OAC:

$$\beta = \alpha + i \quad \text{or} \quad i = \beta - \alpha,$$

and for triangle CAI: $\gamma = \beta + r \quad \text{or} \quad r = \gamma - \beta.$

Since $r = i$, we arrive at the result

$$\gamma - \beta = \beta - \alpha,$$

or
$$\alpha + \gamma = 2\beta.$$

Now the angle β equals the arc AS divided by the radius $R = CS$. We must now introduce the condition that the angles α and γ be small (meaning a small fraction of a radian). If these angles are small, they can be measured to a good approximation by the ratios

$$\alpha = AS/OS; \qquad \gamma = AS/IS.$$

In this case the equation $\alpha + \gamma = 2\beta$ becomes

$$\frac{AS}{OS} + \frac{AS}{IS} = 2\,\frac{AS}{R}, \qquad \text{or} \qquad \frac{1}{OS} + \frac{1}{IS} = \frac{2}{R}.$$

This is the equation that determines the distance IS in terms of the distance OS and the radius R. The distance IS is seen to be independent of the angle α, provided the angles α and γ are both small. If α and γ are both small, their sum 2β will be small; and since 2β is the angular aperture of the mirror as defined above, this angular aperture must be small. When the angular aperture is small, the distance IS will be independent of the angle α, and all rays starting from O will pass through the *same* point I, as indicated in Fig. 6(b). This point will then be an *image* of the object O.

It is customary to call OS the *object distance* and to designate it by the symbol p; and to call IS the *image distance* and to designate it by the symbol q. In terms of these symbols, the above equation becomes

$$\frac{1}{p} + \frac{1}{q} = \frac{2}{R}. \qquad \left\{ \begin{array}{l} p = \text{object distance} \\ q = \text{image distance} \\ R = \text{radius of curvature} \end{array} \right\} \quad (1)$$

This is called the *mirror equation*.

In the case we have been discussing, I is said to be a *real image*, because the rays from O that are reflected from the mirror really do pass through I. If an observer places his eye in the cone of rays proceeding to the left from I in Fig. 6(b) and looks toward the mirror, he will apparently see a source of light at I, if O is a luminous point. Or the real image at I can be observed by placing a small screen at this position; the introduction of the screen will cut off some of the rays from O before they reach the mirror, but an image can still be observed at I unless *all* the light from O is stopped before it reaches the mirror. A *real* image can be caught on a screen, a *virtual* image cannot.

Now let us look more closely at equation (1). We note first that the equation is symmetric in p and q; that is, p and q can be interchanged without altering the equation. This symmetry is associated with the geometrical fact that object and image positions can be interchanged in Fig. 6. If the object were placed at point I in Fig. 6 and rays were then drawn from this point *to* the mirror, they would be reflected back to a focus at point O. In fact, they would be just the rays shown in Fig. 6 *traced backwards.*

Equation (1) tells us that when $p = R$, q also equals R. This statement is correct because a set of rays proceeding outward from the center of curvature would all strike the mirror normally and be reflected right back through the center of curvature. Now let us see what happens as the object distance increases. As p increases in (1), q decreases. The largest value p can have is ∞; in this case $1/p = 0$ and $q = \frac{1}{2} R$ (see Fig. 7). 'Object at infinity' means, physically, that the rays coming from the object are parallel. The image position in this case—the position at which *parallel light* is focused—is called the *principal focus* of the mirror, and the distance of the principal focus from the mirror, $\frac{1}{2} R$, is called the

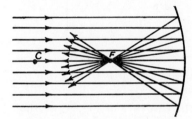

focal length of the mirror. Thus, the focal length of a concave mirror, denoted by f, is

$$f = \frac{1}{2} R. \tag{2}$$

If equation (1) be rewritten in terms of the focal length, it takes the form

Fig. 7. Parallel light rays converge at the principal focus F.

$$\frac{1}{p} + \frac{1}{q} = \frac{1}{f}. \tag{3}$$

Study of this equation shows that as the object distance p decreases from ∞ to f, the image distance q increases from f to ∞. But what happens when the object distance is less than f—that is, when the object is 'inside' the principal focus of the mirror? Formal application of (3) would give a *negative* value for q, which would suggest that the image was *behind* the mirror, and hence *virtual*. Accurate analysis of this case, similar to the above analysis of Fig. 6(a), shows that these suppositions are correct. We omit this analysis, which shows that we arrive at the situation of Fig. 8, where the object O is inside the principal focus,

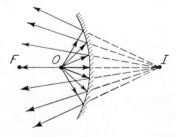

Fig. 8. Formation of a virtual image of a point object by a concave mirror.

marked F, and the image is virtual. *Equations (1) and (3) still apply when the object distance p is less than f = ½R; the fact that the image distance q comes out negative indicates that the image is virtual and behind the mirror.*

So far, we have considered only the image of a point. Now we shall consider the image of an extended object AO lying in a plane normal to the mirror axis in Fig. 9. We know that an image of A is formed at a position B given by equation (1). By the previous analysis we know also that an image of O will be formed at some point I along the radius OC of the sphere, provided none of the rays from O to the mirror make too large an angle of incidence. Since we know that under these conditions all rays from O are focused at a common point, we can determine the position

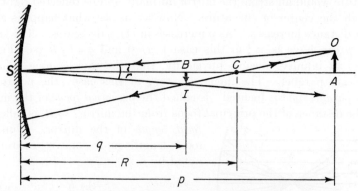

Fig. 9. Formation of a real image BI of an extended object AO by a concave mirror.

of this point from any two rays. Using the two rays of Fig. 9, we shall show that the point I lies immediately beneath B, and hence that *a plane object has a plane image.* Of the two rays chosen, one passes through the center of curvature C and is reflected back along itself; the other strikes the mirror at point S on the axis and is reflected with angles i and r equal. To prove the above statements we shall show that the distance q of the point of intersection of these two rays satisfies exactly the relation (1).

For the moment, then, forget that B in Fig. 9 is intended to represent the image of A and consider it merely as the foot of the perpendicular dropped from the point of intersection I to the axis. Since the triangles OAC and IBC are similar,

$$OA/IB = CA/BC.$$

Since the triangles OSA and ISB are similar,

$$OA/IB = SA/SB.$$

Combining these relations, we obtain

$$\frac{CA}{BC} = \frac{SA}{SB}.$$

When these quantities are written in terms of the image distance q, the object distance p, and the radius of curvature R, the equation becomes

$$\frac{p-R}{R-q}=\frac{p}{q},$$

which by cross multiplication gives

$$pq-Rq=Rp-pq$$

or
$$Rq+Rp=2pq.$$

On dividing this equation by pqR, we obtain

$$\frac{1}{p}+\frac{1}{q}=\frac{2}{R}.$$

Here q represents the distance BP when B is considered as the foot of the perpendicular dropped from the image I of point O. But this is the same relation as (1), which gives the distance of the *image B* of point A. Hence the images of O and A lie at the same distance from the mirror.

An exactly similar argument can be applied when the image is virtual to show that a plane object has a plane virtual image. This is left to the student as an exercise.

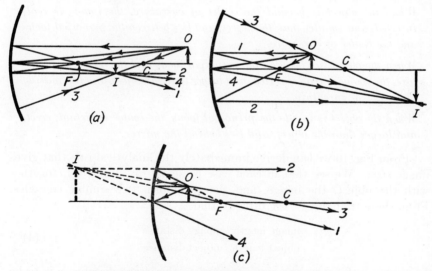

Fig. 10. Principal-ray diagrams for a concave mirror.

The best understanding of the characteristics of image formation by concave mirrors is obtained by drawing principal-ray diagrams. Such diagrams are shown in Fig. 10 for the cases in which the object is (a) beyond the center of curvature, (b) between the principal focus and the center of curvature, and (c) inside the principal focus. The so-called *principal rays* are four rays whose paths, from point O of the object in Fig.

10 to the mirror and back, are very easy to trace. The principal rays, numbered correspondingly in Fig. 10, are:

1. The ray that leaves O parallel to the axis and is reflected back through the principal focus F (a ray of Fig. 7).
2. The ray that leaves O along the line through the principal focus and is reflected parallel to the axis (a reversed ray of Fig. 7).
3. The ray that leaves O along the line through the center of curvature C and is reflected back along itself (as in Fig. 9).
4. The ray that strikes the mirror at the axis and is reflected back at an equal angle on the opposite side of the axis (as in Fig. 9).

These four rays intersect at the point I of the image, and serve to locate the position, size, and orientation of the image graphically. The student will find that the sketching of rough principal-ray diagrams like those of Fig. 10 will assist him in the understanding of image formation, and will furnish a valuable check on analytical work. While any two rays, accurately traced, will locate the image, it is safer in making rough diagrams to trace at least three.

It is good practice to sketch a principal-ray diagram in connection with *every* problem on optical image formation. From the three diagrams of Fig. 10 we see at once that:

When the object is beyond the center of curvature, the image is real, inverted, and smaller than the object, and lies between the principal focus and the center of curvature.

When the object lies between the principal focus and the center of curvature, the image is real, inverted, and larger than the object, and lies outside the center of curvature.

When the object is inside the principal focus, the image is virtual, erect, and larger than the object, and lies behind the mirror.

From Fig. 10 we can derive immediately the analytical rule that gives image size. We see that in each case principal ray number 4, together with the object, the image, and the axis, form two similar triangles. From these triangles we see directly that

$$\frac{\text{image length}}{\text{object length}} = \frac{\text{image distance}}{\text{object distance}}. \tag{4}$$

In applying this rule, the sign attached to the image distance q is to be ignored.

Example. *A concave mirror of 2-ft radius of curvature is used to project the image of a lamp filament on a wall 15 ft from the mirror. Where must the filament be placed, and what is the size and character of the image?*

A real image beyond the radius of curvature can only occur in the case of Fig. 10(b), in which the object is between the focus and the center of curvature. From this figure we see that the image is *real, inverted,* and *enlarged.* We obtain the object distance p by substituting $R=2$ ft and $q=15$ ft in (1):

$$\frac{1}{p}+\frac{1}{15\ \text{ft}}=\frac{2}{2\ \text{ft}}, \quad \text{or} \quad p={}^{15}\!/_{14}\ \text{ft.}$$

The enlargement is given by (4) as

$$\text{enlargement}=\frac{\text{image length}}{\text{object length}}=\frac{15\ \text{ft}}{{}^{15}\!/_{14}\ \text{ft}}=14.$$

The image is 14 times the size of the filament in any linear dimension (height, width, etc.).

In our discussion of the formation of images by concave mirrors, we have assumed that the mirrors were of small angular aperture. If the

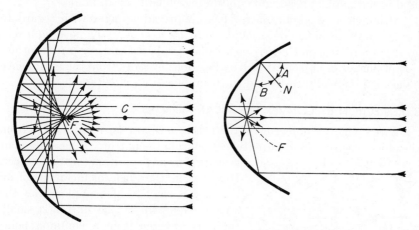

Fig. 11. Reflection of parallel rays by a spherical mirror of large angular aperture.

Fig. 12. Reflection of parallel rays by a parabolic mirror.

mirror has a large angular aperture, image formation is imperfect because the reflected rays do not all pass through a single point. This effect is known as *spherical aberration.* Figure 11 shows a concave spherical mirror of large aperture, on which parallel rays are incident. It will be noted that reflected rays cross the mirror axis farther and farther from the principal focus as the paths of the incident rays are drawn farther and farther from the axis. The envelope of these rays forms a 'caustic curve' which has a cusp at the principal focus F.

It is possible to eliminate spherical aberration for distant objects by using a mirror that is not spherical but is in the shape of the paraboloid of revolution obtained by rotating a parabola about its own axis. Such a mirror is usually called a *parabolic mirror* (rather than a paraboloidal mirror). The parabolic section of such a mirror is shown in Fig. 12. It is a geometrical property of the parabola that the normal to the curve at any point bisects the angle between a line drawn to that point parallel to the axis of the parabola and a line drawn from the focus of the parabola to the point in question.   Therefore, the angles A and B in Fig. 12 are equal for all lines drawn parallel to the axis.   Since this equality of angles is also the condition for regular reflection, it follows that all rays parallel to the axis pass through the focus F after reflection and also that all rays emanating from a point source at the focus are reflected from the mirror as rays parallel to the axis.   The parabolic mirror may therefore be used either to concentrate parallel rays from a distant point source at a sharply defined focus or to send out a parallel beam of light from a point source at F.   The first use is illustrated in the large reflecting mirrors in astronomical telescopes.   The second use is illustrated in the parabolic reflectors used in automobile headlights and in searchlights of all kinds.

Although a parabolic mirror has unique advantages with regard to formation of an image of an object *near the axis of the parabola at a very great distance*, it is not nearly so good as a spherical mirror in the formation of images of objects at nearby locations or away from the axis; hence its use is practically restricted to the applications cited above.

3. REFLECTION BY CONVEX SPHERICAL MIRRORS

WHEN A POINT object is on the axis of a *convex* mirror, the rays from the object clearly *diverge* after reflection from the mirror.   This statement is true for any position of the object. However, if the angle of incidence of all the rays is small, which implies that the angular aperture of the mirror is small, the rays diverge from a common point as indicated schematically in Fig. 13. This point constitutes a virtual image of the object.   A person looking into the convex mirror of Fig. 13 sees a mirrored image of O at I, much as in the case of a plane mirror.

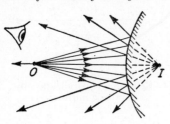

Fig. 13. Formation of a virtual image of a point object by a convex mirror.

A proof that such an image is formed can be given by methods similar to those we used in connection with Fig. 6.   Also, we can show that a plane object such as OA in Fig. 14 has a plane image IB.   We shall omit these proofs; but granted that an image of point O in Fig. 14 is formed at some point I, we shall determine the location of I by finding the intersection of the two rays shown in Fig. 14.   One of these rays heads from O toward the center of curvature and is reflected back along itself; the other strikes the mirror at the axis and is reflected symmetrically.   In the case of convex mirrors, *the radius of curvature R is considered to be a negative number;* hence, the distance from the mirror to the center of curvature is represented by $-R$.   As is customary in the case of virtual images, *the image distance q is considered to be a negative number;* hence, the distance from the image to the mirror is represented by $-q$.

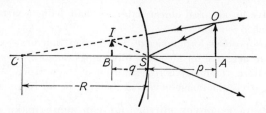

Fig. 14. Image formation by a convex mirror.

From the similar triangles IBS and OAS, $OA/IB = SA/BS$.
From the similar triangles IBC and OAC, $OA/IB = CA/CB$.

Hence
$$\frac{SA}{BS} = \frac{CA}{CB}.$$

Inserting the values of these lengths in terms of p, q, and R gives

$$\frac{p}{-q} = \frac{(-R)+p}{(-R)-(-q)} = \frac{p-R}{q-R}.$$

Clearing fractions gives $-pq + qR = pq - pR$
or $qR + pR = 2pq.$

Dividing through by pqR, we again obtain the *mirror equation*

$$\frac{1}{p} + \frac{1}{q} = \frac{2}{R}. \tag{5}$$

For a convex mirror we must remember that R is a negative number; this convention makes q come out negative for any positive value of p, indicating that *the image is always virtual and behind the mirror.*

A study of equation (5) shows that as the object distance p varies from 0 to ∞, the image position varies from $q = 0$ to $q = \frac{1}{2} R$. Object at infinity corresponds to parallel light incident on the mirror as in Fig. 15. The virtual-image point in this case is called the *principal focus* of the convex mirror. The distance of the principal focus from the mirror, $q = \frac{1}{2} R$, is called the *focal length* and is denoted by f. Just as R is taken as a negative number, *the focal length $f = \frac{1}{2} R$ is a negative number in the case of a convex mirror.* In terms of focal length the mirror equation takes the form

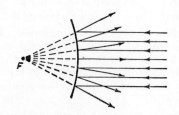

Fig. 15. Parallel light rays diverge from the principal focus F of a convex mirror. The principal focus is behind the mirror, halfway between the mirror and the center of curvature C.

$$\frac{1}{p} + \frac{1}{q} = \frac{1}{f} = \frac{2}{R}. \tag{6}$$

It is convenient that *equation* (6) *applies to all types of spherical mirrors with the sign conventions we have adopted:*

> p is positive for any real object (later we shall define a virtual object for which p is negative).
> f and R are positive for a concave (converging) mirror.
> f and R are negative for a convex (diverging) mirror.
> If q is positive, the image is real (in front of the mirror).
> If q is negative, the image is virtual (behind the mirror).

In the case of a convex mirror, one can again make good use of a principal-ray diagram such as that in Fig. 16. The four principal rays shown in Fig. 16 are the same as the four listed on p. 456 in the discussion of the concave mirror.

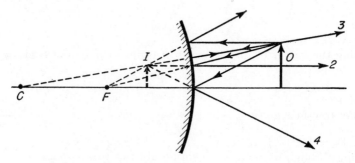

Fig. 16. Principal-ray diagram for a convex mirror.

From Fig. 14, we conclude that the image is always erect and smaller than the object, and we obtain the same analytical expression (4) for image length as in the case of a concave mirror.

PROBLEMS

1. A man strikes a match in a dark room and sees the virtual image of the match by light reflected by a plane mirror. If the image *appears* to be 16 ft from the lighted match, what is the distance from the match to the mirror?   Ans: 8 ft.

2. A man 6 ft tall stands 4 ft in front of a large vertical plane mirror. Where will a virtual image of the man be formed? How tall will the image be?

3. A woman's eyes are 5 ft from the floor while she is wearing shoes. The top of her hat is 6 ft from the floor. At what height from the floor should the lower edge of a 3-ft vertical mirror be placed so that she can see herself, with hat, at full length? Show that the answer is independent of the distance the woman stands from the mirror, and draw a ray diagram to illustrate this point clearly.
Ans: 2.5 ft.

4. A young woman 5 ft 2 in tall wishes to purchase a mirror just long enough to enable her to see a full-length image of herself. How long should the mirror be?

5. Show that if two adjacent walls of a rectangular room are mirror surfaces, an observer sees exactly three images of himself and of all other objects in the room. Locate the images for arbitrary position of the object, and trace the rays associated with each image. The rays should be traced from a point of the object to the observer's eye.

6. Show that if the mirror walls of Prob. 5 include an angle of 60°, there are five images. Locate the images and trace rays as in Prob. 5.

7. What does an observer see if two adjacent walls and the ceiling of a rectangular room are mirror surfaces? Explain clearly. Ans: seven images.

8. What does an observer see if two opposite walls of a rectangular room are mirror surfaces? if three walls are mirror surfaces?

9. In Prob. 7 show that if a narrow beam of light strikes near the mirrored corner of the ceiling from any direction, it is reflected back in a direction exactly opposite. How is this properly employed in retrodirective reflectors used for highway markers?

10. Sensitive instruments (for example the Cavendish apparatus, p. 96) frequently measure the twist of a fiber by attaching a tiny plane mirror to the fiber and reflecting a narrow beam of light from the mirror to a scale. In this arrangement the light beam acts as an inertialess pointer. Show that if the mirror turns through angle θ, the reflected light beam turns through the angle 2θ. If it is desired that each minute of arc that the fiber twists result in a motion of 1 mm of the reflected beam on the scale, how far must the scale be from the mirror?

11. Prove geometrically that all rays from O in Fig. 3 that are reflected from the mirror appear to come from a common point I located as described in the text.

12. An object 4 cm tall is placed at a distance of 50 cm from a concave mirror with radius of curvature 40 cm. Find the image distance, size, and character (real or virtual, erect or inverted?). Sketch the principal-ray diagram.

13. An object 4 cm tall is placed 30 cm from a concave mirror with radius of curvature 40 cm. Find the image distance, size, and character. Sketch the principal-ray diagram. Ans: 60 cm; 8 cm.

14. An object 2 cm tall is placed 6 cm from a concave mirror of 10 cm radius of curvature. Determine image distance, size, and character. Sketch the principal-ray diagram.

15. An object 4 cm tall is placed 10 cm away from a concave mirror with radius of curvature 40 cm. Find the image distance and the image size. Sketch the principal-ray diagram. Ans: −20 cm; 8 cm.

16. An object 0.5 cm tall is placed 1.5 cm away from a concave mirror of radius of curvature 10 cm. Determine image distance, size, and character. Sketch the principal-ray diagram.

17. An object 4 cm tall is placed 40 cm away from a concave mirror of 40 cm radius of curvature. Determine the image distance, size, and character. Sketch the principal-ray diagram. Ans: 40 cm; 4 cm.

18. An object 8 cm tall is placed 20 cm away from a concave mirror of 40 cm radius of curvature. Determine the image distance. Place the head of the object 4 cm above the axis, the tail 4 cm below the axis, and draw a ray diagram showing clearly the course of a number of rays from each end of the object and from the mid-point of the object, after reflection from the mirror. Be prepared to discuss thoroughly this important case of an object at the principal focus. Discuss the image character as a limiting case of what happens if the object moves toward the focus (a) from positions slightly inside, (b) from positions slightly outside.

19. By an argument exactly like that used in the text in connection with Fig. 9, derive the mirror equation for the case in which the object is inside the principal focus and the image is virtual. Draw a new diagram similar to Fig. 9 for this case, and denote the distance of the image behind the mirror by $-q$.

20. Let R be the radius of curvature and f be the focal length of a concave mirror. Five possible object positions are (1) $p > R$, (2) $p = R$, (3) $f < p < R$, (4) $p = f$, (5) $0 < p < f$. Which ones of these five positions give (a) an inverted diminished image? (b) an inverted enlarged image? (c) an inverted image equal in size to the object? (d) an image at infinity? (e) an erect image equal in size to the object? (f) an erect enlarged image? (g) a real image?

21. An object is placed x cm in front of a concave mirror of radius of curvature 10 cm. What are the least and greatest values of x for which (a) the image is real? (b) the image is erect? (c) the image is larger than the object?

22. Concave mirror A has a linear aperture of 10 cm and radius of curvature 10 cm, and concave mirror B has an aperture of 15 cm and focal length 12 cm. For which of these mirrors will the effects of spherical aberration be the more troublesome? Why?

23. An object 4 cm tall is placed on the axis at a distance of 50 cm from a convex mirror with radius of curvature -40 cm. Find the image distance, size, and character. Sketch the principal-ray diagram.   Ans: -14.3 cm; 1.14 cm.

24. An object 4 cm tall is placed on the axis at a distance of 10 cm from a convex mirror of radius of curvature -40 cm. Find the image position, size, and character. Sketch the principal-ray diagram.

25. How far from a convex mirror with radius of curvature -40 cm should an object be placed in order to produce an image one-half as tall as the object?
Ans: 20 cm.

26. When an object is placed 30 cm away from a convex mirror, a virtual image one-third as tall as the object is produced. Find the focal length and radius of curvature of the mirror.

CHAPTER 23

REFRACTION OF LIGHT

IN THIS CHAPTER we first state the laws governing the refraction of light when it passes from one medium into another. We then give a treatment of image formation by lenses in much the same way as we treated image formation by mirrors in the preceding chapter. Optical instruments utilizing lenses and mirrors form the subject of the next chapter.

1. REFRACTION OF LIGHT

WHEN LIGHT strikes the surface of a *transparent* substance like glass, a considerable fraction of the incident light penetrates the glass; unless the incidence is normal to the surface, this light experiences an abrupt change in direction. The bending of a light ray in passing from one medium to another is called *refraction*.

The behavior of light in passing from one medium into another medium is shown in Fig. 1, which uses air and water as examples of the two media. Rays passing from air to water or glass are bent *toward* the normal at the interface; rays passing from water or glass into air are bent *away* from the normal. Water and glass are said to be *optically denser* than air. It will be noted from the figure that a portion of the light is reflected at the interface and a portion is transmitted. The ratio of the light transmitted to that reflected depends upon the nature of the two media and upon the angle of incidence.

Refraction takes place in accordance with two experimental laws:

FIRST LAW OF REFRACTION: *The refracted ray lies in the plane containing the incident ray and the normal to the interface at the point of incidence.*

SECOND LAW OF REFRACTION: *The ratio of the sine of the angle of incidence to the sine of the angle of refraction when light passes from one medium into a second is a constant that is independent of the angle of incidence, but that may depend on the wavelength of the light. (Angles of incidence and of refraction are measured from the normal.)*

In Fig. 1 the incident ray, the refracted ray, and the normal to the interface are all in the plane of the paper; the plane surface of the water is at right angles to the plane of the paper.   The second law of refraction can be written for the cases shown in (a) and (b) in the forms

$$\frac{\sin i}{\sin r} = \mu_{WA} \quad \text{and} \quad \frac{\sin i'}{\sin r'} = \mu_{AW}, \tag{1}$$

where the constant μ_{WA} is called the *index of refraction* of water with respect to air, and μ_{AW} the index of refraction of air with respect to water.

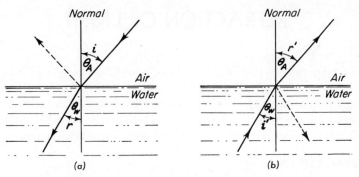

Fig. 1. Refraction at a plane surface. Broken lines indicate reflected rays.

It is found experimentally that the path of the refracted ray is completely reversible; that is, if i' in Fig. 1(b) equals r in Fig. 1(a), then r' will equal i.   Hence we conclude that

$$\mu_{AW} = 1/\mu_{WA},$$

and, if we let θ_A be the angle between the normal and the ray in air, and θ_W be the angle between the normal and the ray in water, both of the equations (1) take the form

$$\frac{\sin\theta_A}{\sin\theta_W} = \mu_{WA}. \tag{2}$$

The first law of refraction has been known since the third century B.C.; the second law of refraction is known as *Snell's law* and was discovered early in the seventeenth century.*

Refraction can be readily understood in terms of a difference of the speed of light in the two media.   Consider the situation shown in Fig. 2. OA and PB represent two rays normal to a plane wave-front, a portion of which is represented by a line such as AB.   Seven successive positions of this wave-front, with equal time intervals, are shown in Fig. 2.   After refraction of the light, the wave-front reaches position CD.   Now

---

* The Dutch astronomer Willebrord Snell (1591–1626) was the first to discover the second law of refraction, but the results of his investigations were not published until after his death.   The law was discovered independently and first reported by René Descartes (1596–1650).

$\angle BAD = i$, since the sides of the angles BAD and i are mutually perpendicular; $\angle ADC = r$ for the same reason. Thus, Snell's law can be written as

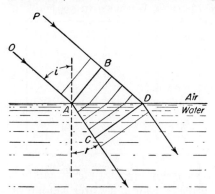

$$\mu_{WA} = \frac{\sin i}{\sin r} = \frac{\sin BAD}{\sin ADC}$$

$$= \frac{BD/AD}{AC/AD} = \frac{BD}{AC}. \quad (3)$$

Since A and B are points on an incident plane wave and C and D are points on the same wave-front after refraction has occurred, it follows that the time required for the wave-front to move from B to D in air must be equal to the time for the refracted wave-front to move from A to C in water. If c_A represents the speed of light in air and c_W the speed of light

Fig. 2. Refraction at a plane surface. The wave-front turns because the speed of light in water is less than in air. It is useful to visualize a line of soldiers marching from a dry field (air) into a muddy field (water) where the marching speed is less. The line would tend to turn as indicated.

in water, equating these two times gives

$$BD/c_A = AC/c_W, \quad \text{or} \quad BD/AC = c_A/c_W.$$

Therefore, in (3), $\mu_{WA} = c_A/c_W.$ (4)

Equation (4) states that the index of refraction of water with respect to air is equal to the ratio of the speed of light in air to the speed of light in water. Direct experimental measurements of the speeds of light in air and water are in agreement with this equation and furnished early support for the wave theory of light.

In view of the fact that the speed of light is greater in vacuum than in any transparent material medium, it is desirable to refer the indices of all optical media to vacuum.

> The **absolute index of refraction** of any medium is defined as the index of refraction of the medium relative to vacuum.

If we let c be the speed of light in vacuum, and c_M the speed of light in medium M, the absolute refractive index of medium M is

$$\mu_M = c/c_M.$$

The absolute index of refraction is usually called just *the index of refraction* or the *refractive index* of the medium.

Table I gives indices of refraction for various gases, liquids, and solids, for light of a particular wavelength. Since the index of refraction of air is very nearly equal to 1, it is usually possible to treat it as unity.

TABLE I

INDICES OF REFRACTION FOR YELLOW LIGHT OF WAVELENGTH 590 mμ

Gases at NTP		Solids at 20° C	
Dry air	1.00029	Diamond	2.419
Carbon dioxide	1.00045	Fluorite	1.434
Liquids at 20° C		Glass (typical values)	
Benzene	1.501	Crown	1.517
Carbon disulfide	1.642	Commercial plate	1.523
Carbon tetrachloride	1.461	Light flint	1.574
Ethyl alcohol	1.354	Dense flint	1.656
Water	1.334	Quartz (fused)	1.458

The relative index of refraction μ_{WA} occurring in equation (4) can now be rewritten in terms of the absolute indices for air and water as follows:

$$\mu_{WA}=\frac{c_A}{c_W}=\frac{c/c_W}{c/c_A}=\frac{\mu_W}{\mu_A}.$$

When this expression is substituted in (2), we get the most convenient form of Snell's law:

$$\frac{\sin\theta_A}{\sin\theta_W}=\frac{\mu_W}{\mu_A}, \quad \text{or} \quad \mu_A\sin\theta_A=\mu_W\sin\theta_W.$$

This relation can be immediately generalized to apply to the passage of a light ray through the interface between any two media I and II:

$$\mu_I\sin\theta_I=\mu_{II}\sin\theta_{II}, \qquad \left(\begin{matrix}\text{SNELL'S}\\\text{LAW}\end{matrix}\right) \quad (5)$$

where μ_I and μ_{II} are the absolute refractive indices of media I and II and θ_I and θ_{II} are the angles between rays and normals in media I and II, respectively. Equation (5) applies equally well for rays incident on either side of the interface. This is the easiest form in which to remember and to use Snell's law.

We are now in a position to discuss the phenomenon of *total reflection*. Figure 3 shows the interface between two media I and II, of which medium II is assumed to have the higher index of refraction—one says that II is *optically denser* than I. According to (5), if $\mu_{II}>\mu_I$, then $\theta_{II}<\theta_I$. A ray passing from I into II is bent toward the normal, and no peculiarities arise. But consider the three rays (a), (b), (c) *within the denser medium* in Fig. 3, heading

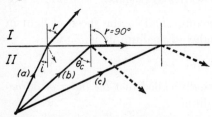

Fig. 3. Total reflection.

toward the interface. Ray (a) has a small angle of incidence and is refracted away from the normal. As the angle of incidence increases, we reach the situation shown in (b) where the angle of refraction is 90°. The angle of incidence for which the angle of refraction is 90° is called the *critical angle* θ_c. Substituting $\theta_I = 90°$ ($\sin\theta_I = 1$) in (5) gives the formula

$$\sin\theta_c = \mu_I/\mu_{II}. \qquad\qquad (\mu_I < \mu_{II}) \quad (6)$$

Substitution of a value of θ_{II} larger than the critical angle in (5) gives a value for $\sin\theta_I$ that is greater than unity, and θ_I does not represent any real angle. No refracted ray is possible. For angles of incidence greater than θ_c, as in the case of ray (c) in Fig. 3, the ray is *totally reflected* at the interface, and no light passes into the other medium. Notice that *total reflection takes place only for light within a medium of higher optical density at a surface of contact with a medium of lower optical density.*

The relation (6) furnishes the basis for a number of types of convenient refractometers designed to determine an unknown index of refraction by measurement of a critical angle. For example, the index of refraction of a small drop of liquid can be measured by placing the drop on the surface of glass of known index and measuring the critical angle for total reflection of light traveling within the glass and reflected at the surface of liquid contact, provided that the liquid has lower optical density than the glass.

Because total reflection is really *total*, it furnishes the basis for a perfect mirror which is utilized in various ways in optical instruments. A

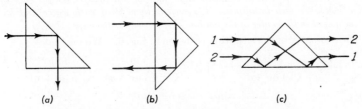

(a)   (b)   (c)

Fig. 4. Total internal reflection in glass prisms.

beam of light may be turned through 90° or 180° by a glass prism with 45° and 90° angles. These applications of total reflection are shown in Fig. 4, (a) and (b). Another utilization of total reflection is illustrated in Fig. 4(c), which shows a glass prism that can be used to invert an image without changing the direction of the light beam. Prisms giving total internal reflection are frequently used in binoculars.

Refraction causes an object immersed in water to appear closer to the surface than it actually is. In order to understand this phenomenon, consider Fig. 5. In this sketch, O represents a point on a submerged object. Because of refraction, the ray OP would appear to an observer in the air to come from point D. Now $\angle AOP = i$ and $\angle ADP = r$. Therefore,

$$\frac{\tan i}{\tan r} = \frac{AP/AO}{AP/AD} = \frac{AD}{AO} = \frac{\text{apparent depth}}{\text{actual depth}}.$$

If i is small, the tangents of i and r are almost equal to the sines of i and r, and we may write

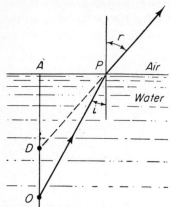

$$\frac{\sin i}{\sin r} = \frac{AD}{AO} = \frac{\text{apparent depth}}{\text{actual depth}} = \frac{1}{\mu_W},$$

where μ_W is the refractive index of water and the refractive index of air is taken as 1. Therefore, for a submerged body *viewed almost vertically:*

$$\text{apparent depth} = (\text{actual depth})/\mu_W. \quad (7)$$

Fig. 5. Apparent depth of a submerged object.

In deriving (7), we have used only a single ray. Actually, many rays will reach the eyes of an observer looking vertically downward at the object in the water, but these rays will all have angles of incidence and refraction small enough to permit the tangents to be approximated by sines. Equation (7) will apply to all such rays, so we see that point D will be the image of O. Submerged objects viewed from directions other than the vertical appear closer to the surface than is indicated by (7).

Example. *A cylindrical tin cup is 3 inches in diameter. A person looks into the cup over the rim at such an angle that he can just see the far edge of the bottom when the cup is empty. The cup is then filled with water and he can just see a spot in the center of the bottom. How deep is the cup?*

The geometry of the situation is shown in Fig. 6. We see that

$$\sin\alpha = \frac{3\text{ in}}{\sqrt{9\text{ in}^2 + d^2}}; \qquad \sin\beta = \frac{1.5\text{ in}}{\sqrt{2.25\text{ in}^2 + d^2}} = \frac{3\text{ in}}{\sqrt{9\text{ in}^2 + 4d^2}}.$$

Hence

$$\frac{\sin\alpha}{\sin\beta} = \sqrt{\frac{9\text{ in}^2 + 4d^2}{9\text{ in}^2 + d^2}}. \qquad (i)$$

When this ratio equals 1.33, the refractive index of water, the bent line in Fig. 6 will suitably represent a light ray refracted at the water surface. Setting this ratio equals to 1.33 gives

$$d = 1.78\text{ in}$$

as the critical depth of the cup.

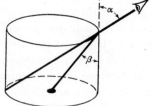

Fig. 6. A cup 3 inches in diameter and of depth d.

We notice that the ratio (i) increases if d increases; hence for a deeper cup, the ray from the spot to the rim is not refracted sufficiently to reach the eye. On the other hand, if d is less than 1.78, the ratio (i) is less than 1.33, so the ray from center to rim will be refracted too much to reach the eye. This means, as you should verify, that the eye can see the spot (by some other ray through the water surface) as well as some of the bottom of the cup to the right of the spot.

2. IMAGE FORMATION BY LENSES

WE ARE now in a position to consider the ways in which the refractive properties of transparent substances can be used in the design of the lenses used to produce images in optical instruments. Lenses are made of transparent materials with polished surfaces, at least one of which is curved.
The commonest form of simple lens has two surfaces that can be considered as parts of spheres as in Fig. 7. The line joining the centers of the two spheres is called the *principal axis*, or merely the *axis* of the lens. We shall consider chiefly lenses made of dense optical materials such as glass, and designed for use in air. Lenses are usually classified as *converging* or *diverging*, depending upon their effects upon incident parallel rays. A lens is regarded as 'thin' if the lens thickness t is

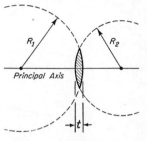

Fig. 7. Geometry of lens surfaces.

small compared with the radii of curvature, R_1 and R_2.

As indicated in Fig. 8, a lens thicker in the middle tends to *converge* incident parallel rays; a lens thicker at the edges than in the center tends to *diverge* parallel rays. The cross sections of common types of lenses are shown in Fig. 9; the first three are converging, the last three diverging.

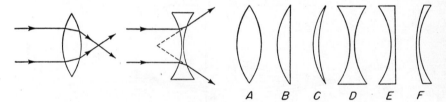

Fig. 8. Deviation of parallel light rays by lenses.

Fig. 9. Common lens types: A, double-convex; B, plano-convex; C, concavo-convex; D, double-concave; E, plano-concave; F, convexo-concave.

Lenses produce images of luminous or illuminated objects. In order to show how images are produced, let us consider Fig. 10. Part (a) of this figure shows a ray leaving a point object O on the lens axis at a distance p from the lens; after passing through the lens, this ray again reaches the lens axis at point I at a distance q from the lens. Part (b) shows the refraction of the ray at the first surface only. By Snell's law, we may write

$$\sin i_1 = \mu \, \sin r_1, \qquad (8)$$

where the index of refraction of air is taken as unity and that of the glass as μ, and where i_1 and r_1 are the angles of incidence and of refraction. If i_1 and r_1 are sufficiently small, the sines of these angles may be replaced by the angles themselves, and (8) becomes

$$i_1 = \mu r_1.$$

By consideration of the exterior angles of the triangles in part (b) of Fig. 10, it can be seen that

$$i_1 = \theta + \alpha \quad \text{and} \quad r_1 = \alpha - \gamma;$$

therefore,
$$\theta + \alpha = \mu(\alpha - \gamma). \tag{9}$$

Similarly, Fig. 10(c) shows the refraction at the second lens surface. The ray coming from the left in this figure is the same ray, in the glass, as

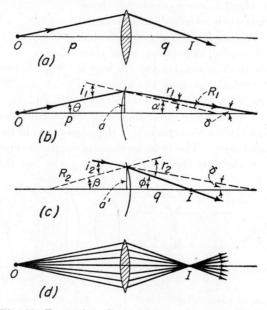

Fig. 10. Formation of a real image of a point object.

that which proceeds to the right in (b). By writing Snell's law for the second lens surface and considering the triangles shown in part (c) of Fig. 10, we may write, for small angles,

$$r_2 = \mu i_2;$$

or
$$\beta + \phi = \mu(\beta + \gamma). \tag{10}$$

By adding relations (9) and (10), we obtain

$$\theta + \alpha + \beta + \phi = \mu(\alpha + \beta)$$

or
$$\theta + \phi = (\mu - 1)(\alpha + \beta). \tag{11}$$

If we assume that the thickness of the lens is negligible compared with p, q, R_1, and R_2, then it does not matter from exactly what point of the lens p and q are measured, and the height a in Fig. 10(b) can be set equal to the height a' in (c). Then by considering that all angles are small enough to be replaced by their sines or tangents, we can write the following approximate values for the angles:

$$\theta = a/p, \quad \phi = a/q, \quad \alpha = a/R_1, \quad \beta = a/R_2.$$

Substituting these values for the angles in (11) and dividing by a gives the *lens equation:*

$$\frac{1}{p} + \frac{1}{q} = (\mu - 1)\left(\frac{1}{R_1} + \frac{1}{R_2}\right), \tag{12}$$

where p is the object distance, q is the image distance, and R_1 and R_2 are the radii of curvature of the lens surfaces.

Since there is nothing unique about the particular ray shown in Fig. 10, this relation holds for all rays passing from the object to the lens, provided that only small angles are involved, and we may therefore conclude that all such rays passing from the point object O to the lens also pass through point I, as indicated in part (d) of Fig. 10. Hence, a real image appears at point I. Although we have derived the above relation only for a point source on the axis, the same relation holds for point objects slightly off the axis, provided the angles of incidence at the first lens surface are small. Since objects of finite size may be treated as collections of point sources, the lens can be used to produce an image of an object of finite size lying in a plane perpendicular to the axis, provided all angles of incidence are small. For objects of finite size, p in the above equation is the distance from the lens to the plane in which the object lies and q is the distance from the lens to the plane in which the image lies.

In discussing the formation of images by thin lenses, let us first consider the effects of a thin lens on incident parallel light rays. If we have a lens like that shown in Fig. 11, we find that parallel rays coming from the left are brought to a focus at point F. This point is called a *principal focus* of the lens, and its distance from the lens is known as the *focal length* f of the lens. We can determine the focal length by setting $p = \infty$ in (12), corresponding to incident parallel rays, in which case q becomes equal to f and we find that

$$\frac{1}{f} = (\mu - 1)\left(\frac{1}{R_1} + \frac{1}{R_2}\right). \tag{13}$$

This relation is called the *lensmaker's equation.*

Unlike a mirror, a lens is two-sided, and light can pass through it in either direction. Furthermore, because (12) is symmetric with respect to R_1 and R_2, we see that even though the radii of curvature may be different, the image-forming properties are identical for light traveling in the two directions. Consequently, in Fig. 11, parallel rays coming from the right will be brought to a focus at point F', which is at the same distance f from the lens as point F.   The points F and F' are called the two *principal foci*. They are equidistant from the lens, at the distance given by (13).

As a result of the reversibility of light rays, a point source of light placed either at F or at F' will produce a parallel beam of light, as shown

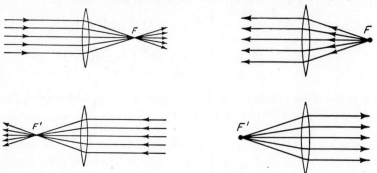

Fig. 11. Action of a converging lens on parallel light rays. Parallel rays intersect at the principal focal points of the lens.

Fig. 12. Action of a converging lens on light rays from point objects at the principal foci.

in Fig. 12.   On the basis of this knowledge, it is possible to find image positions by graphical methods, since (a) any ray coming to the lens parallel to the principal axis passes through the principal focus beyond the lens after refraction, and (b) any ray passing through the principal focus in front of the lens will be refracted in such a manner as to leave the lens in a direction parallel to the principal axis.

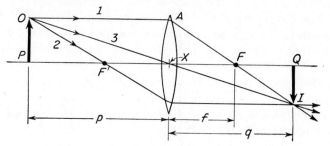

Fig. 13. Principal-ray diagram for a converging lens.

In order to illustrate the graphical method of locating images formed by a converging lens, let us consider Fig. 13, in which the end of an object is located at position O.   We can readily trace the following three *principal rays* from the tip O of the object to the tip I of the image; these rays are numbered as in Fig. 13:

1. The ray that leaves O in a direction parallel to the principal axis and after refraction passes through the principal focus F.

2. The ray that passes through the principal focus F' and after refraction is parallel to the principal axis.

3. The ray that passes through the optical center X of the lens and is undeviated.

Principal ray number 3 is defined by a straight line intersecting the principal axis at point X, which is called the *optical center* of the lens. All rays passing through point X traverse the lens without deviation; this point divides the rays that are bent downward by the lens from those that are bent upward.

It is instructive to derive the relation between p, q, and f from the principal-ray diagram. In Fig. 13, the right triangles OPX and IQX are similar. Therefore, we may write

$$OP/IQ = PX/QX.$$

Triangles AXF and IQF are also similar, and we may write

$$AX/IQ = XF/QF.$$

But since $AX = OP$, this relation can be rewritten as

$$OP/IQ = XF/QF.$$

By equating the two expressions for OP/IQ, we obtain

$$\frac{PX}{QX} = \frac{XF}{QF}.$$

Rewriting this relation in terms of the object distance p, the image distance q, and the focal length f, we obtain

$$\frac{p}{q} = \frac{f}{q-f},$$

which can be rewritten in the form

$$\frac{1}{p} + \frac{1}{q} = \frac{1}{f}. \tag{14}$$

as in (12) and (13).

We further note from similar triangles OPX and IQX in Fig. 13 that

$$\frac{\text{image length}}{\text{object length}} = \frac{\text{image distance}}{\text{object distance}}. \tag{15}$$

3. THIN SIMPLE LENSES

WE HAVE DISCUSSED in detail the formation of a real image by a double-convex lens. There are many other cases of image formation by lenses to be discussed. These we shall treat less rigorously, making full use of principal-ray diagrams to achieve an understanding of the phenomena involved.

First we note that the image formed by a converging lens is not necessarily real. If we insert a value of p less than f in (14), q comes out nega-

tive.   As shown by the principal-ray diagram for this case in Fig. 14, this
negative value of q implies a virtual image in front of the lens rather than

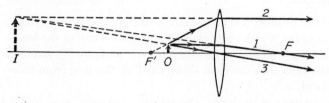

Fig. 14. A converging lens forms a virtual image when the object is inside
the focus.

a real image back of the lens.   (The *front side* of a lens is the side from
which the light comes, and the *back side* is the side from which the light

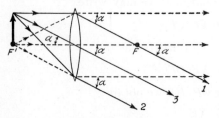

Fig. 15. Object at the principal focus;
image at infinity.

emerges; 'back of the lens' means
to the right of the lens in Figs. 14
and 15.)   From similar triangles in
Fig. 14, we again see that (15) gives
the image size.

If we substitute $p = f$ in the lens
equation, we find $q = \infty$.   Fig. 15
illustrates the meaning of image at
infinity.   Principal rays 1 and 3 are
parallel by simple geometry.   All
other rays from the head of the arrow are parallel to these rays after
they pass through the lens, and make the same angle α with the principal
axis that the object subtends at the
center of the lens.

Tracing the rays backwards through
the lens in Fig. 15 shows that a bundle
of parallel rays making an angle α with
the principal axis is brought to a focus
at a point in the plane, distant f from
the lens, that contains the principal
focus.

A glass lens thinner at the center
than at the edge acts, as we have noted,
as a *diverging* lens.   Fig. 16 illustrates
its action on parallel rays.   It will be
noted that parallel rays incident from
the left upon a diverging lens are refracted in such a manner as to make
them *appear* to come from a point

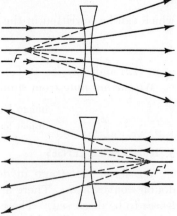

Fig. 16. Action of a diverging lens
on parallel light rays.

called the principal focus F on the left side of the lens.   Similarly, parallel rays reaching the lens from the right are refracted in such a way as to make them *appear* to come from a point called the principal focus F' on the right side of the lens.

A diverging lens cannot be used to produce a parallel beam from a diverging beam as is done in Fig. 11. However, by considering the rays in Fig. 16 reversed, we see that if a converging beam of light is incident upon a diverging lens, it is possible for the lens to render the beam parallel. Such a situation is indicated in Fig. 17. If a beam of light converging toward the point F' approaches the lens from the left, the diverging lens will render the beam parallel. A converging beam like that incident on the lens in Fig. 17

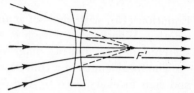

Fig. 17. Rays directed toward the principal focus behind a diverging lens become parallel after passing through the lens.

can be considered to represent a *virtual object* at F'. The converging beam would have come to a point focus at F' if the beam had not been intercepted by the diverging lens.

Graphical construction of the images formed by diverging lenses can be carried out by the use of principal rays as in Fig. 18. Principal ray 1 approaches the lens in a direction parallel to the principal axis and is refracted in such a way that it *appears* to come from principal focus F.

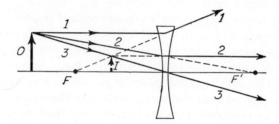

Fig. 18. Principal-ray diagram for a diverging lens.

Principal ray 2 approaches the lens in such a direction that it would pass through principal focus F' if the lens were absent; after refraction, it leaves the lens parallel to the principal axis. Principal ray 3 passes without deviation through the center of the lens. After passage through the lens, these three rays appear to come from a point which defines the end of the virtual image I. Again we see from similar triangles that the relation (15) will give the image length.

The equation
$$\frac{1}{p}+\frac{1}{q}=\frac{1}{f} \qquad (16)$$

applies to all types of lenses and mirrors with the following sign conventions:

$$\text{Object distance } p \text{ is } \left\{ \begin{array}{l} + \text{ for a real object,} \\ - \text{ for a virtual object.} \end{array} \right.$$

$$\text{Image distance } q \text{ is } \left\{ \begin{array}{l} + \text{ for a real image,} \\ - \text{ for a virtual image.} \end{array} \right.$$

$$\text{Focal length } f \text{ is } \left\{ \begin{array}{l} + \text{ for a converging lens or mirror,} \\ - \text{ for a diverging lens or mirror.} \end{array} \right.$$

Equation (15), with signs of p and q ignored, will always give the image length. Whether the image is erect or inverted is best determined by sketching a principal-ray diagram.

The focal length of a thin lens is determined correctly as to magnitude and sign in every case by the *lensmaker's equation* (13). In using this equation we must take the radii R_1 and R_2 as *positive for convex surfaces, negative for concave surfaces.* Equation (13) assumes that the lens is immersed in material, such as air, having index of refraction unity. If this is not true, equation (13) is still valid if μ represents the ratio of the index of refraction of the lens material to the index of refraction of the material in which the lens is immersed.

We should mention the unit used by opticians in describing lenses. Opticians measure the *power* of a lens in *diopters.* A lens having a focal length of 1 meter has a power of 1 diopter. The power of a lens in diopters may be expressed as

$$P = 1/f, \tag{17}$$

where f is the focal length of the lens in meters. Opticians call diverging lenses *negative lenses;* converging lenses are termed *positive lenses.*

There are several reasons why spherical lenses fail to produce perfect images. First, rays parallel to the axis striking the lens at points far from the axis do not pass through the principal focus defined for rays close to the axis. This defect, called *spherical aberration,* can be minimized by using a diaphragm to limit the useful portion of the lens to an area close to the axis. A second defect results from the fact that the index of refraction of a lens material is not the same for all colors; hence, if white light is incident upon a lens, the rays of the component colors are not brought to a focus at the same point. This defect, called *chromatic aberration,* can be partially corrected by the use of a compound lens composed of simple lenses made of different glasses; a compound lens of this type is called an *achromatic lens.* A full discussion of lens defects can be found in intermediate optics texts. We shall consider chromatic aberration and discuss achromatic lenses in Chap. 26.

Example. *In a familiar illusion, a person looks into a black box and apparently sees a girl in a bathing suit. The girl moves her arms and legs as if swimming, but she is only 6 in tall. How can a projection lens be used to create this illusion?*

The arrangement is shown in Fig. 19. The box stands on a suitable enclosed pedestal and the girl is in a room below lying on a black table but brightly illuminated from above.   A projection lens and a 45-degree mirror form a real reduced image in the box.   The projection lens would form a real image at I'; the mirror causes this image to be formed at I, an equal distance in front of the mirror.   (Look at Fig. 3 on p. 449, imagining all light rays to be reversed in direction, to be convinced of this last statement. I' is in this case known as a virtual object for the mirror, I being the real image.)   If the reduction is by a factor of 10, from 5-ft height to 6 in, and if the distance LI' is 1.5 ft, the distance LO would be 15 ft, by relation (15). Inserting $p = 15$ ft, $q = 1.5$ ft in (16) gives

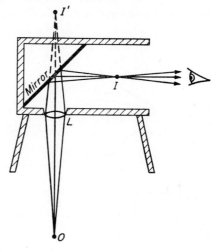

$$\frac{1}{f} = \frac{1}{15\,\text{ft}} + \frac{1}{1.5\,\text{ft}} = \frac{11}{15\,\text{ft}}, \quad f = 1.36\,\text{ft}$$

as the required focal length of the lens.

If the girl is to appear horizontal, as if swimming, she would lie on the table at O, with her head out of the paper and her feet into the paper.   Since the image is in-

Figure 19

verted at I, she would appear to the observer to have her head to the right and her feet to the left.

4. COMBINATIONS OF LENSES

IF LIGHT from an object passes through two lenses one after the other, the combined action of the two can be deduced by considering that the image which would be formed by the first lens is the object for the second lens.   If the first lens produces an image in front of the second lens, this first image may be treated as a real object for the second lens.   In lens

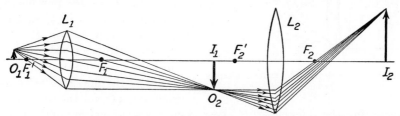

Fig. 20. The image I_1 formed by the first lens acts as a real object O_2 for the second lens.

arrangements such as that in Fig. 21, the image from the first lens may not be formed before the light beam is intercepted by the second lens; in this case the image which would have been formed by the first lens must be treated as a *virtual object* for the second lens.

In the lens arrangement shown in Fig. 20, lens L_1 forms a real image I_1

of object O_1.   Image I_1 can be treated as a real object O_2 for lens L_2. Lens L_2 forms a real image I_2 at the position indicated.   Lens L_2 is drawn larger than L_1 so that all rays from O_1 that pass through L_1 will also pass through L_2.   However, only one of the rays from the end of O_2 in this drawing is a principal ray.   To determine graphically the position of I_2, the other principal rays from O_2 may be sketched, even though no light actually proceeds along them in this particular combination.

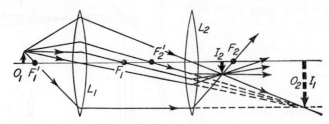

Fig. 21. The image I_1 formed by the first lens acts as a virtual object O_2 for the second lens. In this graphical construction, the three principal rays for lens L_1 are indicated by arrowheads to the left of L_1, those for L_2 by arrowheads to the left of L_2.

In the lens arrangement shown in Fig. 21, lens L_1 would have formed a real image I_1 if the light beam had not been intercepted by the second lens L_2.   In finding the position of the final image I_2 formed by the second lens, we must treat I_1 as the virtual object O_2 for the second lens.   It will be remembered that the object distance of a virtual object is regarded as negative when used in the lens equation.

As an example of a compound lens, let us consider the case of two

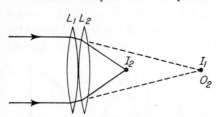

Fig. 22. Image formed by two thin lenses in contact.

thin lenses in contact as shown in Fig. 22.   The focal length of the first lens if f_1, that of the second lens is f_2.   Consider parallel rays reaching the first lens from an infinitely distant point object.   Then the image distance for the first lens is $q_1 = f_1$.   Now let the image I_1 formed by the first lens serve as a *virtual object* O_2 for the second lens.

Neglecting the thicknesses of these thin lenses, we can write the following equation for the second lens, with object distance $p_2 = -f_1$:

$$\frac{1}{-f_1}+\frac{1}{q_2}=\frac{1}{f_2}, \quad \text{or} \quad \frac{1}{q_2}=\frac{1}{f_1}+\frac{1}{f_2}.$$

It is possible to treat the two thin lenses in contact as a compound lens. Remembering that the focal length of a lens is the image distance when the object distance is infinite, we note that q_2 in the above equation is equal to the focal length of the lens combination, and we may write

$$\frac{1}{f_{\text{Comp}}} = \frac{1}{f_1} + \frac{1}{f_2}, \tag{18}$$

where f_{Comp} is the focal length of the compound lens.

PROBLEMS

NOTE: In working most of these problems, the refractive index of air can be taken as unity.   Take other indices of refraction from Table I.

1. A ray of light in air strikes a water surface at an angle of incidence of 30°. What is the angle of refraction?   Show diagram.   Ans: 22°.0.

2. A ray of light in air strikes the surface of a diamond at an angle of incidence of 30°.   What is the angle of refraction?   Show diagram.

3. The index of refraction of a certain type of glass is 1.52.   Taking $c = 3 \times 10^8$ m/sec, calculate the speed of light in this glass.   Ans: 1.97×10^8 m/sec.

4. What is the speed of light in water? in diamond?

5. A shallow tank with a flat glass bottom contains carbon disulfide.   A ray of light in air is incident at the surface of the carbon disulfide at an angle of 45°. If the refractive index of the glass is 1.517, find the angle of refraction of the light inside the glass.   Show diagram.   Ans: 27°.8.

6. If the tank described in Prob. 5 were filled with water instead of carbon disulfide, what would be the angle of refraction of the light ray inside the glass? Show that an empty tank would give the same angle.

7. A ray of light in air has an angle of incidence of 30° at the surface of a plate of glass 4.0 cm thick, with $\mu = 1.523$.   The ray emerging from the glass is parallel to the incident ray but is displaced laterally with respect to the incident ray. What is the magnitude of the lateral displacement?   Ans: 0.796 cm.

8. A stick 4 ft long, marked off in feet, is placed vertically at the shallow end of a swimming pool, where the water is 3 ft deep.   The 1-ft mark is at the surface of the water, the 4-ft mark at the bottom.   An observer stands at the opposite end of the pool with his eyes 20 ft horizontally from the stick and 7 ft above the water surface.   What is the apparent depth of the 2-, 3-, and 4-ft marks below the surface, as the observer would judge by comparison with the distance from the top of the stick to the 1-ft mark?

9. An observer looks from directly above at a small stone at the bottom of a pool of water.   The stone appears to be 3 ft beneath the surface of the water. What is the actual depth of the pool?   Ans: 4.00 ft.

10. A ray of light in water strikes the horizontal surface of the water at angle of incidence of 30°.   What is the angle of refraction in air?   What is the angle of incidence in water when the angle of refraction in air is 90°?   Show diagrams.   What is the critical angle for water?

11. What is the angle of deviation D when yellow light is incident at an angle of 50° on the dense flint-glass prism in Fig. 23?   Ans: 52°.7.

12. What is the angle of deviation D when yellow light is incident at an angle of 70° on the dense flint-glass prism in Fig. 23?

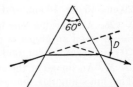

Figure 23

13. Neglecting the curvature of the earth, compute the deviation of starlight incident at an angle of 80° (the star is 10° above the horizon) on the top of the earth's atmosphere if the index of refraction of the air at the earth's surface is 1.00030.   Ans: $0°097 = 5'.8$.

14. The index of refraction of air depends only on temperature, pressure, and humidity. An astronomer reads temperature, pressure, and humidity at the earth's surface, and measures the apparent angle of a star from the zenith. He then looks up in a table the correction to be applied to give the true angle. To the approximation in which the curvature of the earth can be neglected and in which the atmosphere can be assumed to have characteristics that vary with altitude but do not vary in any given horizontal plane, show that these tables can be rigorously compiled because the angle of deviation depends only on the index of refraction at the earth's surface and is independent of the manner in which this index varies as one ascends to the top of the atmosphere.

15. Why do stars twinkle? Why does the air over a hot radiator seem to shimmer?

16. What is the minimum index of refraction glass can have and still give total reflection for the light paths shown through the 90° prism of Fig. 4(c)?

17. What is the minimum index of refraction glass can have and still give total reflection in the case of the 90° prisms shown in (a) and (b) of Fig. 4? Ans: 1.414.

18. What is the critical angle for diamond? Explain how the high index of refraction of diamond accounts for its extraordinary 'sparkle' when cut as a gem.

19. A large slab of glass of index 1.650 has a small air bubble a short distance below the surface. A dime (diameter 1.75 cm) placed on the surface of the glass is just large enough to completely prevent the bubble from being seen through the surface. How far down is the air bubble?   Ans: 1.15 cm.

20. Why is a camera lens with a 180° field of view called a 'fish-eye lens'? What is the angle of the cone in which a fish would see the whole of the world above the level surface of a fresh-water lake?

21. A double-convex lens of crown glass has surfaces with radii of curvature of 40 cm and 50 cm, respectively. What is its focal length?   Ans: 43.0 cm.

22. What should be the radius of curvature of the curved surface of a plano-convex crown-glass lens if the lens is to have a focal length of 20 cm?

23. An object 4 cm tall is placed near the axis of a thin converging lens at a distance of 33.3 cm from the lens. If the focal length of the lens is 20 cm, where will the image be formed and what will be the size of the image? Sketch the principal-ray diagram.   Ans: 50 cm behind; 6 cm.

24. An object 2 cm tall is placed 10 cm from a diverging lens of −10-cm focal length. Where will the image be formed? What will be the size of the image? Sketch the principal-ray diagram.

25. A converging lens has a focal length of 10 cm. Determine the image distances when an object is placed at the following distances from the lens: 25 cm, 20 cm, 15 cm, 10 cm, and 5 cm.   Ans: $+16.7, +20, +30, \infty, -10$ cm.

26. A diverging lens has a focal length of −10 cm. Locate the images produced when an object is placed at the following distances from the lens: 25 cm, 20 cm, 15 cm, 10 cm, and 5 cm.

27. An image of the sun is formed by a converging lens of 2-m focal length. The sun's angular diameter is 32' of arc. What is the diameter of the image? Sketch the principal-ray diagram.   Ans: 1.86 cm.

28. Two distant stars are imaged on a photographic plate by a converging telescope lens of 8-m focal length. The distance between the images is 1 mm. What is the angular separation of the stars in the sky?

29. A concavo-convex spectacle lens has a power of $+2$ diopters. If the glass has a refractive index of 1.6 and the concave surface a radius of -1 m, what is the radius of the convex surface? Ans: 23.1 cm.

30. Why does a piece of glass of irregular shape become invisible when it is immersed in a liquid of the same index of refraction?

31. A converging lens of 10-cm focal length is made of glass of refractive index 1.523. What is its focal length when immersed in water? Ans: 36.9 cm.

32. Insert a pencil through a water surface at an angle of 45°, and observe that the pencil appears to be bent through a certain angle at the point where it enters the water. Compute this angle of bend for the case where your line of sight to the point of entry is at 45° to the water surface, and the vertical plane containing the pencil is perpendicular to the vertical plane containing the line of sight.

33. Two converging lenses are placed 10 cm apart. The focal length of the first lens is 20 cm and that of the second is 30 cm. If an object is placed 40 cm in front of the first lens, where will the final image be formed? Sketch the principal-ray diagram. Ans: 15 cm behind second lens.

34. A converging lens of focal length 10 cm is placed 20 cm in front of a diverging lens of focal length -10 cm. If an object is placed 40 cm in front of the converging lens, where will the final image be formed?

35. Two converging lenses of focal lengths 40 and 50 cm are placed in contact. What is the focal length of this lens combination? What is the power of the combination in diopters? Ans: 22.2 cm; 4.5 diopters.

36. A 4-diopter converging lens and a 2-diopter diverging lens are placed in contact. What is the focal length of the resulting compound lens?

37. A converging lens of focal length 20 cm is placed in front of a converging lens of focal length 4 cm. What is the distance between the lenses if parallel rays entering the first lens leave the second lens as parallel rays? Ans: 24 cm.

38. A converging lens of focal length 50 cm is placed in front of a diverging lens of focal length -5 cm. What is the distance between the lenses if parallel rays entering the first lens leave the second lens as parallel rays?

39. An object is placed 8 cm in front of a diverging lens of focal length -8 cm. A converging lens of focal length 15 cm is placed behind the diverging lens and forms a final image at infinity. What is the distance between the lenses? Sketch the principal-ray diagram. Ans: 11 cm.

40. An object is placed 16 cm in front of a converging lens of focal length 8 cm. A diverging lens of focal length -12 cm is placed behind the converging lens and forms a final image at infinity. What is the distance between the lenses? Sketch the principal-ray diagram.

41. An object is placed 8 cm in front of a converging lens of focal length 8 cm. A diverging lens of focal length -12 cm is placed 4 cm behind the converging lens. Find the position, size, and character of the final image.
    Ans: Erect, virtual image at same location as object; 1.5 times object size.

42. An object is placed 8 cm in front of a converging lens of focal length 8 cm. A converging lens of focal length 12 cm is placed 4 cm behind the first lens. Find the position, size and character of the final image.

43. A converging lens of focal length 20 cm is placed 20 cm from a diverging mirror of focal length -10 cm. A candle is midway between the lens and the mirror. Where should a screen be placed to catch a real image of the candle flame? What is the image size? Is the image erect or inverted?

Ans: 100 cm from the lens; twice the size of the flame; inverted.

44. A converging lens of focal length 20 in is placed 20 in from a converging mirror of focal length 4 in. A candle is placed midway between the lens and the mirror. Describe the two images of the candle flame (position, size, character) seen when one looks through the lens. Sketch the principal-ray diagram.

45. By the method used on p. 473 to derive the lens equation from the principle-ray diagram of Fig. 13 in the case of formation of a real image by a converging lens, derive the same equation for the following cases, using the sign conventions given at the top of p. 476:

(a) The formation of a virtual image by a converging lens, as in Fig. 14.

(b) The formation of a virtual image by a diverging lens, as in Fig. 18.

(c) The formation of the image of a virtual object by a converging lens, as in the case of lens L_2 in Fig. 21.

(d) The formation of a real image of a virtual object by a diverging lens.

(e) The formation of a virtual image of a virtual object by a diverging lens.

CHAPTER 24

OPTICAL INSTRUMENTS

In the preceding chapters, the laws of reflection and refraction were stated and the properties of mirrors and lenses were described. The present chapter deals with optical instruments of which lenses and mirrors are the component parts. Although, in order to minimize aberrations, the lenses actually used in good optical instruments are thick compound lenses, here they will be treated as thin simple lenses. The basic theory of these optical instruments is not altered by this simplification. The instruments to be discussed are the camera, the projector, the human eye, the simple magnifying glass, the microscope, and the telescope.

1. THE PHOTOGRAPHIC CAMERA

One of the simplest optical instruments is the photographic camera, in which a lens is used to produce a real image of an illuminated or luminous object, as in Fig. 1. The lens is mounted at the end of a light-tight bellows; the real image is formed on a light-sensitive photographic plate or film during the period when the camera shutter is open. The portions of the film illuminated during the exposure experience chemical changes which are later made visible during the process of developing. This process is followed by treatment in a fixing bath in order to remove further sensitivity to light.

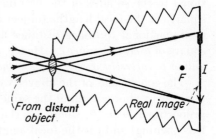

Fig. 1. Image formation in the camera.

Usually, the object being photographed is at a considerable distance from the camera, and a diminished real inverted image is formed on the plate. If the object is at a distance large compared to the focal length, the image is formed in the plane of the principal focus of the lens; the film position is permanently fixed in this plane in so-called 'box cameras,' which can be used satisfactorily in photographing distant objects. In photographing nearer objects, the distance between lens and plate must be increased to slightly more than the focal length, as indicated in Fig. 1, and a camera equipped with a movable lens must be used. If the object distance is equal to $2f$, the image distance is also $2f$ and the image and object are of equal size; special copying cameras arranged in this way are used for reproducing drawings or manuscripts without change in size. Enlarging cameras use an object distance less than $2f$ and produce an enlarged image at the plate position.

To obtain a satisfactory picture, the total light energy per unit area, in the wavelength region to which the film is sensitive, must be within certain limits; otherwise the film will be under- or overexposed. This energy per unit area can be measured by the *product of the exposure time by the illumination of the film.* Most shutters provide for a selection of values of exposure time. *Other things being equal, the illumination of the film is proportional to the area of the lens opening;* this area can be varied in most cameras by changing the setting of a diaphragm that allows light to pass only through a circular portion surrounding the principal axis of the lens.

Now let us consider two different cameras having lenses of *different focal lengths,* but lens openings of the *same diameter.* Let the two cameras photograph the *same distant scene.* The distances from lens to film must then be different, since this distance must equal the focal length for a scene whose distance is large compared to the focal length. From a given portion of the scene the same amount of light passes through the two lenses, but is used to illuminate different areas of the film—areas proportional to the squares of the film distances and hence proportional to the squares of the focal lengths (object distance being constant, image length is proportional to image distance and image area is proportional to the square of image distance). Hence, *other things being equal, the film illumination is inversely proportional to the square of the focal length.*

The conclusions of the above two paragraphs can be combined by saying that in photographing the same distant scene, the film illumination is proportional to a^2/f^2, where a is the *aperture* (the diameter of the circular lens opening) and f is the focal length. *The ratio f/a is called the* 'f-number.' Hence, illumination is proportional to $1/(\text{f-number})^2$. To get the same film exposure when photographing the same distant scene with two different cameras, *the exposure times must be proportional to the squares of the f-numbers.* The camera with the higher f-number has lower film illumination and hence requires longer exposure time. The lower the minimum f-number of a given camera lens (diaphragm wide open), the 'faster' the lens. The series of stops marked on most diaphragms—a series such as f:1.6, 2.3, 3.2, 4.5, 6.3, 9, 13, 18—are a set such that the square of each f-number is approximately double the square of the preceding one. Hence, a shift to the stop of next higher f-number requires double the exposure time for given lighting or double the light intensity of the scene for given exposure time. To summarize:

> The **f-number** is the ratio of the focal length f of a camera lens to the diameter a of the diaphragm opening.

If we let W be the light energy per unit area of film, E the film illumination (in lumens/ft^2, for example), and t the exposure time,

$$W \propto Et, \qquad E \propto a^2/f^2,$$

hence
$$W \propto (a^2/f^2)\, t = t/(\text{f-number})^2. \qquad (1)$$

Hence, in photographing the same scene, if the f-number is increased by $\sqrt{2}$, the exposure time must be doubled.

> **Example.** *What is the f-number of a lens of 12-in focal length used with a diaphragm of ¾-in diameter? If this camera requires ⅟₅₀-sec exposure time to photograph a distant scene, what exposure time would be required with a lens of 6-in focal length and aperture ¾ in to photograph the same scene on the same type of film?*
>
> The f-numbers of the two lenses are $(12 \text{ in})/(¾ \text{ in}) = 16$ and $(6 \text{ in})/(¾ \text{ in}) = 8$ respectively. By (1), $t \propto (\text{f-number})^2\, W$. Since we desire the same film energy W per unit area, the second camera, of ½ the f-number, would require ¼ the exposure time, or ⅟₂₀₀ sec. We note that the second camera has the same aperture as the first, so light energy passes through its lens at the same rate, but this energy is distributed on a film of only ¼ the area; hence the exposure time is reduced in this proportion.

2. THE PROJECTION LANTERN

OPTICALLY, the slide or film projector is similar to an enlarging camera, since a lens is used to form a real image on a screen.   In Fig. 2, the slide O is located at a distance from the lens only slightly greater than the focal length, and the image I is enlarged, real, and inverted.   Great enlargement is possible provided the slide is sufficiently well illuminated.   The primary source of illumination may be a carbon arc or an incandescent lamp with its filament concentrated in a small flat zone. A converging mirror and a converging lens (condensing lens) are usually used to cause as much as possible of the light of the source

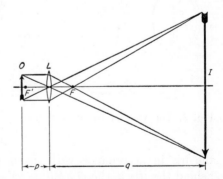

Fig. 2. Image formation by the lens of a projection lantern.

to pass through the slide or film and head in the direction of the projection lens.   While these optical parts are necessary in order to get adequate illumination on the screen, they have no role in forming the image on the screen and need not be of high quality; they are not shown in Fig. 2. The projection lens L must be of high optical quality and is usually compound.

> The **enlargement** produced by a projector is defined as the ratio of image length to object length.

From (15), p. 473, we see that the enlargement is equal to the ratio of image distance to object distance; that is,

$$\text{enlargement} = q/p. \tag{2}$$

3. THE EYE

OPTICALLY, the human eye is similar in many respects to the camera since it contains a lens system equipped with a shutter (the eyelid), a variable diaphragm (the iris), and a screen (the retina) on which are produced real inverted images of external objects. While the eye is relatively simple optically, it is very complex physiologically, the complexity arising chiefly from the mechanisms required for making various mechanical adjustments and from the as-yet-little-understood processes of detection at the retina. The chief optical properties are discussed briefly in the following paragraphs.

The eye consists of a roughly spherical eyeball supported in a bony socket in the skull, a system of muscles for moving the eyeball, and tear ducts for moistening the anterior surface of the eyeball. The chief features of the eyeball itself are shown in cross section in Fig. 3. Light enters the eye through a transparent curved shell called the *cornea*, the space immediately behind which is filled with a liquid material called the *aqueous humor*. Next the light passes through the *pupil*, a circular aperture in a colored membrane called the *iris*. The diameter of the pupil is changed automatically by the expansion or contraction of the iris in accordance with the brightness of the light. Immediately behind the iris is the *crystalline lens*, a somewhat plastic lens, the curvatures of whose surfaces can be changed by muscles around the edge in order to vary the focal length. The interior portion of the eyeball is filled with a jellylike substance called the *vitreous humor*, and the inner coating of the back wall is the light-sensitive surface called the *retina*. The retina includes many millions of light receivers called *rods* and *cones*

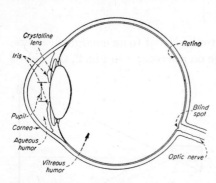

Fig. 3. Top view of the right human eye.

because of their shapes. These are imbedded in the tissue with their lengths normal to the retinal surface. Each of these receivers is connected to a ramification of the optic nerve.

Approximate values for the indices of refraction of the transparent portions of the eye are given in the accompanying table. Since these indices range only from 1.34 to 1.44, light experiences the greatest refraction as it first enters the eye at the cornea. The cornea, aqueous humor, crystalline lens, and vitreous humor must all

Cornea	1.351
Aqueous humor	1.337
Crystalline lens	1.437
Vitreous humor	1.337

be considered as components of the lens system of the eye. The effect of all the refractions is to form a real image on the retina in the manner we have already discussed for simple lenses.

If the eye muscles are *relaxed*, sharply defined images of *distant objects* are produced on the retina of a normal eye. In order to produce sharp images of nearby objects, the muscles attached to the crystalline lens increase the curvature of the lens surfaces, decreasing the focal length sufficiently to bring the desired images into sharp focus. This adjustment of focus is called *accommodation*. It is possible for the normal adult eye to deform the crystalline lens sufficiently to produce sharp images of objects as close as 25 cm (10 in), which is known as the distance of the *near point of the normal eye*. Children can see objects clearly at shorter distances, since the crystalline lens is more readily deformable in early life. Normally, the near point moves beyond 25 cm at about the age of 40.

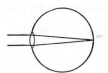

(*a*) Normal vision; object at ∞, lens fully relaxed; or, object at 25 cm, lens fully converged.

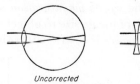

Uncorrected　　　　　　　Corrected

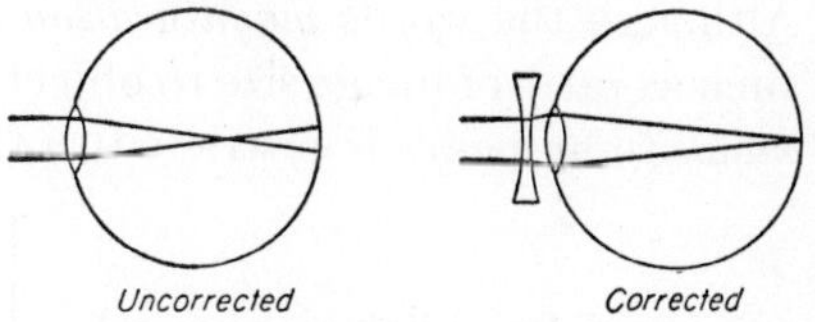

(*b*) Nearsightedness (myopia); object at ∞, lens fully relaxed.

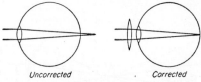

Uncorrected　　　　　　　Corrected

(*c*) Farsightedness (hypermetropia); object at 25 cm, lens fully converged.

Figure 4

There are several rather common defects of vision that deserve brief consideration. The normal eye produces sharp images of distant objects when the eye muscles are relaxed, and is capable of sufficient convergence to produce sharp images of objects as close as 25 cm, as in Fig. 4(a). However, the size and shape of the eyeball and the focal length of the lens system are not always properly matched. If the lens is effectively too convergent, the images of distant objects will fall in front of the retina so that on the retina itself the image will be blurred. Only objects close to the eye can be focused sharply on the retina; eyes with this type of defect are said to be *myopic* or *nearsighted*. The *far point* of a myopic eye is not at ∞ but at some inconveniently close distance. As indicated in Fig. 4(b), this defect can be remedied by using a suitable diverging spectacle lens. A lens incapable of sufficient convergence leads to *farsightedness*, or *hypermetropia*, which, as indicated in Fig. 4(c), can be remedied by the use of converging spectacle lenses. The *near point* of a hypermetropic eye is beyond 25 cm. Normally, persons over 40 become hypermetropic and reading glasses are required.

A third common type of defect in vision occurs when one or more of the refracting surfaces of the eye, such as the cornea or crystalline lens, are not perfectly spherical. In this case light from a point source will not be focused in a point image. An eye having this characteristic is said to be *astigmatic*. This defect can be corrected by using a cylindrical spectacle lens so placed in front of the eye that its unsymmetric curvature corrects the asymmetric curvature of the crystalline lens or cornea.

4. DEFINITION OF MAGNIFYING POWER

MAGNIFYING glasses, microscopes, and telescopes enable us to see objects more clearly than is possible with the unaided eye. The greater clarity is obtained because, with the aid of the optical instrument, a larger image is formed on the retina of the eye than would be formed if the object were viewed directly. The ratio of the lengths of these images on the retina is known as the *magnifying power* of the optical instrument. Although the words *magnification* and *enlargement* have other meanings, such as ratio of image size to object size in the case of a projector, the term *magnifying power* is restricted to the dimensionless ratio defined as:

$$\begin{Bmatrix} \text{magnifying power of} \\ \text{an optical instrument} \end{Bmatrix} = \frac{\begin{Bmatrix} \text{length of image on retina when} \\ \text{object is viewed through the} \\ \text{optical instrument} \end{Bmatrix}}{\begin{Bmatrix} \text{length of image on retina when} \\ \text{object is viewed directly in the} \\ \text{most favorable manner} \end{Bmatrix}}. \qquad (3)$$

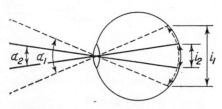

Fig. 5. Magnifying power $= i_1/i_2 = \alpha_1/\alpha_2$, where i_1 and α_1 refer to observation through an optical instrument, i_2 and α_2 refer to direct observation. The angle of the field of view is much exaggerated in this sketch.

In Fig. 5, rays are traced from the ends of the object (or from any two definite points of the object) through the center of the lens of the eye. The distance from the lens of the eye to the retina does not change when the focal length of the eye lens is changed to view objects at different distances. Hence we see in Fig. 5 that the ratio of image lengths in (3) equals the ratio of angles subtended at the eye by rays from the ends of the object, provided these angles are small.   The assumption of small angles is always valid, because the eye sees distinctly only the small central portion of the field of view, which subtends a small angle α.   These considerations lead to the following useful expression for magnifying power:

$$\begin{Bmatrix} \text{magnifying power of} \\ \text{an optical instrument} \end{Bmatrix} = \frac{\begin{Bmatrix} \text{angle } \alpha_1 \text{ subtended at lens of eye} \\ \text{when object is viewed through} \\ \text{the optical instrument} \end{Bmatrix}}{\begin{Bmatrix} \text{angle } \alpha_2 \text{ subtended at lens of eye} \\ \text{when object is viewed directly} \\ \text{in the most favorable manner} \end{Bmatrix}}. \qquad (4)$$

The denominators of the above expressions contain the phrase 'in the most favorable manner,' which we must now discuss.   As we have seen, the normal or properly corrected eye has a lens of variable focal length so that it can focus on the retina an image of an object at any distance between 25 cm and ∞.   But for a given object size, the size of the image on the retina varies inversely as the object distance.   When this page is held at 25 cm, the words on this page form images on the retina that are four times as high as when the page is held at 100 cm.   Hence the normal eye can distinguish letters at 25 cm (10 in) that are one-quarter the height of those that can be distinguished at 100 cm (40 in).

In defining the magnifying power of a magnifying glass or a microscope, we assume that direct observation, in the denominator of (3) or (4), is made with the object held at 25 cm, the near point of the normal or properly corrected eye.   On the other hand, a telescope or opera glass is specifically intended for viewing *distant* objects.   Hence, in defining their magnifying powers we must assume that, in the denominator of (3) or (4), the object is viewed at the distance of its actual location.

Example.   *What is the magnifying power of a concave shaving mirror of radius of curvature 24 in?   The computation should be based on a comparison with a plane mirror, the most favorable manner of shaving in each case being to hold the face 8 in from the mirror.*

Consider a line 1 in long drawn on the face.   In the case of the plane mirror this line is imaged normal size 8 in behind the mirror or 16 in from the eyes.   The angle α_2 in Fig. 5 is thus $\frac{1}{16}$ rad for this 1-in line.

The concave mirror has a focal length of 12 in.   Setting $p = 8$ in, $f = 12$ in, in the mirror formula gives $q = -24$ in; the image is 24 in behind the mirror. The enlargement is (image distance)/(object distance) $= 3$; hence the 1-in line is 3 in long in the image, which is 32 in from the eyes.   The angle α_1 in Fig. 5 is $\frac{3}{32}$ rad.

The magnifying power is the ratio

$$\alpha_1/\alpha_2 = \frac{3}{32}/\frac{1}{16} = 1.5$$

Each whisker makes an image on the retina $1\frac{1}{2}$ times as long when the shaving mirror is used.

5. THE MAGNIFYING GLASS

A SINGLE converging lens can be used as a magnifying glass to form enlarged virtual images of small objects. As indicated in Fig. 6, the object is placed between the principal focus and the lens. The eye is placed at some distance d from the lens, and an enlarged virtual image is observed at a conveniently large distance D from the eye. We shall first compute the magnifying power of this system and then discuss the two methods of employment according to which the magnifying glass is known either as a *simple microscope* or as a *reading glass*.

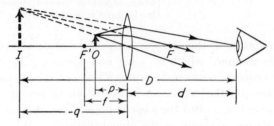

Fig. 6. Magnifying glass.

If we let O be the length of the object and I the length of the image, then, for small angles,

$$\begin{Bmatrix} \text{angle subtended at lens of} \\ \text{eye when object is viewed} \\ \text{through magnifying glass} \end{Bmatrix} = \frac{I}{D}, \qquad \begin{Bmatrix} \text{angle subtended at lens of} \\ \text{eye when object is viewed} \\ \text{directly at 25 cm} \end{Bmatrix} = \frac{O}{25 \text{ cm}}.$$

Hence, according to (4),

$$\text{magnifying power} = M = \frac{I/D}{O/25 \text{ cm}} = \frac{I}{O} \times \frac{25 \text{ cm}}{D}.$$

But
$$\frac{I}{O} = \frac{-q}{p} = \frac{D-d}{p}; \quad \text{hence,} \quad M = \frac{D-d}{p} \times \frac{25 \text{ cm}}{D}.$$

The lens equation gives
$$\frac{1}{p} = \frac{1}{f} - \frac{1}{q} = \frac{1}{f} + \frac{1}{D-d}.$$

Substituting this in the above expression for M gives

$$M = \frac{25 \text{ cm}}{f} \left(1 - \frac{d}{D} \right) + \frac{25 \text{ cm}}{D}. \tag{5}$$

The distance D of the image from the eye may be anywhere between the near point and the far point of the eye—between 25 cm and ∞ for the normal eye. For continuous use of a magnifying glass, it may be assumed that the image is placed at a large distance ($D = \infty$) since this corresponds to the relaxed position of the eye. Placing the image near ∞ does not decrease the clarity of the image, since of course the light actually comes from the object through the lens to the eye as in Fig. 6. For $D = \infty$, (5) gives $M = (25 \text{ cm})/f$, independent of d. The required lens aperture does

vary with d, however.   To see a circular object of *diameter* O requires a
lens aperture (diameter)

$$a = (d/f)\, O \qquad\qquad\qquad (6)$$

when $D = \infty$; for smaller values of D, slightly smaller apertures will suffice.
Proof of (6) is left as an exercise.

One way of employing a magnifying glass is as a *reading glass*.   The
glass is of short focal length (say 10 cm), is held near the page being read,
and at a convenient distance d (say 20 cm) from the eye.   According to
(5), there is little magnification unless the glass is held at such a distance
from the page as to make D very large, in which case $M = (25\text{ cm})/f$.
A glass of 10-cm focal length would be held 10 cm from the page ($p = f$,
$D = \infty$) and give $M = 2.5$.   Magnifying powers much larger than this are
impractical with a reading glass because, according to (6), if f is decreased
to increase M, the aperture a must be increased in comparison with the
size of the object; but large aperture and short focal length are inconsistent in a simple uncorrected lens if the lens is to be free from excessive
spherical aberration.

This limitation of aperture is removed if the lens is placed very close
to the eye ($d \ll f$ in (6)); a lens so used is called a *simple microscope*.
Examples are the familiar jeweler's lens and the eyepiece of a telescope.
In this case we can, to a good approximation, set $d = 0$ in (5) and obtain
the expression

$$M = \frac{25\text{ cm}}{f} + \frac{25\text{ cm}}{D}. \qquad \left(\begin{array}{c}\text{simple}\\\text{microscope}\end{array}\right) \quad (7)$$

If $f \ll 25$ cm, M decreases only slightly as D varies between 25 cm and ∞.

Example.   *If the reading glass described in the text above is to enable 5 cm of
a line of type to be seen at once, how wide must the glass be?*

The 5 cm of type is seen *through the glass* magnified by a factor of 2.5 as compared with normal vision at 25 cm.   For normal vision, this type subtends
an angle of $(5\text{ cm})/(25\text{ cm}) = \frac{1}{5}$ rad at the eye.   Seen through the glass, it
must subtend 2.5 times this angle, or $\frac{1}{2}$ rad.   Hence the glass itself must subtend an angle of $\frac{1}{2}$ rad.   At 20 cm from the eye, this requires a glass 10 cm
wide.

We get the same result from (7) by substituting $d = 20$ cm, $f = 10$ cm,
$O = 5$ cm, to obtain

$$a = (20\text{ cm}/10\text{ cm})(5\text{ cm}) = 10\text{ cm}$$

as the width of the reading glass.

Now we should note that it is impossible to make a satisfactory lens 10 cm
wide of focal length 10 cm.   A double-convex lens of this focal length made
from glass of $\mu = 1.6$ would have radii of curvature of only 12 cm!   For M
as large as 2.5, we would have to settle for seeing much less than 5 cm of a
line of type at a time.

Example.   *The converging spectacle lenses employed by a far-sighted person
for reading are actually simple microscopes.   If the near point of such a person
is at 50 cm and glasses are prescribed that enable him to read at 25 cm, what*

magnifying power does he acquire as compared with the normal eye reading at 25 cm?

To move the near point in from 50 cm to 25 cm, the glasses must form a virtual image at 50 cm of an object at 25 cm. The lens formula shows that this requires a focal length of 50 cm or a power of 2 diopters. If the person holds the page at 25 cm when reading, his image distance D will be 50 cm, and (7) gives

$$M = \frac{25 \text{ cm}}{50 \text{ cm}} + \frac{25 \text{ cm}}{50 \text{ cm}} = 1.$$

Spectacle lenses are close to the eyes. Therefore the angle subtended by the object at the eye equals the angle subtended by the image at the eye. So long as the object is held at 25 cm, no matter where the image is placed in order to enable the eye to see it distinctly, the angle subtended by the image is the same as that subtended by the object at 25 cm from a normal eye.

6. THE COMPOUND MICROSCOPE

WHEN IT IS desired to view a small object with very great magnifying power, it is necessary to utilize two lenses, each of which contributes to

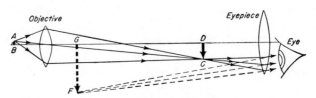

Fig. 7. Image formation in a compound microscope.

the magnifying power. Such an arrangement, called a *compound microscope,* is shown schematically in Fig. 7, in which the high-quality, corrected, compound lenses that must actually be employed are represented by thin simple lenses.

A converging lens of short focal length produces an enlarged real image CD of the small object AB. This lens is called the *objective.* A second lens, called the *eyepiece,* is then used to form an enlarged virtual image FG which is viewed by the observer. *The objective acts as a projector,* and *the eyepiece is used as a simple microscope* to view the real image formed by the objective. As in the case of a slide in the projector, the object AB must be well illuminated; adequate illumination is usually accomplished by means of an incandescent lamp and concave mirror.

The magnifying power produced by a compound microscope is equal to the product of the enlargement E_o produced by the objective and the magnifying power M_E of the eyepiece, because the simple microscope which constitutes the eyepiece can form on the retina an image of CD which is E_o times as large as the image it could form of the object AB. This magnifying power can be expressed in terms of the distances given

on the simplified diagram of the microscope shown in Fig. 8.   In this
figure the object AB and images
CD and FG are shown as before; p
and q denote object and image distances from the objective; and the
final virtual image FG is formed at
the distance D (between 25 cm
and ∞) from the eyepiece.   Under
these conditions, the enlargement
E_o produced by the objective is given
by the relation $E_o = q/p$, as in equation (2) for the projector.   The mag-

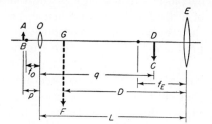

Fig. 8. Positions of object and images
in a compound microscope.

nifying power M_E of the eyepiece is given by equation (7).   Therefore,
the total magnifying power is

$$M = E_o\,M_E = \frac{q}{p}\left(\frac{25\text{ cm}}{f_E} + \frac{25\text{ cm}}{D}\right), \tag{8}$$

where f_E is the focal length of the eyepiece.

We can best appreciate the meaning of this formula by noting that in
actual cases (a) f_E is small compared to D, so that the term 25 cm/D can
be neglected in comparison with 25 cm/f_E; (b) p is only negligibly larger
than f_o, the focal length of the objective, so that we can write f_o for p; (c)
f_E is small compared to the 'tube length' L, so that to a rough approximation we can replace q by L.   With these approximations, the formula
for the magnifying power becomes

$$M \approx \frac{L}{f_o} \times \frac{25\text{ cm}}{f_E} = \frac{L\,(25\text{ cm})}{f_o\,f_E}.$$

From this expression, it can be seen that for large magnifying power, the
focal lengths of both the eyepiece and the objective should be very small
and the tube length should be made as large as convenience permits.

There are several practical limitations to the magnification obtainable
with a compound microscope.   One of these is the illumination that can
be used on the object; for biological specimens, the maximum illumination
tolerable without damage to the specimen is sometimes rather low.   A
second limitation to magnification is involved in the increasingly serious
problem of lens aberrations; the compound lenses used in good microscopes must be carefully designed to minimize chromatic and spherical
aberration and other types of distortion.   A third and more fundamental
limitation to magnification is imposed by the wave properties of light
itself, as we shall discuss in the following chapter.

7. THE ASTRONOMICAL TELESCOPE

TELESCOPES are instruments used for the purpose of improving the
observer's vision of distant objects.   Like the compound microscope, the

telescope consists essentially of two components: the objective and the eyepiece. In the case of the telescope, the *objective* forms a real image of a distant object and hence serves the same purpose as a *camera lens;* the *eyepiece* is used to produce an enlarged virtual image of the real image produced by the objective and hence serves as a *simple microscope.*

Figure 9 shows a diagram of a refracting astronomical telescope. An objective lens forms a real inverted image AB of a distant erect object that subtends an angle α at the objective. This real image AB is then viewed through the eyepiece which produces the enlarged inverted virtual image CD, which subtends the angel β at the eyepiece. Owing to the great distance of the object, the rays from any point of it can be considered parallel on reaching the objective; hence, the real image AB is formed in the principal focal plane of the objective.

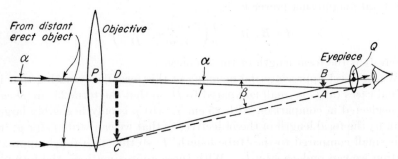

Fig. 9. Image formation in a refracting astronomical telescope. The two rays shown here both originate at the top of a very distant erect object.

In observing a distant object, it is the apparent size that is important, and this is determined by the angle subtended at the eye. Without the telescope, the angle subtended would be α; with the telescope, the angle subtended is β (if the eye is close to the eyepiece). Hence, the magnifying power of the telescope is given by $M = \beta/\alpha$. As in previous discussions, the angles α and β may be approximated by their tangents, and we may write

$$M = \frac{\beta}{\alpha} = \frac{AB/QB}{AB/PB} = \frac{PB}{QB}.$$

In focusing the telescope, let us assume that the observer arranges the eyepiece position so that the distance QB is the focal length of the eyepiece, f_E, and the image CD is at infinity. Since PB is simply f_o, the focal length of the objective, the above expression for the magnifying power can be written as

$$M = f_o/f_E. \tag{9}$$

The magnifying power is equal to the ratio of the focal length of the objective to the focal length of the eyepiece, provided the telescope is focused for final image at infinity.   Hence, in order to achieve high magnification, the focal length of the objective should be made large and the focal length of the eyepiece should be made small.

In astronomical work, although a certain amount of attention must be paid to magnifying power, the principal emphasis is on seeing fainter and fainter objects by increasing the *light-gathering power* of the telescope. Because of inherent limitations imposed by the wave nature of light, we cannot hope to see any star outside of our own solar system as other than a point; but in order to see fainter and more distant objects, it is desirable to gather as much light as possible from the object, all focused as accurately as possible at a point on a photographic plate.   Hence emphasis is placed on increasing the size of the telescope objective.   There are difficult problems involved in increasing the size of an objective *lens*, since both the production of large pieces of glass of high optical quality and the grinding and polishing of the large compound-lens components needed to correct aberrations involve great difficulties.   The largest objective lens that has been made is the one of 40-inch diameter at the Yerkes Observatory of the University of Chicago.

One method of overcoming some of these optical problems is to replace the objective lens by a large, concave, front-surface, parabolic mirror. With an objective of this type, glass of high optical quality is not needed, since the light is reflected from the surface and does not traverse the glass; furthermore, in the case of a concave mirror, there is only one optical surface to be ground and polished.

There are various ways in which a *reflecting telescope* may be arranged; one is shown diagrammatically in Fig. 10.   Light from a distant object or from two neighboring stars, subtending angle α at the mirror surface, is focused by the objective in such a manner as to form a real image at $A'B'$. A small plane mirror M is placed on the telescope axis to change the direction of the reflected light in such a way that the real image is actually formed at AB, where it may be viewed through the eyepiece E.   At the eyepiece the image subtends angle β.   The magnifying power is given by $M = \beta/\alpha$, and formula (9) applies to this case if f_o is the focal length of the objective mirror.   Since an astronomical telescope is used only for viewing distant objects very nearly on the telescope axis, the objective mirror is ground with a paraboloidal surface so as to eliminate spherical aberration.   A mirror has inherently no chromatic aberration.   The largest objective mirror is the one of 200-in diameter at Mount Palomar in California.

We have discussed only an astronomical telescope arranged for visual observation.   If the telescope is arranged to follow the stellar apparent motion accurately, a photographic plate can integrate the light received over a period of many hours, and hence can detect objects very much fainter than can be visually observed.   In photographic observation,

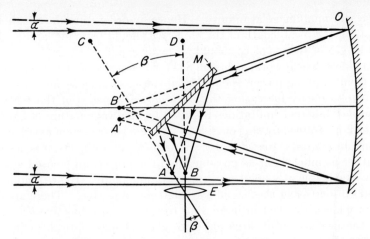

Fig. 10. Reflecting telescope. Incoming light from one point of the object, located on the axis, is shown in solid lines. Light from a point of the object located at an angle α away from the axis is shown by long dashes. The focal length of the objective is ordinarily much longer in comparison with its aperture than shown here, so the mirror M cuts off a smaller fraction of the incoming light.

either the plate can be put directly at the position of the image formed by the objective, or a camera can be used to photograph this image with further linear magnification.

8. TERRESTRIAL TELESCOPES

WHEN A telescope is used for astronomical purposes, the fact that the image is inverted is of no inconvenience; but when terrestrial objects are to be viewed, it is necessary to have an erect final image. The erection

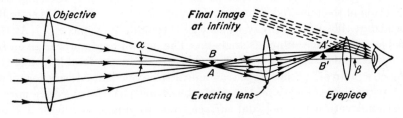

Fig. 11. Terrestrial telescope.

can be accomplished by introducing a third lens, called the *erecting lens*, between the objective and eyepiece. The arrangement is shown schematically in Fig. 11. In this figure a bundle of rays from one end of an erect object is shown passing through the objective, the erecting lens, and the eyepiece. If the erecting lens is placed twice its focal length from the real inverted image AB, it forms a reinverted image $A'B'$ of equal size, which is then viewed through the eyepiece.   Since there is no difference in the sizes of AB and $A'B'$, the magnifying power is still given by (9). However, it should be noted that a terrestrial telescope is longer by four times the focal length of the erecting lens than an astronomical telescope giving equal magnification.

This increased length is sometimes inconvenient and can be avoided by using totally reflecting prisms (described in Chap. 23) instead of an erecting lens for producing the reinversion.   Such an arrangement is shown in Fig. 12.   Light from the objective O reaches prism P_1, which produces a right-left inversion.   From prism P_1 the light passes to prism P_2, which produces a vertical inversion.   As a result of these two inversions the real image produced by the objective is erect and properly oriented and can be observed through the eyepiece E in the usual manner.   Owing to the reflections occurring at P_1 and P_2, the optical length of the instrument is almost three times the actual distance between objective and eyepiece.   A terrestrial telescope of the same optical characteristics would have to be over three times as long, since it would have to provide for an erecting lens.   Since prism instruments are usually made in pairs, one for each eye, the combinations are generally termed

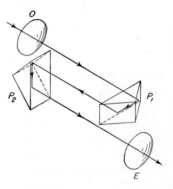

Fig. 12. Arrangement of lenses and prisms in the prism binocular.

prism binoculars.   There is one other interesting optical property of prism binoculars: it is possible to have the distance between the two objectives greater than the distance between the observer's eyes.   This feature increases the stereoscopic effect involved in binocular vision and hence enhances the observer's perception of differences in distance.

One other type of telescope that produces an erect image is the very earliest form of telescope, invented by Galileo in 1609.   This instrument survives today almost exclusively in the opera glass of magnifying power usually about 3.   The Galilean telescope employs a converging lens as objective and a diverging lens as eyepiece, as indicated in Fig. 13.   Two rays are shown reaching the objective from a point of a distant object at an angle α off the axis.   The objective would produce a real inverted image at position AB if the eyepiece E were not present.   However, since the eyepiece is interposed, the image AB forms a virtual object for the eyepiece.   The observer sees the erect virtual image CD formed by lens E.   The magnifying power of this telescope is given, as usual, by the ratio of angle β to angle α.   When the final image CD is at infinite distance the image AB is at the principal focus of the eyepiece and the magnifying power is given by $M = f_O/f_E$, as in the case of the astronomical telescope.   In this relation the negative sign usually attached to the focal length f_E of a diverging lens is to be ignored.   It is noted that the tube length is shorter than for an astronomical telescope and much shorter

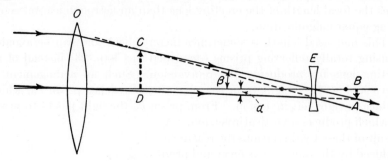

Fig. 13. Galilean telescope.

than for a terrestrial telescope of the same magnifying power; hence the compact size of opera glasses.

> **Example.** *A private detective desires a pair of binoculars that will enable him to read the license plate on a car* 300 ft *away when he can normally read such a plate readily at* 20 ft.   *What magnifying power does he need?   If the objective has a focal length of* 12 in, *what should be the focal length of the eyepiece?*
>
> The necessary magnifying power is 300 ft/20 ft = 15, since the height of the image of a licence plate on the retina varies inversely as its distance.   From the formula $M = f_O/f_E$, we see that if $M = 15$ and $f_O = 12$ in, f_E must be $1\frac{2}{15}$ in = 0.8 in.

PROBLEMS

1. A camera lens has a focal length of 10 cm.   What should be the distance between lens and plate when the object being photographed is 2 m from the lens?   Sketch the principal-ray diagram.   Ans: 10.5 cm.

2. An enlarging camera has a lens of 10-cm focal length.   If it is desired to make an 8×10-inch print from a 2×2.5-inch film, what should be the distances from film to lens and from lens to print?

3. A certain camera lens has a focal length of 4 in and is to be used in photographing an object 2 ft tall.   How far from the object should the lens be placed if the photographic image is to be 2 in tall?   What should be the distance from the lens to the photographic plate?   Ans: 52.0 in; 4.33 in.

4. A lens is to be used in a box camera in which the plate distance has a fixed value of 4 in.   What should be the focal length of the lens?   A camera of this type must use a 'slow' lens of small aperture in order to perform satisfactorily.   By consideration of ray diagrams, show that the smaller the aperture of the lens, the closer an object can be and still form an image on the plate that is reasonably sharp.

5. The housing of a camera lens is marked f: 3.2, 9 cm.   What is the diameter of the lens?   If the correct exposure time for a certain scene is $\frac{1}{20}$ sec at f:6.3, what is the correct exposure time at f:3.2?   Ans: 2.8 cm; $\frac{1}{80}$ sec.

6. A camera lens has a focal length of 8 cm and a diameter of 2.5 cm.   What is the f-number of this lens?   What is the proper exposure time for photographing a scene with this lens if an exposure meter indicates that the correct exposure is $\frac{1}{200}$ sec at f:2.8?

7. When a scene is photographed, it is desirable to have objects at various distances in reasonably good focus. If light from an object at distance p is perfectly focused on the plate, light from a point on an object at different distance p' will not fall at a single point on the plate, but will fall within a small circle, known as the *circle of confusion*. Show that for a given lens, and given values of p and p' the diameter of the circle of confusion is directly proportional to the diameter d of the aperture, and hence inversely proportional to the f-number of the stop used. Hence show that the 'depth of focus' increases as the f-number of the stop increases.

8. The total distance between a slide in a projection lantern and the screen is 30 ft. If the projection lens has a focal length of 18 in, what should be the distance between the slide and the lens?

9. A lantern slide has dimensions 3 in $\times$ 4 in. This slide is to be projected in such a way as to produce an image 3 ft $\times$ 4 ft on a screen 20 ft from the projection lens. What should be the focal length of the projection lens? What should be the distance from the slide to the lens?   Ans: 18.5 in; 20 in.

10. It is desired to produce an image of a 3-in $\times$ 4-in lantern slide on a screen 30 ft from the projection lens. The image on the screen is to be 6 ft by 8 ft. (a) What should be the focal length of the projection lens? (b) Where should the slide be placed? (c) If the illumination at the slide is 1000 lumens/ft², what is the maximum possible illumination at the screen?

11. A very nearsighted person cannot see objects clearly when they are farther than 10 in away. What is the focal length of the lens needed to enable this person to see distant objects clearly?   Ans: -10 in.

12. An extremely nearsighted person cannot see objects clearly at distances greater than 12 cm. What power of lens is needed to make reading at 25 cm possible? What power of lens does this person need in order to see distant objects clearly?

13. What power of spectacle lenses is needed for reading at 25 cm by a person who cannot see objects distinctly when they are closer than 250 cm?
                    Ans: 3.6 diopters.

14. A near-sighted person has his far point at 200 cm, his near point at 25 cm. Prescribe glasses for driving an automobile. Where would this person have to hold a book to read with these glasses on? Would he find it inconvenient to leave his glasses on constantly?

15. A converging lens has a focal length of 1 cm. If this lens is to be used as a simple microscope, at what distance from the lens should the object be placed in order that an enlarged virtual image may be formed at a distance of 25 cm from the lens? What is the magnifying power in this case?   Ans: 0.962 cm; 26.

16. If the lens in Prob. 15 were used in such a way as to produce a virtual image at ∞, where would the object be placed? What is the magnifying power in this case?

17. What is the magnifying power of a reading glass whose focal length is 12.5 cm if it is held 10 cm from a book and if the observer's eyes are 30 cm from the lens? Sketch the principal-ray diagram.   Ans: 1.56.

18. How far from the lens in Prob. 17 should the book be located in order for the maximum magnifying power of 2 to be produced?

19. What is the focal length of a jeweler's lens having a magnifying power of 20 when the image is formed at ∞ ? What should the object distance be?

Ans: 1.25 cm; 1.25 cm.

20. Derive equation (6), p. 491.

21. In a compound microscope, the focal length of the objective lens is 1.0 cm, that of the eyepiece is 5 cm, and the distance between the lenses is 20 cm. If the observer places the final image at a distance of 25 cm from his eye, what is the distance from the object to the objective lens? What is the magnifying power?

Ans: 1.07 cm; 89.

22. In a compound microscope the focal length of the objective is 0.5 cm and that of the eyepiece is 4 cm. If the distance between the lenses is 30 cm, what should be the distance from the object to the objective lens if the observer focuses for image at ∞ ? What is the magnifying power?

23. The objective lens of a compound microscope has a focal length of 0.5 cm and the eyepiece has a focal length of 2 cm. What is the maximum obtainable magnifying power when the lenses are 10 cm apart? Ans: 206.

24. If the objective of a compound microscope has a focal length of 5 mm, where should the object be placed in order that the objective produce an enlargement of 100 diameters? What would be the focal length of the eyepiece needed to give an over-all magnifying power of 2000 for the microscope when the final image is 25 cm from the eyepiece?

25. A compound microscope has an objective lens of 5-mm focal length and an eyepiece of 8-mm focal length. How far apart should the lenses be in order to obtain a magnifying power of 500 when the final image is formed at infinity?

Ans: 9.3 cm.

26. If an astronomical telescope has a magnifying power of 100 when used with an eyepiece of 3-cm focal length, what is the focal length of the objective?

27. A small astronomical telescope has a distance of 46.2 cm between the objective and the eyepiece. If the magnifying power of this telescope is 20, find the focal lengths of objective and eyepiece. Ans: 44.0 cm; 2.2 cm.

28. In taking a photograph of the moon, a photographic plate is inserted in the focal plane of the objective lens of a telescope. How large a photograph of the moon can be obtained if the objective has a focal length of 80 cm? The diameter of the moon is 2163 mi and the distance to the moon is 240,000 mi.

29. The telescope at the Yerkes Observatory has an objective of diameter 40 in and focal length 65 ft. What is its magnifying power when used with an eyepiece of focal length 1 in and the final image at infinity? Ans: 780.

30. The illumination from direct sunlight on a certain day is 8000 lumens/ft². If the Yerkes telescope were used to view the sun, what would be the illumination measured at the image of the sun's disk in the focal plane of the objective? (Note: The diameter of the sun subtends an angle of 0°.5.)

31. The objective of a terrestrial telescope has a focal length of 80 cm and the telescope has a magnifying power of 20 when adjusted in such a way that parallel rays reach the observer. If the erecting lens has a focal length of 18 cm, what is the total length of the telescope? Show diagram. Ans: 156 cm.

32. The objective of a terrestrial telescope has a focal length of 3 ft. The erecting lens has a focal length of 4 in and the total length of the telescope is 4.5 ft. What is its magnifying power?

33. The total length of the optical path between objective and eyepiece in a pair of prism binoculars is 18 in, although the actual distance between objective and eyepiece is only 7 in. If the magnifying power of this instrument is 8, what would be the length of a terrestrial telescope using the same objective and eyepiece and having an erecting lens of focal length 3 in?   Ans: 30 in.

34. An opera glass measures 6 in between objective and eyepiece. If the focal length of the objective is 8 in, what is the magnifying power?

35. An opera glass measures 3 in between objective and eyepiece. The focal length of the objective is 5 in. What is the magnifying power?   Ans: 2.5.

36. Prove that the magnifying power of the Galilean telescope of Fig. 13 is f_O/f_E when the final image is formed at infinity.

37. A surveyor's transit is a telescope equipped with graduated circles that measure the horizontal and vertical angles through which the tube of the telescope turns when it is pointed first at one object and then at another. To facilitate pointing the axis of the telescope at exactly the object desired, the telescope is equipped with cross hairs, and the telescope is turned so that the object is apparently at the intersection of the cross hairs. Describe exactly how the cross hairs must be built into the tube of the telescope, allowing provision for focussing on objects at various distances.

38. Workers sometimes employ 'telescopic' glasses, in which one pair of lenses is about 8 cm in front of the eyes, the second pair close to the eyes. The purpose is to secure magnification and still keep a distance of 25 cm from object to glasses to leave room to work on the object.

(a) Show that no single lens at any position relative to the eye can have a magnifying power greater than unity if the object is 25 cm or more from the lens.

(b) Design a set of telescopic glasses with the lenses 8 cm apart that will give $M = 1.5$ for an object 25 cm from the front lens, and produce a final erect image at ∞.

39. What are the magnifying powers of the telescopes of Fig. 9 and Fig. 11 when one looks at a distant object *through the wrong end?* If a pair of opera glasses are focused on a distant object, with final image at infinity, and then looked through from the wrong end, what is seen?

40. Opera glasses with $f_O = 5$ in, $f_E = -2$ in, are focused on an object 5 ft from the objectives with final image at infinity. What is the magnifying power? The glasses are turned around and the objectives placed against the eyes. What change in tube length is required to bring the same object, now 5 ft from the eyepieces, into focus with final image at infinity? What now is the magnifying power?

41. Discuss limitations on the magnifying power of prism binoculars associated with problems of light-gathering power and image brightness. What are so-called *night glasses?*

CHAPTER 25

PHYSICAL OPTICS

IN THE DISCUSSION of optical phenomena thus far, we have devoted our attention to phenomena that can be adequately described in terms of rays. The actual wave properties of light were not intimately involved in this treatment by the methods of *geometrical optics*.

The optical phenomena known as *diffraction, interference,* and *polarization* can be adequately described *only* in terms of the wave properties of light. Treatment of optical phenomena from the wave point of view is called *physical optics*. *All* optical problems must be treated by the methods of physical optics if a minutely detailed analysis is desired. Geometrical or ray optics can be regarded as an approximation which proves adequate for many practical optical problems.

1. INTERFERENCE: FRESNEL'S DOUBLE MIRROR

THE GENERAL conditions for interference have been discussed in Chap. 18, Wave Motion. Interference between two waves occurs only (a) if the frequencies of the sources are equal and (b) if there is some definite and constant phase relationship between the vibrations of the two sources. These two conditions are known in optics as the conditions for 'coherence.' It is possible to have coherent waves from two *different* sources of mechanical waves and even of radio waves. However, although it is relatively easy to produce optical sources of equal frequency, the problem of arranging for definite phase relationships between two independent light sources is probably insoluble. Interference between two independent light sources such as two electric arcs or two luminous flames has never been observed. Interference of light waves occurs only when waves from the *same source* proceed along *different paths* enroute to the *same point*.

We note that light waves are radiated by individual atoms or molecules. Each atom or molecule of the source contributes only a tiny part to the light energy, and these parts bear no particular phase relation to each other. Hence it is necessary for the light from each atom or molecule to interfere *with itself* to obtain an interference pattern.

In computing details of any interference pattern, amplitudes are added trigonometrically as in Fig. 8, p. 386, to obtain the *amplitude* of the resultant wave.   But just as in the case of sound waves,

Intensity of illumination is proportional to the square of the amplitude.

Thomas Young was the first (in 1802) to produce effects directly and unambiguously interpretable as interference between light waves; we shall discuss Young's experiment in Sec. 4.   First we shall consider a somewhat later experiment performed by Augustin Jean Fresnel (1788–1827).   The arrangement used by Fresnel is shown in Fig. 1.   Two plane mirrors M_1 and M_2 meet each other along a straight line K.   The two mirrors are inclined toward each other so that there is a small angle, actually only a few minutes of arc, between their planes.   At a distance of a few centimeters from the mirrors, a narrow slit S is set up in such a way that it is parallel to the line of intersection K.   The slit is illuminated from behind by a sodium flame or some other bright source of monochromatic (single-frequency) light so that light passing through the slit reaches both mirrors and is reflected by them.   The mirrors are made of black glass so that the light is reflected only from the front surfaces of the mirrors.

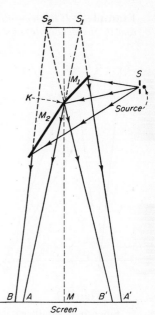

Fig. 1. Fresnel's double mirror.

The slit S is imaged by mirror M_1 at S_1, and light diverging from S_1 reaches the screen in the region between A and A'. The image formed by mirror M_2 is at S_2, and light diverging from S_2 reaches the screen in the region between B and B'. Thus, the portion of the screen between A and B' receives light from both images, S_1 and S_2.   In this way we have created two 'sources' of illumination on the screen that have not only *identical frequencies* but also *a definite phase relationship.*   Therefore, the conditions for interference are fulfilled.   The interference gives rise to alternate bright and dark bands on the white screen.   The bands, or *interference fringes*, as they are usually called, are parallel to the line K and to the slit S.

Note that the distance traversed by a light ray from S to M_1 to a point on the screen is the same as the length of the straight line from S_1 to the point on the screen.   Similarly, a ray reflected from M_2 proceeds the same distance as if it came directly from S_2.   The two rays arriving at the same point on the screen and coming (apparently) from S_1 and S_2 will interfere constructively at point M, which is at the same distance from S_1 and S_2, and at points on either side of M for which the distances to S_1 and S_2

differ by an integral number of wavelengths. These points give the positions of the centers of the *bright* fringes. Between them, at positions where the path lengths differ by $\frac{1}{2}$, $\frac{3}{2}$, $\frac{5}{2}$, $\cdots$ wavelengths, interference is destructive. These positions mark the centers of the dark fringes.

If a sodium arc (a monochromatic source) illuminates the slit S, the interference pattern consists of alternate yellow and black fringes. If, however, white light is used, all the bright bands except the central one at M exhibit spectral colors like a rainbow. This effect is due to the fact that the wavelengths corresponding to different spectral colors are different and hence the positions of destructive and constructive interference are different for different wavelengths.

Example. *If the separation of the virtual sources S_1 and S_2 in Fig. 1 is 0.1 mm and the perpendicular distance from the virtual sources to the screen is 50 cm, find the distance between the central bright fringe and the center of the first bright fringe on either side when the slit is illuminated with yellow sodium light of wavelength $\lambda = 589$ mμ.*

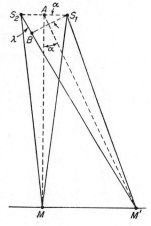

Figure 2

The geometry of this problem is illustrated in Fig. 2, except that in this figure horizontal distances S_2S_1 and MM' are exaggerated in comparison with vertical distances by a factor of about 100. The angle between the central bright fringe M and the next M' turns out to be only about 0.006 rad; it is the smallness of this angle that permits the trigonometric approximations used in the following computation. In Fig. 2, MA is the bisector of $\angle S_2MS_1$, $M'A$ is the bisector of $\angle S_2M'S_1$; S_1B is drawn perpendicular to $M'A$. Hence the lengths $M'S_1$ and $M'B$ are equal. The length S_2M' is greater than S_1M' by S_2B, and for the first bright fringe this length difference must equal λ as indicated on the figure.

Since α is small, we can write $\alpha = \lambda/S_1S_2 = (589 \times 10^{-6}\text{ mm})/(0.1\text{ mm}) = 0.00589$ rad to a good approximation. Also $\alpha = MM'/MA = MM'/(500\text{ mm})$ to a good approximation. Equating these two expressions for α gives

$$MM'/(500\text{ mm}) = 0.00589, \qquad \text{or} \qquad MM' = 2.95\text{ mm}$$

as the distance of the center of the first bright fringe.

2. INTERFERENCE PHENOMENA IN THIN FILMS

INTERFERENCE phenomena are produced by reflection of light from thin films. The colors observed in thin films such as soap bubbles, thin layers of oil on water, and thin layers of oxide on metal surfaces (for example blued steel, the blacksmith's temper colors, and the striking colors placed on aluminum by controlled oxidation) are familiar to everyone. Such films are usually observed by reflection when white light is incident, and the colors are due to the interference of light waves reflected at the front and back surfaces of the films.

The reflection involved in this phenomenon is regular reflection.   In order to understand how the interference arises, let us consider Fig. 3. Rays 1 and 2 proceed *from the same point of a monochromatic source*, are reflected from the front and back surfaces of the film, and then proceed *to the same point* on the retina of the eye or on a photographic plate.   The distances of the source and the eye are so large in comparison with the film thickness t that the rays 1 and 2 are essentially parallel in Fig. 3, and the distances from the source to P and Q, on a wave-front perpendicular to the rays, are equal.   Similarly the distances from P' and Q' to the eye are equal.   The rays 1 and 2 will interfere when they reach the eye.   Whether

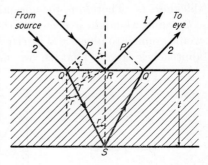

Fig. 3. Reflection from a thin film.

the interference is constructive, destructive, or intermediate will depend on the angle of incidence i.   We note that the path difference between rays 1 and 2 in Fig. 3 arises from the fact that 1 follows the route PRP' while 2 traverses the path QSQ'.   One cannot, however, merely subtract the length PRP' from the length QSQ' to determine the number of wavelengths in this path difference, because the wavelengths in the film and in air are different.

In order to handle problems like this, involving paths in material media, it is convenient to define a quantity called the *optical path length:*

> The **optical path length** of a ray in a material medium is the path length in vacuum that would contain the same number of wavelengths as does the actual path length in the material medium.

Two rays of the same frequency will take the same times to traverse the same optical path lengths since a distance equal to one wavelength is traversed in the fixed periodic time $T = 1/f$.

Since the speed of light in a material medium of index of refraction μ is c/μ, where c is the speed in vacuum, and since the frequency is the same in the material and in vacuum, the wavelength in the material will be λ/μ, where λ is the wavelength in vacuum, as indicated in Fig. 4.   Since the wavelength is less by a factor μ, we see that the number of waves in the material path will be greater by a factor μ, and from the above definition that

$$\text{(optical path length)} = \mu(\text{actual path length}).$$

It is readily seen that the conditions for interference that we have previously stated can be applied to the difference between the total *optical* path lengths of two interfering rays when comparison is made with the vacuum wavelength.

In Fig. 3, then, if we take the index of refraction of air as unity, we see that

$$\text{difference in optical path length} = \mu(QSQ') - PRP'. \qquad (1)$$

For normal incidence, PRP' is zero and QSQ' is simply twice the film thickness t. Therefore, for normal incidence, the optical path difference is $2\mu t$, and we might expect that the light waves traversing paths 1 and 2 would come into phase and interfere constructively as the film thickness t approaches zero. That is, we might expect extremely thin films to

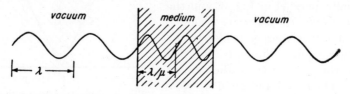

Fig. 4. The wavelength in a material medium is λ/μ, if λ is the wavelength in vacuum.

appear bright when viewed by reflected light at almost normal incidence. A simple experiment with a soap film shows the reverse to be the case; in a region where the soap film is so thin that it is about to break, the film appears *black* when viewed by reflected monochromatic or white light. Note that the reflection processes for rays 1 and 2 are not identical. The reflection at the front surface takes place in a medium of low refractive index (air) at the boundary of a medium of high refractive index (film material); reflection at the back surface occurs in a medium of high refractive index (film material) at the boundary of a medium of low refractive index (air). The above and similar experiments show that, under these circumstances, there is always a phase difference of 180° between the two reflected waves in addition to phase differences caused by differences in optical path.

Because of this phase difference, the rules for constructive and destructive interference *for thin films* are just opposite those we have encountered previously:

For reflection from thin films, maximum destructive interference occurs if the optical path difference is equal to a whole number of wavelengths; maximum constructive interference occurs if the optical path difference is equal to an odd number of half wavelengths.

From Fig. 3, we see that we can write $QS = QT + TS = QR \sin r + t \cos r$, and, since $\mu \sin r = \sin i$, $\mu QS = QR \sin i + \mu t \cos r = PR + \mu t \cos r$. From this last relation, we see that the expression (1) has the value difference in optical path $= 2\mu t \cos r = 2t \sqrt{\mu^2 - \mu^2 \sin^2 r} = 2t \sqrt{\mu^2 - \sin^2 i}.$ (2)

In order to see the interference colors, it is not necessary that the source have any special character—it can be the general illumination of the room. But it is necessary to look *at* the film, that is, to focus the eye on the film, as one naturally does. With the eye focused on the film in Fig. 3, light from the tiny region RQ' is focused say on one cone of the retina. By the laws of regular reflection, this light can come from only one small region of the source and hence the rays reflected from the two surfaces have the necessary coherence for interference.

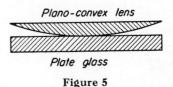

Plano-convex lens

Plate glass

Figure 5

One well-known phenomenon involving interference of light waves in thin films gives rise to *Newton's rings*, first observed scientifically by Sir Isaac Newton. The effect (Fig. 6) can easily be produced by placing a plano-convex lens with a long focal length (approximately 4 meters) on a flat piece of plate glass in the manner indicated in Fig. 5. If the arrangement is illuminated by white light, the point of contact of the lens and plate is surrounded by a system of colored concentric circular rings. If the arrangement is illuminated with monochromatic light, a system of light and dark rings is observed. The observed patterns can be readily explained in terms of interference effects caused by the thin film of air between the lens and the plate.

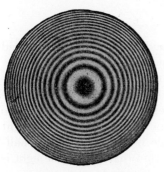

Fig. 6. Photograph of Newton's rings taken with monochromatic light. [*Courtesy of Jemima B. Dutcher.*]

The pattern observed by reflected rays of nearly normal incidence is shown in Fig. 6. The central region around the point of contact between lens and plate is dark, since in this region the film is extremely thin, as in the case of a soap film just before rupture. Beyond this region the conditions for constructive and destructive interference are realized alternately as the distance from the point of contact increases.

The film thickness at horizontal distance r from the point of contact in Fig. 5 can be shown geometrically to be $t = r^2/2R$, where R is the radius of curvature of the lens surface, provided that $r \ll R$. According to the previous discussion, the nth dark ring *surrounding* the central dark spot will occur where the optical path difference is $n\lambda$. This optical path difference is just $2t$ for normal incidence, since $\mu = 1$ for air. Hence the radius of the nth dark ring, calling the center spot the zeroth, is given by

$$r_n^2/R = n\lambda.$$

This relation can be used to determine the wavelength λ of monochromatic light by measurement of the radii of Newton's rings.

Example. *A film of oil of index of refraction 1.5 floats on water on a damp pavement. The eye observes a particular point where the angle of incidence (i in Fig. 3) is 45° and the film thickness is 340 mμ. What color is seen at this point?*

Since the index of refraction of the oil is higher than that of the underlying water, the same phase difference between light reflected from the top and bottom of the film occurs as in the case of a soap film, and the rule for interference stated in italics on p. 506 applies. From formula (2), we find the *difference in optical path:*

$$2t \sqrt{\mu^2 - \sin^2 i} = 2 \ (340 \ \text{m}\mu) \ \sqrt{(1.5)^2 - (0.707)^2}$$
$$= 2 \ (340 \ \text{m}\mu) \ \sqrt{1.75} = 898 \ \text{m}\mu.$$

Let us round this to 900 mμ for purposes of the following qualitative arguments. From Fig. 7 on p. 430, we note that 900 mμ is in the infrared, but that it is 2×450 mμ and $\tfrac{3}{2} \times 600$ mμ. Hence by the rule for interference, the violet color of wavelength 450 mμ will suffer maximum *destructive* interference while the orange color of wavelength 600 mμ will have maximum constructive interference. The yellow-orange-red end of the spectrum will be enhanced while the violet-blue end of the spectrum will be diminished in intensity as compared with the illuminating white light. This particular portion of the oil film will have an orangish color.

3. THE MICHELSON INTERFEROMETER

ONE OF THE most ingenious methods of producing interference is used in the Michelson interferometer, which is shown diagrammatically in Fig. 7. The method consists of dividing a beam of light by partial transmission and partial reflection and sending the two beams over different routes to two mirrors, where they are reflected in such a way as to cause them to recombine and produce interference. Parallel monochromatic light represented by ray S is incident at an angle of 45° on a plane 'half-silvered' mirror M. The silver coating is so thin that half of the light is transmitted as ray 1; the rest of the light is reflected and is shown as ray 2. Ray 1 reaches mirror M_1 and ray 2 reaches mirror M_2. In both cases incidence is normal, and hence the direction of each ray is reversed as indicated in the figure; for the sake of clearness, the reflected rays shown in Fig. 7 have been displaced laterally. On their return journey the two rays reach half-silvered mirror M again and approximately half of the light represented by each ray reaches the observer; the remaining light shown by the dotted ray returns to the source. Glass plate N, identical to M but unsilvered, makes the number of extraneous reflections at glass surfaces that remove energy from the beam identical for rays 1 and 2; hence these rays reach the observer with equal amplitudes.

If the distances of M_1 and M_2 from M are equal, the two rays 1 and 2 traverse identical paths; the glass plate N makes the path in glass the same for both rays. Therefore, the light waves associated with rays 1 and 2 emerge in phase and reinforce each other. Reinforcement also occurs when the optical paths traversed by rays 1 and 2 differ by a whole number of wavelengths. Interference changes from constructive to destructive when one of the mirrors is moved a distance equal to a quarter wavelength, since this movement changes the optical path by a half wavelength. It follows that the Michelson interferometer can be used for the absolute measurement of wavelength if the mirror M_2 is moved in the direction of ray 2 through a distance that can be measured by a micrometer screw, and if the alternations of light and darkness in the field of view are observed while the mirror is being moved.

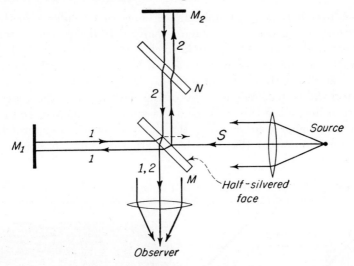

Fig. 7. The Michelson interferometer.

As the apparatus is actually employed, the mirrors are not aligned with perfect accuracy. Very slight tilts from the perfect alignment discussed above are desirable so that the field is crossed by parallel fringes, which move in a direction normal to their length as mirror M_2 is moved. 'Counting the fringes' that move past the crosshairs of an eyepiece will then give the number of *half wavelengths* that the mirror M_2 is moved.

One extremely important application of the Michelson interferometer is the determination of the length of the standard meter in terms of wavelengths of light. Michelson and others performed this measurement in terms of light from an electric-arc source with cadmium electrodes by a method similar in essentials to that described above. The results of the experiments give

$$1 \text{ meter} = 1{,}553{,}161.1 \; \lambda_{Cd,R} = 1{,}966{,}249.7 \; \lambda_{Cd,G} = 2{,}083{,}372.1 \; \lambda_{Cd,B},$$

where $\lambda_{Cd,R}$, $\lambda_{Cd,G}$, and $\lambda_{Cd,B}$ are the wavelengths of the red, green, and blue light emitted by cadmium. An even more accurate evaluation of the meter can be made in terms of green light emitted by the pure mercury isotope 198, which has recently been produced from gold. This evaluation in terms of green light from mercury 198 can be made more precise than the evaluation in terms of light from cadmium because the several isotopes of cadmium give several nearly but not exactly equal frequencies; hence the cadmium light is less monochromatic than that from the pure mercury isotope. The result of the evaluation of the meter in terms of the green light of wavelength λ_{Hg} from mercury 198 is

$$1 \text{ meter} = 1,831,249.21 \ \lambda_{Hg}.$$

This evaluation is of great importance, since it provides a method of duplication of the primary standard meter. If the primary standard were destroyed, it would be possible to construct a new one which would agree with the original standard meter within 1 part in 10,000,000.

It is very likely that in the near future the fundamental unit of length, the meter, will be redefined in terms of the wavelength of the above mercury green line, since this wavelength is more reproducible, and can be measured to higher accuracy, than the distance between two scratches on a platinum-iridium bar that may be suffering unknown mechanical distortions as time passes.

Example. *A Mach interferometer is a variant of the Michelson interferometer that is used to measure density differences at various points in a supersonic*

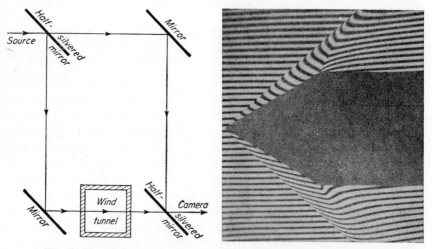

Fig. 8. The Mach interferometer, and photograph of the flow past a cone. The mirrors are tilted so that the region of constant density to the left of the cone gives uniformly spaced parallel fringes. The fringe shift is to be measured by comparison with this uniform spacing. [*Photograph from U.S. Naval Ordnance Laboratory.*]

wind tunnel. A Mach interferogram for the flow past a wedge is shown in Fig. 8. The light beam is split and then reassembled by means of half-silvered mirrors, so that half the light has passed through the glass-sided wind tunnel, half has passed under the tunnel through air of constant density. If the path length through the wind tunnel is 30 cm and the fringes at the left in the photograph corresponds to air of normal density at NTP, what is the percentage change of density for each shift of one fringe at the same horizontal level when sodium light of 590 mμ wavelength is used?

The index of refraction of air at NTP is $\mu = 1.000293$. The *excess* $(\mu - 1)$ over the vacuum index *is proportional to the density*. The optical path through the wind tunnel is $\mu \times (30 \text{ cm})$. Moving from one fringe to the next corresponds to a change in optical path length of one wavelength. This corresponds to a change $\Delta\mu$ in refractive index given by

$$590 \text{ m}\mu = \Delta\mu \times (30 \text{ cm}) = \Delta\mu \times 30 \times 10^7 \text{ m}\mu,$$

since $1 \text{ cm} = 10^7 \text{ m}\mu$. This relation gives

$$\Delta\mu = 590/(30 \times 10^7) = 1.97 \times 10^{-6}$$

for one fringe. For normal air, $\mu - 1 = 293 \times 10^{-6}$. To change this value of $\mu - 1$ by 1.97×10^{-6} involves a density change in the proportion

$$1.97/293 = 0.0067 = 0.67 \%.$$

Thus it is seen that the Mach interferometer gives an accurate way of measuring density changes of air, even though the density of air is very low to begin with.

4. DIFFRACTION PHENOMENA AND HUYGENS' PRINCIPLE

WHEN light waves pass through an aperture, they always spread to some extent into regions that would not be traversed by rays representing

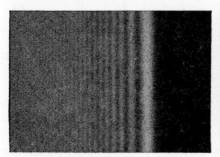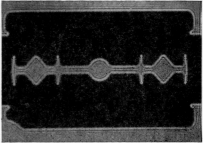

Fig. 9. Shadows of a straight edge and of a razor blade. [*From Francis Weston Sears, Principles of Physics, III (Optics), 2nd ed., by permission of Addison-Wesley Press, Inc., publishers.*]

rectilinear propagation. The shadow of a straight-edge illuminated by a point source does not exhibit a sharp transition from light to dark but has the appearance shown in Fig. 9. Most everyday experience is concerned with extended rather than point sources, so the shadows ordinarily observed merely look 'fuzzy' at the edges, and do not exhibit the interesting diffraction patterns shown in Fig. 9.

The term **diffraction** refers to those phenomena that result from the non-rectilinear propagation of light waves.

When light waves from a point source pass an obstacle that obstructs part of the wave-front, the shadow beyond is not sharp. The behavior of the light can be explained by means of *Huygens' principle* (Christian Huygens, 1629–1695):

HUYGENS' PRINCIPLE: *Every point on an advancing wave-front can be considered as a source of secondary waves which in a homogeneous medium spread out as spherical wavelets. A later position of the wave-front is given by the envelope of the secondary wavelets.*

The application of Huygens' principle to spherical waves in free space can be understood by consideration of Fig. 10. If W_1 is a wave-front spreading out from a source S with speed c, then according to the Huygens hypothesis every point of this wave-front is to be considered as the source of a secondary wavelet whose radius after t seconds would be ct. A later position of the primary wave-front such as W_2 is given by the envelope of the secondary wavelets.

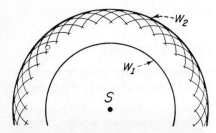

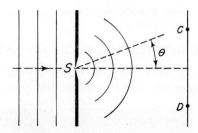

Fig. 10. Huygens' principle for a spherical wave-front.

Fig. 11. Diffraction by a slit of width small compared with the wavelength of the light.

In Fig. 11, let S be a hole or slit *of width small compared with the wavelength of the advancing plane waves.* The narrow opening S will transmit a disturbance to the region beyond the barrier. According to Huygens' principle, the disturbance in this region will be transmitted in the manner shown in the figure; a cross section of the advancing wave-front would consist of semicircles. Experimentally, it is found that the region of screen CD that is illuminated by such a slit is broad. The central portion of the screen is always brighter than the more remote portions, and hence it must be assumed that the amplitudes of the secondary wavelets is greatest in the forward direction; more detailed theory indicates that the amplitude of the wavelet at a given distance from a slit of infinitesimal width is proportional to $(1+\cos\theta)$, a quantity sometimes called the *obliquity factor.*

The original experiment on interference performed by Thomas Young made use of the diffraction of light passing through a narrow slit. Young's experimental arrangement is shown schematically in Fig. 12. Sunlight is first allowed to pass through slit S, and then at a considerable distance away the diffracted light passes through the slits S_1 and S_2. If the slits

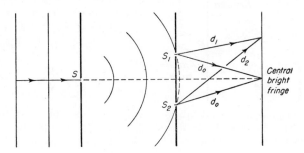

Fig. 12. Young's experiment.

S_1 and S_2 are at equal distances from S, the light waves from S reach these slits in the same phase. Light waves passing through slits S_1 and S_2 therefore produce interference fringes on the screen CD in exactly the same manner as in the interference experiments of Fresnel that involved a

double mirror. Interference patterns obtained in this way are shown in Fig. 13.

The shadows observed in Fig. 9, when a portion of the wave-front is cut off, can be explained by Huygens' principle (the mathematics is somewhat complicated) in the manner suggested by Fig. 14. In this figure the plane wave-front from a very distant source is interrupted by a straight-edge. A point such as P on the screen receives light from the secondary wavelets starting from each point in the region AA of the inter-

Fig. 13. Interference patterns formed in Young's experiment. The pattern on the left is formed by slits of half the separation of those giving the pattern on the right. [*From Francis Weston Sears, Principles of Physics, III (Optics), 2nd ed., by permission of Addison-Wesley Press, Inc., publishers.*]

rupted wave-front. But on arrival at P, these secondary waves have various phases. The actual amplitude at P is an integrated effect, and the integration for various points on the screen in the neighborhood of the edge of the geometrical shadow leads sometimes to a greater amplitude than that along AA, sometimes to a lesser, giving rise to the fringes shown in Fig. 9 and indicated schematically in Fig. 14. It is apparent that the amplitude at the point at the edge of the geometrical shadow (the actual position of P in Fig. 14) is just half the amplitude of the uninterrupted wave-front, since half the Huygens' wavelets have been eliminated in completely symmetrical fashion. Hence the intensity here is $\frac{1}{4}$ the

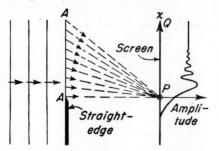

intensity of the full beam. The intensity falls off regularly as one proceeds into the shadow; the fringes occur on the geometrically illuminated part of the screen. The centers of the bright fringes occur at

$$x = 1, \sqrt{3}, \sqrt{5}, \cdots \times \sqrt{\lambda d},$$

Fig. 14. Shadow of a straight-edge (schematic). The distance PQ is about 3.5 mm if the distance AP is 1 m.

where d is the distance to the screen, AP in Fig. 14. Thus Fig. 14 is highly distorted. If $AP = 1$ meter and $\lambda = 490$ m$\mu = 49 \times 10^{-8}$ m (blue-green), the first three bright fringes are at $x = 0.7$, 1.2, and 1.5 *millimeters* from P.

The diffraction patterns we have considered so far are characterized by the fact that *no lenses are involved* in their production. They are known as *Fresnel diffraction* patterns. Another type of diffraction pattern of importance is called a *Fraunhofer diffraction* pattern.

> In **Fresnel diffraction,** light from a very distant point source passes through an aperture and falls on a screen, no lenses being employed.

> In **Fraunhofer diffraction,** a point or line source is placed at the principal focus of a converging lens that renders the light parallel; the light then passes through the aperture at which diffraction takes place, and is then focused on a screen placed at the principal focus of a second converging lens.

The arrangement for observing Fraunhofer diffraction is shown in Fig. 15. Let us consider first the case where the source is a narrow line perpendicular to the paper, emitting monochromatic light. If no diaphragm is present, an image of the line source appears on the screen. If we insert a diaphragm containing a narrow slit parallel to the source, the pattern on the screen changes radically to that shown in Fig. 16. This pattern is the Fraunhofer diffraction pattern of the aperture slit. The bright central portion of the diffraction pattern coincides with the original image but is considerably broader.

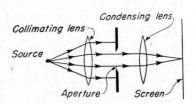

Fig. 15. Arrangement for observing the Fraunhofer diffraction pattern of an aperture slit (schematic).

Several narrower bright and

dark fringes appear on the screen on each side of the central image.   The width of the central image and the spacing of the diffraction fringes are entirely determined by the width of the aperture slit.

The explanation of the observed diffraction pattern is relatively simple, since only plane wave-fronts reaching the condensing lens are focused on the screen.   The simplified drawing in Fig. 17 will be useful in understanding the observed diffraction patterns; in this figure the magnitudes of the angle and the wavelength are enlarged for purposes of clarity.   In the figure the lines I represent the path traversed in the forward direction by the secondary Huygens wavelets from the two edges of the aperture slit.   Since the light approaching the slit consists of a parallel beam, the original wave-front is plane and all sources of Huygens wavelets in the slit opening are in phase.   Therefore, the secondary waves traversing the paths I and all similar paths drawn in the forward direction from the plane of the slit are in phase, and the lens produces a bright image in the forward direction; this bright image is the central maximum of the diffraction pattern. The intensity of images produced at other points on the screen depends on the differences in optical paths traversed by secondary waves from different parts of the slit.   If we are interested in the intensity on

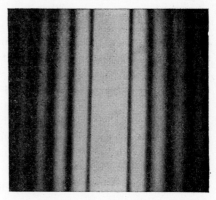

Fig. 16. Fraunhofer diffraction pattern of a single slit. [*From Francis Weston Sears, Principle of Physics, III (Optics), 2nd ed., by permission of Addison-Wesley Press, Inc., publishers.*]

the screen at a point making angle θ (measured at the slit) with the center of the pattern, we must consider the portions of the Huygens' wavelets that leave the slit at angle θ in Fig. 17. The lines II_a and II_b represent paths traversed by such secondary waves. It will be noted that the path II_a traversed by waves from the upper limit of the slit is longer than the path II_b by an amount Δp. If this path difference Δp is λ, the slit can be divided into two zones indicated in the figure by AB and BC, respectively; the *mean difference* in path length for the secondary waves coming from the two zones is then $\frac{1}{2}\lambda$ and the waves from the two zones cancel

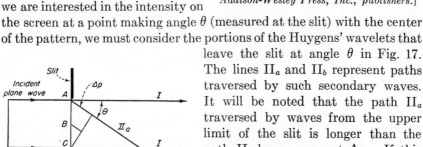

Fig. 17. Diffraction at an aperture slit (schematic).

completely when the lens brings the waves together on the screen. Therefore, at an angle θ for which Δp is λ, complete cancellation occurs, and a dark fringe or region of zero intensity results. Similar reasoning shows that the intensity is zero when Δp is equal to 2λ, 3λ, 4λ, 5λ, $\cdots$.

The situation is different when Δp is equal to an odd number of half wavelengths. For $\Delta p = \frac{1}{2}\lambda$, the phase difference between waves from the center and the edges is only $\frac{1}{4}\lambda$; this leads to only a slight decrease in amplitude, actually to $2/\pi$ that of the central maximum, or intensity $4/\pi^2$ that at the center, apart from the obliquity factor. Now consider the case for $\Delta p = \frac{3}{2}\lambda$. The slit can be divided into three zones, and the mean difference in path traversed by the secondary waves coming from successive zones is $\frac{1}{2}\lambda$. Therefore, the waves from two of the zones will lead to complete cancellation at the screen, but the secondary waves from the third zone are not canceled and a bright fringe or maximum will appear on the screen. Apart from the obliquity factor, the amplitude of this maximum will be $\frac{1}{3}(2/\pi)$ times the amplitude of the central maximum, so the intensity will be $\frac{1}{9}(4/\pi^2)$. Similar arguments show that bright fringes occur when Δp is equal to $\frac{5}{2}\lambda$, $\frac{7}{2}\lambda$, $\cdots$, with amplitudes $\frac{1}{5}(2/\pi)$, $\frac{1}{7}(2/\pi)$, $\cdots$ of that of the central maximum, and thus with rapidly decreasing intensities. Since the first dark fringe occurs at $\Delta p = \lambda$, and $\Delta p = 0$ gives a maximum, the distance between the centermost dark fringes is twice as great as that between succeeding dark fringes; the result is that the observed central maximum is twice as wide as the other maxima, as in Fig. 16.

As for the angles at which the maxima and minima occur, it will be noted that in Fig. 17 $\sin\theta = \Delta p/w$, where w is the slit width. Fig. 18

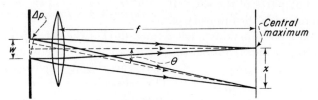

Fig. 18. Fraunhofer diffraction patterns on a screen.

shows the way in which the light is focused on the screen. Since parallel light is focused at a point, the distance from the lens to the screen must equal the focal length f of the lens. Parallel light making angle θ with the axis of the lens will be focused at the point x for which $x/f = \tan\theta$, as shown by the broken ray drawn through the center of the lens. Since the angle θ is small for those parts of the diffraction pattern that have appreciable intensity, we may replace $\tan\theta$ by $\sin\theta$ and write

$$\sin\theta = \frac{\Delta p}{w} = \frac{x}{f}, \qquad \text{or} \qquad x = \frac{\Delta p}{w} f.$$

In the above discussion and in that of Fig. 7 we have employed implicitly the following important principle:

> *When a lens forms a point image of a point object, the optical path lengths of all rays through the lens are equal; hence rays leaving the object in phase will arrive at the image in phase.   When a parallel beam is focused at a point, the optical path lengths of all rays from a plane wave-front to the point are equal; a similar statement applies when light from a point is rendered parallel by the lens.*

Proof of this property of a lens, which is necessary to permit interference between light passing through different parts of the lens, is simply a matter of geometry.

Example.   *At what angles do the centers of the first and second bright diffraction fringes appear in the Fraunhofer pattern of a slit 0.1 mm wide illuminated with 590-mμ sodium light?   If these fringes are focused on a screen by a lens of 1-m focal length, what are their distances from the center of the pattern?*

The first maximum occurs when Δp in Fig. 17 is $\frac{3}{2}\,\lambda$, the second when Δp is $\frac{5}{2}\,\lambda$.   Since $\frac{3}{2}\,\lambda = 885$ mμ and $\frac{5}{2}\,\lambda = 1475$ mμ, and since 0.1 mm = 100,000 mμ, these maxima occur at angles given by

$$\theta \approx \sin\theta = \frac{885}{100,000} = 0.00885 \text{ rad}$$

and

$$\theta \approx \sin\theta = \frac{1475}{100,000} = 0.01475 \text{ rad},$$

corresponding to 0°.50 and 0°.84.   Since the angles are small, we can write $x = f\theta$, which, with $f = 100$ cm, gives $x = 0.885$ cm and 1.475 cm for the distances from the center of the pattern.

5. RESOLVING POWER OF OPTICAL INSTRUMENTS

IF IN Fig. 15 we have a *point source* and a *circular aperture*, the calculation of the diffraction pattern on the screen is similar in essentials to our previous calculation for a line source and a slit aperture.   Instead of a point image on the screen we find a circular image surrounded by circular dark and light fringes.   We have seen that the first minimum in the diffraction pattern of a slit occurs at an angle $\theta = \lambda/w$.   In the case of a circular aperture, the first minimum occurs at angle $\theta = 1.22\,\lambda/a$, where a is the diameter of the circular opening (the linear aperture).

Now suppose that in Fig. 15 we remove the aperture.   The wave-front proceeding forward from the collimating lens is still limited; it is limited by the diameter of the collimating lens itself.   The image of the point source on the screen will still not be perfect; it will be the diffraction pattern of a circular aperture of diameter a equal to that of the collimating lens.

Now consider the case in which there are *two* point sources subtending angle α at the collimating lens.   These two sources will have two images on the screen subtending angle α at the condensing lens.   Each image will be a diffraction pattern.   If the angle α is $1.22 \lambda/a$, the center of one pattern will fall on the edge of the central maximum of the other, and the two central maxima overlap so much that it is difficult to distinguish between the two images.   Experimentally it has been found that the two images can be *resolved* for $\alpha > 1.22 \lambda/a$.   For $\alpha < 1.22 \lambda/a$, the images cannot be resolved and it is difficult to tell whether there are two images or one.   The criterion $\alpha > 1.22 \lambda/a$ for resolution is known as the *Raleigh criterion*.   The wavelength normally used in Rayleigh's criterion when white light is involved is an average value of 500 m$\mu = 5 \times 10^{-5}$ cm.

An extension of the above arguments shows how diffraction effects set the ultimate limitation on the usefulness of optical instruments such at telescopes and microscopes.   In the preceding chapter, we discussed the magnification obtainable with these instruments and indicated that limits of *useful* magnification were imposed by the wave nature of light itself.   It is useless, for example, to try to resolve two stars by increasing the magnifying power of a telescope merely by using an eyepiece of shorter focal length if the stars subtend an angle of less than $\alpha = 1.22 \lambda/a$, where a is the diameter of the objective.   If the angle subtended is less than this, the objective can produce only a fuzzy image consisting of over-lapping diffraction patterns in which separate images of the two stars cannot be distinguished, regardless of the power of the eyepiece.

The ultimate resolution attainable with a microscope is similarly limited.   Although parallel light beams are not involved in a microscope, one can say *approximately* that in order to be resolved by a microscope, two points must subtend an angle at the objective at least as large as $1.22 \lambda/a$, where a is the diameter of the microscope objective.   However, there *is* a way in which the resolving power of a microscope can be increased.   If ultraviolet light is used to illuminate the object, the limit-ing angle α is smaller, since ultraviolet light is of shorter wavelength than visible light.   It is necessary to use a photographic plate to receive the image in an ultraviolet microscope.

We notice that the *larger* the aperture of a telescope or microscope, the *better* is the resolution, that is, the *smaller* is the angle between two points that can be just resolved.

6. DIFFRACTION GRATINGS

WHEN THE aperture in Fig. 15 consists of a large number of narrow slits placed side by side, it is known as a *diffraction grating*.   Diffraction grat-ings are extensively used in the determination of the wavelengths of light emitted and absorbed by various materials.

In Fig. 19(a) a parallel beam of monochromatic light is shown ap-proaching a transmission grating consisting of a large number of extremely narrow slits, only a few of which are shown.   The distance between adjacent slits is d.   Since the beam is parallel and normal to the grating, all Huygens sources in the plane of the grating are in the same phase. The secondary waves are in phase in the forward direction, since the paths traversed by all waves in this direction are of equal length.   If the light waves traveling in the forward-direction are focused on a screen, a bright *central image* of the original slit is formed.   In certain other directions, the secondary waves will also be in phase at a plane wave-front.   One of these directions is denoted by θ in Fig. 19(b).   At this angle the paths traversed by secondary waves from successive slits differ by an amount equal to the wavelength of the light.   Hence the condensing lens will produce an image of the original slit on the screen; this image is called the *first-order* image.   Consideration of Fig. 19 shows that the angle θ for the first order is defined by the relation $\sin\theta = \lambda/d$.

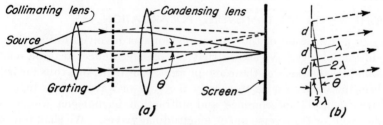

Fig. 19. Transmission grating.

Other directions in which secondary waves from the slits can produce a common plane wave-front are those directions in which the paths traversed by the secondary waves from successive slits differ by 2λ, 3λ, 4λ, $\cdots$.   The directions in which diffraction maxima may be produced are accordingly given by the general relation

$$\sin\theta_n = n\lambda/d, \tag{3}$$

where $n = 1, 2, 3, 4, \cdots$.   These values of n give the *order number* of the diffraction maxima.   Since θ_n can be accurately measured and d is known for a given grating, it is possible to use a grating to measure the wavelength of light.   When the angle θ is large it is desirable to turn the condensing lens as in the spectrometer illustrated on p. 536.

The gratings actually used in most research investigations are *reflection* gratings.   Frequently, reflection gratings are concave metal mirrors on which equally spaced narrow lines have been ruled with a diamond. When the grating is illuminated, the strips between these lines become the sources of Huygens wavelets, just as do the parallel slits in a transmission grating.   The light is brought to a focus on a photographic plate by the concave mirror itself.   Since the spacing of grating lines must be constant for all parts of a grating surface and since optical gratings have several thousand lines per centimeter, the fabrication of a grating is a difficult and expensive process.

Example. *A reflection grating having* 10,000 *lines/cm is illuminated by parallel light of* 590-mμ *wavelength, incident normally. At what angles are the diffraction images formed?*

The grating spacing d is 10^{-4} cm $= 10^3$ mμ $= 1000$ mμ. Hence the first-order image is formed at

$$\sin\theta_1 = \lambda/d = 590 \text{ mμ}/1000 \text{ mμ} = 0.590$$
$$\theta_1 = 36°2.$$

The second-order image would be formed at

$$\sin\theta_2 = 2\,\lambda/d = 1.08,$$

but this is an impossible angle. The grating spacing is less than $2\,\lambda$ so it is impossible to have a wavelength difference of $2\,\lambda$ from successive slits. There is only one diffraction image.

7. LIGHT WAVES ARE TRANSVERSE; POLARIZATION

In our discussion of the optical phenomena involved in interference and diffraction, we have shown that the observed effects can be readily explained on the basis of the wave properties of light, but thus far it has not been necessary for us to specify the type of wave motion involved. Our treatment of interference and diffraction phenomena would hold equally well for transverse or for longitudinal waves. We shall now discuss other phenomena that show definitely that *light waves are transverse in character*.

In longitudinal waves such as sound waves, there is always symmetry around an axis in the direction of propagation, since the vibrations are in this direction. In transverse waves the vibrations are at right angles to the direction of propagation, and hence symmetry around an axis in this direction may not exist. For example, a transverse wave traveling along a horizontal string may involve up-and-down vertical motion of the particles of the string, or it may involve left-and-right horizontal motion, or any combination of these. Similarly, a transverse elastic wave in a solid may involve particle motions in various different directions all perpendicular to the direction of propagation; we say that the wave may have different *polarizations*.

Whenever there is a lack of symmetry around an axis in the direction of propagation of a wave motion, we say that the wave motion is *polarized*. Polarization can occur only with transverse waves. Since a beam of light can be polarized, we conclude that light waves are transverse waves. The ways in which polarization of light can be produced include absorption (dichroism), reflection, refraction, scattering, and birefringence.

The production of polarized light by absorption (dichroism) is exhibited by crystals of certain minerals and organic compounds. The best known of these minerals is *tourmaline*. When a light beam passes through a single properly cut slab of clear tourmaline, it emerges diminished in intensity but not otherwise changed in appearance so far as the human eye can discern.   However, if two slabs of tourmaline are introduced into a light beam, the intensity of the transmitted light depends on the relative orientation of the two slabs, as illustrated in Fig. 20.   In (a) the two slabs are oriented with crystalline axes parallel and light is transmitted.   In (b) one of the slabs has been rotated through an angle θ with respect to the other slab and less light is transmitted.   In (c) one of the slabs is oriented at 90° with respect to the other slab and *no light is transmitted through the pair*.   These effects can be interpreted *only* if light waves are assumed to be transverse.

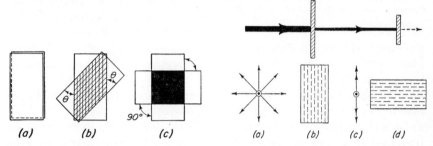

Fig. 20. Transmission of light through tourmaline crystals.

Fig. 21. Transmission of light waves through 'crossed' tourmaline crystals.

In an ordinary light beam the transverse vibrations have no preferred direction with respect to the direction of propagation; in other words, the different 'pieces' of the light wave that originate in different atoms of the radiating source have their vibrations randomly oriented in all possible planes transverse to the direction of propagation.   Then a pencil of light approaching the reader would involve various transverse vibrations as shown in Fig. 21(a).   The tourmaline slab shown in Fig. 21(b) transmits only the light associated with vibration components in the vertical direction and absorbs all the light associated with vibration components in the horizontal direction.   If the tourmaline slab is placed in the light beam approaching the reader, the transmitted light has only vibrations in the vertical direction as indicated in (c).   If a second tourmaline slab is oriented at right angles to the first as in (d), it can transmit only light associated with horizontal vibrations.   Since light associated with horizontal vibrations has already been removed by the first tourmaline slab, no light reaches the observer.   This explanation is necessary to account for the observed phenomena depicted in Fig. 20 and many other experiments, and hence we must conclude that light waves are transverse.

Owing to the fact that most tourmaline crystals are colored, they are not very useful in optical instruments.   Small needle-shaped crystals of the organic compound quinine iodosulphate having similar optical properties were grown as early as 1852.   Because of their small size, they were not useful in optical work until 1935, when Edwin H. Land developed a method of orienting large numbers of crystals of this type.   The mate-

rial (called *Polaroid*) that was developed by Land consists of a film of cellulose acetate or nitrocellulose in which are suspended large numbers of minute crystals having optical properties similar to those of tourmaline.   These minute crystals are given the same orientation by giving the film a stretch in one direction during the manufacturing process.   For optical use, the films

Fig. 22. Transmission of light through Polaroid films. [*Courtesy of the Polaroid Corporation.*]

are mounted between glass plates.   As indicated in Fig. 22, two Polaroid plates can be used to produce effects similar to those produced by tourmaline crystals.

The light transmitted by the first tourmaline crystal or Polaroid plate inserted in a light beam is said to be *plane-polarized*, since the vibrations are in a single plane.   For example, the vibrations shown in Fig. 21(c(are polarized in a vertical plane.   The device, such as the first tourmaline slab or first Polaroid plate, that produces the polarization is called the *polarizer*.   Ordinarily, the eye cannot detect any difference between polarized and unpolarized light without the assistance of a second tourmaline slab, Polaroid plate, or similar device; the second device is called the *analyzer*.   A polarizing plate is said to be *perfect* if it transmits *all* light polarized along a given transverse axis, called the *axis of the plate*, and absorbs *all* light polarized normal to this axis.   Commercial plates only approximate this perfection.

In ordinary light, the amplitudes of the different 'pieces' of the light originating in different atoms of the source can be resolved vectorially into components along any two axes normal to the direction of propagation. Since the energy of a light vibration is proportional to the square of the amplitude, this resolution is energetically correct, the sum of the squares of the two rectangular components of a vector being equal to the square of the length of the vector.   After passing through a perfect polarizer, an unpolarized beam is reduced to 50% of its original intensity, since one component is completely eliminated.   If the resulting plane-polarized beam passes through a perfect analyzer making an angle θ with the plane of polarization, the resulting amplitude is $\cos\theta$ and intensity $\cos^2\theta$ times that of the plane-polarized beam that leaves the polarizer.

Example. *Four perfect polarizing plates are stacked so that the axis of each is turned 30° clockwise with respect to the preceding plate, the last plate therefore being 'crossed' with the first.   How much of the intensity of an incident unpolarized beam of light is transmitted by the stack?*

The first plate transmits ½ of the incident intensity. Each succeeding plate makes a vector resolution at angle 30° and transmits a fraction $\cos 30°$ of the amplitude or $\cos^2(30°)$ of the intensity. Since $\cos 30° = \sqrt{3}/2$ and $\cos^2(30°) = \frac{3}{4}$, the intensity transmitted by the stack is

$$\frac{1}{2} \cdot \frac{3}{4} \cdot \frac{3}{4} \cdot \frac{3}{4} = \frac{27}{128} = 0.211,$$

or 21.1 per cent of the original intensity.

8. POLARIZATION OF LIGHT

WE HAVE discussed the polarization of light by absorption in certain crystals. We shall now discuss other ways in which light becomes polarized.

When light is *reflected* from a *non-metallic* surface, the reflected light is partially plane-polarized, and, at one angle of incidence, is completely plane-polarized. This angle, about 57° for glass, is such that the reflected and refracted beams are exactly 90° apart. It is known as *Brewster's angle*. The efficacy of Polaroid glasses in relieving glare from a non-metallic surface, such as a road surface, depends on this polarization.

Since the light reflected from a glass plate is at least partially plane-polarized, that *refracted* into the plate is also partially plane-polarized. The light transmitted through a stack of a large number of thin clear glass plates, separated by air spaces and arranged so the light is incident at Brewster's angle, will be almost completely plane polarized; such an arrangement can be used as a polarizer for transmitted light.

Light *scattered* by small particles or by density variations of a gas, as in the case of the blue light of the sky, is completely plane-polarized when observed at 90° to the incident light. Thus Polaroid glasses and camera filters can be used to reduce the glare from blue skylight when observation is made in a direction nearly 90° from the direction of the sun.

We shall now consider the phenomenon of *double refraction*, or *birefringence*, which results when light traverses an optical medium that is not isotropic. In Fig. 23(a), the small crosses represent the positions of

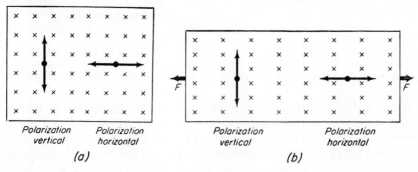

Fig. 23. Transmission of light through (a) isotropic material, (b) anisotropic material.

molecules or atoms in an *isotropic* medium traversed by light beams plane-polarized in the vertical direction and horizontal direction. The arrangements of the atoms or molecules relative to vibrations in these two directions are identical. The vertical and horizontal vibrations interact in the same manner with the medium, and the light waves associated with vertical and horizontal vibrations consequently have the same speed.

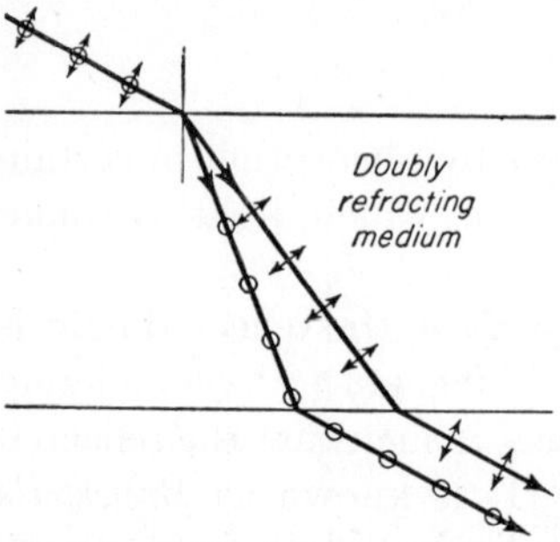

Doubly refracting medium

When the isotropic medium is subjected to a tensile stress as shown in Fig. 23(b), the resulting strain involves a change in the relative positions of the atoms and molecules of the medium, which is therefore no longer isotropic. The polarized light with vertical vibrations will not interact with the medium in the same manner as the light with horizontal vibrations and will therefore have a different speed in the strained medium. The unpolarized light will actually be divided by the medium into two disturbances traveling with different speeds, and the medium is said to be *doubly refracting* or *birefringent*. An isotropic medium like glass or Lucite becomes doubly refracting when strained; certain crystals like quartz and calcite are naturally anisotropic and exhibit double refraction even when not subjected to external forces.

Fig. 24. Double refraction by an anisotropic medium.

Fig. 25. Photograph of a printed word viewed through a doubly refracting crystal, and through ordinary glass. No Polaroid is involved, but the photograph was furnished through the courtesy of the Polaroid Corporation.

Since a doubly refracting medium has two different indices of refraction, a ray of unpolarized light incident at an angle with the normal to the surface is usually split into two refracted rays polarized at right angles, as shown in Fig. 24. This phenomenon can lead to some rather interesting effects such as the one depicted in Fig. 25, in which the incident light is separated into polarized components laterally displaced.

When a medium of variable birefringence, such as a crystal of varying thickness or a strained glass plate, is placed between a polarizer and an analyser, an interesting interference pattern is created.   The birefringent medium splits the incident plane-polarized light into two plane-polarized components that are out of phase.   The analyzer reassembles part of each component into a single plane-polarized beam.   In this beam the components interfere to an extent that is dependent on the phase difference, and hence create a pattern if these phase differences vary from point to point of the birefringent medium.   Imagine the two polarizing plates to be 'crossed,' and let a parallel beam of monochromatic light be incident on

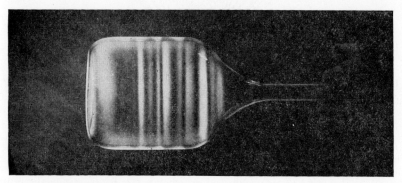

Fig. 26. Use of polarized light in detecting strains in glassware.

the polarizer.   If the strained body of Fig. 23(b) is placed between these plates at such orientation that the incident light has its plane of polarization at 45° to the horizontal and vertical, the strained body splits the incident beam into two coincident beams, with horizontal and vertical polarizations, that travel at different speeds.   Unless the optical path difference of these two beams in the strained material is exactly a whole number of wavelengths, some light will be transmitted when these two beams are recombined into a single plane-polarized beam by the 'crossed' analyzer.   If the strain of the material varies with position, light and dark bands will appear as the phase difference of the two emerging beams varies; these bands are illustrated in Fig. 26.

The use of polarized light to reveal strains in transparent materials is finding extensive application in the field of mechanical stress analysis. The distribution of internal stresses in structural units or machine parts may be determined by passing polarized light through scale models made of celluloid or transparent bakelite, which are subjected to external forces simulating those in the actual structures or machines.   The internal strains can be determined from the patterns observed through an analyzer. Fig. 27 shows the pattern resulting from compression of a disk or cylinder.

Fig. 27. [*Courtesy of Prof. M. M. Frocht.*]

This important method of solving problems in the theory of elasticity is called *photoelasticity*.

PROBLEMS

1. A narrow slit used in a Fresnel experiment of the type illustrated in Fig. 1 is illuminated by red light of wavelength 700 mμ. If the separation of the virtual source-slits S_1 and S_2 is 0.2 mm and if the perpendicular distance from these virtual sources to the screen is 1 m, what is the distance from the central bright fringe to the nearest bright fringes on either side?   Ans: 3.5 mm.

2. If light of another color is used in the experiment of Prob. 1, and the distance between the central bright fringe and the next fringe is found to be 2.4 mm, what is the wavelength of the light?

3. Show that the successive fringes observed in the Fresnel experiment of Fig. 1 are uniformly spaced so long as the angle α in Fig. 2 is very small compared to 1 radian.

4. Show that the thickness t of air space in Fig. 5, p. 507, at horizontal distance r from the point of contact, is $t = r^2/2R$ if $r \ll R$. Here R is the radius of curvature of the lens.

5. What is the minimum thickness of a soap film of refractive index 1.33 if the film gives constructive interference of orange light of wavelength 600 mμ at normal incidence?   Ans: 1.13×10^{-5} cm.

6. Find the thickness of a soap film that gives constructive second-order reflection of red light of wavelength 700 mμ. Take $\mu = 1.33$ for the film and assume normal incidence. NOTE: Second-order reflection occurs when the optical path difference is equal to $\frac{3}{2}$ wavelengths.

7. A beam of sodium light ($\lambda = 589$ mμ) strikes a film of olive oil floating on water, and interference fringes are observed. The refractive index of the oil is 1.46. When the film is viewed at an angle of 30° from the normal, the eighth *dark* band of the system is seen. This band corresponds to an optical path difference of 7 λ. What is the thickness of the film?   Ans: 1.50μ.

8. The flatness of glass plates such as are used in interferometers can be tested by placing two such plates in contact along one edge, separated by the thickness of a sheet of thin paper along the opposite edge, and observing the reflection of monochromatic light at normal incidence.

(a) Show that if the plates are perfect, a system of straight, parallel, uniformly spaced interference fringes will be observed. Determine the spacing of the fringes in terms of the thickness of the paper, the dimensions of the plates, and the wavelength of the light.

(b) A plate is perfect except for one low spot. This plate is tested against a perfect plate and the fringe pattern photographed. What will be the appearance of the fringe pattern? Show how, by measurements on the photograph, the depth of the low spot can be determined to within an accuracy of a fraction of the wavelength of light.

9. A parallel beam of sodium light ($\lambda = 589$ mμ) falls normally on the plane surface of a plano-convex lens whose convex surface is in contact with a plane glass surface. The radius of curvature of the lens surface is 50 cm. Find the radius of the 50th dark ring observed by reflection, not counting the central dark spot.   Ans: 0.384 cm.

10. Show that as the angle of incidence i in Fig. 3 increases from 0 to 90°, the difference in optical path *decreases* from $2\mu t$ to $2\mu t \cos\theta_C$, where θ_C is the critical angle for the film material. If one takes a square of thin film diffusely illuminated by monochromatic light such that $2\mu t = 10 \lambda$ and $\cos\theta_C = 0.7$, how many changes from dark to bright and from bright to dark take place in the appearance of the film as it is slowly tilted from the position where it is observed at normal incidence to that where it is observed at grazing incidence?

11. A glass plate 0.50 micron thick is illuminated by white light. The refractive index of the glass is 1.50. What wavelength in the visible spectrum (400 mμ to 700 mμ) will be intensified in the reflected light observed at an angle of 45° from the normal?   Ans: 529 mμ.

12. While moving one mirror of a Michelson interferometer a distance of 1.000 mm, an observer counted 4218 fringes. What was the wavelength of the light used?

13. While moving one mirror of a Michelson interferometer a distance of 0.250 mm, an observer counted 909 fringes. Calculate the wavelength of the light used.   Ans: 550 mμ.

14. In order to check the accuracy of a certain precision micrometer gauge, an observer uses the micrometer to measure the distance moved by an interferometer mirror. Using the red light from a cadmium source, an observer counts 4162 fringes while the mirror is being moved a distance of 1.330 mm *as measured by the gauge*. What is the actual distance moved? What is the per-cent error in the distance as given by the gauge?

15. A lens of focal length 40 cm is used to form a Fraunhofer diffraction pattern of a slit 0.3 mm wide. Calculate the distance on the screen from the center of the central maximum to the center of the first dark band and to the next bright band when the slit is illuminated by yellow light from a sodium flame ($\lambda = 589$ mμ).   Ans: 0.79 mm; 1.18 mm.

16. Parallel light of wavelength 546.1 mμ is incident normally on a slit 1 mm wide. If a lens of 100-cm focal length is mounted just behind the slit and the light is focused on a screen, what will be the distance from the center of the diffraction pattern to (a) the first minimum, (b) the first maximum, and (c) the third maximum?

17. In the Fraunhofer diffraction pattern of a single slit, the distance from the first minimum on one side of the central maximum to the first minimum on the other side of the central maximum is 6.75 mm. If the wavelength of the light is 546.1 mμ and the lens used to form the diffraction pattern has a focal length of 60 cm, find the width of the slit. Ans: 0.097 mm.

18. Parallel white light is incident normally on a slit; a lens of focal length 60 cm mounted behind the slit focuses the light on a screen. Find the wavelength of light for which the *third* maximum coincides in position with the *second* maximum for red light of wavelength 640 mμ.

19. What is the theoretical angular limit of resolution of the Yerkes telescope, whose objective is 40 inches in diameter? Ans: 0″.124.

20. Taking 240,000 mi as the distance from the earth to the moon, find the linear separation of two objects on the moon's surface that can just be resolved by the 200-in telescope on Mount Palomar.

21. The focal length of the objective of a certain microscope is 3.2 mm and its diameter is 4.0 mm. What is the *approximate* value of the separation of two point objects that can just be resolved when they are illuminated by light of mean wavelength 500 mμ?
Ans: 488 mμ. NOTE: Calculation on basis of more detailed theory gives 380 mμ.

22. What would be the *approximate* value for the smallest separation of two point objects that could just be resolved if ultraviolet light of wavelength 230 mμ were used with the microscope described in Prob. 21 and photographic methods of detection were used?

23. A transmission grating has 4000 lines/cm. Calculate the angular deviation of the second order diffraction maximum for sodium light of wavelength 589.3 mμ when a parallel beam of light strikes the grating at normal incidence. Show diagram. Ans: 28°.1.

24. When a parallel beam of light is normally incident, a transmission grating produces a diffraction pattern in which the third-order maximum for sodium light appears at an angle of 45° away from the central image. Find the distance between the lines on the grating.

25. When plane light waves are normally incident, a diffraction grating ruled with 6000 lines/cm forms the first-order diffraction maximum for light of a certain wavelength at an angle of 18°.0. What is the wavelength of the light? Show diagram. Ans: 515 mμ.

26. Plane monochromatic waves of wavelength 600 mμ are incident normally on a plane transmission grating having 5000 lines/cm. Find the angles at which the first-, second-, third-, and fourth-order diffraction maxima appear.

27. Three perfect polarizing plates are stacked. The first and third are crossed; the one between has its axis at 45° to the axes of the other two. Find the fraction of the intensity of an incident unpolarized beam that is transmitted by the stack. Ans: ⅛.

28. Three perfect polarizing plates are stacked. The first and third have their axes parallel; the one between has its axis at 30° to the axes of the other two. Find the fraction of the intensity of an incident unpolarized beam that is transmitted by the stack.

29. Light of wavelength 589.0 mμ is normally incident on a sheet of quartz crystal cut in such a way that the index of refraction for polarization along one crystal axis is 1.553 and for polarization along the other is 1.544, where the two polarizations are analogous to those indicated in Fig. 22(b). What are the two wavelengths of the light in the crystal? Ans: 379.3, 381.5 mμ.

30. The plate of crystal is said to be a 'half-wave' plate if, when light is incident as in Prob. 29, there is one-half wavelength more of one polarization than of the other as the light passes through the plate. (That is, if the difference in optical path length is $\frac{1}{2} \times 589.0$ mμ.) Determine the thickness of a quartz half-wave plate for 589-mμ light.

31. Show that if a quartz half-wave plate (see Prob. 30) is placed between *parallel* polarizing plates oriented at 45° to the orientation of the crystal axes, *no* light is transmitted through the combination. Show that if the polarizing plates are *crossed*, with the same 45° orientation, *all* the light transmitted by the first polarizing plate is transmitted by the combination.

32. When a uniform tensile stress within the Hooke's-law range is applied to a transparent sheet of isotropic material as in Fig. 22, it is found that the difference in optical path length for the two polarizations is proportional to the stress. If such a sheet were placed between crossed polarizing plates oriented at 45° to the horizontal and vertical, and were unstressed, it would be dark. At what differences in optical path length does it become first bright, then dark, again bright, etc.? Note that the uniformly stressed sheet is uniformly bright or dark; one obtains fringes as in Fig. 27 only when the stress varies from one region to another.

33. Verify the principle stated in italics near the top of page 517 for the case of a thin double-convex lens of small angular aperture. Consider a point object on the axis at distance $2f$, forming a point image at $2f$. Show that the optical path length of the ray through the periphery of the lens, where it has zero thickness, equals the optical path length of the ray through the center. Make the same comparison for a parallel beam with plane wave-front arriving at the lens and imaged at the principal focus.

CHAPTER 26

DISPERSION AND SPECTRA

By *dispersion* of light is meant the separation of the light into its component wavelengths or spectral colors. A *spectroscope* is an instrument designed to disperse the light from a source so that its component wavelengths can be observed. These component wavelengths constitute the *spectrum* of the source. In this chapter we shall describe dispersion by refraction; the elimination of such dispersion in achromatic lenses; prism and grating spectroscopes depending on dispersion by refraction and diffraction respectively; and the various types of emission and absorption spectra that are observed.

1. DISPERSION BY REFRACTION

THE INDEX of refraction that occurs in Snell's law is not the same for all wavelengths. For most transparent media, the index increases slightly as the wavelength decreases; that is, it is slightly greater for violet light than for red light. As a result of this difference in refractive index, rays of violet light are bent more sharply than rays of red light in passing from air into most transparent media, as shown in Fig. 1.

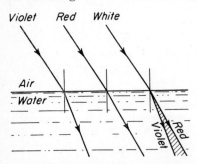

Fig. 1. Dispersion of white light by refraction at a water surface. (The amount of dispersion is exaggerated in this sketch.)

If a ray of white light is incident on the water surface in Fig. 1 at the same angle as the violet and red rays, it splits after passing through the water surface into a group of colored rays with a violet ray at one boundary of the group and a red ray at the other boundary. The white ray is said to be *dispersed*. Such dispersion is observed when a narrow pencil of sunlight is incident on the surface of water in an aquarium. The explanation of the splitting of the white-light ray into colored rays appears obvious now; we immediately conclude that the original white light is a complex wave motion that can be analyzed into components of different frequencies corresponding to the colored components, which are separated from one another by refraction at the water surface. In other words, white light is actually a compound wave produced by superposition of the waves corresponding to the different colors. Before Newton's time it was thought that the colors were somehow *created* in the refracting medium. Using glass prisms to produce dispersion as in Fig. 2, Newton showed that the colored light produced by dispersion could be recombined to produce white light, but that a single color produced by dispersion was not changed into still other colors by a second refraction process. Thus he concluded that "*Light* is not similar or Homogenial, but consists of Difform Rays, some of which are more Refrangible than others."

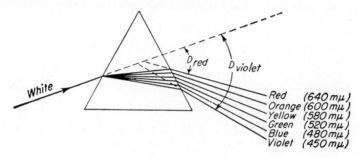

Fig. 2. Dispersion of white light by a prism.

The observed spectrum or band of colors produced when white light is dispersed actually varies in hue continuously from the violet to the red end of the spectrum, but we are still accustomed to use the terminology of Newton in dividing these 'colors of the rainbow' into the seven bands: violet, indigo*, blue, green, yellow, orange, and red, in order of increasing wavelength. Since Newton did not believe that light transmission involves a wave motion, he did not, of course, attribute a different frequency and wavelength to each spectral color as we do today. None the less, he clearly demonstrated that the spectral colors are merely components of white light.

When light contains colored components in the same proportion in which they are present in sunlight, the light appears *white*. If some components are relatively more abundant than in sunlight, the light appears slightly colored; for example, the light from an ordinary tungsten lamp contains a larger proportion of red light than does sunlight, and hence the light from a tungsten lamp appears slightly more orange than the *white* light from the sun.

The separation of light into its spectral colors is conveniently accomplished by a prism, as in Fig. 2. Since a prism has two useful refracting surfaces, the resulting angular separation is greater than that at a single

* The term *indigo* is obsolescent.

surface.   The *deviation* (angle D in Fig. 2) of light by a prism is, for a prism of given shape, roughly proportional to the difference $\mu - 1$ between the index of refraction of the prism material and that of air.   Thus the change in deviation with change in wavelength, which is a measure of the dispersion, is roughly proportional to $d\mu/d\lambda$, the rate of change of refractive index with wavelength.   Since the refractive index ordinarily decreases with increasing wavelength, so that $d\mu/d\lambda$ is negative, $-d\mu/d\lambda$ is called the *dispersive power* of the refracting material at wavelength λ.

Table I gives the refractive indices of several materials for wavelengths in the red, yellow, and blue.   It also gives the mean dispersive power, $-\Delta\mu/\Delta\lambda$, in the region between red and blue.   The specific wavelengths given are those of three easily reproducible spectral colors.   The red and

TABLE I

REFRACTIVE INDICES AND MEAN DISPERSIVE POWERS AT 20° C

Material	Refractive index for wavelength			Mean dispersive power
	λ_R (red) 656.3 mμ	λ_Y (yellow) 589.3 mμ	λ_B (blue) 486.1 mμ	$\dfrac{\mu_B - \mu_R}{\lambda_R - \lambda_B}$
Water................	1.3312	1.3330	1.3372	35×10^{-6}/mμ
Carbon disulfide........	1.6182	1.6276	1.6523	201
Crown glass (typical)...	1.5145	1.5172	1.5240	56
Flint glass (typical).....	1.6221	1.6270	1.6391	100

blue wavelengths appear in the spectrum of hydrogen and the yellow in the spectrum of sodium.

Example.   *The rainbow is formed by internal reflection of sunlight in water droplets as indicated in Fig. 3.   If one analyzes the angle of deviation D as a*

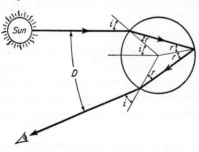

function of the angle of incidence i for values of i from $0°$ to $90°$, it is found that D goes from $0°$ to a maximum value and then decreases.   In the neighborhood of the maximum, D changes very little for a considerable change in i; hence there is a considerable concentration of reflected light at this maximum value of D, and this light forms the rainbow.   Show that the rainbow is formed at $D \approx 42°$, and that the red is on the outside (larger D)

Figure 3

and the violet on the inside (smaller D).

The geometry of the circle is such that it is easy to trace the ray—all the angles inside are equal and the two angles outside are equal, as indicated by r

and i in Fig. 3. From Snell's law,

$$\sin i = \mu \sin r.$$

It is a simple matter of geometry to determine that

$$D = 4r - 2i.$$

Since

$$r = \arcsin\left(\frac{1}{\mu} \sin i\right),$$

we can write

$$D = 4 \arcsin\left(\frac{1}{\mu} \sin i\right) - 2i.$$

To determine the maximum of D, we compute dD/di and set this derivative equal to zero:

$$\frac{dD}{di} = 4 \frac{1}{\sqrt{1 - (1/\mu^2)\sin^2 i}} \frac{1}{\mu} \cos i - 2 = 0.$$

Simplification of this equation gives

$$\cos^2 i = \tfrac{1}{3}(\mu^2 - 1).$$

For water $\mu = 1.333$ and $i = 59°.4$. Therefore $r = 40°.2$ and

$$D = 4r - 2i = 4(40°.2) - 2(59°.4) = 42°.0$$

is the maximum deviation angle.

We note from Table I that as we go from red to violet the index of refraction of water increases. The value $\mu = 1.333$ that we used above is for yellow light in the middle of the spectrum. If we make the same computations for $\mu = 1.331$ (red) and $\mu = 1.337$ (blue), we find angles of maximum deviation

$$D_{\text{Red}} = 42°.6, \qquad D_{\text{Blue}} = 41°.2.$$

Since this angle is the angle between the observer's line of sight and the line to the sun, the red is on the outside of the rainbow.

2. ACHROMATIC LENSES

IT WILL be noted from Table I that the refractive indices for a given wavelength are different for different materials and also that the values of $\Delta\mu = \mu_B - \mu_R$ are different for different materials. These properties make it possible to correct in part the *chromatic aberration* always associated with simple thin lenses. We recall from Chap. 23 that chromatic aberration results from the fact that the index of refraction of a lens material is not the same for all wavelengths. The result of this variation in μ can be seen from the drawing of a simple lens in Fig. 4(a). Here white light is incident on the lens; but as a result of the variation of refractive index with wavelength, colored images are produced at different points by the lens.

By making a compound lens from two simple lenses of different materials such as crown and flint glass, it is possible to make the red and blue images coincide, as in Fig. 4(b). When the lens is so constructed that red and blue images coincide, it is found that the images of colors of intermediate wavelengths also coincide fairly accurately. Such a two-component lens is called an *achromatic* (Gk: without color) *doublet*. The diverging lens must have a focal length greater in absolute magnitude than that of the converging lens if the combination is still to act as a converging lens, and the material of the diverging lens must have a mean dispersive power higher than that of the converging lens if the colors are to be returned to coincidence. From the values given in Table I, it can be seen that crown and flint glass are suitable for use in making an achromatic combination, since the refractive indices of these materials are not greatly different but the mean dispersive power of flint glass is nearly twice that of crown glass. Therefore, as indicated in Fig. 4(b), it is customary to use a converging crown-glass lens C and a diverging flint-glass lens F for making an achromatic converging lens.

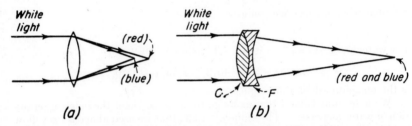

Fig. 4. Construction of an achromatic lens. Typically, the components would be of crown and flint glass.

Equation (18) of Chap. 23 (p. 479) gives the relation between the focal length f_{Comp} of a compound lens and the focal lengths f_C and f_F of the component simple lenses. Since we wish the focal length f_{Comp} of the compound lens of Fig. 4(b) to be the same for red and blue wavelengths, we may write the condition for achromatism in the form

$$\frac{1}{(f_{\text{Comp}})_R} = \frac{1}{(f_{\text{Comp}})_B} \quad \text{or} \quad \frac{1}{f_{CR}} + \frac{1}{f_{FR}} = \frac{1}{f_{CB}} + \frac{1}{f_{FB}}, \tag{1}$$

where the subscripts C and F refer to crown and flint glass, and the subscripts R and B refer to red and blue wavelengths.

To see how equation (1) is used to compute an achromatic lens, let us work through an example employing the refractive indices for crown and flint glass given in Table I. According to the lensmaker's equation (13), p. 471, the focal length of a lens of given radii of curvature is inversely proportional to $\mu - 1$. Thus for any crown-glass lens the focal lengths for red and blue light are related by

$$f_{CR} = (0.5240/0.5145)f_{CB} = 1.0185 f_{CB}, \qquad \text{(crown)}$$

while for any flint-glass lens

$$f_{FR} = (0.6391/0.6221)f_{FB} = 1.0273 f_{FB}. \qquad \text{(flint)}$$

If we substitute $1/f_{CB} = 1.0185/f_{CR}$ and $1/f_{FB} = 1.0273/f_{FR}$ in (1), we find

$$f_{FR} = -(273/185)f_{CR} = -1.476\,f_{CR}$$

as the condition that the combination be achromatic. The resulting focal length of the combination then comes out as

$$f_{\text{Comp}} = (273/88)f_{CR} = 3.102\,f_{CR}.$$

This will be the focal length for either red or blue light.

Example. *What will be the focal lengths in the red and blue of the crown- and flint-glass components of an achromatic doublet of 62.04-cm focal length?*

We desire that f_{Comp} be 62.04 cm in both the red and blue. The last relation in the text above gives

$$f_{CR} = (62.04 \text{ cm})/3.102 = 20.00 \text{ cm}$$

as the focal length of the converging crown-glass component in the red. In the blue, this lens will have focal length

$$f_{CB} = (20.00 \text{ cm})/1.0185 = 19.64 \text{ cm}.$$

According to the next to the last equation in the text above, with this lens we use a diverging flint-glass lens of focal length in the red

$$f_{FR} = -1.476 \ (20.00 \text{ cm}) = -29.52 \text{ cm}.$$

In the blue this lens will have focal length

$$f_{FB} = (-29.52 \text{ cm})/1.0273 = -28.73 \text{ cm}.$$

To check that we have achieved an achromatic doublet of the desired focal length, we compute

$$\frac{1}{(f_{\text{Comp}})_R} = \frac{1}{f_{CR}} + \frac{1}{f_{FR}} = 0.05000 - 0.03389 = 0.01611, \quad \text{or} \quad (f_{\text{Comp}})_R = 62.07 \text{ cm},$$

$$\frac{1}{(f_{\text{Comp}})_B} = \frac{1}{f_{CB}} + \frac{1}{f_{FB}} = 0.05092 - 0.03481 = 0.01611 \quad \text{or} \quad (f_{\text{Comp}})_B = 62.07 \text{ cm},$$

which checks within the accuracy of the computation.

While an achromatic doublet makes the red and blue images coincide perfectly, the coincidence is not perfect for colors between. Very fine lenses have more than two components so that the achromatism can be made perfect at more than two points in the spectrum and hence better throughout the whole spectrum.

3. SPECTROSCOPES

A SPECTROSCOPE is an instrument that disperses the light from a source so that the component colors can be observed visually. The dispersion may be effected by either a prism or a grating.

When a spectroscope is provided with an accurate scale for measurement of the positions of the dispersed colors, such as the divided circles indicated in Figs. 5 and 7, it is called a *spectrometer*. In these instruments, the light of the source illuminates a slit S perpendicular to the plane of the diagram. If the source gives monochromatic light, a single image of the slit is seen in the telescope in light of the monochromatic color. If the source gives several monochromatic wavelengths, several images of the slit are seen in the light of the different colors as the telescope is moved

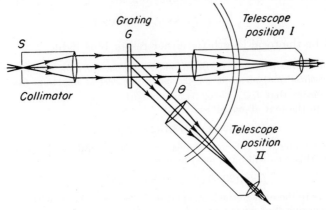

Fig. 5. Schematic diagram of a grating spectrometer.

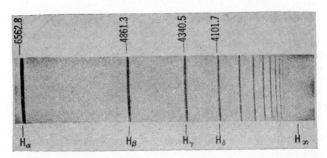

Fig. 6. Spectrogram of atomic hydrogen. Divide numbers by 10 to get wavelengths in mμ. This is a photographic *negative;* hence the bright emission lines appear as dark lines on a light background, the reverse of the way they would appear to the eye in a spectroscope. [*From Herzberg, Molecular Spectra and Molecular Structure (Prentice-Hall).*]

around the circle. Because the different images of the slit appear to the observer as parallel narrow lines, it is customary to speak of them as *spectral lines.*

If the spectroscope is arranged for photographic observation, so the spectral lines can be photographed side by side on a film or plate, the instrument is called a *spectrograph,* and the picture a *spectrogram.* Fig. 6 shows the spectral lines emitted by atomic hydrogen.

In the grating spectrometer of Fig. 5, the wavelength of a spectral line can be accurately determined by measuring the angle θ that the telescope must be moved from the position I of the central image to the position II of a diffracted image. As the telescope is moved, the first-, second-, third-, ··· order images will be successively observed. Equation (3), p. 519 gives the wavelength for the nth-order image as

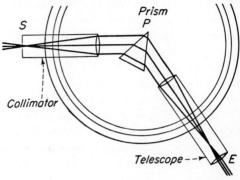

$$\lambda = \sin\theta_n / Nn$$

where N is the number of grating lines per unit width of the grating (the reciprocal of the grating spacing d).

The prism spectrometer of Fig. 7 does not provide an absolute measurement of wavelength. For any given prism, the angular scale must be calibrated by using a source

Fig. 7. Schematic diagram of a prism spectrometer.

whose wavelengths are known because they have been measured by using a grating or other device depending on the principles of interference.

4. EMISSION AND ABSORPTION SPECTRA

THE SPECTRUM produced when the light from a luminous source is dispersed is called the *emission spectrum* of the source. Its appearance is determined by the composition and physical state of the source.

Incandescent solids and liquids, and incandescent gases under extremely high pressure produce *continuous spectra*, which include light of all colors. Thus, the spectrum of a hot tungsten filament consists of all colors from the violet end of the spectrum to the red end. The spectrum is not interrupted by any dark regions. These spectra will be considered further in Sec. 2 of Chap. 37.

Luminous gases and vapors at low pressure have spectra quite different from the spectra of incandescent solids. The emission spectra of such materials consist of distinct lines, or groups of closely spaced lines, and are called *line* or *band spectra*.

It is found that every chemical element emits a characteristic *line spectrum* when the *atoms* of the element are excited in a flame, a furnace, or an electric discharge. Thus, if different materials containing sodium are introduced into a hot Bunsen flame or an electric arc, a characteristic yellow line appears in the spectrum at 589 mμ, the same position as in the spectrum of a sodium-vapor light such as is used for highway illumination. Therefore, we might conclude that the mechanism involved in the emission of this yellow line is to be found in the sodium *atom* itself. This conclusion is correct and can be generalized by the statement that *line spectra originate in the atoms of the chemical elements*. Figure 6 shows the spectrum of the hydrogen atom in the visible and near-ultraviolet regions.

With strong excitation, as in an electric spark, line spectra characteristic of positive *atomic ions* are observed.

Other types of emission spectra are sometimes produced by incandescent gases at low pressure. These spectra are called *band spectra* and consist of large numbers of spectral lines closely spaced in groups called *bands*. In the bands, the lines are usually so closely spaced that they cannot be separated by low-dispersion instruments. *Band spectra have their origin in molecules or molecular ions.* Fig. 8 shows a portion of the band spectrum of the phosphorus-nitride molecule in the ultraviolet. The molecules of any compound will emit a characteristic band spectrum if excitation can be produced without causing the molecules to dissociate. Many types of molecules dissociate at relatively low temperatures; for example, when sodium chloride is placed in a Bunsen flame, the molecules

267.71mμ 238.13mμ

Fig. 8. Photographic negative of the band spectrum of the PN molecule. *[From Herzberg, Molecular Spectra and Molecular Structure (Prentice-Hall).]*

are readily dissociated and the bright yellow line of *atomic* sodium predominates in the spectrum of the hot vapor. On the other hand, in an electrical-discharge tube containing air, molecular excitation results in the emission of band spectra characteristic of the O_2 and N_2 molecules.

When light from a source with a continuous spectrum is allowed to pass through a relatively cool gas or vapor before entering the spectrograph, the observed spectrum consists of the continuous spectrum of the source crossed by dark lines or bands. The dark lines or bands are present as a result of selective absorption by the cool gas or vapor. For example, if light from an incandescent tungsten-filament lamp is allowed to pass through a tube containing sodium vapor, the observed spectrum is continuous except for a dark line appearing in the yellow region. This line denotes a wavelength *absorbed* by the sodium vapor. The dark line appears at exactly the same position as the yellow line appears in the emission spectrum of sodium. This correspondence between the positions of the lines in the emission and absorption spectra is quite general. The wavelengths absorbed by a given type of atom or molecule are identical with wavelengths emitted when the emission spectrum of the atom or molecule is excited. The dark lines or bands in the spectrum, observed when white light is allowed to pass through an absorbing gas, constitute the *absorption spectrum* of the atoms or molecules of the gas.

Liquids and solids have broad regions of absorption exhibiting no line structure. For example, the ruby glass commonly used in photographic darkrooms has an absorption region covering the entire visible spectrum except the red and deep orange; the absorption is very intense and shows no line structure. An aqueous solution of copper sulfate absorbs strongly in most regions of the visible spectrum except in the blue and green.

Dark lines are observed in the otherwise continuous visible spectrum of the sun (see Fig. 9). Although these lines were first observed by Wollaston in 1802, they are known as the *Fraunhofer lines*, since Joseph von Fraunhofer made a careful study of about 600 dark lines in the solar spectrum in the years following 1814.

The light emitted by the sun is generally the continuous spectrum of a gas at a very high pressure, but this light experiences selective atomic absorption in passing through the relatively cooler gases at the surface of

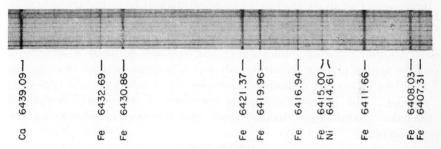

Fig. 9. Part of the spectrum of the sun in the red region, showing Fraunhofer lines arising from absorption by atoms or positive ions of Fe, Ca, and Ni. Divide numbers by 10 to get wavelengths in mμ. This is a photographic *positive*, so the spectrum appears as it would to the eye in a spectroscope—dark absorption lines against a bright continuous background. [*From Astrophys. Jl. 75, plate XVIII (1932).*]

the sun. Most of the structure of the otherwise continuous solar spectrum originates in this process, but some dark bands arise from absorption by molecules in the atmosphere of the earth. Comparison of the wavelengths of the Fraunhofer lines with those emitted by atoms in the laboratory enables astrophysicists to determine the composition of the gases in the sun's outer layers. Absorption lines of *helium* were first found in the Fraunhofer spectrum of the sun (hence the name helium) and recognized as arising from an element unknown at the time on the earth. This element was later (1895) found by Ramsey in the earth's atmosphere.

The detailed study of emission and absorption spectra is called *spectroscopy*. This study led directly to the modern knowledge of the internal structure of atoms that we shall discuss later in this book. Spectroscopic investigations have been extended from the visible to the ultraviolet and infrared portions of the electromagnetic spectrum; since glass has absorption bands in these regions, other optical materials must be used in the spectrographs. In the near-ultraviolet region, quartz lenses and quartz prisms are frequently used; photographic plates are used as detectors for the radiation. In the infrared, metallic mirrors are used in place of lenses in the optical systems of spectrographs. Prisms of fluorite, rock salt, or potassium bromide, or coarse reflection gratings are used to disperse the infrared radiation, and thermoelectric methods of detection are generally employed.

Spectroscopy has proved to be of great industrial importance in providing a very sensitive and convenient method of chemical analysis. In the analysis of a chemical for constituent elements, a sample of the unknown is usually placed on the carbon electrodes of an electric arc and the resulting emission spectrum is observed. Extremely small quantities of elements can be detected by their characteristic emission lines. The processes of analysis are rapid and accurate and have the advantage of requiring only very small samples. Special analyses for impurities in certain metallurgical processes are obtainable in a matter of seconds.

Another valuable application of spectroscopic methods of analysis is in the field of organic chemical analysis. Chemical methods of analyzing mixtures of organic compounds are sometimes laborious and time-consuming. The infrared absorption spectrum of an organic compound includes characteristic bands which can be used in identifying the compound.

PROBLEMS

1. A light ray consisting of wavelengths 656.3 mμ and 486.1 mμ is incident on the surface of carbon disulfide contained in a beaker. If the angle of incidence is exactly 30°, find the angles of refraction in carbon disulfide. Ans: 18°.00; 17°.61.

2. A ray of light containing only wavelengths 656.3 mμ and 486.1 mμ strikes a water surface at angle of incidence of 45°. Find the angular separation of the two refracted rays beneath the water surface.

3. A ray of white light is incident at an angle of 60° with the normal to the face of a 60° flint-glass prism as in Fig. 2. Make a large drawing showing the passage of rays of the red, yellow, and blue light of Table I through this prism, including accurate values of all angles involved.

Ans: resultant deviations are 49°.01, 49°.45, 50°.56.

4. For the example worked out in the text on p. 535, determine the focal lengths of the crown- and flint-glass components and the resulting focal length of the achromatic doublet for the yellow light of Table I.

5. If a flint-glass lens has focal length 50.00 cm for the yellow light of Table I, what is its focal length for the red and the blue light? Ans: 50.39, 49.05 cm.

6. If a flint-glass lens has focal length −80.00 cm for the yellow light of Table I, what is its focal length for the red and the blue light?

7. It is desired to make a converging achromatic lens of focal length 40 cm from a flint-glass lens and a crown-glass lens. Each of the component lenses has one plane surface, and it is the plane surfaces that are in contact. What should be the radius of curvature of the curved surface (a) of the flint-glass lens and (b) of the crown-glass lens? Ans: (a) −11.9 cm; (b) +6.67 cm.

8. It is desired to make a diverging achromatic lens of focal length 25 cm from flint- and crown-glass lenses. If the lens surfaces that are in contact are plane, what should be the radii of curvature of the outer curved surfaces?

9. What is the focal length of an achromatic crown-flint doublet in which the *flint*-glass component has a focal length of exactly $+20$ cm for blue light?

Ans: -43.2 cm.

10. A doublet for an enlarging camera is to be used with photographic paper insensitive to the red. Hence it is desired to make it achromatic for yellow and blue light. If the focal length is 62.04 cm, determine the focal lengths of the crown- and flint-glass components for the yellow and blue light of Table I.

NOTE: By the *angular dispersion* of a spectrometer is meant the change in angle on the circles of Fig. 5 or Fig. 7 per unit change in wavelength, that is, $d\theta/d\lambda$. The mean angular dispersion over a wavelength range $\Delta\lambda$ would be $\Delta\theta/\Delta\lambda$. If the spectrometer is arranged for photographic observation, a photographic plate is placed at the focal plane of the objective of the telescopes in these figures, so that the objective acts as a camera lens. The *linear dispersion* is then defined as $dX/d\lambda$, where dX would be the separation on the plate of two spectral lines differing in wavelength by $d\lambda$.

11. Show that the angular dispersion of a grating spectrometer at angle θ in the nth order is $d\theta/d\lambda = nN/\cos\theta$. Show that the linear dispersion on a photographic plate is $dX/d\lambda = nNf/\cos\theta$, where f is the focal length of the camera lens.

12. A 5000-line/cm transmission grating is mounted as in Fig. 5. Determine its mean angular dispersion in the first-order spectrum in the region between the blue and red wavelengths of Table I. Compare with the mean angular dispersion of the prism of Prob. 3 in this same region.

13. What is the angular dispersion of a 5000-line/cm grating in the vicinity of 589 mμ in the second order when the grating is used at normal incidence?

Ans: $4\,!25/$mμ.

14. A 5000-line/cm grating is used at normal incidence in a spectrograph in which the camera lens has a focal length of 150 cm. What is the linear dispersion at the plate in the vicinity of 589 mμ when the second-order spectrum is photographed?

PART V

ELECTRICITY AND MAGNETISM

CHAPTER 27

ELECTROSTATICS

Electrostatics is the branch of science that deals with the laws of electricity at rest.

Almost everyone has had the experiences, especially in dry interiors in winter, of getting a shock when touching a doorknob after walking across a rug, of having his comb crackle in his hair, and of having sheets of writing paper cling obstinately together. Of course he has seen lightning; he may have had the interesting experience of standing on a dock during the approach of a summer thunderstorm and seeing everyone's hair pulled tautly erect by the electrical forces that precede a lightning discharge. These are all manifestations of static electricity—electricity at rest, as distinguished from the currents of electricity in wires with which we are so familiar nowadays.

The laws of static electricity are not only fundamental to a study of those of current electricity, they are also directly applied in describing the performance of many familiar modern devices such as the condensers and vacuum tubes in every radio set. We therefore begin the systematic study of electricity by considering the basic laws of *electrostatics*.

1. ELECTRIC CHARGES

WE CAN ELECTRIFY, or charge, a hard-rubber rod by rubbing it with cat's fur. We can charge a glass rod by rubbing it with silk. The electrified rods acquire the power of attracting bits of paper or small balls made of some light material such as pith or cork and suspended by silk threads.

By playing with very light 'metal' balls such as pith balls coated with metal foil or painted with metal paint, we can easily convince ourselves that there is a difference between the type of electric charge on the hard rubber and that on the glass. The metal ball is attracted by either charged rod until it is permitted to touch the rod; then it bounces away from the rod it has touched and is thereafter strongly repelled by it. The metal ball has become charged by contact with the charged rod. A charged metal ball that is repelled by the hard-rubber rod is attracted by the glass rod, and one that is repelled by the glass rod is attracted by the hard-

545

rubber rod. Furthermore, a metal ball that has touched a charged glass rod and another that has touched a charged hard-rubber rod attract each other; but if two metal balls have touched the same charged rod, they repel each other. Evidently the two charged rods must have two different *kinds* of electric charge. Any two dissimilar materials when brought into contact or rubbed together become more or less charged, but two centuries of search have produced no more than the two kinds of electric charge that are produced in considerable quantity on hard rubber and glass when rubbed with cat's fur and silk, respectively. Thus we conclude that there are two and only two different kinds of electric charge.

The two kinds of electric charge are arbitrarily called *positive* and *negative*, or + and −, according to conventions introduced by Benjamin Franklin:

Positive electricity is the kind of electricity on glass that has been electrified by rubbing with silk.

Negative electricity is the kind of electricity on hard rubber that has been electrified by rubbing with cat's fur.

From the experiments discussed above, we conclude that charged objects exert forces on each other in accordance with the following law:

Like charges repel each other and unlike charges attract each other.

For example, the metal ball that touches the positively charged glass rod acquires a positive charge like that of the rod and is repelled by the rod, but it will be attracted to the negatively charged hard-rubber rod or to the negatively charged ball that has touched the hard-rubber rod.

A little further experimenting with charged metal balls will show that the electrostatic force between a given pair of charges decreases rapidly as the distance between the charges increases. The law of dependence on distance was first determined experimentally by Coulomb* in 1785. Using a torsion balance to measure the forces, he showed that *the mutual force between two given charges varies inversely as the square of the distance between them:*

$$F \propto 1/d^2. \tag{1}†$$

Thus, if the distance between two charges is doubled, the force between them is decreased to ¼ its original value; if the distance is halved, the force is increased to 4 times its original value. Of course, by Newton's

* Charles Augustin Coulomb (1736–1806), French physicist; discoverer of the inverse-square laws of electrostatics and magnetostatics.
† This law holds rigorously only for 'point' charges or, more practically, for charged bodies, such as pith balls or atomic ions, separated by distances large compared with the dimensions of the bodies. Charges that are physically very small compared with distances of interest will be referred to as *point charges*, the word *point* to be understood in this physical sense and not in the idealized mathematical sense.

third law, the electrical force exerted by one charge on a second charge is equal in magnitude but opposite in direction to the force exerted by the second charge on the first.   The directions of the force vectors are along

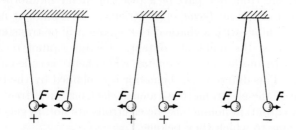

Fig. 1. Unlike charges attract; like charges repel.

the line connecting the charges, in an attractive or repulsive sense according to the signs of the charges, as in Fig. 1.

2. ELECTRICAL STRUCTURE OF MATTER; COULOMB'S LAW

INSTEAD of stumbling along tortuous historic paths that eventually led to a complete understanding of the behavior of electric charges, we can profitably utilize the modern knowledge of the atomic constitution of matter.   There is so much physical and chemical evidence for the correctness of the modern atomic picture that there can be no reasonable doubt of its validity.   Use of this knowledge of the structure of matter greatly simplifies the presentation and understanding of electrical phenomena.

An atom contains a positively charged central core, or *nucleus*.   Most of the mass of the atom is in the nucleus, which has a diameter of only about 10^{-15} m.   Revolving around the nucleus, out to a distance of the order of 10^{-10} m, are a number of negatively charged particles called *electrons*.   The electrons are all alike; each is of much smaller mass than the nucleus and carries a charge denoted by $-e$.   Ordinarily, the atom as a whole appears to be electrically neutral or uncharged, so we say that *the total negative charge on all the electrons is equal in magnitude to the positive charge on the nucleus*.   The number of electrons in a neutral atom is called the atomic number and varies from 1 to 100 through the known periodic table.   Thus,

> H has a nucleus of charge $+e$ and 1 electron,
> He has a nucleus of charge $+2e$ and 2 electrons,
> Li has a nucleus of charge $+3e$ and 3 electrons,
> and so forth.

If one or more electrons are removed from a normal atom, it becomes a positive ion, familiar from the study of chemistry; if one or more extra electrons are added to a normal atom, it becomes a negative ion.

Metals and nonmetals behave quite differently with respect to electric charges. If a piece of metal is brought into contact with a charged rod, the entire surface of the metal becomes charged immediately. Charge can travel easily from one part of a piece of metal to another, and the metal is said to be a *conductor* of electricity. If a piece of nonmetal is brought into contact with a charged rod, charge will be transferred to the nonmetal only at the point of contact. Charge cannot readily travel from one part to another of a nonmetal, which hence is called an *insulator* or *dielectric*. This difference in behavior is explained by the fact that in metals some of the electrons (the valence electrons) are 'free' to wander from atom to atom; in nonmetals the electrons are not, in general, free to leave the atoms to which they belong.

The 'free' electrons in a metal move around inside the metal much like the molecules in a gas. In the neutral or uncharged state of a metal, the electrons are uniformly distributed throughout the volume of the metal. If an uncharged metal ball is brought near a positively charged rod as in Fig. 2(a), the electrons in the ball are attracted by the rod and the positive

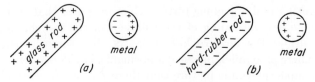

Fig. 2. Induced charges.

nuclei in the ball are repelled by it. The mobile free electrons concentrate on the side of the ball near the rod. The side of the ball nearer the charged rod acquires a net negative charge; the other side of the ball is left with a deficiency of electrons and hence an *equal* net positive charge. The reverse happens in Fig. 2(b), in which the electrons are repelled by the negatively charged rod. Charges acquired by portions of an uncharged object in this manner are said to be 'induced' by the near-by charged body.

If the metal ball in Fig. 2(a) is made so that the two halves can be separated, one can obtain equal and unlike charges on the two halves by separating them before the charged rod is removed. The sequence of events is shown in Figs. 3(a)–(e), which are intended to be self-explanatory. Instead of a single metal sphere that can be split, two spheres originally in contact can be used as in Figs. 4(a)–(e). The two spheres in Fig. 4(e) have charges that are equal and unlike, since the spheres in Fig. 4(a) were uncharged, and the excess of electrons on the left sphere must exactly equal the deficiency of electrons on the right sphere. These spheres must be held by insulating nonmetallic supports, such as silk threads or glass rods, through which electrons cannot flow.

In this way, Coulomb obtained on small spheres charges which he knew were equal and unlike.   With his torsion balance he then found that

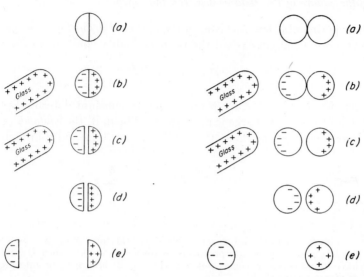

Fig. 3. By induction, equal and opposite charges are obtained on the two halves of a metal sphere.

Fig. 4. By induction, equal and opposite charges are obtained on two metal spheres.

a third charge would exert equal but opposite forces on the equal but unlike charges.   In other words, like charges repel each other with the same forces as unlike charges attract, if the charges are numerically equal.

Finally, Coulomb found that the force that either of two charges exerts on the other is proportional to the product of the sizes or magnitudes of the charges.   He verified this fact by a technique of splitting a given charge into two, four, or more equal parts that is illustrated in Fig. 5.   When the two identical spheres in Fig. 5 are separated, they are found to be equally charged (they exert equal forces on any other charge) as would be expected from symmetry.   The charge on one of these spheres can again be divided into two, and so on.

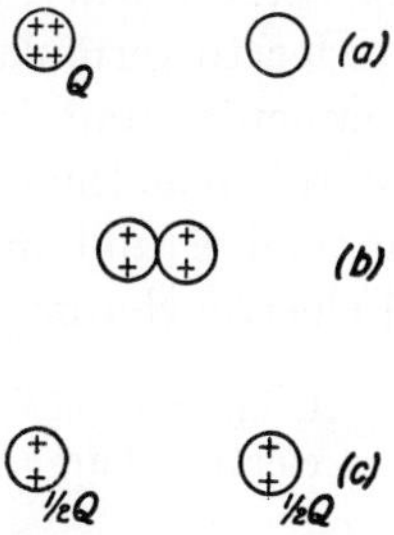

Fig. 5. By touching a charged metal sphere to an uncharged sphere of the same size, the charge is divided into two equal parts.

Coulomb found that the force between two charges, denoted by Q_1 and Q_2 (Fig. 6), is proportional to Q_1, to Q_2, and to $1/d^2$; that is,

$$F \propto \frac{Q_1 Q_2}{d^2}.$$

COULOMB'S LAW: *The electric force between two point charges is proportional to the magnitude of each of the charges and inversely proportional to the square of the distance between the charges.*

This experimental law furnishes an *operational definition of magnitude of charge*, once we have selected the proportionality constant in the relation

$$F = \text{const} \times \frac{Q_1 Q_2}{d^2}.$$

The choice of this arbitrary proportionality constant determines the size of the unit in which charge is measured. The unit, the *coulomb* (abbreviated coul or c), is chosen so that if F is in newtons and d in meters, the

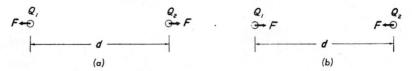

Fig. 6. When Q_1 and Q_2 have like signs, the force F in (2) comes out positive and is to be interpreted as repulsive, as in (a); when Q_1 and Q_2 have unlike signs, F comes out negative in (2) and is to be interpreted as attractive, as in (b).

proportionality constant will be 8.9878×10^9 nt·m²/coul². This proportionality constant should not be considered as dimensionless, because to do so would imply that the coulomb is a unit that is expressible in terms of the mechanical units of length, mass, and time, and this is basically incorrect. Rather, *the coulomb is itself a fundamental unit of a new type.* In order to formulate the laws of electricity and magnetism, one new fundamental unit is required. This new fundamental unit is conveniently taken as the unit of charge. *All* physical units can be expressed in terms of five fundamental units—those of length, mass, time, temperature, and electric charge.

Coulomb's law having been established experimentally, the unit of electric charge, the **coulomb,** is defined by the equation

$$F = (8.9878 \times 10^9 \text{ nt·m}^2/\text{coul}^2) \frac{Q_1 Q_2}{d^2}.$$

This coefficient is inconvenient to write, and will occur in many formulas.*

* In advanced texts, an algebraic symbol is usually used in writing Coulomb's law. In the so-called 'rationalized' system of units, coulomb's law is written

$$F = \frac{1}{4\pi\epsilon_0} \frac{Q_1 Q_2}{d^2},$$

where ϵ_0 is a dimensional constant called 'the permittivity of free space' and the numerical factor 4π is introduced in order that certain equations appearing in electromagnetic theory may be written in a convenient form. In the 'non-rationalized'

For most purposes it is sufficiently accurate to use 9×10^9 as the numerical factor, and this will be done in all the examples and problems in this book. To keep track of units but avoid repeating the long parenthesis above, we shall abbreviate this parenthesis to $(9 \times 10^9 \text{ nt·m}^2/\text{c}^2)$, writing

$$F = (9 \times 10^9 \text{ nt·m}^2/\text{c}^2) \frac{Q_1 Q_2}{d^2}, \qquad \left\{ \begin{array}{l} F \text{ in nt} \\ Q_1, Q_2 \text{ in coul} \\ d \text{ in m} \end{array} \right\} \quad (2)$$

where it is understood that

$$9 \times 10^9 \text{ nt·m}^2/\text{c}^2 \sim 8.9878 \times 10^9 \text{ nt·m}^2/\text{coul}^2.$$

The coulomb is chosen to be a unit of convenient size in working with electric *currents*. From the standpoint of electrostatics it is an enormous unit, and electrostatic charges are usually expressed in terms of the submultiples:

$$1 \ \mu\text{c} = 1 \text{ microcoulomb} = 10^{-6} \text{ coulomb}$$
or $\qquad 1 \ \mu\mu\text{c} = 1 \text{ micromicrocoulomb} = 10^{-12} \text{ coulomb.}$

The positive charge on the hydrogen nucleus (the *proton*) and the negative charge on the electron are the smallest (non-vanishing) charges that have ever been observed. The absolute magnitudes of these charges are universally denoted by the symbol e, where

$$e = 1.6021 \times 10^{-19} \text{ coul.} \qquad (3)$$

Thus, the charge on the electron is $-e$; that on the proton is $+e$. Experimental evidence to date indicates that *all* charges are positive or negative integral multiples of the charge e.

Equation (2), with the sign convention explained in Fig. 6, gives the force acting between two charges. Where more than two charges are present, the total force acting on one of the charges is the vector sum of the forces arising from each of the other charges individually. For example, in Fig. 7, where there are four charges, we may compute the total force on the -0.2-μc charge by adding vectorially the three forces of repulsion from the other three charges, in the manner indicated.

We are now in a position to see why an *uncharged* metal-coated pith ball is attracted to a charged rod. Looking back to Fig. 2, we can see that

---

system of units, Coulomb's law is written

$$F = \frac{1}{\epsilon_0'} \frac{Q_1 Q_2}{d^2},$$

where ϵ_0' is the dimensional constant. It is noted that

$$\frac{1}{4\pi\epsilon_0} = \frac{1}{\epsilon_0'} = 8.9878 \times 10^9 \text{ nt·m}^2/\text{coul}^2.$$

In advanced courses, the student should have little difficulty in making the identification of our 9×10^9 nt·m^2/c^2 with $1/4\pi\epsilon_0$ or $1/\epsilon_0'$. Further discussion of various systems of electrical units is given in Sec. 2 of the Appendix. The relation between 9×10^9 and the square of the speed of light is pointed out in Chap. 36.

when the pith ball is brought near the charged rod, equal and opposite charges are induced on the two sides of the pith ball. But the charges of sign unlike the charge on the rod are closer to the rod than are the charges of like sign. Because of this difference in average distance, the force of attraction experienced by the unlike charges is greater than the force of repulsion experienced by the like charges, and the pith ball experiences a net force of attraction. When the pith ball actually touches the rod, some or all of the unlike charges are neutralized by transfer of charge from the surface of the rod to the ball; this leaves a preponderance of like charge to be strongly repelled.

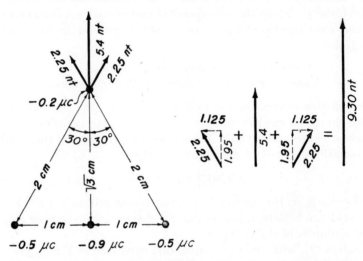

Fig. 7. The resultant electrical force on the -0.2-μc charge is 9.30 nt directed upward.

The fact that an uncharged *nonmetallic* object, such as an *uncoated* pith ball or a piece of paper, is attracted to a charged rod is associated with a phenomenon called *polarization,* or *dielectric polarization.* In spite of the fact that electrons in a nonconductor cannot leave the atom to which they belong and move to the side of the ball, as they do in the conductor of Fig. 2, the electrons in each atom are pulled or pushed so that they lie, on the average, closer to or farther from the charged rod than the positive nucleus. When the charges of the nonmetal (the dielectric) are disturbed thus, it is said to become *polarized.* In Fig. 8(a) the electrons in each atom are on the average closer to the positive charges of the rod than is the positive nucleus. Thus, each atom experiences a net force of attraction toward the rod and the whole ball is attracted toward the rod. A similar effect takes place in Fig. 8(b) with a negative rod. The force of attraction between an uncharged dielectric body and a charged rod is in general much smaller than that between an uncharged conducting (metal) body and the same charged rod.   The laws governing dielectric polarization will be considered later.

The fact that a material medium (even air) becomes polarized in the neighborhood of an electric charge has an influence on the force between two charged bodies immersed in the material medium.   Thus, formula

Fig. 8. Dielectric polarization. The cross-hatched circles are intended to represent individual atoms, each with a positive nucleus and a 'cloud' of negative electrons.

(2) is strictly true only in the absence of all other material media, that is, when the charges are in empty space.   However, the polarization of air is so slight that for all ordinary purposes formula (2) can be assumed to hold for charges immersed in air.

3. ELECTRIC FIELD

An *electric field* is said to exist in any region of space in which an electric charge would experience an electrical force, for example in the region around a charged body.   The intensity of the electric field at a point is defined in terms of the electrical force F that would be exerted on a very small positive test charge $+q$ placed at the point.   *The test charge must be so small that it does not appreciably disturb the charges on the bodies that set up the field;* that is, it must not cause appreciable redistribution of the charges on conductors or alteration of the polarization of dielectrics in its neighborhood.

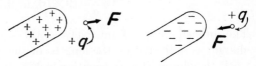

The net force F on the test charge $+q$ (see Fig. 9, for example) is the vector resultant of all the forces on

Fig. 9. The electric field has the same direction as the force F acting on a small positive test charge $+q$, and has the magnitude F/q.

q exerted by the various individual charges or elements of charge on the charged bodies in the neighborhood.   By Coulomb's law, each of these component forces is proportional to the magnitude of q.   Hence, the resultant force F has a magnitude proportional to q, and we may write

$$F = q\mathcal{E}. \qquad (4)$$

In this equation, $$\mathcal{E} = F/q, \qquad (5)$$

the force in newtons per coulomb of test charge, is known as the *electric intensity.*

The **electric intensity** at a point is a vector having the direction of the force that would be exerted on a small positive test charge placed at the point and a magnitude equal to the magnitude of this force divided by the magnitude of the test charge.

Thus, in an electric field there is a vector **ε** associated with each point of space.   In terms of this vector, equation (4) gives the force on a small charge placed at that point.   Equation (4) is valid for negative charges (*q* negative) as well as for positive charges (*q* positive).   *If the small charge q is positive, the force F has the same direction as ε; if the small charge is negative, the force F has the direction opposite to the vector ε.*

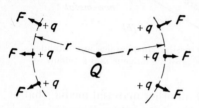

Fig. 10. The field at distance *r* from a positive charge *Q* is determined by the force *F* on a small test charge +*q*.

In learning to compute electric intensities, let us start with the field in the neighborhood of a single isolated positive point charge of magnitude *Q*. To measure the intensity at a distance *r* from charge *Q*, we imagine that we place a small test charge +*q* (Fig. 10) at a distance *r* (in meters) from the charge *Q*.   At any point on a sphere of radius *r* drawn around the charge *Q*, the force on the test charge would be radially outward and of magnitude

$$F = (9 \times 10^9 \ \text{nt·m}^2/\text{c}^2) \ Qq/r^2.$$

The electric intensity is, then, by definition (5), directed radially outward and of magnitude

$$\varepsilon = \frac{F}{q} = (9 \times 10^9 \ \text{nt·m}^2/\text{c}^2) \ \frac{Q}{r^2}. \qquad \left\{ \begin{array}{l} \varepsilon \ \text{in nt/coul} \\ Q \ \text{in coul} \\ r \ \text{in m} \end{array} \right\} \quad (6)$$

The intensity falls off inversely as the square of the distance from the charge, as indicated by the lengths of the vectors in Fig. 11.

If the charge *Q* were negative in Fig. 10, the force *F* on a positive test charge would be directed radially inward rather than outward.   Since the intensity is in the direction of the force on a positive test charge, the electric intensity would be directed inward as in Fig. 12.   Its magnitude would still be given by (6).

It is convenient to visualize a set of lines, called *electric lines*, whose direction gives at every point in space the direction of the electric-intensity vector at that point.

An **electric line** is a line whose tangent at each point is in the direction of the electric intensity at that point.

As so defined, electric lines are not intended to give information about the magnitude of the electric intensity, but only about its direction. Electric lines about the positive and negative point charges of Figs. 11 and 12 are shown in Figs. 13 and 14. Of course these figures can show only sample electric lines in one plane. Electric lines must be imagined to bristle out from the charges in every direction in space like the quills of a curled-up porcupine. Through every point in space there is an electric line starting

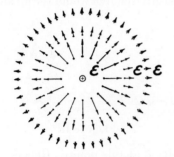

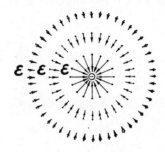

Fig. 11. Electric intensities $\mathcal{E}$ at points near a positive charge.

Fig. 12. Electric intensities $\mathcal{E}$ at points near a negative charge.

at the $+$ charge and going out to infinity, or starting at an infinite distance and ending on the $-$ charge. This description assumes that in the whole of space there is only a single positive charge (Fig. 13) or a single negative charge (Fig. 14). This is obviously an absurd assumption, but the pictures of Figs. 11–14 hold in practice if the charge we are considering is well isolated from all other charges so that the forces exerted on our test charge by other charges are negligible. The electric lines in Figs. 13 and

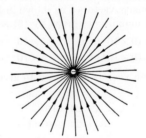

Fig. 13. Electric lines go radially out from a positive point charge.

Fig. 14. Electric lines go radially into a negative point charge.

14 do not really go on indefinitely to infinity but are disturbed as soon as they come near other charges.

Now let us see how we would compute the field arising from more than one charge. Consider first the field of two charges, for example the two charges of opposite sign in Fig. 15. To determine the field at point A, we imagine a small test charge $+q$ at this point. The test charge will experience an attractive force $\boldsymbol{F}_1$ toward the negative charge and a repulsive force F_2 from the positive charge.   These two forces must be added vectorially to obtain the total force F:

$$F = F_1 + F_2; \quad \text{hence} \quad (F/q) = (F_1/q) + (F_2/q).$$

But F_1/q is the electric intensity $\mathcal{E}_1$ that the negative charge would set up alone; F_2/q is the intensity $\mathcal{E}_2$ that the positive charge would set up alone;

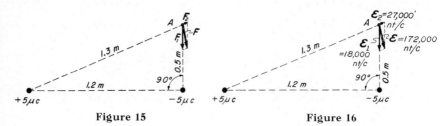

Figure 15   Figure 16

F/q is, by definition, the electric intensity $\mathcal{E}$ at this point.   Hence,

$$\mathcal{E} = \mathcal{E}_1 + \mathcal{E}_2.$$

This result can be immediately generalized to the field set up by any number of charges, and shows that

The electric intensity arising from any number of individual charges is the vector sum of the intensities that the charges individually contribute.

Example.   *Determine the electric intensity at point A for the charges shown in Fig. 15.*

Instead of working with force vectors F, we can work directly with intensity vectors $\mathcal{E}$ as shown in Fig. 16. $\mathcal{E}_1$ and $\mathcal{E}_2$ have the directions shown and magnitudes given by (6) as

$\mathcal{E}_1 = (9 \times 10^9 \text{ nt·m}^2/\text{c}^2)(5 \times 10^{-6} \text{ c})/(0.5 \text{ m})^2 = 180 \times 10^3 \text{ nt/coul},$
$\mathcal{E}_2 = (9 \times 10^9 \text{ nt·m}^2/\text{c}^2)(5 \times 10^{-6} \text{ c})/(1.3 \text{ m})^2 = 27 \times 10^3 \text{ nt/coul}.$

These vectors are added to give $\mathcal{E}$, as follows:

$\mathcal{E}_{1X} = 0$ nt/c	$\mathcal{E}_{1Y} = -180 \times 10^3$ nt/c
$\mathcal{E}_{2X} = 24 \times 10^3$	$\mathcal{E}_{2Y} = 10 \times 10^3$
$\mathcal{E}_X = 24 \times 10^3$ nt/c	$\mathcal{E}_Y = -170 \times 10^3$ nt/c

Hence $\mathcal{E} = 172 \times 10^3 \text{ nt/c}; \quad \theta = 8°.1.$

It will be noticed from this example that the inverse-square law represents a very rapid decrease of force with distance.   The intensity at point A is principally determined by the charge 0.5 m away; the charge of equal magnitude at 1.3 m has a very much smaller effect, so that $\mathcal{E}$ does not differ very much from $\mathcal{E}_1$ in magnitude or direction.

Figure 17 illustrates the computation of the electric intensity at four other points in the field of the two charges of Fig. 16.   Figure 18 shows the system of electric lines for the field of these two charges. Electric lines through the points A, B, C, D, E of Figs. 16 and 17 are shown, and a

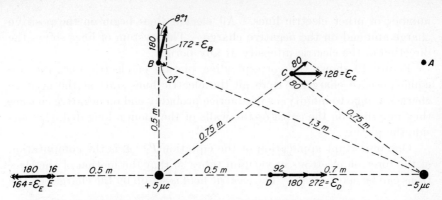

Fig. 17. Computation of the electric intensity at four points near the charges of Fig. 16. Values of the intensity are given in units of 10^3 nt/c.

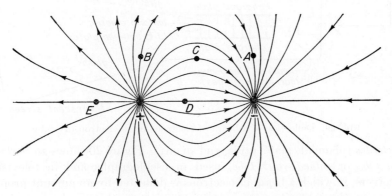

Fig. 18. Electric lines in the vicinity of equal but unlike charges.

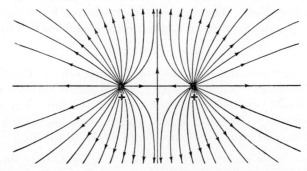

Fig. 19. Electric lines in the vicinity of two equal positive charges.

number of other electric lines. All electric lines begin on the positive charge and end on the negative charge. This system of lines shows the direction of the electric intensity at any point.

Figure 19 shows the corresponding picture of electric lines for two equal positive charges. Here all the electric lines start at the positive charges and go to infinity, or in practice probably end on negative charges they may find on the earth or the walls of the room a long distance outside the picture.

One important application of the equation $F = q\mathcal{E}$ is the computation of the force on electrons in vacuum tubes so that the motion of the electrons can be determined. The electric field is set up by the charges on the

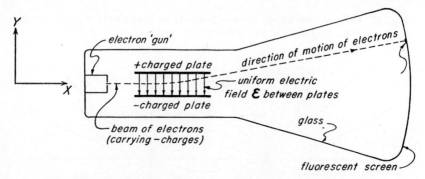

Fig. 20. Deflection of a beam of electrons in an electron-ray tube.

electrodes (filament, plate, grids, and so on). Figure 20 shows an *electron-ray tube* or *cathode-ray* tube*, used in oscillographs and in television receivers, in which a beam of electrons is deflected by an amount proportional to the intensity of an electric field between two charged plates. Deflections of electron beams by electrostatic fields also take place in television iconoscopes, 'magic-eye' tubes, beam power tubes, and electron-multiplier tubes. The charge on each electron is $q = -e = -1.60 \times 10^{-19}$ coul. In an electric field $\mathcal{E}$, the electron experiences a force

$$F = q\mathcal{E} = -e\mathcal{E} = -(1.60 \times 10^{-19} \text{ coul}) \, \mathcal{E}. \tag{7}$$

The minus sign indicates that this force is opposite in direction to the electric intensity $\mathcal{E}$. A small positive charge placed between the plates of Fig. 20 would experience a downward electrical force, but a negative charge is repelled by the lower negative plate, attracted toward the upper positive plate, and experiences an upward electrical force.

Example. *In the electron-ray tube of Fig. 20, if the speed of the electrons is 10^7 m/sec, the length of the plates 1 cm, and the distance from plates to screen 30 cm, determine the deflection of the beam on the screen when a field of intensity 15,000 nt/coul is set up between the plates. Show that the deflection*

---

* The term *'cathode-ray'* originated because the electrons come from a negative electrode called the *cathode*.

is proportional to the intensity of the field and that the effect of gravity on the motion of the electrons is negligible.

Since the electron is initially moving horizontally and neither electric nor gravitational forces act horizontally, the horizontal component v_X of the electron's velocity remains constant: $v_X = 10^7$ m/sec. The time t that the electron spends in the uniform field between the deflecting plates is therefore $t = l/v_X$, where l is the length of the plates; the time t' required for the electron to traverse the distance d from deflecting plates to screen is $t' = d/v_X$.

Electric forces. First let us ignore the effects of gravity. During its passage through the uniform field $\mathcal{E}$ between the deflecting plates, the electron experiences a constant upward force $F_Y = e\mathcal{E}$ and hence, from Newton's second principle, has a constant vertical acceleration $a_Y = F_Y/m = e\mathcal{E}/m$, where m is the mass of the electron (9.11×10^{-31} kg). Therefore, while passing between the deflecting plates, the electron acquires an upward velocity component $v_Y = a_Y t$. After leaving the deflecting plates, the electron moves with constant velocity; hence by the time it strikes the screen, it has an upward displacement $Y = v_Y t'$. (It should be noted that the above computation is rigorous if the distance $d = 30$ cm is measured from the midpoint of the uniform field to the screen.) To find the magnitude of this vertical displacement, we use the numerical data given in the example:

$$t = l/v_X = (10^{-2}\ \text{m})/(10^7\ \text{m/sec}) = 10^{-9}\ \text{sec},$$
$$t' = d/v_X = (0.3\ \text{m})/(10^7\ \text{m/sec}) = 3 \times 10^{-8}\ \text{sec},$$
$$a_Y = e\mathcal{E}/m = (1.6 \times 10^{-19}\ \text{c})(1.5 \times 10^4\ \text{nt/c})/(9.11 \times 10^{-31}\ \text{kg})$$
$$= 2.6 \times 10^{15}\ \text{m/sec}^2,$$
$$v_Y = a_Y t = (2.6 \times 10^{15}\ \text{m/sec}^2)(10^{-9}\ \text{sec}) = 2.6 \times 10^6\ \text{m/sec},$$
$$Y = v_Y t' = (2.6 \times 10^6\ \text{m/sec})(3 \times 10^{-8}\ \text{sec}) = 7.8 \times 10^{-2}\ \text{m} = 7.8\ \text{cm}.$$

If we substitute successively in the equation for Y, we obtain the expression $Y = (eld/mv_X{}^2)\ \mathcal{E}$, which shows that the deflection in a given electron-ray tube is directly proportional to $\mathcal{E}$.

Effect of gravity. Now let us consider the effect of gravity on the electron's trajectory. The weight of the electron is $w = mg$, and like any other particle near the earth's surface the electron has a constant downward acceleration g during its entire flight. The downward displacement resulting from gravity during the time t' is $\frac{1}{2} gt'^2 = \frac{1}{2}(9.8\ \text{m/sec}^2)(3 \times 10^{-8}\ \text{sec})^2 = 4.4 \times 10^{-15}\ \text{m} = 4.4 \times 10^{-13}\ \text{cm}$, a displacement completely negligible compared with that produced by the electric field, and completely undetectable by observation of the screen. Alternatively, we note that the acceleration a_Y arising from electrical forces is about 3×10^{14} times the acceleration of gravity; hence the electrical forces have an effect that is *enormous* in comparison with the effect of gravity.

4. DIFFERENCE OF POTENTIAL

WE NOW COME to a very important concept, that of *difference of potential*. This concept is fundamental to an understanding of electrical energy and power. Difference of electric potential is measured in a unit called the *volt**; the measuring instrument is called a *voltmeter*, and difference of potential itself is commonly called *voltage*.

* Named for Alessandro Volta (1745–1827), Italian scientist and professor; inventor of the electroscope and the voltaic cell.

In a region in which there is an electric field, an electric charge experiences a force. If the charge moves from one point A to another point B, either the field does work on the charge (like the work that gravity does on a sled when it coasts downhill) or outside energy is required to overcome the electrical forces and to effect the motion (like the outside energy required to pull a sled uphill against the force of gravity). It can be rigorously proved that if the charge is small enough so that it does not appreciably disturb the charges that are setting up the field, *the magnitude of this work is independent of the path taken from A to B*, just as the change in potential energy in motion under the force of gravity is independent of the path.

> The **difference of potential** between A and B, in volts, is a *scalar* quantity defined as the work in joules per coulomb done by the electrical forces when a small positive test charge is moved from A to B.

If this work is positive, A is said to be at a higher potential than B—the forces exerted by the electric field push the positive charge down the potential hill from A to B. If, on the other hand, this work is negative, indicating that outside energy must be supplied to overcome the forces of the electric field, A is said to be at a lower potential than B. Notice that difference of potential is defined in terms of work done on a *positive* charge. Unlike the gravitational case, where all masses tend to move downhill, *negative* electric charges would tend to move *up* a potential hill.

In an electric field, the electrical forces tend to move a positive charge from a region of higher to one of lower potential, and tend to move a negative charge from a region of lower potential to one of higher.

Let us first consider the difference of potential for two charged plates between which there is a uniform electric field, as in Fig. 21. At any

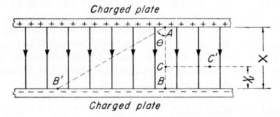

Charged plate

Figure 21

point between the plates, a small test charge $+q$ experiences a *downward* electrostatic force

$$F = q\mathcal{E},$$

by (4). In the motion from A to B, this force does work

$$W_{A \to B} = F \cdot X = q\mathcal{E} \cdot X.$$

The work done per coulomb of charge is

$$W_{A \to B}/q = \mathcal{E} \cdot X. \tag{8}$$

With $\mathcal{E}$ in nt/coul and X in m, the right side comes out in nt·m/coul or joules/coul. By definition, this is the difference of potential between A and B in volts. This difference of potential is usually denoted by $V_A - V_B$ (V for voltage). We have, then,

$$V_A - V_B = \mathcal{E}X. \qquad \left\{\begin{matrix} V \text{ in volts} \\ \mathcal{E} \text{ in nt/coul} \\ X \text{ in m} \end{matrix}\right\} \tag{9}$$

The deflection of the beam in the electron-ray tube was found in Sec. 3 to be proportional to the field strength $\mathcal{E}$; hence, for a given plate spacing X, it is proportional to the difference of potential between the plates. The electron-ray tube acts as a voltmeter to measure the difference of potential between its plates.

Since
$$1 \text{ volt} = 1 \; \frac{\text{joule}}{\text{coulomb}} = 1 \; \frac{\text{newton·meter}}{\text{coulomb}}, \tag{10}$$

$$1 \; \frac{\text{volt}}{\text{meter}} = 1 \; \frac{\text{newton}}{\text{coulomb}}, \tag{11}$$

and *volt/meter* is usually used as the name of the unit of electric intensity in place of *newton/coulomb*. Because of this fact, electric intensity is frequently called *potential gradient;* it is the change of potential per unit of distance. If the difference of potential in Fig. 21 is known, equation (9) shows that the field strength is given by

$$\mathcal{E} = (V_A - V_B)/X. \tag{12}$$

Example. *If the difference of potential between the plates in Fig. 21 is 240 volts (240 v) and the distance between the plates is 0.8 cm, determine the electric intensity.*

From (12), $\mathcal{E} = 240 \text{ v}/0.008 \text{ m} = 30,000 \text{ v/m}.$

Now consider the difference of potential $V_A - V_{B'}$ in Fig. 21. We can imagine a small test charge $+q$ to move from A to B' along the straight line AB'. The component of electrostatic force along this line is $q\mathcal{E} \cos\theta$. The distance AB' is $X/\cos\theta$. The work done is

$$(q\mathcal{E} \cos\theta)(X/\cos\theta) = q\mathcal{E}X,$$

and hence $V_A - V_{B'} = q\mathcal{E}X/q = \mathcal{E}X.$

We have obtained the same answer for $V_A - V_{B'}$ that we obtained in (9) for $V_A - V_B$. This identity implies that B and B' are at the same potential: $V_B - V_{B'} = 0$. We can see why this must be so if we imagine moving a charge from B to B' directly, just outside the surface of the plate. Since the motion takes place perpendicularly to the electric intensity, no work is done by the electrical forces, so $V_B - V_{B'} = 0$.   The surface of the plate is said to be an *equipotential surface.*

Any horizontal plane between the plates is an equipotential surface, since no work is done in moving a charge from one point to another in the same horizontal plane, for example from C to C' in Fig. 21.   The potential between the plates may be marked on a whole plane at a time, as

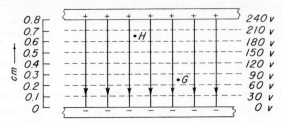

Fig. 22. Equipotential surfaces (broken lines) and lines of force for the plates of Fig. 21, 0.8 cm apart with a difference of potential of 240 v. The potential of the negative plate is arbitrarily called 0 v, but differences between values of potential are the only quantities with physical significance.

illustrated in Fig. 22 for plates 0.8 cm apart at a difference of potential of 240 v.   In this case, the electric field $\mathcal{E} = (V_A - V_B)/X = 30{,}000$ v/m. In Fig. 21, we see that $V_C - V_B$ is proportional to the distance X_1 since $V_C - V_B = \mathcal{E}X_1 = (30{,}000 \; v/\mathrm{m}) \; X_1$.

Since no work is done in moving a charge along an equipotential surface, we conclude that

Electric lines are normal to equipotential surfaces.   The direction of the electric intensity is from higher to lower potential.

As a second example of computation of differences of potential, we shall compute the difference of potential between two points in space near a single point charge.   The equipotential surfaces are clearly spheres surrounding the charge, as indicated in Fig. 23, since the surface of one of

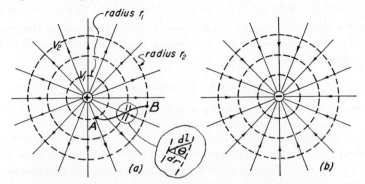

Fig. 23. Equipotential surfaces (broken lines) are spheres surrounding an isolated point charge Q, positive in (a) and negative in (b).

these spheres is everywhere perpendicular to the electric lines, and a test charge may be moved about freely on one of these spheres without the electrostatic forces doing any work. The difference of potential, $V_1 - V_2$, between the sphere of radius r_1 and that of radius r_2 in Fig. 23(a) is, by definition, the work in joules per coulomb that would be done by the electrostatic forces on a test charge $+q$ moved from radius r_1 to radius r_2. When the test charge $+q$ is at radius r, it experiences electrostatic force $F = (9 \times 10^9 \text{ nt·m}^2/\text{c}^2) Qq/r^2$, radially outward. When the charge moves a distance dl along the path AB in Fig. 23(a), the work done by this electrostatic force (see inset) is $F \, dl \cos\theta = F \, dr = (9 \times 10^9 \text{ nt·m}^2/\text{c}^2) (Qq/r^2) \, dr$. The total work done when the charge moves from A to B is

$$W = (9 \times 10^9 \text{ nt·m}^2/\text{c}^2) \int_{r_1}^{r_2} \frac{Qq}{r^2} \, dr = (9 \times 10^9 \text{ nt·m}^2/\text{c}^2) \, Qq \int_{r_1}^{r_2} \frac{dr}{r^2},$$

and the difference of potential between any point A at radius r_1 and any point B at radius r_2 is

$$V_1 - V_2 = \frac{W}{q} = (9 \times 10^9 \text{ nt·m}^2/\text{c}^2) \, Q \int_{r_1}^{r_2} \frac{dr}{r^2} = -(9 \times 10^9 \text{ nt·m}^2/\text{c}^2) \frac{Q}{r} \Big]_{r_1}^{r_2}$$

$$= (9 \times 10^9 \text{ nt·m}^2/\text{c}^2) \left(\frac{Q}{r_1} - \frac{Q}{r_2} \right). \tag{13}$$

This quantity is seen to be positive if Q is positive and $r_1 < r_2$. The closer we are to the positive charge in Fig. 23(a), the higher the potential. If Q is negative in (13), as in Fig. 23(b), $V_1 - V_2$ comes out negative, so that V_2 is greater than V_1; the closer we get to the negative charge, the lower the potential.

The difference of potential between the sphere at r_1 and a concentric sphere of infinite radius is obtained by setting $r_2 = \infty$ in (13), to get

$$V_1 - V_\infty = (9 \times 10^9 \text{ nt·m}^2/\text{c}^2) \, Q/r_1. \tag{14}$$

Sometimes it is convenient to arbitrarily call the potential at infinity *zero*, in which case $V_1 = (9 \times 10^9 \text{ nt·m}^2/\text{c}^2) \, Q/r_1$, and, in general,

$$V = (9 \times 10^9 \text{ nt·m}^2/\text{c}^2) \, Q/r. \tag{15}$$

In Fig. 24, the potential values are shown for charges of $\pm 10^{-3} \mu c$, with this convention. Again we notice that the direction from higher to lower potential is the direction in which the field tends to move a positive test charge; this direction is away from the positive charge, but toward the negative charge, in Fig. 24.

In the above derivation we have rigorously proved that for the field of a single point charge the work done in the motion of a test charge from A to B is independent of the path taken from A to B. This proof is still valid as B moves out to infinity. This is a special case of the general theorem that in any electrostatic field the work done in moving a test charge from one point to another is independent of path.   The general

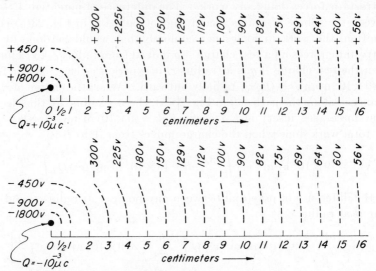

Fig. 24. Potential values near charges of $+10^{-3}$ and -10^{-3} microcoulomb with the zero of potential taken at infinity.

theorem is proved by using the fact that any electrostatic field is actually a superposition of the fields of point charges (see Prob. 37).

5. GAUSS'S LAW

OF FUNDAMENTAL importance in the study of electrostatics is a relation known as *Gauss's law*.   It is desirable to derive this law before we proceed further with discussions of such subjects as charges on conductors, shielding, and capacitance.   This law states

GAUSS'S LAW: *The surface integral over any imaginary closed surface of the outward-normal component of the electric intensity set up by any charge distribution whatsoever equals $(36\,\pi \times 10^9$ nt·m²/c²$)$ times the total electric charge inside the closed surface.*

As an illustration of this law, which will help us get started on the general proof, let us consider the lines of force that leave an isolated positive point charge Q and pass out through an imaginary sphere S (Fig. 25).   At any point on the sphere of radius R surrounding the charge, the field strength is $\mathcal{E} = (9 \times 10^9$ nt·m²/c²$)$ Q/R^2 by (6). If we consider the element of area dA, the product of $\mathcal{E}$ (which is perpendicular to the surface) by dA is $\mathcal{E}\, dA = (9 \times 10^9$ nt·m²/c²$)\,Q\,dA/R^2$.

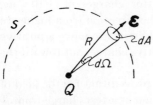

Figure 25

But dA/R^2 is the element $d\Omega$ of solid angle, and the integral over a whole sphere of $d\Omega$ is 4π. Hence the surface integral over the sphere of the outward-normal component of electric intensity has the value

$$\iint_S \mathcal{E}_\perp \, dA = \iint_S (9\times10^9 \text{ nt·m}^2/\text{c}^2)\, Q \, dA/R^2$$

$$= (9\times10^9 \text{ nt·m}^2/\text{c}^2)\, Q \iint d\Omega = (36\,\pi\times10^9 \text{ nt·m}^2/\text{c}^2)\, Q,$$

in agreement with the law. Figure 25 is drawn for a positive charge, and the lines of force pass *outward* through the sphere. If the charge were negative, the electric lines would pass *inward*, the *outward*-normal component of electric intensity would be negative, and the law would still be satisfied.

Let us now derive the law for a point charge Q and the imaginary closed surface S shown in Fig. 26. Let a cone subtending solid angle $d\Omega$ at the charge Q cut an area dA out of the surface at a distance R from the charge. At the surface the electric intensity is $\mathcal{E} = (9\times10^9 \text{ nt·m}^2/\text{c}^2)$ Q/R^2, directed away from Q along

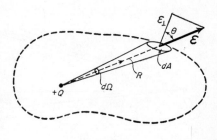

Figure 26

the radius vector. The integrand in Gauss's law is $\mathcal{E}_\perp \, dA$, where $\mathcal{E}_\perp$ is the component of $\mathcal{E}$ perpendicular to dA, $\mathcal{E}_\perp = \mathcal{E}\cos\theta$. Hence the integrand becomes

$$\mathcal{E}_\perp \, dA = \mathcal{E}\cos\theta \, dA = (9\times10^9 \text{ nt·m}^2/\text{c}^2)\, Q \, dA \, \cos\theta/R^2$$

$$= (9\times10^9 \text{ nt·m}^2/\text{c}^2)\, Q \, d\Omega,$$

since $d\Omega = dA \cos\theta/R^2$, as we have already noted on p. 442. The integral over the surface S of the above integrand reduces to integration over a sphere of $d\Omega$, which gives 4π. Hence, once again,

$$\iint_S \mathcal{E}_\perp \, dA = (36\,\pi\times10^9 \text{ nt·m}^2/\text{c}^2)\, Q.$$

We notice from the above that the contribution to the integral from the electric lines starting out from a charge Q in solid angle $d\Omega$ has the value $(9\times10^9 \text{ nt·m}^2/\text{c}^2)\, Q \, d\Omega$ independent of the radius R, when these electric lines pass *outward* through the closed surface. If the electric lines from a positive charge pass *inward*, as at various points in Figs. 27 and 28, the contribution would be the negative of this since $\cos\theta$ and the outward-normal component $\mathcal{E}_\perp$ would be negative. Figure 27 shows a surface of a more general type than that in Fig. 26, in which it is seen that the electric lines from a positive charge Q inside the surface that start out in solid angle $d\Omega$ may pass through the surface more than once. But for a charge inside the surface, these lines necessarily pass *out* of the surface *once more* than they pass *in*. Since the contributions to the surface integral are $\pm (9 \times 10^9 \text{ nt·m}^2/\text{c}^2) \, Q \, d\Omega$ at each passage, $+$ for passages out and $-$ for passages in, the net contribution from each solid angle is the same, $(9 \times 10^9 \text{ nt·m}^2/\text{c}^2) \, Q \, d\Omega$, as in the simple case of Fig. 26, and the surface integral has the same value, given by Gauss's law.

Now consider a point charge lying outside the closed surface, as in Fig. 28. In this case any cone from the point charge cuts the surface an *even* number of times. The net contribution of each cone, and hence of all electric lines from Q, to the integral of $\mathcal{E}_\perp \, dA$ is zero, as required by the law, since the charge inside the closed surface is zero.

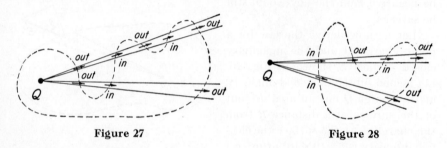

Figure 27   **Figure 28**

Having thus proved the law for a single point charge, either inside or outside the surface, we can proceed to prove it for any collection of charges whatever. Let the charges in the interior of the surface be $Q_1, Q_2, Q_3, \cdots$. There can be as many such charges as we please—in the last analysis, as many charges as there are electrons and nuclei within the surface. Then let there be charges $Q_1', Q_2', Q_3', \cdots$ outside the surface—these charges should include all the rest of the electrons and nuclei in the universe. The electric intensity $\mathcal{E}$ at any point of the closed surface will be the vector sum of the contributions from these different charges. Since the outward-normal component of the vector sum is the sum of the outward-normal components of the vectors, we can write

$$\mathcal{E}_\perp = \mathcal{E}_{1\perp} + \mathcal{E}_{2\perp} + \mathcal{E}_{3\perp} + \cdots + \mathcal{E}_{1\perp}' + \mathcal{E}_{2\perp}' + \mathcal{E}_{3\perp}' + \cdots,$$

and $\displaystyle \iint_S \mathcal{E}_\perp \, dA = \iint_S \mathcal{E}_{1\perp} \, dA + \iint_S \mathcal{E}_{2\perp} \, dA + \cdots$

$$+ \iint_S \mathcal{E}_{1\perp}' \, dA + \iint_S \mathcal{E}_{2\perp}' \, dA + \cdots,$$

where $\mathcal{E}_1$ is the intensity arising from Q_1, $\mathcal{E}_1'$ is the intensity from Q_1', and so forth. Since the primed charges are outside the surface, the last group of integrals above all vanish, while the first group, for charges inside the surface, have values that we have already computed. Hence we see that

$$\iint_S \mathcal{E}_\perp \, dA = (36\,\pi \times 10^9 \text{ nt·m}^2/\text{c}^2)(Q_1 + Q_2 + Q_3 + \cdots)$$

$$= (36\,\pi \times 10^9 \text{ nt·m}^2/\text{c}^2) \, \Sigma \, Q, \tag{16}$$

where the summation includes only charges interior to the surface.

This completes the derivation of Gauss's law, which we shall find is a powerful tool in the subsequent discussions of electrostatics.

Example. *Determine the electric intensity inside and outside the hollow spherical conductor of Fig. 29, carrying total charge Q.*

By symmetry, if there are no other charges in the neighborhood, the charge will be uniformly distributed around the sphere and *the electric lines will be radial.*

Consider an imaginary sphere, of radius $r_1 < R_1$, inside the hollow conductor. Since there is no charge inside this imaginary sphere, the surface integral of $\mathcal{E}_\perp$ must vanish. Since $\mathcal{E}_\perp = \mathcal{E}$, by symmetry, $\mathcal{E}$ must vanish. *There is no field inside the charged conductor.*

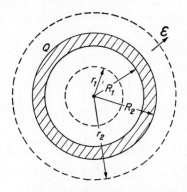

Fig. 29. A hollow charged spherical conductor with internal and external radii R_1 and R_2.

Consider an imaginary sphere, of radius $r_2 > R_2$, outside the conductor. Again setting $\mathcal{E}_\perp = \mathcal{E}$, Gauss's law gives

$$\iint_S \mathcal{E}_\perp \, dA = \mathcal{E} \times 4\,\pi\, r_2^2 = (36\,\pi \times 10^9 \text{ nt·m}^2/\text{c}^2)\, Q$$

or
$$\mathcal{E} = (9 \times 10^9 \text{ nt·m}^2/\text{c}^2)\, Q/r_2^2.$$

The intensity outside the charged spherical conductor is the same as if the charge Q were concentrated in a point at the center.

We note that in the case of *gravitational* forces, which are also inverse-square forces, there is a law exactly similar to Gauss's law. Use of this law in the same manner as in the example above proves that the gravitational force of a spherical earth on a particle near its surface is exactly the same as if the whole mass of the earth were concentrated at its center, a fact that we made use of on p. 97 (see Probs. 48–50).

6. CHARGES ON CONDUCTORS; SHIELDING

ELECTROSTATICS implies that all charges are at rest (static); if there were a field within the material of a conductor, forces would be exerted on the free electrons and would cause them to move. As we shall see later, in current electricity an electric field is continuously maintained within a conductor and the electrons do continue to move. But in static problems, the electrons in a conductor must have settled down in such a configuration that there is no electric field and therefore no electric lines within the conductor. This settling down takes place very quickly, as indicated in Fig. 30.

There is no static electric field within the material of a conductor.

Since no static electric field can exist within a conductor,

In the static case, there is no difference of potential between two points in the same conductor.

The difference of potential between two points is determined by the work done by the electric field on a test charge moved from one point to the

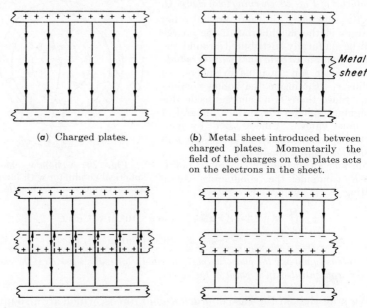

(a) Charged plates.

(b) Metal sheet introduced between charged plates. Momentarily the field of the charges on the plates acts on the electrons in the sheet.

(c) This field causes the electrons to move to the top of the sheet. The charges on the sheet then set up a field (broken lines) opposing the original field. When enough electrons have moved so that this field exactly balances the original field . . .

(d) . . . there is no longer any force on the electrons in the sheet and we have electrostatic equilibrium with no electric field within the conducting sheet. The whole process of establishment of equilibrium takes place in about 10^{-17} sec.

Fig. 30. In electrostatic equilibrium there is no electric field within a conductor.

other; and if the two points are within the same conductor, no electric field exists along a path joining the two points and lying entirely within the material of the conductor, so that no work is done when a test charge is moved along such a path; thus

The whole of a single conducting body is an equipotential region.

The absence of electric field within a conductor implies that

All the charge on a conductor lies on its surface.

To prove this statement from Gauss's law, consider an imaginary closed surface that lies entirely within the material of the conductor.   Since the electric intensity vanishes everywhere inside a conductor, it vanishes on this imaginary surface, so the net charge inside the surface must vanish. Therefore the net charge must vanish in any volume whatsoever inside the conductor, and so much vanish everywhere.   Only the layers of atoms nearest the surface can have an excess or deficiency of electrons; the atoms in the interior must be neutral.

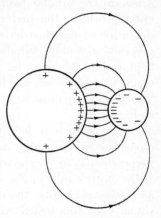

Since the field vanishes inside a conductor, electric lines will begin or end on the surface of a conductor.   Because the surface of the conductor is an equipotential surface, and electric lines are perpendicular to equipotential surfaces,

Fig. 31. Electric lines are perpendicular to the surface of a conductor.

Electric lines start out perpendicularly from the surface of a conductor.

From a positively charged region of the surface of a conductor, electric lines start out; on a negatively charged region, electric lines end, as in Fig. 31.

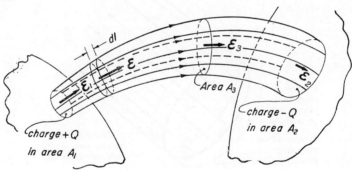

Fig. 32. An electric tube.

Now consider a bundle of electric lines called an *electric tube*, starting from an area A_1 of one conductor and ending on an area A_2 of another, as in Fig. 32.

An **electric tube** is a tubular region of space bounded by electric lines.

We shall show that the magnitude of the positive charge in the area A_1 at the beginning of the electric tube in Fig. 32 precisely equals the magnitude of the negative charge in the area A_2 at its end:

An electric tube has equal charges of opposite sign at beginning and end.

To prove this, apply Gauss's law to the imaginary surface whose boundaries are the tubular boundaries of the electric tube plus surfaces lying entirely within the materials of the conductors at the ends. By the definition of the electric tube, there is *no component* of electric intensity *perpendicular* to the tubular boundaries, and we have seen that there is no field inside the material of the conductors. The surface integral in Gauss's law vanishes, and hence the *net* charge inside this surface vanishes. Therefore there must be *equal and opposite* charges at the ends of the tube in Fig. 32.

Also, there is a definite relationship between the electric intensity along the electric tube, its area (measured on an equipotential surface perpendicular to the electric lines), and the amount of charge on its ends. If the electric tube in Fig. 32 is sufficiently thin so that ε can be regarded as a constant across the cross section, we can easily show by applying Gauss's law to a restricted section of the length of the tube that

$$\varepsilon_1 A_1 = \varepsilon_2 A_2 = \varepsilon_3 A_3. \tag{17}$$

The product of electric intensity by area is constant along a thin electric tube.

Now apply Gauss's law to the pill-box shaped imaginary surface in Fig. 33, which is drawn near the left end of the electric tube of Fig. 32.

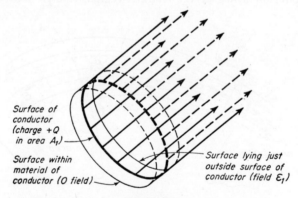

Surface of
conductor
(charge +Q
in area A_1)

Surface within
material of
conductor (O field)

Surface lying just
outside surface of
conductor (field ε_1)

Figure 33

The only contribution to the surface integral of $\varepsilon_\perp \, dA$ is on the surface lying just outside the conductor, which contributes $\varepsilon_1 A_1$. The charge within the surface is Q. Hence Gauss's law gives

$$\varepsilon_1 A_1 = (36\,\pi \times 10^9 \ \text{nt·m}^2/\text{c}^2)\, Q. \tag{18}$$

From this equation we get a relation between the surface charge density Q/A_1 and the electric intensity immediately outside the conductor:

$$Q/A_1 = \varepsilon_1/(36\,\pi \times 10^9 \ \text{nt·m}^2/\text{c}^2). \tag{19}$$

A corresponding computation near the right end of the tube of Fig. 32 would give the same relation between the negative surface charge density on this surface and the electric intensity directed *inward* toward this surface.

The surface charge density near a point on a conductor equals the electric intensity immediately outside the point divided by $36\,\pi \times 10^9$ *nt·m²/c². The sign of the surface charge density is positive if the electric intensity is directed outward, negative if the electric intensity is directed inward.*

The difference of potential between the two conductors of Fig. 32 is measured by the work that the field would do on a test charge moved along the electric tube from one conductor to the other, divided by the size of the test charge.   Let the magnitude of the test charge be denoted by q.   The force on this charge is $\mathcal{E}q$.   The work done on this charge in moving the distance dl is $\mathcal{E}q\,dl$, and the total work is $\int \mathcal{E}q\,dl = q \int \mathcal{E}\,dl$, the integration being carried from one conductor to the other.   The difference of potential is, then, this integral divided by q, or

$$V_1 - V_2 = \int \mathcal{E}\,dl. \tag{20}$$

The difference of potential between two conductors is the integral, along an electric line, of electric intensity multiplied by the element of length of the electric line.

Or, since we can write $\int \mathcal{E}\,dl = \mathcal{E}_{Av} \int dl$, we can state that

The average electric intensity along an electric line connecting two conductors is the difference of potential divided by the length of the electric line.

In general, then, the electric intensity between two conductors is high where the *electric* lines are short, low where they are long (note Fig. 31).   Since the surface charge density is proportional to the electric intensity at the surface, this statement means that the charges on oppositely charged conductors tend to congregate on the parts of the surface facing each other where the electric lines are shortest.   The extreme example of this congregation is in the case of two large oppositely charged plane-parallel conductors close to each other.   Except near

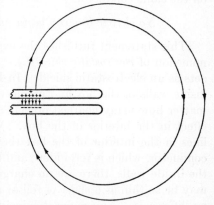

Fig. 34. Schematic diagram of representative electric lines near the edges of oppositely charged parallel plates.

the very edges of the plates, the charge can be considered to be *all* on the *facing* surfaces, uniformly distributed. This distribution is associated (Fig. 34), with the constant length of electric lines between the plates, and with the comparatively enormous length of electric lines connecting charges on the outer surfaces, which makes for very low electric intensities and very low charge densities on the outer surfaces.

Electric lines either begin at positive charges and end at negative charges, or they may go out to or come in from infinity as in the case of the lines from an isolated point charge or the charged conductor of Fig. 29. We easily see that relation (17) is satisfied for the infinite conical electric tube that proceeds outward to infinity in these cases, for the area of the tube varies as the square of the radial distance, while the electric intensity falls off inversely as the square of this distance. An electric line could not *end* in free space without violating (17). We also see that electric lines cannot form closed curves in space because the integral in (20), extended once around such a closed curve, would not vanish if there really were such an electric line; but the left side of (20) would vanish because we get back to the same point and the same potential; this contradiction shows that there cannot be such a line. To summarize,

Electric lines always begin and end on electric charges, or one end of an electric line may proceed to infinity. Electric lines cannot terminate in free space nor can they form closed curves in free space.

The existence of electric lines joining the two conductors in Fig. 31 or Fig. 32 implies that there *must* be a difference of potential between the conductors. Hence, they must be *different* conductors not electrically connected, since no difference of potential can exist between two points on the same conductor.

No electric line can begin and end on the same conductor.

This statement furnishes the explanation of the very important phenomenon of *electrostatic shielding*. A closed box made entirely of metal acts as an electrostatic shield. In Fig. 35 there can be no charge on the inside walls of the box and no electric lines in the interior volume. No matter how many charged objects are near the shielded box, there is no effect in the interior of the box. Why?—because if there were electric lines in the interior of the box they would begin and end on the same conductor, which is forbidden; and if there are no electric lines ending on the inside walls, there are no charges on the walls, by (19). The shield may be as thin as a sheet of foil or a coat of aluminum paint. It makes no difference. Any apparatus inside the shield is completely unaffected by electrified bodies outside.

If a charged metal body is placed inside a shield, an equal and opposite charge is induced on the inner walls of the shield (Fig. 36), but the distribution of charge on the body and on the inner walls is completely unaffected by charges outside the shield. *If now the charged body is electrically connected to the shield, it becomes completely discharged* (Fig. 37), because all the surfaces inside the shield are now at the same potential and no surface charges can exist there. The charge on the body has moved to the outside wall of the shield, where it has no effect on the interior.

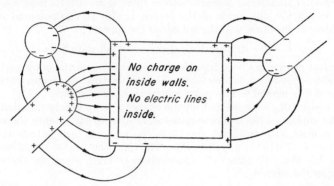

Fig. 35. There is no charge on the inside walls of a hollow conductor unless there are charges inside the hollow and insulated from the conductor (as in Fig. 36).

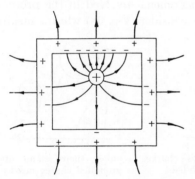

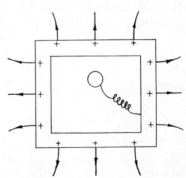

Fig. 36. If a charged conductor is placed inside a shield, an equal and opposite charge appears on the inner wall of the shield.

Fig. 37. If the charged body in Fig. 36 is electrically connected to the shield, it becomes *completely* discharged.

Shielding is familiar to everyone who has looked inside a radio set. It is designed to keep electric fields originating in other components of the set, or outside, from interfering with the operation of the various vacuum tubes and other field-sensitive parts.

Example. *Determine the potential at all radii for the charged hollow conductor of Fig. 29, p. 567. Also verify the correctness of equation (19).*

In the example on p. 567, we showed that the electric intensity outside the sphere $(r_2 > R_2)$ has exactly the value for a point charge Q. Hence, taking $V_\infty = 0$, the computation on p. 563 is applicable, and the potential out-side the sphere has the same value as for a point charge:

$$V = (9 \times 10^9 \text{ nt·m}^2/\text{c}^2) \, Q/r_2. \qquad (r_2 > R_2)$$

By setting $r_2 = R_2$ in this expression, we find the potential at the outer surface of the conductor. Since the whole of the material of a conductor is an equi-potential region, this value also gives the potential throughout the con-ductor and at its interior surface. Since there is no electric field inside the hollow conductor, the inside of the hollow is also an equipotential region, with potential the same as at the outside of the sphere:

$$V = (9 \times 10^9 \text{ nt·m}^2/\text{c}^2) \, Q/R_2 \qquad \text{at all radii} \leq R_2.$$

Once a test charge has been brought in from infinity to the outer surface of the conductor, it encounters no further electric field and no further work need be done if it is moved to any point within this outer surface.

To verify (19), we note that all the charge Q is uniformly distributed on the *outer* surface of the hollow conductor, of area $4\pi R_2^2$. Hence the surface charge density is $Q/4\pi R_2^2$. $\mathcal{E}_1$ in (19) is the intensity just outside the sur-face, which is $(9 \times 10^9 \text{ nt·m}^2/\text{c}^2) \, Q/R_2^2$. The right side of (19) is this intensity divided by $36\pi \times 10^9 \text{ nt·m}^2/\text{c}^2$, which gives $Q/4\pi R_2^2$, equal to the charge density on the left side.

7. CHARGING BY INDUCTION; THE ELECTROSCOPE

THE IDEAS about electric lines which were presented in the previous section are useful in explaining the phenomena involved in the process of charging by induction. First, let us consider (Fig. 38) what is meant

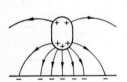 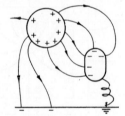

Fig. 38. A charged metal body...   loses all of its charge when it is grounded...   unless there is an un-grounded charge nearby.

by *grounding* a conductor. At the left of Fig. 38, all the electric lines from the charged conductor are shown ending on the ground; none of them go to infinity. This is the situation when charged objects are near an infinite conducting plane, and the earth is, for practical purposes, such an infinite conducting plane. Equal and opposite charge are induced in the nearby areas of the earth's conducting surface, so that all the electric lines begin or end there. When the charged body in Fig. 38 is grounded (electrically connected to the earth), it and the whole earth become a single conductor. The charge that was on the body is distributed over the whole surface of the earth, which is so enormous that the resulting charge density is negligible, and the body is, for practical purposes, left uncharged (unless there is another ungrounded charge nearby).

The process of *charging by induction* should be clear from Fig. 39, with the possible exception of one point, namely, why *all* the negative charge leaves the ball when it is grounded, in Fig. 39(b).   The answer is that if negative charges did remain on the ball, there would have to be positive charges at the beginnings of the electric lines that ended on these

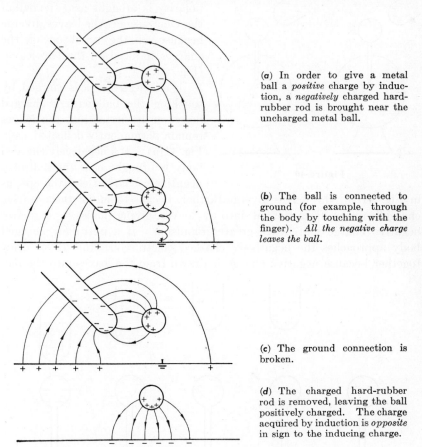

(*a*) In order to give a metal ball a *positive* charge by induction, a *negatively* charged hard-rubber rod is brought near the uncharged metal ball.

(*b*) The ball is connected to ground (for example, through the body by touching with the finger).   *All the negative charge leaves the ball.*

(*c*) The ground connection is broken.

(*d*) The charged hard-rubber rod is removed, leaving the ball positively charged.   The charge acquired by induction is *opposite* in sign to the inducing charge.

Fig. 39. Charging by induction. Lines of force are schematic only.

negative charges.   But there are no positive charges on the hard-rubber rod.   Moreover, the positive charges at the other ends of the electric lines could not be on the ball or the earth because these now form one single conductor, and an electric line cannot begin and end on the same conductor.   This absence of necessary positive charges guarantees that all negative charge will leave the ball when it is grounded.

The *electroscope* (Fig. 40) is a useful and instructive instrument.   It usually consists of two thin gold leaves fastened to a metal rod terminated by a metal ball or plate.   The leaves are more or less completely surrounded by a grounded metal case, from which the protruding metal rod is insulated. Grounding the case removes the possibility that the case will have a charge of its own that will influence the ball and hence the leaves. The grounded case will have only such charge as may be *induced*

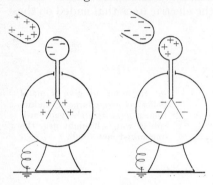

Figure 40

on it. If a charged body of either polarity is brought near the ball of the electroscope, the leaves diverge because of the repulsion of the charges induced on the two leaves (Fig. 40).

If the electroscope is charged, by touching the ball with a charged body, or by induction, the leaves remain permanently deflected, as in Fig. 41(a). If a negatively charged body is brought near the ball of a negatively charged electroscope, as in Fig. 41(b), the leaves diverge further, because some of the negative charge is driven from the ball into the leaves, giving the leaves a greater negative charge and hence greater repulsion. If a positively charged body approaches the negatively charged electroscope, the leaves draw together because negative charge is drawn from the leaves into the ball

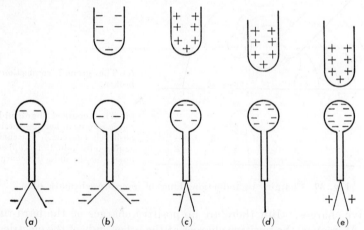

Fig. 41. The effect of an external charge on a charged electroscope. (The electroscope shield is omitted from these schematic drawings.)

as in Fig. 41(c). If the body has a sufficiently strong positive charge, as it approaches still closer the leaves collapse completely and then diverge again as more and more negative charge moves from the leaves into the ball as in (d) and (e).

Note that the shield prevents any direct action of an external charge on the leaves. No electric lines can go directly from an external charge to the leaves.   The effect on the leaves is due entirely to charges induced on them because they are connected to the ball by a conductor insulated from the shield.

The electroscope will serve as the simplest type of electrostatic voltmeter to measure the potential, relative to ground, of a charged conductor.   For this purpose the ball is connected by a long, fine, insulated wire to the body whose potential it is desired to measure.   Some of the charge flows to the ball and leaves of the electroscope, charging them so that they have the same potential as the conductor.   If the amount of charge that flows to the electroscope when it is connected is small compared with the total charge on the conductor, the potential of the conductor is not appreciably altered by connecting the electroscope.   If the amount of charge is not small compared with the total charge, at least the electroscope leaves and the conductor come to the same potential, and the electroscope measures the potential that exists after it is connected.

The deflection of the electroscope is a measure of the potential difference between the electroscope leaves and the grounded case.

This statement follows from the fact that the deflection is directly related to the charge on the leaves by Coulomb's law, the charge on the leaves is related to the electric intensity near the leaves by (19), and the electric intensities within the shield are directly related to the difference of potential between the leaves and shield by (20). While the deflection is not proportional to the difference of potential, the deflection increases in regular fashion as the potential difference increases.

The same principles are utilized in a more rugged but less sensitive instrument called an *electrostatic voltmeter*, a commercial type of which is illustrated in Fig.

Fig. 42. Movement of commercial electrostatic voltmeter [*courtesy of Sensitive Research Instrument Corporation*].

42.   In this instrument a set of rotating vanes bearing one kind of charge is pulled by electrostatic forces into a position between a set of oppositely charged stationary vanes.   Rotation of the vanes is resisted by the restoring torque of a spring, and the amount of rotation is a measure of the difference of potential between the two sets of vanes.

PROBLEMS

1. Two small metal balls, each suspended by a 15-in silk thread from a horizontal east-west wooden rod, hang a short distance apart.   Each is negatively charged. The west ball is subjected to an electrical force of 0.02 nt because of the presence of the east ball. (a) What is the direction of the electrical force on the west ball? (b) What is the direction of the electrical force on the east ball? (c) What is magnitude of electrical force on the east ball?

Ans: (a) toward the west; (b) toward the east; (c) 0.02 nt.

2. Two small metal balls hang at the ends of 15-in silk threads from a horizontal north-south wooden rod. The ball to the north is positively charged. It experiences an electrical force toward the south. (a) What is the sign of the charge on the south ball? (b) What is the direction of the force on the south ball? (c) How do the electrical forces on the two balls compare in magnitude?

3. If two point charges each experience an electrical force of repulsion of 0.06 nt when they are 10 cm apart, what will be the force when they are (a) 100 cm apart? (b) 50 cm apart? (c) 5 cm apart? (d) 2.5 cm apart? (e) 1 cm apart?

Ans: (a) 0.0006 nt; (b) 0.0024 nt; (c) 0.24 nt; (d) 0.96 nt; (e) 6 nt.

4. If two point charges each experience an electrical force of attraction of 0.04 nt when they are 5 cm apart, what will be the force when they are (a) 100 cm apart? (b) 50 cm apart? (c) 10 cm apart? (d) 2.5 cm apart? (e) 1 cm apart?

5. Charges of +20 and +30 μc are 3 m apart. What is the force between them?   Ans: 0.6 nt repulsion.

6. Charges of +10 and −15 μc are 6 m apart. What is the force between them?

7. Two small spheres carrying unequal positive charges repel each other with a force of 0.1 nt when 3 cm apart. If the charge on each of the spheres is doubled, and the distance between them is doubled, what is the force of repulsion?

8. In each of the three sketches in Fig. 1, assume that the two strings are of equal length and that the signs of the charges are as indicated. Which of the two strings makes the greater angle with the vertical if (a) the charges are equal in magnitude and the balls equal in weight? (b) the left-hand charge is greater in magnitude than the right-hand charge and the balls are equal in weight? (c) the charges are equal in magnitude but the left-hand ball is heavier than the right-hand one? (d) the left-hand charge is greater in magnitude than the right-hand and the left-hand ball is heavier than the right-hand one? (Give adequate reasons for your answers to the above questions.)

9. Two small metal-coated pith balls, each having a mass of 14 g, are held at the ends of silk threads 70 cm long. The other ends of the threads are fastened at a common point. Charges are placed on the two balls and they come to equilibrium at a distance apart of 10 cm. If the charge on one ball is −0.04 μc, what is the charge on the other ball?   Ans: −0.273 μc.

10. Two charges, of +10 and −10 μc, are 20 cm apart in air, the + charge being to the left, the − charge to the right. (a) What force does each exert on a +5-μc charge placed halfway between them? (b) What is the total force on the +5-μc charge? (c) on the +10-μc charge? (d) on the −10-μc charge?

11. Two charges, +10 and −5 μc, are 10 cm apart. Where must a third charge be placed in order that the resultant force acting upon it should be zero?

Ans: 24.14 cm from the −5-μc charge (in what direction?).

12. Two charges of +20 and −5 μc are 5 cm apart. Where must a third charge be placed in order that the resultant force acting on it should be zero?

13. Two charges of +10 and −10 μc are 8 cm apart. Find the magnitude

and direction of the total force exerted by these charges on a third charge of $+0.5\ \mu c$ that is 5 cm distant from each of the two charges.

Ans: magnitude 28.8 nt (in what direction?).

14. Two charges of $+10\ \mu c$ each are 8 cm apart in air. Find the magnitude and direction of the total force exerted by these charges on a third charge of $+0.5\ \mu c$ that is 5 cm distant from each of the two charges.

15. (a) In the normal hydrogen atom, the proton and electron are an average distance of 0.529×10^{-10} m apart. What is the force of attraction at this distance? (b) The electron mass is 9.11×10^{-31} kg. What acceleration (direction and magnitude) does this force of attraction give the electron? (c) Considering the electron as revolving in a circular orbit around the much heavier proton, what is its speed in this orbit? (d) What is its frequency, that is, how many revolutions per second does it make? Ans: (a) 8.23×10^{-8} nt; (b) 9.03×10^{22} m/sec^2 toward the proton; (c) 2.18×10^6 m/sec; (d) 6.56×10^{15}/sec.

16. How far apart in a vacuum must two electrons be if the force of electrostatic repulsion on each electron is just equal in magnitude to the weight of the electron? (The electron mass is 9.11×10^{-31} kg.)

17. (a) Two bodies attract each other electrically. Are they necessarily both charged? (b) Two bodies repel each other electrically. Are they necessarily both charged? Explain the reasons for your answers.

18. Two charges of $-2\ \mu c$ each are 16 cm apart. Find the electric intensity at a point distant 10 cm from each of the charges.

19. If a charge of $+4\ \mu c$ experiences a force of magnitude 8 nt at a certain point in an electric field, what is the magnitude of the electric intensity at that point? Ans: 2×10^6 nt/coul.

20. What are the magnitude and direction of the electric intensity at a point 50 cm from a charge of $-200\ \mu c$?

21. Two charges of $+4$ and $-2\ \mu c$ are 16 cm apart. Find the electric intensity at a point that is 20 cm from the positive charge and 12 cm from the negative. Ans: 10.1×10^5 nt/coul at angle $44°6$ from line from $+$ to $-$ charge.

22. Two charges of $+4$ and $-2\ \mu c$ are 16 cm apart. Find the electric intensity at a point that is 12 cm from the positive charge and 20 cm from the negative.

23. A charged particle of 0.003-g mass is held stationary in space by placing it in a downwardly directed electric field of 24×10^4 nt/coul. Find the charge on the particle in μc. Ans: $-1.23\times10^{-4}\ \mu c$.

24. An oil drop has a net negative charge of $-6\ e$, representing an excess of 6 electrons. It remains at rest under the action of the force of gravity and the electrical force when it is placed in a downward electric field of 3×10^6 nt/coul. Find the mass of the droplet.

25. Verify the values of electric intensity given in Fig. **17** at points B, C, D, and E.

26. If the charges of Fig. 19 are each $+5\ \mu c$, separated by 1.2 m, find the electric intensity at points A, B, C, D, and E, located at the same geometrical positions as in Figs. 16–18. Note that the directions you obtain should agree with the directions of the electric lines shown in Fig. 19.

27. What is the acceleration of an electron in a field of 1000 nt/coul? Express this in terms of the acceleration of gravity. Ans: 1.76×10^{14} m/sec^2; 1.79×10^{13} g.

28. In the field mentioned in Prob. 27, how long would be required for the electron to attain the speed of light? What would be the energy of the electron moving at this speed? (After making this calculation, consult Chap. 38, Sec. 3.)

29. What is the magnitude of the force on a charge of 6 μc placed at a point where the potential gradient has a magnitude of 400,000 v/m?   Ans: 2.4 nt.

30. What is the magnitude of the force on a charge of -12 μc placed at a point where the potential gradient has a magnitude of 30,000 v/m?

31. If the potential at H, Fig. 22, is 195 v and that at G is 75 v, how much work is required to move a charge of 6 μc from G to H?   Ans: 0.00072 joule.

32. If the potential at H, Fig. 22, is 195 v and that at G is 75 v, how much work is required to move one electron from H to G?

33. (a) What is the difference of potential between two points 20 and 40 cm distant from a charge of -120 μc? (b) Which point is at the higher potential? (c) How much work must be done on a $+2$ μc charge to move it from the point of lower potential to that of higher?   Ans: (a) 2.7×10^6 v; (c) 5.4 joules.

34. What is the potential difference between two points 50 and 20 cm from a $+100$-μc charge? Which point is at the higher potential? How much work does the field do on a 6-μc charge moved from the higher- to the lower-potential point?

35. Two large parallel plane plates 5 cm apart are held at a potential difference of 12,000 v. (a) How much work is necessary to carry 0.3 μc of charge from the lower-potential plate to the higher-potential plate? (b) What are the magnitude and direction of the force acting on this charge? (c) What is the intensity of the electric field between the plates?
     Ans: (a) 3.6×10^{-3} joule; (b) 7.2×10^{-2} nt; (c) 2.4×10^5 nt/coul.

36. Two large parallel plates 2 mm apart are held at a potential difference of 900 v. (a) How much work, in joules, is necessary to carry 0.2 μc of charge from the lower- to the higher-potential plate? (b) What are the magnitude and direction of the force acting on this charge? (c) What is the electric intensity between the plates, in nt/coul? (d) How much work, in joules, would be necessary to carry a total of 1 coul of charge from the lower- to the higher-potential plate, the potential difference being maintained at 900 v?

37. Prove that *the potential at a point P (Fig. 43) in the neighborhood of charges* Q_1, Q_2, Q_3, $\cdots$, *at distances* r_1, r_2, r_3, $\cdots$, *is*

$$V_P = (9 \times 10^9 \text{ nt·m}^2/\text{c}^2) \left(\frac{Q_1}{r_1} + \frac{Q_2}{r_2} + \frac{Q_3}{r_3} + \cdots \right),$$

when the zero of potential is taken at infinity. In this formula, the various Q's can be either positive or negative. In your proof choose an arbitrary path from P to ∞; then show that the work done by the resultant electric field is the sum of the works done by the parts of the electric field resulting from

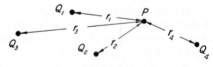

Figure 43

each charge individually, and hence that the potential at P is the scalar sum of the potentials arising from each charge separately.

38. Making use of the formula of Prob. 37, find the potentials at points A, B, C, D, and E in Figs. 16–17.

39. What is the electric intensity adjacent to the surface of a sphere uniformly charged with -0.2 μc/cm^2?   Ans: $72 \pi \times 10^6$ v/m.

40. A sphere of radius 1.5 cm has a total charge of 9 μc uniformly distributed over its surface. What is the electric intensity at the surface of the sphere?

41. Two large parallel plane plates are 0.4 cm apart and have a difference of potential of 1000 v. What is the density of charge, in $\mu c/m^2$, on each plate?

Ans: $2.21\ \mu c/m^2$.

42. Two large parallel plane plates are 0.4 cm apart and are charged to densities of $\pm 3\ \mu c/m^2$. (a) What is the electric intensity between the plates? (b) What is the difference of potential?

43. Two concentric, thin, metallic spherical shells of radii R_1 and R_2 $(R_1 < R_2)$ bear charges Q_1 and Q_2. Using Gauss's law, show that (a) the electric intensity at radius $r < R_1$ is zero; (b) the electric intensity at radius r between R_1 and R_2 is $(9 \times 10^9\ \text{nt·m}^2/\text{c}^2)\ Q_1/r^2$; (c) the electric intensity at radius $r > R_2$ is

$$(9 \times 10^9\ \text{nt·m}^2/\text{c}^2)\ (Q_1 + Q_2)/r^2.$$

44. For the system of charges in Prob. 43, show that the potential, relative to a zero at infinity, is

$$\begin{array}{lll} (9 \times 10^9\ \text{nt·m}^2/\text{c}^2)\ (Q_1 + Q_2)/r & \text{for} & r > R_2; \\ (9 \times 10^9\ \text{nt·m}^2/\text{c}^2)\ [Q_1/r + Q_2/R_2] & \text{for} & R_2 > r > R_1; \\ (9 \times 10^9\ \text{nt·m}^2/\text{c}^2)\ [Q_1/R_1 + Q_2/R_2] & \text{for} & r < R_1. \end{array}$$

45. For the system of charges of Prob. 43, find the charge per unit area on the inner and outer surfaces of each spherical shell. Find the answers in the two different ways given below, and check.

(a) Use the total charge on each shell, the area of the shell, and the theorem that equal and opposite charges reside at the two ends of a line of force.

(b) Use the fact that the electric intensity just outside a conductor is $36\ \pi \times 10^9$ nt·m^2/c^2 times the charge per unit area. From the electric intensities in Prob. 43, compute the values of the charge per unit area.

46. Charge is *uniformly* distributed throughout the interior of a non-conducting sphere of radius R, the *total* charge being Q. Using Gauss's law, show that
(a) the electric intensity at radius $r > R$ is $(9 \times 10^9\ \text{nt·m}^2/\text{c}^2)\ Q/r^2$;
(b) the electric intensity at radius $r < R$ is $(9 \times 10^9\ \text{nt·m}^2/\text{c}^2)\ Qr/R^3$.

47. Show that the electric intensity at distance r from an infinite straight fine wire with linear charge density q, in coulombs per meter length, is $(18 \times 10^9\ \text{nt·m}^2/\text{c}^2)\ q/r$.

48. The gravitational acceleration **g** represents force per unit mass and hence is quite analogous to electric intensity, which represents force per unit charge. Show that Gauss's law for the gravitational case, analogous to (16), is

$$\iint_S g_\perp\, dA = 4\pi\, G \sum m,$$

where G is the universal gravitation constant (see p. 96), and the summation is over all masses *interior* to the imaginary surface S.

49. Consider a massive spherical body whose density is not necessarily constant, but is a function only of the radius r from its center (the earth approximates such a body). Using the law derived in Prob. 48, show that the gravitational attraction of such a body for a particle is the same as if all the mass of the body were concentrated at its center.

50. By simple logical argument, starting with the result of Prob. 49, show that the gravitational force between two massive spherically symmetric bodies of any size is the same as if all the mass of each body were concentrated at its center.

51. If we assume that the earth is a sphere of *uniform* density, show that Gauss's law (Prob. 48) implies that a particle in a hole within the earth would have gravitational acceleration directly proportional to its distance from the center of the earth, decreasing from the surface value to zero as the center of the earth is approached.

52. Assume that the earth is a sphere of uniform density and that a straight well is dug from Brazil to China through the center of the earth. Show that a stone dropped into the well would execute simple harmonic motion and determine the period of the motion.

53. Show that if a total charge Q is uniformly distributed along a thin wire forming the perimeter of a circle of radius R lying in the XY-plane centered at the origin, then the electric intensity at any point on the Z-axis (the axis of the circle) is given by a formula of the type

$$\mathcal{E} = (9 \times 10^9 \text{ nt·m}^2/\text{c}^2) \frac{Q \cos\phi}{R^2 + Z^2}.$$

Draw a diagram that properly locates the angle ϕ in this formula, and the direction of the electric intensity.

54. Let a charge be uniformly distributed over the whole XY-plane with uniform density q, in coul/m². By splitting this charge into rings and integrating the formula in the preceding problem, compute the electric intensity at any point along the Z-axis and verify that you obtain the same value as is obtained by application of Gauss's law to this geometrical situation.

Ans: $(18 \pi \times 10^9 \text{ nt·m}^2/\text{c}^2) \, q$.

NOTE: Much of our knowledge of the atomic nucleus has been obtained by firing high-energy 'atomic projectiles' into thin 'targets' of various materials and observing the results. The atomic projectiles most frequently used have been electrons, protons, deuterons, and doubly ionized helium atoms (called alpha-particles). The results of nuclear 'bombardments' by these projectiles are discussed in Chap. 38, in which the types of particles and radiation emerging from the 'struck' nuclei are listed in some detail. As the methods used in accelerating atomic projectiles and the methods of detecting the emerging particles and radiation involve for the most part the elementary principles of mechanics already studied and the elementary principles of electricity and magnetism being introduced in the present chapter and the next few chapters, it will be instructive to examine some of these methods in problems.

It is interesting and even amazing that the general physical principles developed on the basis of observations of such macroscopic things as collisions between billiard balls, forces between electrically charged pith balls, etc., can be applied so successfully to microscopic particles such as electrons, protons, nuclei, atoms, and molecules. No one has ever 'seen' any of these microscopic particles and yet by applying elementary physical principles to them we can explain satisfactorily observed macroscopic phenomena and design instruments involving microscopic particles. Although we have never seen an electron, we can design· television picture tubes. Although we have never seen a U^{235} nucleus, we can design an atomic bomb.

In working the problems below, the student should refer to the table in Sec. 3 of the Appendix for data on microscopic particles.

55. The most direct method of obtaining high energy projectiles is to produce ions in a region of high potential and allow electrical forces to accelerate them through an evacuated tube toward a target at ground potential. Such an arrangement is shown in Fig. 44.

Positive ions produced inside an 'ion source' maintained at high positive potential are accelerated toward a hollow metal 'focus tube' maintained at a somewhat lower potential. Ions entering the focus tube move downward at constant velocity (since there is no electric field *inside* a hollow conductor) until they emerge at the lower end. The emerging ions are immediately given a further downward acceleration toward the first 'accelerator section,' which is at a considerably lower potential. Ions entering the first hollow cylindrical accelerator section again move with constant downward velocity until they emerge and are accelerated toward the next accelerator section, etc. The use of many accelerator sections maintained at successively lower potentials makes it possible to direct a narrow beam of high energy ions to the target, which is at ground potential. Low pressure inside the accelerator tube is maintained by vacuum pumps.

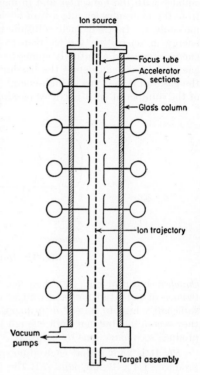

Fig. 44. Accelerator tube.

Suppose that hydrogen atomic ions H^+ (protons) are produced in the ion source, which is at a positive potential of 1.5 million volts with respect to ground. What is the kinetic energy of a proton striking the target, which is at ground potential? If the distance from the ion source to the target is 2.5 m, what average force is exerted on the proton? What is the average acceleration of the proton? Ans: 2.4×10^{-13} joules, 9.6×10^{-14} nt, 5.75×10^{13} m/sec².

56. Answer the questions in Prob. 55 for a case in which doubly charged helium ions He^{++} (alpha particles) are produced in the ion source. How would the speed of an alpha particle striking the target compare with that of a proton in Prob. 55? Answer the same questions for deuterons (hydrogen atomic ions of atomic mass 2).

57. Although the acceleration of protons by the method shown in Fig. 44 is simple in principle, it is not a simple matter to obtain and maintain potential differences of several million volts between the ion source and the target. One method of obtaining such a potential difference is that used in the Van de Graaff generator shown schematically in Fig. 8 of Chap. 38. In this device, static charges are transported on a rapidly moving endless belt from ground potential to a large hollow sphere insulated from the ground. The ion source and focus tube are located inside the sphere. If the spherical electrode has a constant positive potential of 1.8 million volts with respect to ground, how much work is done in placing a charge of 6 μcoul on the sphere? Ans: 10.8 joules.

58. What becomes of the kinetic energy of the ions in a tube such as that in Fig. 44 when the ions strike a thick target? Why is it necessary to use water cooling on some types of targets?

Note: When a charged particle of high kinetic energy passes through a gas, it collides with the molecules and in many of these collisions tears electrons away from the molecules leaving a trail of 'ion pairs' (electrons and positively charged molecules). In each such collision the high-energy particle loses some of its energy in separating the electron from the molecule and thereby 'fritters' its energy away and eventually comes to rest. By collecting the ions produced in a gas sample, we can detect the passage of high-energy ionizing particles through the gas and if the type of high-energy particles is known, we can get an estimate of the number of such particles passing through the gas sample. The *ionization*

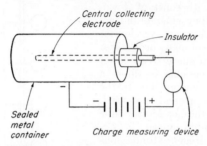

Fig. 45. Ionization chamber.

chamber shown in Fig. 45 is a device for making such measurements. The difference of potential between central electrode and the container is maintained sufficiently high to collect *all* primary ions formed by the original particle before they recombine but not high enough to give the ions sufficient kinetic energy to produce secondary ions by collision.

59. It is known that each alpha particle from a certain radioactive element produces 1.4×10^5 ion pairs. If the positive central electrode in an ionization chamber collects 2.24×10^{-12} coul in one second, how many alpha particles of the type mentioned have passed through the gas in the chamber?   Ans: 100.

60. It will be noted that the charge per second collected in an ionization chamber is extremely small. Larger amounts of charge can be collected if the potential of the inner electrode is raised so that each of the primary ions produced by the original particle is given sufficient kinetic energy to produce secondary ions before being collected; over a limited range of potential the number of secondary ions is directly proportional to the number of primary ions. If the central electrode potential in the chamber mentioned in Prob. 59 is slowly raised while the number of alpha particles passing through the chamber per second remains constand, the charge collected per second increases. Find the ratio of the number of ions collected each second to the number of primary ions formed for an electrode potential at which the central electrode collects (a) 10^{-11} coul/sec, (b) 2.2×10^{-10} coul/sec, and (c) 0.001 μc/sec. (This ratio is sometimes called the *gas amplification factor*. The microscopic processes involved are considered further in a problem in the next chapter.)

CHAPTER 28

CAPACITANCE

THE MOST FAMILIAR device whose action is entirely electrostatic is the *condenser* (or *capacitor*), of which a considerable number occur in every radio set or electronic circuit. In such applications, electric charge flows through the wires leading to the condenser but does not flow *through* the condenser—it merely piles up as charge on the plates of the condenser. The relation between the charge on the plates and the difference of potential between the plates is governed by the laws of electrostatics, the charge on the plates being at rest. The ratio between the magnitude of charge on either plate and the difference of potential is a constant, called the *capacitance* of the condenser. Many circuit elements that are not actually called condensers behave like condensers, and a consideration of their capacitance is necessary to an understanding of their performance. One example of such circuit elements is the cable discussed in Sec. 2; others are alternating-current power lines, telephone lines, and the metallic elements of any vacuum tube.

1. THE PARALLEL-PLATE CONDENSER

FIGURE 1 shows two parallel plane plates, each of area A, separated by distance d, and charged with equal and opposite charges $\pm Q$. The

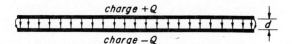

Fig. 1. Parallel-plate condenser. The area of each plate is A. The plates are in vacuum (or in air).

separation d is assumed to be small compared with the linear dimensions of the plates. For the reasons that we indicated on p. 571, the charges are almost entirely on the inside surfaces of the plates and, except near the edges, the electric lines go perpendicularly from one plate to the other.

For plates of size large compared with the separation d, edge effects are negligible, and the charge per unit area on the plates is $\pm Q/A$. Then,

585

by (19), p. 570, the electric intensity is

$$\mathcal{E} = (36\,\pi \times 10^9 \text{ nt·m}^2/\text{c}^2)\, Q/A, \tag{1}$$

independent of the plate separation d. The difference of potential between the plates is

$$V = \mathcal{E}d = (36\,\pi \times 10^9 \text{ nt·m}^2/\text{c}^2)\, Qd/A. \tag{2}$$

A combination of two conductors in proximity is called a *condenser*. The electrical characteristics of a condenser are determined by its *capacitance*, defined as follows:

> The **capacitance** between two conductors is the ratio of the magnitude of the charge on either conductor to the resulting potential difference when the conductors have equal and opposite charges.

The capacitance is a measure of the ability of the conductors to store charge when a potential difference is produced between the conductors, whether by a battery, a radio wave, or any other source of potential difference. Capacitance, denoted by C, equals Q/V, the charge in coulombs per volt of potential difference. The unit, 1 coulomb/volt, is given the name *farad**, abbreviated f.

> One **farad** is the capacitance of a condenser that stores one coulomb on each plate for each volt of potential difference.

From (2), it follows that the capacitance of the parallel-plate condenser in Fig. 1 is given by the expression

$$C = \frac{Q}{V} = \frac{A}{(36\,\pi \times 10^9 \text{ nt·m}^2/\text{c}^2)\, d}. \qquad \left\{ \begin{smallmatrix} C \text{ in f} \\ A \text{ in m}^2 \\ d \text{ in m} \end{smallmatrix} \right\} \tag{3}$$

The capacitances of condensers are ordinarily very small fractions of a farad; hence, capacitances are ordinarily specified in *microfarads* (μf) or *micromicrofarads* ($\mu\mu$f):

$$1\ \mu\text{f} = 10^{-6}\ \text{f} = 1\ \mu\text{c}/\text{v}, \qquad 1\ \mu\mu\text{f} = 10^{-12}\ \text{f} = 1\ \mu\mu\text{c}/\text{v}.$$

Example. *Find the capacitance of a parallel-plate condenser formed when two sheets of aluminum, each 1 m² in area, are separated by a 0.1-mm layer of air. What is the charge on either plate of this condenser when the difference of potential between the plates is 100v?*

Substitution in (3) gives

$$C = \frac{1 \text{ m}^2}{(36\,\pi \times 10^9 \text{ nt·m}^2/\text{c}^2)\cdot 10^{-4} \text{ m}} = 8.85 \times 10^{-8}\ \text{f} = 0.0885\ \mu\text{f} = 88{,}500\ \mu\mu\text{f},$$

and $\qquad Q = CV = 8.85 \times 10^{-8}\ \text{f}\cdot 10^2\ \text{v} = 8.85 \times 10^{-6}\ \text{coul} = 8.85\ \mu\text{c}.$

---

* After MICHAEL FARADAY (1791–1867), director of the laboratory of the Royal Institution, London, who conceived the idea of representing an electrostatic field by electric tubes and formulated its properties in terms of them, and who discovered electromagnetic induction and the laws of electrolysis.

Parallel-plate condensers are frequently made with a stack of plates connected alternately. The plates are stacked as in Fig. 2. With the exception of the end plates, each plate carries charges on both sides, at the ends of the electric lines going to both adjoining plates. The condenser of Fig. 2, which has five sets of electric lines has as much positive and negative charge as five condensers like that of Fig. 1. Hence, for the same potential difference it has five times the charge, corresponding to five times the capacitance. In general, if a condenser has N plates, there

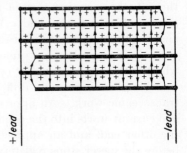

Fig. 2. A 6-plate condenser.

are $N-1$ sets of electric lines and the capacitance is $N-1$ times (3), or

$$C = (N-1)A/(36\,\pi \times 10^9 \text{ nt·m}^2/\text{c}^2)\,d. \qquad (4)$$

In the variable tuning condenser used in radios, the capacitance is varied by moving one mesh of plates into and out of the other mesh, so that the area A of plates facing each other is varied.

2. THE CYLINDRICAL CONDENSER

A CYLINDRICAL condenser is formed from one long cylindrical conductor inside another. The most common example is a cable, either metal-sheathed, or buried in a conducting medium such as earth or water. The effect of the capacitance of an underwater cable on transoceanic telegraphy, studied by Kelvin, was one of the earliest instances of the impact of a purely electrostatic phenomenon, *capacitance*, on what otherwise should have been purely an advance in the use of current electricity.

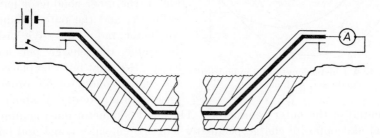

Fig. 3. An underwater telegraph cable.

The cable (Fig. 3) consists of a conductor inside a cylindrical lead and steel protecting sheath which is in intimate contact with conducting sea water and hence effectively grounded. The essential ideas of telegraphy are the following: A battery is attached at one end of the cable so that when the key is closed the conductor is raised to a certain potential relative to the grounded shield. Because of this potential, a small current (a *current* is a flow of electric charge) passes through the conductor and through the sensitive current-measuring instrument, denoted by A (for ammeter), at the other end. When the key is released, the current stops and the conductor returns to ground potential, since it is connected to ground through the instrument A. Thus, the pointer on A detects whether the key is closed or open, and telegraphic signaling is possible.

This scheme presents difficulties where the cable is very long, as in transoceanic work. An appreciable time elapses after the key is closed and current starts into the conductor before the meter registers current at the other end, and an appreciable time elapses after the key is opened before the meter stops registering current. The reason for this behavior is that appreciable time is required merely to *charge* the conductor. Current is a flow of charge, and the current at first charges the conductor and is not available to pass through the meter. Only as the conductor is charged does the potential appear at the other end. Correspondingly, after the key is opened, the charge on the conductor must flow out through the meter, and only as the conductor is discharged does the potential drop

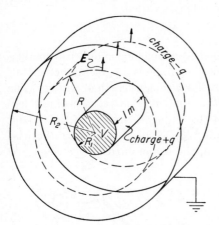

Fig. 4. A 1-meter length of a cylindrical condenser, with charge q.

to zero. The delayed response renders transoceanic telegraphic communication sluggish and makes telephonic communication, in which the current must vary with the frequency of sound, impossible with a simple cable such as that of Fig. 3.

We represent the cable by two long concentric cylindrical conductors illustrated in cross section in Fig. 4, the inner conductor having radius R_1 and the outer grounded conductor, radius R_2. We wish to determine the charge per meter length, $+q$, that must be placed on the inner conductor in order to raise it to a potential V above the potential of the outer conductor. The outer conductor must acquire an equal and opposite charge per meter length, $-q$, since equal and opposite charges lie at the two ends of each electric tube.

By symmetry, the charges must be distributed uniformly around the conductors, and the electric lines must point radially outward. For the moment we shall assume that there is air between the inner conductor and the sheath, though in practice there would be some insulating material such as rubber. The effect of this dielectric will be discussed in Sec. 3.

We can find the intensity ε as a function of radius R by applying

Gauss's law to an imaginary cylinder of 1-m length and radius R, which will enclose total charge $+q$. Since the only electric lines penetrating this imaginary cylinder are at its outer surface, of area $2\pi R$, Gauss's law gives

$$\mathcal{E}\cdot 2\pi R = (36\,\pi\times10^9 \text{ nt·m}^2/\text{c}^2)\,q, \quad \text{or} \quad \mathcal{E} = (18\times10^9 \text{ nt·m}^2/\text{c}^2)\,q/R. \quad (5)$$

This equation gives the intensity at any radius R for linear charge densities $\pm q$ in coul per m length of the conductors. The intensity is proportional to q, varies inversely with R, and does not depend on the radii of the conductors. However, the difference of potential between the conductors, which is the integral of $\mathcal{E}\,dR$ from R_1 to R_2, does depend on these radii. This difference of potential is

$$V = \int_{R_1}^{R_2} \mathcal{E}\,dR = \int_{R_1}^{R_2} (18\times10^9 \text{ nt·m}^2/\text{c}^2)\,(q/R)\,dR$$

$$= (18\times10^9 \text{ nt·m}^2/\text{c}^2)\,q\,\log_e R \Big]_{R_1}^{R_2}$$

$$= (18\times10^9 \text{ nt·m}^2/\text{c}^2)\,q\,[\log_e R_2 - \log_e R_1],$$

or
$$V = (18\times10^9 \text{ nt·m}^2/\text{c}^2)\,q\,\log_e(R_2/R_1). \quad (6)$$

This equation gives the potential, in volts, to which the conductor of a cable is raised, relative to the sheath, by charge q, in coul/m. Alternatively, it gives the charge per meter length that must be supplied if the potential is to be raised to V, in volts. It will be noticed that the linear charge density is proportional to the potential.

If a cable or cylindrical condenser is of length l, in meters, and has linear charge density q, in coul/m, its whole charge will be $Q=ql$, and according to (6) its capacitance will be

$$C = \frac{Q}{V} = \frac{ql}{V} = \frac{l}{(18\times10^9 \text{ nt·m}^2/\text{c}^2)\,\log_e(R_2/R_1)}. \qquad \left\{\begin{matrix} c \text{ in f} \\ l \text{ in m} \end{matrix}\right\} \quad (7)$$

Even for a cable crossing the ocean, this capacitance is only a small fraction of a farad.

3. DIELECTRIC CONSTANT

The discussion of the previous sections assumed that there was air or vacuum between the plates of the condenser. This condition obtains in the case of variable radio tuning condensers, but in most condensers some solid insulating material fills the space between the plates. Fixed radio condensers use mica or paraffined paper; underground or underwater cables have a rubber compound between the conductor and the sheath or between the two conductors in a two-wire cable; large high-voltage condensers are made with plates of metal foil placed on opposite sides of a sheet of glass.

A non-conducting material medium is called a **dielectric.**

The reason for using a dielectric between the plates is not solely *mechanical* convenience. A dielectric improves the condenser *electrically* in two ways: it *increases the capacitance,* and it *permits the use of higher voltages without danger of breakdown or flashover between the plates.* Breakdown is related to a property of a dielectric called *dielectric strength,* which will be discussed in Sec. 6. We turn here to an explanation of the increase in capacitance.

Consider first the effect of inserting a sheet of insulating material that almost completely fills the space between the plates of a parallel-plate condenser. Let Fig. 5(a) represent a small section of the condenser with the plates uncharged. By smoothing out the atomic irregularities, we can imagine the dielectric to be composed of uniform distributions of positive and negative charges as indicated. When the condenser plates

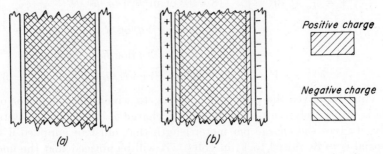

Fig. 5. Illustrating the relative displacement of positive and negative charge when a dielectric becomes polarized.

are charged, as in (b), the dielectric becomes *polarized* as discussed on p. 533. The electrons are not free to leave their own nuclei, but on the average there is a slight shift of the negative charge toward the positive plate. This shift results in a very slight relative displacement of the smoothed-out negative- and positive-charge distributions as indicated schematically in Fig. 5(b). Since the positive and negative charge distributions in the center of the dielectric still neutralize each other, the net effect of this polarization is to leave an unneutralized layer of negative charge on the surface of the dielectric near the positively charged plate and a layer of positive charge near the negatively charged plate. The charges on the plates are called *free charges,* and those on the dielectric surface, *bound charges,* for obvious reasons.

The magnitude of the bound charge in each layer is less than the magnitude of the free charge, but for any given dielectric material, the ratio of bound charge to free charge is a definite constant. The field in the dielectric is determined by the net effective charge, which will be a certain fraction Q/K of the free charge, as indicated in Fig. 6. For example, if $K = 5$, the bound charge is $-\frac{4}{5} Q$ and the net effective charge is $\frac{1}{5} Q$. For ordinary condenser dielectrics, K varies from 2 to 8.

Because of the presence of the dielectric, the net effective charge on each plate is reduced by a factor K. Hence the electric intensity between the plates and the difference of potential between the plates are also reduced by the factor K, so that in place of (1) and (2) we have

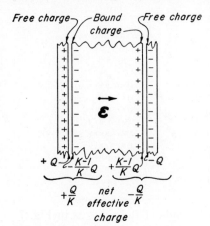

$$\mathcal{E} = \frac{(36\,\pi \times 10^9 \text{ nt·m}^2/\text{c}^2)\,Q}{KA},$$

$$V = \frac{(36\,\pi \times 10^9 \text{ nt·m}^2/\text{c}^2)\,Qd}{KA}.$$

The capacitance, which is defined as the ratio of *free* charge (the charge that would flow through the leads) to voltage, is increased by a factor K to

Fig. 6. Bound and free charges for a dielectric constant K.

$$C = Q/V$$
$$= KA/(36\,\pi \times 10^9 \text{ nt·m}^2/\text{c}^2)\,d. \quad (8)$$

For an N-plate condenser, as in Fig. 2, with dielectric between all pairs of plates, the capacitance becomes

$$C = K(N-1)A/(36\,\pi \times 10^9 \text{ nt·m}^2/\text{c}^2)\,d. \qquad (9)$$

The dimensionless constant K is called the *dielectric constant* or *specific inductive capacity* of the dielectric material. For a given kind of material it has a given fixed value.

> The **dielectric constant** of a material is the ratio of the capacitance of a condenser with the material between the plates to the capacitance with vacuum between the plates.

Values of the dielectric constant K for some of the dielectrics of interest are given in Table I. Values are also given for certain gases. It is not strictly true, as we have assumed so far, that the capacitance of an air condenser is the same as that of the condenser evacuated. But the increase of capacitance arising from the polarization of the air is only 6 parts in 10,000, a change that is not of importance for most purposes and that requires apparatus of high precision to detect experimentally.

So far, we have discussed the effect of polarization on the field between parallel plates only. However, if the space between plates of any shape be completely filled with a dielectric, the capacitance of the resulting condenser is increased by a factor of K—the same K as given in Table I, no matter what the shape of the plates. This increase arises from the fact that the polarization of the dielectric along any electric tube results

TABLE I

TYPICAL VALUES OF DIELECTRIC CONSTANT AND DIELECTRIC STRENGTH

	K	Dielectric strength (kv/cm)
Insulator porcelains.........	6	100–200
Glass.....................	5–10	200–400
Rubber, vulcanized.........	3.0	160–500
Transformer oils...........	2.1	50–150
Mica......................	4.5–7.5	250–2000
Paraffined paper...........	2	400–600
Nitrocellulose plastics.......	6–12	100–400
Dry air at 1 atm...........	1.0006	30
Carbon dioxide at 1 atm.....	1.0010	28

in the appearance of bound charges at the ends of the tube, as in Fig. 7. The result is that the net effective charges, the electric intensity at any point, and the difference of potential are all reduced by the factor K.

As a result of dielectric polarization, the force between two charged bodies immersed in a fluid dielectric such as oil is reduced by the factor K. To see this, note that the free charge that is attached to one of the bodies is attracted by both the free and bound charges of the other body. In this case the formula for the force between two point charges Q_1 and Q_2 separated by distance d becomes $F = (9 \times 10^9 \text{ nt·m}^2/\text{c}^2) Q_1 Q_2 / K d^2$.

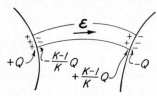

Fig. 7. Bound charges appear at the ends of every electric tube.

Two ways have been found of substantially increasing the capacitance of a condenser by using different dielectric materials from the older ones listed in Table I. One way, employed in the *electrolytic condenser*, uses an *extremely thin*, tough, insulating layer of aluminum oxide as the dielectric. The oxide is deposited on aluminum metal, which serves as one plate of the condenser, and is in intimate contact with a conducting solution of hydrochloric acid, which serves as the other plate. Because d is extremely small in the denominator of (8), an electrolytic condenser of given size can have a capacitance many times that of a condenser of the same size employing a conventional dielectric. The other way of greatly increasing the capacitance of a condenser depends on the rather recent development of solid materials designated as *ferroelectric*. The name comes from the fact that such materials have *electrical* properties exactly analogous to the *magnetic* properties of ferromagnetic materials which we shall study in Chap. 33. They can be permanently electrified, exhibit electrical hysteresis, and have extremely high dielectric constant. In particular, a multicrystalline barium-titanate ceramic has a dielectric constant of 1400 or more.

The fact that a dielectric increases the capacitance of a condenser is usually, but not always, desirable. In radio condensers, where the aim is to store charge in as small a space as possible, the increase is desirable. In telephone and power cables, where storage of charge is wasteful and leads to sluggish operation, the increase is undesirable.

4. ENERGY OF A CONDENSER

ENERGY MUST be supplied to charge a condenser; and when the condenser is discharged by connecting a wire between its plates, this energy is released in another form such as heat. The heat made available by a condenser discharge is used, for example, to fire detonators in ordnance devices such as mines, torpedoes, and shells. It is important in many uses of condensers to know the amount of energy stored. The computation can be made as follows:

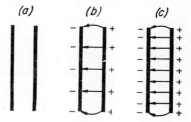

Fig. 8. Charging a condenser.

Consider a condenser of capacitance C, in farads, initially uncharged as in Fig. 8(a). We start to charge this condenser by moving electrons, a few at a time, from the right-hand plate to the left. We may imagine that we move the electrons through the space between the plates, although in practice the electrons are usually impelled by a battery or generator through a wire that connects the two plates. This difference is unimportant, since the difference of potential and hence the work is independent of the route followed by the electrons.

At first the work that must be done on the electrons to force them from one plate to the other is small, since the difference of potential is low. But as the charge on the plates builds up, the work that must be done on each electron increases because the difference of potential increases. Finally, the last electron must be moved through practically the full difference of potential V. Since the difference of potential increases in proportion to the charge, that is in proportion to the number of electrons that have been moved, the *average* difference of potential through which the electrons are moved is $\frac{1}{2} V$. If the total charge that is moved is Q, the work required to move this charge, piece by piece, through an average difference of potential $\frac{1}{2} V$ is $W = Q\,(\frac{1}{2} V)$. By using the relation $C = Q/V$, we can write this work in three alternative forms:

$$W = \tfrac{1}{2}\,QV = \tfrac{1}{2}\,CV^2 = \tfrac{1}{2}\,(Q^2/C). \qquad \left\{\begin{array}{l} W \text{ in joules} \\ Q \text{ in coul} \\ V \text{ in volts} \\ C \text{ in farads} \end{array}\right\} \quad (10)$$

This can be considered as the *electrostatic potential energy* that is stored in a charged condenser.

When a charged condenser is discharged by connecting a wire across its plates, this electrostatic energy disappears. It is transformed into heat in the wire. As we shall see later, whenever current flows in a wire, heat is generated. When a wire is connected between the plates of a charged condenser, the first passage of the electrons from the negative to the positive plate does not usually generate enough heat to take up all the energy of the condenser. Rather, like the oscillations of a pendulum, the flow of electrons overshoots, making the positive plate negative; then the flow reverses. Charge oscillates back and forth from one plate to the other until all the energy has been used up in heating the wire.

5. CONDENSERS IN PARALLEL AND SERIES

IF A NUMBER of condensers are connected in *parallel* as in Fig. 9 and placed in a (real or imaginary) box, at the terminals on the box they

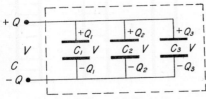

Fig. 9. Condensers in parallel.

appear indistinguishable from a single condenser of capacitance equal to the *sum* of the capacitances of the individual condensers. The reason for this result is that the difference of potential across each condenser is the same (their positive plates form a single conductor and their negative plates a single conductor) and is equal to the difference of potential across the terminals. But the charge Q that must flow in or out through the terminals on charge or discharge is the sum of the charges on the several condensers. Hence, in the notation of, Fig. 9,

$$Q = Q_1 + Q_2 + Q_3 = (C_1 + C_2 + C_3) V,$$

and
$$C = Q/V = C_1 + C_2 + C_3. \qquad \text{(parallel)} \quad (11)$$

If a number of condensers are connected in *series* as in Fig. 10 and placed in a (real or imaginary) box, the determination of the resultant capacitance is somewhat more complicated than in the parallel case. By *resultant capacitance* we mean the capacitance of a single condenser that could replace the series combination in the box with no detectable difference in behavior as observed at the terminals of the box.

We first note that the voltages across the individual condensers are not the same as V, but rather that they add up to V: $V_1 + V_2 + V_3 = V$. Fundamentally, this relation expresses the fact that as a test charge is moved from one terminal to the other through the wire and through the three condensers, work is done on the test charge in three steps as it passes through the three condensers, and the total work is the same as if the test charge were moved directly from one terminal to the other.

On the other hand, in the series case, the charge on each condenser is the same. Consider what happens when a battery is connected to the initially uncharged group of condensers. The charge $-Q$ represents the quantity of electrons that flows out of the negative terminal of the battery; all of these electrons appear as $-Q_3$ on condenser 3. The opposite plate of condenser 3 has the opposite induced charge $+Q_3 = +Q$. The top plate of condenser 3 and the bottom plate of condenser 2 form one conductor of net charge zero; hence $Q_2 = Q_3$, and so on. Hence, $Q_1 = Q_2 = Q_3 = Q$.

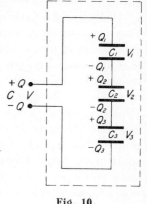

Fig. 10.
Condensers in series.

We derive the formula for the resultant capacitance as follows:

$$V = V_1 + V_2 + V_3 = \frac{Q_1}{C_1} + \frac{Q_2}{C_2} + \frac{Q_3}{C_3} = \frac{Q}{C_1} + \frac{Q}{C_2} + \frac{Q}{C_3};$$

hence
$$\frac{V}{Q} = \frac{1}{C} = \frac{1}{C_1} + \frac{1}{C_2} + \frac{1}{C_3}. \qquad \text{(series)} \quad (12)$$

The reciprocal of the resultant capacitance C equals the sum of the reciprocals of the individual capacitances of any number of condensers in series. It is best to leave the formula in the form (12), first computing $1/C$ and then taking its reciprocal to obtain C.

6. DIELECTRIC STRENGTH

WE HAVE previously stated that when an electric field exists within an insulating dielectric material in a condenser of any type, the electrons become slightly displaced relative to the nuclei but still remain bound to the nuclei. This situation obtains so long as the electric intensity is sufficiently low, but there is a certain value of electric intensity that is sufficient actually to pull electrons away from the atoms to which they belong. When this separation occurs in a gaseous or a liquid material, the material becomes ionized; when it occurs in a solid material, the material becomes ruptured or broken or punctured. Exceeding the critical electric intensity usually results in disruptive discharge of the condenser by sparks that pass through the dielectric material, although the discharge may take place quietly in air in the form of the corona that is observed around lightning rods or high-tension wires.

The critical electric intensity at which breakdown will take place is called the *dielectric strength:*

The **dielectric strength** of a material is the maximum potential gradient that the material can withstand without rupture.

Dielectric strength must not be confused with dielectric constant. They are essentially unrelated. The dielectric constant determines how much charge a given condenser will store up with a given potential difference; dielectric strength determines how much voltage this condenser will stand without breaking down.

Dielectric strength is usually expressed in volts/cm or kilovolts/cm. Typical values are given in Table 1 on p. 592. It will be noticed that the dielectric strengths of most solid and liquid insulators are higher than that of air. Thus a parallel-plate condenser composed of plates 1 mm (0.1 cm) apart in air would break down at a potential difference of about 3.0 kv (3000 volts), since the electric intensity would then be $(3.0 \text{ kv})/(0.1 \text{ cm})$ $= 30$ kv/cm, which is the value of dielectric strength given in Table I. This same condenser immersed in transformer oil would stand between 5 and 15 kv, depending on the type of oil. With mica between the plates, the condenser would withstand a potential difference of from 25 to 200 kv, depending on the quality of the mica.

Example. *A high-voltage underground power cable has a wire of 0.5-cm diameter in a lead sheath of inside diameter 1.5 cm. The insulating material is rubber of dielectric strength 400 kv/cm. What is the voltage of the wire, relative to the grounded sheath, at which breakdown occurs?*

The electric intensity is given by expression (5) divided by the dielectric constant K of the rubber. The capacitance is given by (7) multiplied by K. With these modifications, if we solve (7) for q and substitute in (5) we obtain the relation

$$\mathcal{E} = \frac{V/R}{\log_e(R_2/R_1)},$$

independent of the value of K. This electric intensity is greatest for the smallest value of R, namely $R = R_1$, at the surface of the wire. Breakdown will occur when this maximum intensity exceeds the dielectric strength, 400 kv/cm. Substituting $R = R_1 = 0.25$ cm and $\mathcal{E} = 400$ kv/cm in the above equation, we determine

$$V = \mathcal{E}R_1 \log_e(R_2/R_1)$$
$$= (400 \text{ kv/cm})(0.25 \text{ cm}) \log_e 3$$
$$= 400 \times 0.25 \times 1.10 \text{ kv} = 110 \text{ kv}$$

as the breakdown voltage. In engineering practice a factor of safety would be applied, and such a cable would not be used for a voltage above about ⅓ of this value, or 37,000 volts.

The action of a well-grounded and sharply pointed *lightning rod* is primarily to discharge quietly into the air the charge that is induced in the surrounding earth by a charged thundercloud above. The electric intensity in the vicinity of the sharp point is high enough to break down the immediately surrounding air, but the continual discharge of the ground prevents building up sufficient voltage over the whole cloud-ground path to break down this long path and give rise to a stroke of lightning at this location.

PROBLEMS

1. A condenser is made of two parallel plates 15 cm square and 0.2 cm apart in air. (a) What is its capacitance in farads and in $\mu\mu f$? (b) What is the charge on each plate when the potential difference is 90 v?

Ans: (a) 9.97×10^{-11} f, 99.7 $\mu\mu f$; (b) 8.97×10^{-9} coul.

2. A condenser is made of two parallel plates 12 cm square and 1 mm apart in air. (a) What is its capacitance in farads and in $\mu\mu f$? (b) What is the charge on each plate when the potential difference is 150 v?

3. What is the maximum capacitance of a radio tuning condenser consisting of 13 fixed plates and 12 movable plates if the effective area of each plate in the interleaved position is 30 cm² and the air gaps between fixed and movable plates are 1.8 mm? Express your answer in $\mu\mu f$. Ans: 354 $\mu\mu f$.

4. What is the maximum capacitance of a radio tuning condenser consisting of 12 fixed plates and 11 movable plates if the effective area of each plate in the interleaved position is 22 cm² and the air gaps between fixed and movable plates are 1.5 mm? Express your answer in $\mu\mu f$.

5. The condenser of Prob. 3 is charged with a 144-v battery when it has its maximum capacitance. The battery is disconnected, leaving the condenser charged. The knob is then turned to reduce the effective area to 10 cm². What then is the charge on the condenser and its voltage? Ans: 51,000 $\mu\mu c$; 432 v.

6. The condenser of Prob. 4 is charged with a 120-v battery when it has its maximum capacitance. The battery is disconnected, leaving the condenser charged. The knob is then turned to reduce the effective area to 5.5 cm². What then is the charge on the condenser and its voltage?

7. A condenser consists of two large metal plates 1 mm apart in air. When it is connected to a 1000-v battery, each plate becomes charged with 1 μc. What is its capacitance in $\mu\mu f$? Ans: 1000 $\mu\mu f$.

8. The plates of a condenser become charged with 0.6 μc when a potential difference of 1200 v is applied. What is the capacitance of the condenser in $\mu\mu f$?

NOTE: The student is reminded that there are four convenient ways of finding logarithms to the base e: first by using a log-log slide rule; second, by using a table of natural logarithms; third, by using the relation $\log_e N = \log_e 10 \ \log_{10} N = 2.3026 \ \log_{10} N$; fourth, by inverse interpolation in a table of exponentials, such as that in Sec. 7 of the Appendix, using the relation $\exp(\log_e N) = N$.

9. Find the capacitance per meter length of two concentric cylinders of radii 0.5 cm and 1.0 cm in air. Ans: 80.2 $\mu\mu f/m$.

10. Find the capacitance per meter length of two concentric cylinders of radii 0.5 cm and 2.0 cm in air.

11. The cylinders of Prob. 9 have a potential difference of 5000 v. Find (a) the charge per meter length; (b) the maximum electric intensity between the cylinders; (c) the minimum electric intensity between the cylinders.

Ans: (a) 0.401 $\mu c/m$; (b) 14.4×10^5 v/m; (c) 7.22×10^5 v/m.

12. The cylinders of Prob. 10 have a potential difference of 5000 v. Find the same quantities as in Prob. 11.

13. A 100-plate condenser has plates 40 cm × 30 cm separated by glass plates 3 mm thick of dielectric constant 7.0. Find the capacitance in μf. Ans: 0.246 μf.

14. A condenser is formed from 50 parallel metal plates 20 cm × 20 cm separated by glass sheets ($K = 7.0$) 1.5 mm thick. What is its capacitance in μf?

15. A condenser with air dielectric ($K = 1.00$) is charged by connecting it across a battery. A meter measures the charge that flows to one of the condenser plates as 150 μc. Without disconnecting the battery, the condenser is completely immersed in an insulating oil, and an *additional* charge of 225 μc flows to the plate. What is the dielectric constant of the oil?　　　Ans: 2.5.

16. A condenser with air dielectric ($K = 1.00$) is charged by connecting it across a 100-v battery. Without disconnecting the battery, the condenser is completely immersed in an insulating oil of $K = 3.00$. As a result of immersion, the charge on each condenser plate *increases* in magnitude by 300 μc. What is the capacitance of the condenser with air dielectric?

17. What would be the size of a single pair of square tin-foil plates on glass ($K = 6$) 3 mm thick if the resulting condenser has a capacitance of 1 μf?
　　　　　　　　　　　　　　　　　　　　　　　Ans: 7.5 m square.

18. What would be the number of plates required for a parallel-plate condenser with metal-foil plates of effective area 2 cm × 2 cm and mica dielectric ($K = 6$) 0.1 mm thick, if the condenser is to have a capacitance of 0.02 μf?

19. The small fixed-capacitance condensers used throughout radio sets and other electronic apparatus are frequently constructed as in Fig. 11. An approximate value of their capacitance can be obtained by using the parallel-plate formula, since the dielectric is very thin compared with the radius of curvature throughout most of the condenser. Consider such a condenser rolled from two strips of paper and two strips of aluminum foil. Each strip of foil is 2.5 inches wide. If the foil is 0.0005 inch thick and the paper 0.001 inch thick, with $K = 2$, compute approximately (a) the length of strips required for a 0.5-μf condenser, and (b) the outside diameter of the complete roll.　　　Ans: 220 in; 0.9 in.

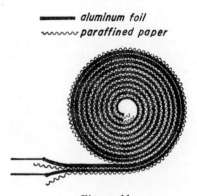

aluminum foil
paraffined paper

Figure 11

20. Find the capacitance per mile (5280 ft) of cable having a conductor of diameter 0.2 in and a lead sheath of inner diameter 0.6 in, the space between being filled with rubber of $K = 3$.

21. In making an electrolytic condenser, the aluminum sheet is *etched* before being oxidized. This doubles its effective area. The oxide has a thickness of 2×10^{-5} in and a dielectric constant of 10, and both sides of the sheet are oxidized and in contact with the acid. Compare the capacitance of an electrolytic condenser made from a sheet of aluminum of area A with that of a parallel-plate condenser made with paper 0.001 inch thick and the same area A.　　　Ans: 1000:1.

22. As in Prob. 17, find the size of plates required for a 1-μf condenser for the case in which a 1-mm layer of barium titanate with $K = 1400$ is the dielectric.

23. What is the energy in joules in a 6-μf condenser charged to 1200 v?
　　　　　　　　　　　　　　　　　　　　　　　Ans: 4.32 joules.

24. A condenser of 50-μf capacitance is charged to 80 v. Calculate the stored energy in joules.

25. How many joules are stored in a 0.50-μf condenser charged with 0.0125 coul? • Ans: 156.2 joules.

26. A condenser consists of two large parallel plates 0.5 mm apart in air. Its capacitance is 200 μf. It is charged to 600 v by means of a battery. (a) What is its energy? (b) The charged condenser is disconnected from the battery. The plates are so mounted that they will remain parallel and insulated when a glass rod is used to push them 3 mm apart. What is the energy of the condenser after this separation is made? What is the source of the extra energy? (c) What is the difference of potential between the plates after they have been separated?

27. A condenser has a capacitance of 2 μf when its plates are separated by a layer of air. It is charged to 400 v by means of a battery. (a) Find the charge on the plates and the energy stored in the condenser. (b) The charged condenser is first disconnected from the battery and then immersed in an oil having a dielectric constant of 3. What is the difference of potential between the plates? What is the energy of the condenser? What is the source of the energy change?

28. Three condensers of respective capacitances 1, 1.5, and 3 μf are connected in *parallel* across a 120-v battery. Find (a) the resultant capacitance; (b) the charge that flows from the battery, using the capacitance obtained in (a); (c) the total energy in joules stored in the condenser combination, using the results of (a) or (b); (d) the charge on each condenser, comparing the total with (b); (e) the energy of each condenser, comparing the total with (c).

29. Three condensers, of respective capacitances, 1, 1.5, and 3 μf, are connected in *series* across a 120-v battery. Find (a) the resultant capacitance; (b) the charge that flows from the battery, using the capacitance obtained in (a); (c) the total energy in joules stored in the condenser combination, using the results of (a) or (b); (d) the voltage across each condenser, checking the total; (e) the energy of each condenser, comparing the total with (c). Ans: (a) 0.5 μf; (b) 60 μc; (c) 3600 μjoules; (d) 60, 40, 20 v; (e) 1800, 1200, 600 μjoules.

30. (a) Two condensers, of 2-μf and 4-μf capacitance, are connected in series and charged from a 120-v battery. What are the charge, voltage, and energy for each condenser? (b) If these two condensers are now disconnected without discharging and are then connected to each other, + plate to + plate and − to −, what are the new values of charge, voltage, and energy for each condenser?

31. If a 1-μf condenser charged to 100 v and a 2-μf condenser charged to 200 v are connected in parallel, + plate to + plate, find the resulting difference of potential, the charge on each condenser, and the loss of energy.
Ans: 167 v; 167, 333 μc; $\frac{1}{3} \times 10^{-2}$ joule.

32. If a 1-μf condenser charged to 100 v and a 2-μf condenser charged to 200 v are connected, + plate of each to − plate of the other, find the resulting difference of potential, charge on each condenser, and loss of energy.

33. Condensers A, B, and C of respective capacitances 4, 3, and 2 μf are connected as shown in Fig. 12. Before the switch is closed, A is charged to a potential difference of 100 v, B and C are uncharged. What will be the charge and voltage of each condenser after the switch is closed?
Ans: $V_A = 76.9$ v, $V_B = 30.8$ v, $V_C = 46.1$ v; $Q_A = 308$ μc, $Q_B = Q_C = 92.3$ μc.

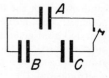

Figure 12

34. Condensers A, B, and C of respective capacitances 4, 3, and 2 μf are connected as shown in Fig. 12. Before the switch is closed, B and C are each independently charged to 100 v, the left-hand plate being positive in each case; A is uncharged. What will be the charge and voltage of each condenser after the switch is closed?

35. How thick must the mica dielectric be in a parallel-plate condenser built to withstand 10,000 v if the mica has dielectric strength 900 kv/cm?

Ans: 0.111 mm.

36. At what voltage will a parallel-plate condenser with dielectric of dry air 1.5 mm thick break down?

37. What are the approximate relative volumes of condensers made of stacked parallel plates with the following dielectrics? (a) Air, $K=1$, dielectric strength 30 kv/cm. (b) Paraffined paper, $K=2$, dielectric strength 500 kv/cm. (c) Mica, $K=6$, dielectric strength 900 kv/cm. The condensers are to have the same capacitance and the same breakdown voltage. Neglect the thickness of the metal plates in your computation.

Ans: 5400 : 9.7 : 1.

38. From Gauss's law, find an expression for the capacitance of an isolated metal sphere of radius R. What is the charge on a sphere of 1 m radius when the sphere is at a potential 1 million volts relative to ∞, where we imagine the other plate of the condenser to be?

39. To what potential can a single isolated sphere 1 cm in diameter in dry air be raised before breakdown occurs?

Ans: 15,000 v.

40. To what potential can a single isolated sphere 1 m in diameter in dry air be raised before breakdown occurs?

41. A method of obtaining high voltage is the 'Marx circuit,' in which a switching mechanism allows a set of condensers to be 'charged in parallel' and 'discharged in series.' Design such a circuit. What is the maximum voltage attainable with a 1000-v battery and ten identical condensers, each capable of withstanding 1200 v between its plates?

Ans: 10 kv.

42. Show that the capacitance of a so-called 'spherical' condenser, formed from two thin concentric metal spheres of radii R_1 and R_2, is given by $C = KR_1R_2/(9 \times 10^9 \text{ nt·m}^2/\text{c}^2)(R_2 - R_1)$.

43. A spherical condenser is formed from two concentric spheres of thin metal, one 0.5 m in radius, the other 1 m, with air dielectric. The outer sphere is grounded, the inner charged with $+3$ μc. Find the electric intensity and the potential relative to ground at points (a) 0.2 m from the center, (b) just outside the inner sphere, (c) 0.8 m from the center, (d) just inside the outer sphere. (e) What is the capacitance of the condenser? (f) What is the maximum charge that can be stored on the inner sphere before dielectric breakdown occurs?

Ans: (a) 0 v/m, 27,000 v; (b) 108,000 v/m, 27,000 v; (c) 42,200 v/m, 6750 v; (d) 27,000 v/m, 0 v; (e) 111 $\mu\mu f$; (f) 83.3 μc.

44. The large spherical electrode in a Van de Graaf generator (Fig. 8, p. 843) used in the open atmosphere can be considered as one 'plate' of a spherical condenser with the other 'plate' at infinite distance. (a) What is the maximum potential obtainable with an electrode 1 m in diameter? More frequently, Van de Graaf generators are mounted in tanks and the situation is more nearly approximated by the arrangement described in Prob. 43, with the outer sphere grounded, except for the use of a mixture of gases at high pressure between the electrode and the tank wall. (b) Find the maximum difference of potential obtainable between the two spheres of Prob. 43 if the space between the two spheres is filled with a mixture of gases having a dielectric strength 10 times that of air. (c) How much charge is on the inner sphere when the sphere has its maximum potential? (d) What is the maximum energy stored in the condenser formed by the high-voltage electrode and the surrounding tank?

45. Find an expression for the energy stored in a parallel-plate condenser in terms of the electric intensity $\mathcal{E}$ between the plates. Considering this energy to be stored in the dielectric between the plates, find an expression for the energy per unit volume in the dielectric in terms of $\mathcal{E}$ and the dielectric constant.

Ans: $\frac{1}{2} C\mathcal{E}^2 d^2$; $K\mathcal{E}^2/(72 \pi \times 10^9 \text{ nt·m}^2/\text{c}^2)$.

46. Returning to a consideration of the ionization chamber shown in Fig. 45, p. 584 find the maximum value of potential difference possible for an ionization chamber filled with air in which the outer grounded electrode has a radius of 3 cm and the inner electrode has a radius of (a) 1 mm, (b) 0.1 mm, and (c) 0.01 mm.

47. In an ionization chamber like that in Fig. 45, p. 584, as one raises the voltage on the inner electrode, (a) when the potential of the inner electrode is very low, most of the primary ions produced by the original particle will recombine to form neutral molecules before the ions can be collected, and hence the rate of charge collection is low; (b) as the potential is increased, the charge collected per second at first rises and then becomes constant for a considerable range of inner electrode potentials; under this condition all the primary ions produced by the original high-energy particle are being collected; (c) as the potential is further increased, the rate at which ions are collected begins to increase once more; (d) at very high potentials, charge is continuously collected by the central electrodes even if the source of high energy particles is removed from the vicinity of the chamber. Discuss the processes occurring in (c) and (d). In your discussion assume that a negative ion or electron must move through a potential difference of 15 volts between collisions before it has enough energy to ionize a neutral molecule with which it may collide. At NTP, an ion moves approximately 10^{-5} cm between collisions. In what part of the ionization chamber do the primary ions formed by the original high-speed particle produce secondary ions? What value of electric intensity is required to produce secondary ionization?

CHAPTER 29

CURRENT ELECTRICITY

IN THIS CHAPTER we make the transition from *static* electricity to *current* electricity—the flow of electric charge in wires. Our previous definitions of charge and difference of potential will still be useful, but we shall have to introduce the additional concepts of *current* as a rate of flow of charge, *resistance* to the flow of charge, and *electromotive force* as a measure of work done on charges in order to maintain a continuous difference of potential. This chapter lays the groundwork for the detailed discussion of direct-current electric circuits and measuring instruments in the following chapter, and introduces basic concepts useful throughout the study of electricity and magnetism.

1. CURRENT ARISING FROM A CONDENSER DISCHARGE

AN ELECTROSCOPE or electrostatic voltmeter connected across the charged condenser of Fig. 1 will serve to measure the difference of poten-

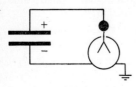

Figure 1

tial between the condenser plates. If now a short, thick wire be connected across the condenser plates, the plates will be discharged almost instantaneously, as indicated by the sudden collapse of the electroscope leaves. But if a very long and very fine wire be connected across the condenser plates, the electroscope leaves will collapse gradually over a period of seconds or minutes; the longer and finer the wire, the longer the time required for the condenser to discharge. Although any wire connected across the condenser plates permits electrons to flow from the negative to the positive plate, a long, fine wire appears to offer more 'resistance' to the flow than a short, thick wire. Furthermore, wires made of certain metals such as nichrome offer much more resistance to the flow than wires of the same size made of other metals such as copper.

In Fig. 2, the conventional symbol for 'resistor' is used to indicate that the wire connected across the condenser plates presents resistance.

During the period in which the condenser is discharging, electrons move from the negative plate through the resistor to the positive plate.

A current is said to exist.   However, by an unfortunate convention originated before the days of the electron theory, the *current* is said to have
the direction *opposite* to that in which the electrons really move.   This
convention is so firmly established that no attempt is being made to
change it.   *We must always specify the direction of current as the direction
in which positive charges would move if the charge were transferred by means
of positive charges rather than by means of electrons.*   Thus, the current in
Fig. 2 is directed from the positive plate of the condenser to the negative.

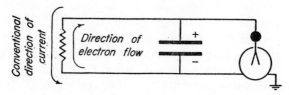

Fig. 2. Rate of decrease of voltage indicates magnitude of current.

If C is the capacitance of the condenser in Fig. 2 and Q is the charge on
either plate, we have, at any instant, $Q = CV$, or, differentiating,

$$dQ/dt = C \, dV/dt.$$

The rate of decrease of charge in coul/sec equals C times the rate of
decrease of potential in v/sec.   But this rate of decrease of charge must
represent the rate of flow of charge in coul/sec through the resistor.   The
rate of flow of charge, in coul/sec, is called the *current* through the wire in
amperes* (abbreviated amp or a) and is denoted by the symbol I.

> A **current** of one **ampere** represents a flow of charge at a rate of one
> coul/sec past any point.   The direction of the current is opposite to
> that in which the electrons actually move when the current repre-
> sents a flow of electrons, as in the case of a current in a wire.

Thus,   1 amp = 1 coul/sec.   (1)

An instrument called an *ammeter* may be connected into the circuit to
measure the current in amperes.   We shall discuss the construction of
such an instrument later.

2. CONSTANT CURRENTS

THE CURRENTS considered in the preceding section were *transient currents* in that charge flowed only during the period required for the condenser to discharge.   If it is desired to maintain a *constant current* for an
indefinite period, some means must be found for keeping the condenser
continuously charged, that is, for renewing the supply of electrons on the
negative plate as fast as they flow around through the wire.   Energy

---

* After ANDRÉ MARIE AMPÈRE (1775–1836), French physicist who formulated the
fundamental laws of the magnetic effects of electric currents.

must be supplied to move these electrons from the positive to the negative plate through the difference of potential existing between these plates. This energy could be supplied and the potential difference maintained by an electrostatic generator of some type, but there are more practical and convenient means.   In discussing this question, *let us agree to ignore our knowledge that in most cases it is negative electrons, rather than positive charges, that move, and speak as if it were really positive charges that move.* This procedure will lead to no essential error and will avoid much confusion because it is consistent with the conventional current direction.

What we need, then, is a 'charge pump' that will pump charge up the 'potential hill' from the negative plate of the condenser to the positive plate, as in Fig. 3, as fast as the charge runs back downhill through the resistor.   This charge pump must do work V, in joules per coulomb of charge, if a difference of potential V is to be maintained.   If the current

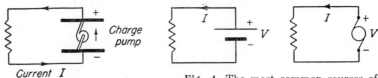

Fig. 3. In order to maintain a continuous current, a 'charge pump' is required.

Fig. 4. The most common sources of constant EMF (charge pumps) are the electric battery and the direct-current electric generator.

is I, charge must be pumped at the rate I, in coul/sec, and the power that must be supplied is IV, in joules/sec or watts.   In Fig. 3, the pump must supply energy at the rate

$$P = IV. \qquad \left\{ \begin{matrix} P \text{ in watts} \\ I \text{ in amp} \\ V \text{ in volts} \end{matrix} \right\} \quad (2)$$

This energy must be supplied to the charges by some outside means since the charges are being moved *against* the electrical forces; the energy reappears as heat in the resistor as the charges flow back down the potential hill through the resistor, in the direction of the electrical forces.

A 'charge pump,' which converts some other form of energy to electrical potential energy by moving charges against an electric field is called a *source of electromotive force*.   The first source of *electromotive force* (EMF) suitable for the production of continuous currents was discovered by Volta in 1799 and called the galvanic pile or voltaic *battery*.   This source was the prototype of our modern dry cells and storage batteries, which obtain their power from stored *chemical energy*.   A second type of source of EMF, based on the discovery of electromagnetic induction in 1831, converts *mechanical energy* into electrical energy.   The modern direct-current electric generator is of this type.   These sources of EMF are illustrated in the circuits of Fig. 4, where of course we can now dispense with the condenser and hook our wires directly to the plates of the battery or to the terminals of the generator.

The operation of sources of electromotive force will be discussed in detail in later chapters. For the present, we need only understand that EMF is measured in volts and that:

> A source of EMF of one volt is a source that does one joule of work on each coulomb of charge that passes through it from the low potential side to the high.

To maintain current I, a source of EMF V must furnish power at the rate given by (2).

3. RESISTANCE; OHM'S LAW

WHENEVER there is a difference of potential (voltage) between the ends of a wire, there is a current through it. The current is caused by the electric field (potential gradient) in the wire. If the voltage is continuously maintained by a source of EMF, the current is continuous. The current meets resistance in its flow which causes generation of heat, just as liquid flowing through a pipe meets frictional and viscous resistance which causes generation of heat. Just as the magnitude of the current of liquid (in ft³/sec) that will flow down-hill through a pipe depends on the difference in elevation of the ends of the pipe, on the diameter, length, and internal roughness of the pipe, and on the temperature (viscosity effect), so does the magnitude of the electric current through a wire depend on the potential difference between the ends of the wire, its diameter, length, and material, and the temperature. The laws determining the dependence of the magnitude of the current on these various factors are simple and will be discussed in order.

The dependence of current on voltage is expressed by *Ohm's law*, discovered experimentally by Ohm* in 1826:

> OHM'S LAW: *For a given conductor at a given temperature, the current is directly proportional to the difference of potential between the ends of the conductor.*

If, in Fig. 5, V is the difference of potential between the ends of a conductor R as measured by a voltmeter V, and I is the current in amperes through the conductor as measured by the ammeter A, and if the temperature is kept constant, Ohm's law states that the current is proportional to V:

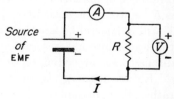

Figure 5

$$I \propto V. \quad \text{(Ohm's law)}$$

* GEORG SIMON OHM (1787–1854), German physicist.

The proportionality constant is called the *conductance G* in *mhos:*

$$I = GV.$$

The reciprocal of the conductance G in mhos is the *resistance R* in *ohms:*

$$R = \frac{1}{G} = \frac{V}{I}; \qquad I = \frac{V}{R}; \qquad V = RI. \tag{3}$$

Thus the unit

$$1 \text{ ohm} = 1 \text{ v/amp.} \tag{4}$$

The abbreviation used for the word ohm is the Greek letter ω (or Ω).

The value of the resistance R depends on the size, shape, material, and temperature of the conductor, but within wide limits does not depend on the voltage V. This rule is true for metals but is not obeyed very accurately by non-metals (see Sec. 6). R is called the *resistance* because the voltage $V = RI$ required for a particular current I is greater the greater the value of R; or, the current $I = V/R$ set up by a particular voltage is smaller the greater the value of R.

Since the electrical forces do work of amount V per coulomb of charge passing through the wire, and since all of this work appears as heat in the wire, *the heat generated per coulomb of charge is $V = IR$*, in joules/coulomb.

To get the power expended in the resistor, which is the same as the rate of heat generation, in watts or in joules/sec, we merely multiply the energy per coulomb ($V = IR$) by the number of coulombs per second (I). The expression for power can then be written in several convenient forms:

$$P = IV = I^2R = V^2/R. \qquad \begin{Bmatrix} P \text{ in watts} \\ I \text{ in amp} \\ V \text{ in volts} \\ R \text{ in ohms} \end{Bmatrix} \tag{5}$$

The amount of heat generated in time t can then be written as

$$W = Pt = IVt = I^2Rt = V^2t/R. \qquad \begin{Bmatrix} W \text{ in joules} \\ P \text{ in watts} \\ t \text{ in sec} \end{Bmatrix} \tag{6}$$

This value may be changed into calories or BTU by using the equivalents:

$$1 \text{ calorie} = 4.186 \text{ joules}, \quad 1 \text{ BTU} = 1055 \text{ joules.}$$

It must be emphasized that the symbol V in (5) and (6) represents the difference of potential between the two ends of the wire whose resistance is R, as would be measured by a voltmeter connected as in Fig. 5. This V will in general be *less* than the battery voltage because of resistance in the leads, internal resistance in the battery, etc. These points will be discussed in succeeding sections.

Electrical energy is usually measured and paid for in kilowatt·hours, rather than in joules (watt·seconds). The kilowatt·hour (kwh) is the amount of energy delivered in a period of one hour if it is being delivered at the rate of one kilowatt. In other words, we get energy in kwh from the formula $W = Pt$ if P is expressed in kw and t in hours.   We note that

$$1 \text{ kwh} = (1 \text{ kw}) \cdot (1 \text{ hr}) = (1000 \text{ w}) \cdot (3600 \text{ sec}) = 3.6 \times 10^6 \text{ joules.}$$

This is a unit of energy of a size convenient for commercial purposes; it usually retails for somewhere between 1 cent and 6 cents.

Example. *A 600-watt radiant heater is designed for operation at 115-volts. What current is drawn by the heater from the* DC *power lines? What is the resistance of the heating coil? How many* BTU's *are generated in one hour?*

From (5), we find the heater current $I = 600 \text{ w}/115 \text{ v} = 5.22 \text{ amp}$.   Then, from (3), the heating-coil resistance $R = 115 \text{ v}/5.22 \text{ amp} = 22.0 \text{ } \omega$.   From (6), the heat generated in one hour is $W = 600 \text{ w} \times 3600 \text{ sec} = 2,160,000$ joules $= 2,160,000 \text{ } (\frac{1}{1055} \text{ BTU}) = 2050 \text{ BTU.}$

4. RESISTIVITY

Now LET us consider the dependence of resistance on length and cross-sectional area of a wire.   Consider first the dependence of resistance on length, other things being equal. Figure 6 shows three wires, identical except for their lengths, which are l, $2l$, $3l$.   If we denote by v the voltage required to force a certain current I through the shortest wire, it is clear that $2v$ will be required to force the same current I through the second, since each half of the

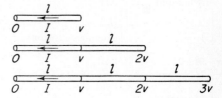

Fig. 6. For a given current, voltage is proportional to length of wire.

second is identical with the first and each half must have a voltage v for current I.   Similarly, each third of the longest wire is identical with the shortest, so that for current I the total voltage must be $3v$.   Since the resistance of a piece of wire equals the voltage between its ends divided by the current, we see that the resistances of the three pieces in Fig. 6

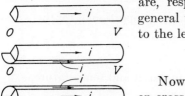

Fig. 7. For a given voltage, current is proportional to cross-sectional area A.

are, respectively, v/I, $2v/I$, $3v/I$; and that in general the resistance varies in direct proportion to the length of the wire:

$$R \propto l. \tag{7}$$

Now, consider the dependence of resistance on cross-sectional area A, length being constant. Figure 7 shows three wires of the same length but with cross-sectional areas in the ratios $1:2:3$.   The second and third wires are equivalent, respectively, to two and three of the first wires, and will carry two and three times the current with the same voltage.   Hence, if the current in the first wire is called i, that in the second will be $2i$ and in the third $3i$ for the same voltage V. Hence, the resistances of the wires will be V/i, $V/2i$, $V/3i$, respectively, and we see that the resistance goes down as the area goes

TABLE I

RESISTIVITY AND TEMPERATURE COEFFICIENT OF COMMON METALS AND ALLOYS

Alloy	Specification	Resistivity at 20° C		Temperature coefficient (per C deg at 20° C)
		(ohm·m)	(ohms per mil ft)	
Copper........	Pure (99.999%)	1.673×10^{-8}	10.06	4.05×10^{-3}
	International standard-annealed (~99.91%)	1.724	10.37	3.93
	Hard-drawn	1.77	10.6	3.8
Aluminum....	Pure (99.96%)	2.655	15.97	4.03
	AIEE standard hard-drawn (99.5%).....	2.828	17.01	4.03
Iron.........	Pure (99.99%)	9.71	58.4	5.76
	Commercial wire	11–13	66–78	5.5
	Cast (typical)........	60	360	5
Steel.........	Rail...............	14–22	84–130	4
Nichrome.....	60%, Ni, 15% Cr, 25% Fe	112	675	0.16
Manganin.....	4% Ni, 12% Mn, 84% Cu...............	48	290	<0.01
Monel........	69% Ni, 28% Cu.....	44	268	1.96
German silver .	18% Ni, 65% Cu, 17% Zn	29	175	0.27
Constantan....	45% Ni, 55% Cu.....	49	294	<0.01
Silver.........	Pure...............	1.59	9.55	3.75
Gold.........	Pure...............	2.44	14.7	3.4
Tungsten......	Pure...............	5.50	33.1	4.7
Platinum......	Pure (99.99%)	9.83	59	3.64

up; in general, the resistance is inversely proportional to the cross-sectional area:

$$R \propto 1/A. \tag{8}$$

From (7) and (8), for wires of given material and temperature,

$$R \propto l/A.$$

The proportionality constant, usually written as ρ, is called the *resistivity*:

$$R = \rho \, l/A. \tag{9}$$

The resistivity depends only on the material and the temperature.

In the metric system, l and A are expressed in m and m²; and since

$$\rho = RA/l, \tag{10}$$

the unit in which ρ is expressed is the ohm·meter. Table I gives the resistivities of various metals and commercial alloys.

In a system convenient for engineering calculations, particularly with round wires, l is expressed in feet and A in circular mils. A circular mil is defined as the area of a circle one mil (0.001 inch) in diameter. The area of a circular wire of diameter d, in mils, is $A = d^2$, in circular mils. In this system the unit of ρ is ohm·circ mil/ft. This unit is commonly written as *ohm per mil ft;* we shall use

TABLE II (WIRE TABLE)

PROPERTIES OF INTERNATIONAL STANDARD-ANNEALED COPPER WIRE AND HARD-DRAWN ALUMINUM WIRE (AIEE STANDARD) ACCORDING TO AMERICAN WIRE GAUGE (BROWN AND SHARPE WIRE GAUGE) NUMBER

Gauge No.	Diameter in mils	Area in circ mils	Copper		Aluminum	
			Ohms per 1000 ft at 20° C	Pounds per 1000 ft	Ohms per 1000 ft at 0° C	Pounds per 1000 ft
6	162.0	26,250	0.3951	79.46	0.648	24.1
7	144.3	20,820	0.4982	63.02	0.817	19.1
8	129.5	16,510	0.6282	49.98	1.03	15.2
9	114.4	13,090	0.7921	39.63	1.30	12.0
10	101.9	10,380	0.9989	31.43	1.64	9.55
11	90.74	8,234	1.260	24.93	2.07	7.57
12	80.81	6,530	1.588	19.77	2.61	6.00
13	71.96	5,178	2.003	15.68	3.29	4.76
14	64.08	4,107	2.525	12.43	4.14	3.78
15	57.07	3,257	3.184	9.858	5.22	2.99
16	50.82	2,583	4.016	7.818	6.59	2.37
17	45.26	2,048	5.064	6.200	8.31	1.88
18	40.30	1,624	6.385	4.917	10.5	1.49
19	35.89	1,288	8.051	3.899	13.2	1.18
20	31.96	1,022	10.15	3.092	16.7	0.939

this designation in spite of the fact that it is *dimensionally incorrect*. With these units we can write the resistance of a *round* wire as

$$R = \rho\, l/d^2, \qquad \left\{ \begin{array}{l} R \text{ in ohms} \\ \rho \text{ in ohms per mil ft} \\ l \text{ in ft} \\ d \text{ in mils} \end{array} \right\}$$

while the resistance of a wire of any cross section is given by (9) with l in ft and A in circular mils. As indicated by Table I, the resistivity in ohms per mil ft, which is the resistance of a circular wire one foot long and 0.001 inch in diameter, is much larger than the resistivity in ohm·m, which is the resistance of a one-meter cube, but the ratio is constant at 6.015×10^8, as may readily be computed. Table II gives data on the characteristics of common sizes of standard round copper and aluminum wires.

In the periodic chart, there is a periodicity of electrical resistivity similar to the periodicity of other properties of the elements. In particular, the three best electrical conductors are Ag, Cu, Au—the three elements that occupy one column of the periodic table. Next comes Al. The resistivities of these four elements will be found in Table I. The periodic table is given in Sec. 9 of the Appendix.

5. TEMPERATURE COEFFICIENT OF RESISTANCE

WE TURN now to a consideration of the dependence of resistance (or resistivity) on temperature. The resistance of a pure metal increases rapidly with temperature, the temperature effect being so pronounced that it must be taken into account in most engineering applications. Figure 8 shows, for example, how the resistivity of copper varies with

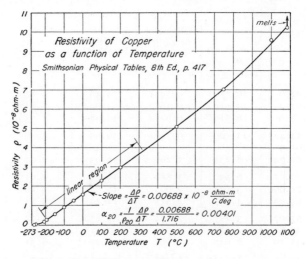

Fig. 8. Typical data on the resistivity of copper.

temperature. The reason for the rapid variation with temperature is that the whole resistance of a metal to electron flow arises from the thermal agitation of the metallic ions that comprise the lattice structure of the metal. This agitation increases rapidly with increasing temperature. These ideas are confirmed by the fact that the resistance of all metals approaches zero as the absolute temperature approaches zero. In fact, in the phenomenon known as *superconductivity*, the resistance of a metal drops entirely to zero at a temperature still a few degrees above absolute zero, so that when a current is once started in a metal ring below such temperature it continues indefinitely without necessity of an EMF to maintain it and without causing any heating of the material. The presence of such a persistent current can be detected by means of the magnetic field it sets up.

Over a wide range of the temperatures of practical interest, the resistivity of a metal can be represented by a linear curve.   The data of Fig. 8 show this statement to be accurately true for copper for temperatures from $-200°$ C to $+300°$ C, and approximately true for still higher temperatures.   It is customary to use the resistivity ρ_{20} at $20°$ C as a reference value, since $20°$ C $=68°$ F is usually taken as the specification of 'room temperature.'   The resistivity ρ_T at temperature T (Centigrade) is written in the form

$$\rho_T = \rho_{20} + \text{const} \times (T - 20° \text{ C}),$$

which is the equation of a straight line for ρ_T as a function of T; the line passes through the point $\rho_T = \rho_{20}$, $T = 20°$ C.   The constant is usually written as $\alpha_{20}\,\rho_{20}$, so that the equation takes the form

$$\rho_T = \rho_{20} + \alpha_{20}\,\rho_{20}\,(T - 20° \text{ C}), \tag{11}$$

or
$$\rho_T = \rho_{20}\,[1 + \alpha_{20}\,(T - 20° \text{ C})]. \tag{12}$$

The constant α_{20} is called the *temperature coefficient of resistance* at $20°$ C.   Since we can write (11) in the form

$$\alpha_{20} = \left(\frac{\rho_T - \rho_{20}}{\rho_{20}}\right) \Big/ (T - 20° \text{ C}),$$

we see that the value α_{20} is independent of the units used for the resistivity ρ; it has the same value whether ρ is in ohm·m or ohms per mil ft. α_{20} is the *relative* change in resistivity per C degree change in temperature.   As seen in Table I, α_{20} has a magnitude of about 0.004 per C degree for most metals.   This value corresponds to an increase in resistivity of about 0.4 per cent per C deg rise in temperature, or 100 per cent for a 250 C deg rise.   Such an increase is very large compared, for example, with linear expansion, where the length increases only about 0.001 per cent per C deg.

Because changes in physical dimensions are only about $\frac{1}{400}$ the change in resistivity with temperature, we can neglect changes in dimensions in discussing the change in resistance of a conductor of given size and shape.   If we multiply (12) on both sides by l/A, where l is the length and A the cross-sectional area of a conductor, we obtain

$$\frac{\rho_T\,l}{A} = \frac{\rho_{20}\,l}{A}\,[1 + \alpha_{20}\,(T - 20° \text{ C})],$$

or, by (9),
$$R_T = R_{20}\,[1 + \alpha_{20}\,(T - 20° \text{ C})]. \tag{13}$$

This very useful equation expresses the resistance of any conductor at temperature T in terms of its resistance at temperature $20°$ C.

Since the change in resistance of a conductor as the temperature changes is large enough to be easily measured, the resistance of a conductor can be used as a thermometer—the so-called *resistance thermometer*.

612   CURRENT ELECTRICITY

In particular, refractory metals like tungsten can be used to measure very high temperatures in this way.

For construction of laboratory apparatus, such as resistance boxes, it is desirable to have a material of very low temperature coefficient so that the resistance will not change when the resistor is heated by current through it. This requirement has been met by certain alloys that have been developed specifically for the purpose—notably manganin and constantan (see Table I).

Example. *A copper wire has resistance of 2 ohms per meter length at 20° C. What must be the electric intensity in the wire if the current is 15 amp? What electric intensity is required to force the same current through the wire at 150° C?*

At 20° C, a voltage of $(15 \text{ amp})(2 \, \omega) = 30$ v is required per meter length. Electric intensity equals voltage gradient so the electric intensity is 30 v/m.

The resistance of the same meter length of wire at 150° C is found by substituting $R_{20} = 2 \, \omega$, $\alpha_{20} = 0.004/\text{C deg}$, $T = 150°$ C in (13) to obtain

$$R_{150} = 2 \, \omega \, [1 + 0.004 \, (130)] = 3.04 \, \omega.$$

The voltage gradient for a 15-amp current thus increases to $(15)(3.04)$ v/m = 45.6 v/m.

6. RESISTANCE OF INSULATORS AND SEMICONDUCTORS

THE RESISTANCE of nonmetallic solids (insulators) is not really infinite —there is some extremely slight conductivity. But the resistance of an insulator is enormous compared with that of a metal; it is greater by a factor of about 10^{20}, and for most practical purposes the resistance can be considered infinite. Typical values of resistivity are

Bakelite: 10^{10} ohm·m,	Mica: 10^{15} ohm·m,	Shellac: 10^{14} ohm·m,
Glass: 10^{12} ohm·m,	Rubber: 10^{16} ohm·m,	Sulfur: 10^{15} ohm·m.

These numbers are intended only to give the correct order of magnitude, because the resistivity varies from sample to sample, decreases with increasing potential gradient so that Ohm's law is not obeyed, and decreases very sharply with increasing temperature.

The above values apply to current conducted through the body of the material. For exposed insulators, the leakage of current over the surface is usually much greater than the charge flow through the body of the material. Particularly when the surface is wet or dusty, the leakage over the surface of transmission-line insulators can be very troublesome, whereas the body leakage is entirely negligible. It is for this reason that such insulators are corrugated to increase the length of surface leakage path, and are made with 'skirts' to keep part of this path dry.

Carbon is one nonmetal that is a fairly good electrical conductor. Its resistivity is about 3500×10^{-8} ohm·m at 20° C. Unlike metals, it has a negative temperature coefficient of resistance of about -0.0005 per C deg. Its resistivity drops to 2700×10^{-8} ohm·m at 500° C, 2100×10^{-8} at

1000° C, and 1100×10^{-8} at 2000° C.   Carbon is used in 'brushes' of electrical machinery, in the carbon-button microphone, and in the carbon-pile rheostat.   Carbon was the only material available for incandescent-lamp filaments before it was discovered how to draw tungsten wire; all other commercial conducting materials soften or melt at too low a temperature.   Carbon is used for one electrode in a dry cell.

There is a class of materials called *semiconductors* which is assuming increasing technical importance.   The most important of these materials are the metallic oxides and sulfides CuO, ZnO, and PbS (galena), and the elements Ge, Si, and Se.   Semiconductors have a feeble electronic conductivity which increases rapidly in exponential fashion with increasing temperature.   For example, CuO has resistivity about 1×10^3 ohm·m at 20° C but only one-tenth this resistivity at 70° C.   The explanation of this behavior is that these materials have no free electrons at the absolute zero of temperature, but as the temperature rises, more and more electrons are 'boiled off' from their parent atoms and become free to wander about in the material and to conduct electricity.   Since at ordinary temperatures the number of free electrons is very low compared with the number in a metal, the resistivity is still very high.

One important application of a semiconductor is the copper-oxide rectifier.   A thin layer of CuO is formed on one side of a sheet of copper. If the type of contact between the copper oxide and the copper is just right, it is found that electrons will flow freely from the copper into the copper oxide but not in the reverse direction.   Hence, when this sheet is placed in a circuit as indicated in Fig. 9, current will flow through it in only one way and an alternating potential will give a rectified unidirectional current.   A rough explanation is that a large current of electrons can pass from the metal into the semiconductor, greatly supplementing the supply of free electrons in the semiconductor and hence permitting the passage of current through it.   In the reverse direction the electron current is necessarily very small, since there are very few free electrons in the semiconductor and a supply cannot enter from the lead sheet because contact conditions at this junction do not satisfy the critical conditions necessary to permit their entry.

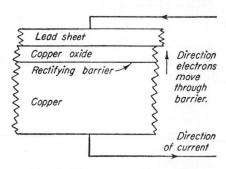

Fig. 9. The copper-oxide rectifier.

Other common types of rectifiers made from semiconductors are the *selenium rectifier* and the *silicon rectifier*.   The selenium rectifier is made by depositing a thin layer of selenium on steel or aluminum and, after heat treatment, applying an alloy of low melting point to the selenium surface. The rectifying barrier is located between the selenium and the alloy; electrons pass readily from the alloy to the selenium, and hence the current direction is from the selenium to the alloy. In the silicon rectifier the rectifying barrier is at a 'point contact' between a fine wire of tungsten, phosphor bronze, or platinum and the surface of a silicon crystal; the current direction is from the silicon to the fine wire. The second contact to the silicon crystal is a soldered connection.

PROBLEMS

1. What is the magnitude of the constant current in a wire if it is found that 2400 coulombs of charge flow through the wire in 2 min?   Ans: 20 amp.

2. An electroplating tank requires 180,000 coulombs per hour. What current must be fed to the tank?

3. How many coulombs are delivered by a storage battery in 24 hr if it is supplying current at the rate of 2 amp?   Ans: 1.73×10^5 coul.

4. There are approximately 10^{29} free electrons per cubic meter of copper (one per atom). For a current of 25 amp in a wire of 1 mm² cross section, what is the *average* speed of 'drift' of the free electrons along the wire?

5. Within limits, the total amount of charge that a storage battery will deliver before it goes 'dead' is independent of the rate at which the charge is delivered. A typical automobile battery is guaranteed for 80 ampere·hours, which means that it will deliver 1 amp for 80 hr, or 2 amp for 40 hr, and so on. (a) How many coulombs is it guaranteed to deliver? (b) How many amperes will it deliver for 5 hr? (c) If the starter draws 500 amp, how long would a fresh battery drive the starter?   Ans: (a) 2.88×10^5 coul; (b) 16 amp; (c) 9.6 min.

6. Why is a coulomb sometimes called an *ampere·second*? How many coulombs are there in an *ampere·hour*?

7. If a storage battery is supplying 20 amp and has an EMF of 6 v, what power is it delivering?   Ans: 120 watts.

8. A 120-v generator delivers 50 kw to an electric furnace. What current is the generator supplying?

9. What voltage should a generator have if it is to supply a 50-kw furnace with a current of 200 amp?   Ans: 250 volts.

10. What current must a 6-v battery deliver if it is to supply 2 hp to an automobile starter?

11. What horsepower must a steam engine have if it is to drive a 3300-v electric generator capable of supplying 150 amp, if the generator converts 90 per cent of the mechanical energy supplied to it into electrical energy?   Ans: 738 hp.

12. If a water turbine delivers 900 hp to an electric generator of 95 per cent efficiency, what current will the generator deliver at 1400 v?

13. The difference of potential between the ends of a wire is 18 v and the current is 2 amp. What is the resistance of the wire?   Ans: 9 ω.

14. What power is expended in a 110-ω resistor connected across a 200-v DC power line?

15. What is the resistance of a 100-w bulb in a 110-v DC power line?   Ans: 121 ω.

16. A current of 5 amp flows through a resistance of 50 ω for 1 hr. How much heat is generated in joules? in kcal?

17. What is the resistance of an immersed coil of wire that heats a liter of water from 19° C to 99° C in 5 min when 110 v are applied?   Ans: 10.9 ω.

18. It is required to generate 1 kcal of heat per minute in a resistor connected to 110 v. What must be the resistance?

19. At 4 cents per kwh, what is the cost of operating fifteen 40-w lamps for 8 hr?   Ans: 19.2 cents.

20. At 3 cents per kwh, what is the cost of operating a 5-hp motor for 12.5 hr?

21. The coil of a powerful electromagnet is made of copper tubing and is cooled by water flowing through the tubing. The current is 500 amp and the resistance 0.24 ω, and 0.6 ft^3/min of water flows through the coil. Find the temperature rise of the water on the assumption that all the heat generated is carried away by the water stream.   Ans: 91.0 F deg.

22. It is desired to design a 220-v water-cooled electromagnet in which the windings carry 350 amp. What flow of cooling water, in ft^3/min, is required to carry off all the heat if the water is to enter at 50° F and leave at 170° F?

23. At 20° C, what is the resistance of a standard-aluminum bus bar $\frac{1}{2}$ cm $\times$ 2 cm in section and 20 m long?   Ans: 5.66 $\times$ 10^{-3} ω.

24. At 20° C, what is the resistance of an annealed-copper bus bar $\frac{1}{2}$ cm $\times$ 2 cm in section and 20 m long?

25. From the resistivity of annealed copper in Table I, compute the resistance of 1000 ft of #10 wire (101.9 mils in diameter), at 20° C. Compare your answer with that given in Table II.

26. What is the resistance of 5000 ft of #10 silver wire at 20° C?

27. If 150 ft of round nichrome resistance wire is to have a resistance of 10 ohms at 20° C, what diameter of wire should be used?   Ans: 101 mils.

28. If 150 ft of round nichrome resistance wire is to have a resistance of 90 ohms at 20° C, what diameter of wire should be used?

29. Magnet wire is sometimes made of square cross section to obtain closer packing. What is the cross-sectional area in circular mils of wire 102 mils square? To what wire gauge is this approximately equivalent in terms of area and resistance?   Ans: 13,200 circ mils; #9.

30. Show that 1 ohm·m = 6.015 $\times$ 10^8 ohms per mil ft.

NOTE: The density at 20° C of standard-annealed copper is 8.89 g/cm^3; that of hard-drawn aluminum is 2.70 g/cm^3; and that of silver is 10.5 g/cm^3. These values should be used in Probs. 31 and 32.

31. If 1000 ft of standard-annealed copper wire has diameter d_{Cu}, weight w_{Cu}, and resistance R, what are the diameters d_{Ag}, d_{Al} and the weights w_{Ag}, w_{Al} of 1000 ft of silver and hard-drawn aluminum wire having the same resistance?
                     Ans: 0.972 d_{Cu}, 1.28 d_{Cu}; 1.12 w_{Cu}, 0.499 w_{Cu}.

32. (a) What are the ratios $R_{Ag}:R_{Cu}:R_{Al}$ of the resistances of silver, annealed copper, and hard-drawn aluminum wires of the same length and the same *diameter?* Which is the best and which the poorest conductor of the three, volume for volume? (b) What are the ratios $R_{Ag}:R_{Cu}:R_{Al}$ of the resistances of silver, annealed copper, and hard-drawn aluminum wires of the same length and the same *weight?* Which is the best and which the poorest conductor of the three, weight for weight?

33. The resistance of a coil of pure copper wire at 20° C is 48.0 ohms. What will be the resistance of the coil at 50° C?   Ans: 53.7 ohms.

34. The resistance of a copper wire is 4.90 ohms at 20° C. What is it at 80° C?

35. Find the resistance at 30° C of 1000 ft of #19 copper wire.

Ans: 8.37 ohms.

36. The resistance of a conductor is 50.3 ohms at 20° C and 55.9 ohms at 50° C. Calculate the temperature coefficient of resistance of the material.

37. The resistance of the copper field coils of a generator is measured when the room temperature is 25° C and is found to be 225 ohms. What will be the resistance of these coils at the operating temperature of 90° C? Ans: 281 ohms.

38. What is the resistance at 20° C of the tungsten filament of a lamp bulb which operates at 2000° C and 100 watts on 110 volts DC?

39. The primary coil of a transformer has a resistance of 5.48 ohms at 20° C. When the transformer is operating at full load, the resistance is 6.32 ohms. What is the operating temperature? Ans: 59.0° C.

40. What will the resistance of a silver wire be at −20° C, if its resistance at 15° C is 19.5 ohms?

41. To prevent insulation damage, it is specified that the field coils of a certain type of motor should not exceed 105° C when it is running continuously under full load. The standard-copper field coils of a particular motor were found to have a resistance of 6.38 ohms at 20°C and 8.26 ohms during a full-load run. Did the motor meet this specification?

42. A platinum wire has a resistance of 254 ohms at 20° C. When it is placed in a furnace, its resistance is 1630 ohms. What is the temperature of the furnace?

43. Show that the resistances of a conductor at temperatures T' and T' are related by the equation

$$R_{T'} = R_T \frac{1 + \alpha_{20} \left(T' - 20° \text{ C}\right)}{1 + \alpha_{20} \left(T - 20° \text{ C}\right)}.$$

44. The temperature coefficient α_{T_0} referred to temperature T_0 is defined by the equation

$$R_T = R_{T_0} \left[1 + \alpha_{T_0} \left(T - T_0\right)\right].$$

(a) Show that

$$\alpha_{T_0} = \frac{\alpha_{20}}{\left[1 + \alpha_{20} \left(T_0 - 20° \text{ C}\right)\right]}.$$

(b) Show that if α_{T_0} and $\alpha_{T_0'}$ refer to any two base temperatures T_0 and T_0',

$$\alpha_{T_0'} = \frac{\alpha_{T_0}}{\left[1 + \alpha_{T_0} \left(T_0' - T_0\right)\right]}.$$

45. A condenser is made by placing sheets of metal foil on the two sides of a glass plate 1 mm thick, of dielectric constant $K = 8.0$. The foil area is 0.25 m² on each side. The condenser is charged to 1000 volts and then disconnected from the voltage source. (a) Find the current conducted through the glass if $\rho = 10^{12}$ ohm·m. (b) With this current, how long would it take the difference of potential to drop by 10 volts? Ans: (a) 0.25 μa; (b) 0.71 sec.

46. Show that the time required for the difference of potential to drop 1 per cent in a charged condenser constructed like that of Prob. 45 is $(8.84 \times 10^{-14}$ sec/ohm·m) $K\rho$, and that this time is independent of the thickness of the plate, the area of the foil, and the voltage.

47. A metal sphere 20 cm in diameter and charged to 1000 volts is supported on a glass rod 1 cm in diameter and 15 cm long. (a) What magnitude of current is conducted through the glass rod to a grounded metal base? (b) If this current were the only source of leakage, how long would it take the potential to drop by 10 volts?

48. The dielectric strength of the glass used in making the condenser described in Prob. 45 is 400 kv/cm. The difference of potential is raised slowly until the glass plate is ruptured. Find the leakage current through the glass plate just before the breakdown occurs. Find also the maximum charge on the condenser plates and the maximum energy that can be stored in the condenser.

CHAPTER 30

DIRECT ELECTRIC CURRENTS

IN THIS CHAPTER we consider direct-current (DC) circuits, and the instruments used in direct-current measurements. Development of the laws governing alternating currents (AC) must necessarily be postponed until after the subjects of electromagnetism and electromagnetic induction have been studied.

1. TERMINAL VOLTAGE OF GENERATORS, MOTORS, AND BATTERIES

WE HAVE DEFINED a source of EMF V as a device that will do work of amount V, in joules per coulomb of charge passing through it, deriving the energy from a mechanical, chemical, or other source. This statement

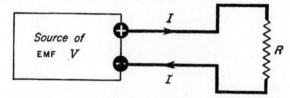

Fig. 1. A source of EMF supplies electrical energy that heats a resistor.

regarding the work done is true if charges pass through the source of EMF in a particular direction, from what is called the *negative terminal* to what is called the *positive terminal*. This situation is illustrated in Fig. 1, in which the source of EMF does work of amount V, in joules per coulomb of charge passing *through it from the − terminal to the + terminal*. This work raises the potential (potential energy per coulomb) of the + terminal by amount V above that of the − terminal.* This difference of potential V across the resistance R causes current in the external circuit from the + terminal to the − terminal, the energy furnished by the source reappearing as heat in the resistor. The magnitude of the current is $I = V/R$, in amperes or coulombs/second. Since each coulomb has been given energy of amount V, the rate of energy delivery is $VI = V^2/R = I^2R$, in joules/sec, or watts, in agreement with (5), p. 606.

---

* In this introductory paragraph we are neglecting a correction, arising from resistance internal to the source of EMF itself, that will be discussed a few pages later.

When current I passes through a resistance R *in either direction*, electrical energy is converted into heat at the rate I^2R, in watts.

But only when current passes through a source of EMF *from the −terminal to the + terminal* is energy of some other form changed into electrical energy at the rate V, in joules per coulomb. If, by employing a higher EMF in the external circuit, current is forced *backward* through the source of EMF as in Fig. 2 (in at the + terminal, through the source from + to −, and out at the − terminal) electrical energy is changed into energy of the other form, and each coulomb passing through the source loses energy of amount V. *A source of EMF represents a reversible device for changing from electrical energy to some other form of energy.* If current is sent backward through a battery, electrical energy is converted into chemical energy—in a recoverable form if the battery is a storage battery, in a form mostly useless if the battery is a dry cell. Send current backward through a generator and you have a motor. There is no difference in principle between a DC generator and a DC motor. All such machines are called *dynamos* and will operate either as generators or motors. If a generator turned at a certain speed in a certain direction changes mechanical energy to electrical energy at the rate V, in joules per coulomb of charge passing through it, then if current is forced through it backward, the generator will turn, as a motor, in the same direction; and when sufficient current is supplied to bring the dynamo up to the same speed, it will convert electrical energy into mechanical energy at the same rate V, in joules per coulomb passed through it.

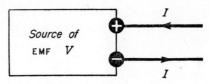

Fig. 2. A current is forced backward through a source of EMF.

In contrast, a resistor is a device that converts electrical energy into heat no matter what the direction of current; it is not possible to reverse the process and regain electrical energy from heat. The potential always *drops* by an amount IR as we traverse a resistor *in the direction* of the current; this change in potential is called the *IR-drop*.

A battery, or a dynamo turning in a certain direction, has one terminal that can be permanently labeled + and one that can be permanently labeled −. When no charge flows, the + terminal has a potential V_E (E for EMF) above that of the − terminal. When charge flows through the source of EMF from − to +, chemical or mechanical energy is converted to electrical energy at the rate V_E, in joules per coulomb of charge. When charge flows in the other direction, the same amount of energy, V_E, in joules per coulomb, is converted from electrical to mechanical or chemical form. The + terminal would always be at potential V_E above the − except for the fact that all dynamos and batteries have *internal* resistance in the internal current path *between* their terminals. As a result of internal resistance, there is a conversion of some energy to heat inside the battery or dynamo, no matter which direction the current has. The copper-wire and carbon-brush path through a dynamo, or the metal-plate and electrolyte path through a battery, has a certain resistance R_I (I for *internal*), so that, for current I in *either* direction, energy is converted into heat at the rate IR_I, in joules per coulomb of charge passing.

Because of internal resistance, the difference of potential V_T between the *terminals* of a battery or dynamo when charge flows is not exactly the same as the EMF V_E, which is the difference of potential when no charge flows, although the difference is usually small for a *good* battery or dynamo. We must distinguish two cases:

Generator, or battery on discharge. Internal current passes from $-$ to $+$ as in Fig. 1. Each coulomb of charge gains energy V_E from mechanical or chemical energy but loses energy IR_I in heat. Net gain is V_E-IR_I, in joules/coulomb. Hence, the difference of potential, V_T, between the $+$ and $-$ terminals is

$$V_T = V_E - IR_I. \qquad \begin{pmatrix}\text{terminal voltage of}\\ \text{generator, or of bat-}\\ \text{tery on discharge}\end{pmatrix} \quad (1)$$

Multiplication of this equation by I gives an equation that expresses the power balance:

$$V_T I \quad = \quad V_E I \quad - \quad I^2 R_I. \qquad (2)$$

$$\left\{\begin{matrix}\text{Electrical power}\\ \text{delivered by the}\\ \text{source of EMF}\end{matrix}\right\} = \left\{\begin{matrix}\text{electrical power}\\ \text{generated in the}\\ \text{source of EMF}\end{matrix}\right\} - \left\{\begin{matrix}\text{electrical power con-}\\ \text{verted into heat in}\\ \text{the source of EMF.}\end{matrix}\right\}$$

Motor, or battery on charge. Internal current passes from $+$ to $-$ as in Fig. 2. Each coulomb of charge loses energy V_E that is changed to mechanical or chemical energy *and* loses energy IR_I in heat. Total loss is V_E+IR_I in joules per coulomb. Hence, in this case the $+$ terminal is at higher potential than the $-$ by

$$V_T = V_E + IR_I. \qquad \begin{pmatrix}\text{terminal voltage of}\\ \text{motor, or of battery}\\ \text{on charge}\end{pmatrix} \quad (3)$$

Multiplication of this equation by I gives the power balance:

$$V_T I \quad = \quad V_E I \quad + \quad I^2 R_I. \qquad (4)$$

$$\left\{\begin{matrix}\text{Electrical power de-}\\ \text{livered to the motor,}\\ \text{or to the battery on}\\ \text{charge}\end{matrix}\right\} = \left\{\begin{matrix}\text{electrical power}\\ \text{converted to}\\ \text{mechanical or}\\ \text{chemical energy}\end{matrix}\right\} + \left\{\begin{matrix}\text{electrical power con-}\\ \text{verted into heat in}\\ \text{the motor, or in the}\\ \text{battery on charge.}\end{matrix}\right\}$$

In the case of a motor, the quantity V_E, which gives the mechanical energy developed in joules per coulomb of charge, is commonly called the *back*-EMF, since it is a voltage in a direction opposing the current, which is given by $I = (V_T - V_E)/R_I$, as we see from (3).

Example. *A* DC *motor has an internal resistance of* 2 ω. *When delivering its rated mechanical power, it draws* 10 amp *from* 120-v *power lines.   What mechanical power is developed by the motor?*

The situation is that depicted in Fig. 2, with the motor acting as a source of EMF.   The motor must be acting as a source of EMF or the current through the motor would be 60 amp in place of 10.   The motor *generates* a back-EMF in a manner that we shall discuss later in Chap. 34, and it is the loss in energy of the charge passing through this generated EMF from high potential to low that represents the gain in mechanical energy.   From (3) we find

$$V_E = V_T - IR_I = (120 - 10\cdot2) \text{ v} = 100 \text{ v}$$

for the back-EMF.   The mechanical power developed is $V_E I = 1000$ w, while the heat developed is $I^2 R_I = 200$ w, the sum of these representing the total power input $V_T I = 1200$ w.

2. SIMPLE CIRCUITS; RESISTORS IN PARALLEL AND IN SERIES

THE SIMPLEST type of electric circuit is illustrated in Fig. 3.   Here the terminal voltage of the generator or battery, given by (1), is applied

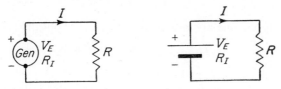

Fig. 3. A resistor connected across a generator or battery.

across the resistor and causes current through it:

$$V_T = IR.$$

Since the terminal voltage itself depends on the current, this relation is an algebraic equation to be solved for I; substituting from (1),

$$V_E - IR_I = IR, \quad \text{or} \quad I = \frac{V_E}{R + R_I}. \tag{5}$$

The current is determined by the EMF and the total resistance in the circuit, both internal and external.   Energetically, the last equation, which may be written as

$$V_E = IR_I + IR,$$

expresses the fact that the chemical or electrical energy V_E given to each coulomb equals the sum of the heat generated by each coulomb in flowing through the internal resistance and that generated in flowing through the external resistance.

A more complicated single-mesh network, in which a battery is being charged by a generator through wires having different resistances, is shown in Fig. 4.   The EMF's and internal resistances of the generator and battery are denoted by V_G, R_G and V_B, R_B.   In this case each coulomb that flows around the circuit gains energy V_G in the generator, and loses V_B to chemical energy in the battery and $IR_G + IR_1 + IR_B + IR_2$ to heat.

Since energy gain must equal energy loss,

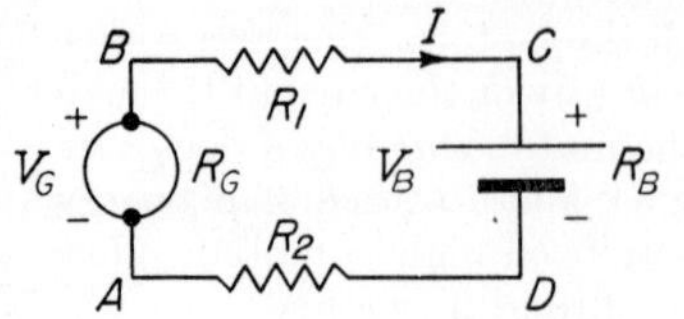

$$V_G = V_B + I(R_G + R_1 + R_B + R_2);$$

hence
$$I = \frac{V_G - V_B}{R_1 + R_2 + R_G + R_B}. \quad (6)$$

Fig. 4. A generator charging a battery.

Alternatively, equation (6) may be derived by considering that the terminal voltages V_{GT} and V_{BT} of the generator and battery oppose each other and that it is only their difference that is available to force current through the external resistances R_1 and R_2. Hence, we write

$$(V_{GT} - V_{BT}) = I(R_1 + R_2). \quad (7)$$

But, from (1),
$$V_{GT} = V_G - IR_G,$$

and, from (3),
$$V_{BT} = V_B + IR_B.$$

When these expressions are substituted in (7), we obtain

$$V_G - IR_G - V_B - IR_B = I(R_1 + R_2),$$

which, when solved for I, gives (6) directly.

It will be readily seen that any simple single-mesh circuit can be solved at once by a generalization of (6). The rule is:

$$\begin{Bmatrix} \text{Current} \\ \text{clockwise} \\ \text{around the} \\ \text{circuit} \end{Bmatrix} = \begin{Bmatrix} algebraic \text{ sum of EMF's counted posi-} \\ \text{tive if they tend to force current} \\ \text{clockwise, negative if they tend to} \\ \text{force current counterclockwise} \end{Bmatrix} \div \begin{Bmatrix} \text{sum of all resist-} \\ \text{ances in the circuit,} \\ \text{both internal and} \\ \text{external.} \end{Bmatrix}$$

If the algebraic sum of EMF's in the above expression comes out negative, the clockwise current also comes out negative; the negative sign indicates that the current is counterclockwise instead of clockwise.

Example. *Determine the current and the differences of potential between point A and points B, C, D in Fig. 4 when $R_1 = 3$ ω, $R_2 = 1$ ω, $V_G = 110$ v, $R_G = 0.2$ ω, $V_B = 24$ v, and $R_B = 0.1$ ω, as in Fig. 5.*

For these constants, equation (6) gives $I = 20$ amp. If we arbitrarily call the potential 0 v at point A, the voltage at B is the terminal voltage of the generator given by (1) as 106 v. There is an IR-drop of 60 v in R_1, which makes the potential at C 46 v. The terminal voltage of the battery on charge is given

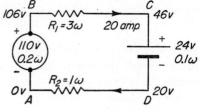

Figure 5

by (3) as 26 v, so the potential drops to 20 v at D. The final drop from D to A is the 20-v IR-drop in R_2. A voltmeter connected between any two of the points A, B, C, D would read the difference between the potential values at these points.

Single-mesh circuits can always be solved by the methods given above. Networks containing more than one mesh will in general need the application of Kirchhoff's laws, which are given in the next section. However some networks can be reduced to a single-mesh circuit by the device of replacing a set of pure resistances by a single equivalent resistance. Suppose that between two points in a circuit, such as A and B in Fig. 6,

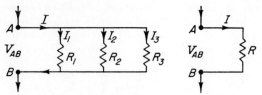

Fig. 6. Resistors in parallel are equivalent to a single resistor of resistance R given by (8).

three resistors are connected in parallel. The voltage across each resistor is the same, V_{AB}. Hence,

$$I_1 = V_{AB}/R_1, \quad I_2 = V_{AB}/R_2, \quad I_3 = V_{AB}/R_3.$$

The current in the external circuit is the sum of these:

$$I = I_1 + I_2 + I_3 = V_{AB}\left(\frac{1}{R_1} + \frac{1}{R_2} + \frac{1}{R_3}\right).$$

The ratio V_{AB}/I is defined as the effective resistance R of the parallel circuit, so that

$$\frac{I}{V_{AB}} = \frac{1}{R} = \frac{1}{R_1} + \frac{1}{R_2} + \frac{1}{R_3}.$$

R, as given by this formula, is the single resistance that will carry the same current with the same voltage as the parallel combination, will generate the same heat, and in general can replace the parallel combination with no effect on the rest of the circuit. For any number N of resistors in parallel, the effective resistance is similarly given by

$$\frac{1}{R} = \frac{1}{R_1} + \frac{1}{R_2} + \cdots + \frac{1}{R_N}. \qquad \binom{\text{resistors}}{\text{in parallel}} \quad (8)$$

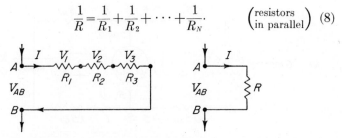

Fig. 7. Resistors in series are equivalent to a single resistor with $R = R_1 + R_2 + R_3$.

In the same way, one can replace a number of resistors in series as in Fig. 7 by a single equivalent resistance

$$R = R_1 + R_2 + \cdots + R_N. \qquad \binom{\text{resistors}}{\text{in series}} \quad (9)$$

To derive this, note that $V_{AB} = V_1 + V_2 + \cdots = I(R_1 + R_2 + \cdots)$, and the effective resistance V_{AB}/I will be $R_1 + R_2 + \cdots$.

Example. *Find the currents through each resistor in the circuit of Fig. 8, where $R_1 = 1 \ \omega$, $R_2 = 2 \ \omega$, $R_3 = 3 \ \omega$, $R_4 = 4 \ \omega$, $R_1 = 0.2 \ \omega$, and $V_E = 6$ v.*

First note that R_3 and R_4 are in parallel connection between the ends of R_1 and R_2; therefore, from (8), R_3 and R_4 can be replaced by a single resistor $R_5 = R_3 R_4/(R_3 + R_4) = (12 \ \omega^2)/(7 \ \omega) = 1.71 \ \omega$. Now R_2 and R_5 are in series connection and can be replaced by $R_6 = R_2 + R_5 = 3.71 \ \omega$. Resistors R_1 and

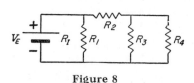

R_6 are in parallel connection across the terminals of the battery and may be replaced by $R_7 = R_1 R_6/(R_1 + R_6) = (3.71 \ \omega^2)/(4.71 \ \omega) = 0.788 \ \omega$. Since R_7 now represents the entire external resistance, the current I through the battery is

Figure 8

given by $I = V_E/(R_1 + R_7) = (6 \text{ v})/(0.988 \ \omega) = 6.07$ amp. The terminal voltage of the battery $V_T = 6.00 \text{ v} - (0.2 \ \omega)(6.07 \text{ amp}) = 4.79$ v. Hence, the current $I_1 = (4.79 \text{ v})/(1 \ \omega) = 4.79$ amp. The current $I_6 = (4.79 \text{ v})/(3.71 \ \omega) = 1.29$ amp, which is also equal to I_2. The voltage drop across R_2 is $(2 \ \omega)(1.29 \text{ amp}) = 2.58$ v; hence the voltage across R_3 and R_4 is $4.79 \text{ v} - 2.58 \text{ v} = 2.21$ v, and $I_3 = (2.21 \text{ v})/(3 \ \omega) = 0.74$ amp, $I_4 = (2.21 \text{ v})/(4 \ \omega) = 0.55$ amp. (It is instructive to redraw the circuit diagram after each successive simplification or replacement of resistance combinations by single resistors such as R_5, R_6, and R_7.)

3. ELECTRICAL NETWORKS; KIRCHHOFF'S LAWS

IN THIS SECTION we shall consider electrical networks more complex than those treated in the previous section. By a *network* we mean an electrical circuit (usually of some complication); like a net, the circuit can be divided into meshes. A *mesh* is one of the separate areas into which the circuit diagram divides the blank paper. Thus Fig. 5 has one mesh; Fig. 9 two; and Fig. 8 three.

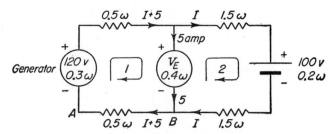

Fig. 9. A generator charges a 100-v battery and drives a motor that draws 5 amp.

There is a straightforward procedure for treatment of a network.   We shall explain the method by using the example of Fig. 9, in which the two unknowns are the charging current I of the battery and the back-EMF V_E of the motor.   We are given that the motor current is 5 amp; hence, we can represent the current delivered by the generator as $I+5$ amp.   This statement is an illustration of

KIRCHHOFF'S FIRST LAW: *At any junction in the circuit the total current flowing toward the junction must equal the total current flowing away.*

Kirchhoff's two laws do not state any new principles, but they do give the two principles that must be systematically applied in the solution of electrical networks.   The second law can be stated as follows:

KIRCHHOFF'S SECOND LAW: *If we start at any point and 'walk' around any closed loop back to our starting point, we must also arrive back at the same electrical potential.   So if, as we walk, we note the different changes in electrical potential arising from* EMF'S, *IR-drops, and IR-rises* (which occur when we happen to walk through a resistance against the current), *and add them all up keeping proper algebraic signs, we must get zero when we have completed our tour of the loop.*

The *loop* contemplated in this law is any closed path in the circuit; for example any of the paths indicated by the fine lines in Fig. 10.

Example.   *In Fig. 9, find the current I and the back-EMF V_E of the motor.*

If we start at point A and walk clockwise around mesh 1 of the net, we encounter successively the following changes in potential:

$+120$ v	(EMF of generator)
$-(0.3\ \omega)(I+5$ amp)	(IR-drop in generator; we walk with the current)
$-(0.5\ \omega)(I+5$ amp)	(IR-drop in line)
$-V_E$	(back-EMF of motor, representing a drop in potential as we walk through it)
$-(0.4\ \omega)(5$ amp)	(IR-drop in motor)
$-(0.5\ \omega)(I+5$ amp)	(IR-drop in line)

The sum must be zero.   This gives the equation

$$120\text{ v}-(0.3\ \omega)(I+5\text{ amp})-(0.5\ \omega)(I+5\text{ amp})-V_E$$
$$-(0.4\ \omega)(5\text{ amp})-(0.5\ \omega)(I+5\text{ amp})=0,$$

or, simplifying, $\qquad 111.5\text{ v}-(1.3\ \omega)I-V_E=0.$ $\qquad$ (i)

This single equation cannot be solved for the two unknowns, but we can get a second equation from the second mesh.   Starting at point B and walking clockwise around mesh 2, we encounter the following changes in potential:

$+V_E$	(this time the back-EMF of the motor represents an increase of potential in the direction we are walking)
$+(0.4\ \omega)(5$ amp)	(an IR-rise, since we are walking against the current)
$-(1.5\ \omega)I$	(IR-drop in line)
-100 v	(drop in potential arising from EMF of battery)
$-(0.2\ \omega)I$	(IR-drop in battery)
$-(1.5\ \omega)I$	(IR-drop in line)

Setting the sum equal to zero gives

$$V_E + (0.4\,\omega)(5\text{ amp}) - (1.5\,\omega)I - 100\text{ v} - (0.2\,\omega)I - (1.5\,\omega)I = 0,$$

or
$$-98\text{ v} - (3.2\,\omega)I + V_E = 0. \qquad \text{(ii)}$$

Equations (i) and (ii) can be solved simultaneously for I and V_E. Adding (i) and (ii) gives

$$13.5\text{ v} - (4.5\,\omega)I = 0,$$

or
$$I = 3\text{ amp}. \qquad \text{(iii)}$$

Substitution in (i) then gives $V_E = 107.6$ v. (iv)

These values of I and V_E check when substituted in (ii).

There is a third equation which could have been used in place of either (i) or (ii), or which can be used as a check on the work. It is derived by walking around the whole outside of the circuit from A clockwise back to A. Let us use it as a check on the current values of $I = 3$ amp through the battery and $I + 5$ amp $= 8$ amp delivered by the generator. When we walk around the outside of meshes 1 and 2 combined, we encounter the following changes in potential in volts:

$+120$ v	(EMF of generator)
$-(0.3\,\omega)(8\text{ amp})$	(IR-drop in generator)
$-(0.5\,\omega)(8\text{ amp})$	(IR-drop in line)
$-(1.5\,\omega)(3\text{ amp})$	(IR-drop in line)
-100 v	(drop arising from EMF of battery)
$-(0.2\,\omega)(3\text{ amp})$	(IR-drop in battery)
$-(1.5\,\omega)(3\text{ amp})$	(IR-drop in line)
$-(0.5\,\omega)(8\text{ amp})$	(IR-drop in line)

The sum of these voltages does equal zero:

$$120 - 2.4 - 4 - 4.5 - 100 - 0.6 - 4.5 - 4 = 0.$$

By a procedure similar to the above, a set of simultaneous equations may be found that will solve any network, provided the number of unknowns is not greater than the number of meshes in the network. The unknowns may be values of current, EMF, terminal voltage, or resistance.

The general procedure for applying Kirchhoff's laws to the solution of networks may be outlined as follows:

1. *Draw the circuit diagram*, and label all known currents, voltages, and resistances. *Put $+$, $-$ signs on all sources of EMF to show the high- and low-potential sides.

2. *Assign letters to all unknown EMF's and to all unknown resistances.* However, in case both the EMF and the internal resistance of a source of EMF are unknown, it will be impossible to solve for both unknowns, and one should work directly with the terminal voltage, assigning a letter to the terminal voltage if it is unknown.

3. *Assign current directions* in all branches of the circuit in which the current is unknown. Frequently it will be impossible to guess the correct direction of the current, but this uncertainty is not important. Guess a *definite* direction; and if you have guessed incorrectly, the computed magnitude of the current will merely come out negative in the final solution.

4. *Assign symbols to all unknown currents,* but in making these assignments keep the number of symbols to a minimum by taking full advantage of Kirchhoff's first law at each current junction. Thus, in Fig. 9, there are two unknown currents; but if the current through the battery is called I, the current delivered by the generator must be $I+5$ amp, so that only one unknown *symbol* need be introduced.

5. *Apply Kirchhoff's second law to a number of loops equal to the number of meshes in the circuit.* You need not use the individual meshes exclusively, but you cannot hope to get more independent equations than there are individual meshes. The loops you choose must altogether traverse each circuit element at least once. Thus, in the four-mesh circuit symbolized in Fig. 10, four loops must be used. These could be the loops labeled 1, 2, 3, and 4, which are the meshes

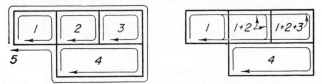

Fig. 10. Various circuit loops can be used in writing Kirchhoff's laws for this four-mesh circuit, as discussed in the text.

themselves; or any *one* of these loops could be omitted and replaced by the outside loop 5. Another alternative would be to choose the loops labeled 1, 1+2, and 1+2+3, along with loop 4. Various other combinations are possible. Now walk around each loop, either clockwise or counterclockwise, back to your starting point. In walking, write down each EMF (or terminal voltage), positive if it represents a rise of potential as you walk, negative if it represents a drop. Also write down the IR-drop or IR-rise associated with each resistance. If you walk through a resistance in the assumed direction of the current, there is a drop in potential which is called negative. If you walk against the assumed direction of the current there is a rise of potential, called positive. When the walk is completed, the algebraic sum of all these changes in potential is equated to zero.

6. *Solve the resulting set of linear equations for the unknowns.* Draw a new diagram, or use a colored pencil, to show the numerical current values and corrected directions of current. Check this final solution against Kirchhoff's first law at each junction, and check also by applying the second law to some circuit loops not previously used.

This procedure is best illustrated by an example somewhat more complex than that of Fig. 9:

Example. *Figure 11 shows a generator and a battery, of known* EMF *and internal resistance, connected in parallel to a motor drawing a known current. In addition to the ordinary leads there is a single low-resistance lead from the motor back to the generator. Find the terminal voltage of the motor and the currents in all the leads.*

Let us assume that since the battery EMF is lower than the generator EMF, the generator will furnish a charging current to the battery as well as furnishing the motor current. Call the battery charging current I_1 and the generator current I_1+12 amp, as in the figure. At the junction below the motor, the motor current splits in an unknown proportion. If we call the current in one wire I_2, the other wire will carry $12\text{ amp}-I_2$, as indicated. All the other currents are now determined, and Kirchhoff's first law is satisfied at each junction, as indicated in Fig. 11.

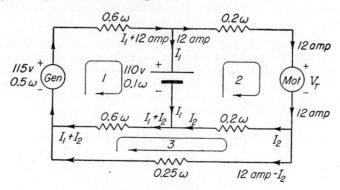

Fig. 11. Three-mesh-network problem.

Now that we have labeled all wires with the current directions and magnitudes, we proceed to apply Kirchhoff's second law to each of the three meshes of the network. The student should carefully check each term in the following equations.

Mesh 1: $115\text{ v}-(0.5\ \omega)(I_1+12\text{ amp})-(0.6\ \omega)(I_1+12\text{ amp})$
$$-110\text{ v}-(0.1\ \omega)I_1-(0.6\ \omega)(I_1+I_2)=0.$$

Mesh 2: $110\text{ v}+(0.1\ \omega)I_1-2.4\text{ v}-V_T-(0.2\ \omega)I_2=0.$

Mesh 3: $(0.6\ \omega)(I_1+I_2)+(0.2\ \omega)I_2-(0.25\ \omega)(12\text{ amp}-I_2)=0.$

These three equations simplify to

$$-8.2\text{ v}-(1.8\ \omega)I_1-(0.6\ \omega)I_2=0, \tag{i}$$
$$107.6\text{ v}+(0.1\ \omega)I_1-(0.2\ \omega)I_2-V_T=0, \tag{ii}$$
$$-3.0\text{ v}+(0.6\ \omega)I_1+(1.05\ \omega)I_2=0. \tag{iii}$$

We can eliminate I_1 by multiplying (iii) by three, which gives

$$-9.0\text{ v}+(1.8\ \omega)I_1+(3.15\ \omega)I_2=0,$$

and adding (i), to get $-17.2\text{ v}+(2.55\ \omega)I_2=0,$

or $I_2=6.75\text{ amp}.$

When this value is substituted in (iii), we find

$$I_1=-6.82\text{ amp}.$$

(The negative sign shows that we guessed the direction of I_1 incorrectly.) Finally, V_T is obtained by substitution in (ii):

$$107.6\text{ v}-0.68\text{ v}-1.35\text{ v}-V_T=0,$$
$$V_T=105.57\text{ v}.$$

The currents that occur in the various other conductors of Fig. 11 are

$I_1+12\text{ amp}=5.18\text{ amp},$ $12\text{ amp}-I_2=5.25\text{ amp},$ $I_1+I_2=-0.07\text{ amp}.$

We guessed incorrectly the directions of the battery current and of the current through the lower 0.6-ω lead. Both the generator and battery furnish current to the motor, and a small part of the battery current, as well as all the generator current, returns by way of the 0.25-ω lead. When the current directions are corrected and numerical values are entered, we get the solution shown in Fig. 12.

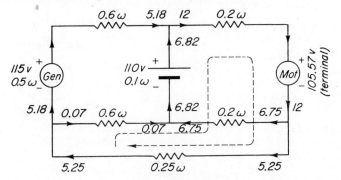

Fig. 12. Solution to the problem of Fig. 11 (currents are in amperes).

A little mental arithmetic shows that this solution satisfies the first law at each junction. As an additional check we shall write Kirchhoff's second law for the loop indicated by the broken arrow in Fig. 12. For this loop we obtain the following equation (in volts):

$$-0.07(0.6)+110-6.82(0.1)-12(0.2)-105.57-5.25(0.25)=0$$

or
$$-0.04+110-0.68-2.40-105.57-1.31=0$$

or
$$0.00=0,$$

a satisfactory check. As a second check we might walk around the whole outside of the circuit beginning at the lower left, to get, in volts,

$$115-5.18(0.5)-5.18(0.6)-12(0.2)-105.57-5.25(0.25)=0$$

or
$$115-2.59-3.11-2.40-105.57-1.31=0$$

or
$$0.02=0,$$

a check within the rounding-off error of the computation.

4. THE DC VOLTMETER

We shall now describe three important DC measuring instruments, the voltmeter, the ammeter, and the potentiometer. The indicating element of all three of these instruments is a galvanometer of the d'Arsonval type, whose operation will be described in Chap. 32. Basically, a galvanometer is an instrument that gives a pointer deflection proportional to the current through itself. It has a certain resistance R_G, and its sensitivity is characterized by the current I_G, or voltage $V_G = R_G I_G$, required for *full-scale deflection*. Good voltmeters and ammeters employ sensitive galvanometers, with I_G and V_G of the order of a thousandth of an ampere or volt, or even less. The galvanometer used in a potentiometer must be even more sensitive.

A voltmeter is made by putting a resistance (called a *multiplier*) in series with a galvanometer, as in Fig. 13. If we want *full-scale deflection of the voltmeter* for voltage V_F, we must add enough resistance R_M so that with voltage V_F across the terminals we get only the small current I_G through the galvanometer. Since

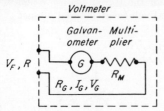

Fig. 13. A DC voltmeter. The symbols V_F, I_G, V_G refer to *full-scale* deflection.

$$I_G(R_G + R_M) = V_F,$$

and

$$I_G R_G = V_G,$$

we find, by division, that

$$\frac{R_G + R_M}{R_G} = \frac{V_F}{V_G}. \tag{10}$$

Example. *In Fig. 13, if* $R_G = 1$ ω, $I_G = 1$ mv, $V_G = 1$ mv, *and we want* V_F *to be* 200 *volts full-scale, find the multiplier resistance.*

Substitution in (10) gives

$$\frac{1\ \omega + R_M}{1\ \omega} = \frac{200}{0.001} = 200{,}000,$$

so that

$$R_M = 199{,}999\ \omega.$$

The total resistance R of this voltmeter would be $R = R_G + R_M = 200{,}000\ \omega$.

A voltmeter must have a very high resistance if it is to serve its purpose because it is intended to measure the difference of potential between two points in a circuit without disturbing the currents in the circuit. No voltmeter, except one of the electrostatic type, actually does this because the voltmeter does draw a minute current. The current drawn, and hence the deflection of the galvanometer, is proportional to the voltage across the terminals. Only if this current is very small compared to the current flowing in the circuit under consideration has the voltmeter accomplished its purpose. The voltmeter always reads the difference of potential between its own terminals, and hence the difference of potential that exists between the two points to which it is connected *after* it is connected. If the voltmeter draws negligible current, this voltage will be the same as that between the same two points *before* it was connected.

Note that (10) can be rewritten in the form

$$\frac{R}{V_F} = \frac{R_G}{V_G} = \frac{1}{I_G} \quad \text{in } \frac{\text{ohms}}{\text{volt}},$$

where R is the total resistance of the voltmeter. Hence, any voltmeter made from a certain galvanometer, characterized by definite values of R_G, V_G, I_G, will have a definite ratio of resistance to full-scale voltage. The ratio for the instrument in the example above is 1000 ohms/volt. The higher this ratio, the better the voltmeter from the standpoint of avoiding disturbance of the circuit. Commercial voltmeters of high quality are ordinarily considerably better than the instrument in the example; they usually have a ratio of 30,000 ohms/volt, and employ a galvanometer element of higher current sensitivity (lower I_G for full-scale deflection) than in the example.

5. THE DC AMMETER

A DC ammeter consists of a galvanometer with an added shunt resistance as in Fig. 14. If we want full-scale deflection with current I_F, we

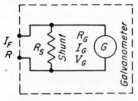

must use a shunt resistance low enough that with current I_F at the terminals, there will be only current I_G through the galvanometer. Since $I_F - I_G$ is the current through the shunt, we have, from Kirchhoff's second law,

$$(I_F - I_G)\,R_S = I_G R_G,$$

Fig. 14. A DC ammeter. The symbols I_F, I_G, V_G **or** refer to *full-scale* deflection.

$$\frac{R_S}{R_G} = \frac{I_G}{I_F - I_G}. \qquad (11)$$

Example. *In Fig. 14, if $I_G = 1$ ma and $R_G = 1$ ohm, and we want an ammeter with $I_F = 10$ amp full-scale, find the proper shunt resistance.*

From (11), $R_S = 1\ \omega \times \dfrac{0.001\ \text{amp}}{9.999\ \text{amp}} = 0.00010001\ \omega.$

The resistance R between terminals of this ammeter can be obtained from the equation $R I_F = V_G$:

$$R = \frac{V_G}{I_F} = \frac{0.001\ \text{v}}{10\ \text{amp}} = 0.0001\ \omega.$$

The resistance of a good ammeter should be low, so that when the ammeter is introduced as a series element in a circuit it does not appreciably change the current in the circuit by introduction of added resistance. An ammeter always measures correctly the current through itself *after* it is connected. Only if its resistance is negligible compared to the other resistances in the circuit is this current the same as the current *before* it was inserted in the circuit. The last equation in the example above shows that the ammeter best from the standpoint of low resistance is the one made with the galvanometer of greatest voltage sensitivity (lowest V_G).

6. ACCURATE COMPARISON OF VOLTAGES: THE POTENTIOMETER

THE POTENTIOMETER is one of the most important instruments in any electrical laboratory making precision measurements. In principle it is a device for accurately measuring the ratio of two voltages. Since one of these is usually the accurately known voltage V_S of a standard cell, the potentiometer serves for precision measurement of the other, unknown, voltage V. It also serves for precision measurement of currents by measuring the voltage across a precision resistor through which the current passes. In this way the potentiometer is used for calibration of both ammeters and voltmeters in terms of the voltage of a standard cell. Standard cells are described in the following chapter.

The basic circuit of the potentiometer is shown in Fig. 15.   A constant current, usually furnished by a lead storage battery, passes through the resistor shown in this figure.   *The whole resistance R across the storage battery remains constant,* but in a commercial instrument this resistance is made up of a combination of fixed resistances and a precision slide wire, all in series, in such a way that *the resistances R_1 and R_2 can be varied and accurately read on knobs and dials.*

In use, first the switch *(1)* is closed, switch *(2)* left open, and R_1 adjusted until the galvanometer G reads zero.   When this adjustment has

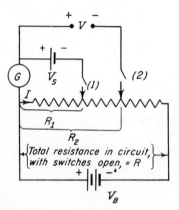

been made, there is no current through the standard cell so its terminal voltage $V_T = V_S$, and we may write

$$V_S = IR_1, \quad \text{where} \quad I = V_B/R,$$

by Kirchhoff's second law.

Then switch *(1)* is opened, switch *(2)* is closed, and R_2 is adjusted until the galvanometer again reads zero.   In this case,

$$V = IR_2, \quad \text{where} \quad I = V_B/R.$$

Since V_B and R have not been changed between the two adjustments, I does not change, so by taking ratios we see that

$$\frac{V_S}{V} = \frac{R_1}{R_2}, \tag{12}$$

Fig. 15. The basic circuit of the *potentiometer*, arranged to compare the unknown voltage V with the voltage V_S of a standard cell.

which determines V in terms of V_S and the known resistances R_1 and R_2.

It is not necessary to know either V_B or I.   The fact that they have not changed between settings can be checked by alternately closing switches *(1)* and *(2)* and verifying that the galvanometer continues to read zero.   The two switches are never both closed at the same time, and the commercial instrument is so constructed that this is impossible.

Figures 16 and 17 show how the potentiometer can be used to calibrate a DC voltmeter or a DC ammeter.   The potentiometer terminals marked + V − correspond to the terminals at the top of Fig. 15.   The potentiometer is used to read the voltage across these terminals, and gives the correct voltmeter reading in Fig. 16.   In connection with Fig. 17, notice that the potentiometer measures the voltage V without drawing current (galvanometer reading zero in Fig. 15).   Since no current is drawn through the terminals V in Fig. 17, the potentiometer reading is R_S times the correct ammeter reading.

In common parlance a *voltage divider* such as that shown in Fig. 16 is sometimes called a 'potentiometer.' This is a misusage. The word *potentiometer* means 'a device for *measuring* potential'; a voltage divider

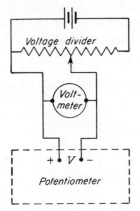

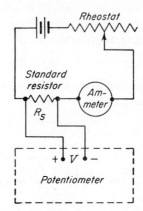

Fig. 16. Potentiometer used to calibrate a DC voltmeter.

Fig. 17. Potentiometer used to calibrate a DC ammeter.

merely *divides* the battery potential and furnishes a fraction of it between the end of the rheostat and the sliding contact.

7. CHARGE AND DISCHARGE OF A CONDENSER

Now THAT we have discussed steady DC circuits and some of the instruments used to measure steady currents and voltages, we shall consider once again the *transient* current from a condenser. Neither the charging nor the discharging of a condenser is instantaneous; we can easily determine the way in which the current varies during the *charge* and *discharge*.

In order to understand the processes occurring while a condenser is being charged, consider the circuit of Fig. 18 containing a condenser C, a resistor R, a battery with EMF V_E and negligible internal resistance, and two switches S_1 and S_2. Let the initial charge on the condenser plates be zero and switches S_1 and S_2 be open. When switch S_1 is closed, the condenser will be charged by a

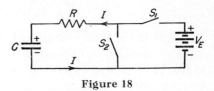

Figure 18

transient current I through R. Following the principles set down in connection with Kirchhoff's laws and recalling that the voltage drop across R is $V_R = RI = R \, dQ/dt$ and that across C is $V_C = Q/C$, where Q is the instantaneous value of the charge on the condenser, we write

$$V_E - R \, dQ/dt - Q/C = 0 \quad \text{or} \quad R \, dQ/dt + Q/C = V_E, \quad (13)$$

a relation that holds for all values of time t, measured in seconds from $t = 0$ at the instant switch S_1 is first closed. We note that at time $t = 0$ the condenser charge $Q=0$ and the entire voltage drop is across the resistance; hence, the initial current $I_0 = V_E/R$. Further, we note that long after the switch is closed ($t = \infty$) the current through R drops to zero and the entire voltage drop is across C; hence, the final and maximum charge on either of the condenser plates is $Q_{Max} = CV_E$. The solution of the differential equation that gives the correct initial and final values of Q is

$$Q = CV_E(1 - e^{-t/RC}). \tag{14}$$

This equation gives the charge on the condenser plate at any intermediate time t, as plotted in the solid curve of Fig. 19. It will be noted that the

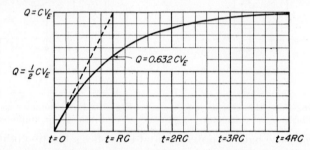

Fig 19. Growth of charge on a condenser of capacitance C when connected to a battery of EMF V_E through a resistance R.

charge Q increases to within $1/e$ of its final value CV_E at a time $t = RC$, which is called the *time-constant* of the circuit. It is interesting to note also that at time $t = RC$ the condenser would have become fully charged if the current I through the resistor had continued to have its initial value $I_0 = V_E/R$; i.e., $Q_{Max} = I_0RC = CV_E$. This is illustrated by the dotted line in Fig. 19, which has slope V_E/R equal to I_0.

The charging current I through R at any time t can be obtained from (14) by differentiation since $I = dQ/dt$; the result is

$$I = (V_E/R)\, e^{-t/RC} = I_0\, e^{-t/RC}. \tag{15}$$

It will be noted that I drops to I_0/e at time $t = RC$.

Now consider the question of *discharge*. We first charge the condenser in Fig. 18 by closing S_1 until the full charge $Q_{Max} = CV_E$ is attained. Then we open switch S_1 and close switch S_2, allowing the condenser to discharge through resistance R. In this case, there is no source of EMF in the circuit and (13) assumes the form

$$R\, dQ/dt + Q/C = 0. \tag{16}$$

The solution of this equation is

$$Q = CV_E\, e^{-t/RC} \tag{17}$$

and the expression for the current is

$$I = -(V_E/R)\, e^{-t/RC}, \tag{18}$$

where t is the time measured from the closing of S_2. Analysis of these equations shows that the charge decays along a curve exactly like that of Fig. 19 turned upside down, with the same time-constant. This analysis is left to the problems.

PROBLEMS

1. Consider a 6-v storage battery, with internal resistance of 0.01 ω, delivering a current of 50 amp. (a) What is the terminal voltage? (b) What is the rate of conversion of chemical to electrical energy? (c) What is the rate of heat generation in the battery? (d) What is the power delivered?

Ans: (a) 5.5 v; (b) 300 w; (c) 25 w; (d) 275 w.

2. Answer the questions (a)–(d) of Prob. 1 for a 1.5-v dry cell, with internal resistance of 0.1 ω, delivering 1.3 amp.

3. Consider a 6-v storage battery, with internal resistance of 0.01 ω, when it is being charged with a current of 50 amp. (a) What is the terminal voltage? (b) At what rate is electrical energy being delivered to the battery? (c) At what rate is heat being developed in the battery? (d) At what rate is electrical energy being changed into chemical energy?

Ans: (a) 6.5 v; (b) 325 w; (c) 25 w; (d) 300 w.

4. Answer the questions (a)–(d) of Prob. 3 for a 110-v bank of storage batteries, consisting of 55 two-volt cells in series, *each cell* having an internal resistance of 0.008 ω, when the bank is being charged with a current of 25 amp.

5. The terminal voltage of a generator is 120 v at no load (no current output). The internal resistance is 0.2 ω. What will its terminal voltage be when it is rotating at the same speed and has the same field excitation (in which case it has the same generated EMF) but is delivering 40 amperes?   Ans: 112 v.

6. The terminal voltage of a generator of 0.2-ω internal resistance is 115 v when the generator is delivering full-load current of 40 amp. Assuming the same generated voltage, what will be its terminal voltage (a) when it is over-loaded and delivering 60 amp? (b) when lightly loaded and delivering 20 amp? (c) at no load?

7. A DC motor has an internal resistance of 0.2 ω. It draws 40 amp at full load from 120-v lines.

(a) What is the back-EMF?

(b) What is the power drawn by the motor?

(c) What is the heat generated in the internal resistance?

(d) What is the mechanical power developed?

(e) Note that not all of the mechanical power computed in (d) appears as useful work at the shaft. Some of it is reconverted to heat within the motor because of friction, windage, and the so-called *iron-losses* (from hysteresis and eddy currents). The amount of mechanical energy reconverted to heat can be determined approximately by a measurement of current drawn at no load, when there is no mechanical output at the shaft. If this motor draws 3 amp from 120-v lines at no load, what is the back-EMF at no load, and what is the mechanical energy developed at no load?

(f) Assuming that the mechanical losses are the same at full load and no load, so that the 358.2 w computed in (e) are to be subtracted from the 4480 w of (d) to get the actual mechanical output at the shaft, compute the over-all efficiency of this motor when running at full load, and the horsepower output.   Ans: (a) 112 v; (b) 4800 w; (c) 320 w; (d) 4480 w; (e) 119.4 v, 358.2 w; (f) 85.9%, 5.52 hp.

8. Make the same computations as in Prob. 7 for the case of a motor of 0.1-ω internal resistance that draws 150 amp from 240-v lines at full load and 4 amp from 240-v lines at no load.

9. Consider the circuit of Fig. 3, p. 621, with EMF $V_E = 6$ v and internal resistance $R_I = 0.5$ ω. Compute (a) the current; (b) the terminal voltage; (c) the generated electrical power; (d) the power lost in internal heat in the generator or battery; (e) the power delivered by the generator or battery and used in heating the external resistance; for each of the following values of external resistance:

(1) $R = 9.5$ ω.   Ans: (a) 0.6 amp; (b) 5.7 v; (c) 3.6 w; (d) 0.18 w; (e) 3.42 w.
(2) $R = 1.0$ ω.   Ans: (a)   4 amp; (b)   4 v; (c)   24 w; (d)   8 w; (e)   16 w.
(3) $R = 0.5$ ω.   Ans: (a)   6 amp; (b)   3 v; (c)   36 w; (d)   18 w; (e)   18 w.
(4) $R = 0.1$ ω.   Ans: (a)   10 amp; (b)   1 v; (c)   60 w; (d)   50 w; (e)   10 w.

10. Show that the answers to Prob. 9 for an external resistance of $R = r$ ω are given by the expressions

(a) $6/(r+\frac{1}{2})$ amp;   (c) $36/(r+\frac{1}{2})$ w;   (e) $36r/(r^2+r+\frac{1}{4})$ w.
(b) $6r/(r+\frac{1}{2})$ v;   (d) $18/(r^2+r+\frac{1}{4})$ w;

From these answers, show that the maximum power is delivered to the external circuit when $R = \frac{1}{2}$ ω. Note that this condition makes $R = R_I$. In analogous fashion, show that in the circuit of Fig. 3, with *any* given values of V_E and R_I, the maximum heat is developed in an external resistance R if R is chosen so that $R = R_I$.

11. In Fig. 5, p. 622, compute (a) the generated electrical power; (b) the heat loss in the generator; (c) the heat developed in R_1; (d) the heat developed in the battery; (e) the heat developed in R_2; (f) the rate of creation of chemical energy. Verify that (a) = (b)+(c)+(d)+(e)+(f).

Ans: (a) 2200 w; (b) 80 w; (c) 1200 w; (d) 40 w; (e) 400 w; (f) 480 w.

12. In Fig. 4, p. 622, take $V_G = 24$ v, $V_B = 6$ v, $R_G = 0.4$ ω, $R_B = 0.2$ ω, $R_1 = 1$ ω, $R_2 = 2$ ω. Compute I. Letting the potential at point A equal 0, compute the potentials at B, C, and D. Also compute all the quantities asked for in parts (a)–(f) of Prob. 11.

13. In Fig. 5, p. 622, to what value would R_2 have to be changed to drop the battery-charging current to 10 amp?   Ans: 5.3 ω.

14. In Fig. 5, p. 622, to what value would R_1 have to be changed to increase the battery-charging current to 30 amp?

15. In Fig. 6, p. 623, let $R_1 = 1$ ω, $R_2 = 2$ ω, $R_3 = 6$ ω, and $V_{AB} = 12$ v. (a) Compute R. (b) Compute I from V_{AB} and R. (c) Compute the total power from V_{AB} and R. (d) Find I_1, I_2, and I_3, and verify that the sum is I. (e) Compute the power developed in R_1, R_2, and R_3 individually, and verify that the sum agrees with (c).

Ans: (a) 0.6 ω; (b) 20 amp; (c) 240 w; (d) 12, 6, 2 amp; (e) 144, 72, 24 w.

16. Answer the same questions as in Prob. 15 for $R_1 = 100$ ω, $R_2 = 20$ ω, $R_3 = 10$ ω, and $V_{AB} = 120$ v in Fig. 6.

17. In Fig. 7, p. 623, let $R_1 = 1$ ω, $R_2 = 2$ ω, $R_3 = 6$ ω, and $V_{AB} = 12$ v. (a) Compute R. (b) Compute I from V_{AB} and R. (c) Compute the total power from V_{AB} and R. (d) Find V_1, V_2, and V_3, and verify that the sum is V_{AB}. (e) Compute the power developed in R_1, R_2, and R_3 individually, and compare the sum with (c).   Ans: (a) 9 ω; (b) 1.333 amp; (c) 16 w; (d) 1.333, 2.667, 8 v; (e) 1.778, 3.556, 10.667 w.

18. Answer the same questions as in Prob. 17 for $R_1 = 100$ ω, $R_2 = 40$ ω, $R_3 = 10$ ω, and $V_{AB} = 120$ v in Fig. 7.

19. A man has five 200-ω resistors. How many different resistances can he obtain by connecting the resistors in any manner he chooses, being free to use any number of the resistors at any one time? Sketch the possible connections, and calculate the resistance of each combination. Ans: 18.

20. In Fig. 8, p. 624, let $V_E = 12$ v, $R_I = 0.2$ ω, $R_1 = 4$ ω, $R_2 = 0.5$ ω, $R_3 = 2$ ω, and $R_4 = 3$ ω. (a) Find the currents I_B, I_1, I_2, I_3, and I_4 through the battery and each of the resistors. (b) Find the voltages V_T, V_1, V_2, V_3, and V_4 across the battery and each of the resistors. (c) Find the power P_T delivered by the battery and the amounts of power P_1, P_2, P_3, and P_4 absorbed in each of the resistors. Verify that $P_T = P_1 + P_2 + P_3 + P_4$.

21. Answer the questions in Prob. 20 for the case $V_E = 105$ v, $R_I = 0.5$ ω, $R_1 = 20$ ω, $R_2 = 5$ ω, $R_3 = 20$ ω, and $R_4 = 60$ ω in Fig. 8. Ans: (a) 10, 5, 5, 3.75, 1.25 amp; (b) 100, 100, 25, 75, 75 v; (c) 1000, 500, 125, 281.25, 93.75 w.

22. In Fig. 9, p. 624, if the motor is loaded so that the motor current is increased to 10 amp, no other constants being changed, what is the charging current of the battery and the back-EMF of the motor? If the motor is loaded so that the motor current is increased to 20 amp, no other constants being changed, what is the charging current of the battery and the back-EMF of the motor?

23. Two generators G_1 and G_2 supply current to two loads I and II in Fig. 20. Calculate the currents in AB, BC, and CD and the voltages V_I and V_{II} across the loads. Ans: $64\frac{1}{3}$ amp A to B; $5\frac{2}{3}$ amp C to B; $80\frac{2}{3}$ amp D to C; $V_I = 114.6$ v; $V_{II} = 115.1$ v.

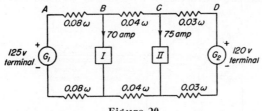

Figure 20

24. In Fig. 20, if the current to load I is 30 amp instead of 70 amp, with no other change, calculate the currents in AB, BC, and CD and the voltages across I and II.

25. The two generators shown in Fig. 21 have nominal ratings of 120 v. Together they supply 100 amp to a transmission line. V_{E1}, the EMF of generator 1, is exactly 120 volts. The EMF of generator 2 may be varied by making variations in the exciting field current, in order to make it carry more or less of the load, as indicated by an ammeter measuring I_2. Compute the exact value of V_{E2} if generator 2 is to supply (a) half the line current; (b) one-quarter of the line current; (c) none of the line current (this is the condition to which the power-station attendant would adjust before he pulled a switch to disconnect generator 2 from the line, leaving generator 1 to carry the whole load); (d) all of the line current. (e) What happens if the EMF of generator 2 is raised to 150 v? Ans: (a) 125 v;

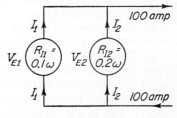

Figure 21

(b) 117.5 v; (c) 110 v; (d) 140 v; (e) $I_2 = 133$ amp, of which 100 amp go into the line and 33 amp go backward through generator 1 to drive it as a motor.

26. In Fig. 21, if $V_{E1} = 120$ v and $V_{E2} = 130$ v, find the currents I_1 and I_2, the voltage across the line, and the effective resistance of the load connected across the line, assuming that this is a pure-resistance load, such as a lighting load.

27. *Wheatstone bridge.* This convenient circuit for the measurement of an unknown resistance is shown in Fig. 22. One of the resistances, say R_1, is unknown. The others are variable but known resistances, which are adjusted until the galvanometer indicates zero current, when the bridge is said to be *balanced.* By applying Kirchhoff's laws show that when the bridge is balanced, the resistances are in the ratio

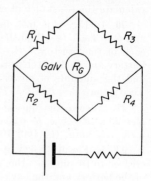

$$R_1/R_2 = R_3/R_4,$$

from which R_1 may be computed if the other three resistances are known.

28. If the bridge of Fig. 22 is balanced with $R_2 = 67.5 \, \omega$, $R_3 = 20.0 \, \omega$, $R_4 = 60.0 \, \omega$, what is the value of the unknown resistance R_1?

Fig. 22. Wheatstone bridge.

29. A two-wire underwater power cable runs across a bay and is 52,000 ft long. Each wire is #0, with resistance 0.0983 ohm per thousand feet. One wire develops a ground to the lead sheath at some point. A Varley-loop test is applied by connecting the two wires together at the far end and setting up a bridge

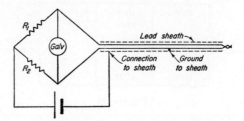

Fig. 23. Varley loop.

circuit at the near end as shown in Fig. 23. The bridge is balanced with $R_1 = 15.00 \, \omega$, $R_2 = 7.63 \, \omega$. Which section of the cable should be pulled up to look for the defect? (The resistance of the grounded circuit through the sheath may be assumed negligible.)   Ans: the section 35,000 ft from the near end.

30. If the bridge of Fig. 23, used as in Prob. 29, is balanced for $R_1 = 6.00 \, \omega$ and $R_2 = 29.7 \, \omega$, approximately where is the defect?

31. Compute the current through the 50-ω galvanometer in the Wheatstone bridge of Fig. 24 when the bridge is *unbalanced*, with $R = 20 \, \omega$. The battery has 24 v and negligible resistance.   Ans: 0.0202 amp upward.

32. Compute the current through the 50-ω galvanometer in the Wheatstone bridge of Fig. 24 when the bridge is *unbalanced*, with $R = 30 \, \omega$. The battery has an EMF of 24 v and negligible resistance.

33. Find the single resistance that is equivalent to the combination shown in Fig. 25.   Ans: 5.35 ω.

34. Find the single resistance that is equivalent to the combination shown in Fig. 26.

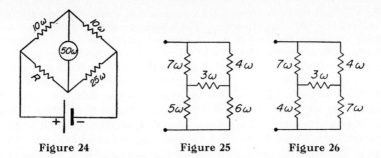

| Figure 24 | Figure 25 | Figure 26 |

35. A storage battery of 550 volts EMF, with an internal resistance of 0.20 ω, is 'floated' across the far end of a 10-mi trolley line in order to help maintain the voltage at that end of the line.   The generator at the near end is so regulated as to maintain its terminal voltage constant at 600 v.   The combined resistance of trolley wire, feeder, and track return is 0.12 ω per mile.   Let there be a single trolley car on the track at a distance X mi from the near end, drawing a current of 100 amp.   As a function of X, find (a) the current delivered by the generator; (b) the current delivered by the battery; (c) the voltage across the trolley car. Also answer the following questions: (d) What is the maximum charging current of the battery?   (e) What is the maximum current delivered by the battery? (f) What is the minimum voltage across the car and at what point of the track does it occur?   (g) If there were no floating battery, what would be this minimum voltage?   Ans: (a) $135.7-8.57X$ amp; (b) $8.57X-35.7$ amp; (c) $600-16.3X+1.03X^2$ v; (d) 35.7 amp; (e) 50.0 amp; (f) 536 v at 7.92 mi; (g) 480 v.

36. A load that draws current I is fed from a 120-volt generator through leads that have a total resistance of 0.2 ohm.   A 110-volt battery is also floated across the load.   The internal resistance of the battery and the resistance of the battery leads total 0.05 ohm.   The load current I varies from 0 to 200 amp.   The generator charges the battery when the load is light, and the battery takes over part of the load and helps to maintain voltage regulation when the load is heavy.

(a) Find the generator current I_G as a function of load current.

(b) Find the battery current I_B as a function of load current, calling discharging current positive and charging current negative.

(c) At what load current does the battery shift from charge to discharge?

(d) Find the load voltage V as a function of load current.

(e) Plot the generator current, battery current, and load voltage as functions of load current, in the range from 0 to 200 amp.

(f) What generator capacity, in kilowatts, is required?

(g) With the battery disconnected, so that the generator supplies the whole load current, what generator capacity would be required?   For this case, plot the load voltage on the same graph as in (e).   Note the great improvement in regulation resulting from the floating battery.

37. A commercial voltmeter reads 150 volts full-scale.   The basic element is a d'Arsonval galvanometer of 100 ohms resistance that gives full-scale deflection on 20 mv.   Find the resistance of the multiplier.   Ans: 749,900 ω.

38. A commercial voltmeter reads 10 volts full-scale.   The basic element is a d'Arsonval galvanometer of 50 ohms resistance that gives full-scale deflection on 0.1 ma.   Find the resistance of the multiplier.

39. A laboratory that possesses the instrument of Prob. 37 desires to convert it to one reading 450 volts full-scale. The laboratory writes to the meter-manu-facturing company and orders a ×3 external multiplier for this particular instrument. The manufacturer sends a box with two binding posts which is to be connected in series with the voltmeter when in use. What is in the box?
Ans: an accurate 1.5-megohm resistance.

40. What is the resistance of the external multiplier that will multiply the readings of the voltmeter of Prob. 38 by 20, converting it to 200 volts full-scale.

41. A typical commercial voltmeter is rated at 30,000 ohms/volt. What is the current for full-scale deflection of the galvanometer element? Ans: $\frac{1}{30}$ ma.

42. It is possible to purchase a commercial voltmeter with a rating of one-million ohms/volt. What is the current required for full-scale deflection of such an instrument?

43. What shunt resistance is required in an ammeter whose galvanometer element has a resistance of 5 ohms and gives full-scale deflection on 50 mv, if the ammeter is to read 25 amp full-scale?   Ans: 0.00200 ω.

44. What shunt resistance is required in a milliammeter whose galvanometer element has a resistance of 50 ohms and gives full-scale deflection on 1 ma, if the milliammeter is to read 60 ma full-scale?

NOTE: In measuring a resistance by the voltmeter-ammeter method, the ammeter is placed in series with the resistance, but the voltmeter can be con-nected in two ways, as indicated in parts (a) and (b) of Fig. 27. Connection (a) has the disadvan-tage that the ammeter measures the current through the voltmeter as well as that through the resistor, (b) has the disadvantage that the volt-meter measures the voltage drop across the am-meter as well as that across the resistor. We call the ratio V/I of voltmeter to ammeter reading the *apparent* resistance of the resistor being measured. In Probs. 45–48, we contemplate measuring a 20.00-ohm resistor by using a dry cell as a current source, together with a 1.5-v full-scale voltmeter and a 50-ma full-scale milliammeter. In each case, the current is adjusted by an external rheostat so that the milliammeter reads full scale.

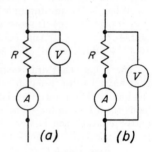

Figure 27

45. (See note above.) If the voltmeter has a resistance of 500 ohms and the milliammeter a resistance of 1 ohm, what is the apparent resistance in case (a)? in case (b)?   Ans: (a) 19.23 ω; (b) 21.00 ω.

46. (See note above.) If the voltmeter has a resistance of 15,000 ohms and the milliammeter a resistance of 1 ohm, what is the apparent resistance in case (a)? in case (b)?

47. (See note above.) If the voltmeter has a resistance of 500 ohms and the milliammeter a resistance of 0.001 ohm, what is the apparent resistance in case (a)? in case (b)?   Ans: (a) 19.23 ω; (b) 20.00 ω.

48. (See note above.) If the voltmeter has a resistance of 15,000 ohms and the milliammeter a resistance of 0.001 ohm, what is the apparent resistance in case (a)? in case (b)?

49. For connection (a) of Fig. 27, show that if I is the ammeter reading, V the voltmeter reading, R_A the ammeter resistance, and R_V the voltmeter resistance, then the true resistance of the resistor is given by $R = V/(I - V/R_V)$. Show also that if $R_{App} = V/I$, then $R = R_{App}(1 + R/R_V)$, so that connection (a) is satisfactory only when the resistance of the voltmeter is large compared to the resistance being measured.

50. For connection (b) of Fig. 27 show that if I is the ammeter reading, V the voltmeter reading, R_A the ammeter resistance, and R_V the voltmeter resistance, then the true resistance of the resistor is given by $R = (V/I) - R_A = R_{App} - R_A$, so that connection (b) is satisfactory only when the resistance of the ammeter is small compared to the resistance being measured.

51. A circuit like that in Fig. 18, p. 633, has $R = 2$ megohms, $C = 4$ μf, and $V_E = 20$ volts. Find the initial value of the current when S_1 is closed, the maximum charge on the condenser plates, and the time-constant of the circuit.

Ans: 10 μa, 80 μc, 8 sec.

52. Solve Prob. 51 for the case $R = 5$ megohms, $C = 2$ μf, and $V_E = 100$ v.

53. In Prob. 51, find the values of voltages V_R and V_C at $t = 0$, 8, 16, 24, ∞ sec.

Ans: $V_R = 20$, 7.36, 2.71, 0.0996, 0 v; $V_C = 0$, 12.6, 17.3, 19.9, 20 v.

54. Show by direct substitution that the value of Q given in (14) is a solution of (13). Show by differentiation of (14) that $I_0 = V_E/R$.

55. In a circuit like that shown in Fig. 18, p. 633, $R = 2$ megohm, $C = 3$ μf, and $V_E = 100$ v. After the condenser is fully charged, switch S_1 is opened and S_2 is closed. Find the charge on the plates of C at times $t = 0$, 6, 12, 18, and ∞ sec after the closing of S_2. What is the initial value of I?

Ans: 300, 110, 40.6, 14.9, 0 μc; 50 μa.

56. Show that the value of Q given in (17) satisfies (16). Derive (18) by differentiation of (17).

57. Show how the time $t = RC$ serves as a *time-constant* for condenser *discharge* in a way similar to the case of *charge*.

58. Plot a curve similar to the one in Fig. 19 for the *discharge* of a condenser.

NOTE: We are now in a position to show how to make a Geiger counter, a device that can be used to detect the passage of a *single* high-energy particle. We have seen in Prob. 60, p. 584, and Probs. 46 and 47, p. 601, that if a chamber like that shown in Fig. 45, p. 584 is equipped with a fine wire as a central electrode mounted in a gas at relatively low pressure, it is possible to collect more ions than are produced by the original high-energy particle. In fact, if the potential of the inner electrode is set slightly lower than the potential giving 'continuous break-down' (determined by the dielectric strength of the gas), multiplications as high as 10^8 are attainable; *i.e.* for each primary ion formed by an original high energy particle, 10^8 secondary ions will be collected.

Consider the tube arranged as shown in Fig. 28. The central electrode connected to the positive terminal of a battery through a high resistance R is initially at a potential just below that at which continuous breakdown occurs. Now sup-

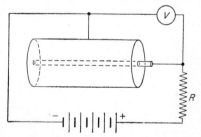

Fig. 28. The Geiger counter.

pose that a high energy particle passes through the gas in the tube. The original particle produces a large number of primary ions, which in passage to the electrode produce large numbers of additional secondary ions. As these ions are collected, a current is produced in the resistor causing an IR-drop sufficiently large to reduce the electrode potential enough to stop the incipient continuous discharge. This large sudden voltage change at the electrode can be registered as a pulse on an oscilloscope or a flash from a neon bulb, or, after electronic amplification, can cause a mechanical counting meter to register. There will be one such voltage pulse each time a high energy particle, or a quantum of ionizing radiation, passes through the tube.

59. The battery EMF in Fig. 28 is 600 v, and a 1-megohm resistor is used to connect the battery to the central electrode. What is the potential of the electrode when no ions are being collected? If the potential of the electrode must be at least 500 volts in order to produce appreciable ion 'multiplication,' what current in the circuit will cause incipient breakdown to be quenched? Answer the same questions for $R = 10^3$ megohms.   Ans: 600 v, 0.1 ma; 600 v, 0.1 μa.

60. If a single high-energy particle produces 10^3 ion pairs in a Geiger-counter tube in which the gas multiplication factor is 10^8, how much charge would be collected? If this charge were collected in 1 μsec, what would be the average collection current during this period? Would this be possible in the circuit shown in Fig. 28 with $R = 1$ megohm?   Ans: 1.6×10^{-8} coul; 0.016 amp; no, why?

61. Now that we have treated Kirchhoff's laws, it is possible to consider from a somewhat different point of view the action of a Geiger counter. Consider the Geiger tube itself as a circuit element having a quiescent resistance of many megohms until a high energy particle or ionizing radiation enters, at which time the resistance is reduced to several hundred thousand ohms. Analyze the action of the circuit of Fig. 28, for a case in which $R = 10^6 \omega$ and the tube resistance is normally $10^{10} \omega$ and is reduced to $10^5 \omega$ when a high-energy particle traverses the tube.

62. Now that we have treated time-constants of RC-circuits, give further consideration to Prob. 61. The effective capacitance in the circuit in question is 2 $\mu\mu$f and is associated with the Geiger-tube electrodes, associated wiring, etc. In this circuit, let the quiescent tube resistance be $10^{10} \omega$ and let this resistance be reduced to $10^5 \omega$ shortly after the passage of a high energy particle. What would be the time-constant of the circuit after the tube resistance decreased? Discuss the effects of the time-constant on the tube's return to its quiescent state. What is the time-constant of the quiescent circuit?   Ans. 2.2 μsec, 0.02 sec.

CHAPTER 31

ELECTROCHEMISTRY; THERMOELECTRICITY

In the preceding chapter we described sources of EMF as *reversible* devices for changing energy from some other form to electrical energy, or from electrical energy to the other form. The other form may be *mechanical, chemical, or thermal*. The principles of operation of motors and generators for the interconversion of mechanical and electrical energy will be described in later chapters. In this chapter we discuss the interconversion of chemical and electrical energy (*electrochemistry*) and the *reversible* interconversion of thermal and electrical energy (*thermoelectricity*). We also mention the *reversible* interconversion of thermal and chemical energy that occurs in batteries. In Chap. 29 we have already described the *irreversible* transformation of electrical energy to heat that occurs in a resistance.

We begin the chapter by defining a new unit of energy, the electron-volt, that is particularly convenient for specifying the energy of a single microscopic particle, and then proceed to relate energies in electron-volts per molecule to the chemist's kilocalories per mole; we also define a new unit of charge, the faraday, that is especially suited for expressing the charge carried by a mole of ions.

1. THE ELECTRON-VOLT (EV) AS A UNIT OF ENERGY

The unit of energy most widely used in modern atomic and nuclear physics is the 'electron-volt.' It must be emphasized at the outset that the electron-volt is simply a unit of energy like the calorie or joule, and that the fact that an energy is expressed in electron-volts does not imply that we are talking about electrons. The electron-volt is of convenient size for specification of the energy of a single electron, atom, molecule, nucleus, photon, or cosmic-ray particle; and is defined in such a way as to simplify the computation of the work done when a particle bearing a multiple of the electronic charge moves through a difference of potential.

> The **electron-volt** is a unit of energy equal to the work done by the electric field when a charge equal to the electronic charge moves through a difference of potential of one volt.

Just as 1 joule = 1 coul × 1 volt, 1 electron-volt = (1 electronic charge) × (1 volt), in accordance with the relation $W = QV$. Thus

$$1 \text{ ev} = 1.6021 \times 10^{-19} \text{ coul} \times 1 \text{ volt} = 1.6021 \times 10^{-19} \text{ joule}. \quad (1)$$

From the definition of the electron-volt, we see that

If a charge Ne, where e is the electronic charge, moves through a difference of potential V, in volts, work NV, in electron-volts, is done.

2. ATOMIC MASS; AVOGADRO'S NUMBER; THE MOLE; THE FARADAY; THE KILOCALORIE/MOLE; THE ELECTRON-VOLT/MOLECULE

SINCE WE have arrived at another point where we need to use atomic masses, we again (see p. 302) point out that there are now two atomic-mass scales, called the 'physical' and the 'chemical.' Chemists developed a convenient scale to represent the *relative masses* of the different elements. The mass of the oxygen atom was taken as exactly 16 units, and this was called the *atomic mass* of oxygen. The atomic mass of hydrogen then came out 1.008, that of silver 107.88, and so on. After the discovery of isotopes by physical methods and in particular the discovery that oxygen has 3 isotopes, of masses in the ratio $16:17:18$ approximately, it was realized that the chemists' atomic mass of 16 did not refer to a definite atomic species but to the *average* of a mixture of three different isotopes of oxygen as they occur in nature. The natural abundances are in the ratio $O^{16}:O^{17}:O^{18} = 2500:1:5$ approximately. Physicists began to measure the relative masses of different *individual* isotopes, and to do so with such accuracy that some of the mass ratios are known to 1 part in 300,000. These accuracies are greater than those that have been achieved by chemical methods.

Because of these developments, physicists need an atomic-mass scale that refers to a definite isotope rather than to a mixture as a standard. They have adopted a *physical scale* in which the mass of the isotope O^{16} is taken as 16 exactly. On this scale the average mass of the atoms in the naturally occurring oxygen mixture is 16.0044, whereas it is 16 exactly on the *chemical scale*, in which the *average* mass of the oxygen isotopes in the natural mixture is taken as 16. Atomic masses on the physical scale are thus greater than those on the chemical scale by 3 parts in 10,000, and each of the quantities named in the title of this section has two values differing in this ratio according to which scale is used.

We shall always use the physical scale in this book.

Average atomic masses of the natural elements are given in Sec. 4 of the Appendix. These are on the physical scale. The difference between the physical scale and the chemical scale is negligible for many purposes.

We now define *Avogadro's number:*

Avogadro's number is the number of atoms in 16 grams of O^{16}.

Because the masses of individual atoms are proportional to the atomic masses, Avogadro's number is also the total number of oxygen atoms in 16.0044 g of natural oxygen; the number of hydrogen atoms in 1.008 g of natural hydrogen; the number of silver atoms in 107.91 g of natural silver; and in general the number of atoms of any element in a quantity whose mass in grams equals the atomic mass. It is equally well the number of molecules of any compound in a quantity whose mass in grams equals the molecular mass. *Avogadro's number*, which we shall denote by $\mathfrak{N}$, has the value

$$\mathfrak{N} = 6.025 \times 10^{23}. \tag{2}$$

This is an enormous number—but then, atoms are really very small!
We now define a *mole:*

> A **mole** of any kind of particle is a quantity containing $\mathfrak{N}$ such particles. Thus, 1 mole $= 6.025 \times 10^{23}$ particles.

This is a generalization of the standard usage of the chemists, who talk about a mole of atoms or of molecules but not about a mole of electrons. However, we shall find this extended definition highly useful in the case of electrons. We can make immediate use of it in defining the unit of charge called the *faraday:*

> The **faraday** is the absolute magnitude of the charge carried by a mole of electrons.

That is, the charge carried by a mole of electrons is -1 faraday. We obtain the size of the faraday in coulombs by multiplying $\mathfrak{N}$, Avogadro's number, by e, the magnitude of the electronic charges:

$$1 \text{ faraday} = \mathfrak{N}e = (6.025 \times 10^{23})(1.6021 \times 10^{-19} \text{ coul}),$$

or
$$\boxed{1 \text{ faraday} = 96,520 \text{ coulombs.}} \tag{3}$$

The faraday is a very convenient unit of charge for treating problems in electrolysis, since it is the absolute magnitude of the charge carried by a mole of monovalent ions of any type. Before we proceed to such problems, it will be advisable to discuss another energy unit.

When hydrogen burns and the resulting steam is condensed to form liquid water, according to the equation

$$H_2 + \tfrac{1}{2} O_2 \rightarrow (H_2O)_{\text{Liq}}, \tag{4}$$

the heat of reaction*, determined calorimetrically, is usually expressed in

---

* In determining a heat of reaction (for example, in a bomb calorimeter), the products of the reaction are allowed to cool to the initial temperature of the substances entering the reaction. Thus the heat of reaction represents the difference of chemical and thermal energy between the substances on the left and right of the reaction equation at the same temperature. In the case of gaseous reactions, the heat of reaction will also depend on whether the reaction takes place at constant volume or at constant pressure. It is customary to specify heats of reaction for the case where all substances in the equation are at NTP.

kilocalories per mole of water molecules formed when one mole of hydrogen molecules reacts with one-half mole of oxygen molecules. This heat of reaction is 69 kcal/mole.

When one mole of water molecules in liquid form is decomposed electrolytically, an equal energy must be supplied from electrical sources. In discussing this topic later, we shall find it desirable to know the reaction energy per *molecule* of water. A suitable and convenient energy unit for expressing the energy of a molecule is the electron-volt. We can determine the correspondence between kcal/mole and ev/molecule from (1) and (2):

$$1 \, \frac{ev}{molecule} = 1.6021 \times 10^{-19} \, \frac{joule}{molecule} \times 6.025 \times 10^{23} \, \frac{molecules}{mole} = 96,520 \, \frac{joules}{mole}.$$

Since 4186 joules = 1 kcal, we divide the above value by 4186 to get

$$1 \, \text{ev/molecule} = 23.06 \, \text{kcal/mole}. \tag{5}$$

This relation means that if we supply 1 electron-volt of energy to each molecule, we supply 23.06 kcal of energy to a mole, which contains $\mathfrak{N}$ molecules. The heat of the reaction (4) is measured calorimetrically as 69 kcal/mole. Hence, if we wish to *reverse* the reaction by electrolysis, we must *supply* 69 kcal/mole or 3.0 ev/molecule.

3. CHARGE TRANSPORT IN ELECTROLYSIS

As we remember from the study of chemistry, the molecules of an acid, base, or salt in water solution are more or less completely dissociated into positively and negatively charged *ions*. It is the availability of these ions to carry the current that enables such a solution to conduct electricity. The ions play the role that free electrons play in metallic conduction. The reason for the dissociation can be understood from our discussion of electrostatics. Water, although it is a poor insulator, is a dielectric of high dielectric constant $K = 81$. If the positive and negative ions making up an acid, base, or salt molecule are once dissociated in water solution (as a result of thermal agitation), the electrostatic force tending to make them recombine into a molecule is only about $\frac{1}{81}$ of what the force would be in vacuum, in accordance with our discussion on p. 592 of the forces between charges immersed in a dielectric. This force is so weak that a large fraction of the molecules of a soluble compound can remain dissociated or *ionized*.

An ionized solution is called an *electrolyte* because it will conduct electricity. In the process of *electrolytic conduction*, electric current enters and leaves a solution at metallic plates called *electrodes*. The combination of electrodes and electrolyte constitutes an *electrolytic cell*. At the electrodes some type of chemical reaction takes place, resulting usually in deposition or solution of solid material or evolution of gas from decomposition of solvent or solute. These chemical changes are said to result from *electrolysis* of the solution.

Let us consider the reactions that take place in the electrolysis of pure water by current that enters and leaves through chemically inert platinum electrodes. Pure water is only weakly ionized, but it does contain in each mole a definite number of hydrogen* ions, H^+, and the same number of hydroxyl ions, OH^-. The number of ions of each type per mole of water molecules is 9×10^{14}, which at first sight looks like a very large number but is actually *very small* compared with Avogadro's number, so that only about one in 10^9 of the water molecules is ionized. With this degree of ionization, pure water is a poor conductor compared with other electrolytes, but it has some conductivity and will carry a feeble current and electrolyze slowly. The ionization, and hence the conductivity, is greatly increased by the addition of a small amount of acid. In the case of sulfuric, perchloric, and some other acids, the net result of electrolysis is decomposition of the water into hydrogen and oxygen, just as in the case of the electrolysis of pure water. While electrolytic generation of hydrogen and oxygen would normally be carried out in acidulated water, it will be simplest if we discuss the phenomena occurring in pure water.

Figure 1 shows two platinum electrodes immersed in water and connected to a source of EMF. The Greek names of the positive and negative

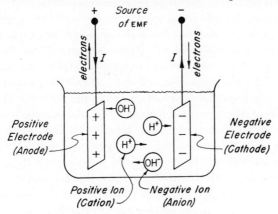

Fig. 1. Electrolysis of water.

electrodes and ions shown on Fig. 1 were given by Faraday and are still in common use.† The source of EMF sets up an electric field in the space

---

* Hydrogen ions are always attached to a neutral water molecule so that the actual ions are $(H_3O)^+ = H^+ + H_2O$, but this detail is unimportant to our discussion.

† The *anode* (Greek for "the way which the sun rises," according to FARADAY, *Experimental Researches in Electricity*), is the electrode at which current enters the cell. The *cathode* (Greek for "the way which the sun sets") is the electrode at which the current leaves. *Anions* are negatively charged ions; *cations* are positively charged ions. Anions move toward the anode, cations toward the cathode, in carrying current through the cell. This notation becomes annoyingly confusing when applied to

between the electrodes.   The H^+ ions slowly drift down the field toward the negative cathode.   Those that reach the negative cathode pick up negative electrons from it and form hydrogen gas in accordance with the equation (we use ε^- as the chemical symbol for an electron)

$$2H^+ + 2\varepsilon^- \rightarrow (H_2)_{Gas}. \qquad (- \text{electrode}) \quad (6)$$

The OH^- ions are attracted to the positive anode.   On reaching it, they give up their electrons to the electrode and form oxygen gas and water in accordance with the equation

$$2OH^- \rightarrow 2\varepsilon^- + H_2O + \tfrac{1}{2}(O_2)_{Gas}. \qquad (+ \text{electrode}) \quad (7)$$

New H^+ and OH^- ions are continuously generated within the water to keep up the ionic concentration at all points, in accordance with the laws of ionic equilibria, which the student can review in his chemistry text.

It will be noticed that one each of reactions (6) and (7) together correspond to the decomposition of one water molecule into one molecule of hydrogen gas and one-half molecule of oxygen gas ($H_2O \rightarrow H_2 + \tfrac{1}{2}O_2$). Also, the combination of these two reactions involves the transfer of two electrons from the solution into the $+$ electrode in (7), and the transfer of two electrons from the $-$ electrode into the solution in (6).   To maintain steady conditions, two electrons must pass through the outside metal circuit from the positive electrode through the source of EMF to the negative electrode.   This movement of electrons corresponds to the flow of an equivalent quantity of conventional positive charge in the opposite direction, as shown by the arrows marked I.   The two electrons enter the electrolyte at the negative electrode (to combine with the H^+) and leave the electrolyte at the positive electrode.   Under steady conditions, the same amount of net negative charge must cross each plane in the electrolyte (from right to left in Fig. 1); otherwise, the net charge of the electrolyte on one side of the plane would increase and that on the other side would decrease.   Hence, under steady conditions the same current crosses each plane of a closed circuit that includes the electrolytic cell of Fig. 1.   The current is carried by electrons in the metallic parts of the circuit; in the electrolyte it is carried by both positive and negative ions.

A nice electrostatic balance will guarantee that, after the process is started, *exactly the same number of reactions* (6) *and* (7) *will occur*.   We

---

a reversible battery cell, because the current direction changes and hence the electrodes exchange names when conditions change from charge to discharge.   For a stabilizing battery floated across a line, an ammeter is required to tell even the names of the plates.   Hence, in discussing batteries, we shall prefer to talk about positive and negative ions and positive and negative electrodes, the positive electrode being the one at higher potential whether the battery is charging or discharging.   These designations are not capricious.

have in Fig. 1 an electrolyte which is normally neutral (no *net* electric charge) and a metal circuit, comprising the plates and the connections through the source of EMF, which is also normally electrically neutral. Suppose that when the electrolysis starts, more of reactions (6) occur than of (7). This inequality results in a net removal of positive charges from the electrolyte, leaving it with a net negative charge, and a net removal of electrons from the metal circuit, leaving the metal with a net positive charge. This difference will set up local fields near the electrodes, as sketched in Fig. 2. These fields are superposed on the field set up by the source of EMF. They strengthen the field near the + electrode, weaken it near the − electrode; thus they help attract negative ions to the + electrode and speed up reaction (7), and they reduce the attraction of positive ions to the − electrode and hence retard reaction (6). The local fields will build up to whatever magnitude is necessary to achieve equality of the rates of these two reactions. If more of reactions (7) were to take place than of (6), local fields of exactly the reverse type would be set up. A very little net

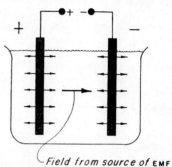

Fig. 2. Local fields that hinder the progress of positive ions toward the − electrode and aid the progress of negative ions toward the + electrode (cf. Fig. 1).

charge transfer from electrolyte to metal will set up sufficient local fields to reach equilibrium between reactions (6) and (7), and it is seen that this equilibrium will be automatically and stably maintained. This is the process that guarantees equality of charge transfer at anode and cathode in any type of electrolysis.

Since reactions (6) and (7) must go on at the same rate, and since two electrons are required for decomposition of each water molecule, we see that two moles of electrons (corresponding to two faradays of charge) must flow through the circuit for each mole of hydrogen gas and each half mole of oxygen gas generated. Thus, 2 faradays $= 2 \times 96,500$ coul $= 193,000$ coul of charge are required to decompose one mole (18 grams) of water into one mole of H_2 gas (2 grams or 22.4 liters at NTP) and one-half mole of O_2 gas (16 grams or 11.2 liters at NTP).

In any electrolysis, the proportionality between charge transferred and mass of material electrolyzed is *exact*. The proportionality factor can be easily obtained by an argument similar to the above as soon as equations corresponding to (6) and (7) for the reactions at the electrodes have been written down. We give two other examples:

Copper plating. Both electrodes are copper in a solution of $CuSO_4$, which ionizes to Cu^{++} and SO_4^{--}. (Even if copper is being plated onto a cathode of some other metal, both electrodes are effectively copper as soon as the process is under way and a thin layer of copper has been deposited.)   At the positive electrode, metallic copper is dissolved and goes into solution as Cu^{++}:

$$Cu_{Metal} \rightarrow 2\varepsilon^- + Cu^{++}, \qquad (+ \text{ electrode})$$

the two electrons going up the wire.   At the negative electrode, the Cu^{++} ions take up two electrons (which come down the wire) and are deposited as metallic copper:

$$Cu^{++} + 2\varepsilon^- \rightarrow Cu_{Metal}. \qquad (- \text{ electrode})$$

Thus, copper metal dissolves from the anode, is transported through the electrolyte, and deposits on the cathode.   *One mole of copper atoms moves from anode to cathode for each two faradays of charge that flow through the circuit.*   The SO_4^{--} ions really play no role in these reactions, and any other soluble salt of copper would give the same effect.   The SO_4^{--} ions help carry the current.   When their concentration near the + electrode, to which they are attracted, gets too high for ionic equilibrium, they combine with Cu^{++} to form $CuSO_4$.   This compound can diffuse back toward the negative electrode, where it can ionize again because of the deficiency of SO_4^{--} near this electrode, from which these negative ions are repelled.

This is the commercial method of purifying copper for electrical purposes, since impurities are in general left behind in this process.   Something over a million tons annually of copper is refined electrolytically at such places as Niagara Falls where cheap electrical power is available.   A single electrolysis from crude copper gives copper of purity better than 99.9 per cent.   Copper of such high purity is needed for electrical use, since very small quantities of impurity greatly increase the electrical resistance.

The silver coulometer.   The previous example involved bivalent Cu^{++} ions, and two faradays were required to deposit one mole of copper.   If silver electrodes are used in a solution of silver nitrate ($AgNO_3$), only one faraday will be required per mole of silver, since the silver is monovalent and forms Ag^+ ions. The electrode reactions are

$$Ag_{Metal} \rightarrow \varepsilon^- + Ag^+, \qquad (+ \text{ electrode})$$
$$Ag^+ + \varepsilon^- \rightarrow Ag_{Metal}. \qquad (- \text{ electrode})$$

These reactions are used in an instrument called a *coulometer*, designed for very accurate measurement of the quantity of electricity that flows through a circuit. The charge to be measured flows through what amounts to a small silver-plating bath in series with the circuit, and the amount of silver dissolved or deposited is accurately weighed.   The charge that flows is determined from the fact that 1 faraday (96,520 coul) deposits 1 mole (107.91 g) of silver.

The laws relating the amount of material deposited, or gas generated, in electrolysis were first determined by Faraday:

FARADAY'S LAWS

(1) *The quantity of material undergoing chemical reaction at an electrode is in direct proportion to the quantity of electric charge passing.*

(2) *The quantity of a given element dissolved or released from solution at an electrode by a given quantity of electric charge is proportional to the ratio of the atomic mass of the element to its valence.   This ratio is called the equivalent mass of the element, and 96,520 coulombs of charge are required per gram-equivalent mass.*

The reason for these laws is clear from the atomic-ionic picture given above.   However, before the knowledge of the electron, the reason why it is 96,520 coulombs that deposits one mole of a monovalent metal or one-half mole of a bivalent metal was not understood in terms of the more fundamental quantities occurring in the computation of (3).

In the case of solution or deposition of a metal, we can summarize Faraday's laws by the formula

$$m = \frac{Q}{96,520 \text{ coul}} \frac{M}{n} \text{ grams.}$$

where m = mass of metal deposited or dissolved, in grams,

Q = quantity of electricity passing through the cell, in coulombs,

M = atomic mass of the metal,

n = valence of the metal—specifically, the number of positive electronic charges carried by the metallic ion in the electrolyte.

In this formula the ratio M/n is called the equivalent mass.   The expression $M/96,520n$ is sometimes called the *electrochemical equivalent* and denoted by z.   Values of z will be found listed in handbooks.   In terms of z, the above equation takes the compact form $m = (z \text{ g/coul}) Q$.

4. VOLTAGE NECESSARY FOR ELECTROLYSIS

WHEN VOLTAGE is applied between platinum electrodes in pure water or in a dilute acid solution that electrolyzes to form H_2 and O_2, no charge flows so long as the difference of potential is below 1.7 volts. Higher applied voltages result in a current proportional to the difference between the applied voltage and 1.7 volts.   When charge is flowing, the electrolytic cell seems to have a back-EMF of 1.7 volts, which, according to what we have learned in the previous chapter, must be related to a change of electrical energy into chemical energy.   In fact, a chemical reaction is taking place:

$$H_2O \rightarrow H_2 + \tfrac{1}{2}O_2,$$

which, as we saw on p. 646, requires 69 kcal of energy per mole of water decomposed, or 3 ev of energy per molecule of water.   For each molecule of water decomposed, a charge of 2 electrons passes through the cell; and in order to furnish 3 ev of energy to a charge of 2 electrons, the charge must pass through a difference of potential of 1.5 v.   This figure is 0.2 v lower than the back-EMF of 1.7 v.   The extra electrical energy of 0.2 ev/electron goes into heat, as we shall discuss in Sec. 6.

In the case we have been considering, charge does not start to flow until we apply a potential of 1.7 volts to furnish the energy absorbed in the reaction that accompanies the flow.   Above this voltage the amount of current will be governed by the terminal voltage and by the internal resistance just as in the case of a battery on charge considered in the previous chapter.

In electrolysis in which copper is being plated from a copper anode to a copper cathode, no chemical energy need be supplied, since for each pair of electrons that traverses the cell, one molecule of solid copper is dissolved, but also one molecule of solid copper is plated, so there is no *net* chemical change. In this case charge will flow with the smallest voltage, and to a certain approximation Ohm's law is obeyed, and current is proportional to voltage. All the electrical energy goes into heat. Since the energy per coulomb is proportional to the voltage, the energy per kilogram of copper that is plated is also proportional to the voltage. To save energy, electrolytic refining is done with low voltages (a fraction of a volt). Large areas of copper plate are used to keep the internal resistance low and the current high.

Example. *Assume that electrolytic refining of copper is done in large cells, each having an internal resistance of 0.0002 ω; that electrical energy costs 0.15 cents per kwh; and that each cell costs 0.4 cent per hour ($2.88 per month) for investment, maintenance, and operating costs in addition to the cost of the electrical energy consumed. At what voltage does the plant produce the cheapest copper, and what is its refining cost per kg?*

If the voltage is x volts, the current will be $(x \text{ v})/(0.0002 \text{ } \omega) = 5000 \text{ } x$ amp. This corresponds to $(3600)(5000 \text{ } x)$ coul/hr $= 18{,}000{,}000$ coul/hr $= 187 \text{ } x$ faradays/hr. One faraday deposits $\frac{1}{2}$ mole $= 31.8$ g $= 0.0318$ kg of bivalent copper, so copper is deposited at the rate

$$(187 \text{ } x)(0.0318 \text{ kg})/\text{hr} = 5.95 \text{ } x \text{ kg/hr}.$$

The power is $IV = 5000 \text{ } x^2$ watts $= 5 \text{ } x^2$ kw. In one hour the energy is $5 \text{ } x^2$ kwh, costing $0.75 \text{ } x^2$ cents. The total cost of operation for an hour is then

$$(0.4 + 0.75 \text{ } x^2) \text{ cents/hr}.$$

We divide this by the production per hour to get the cost per kg:

$$\frac{0.4 + 0.75 \text{ } x^2}{5.95 \text{ } x} \frac{\text{cents}}{\text{kg}} = \left(\frac{0.0672}{x} + 0.126 \text{ } x\right) \frac{\text{cents}}{\text{kg}}.$$

This last expression shows how fixed costs go down and power costs go up with increasing voltage. Setting the derivative equal to zero shows that this expression has a minimum at $x = 0.730$, where the costs amount to 0.184 cents/kg. Hence the most economical voltage is 0.730 v, and the refining costs at this voltage are 0.184 cents/kg, which amounts to $1.67 per ton. NOTE: the costs in this example are not based on actual production costs; they are assumed for purposes of illustration only.

Now suppose that we arrange a cell so that copper will be dissolved and zinc plated out. This process is accomplished in the old Daniell cell, which was used almost universally in the early days of telegraphy. In this cell, illustrated in Fig. 3, solutions of $CuSO_4$ and $ZnSO_4$ are separated by a porous partition through which diffusion of the solutions is very slow.

If we apply sufficient external EMF to drive current through the cell in the direction marked 'charge,' the electrode reactions put copper in solution and plate out zinc, one atom of each for every two electrons:

$$Cu_{Metal} \rightarrow Cu^{++} + 2\varepsilon^-,$$
$$Zn^{++} + 2\varepsilon^- \rightarrow Zn_{Metal}. \qquad \Big\} \quad \text{(charge)} \quad (8)$$

A minimum external voltage of 1.09 volts is required to bring about this reaction.   Hence, it must be that a minimum energy of 2.18 ev/molecule

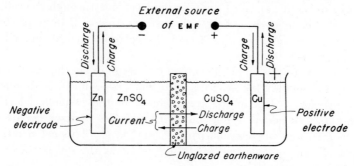

Fig. 3. Schematic diagram of the Daniell cell. Arrows show directions of conventional current in charge and discharge. The cell was usually made with the zinc electrode and $ZnSO_4$ inside a porous cup. This cup was in turn immersed in a glass jar containing $CuSO_4$. A cylindrical copper electrode surrounded the porous cup.

or 50.1 kcal/mole is required to make Cu displace Zn in solution, since the net result of the above reactions is

$$Cu_{Metal} + Zn^{++} \rightarrow Cu^{++} + Zn_{Metal}. \qquad (9)$$

The reverse reaction, Zn displacing Cu in solution, should then release energy at the rate of 50.1 kcal/mole.   The heat of this reaction,

$$Zn_{Metal} + Cu^{++} \rightarrow Cu_{Metal} + Zn^{++}, \qquad (10)$$

can be measured calorimetrically, because it can be made to take place by merely stirring up flakes of zinc metal in $CuSO_4$ solution.   Each zinc flake will start to dissolve from one portion of its surface, while copper plates out on another portion of the surface of the flake (atom for atom, to keep the flake electrically neutral), until what is left is a collection of copper flakes, with all the zinc in solution.   The heat generated in this reaction is found to be 56.0 kcal/mole.   The reason for the difference between this figure and 50.1 kcal/mole is discussed in Sec. 6.

In Fig. 1, when the voltage of the source of EMF drops below 1.7 volts, the current drops to zero and water ceases to be electrolyzed because sufficient energy cannot be supplied.   The cell of Fig. 3 behaves differently.   In Fig. 3, as the voltage of the external source of EMF is reduced to 1.09 volts, the charging current falls to zero right enough, but when the external voltage falls below 1.09 volts, the current *reverses* and the cell begins to discharge.   Charge is now moving through the cell in the reverse direction to that discussed above, the reactions (8) are proceeding in the reverse direction, copper is being plated, and zinc is being dissolved. The net reaction is now (10) instead of (9). Reaction (10) *releases* chemical energy which in this case does not appear as heat, as in the zinc-flake experiment described above, but principally as electrical energy of 2.18 ev per atom, representing an increase of potential energy of $+$ charges moved from the negative to the positive electrode through the cell. *The cell is acting as a source of* EMF. Transformation of 2.18 ev of chemical energy into electrical energy for each 2 electronic charges moved represents an EMF of 1.09 volts.

To discuss the action of the cell on discharge in another way, we may start by noting that the reaction (10) will go by itself, with release of chemical energy. But in the arrangement of the Daniell cell (Fig. 3), the reaction (10) has no opportunity to take place by itself because there are no copper ions in contact with the zinc plate. This net reaction can take place, however, via two electrode reactions, the reverse of (8):

$$\left. \begin{array}{l} Zn_{Metal} \rightarrow Zn^{++} + 2\epsilon^-, \\ Cu^{++} + 2\epsilon^- \rightarrow Cu_{Metal}. \end{array} \right\} \quad \text{(discharge)} \quad (11)$$

But *this pair of reactions can take place only as fast as an external circuit carries the electrons left behind in the zinc plate around to the copper plate to combine with the copper ions.* If the reactions were to go faster than this, the zinc plate would acquire a negative charge that would prevent, by electrostatic forces, any more Zn^{++} from leaving, and the copper plate would acquire a positive charge that would prevent any more Cu^{++} from approaching. The current is carried through the barrier by diffusion through it of Zn^{++} ions in one direction and SO_4^{--} ions in the other.

The fundamental difference in behavior between this cell, which will act as a source of EMF, and the cell of Fig. 1, which will not, is that reactions (8) and (11) are essentially reversible, whereas reactions (6) and (7) are not. In practice, the Daniell cell cannot be successfully charged because the solutions are only imperfectly separated by the porous partition. On discharge, zinc is dissolving and copper is plating out, and there is no tendency for zinc to plate out on the copper even if some Zn^{++} ions get into the copper sulfate, because the reaction (9) does not proceed by itself but requires a large energy to make it go. On the other hand, if we attempt to charge the cell, dissolving Cu and plating out Zn, we do well enough with freshly poured solutions before Cu^{++} ions have had a chance to diffuse through the partition and encounter the Zn plate. But as soon as any Cu^{++} ions do encounter the zinc plate, they will immediately plate out on the zinc, with zinc going into solution, according to (10), which will go by itself with release of thermal energy. This reaction not only wastes energy but also soon spoils the battery by creating two copper plates. With the cell on charge, the electric fields within the cell, corresponding to the IR-drop of the internal resistance, are in a direction to help pull Cu^{++} ions through the partition and to accelerate the above detrimental process.   On discharge, the internal electric fields tend to move positive ions toward the copper plate and to retard the diffusion of Cu^{++} ions into the $ZnSO_4$.   The Daniell cell is never allowed to stand on open circuit. When the cell is not in use, the external circuit is always closed with a resistance of about 100 ohms, so that a small current will continually flow in the direction that prevents Cu^{++} ions from getting into the $ZnSO_4$. As remarked above, no harm results from Zn^{++} ions getting into the $CuSO_4$.   Used in this way, the cell lasts until either the zinc plate is eaten away or all the Cu is plated out of the $CuSO_4$, which is started as a saturated solution.

The Daniell cell is mostly of historical and theoretical interest.   Cells of importance in modern technology, some of which are truly reversible, are discussed in Sec. 7.

5. THE ELECTROCHEMICAL SERIES

THE METALS can be arranged in a list called the *electrochemical series* (or the *electromotive series*) such that each metal will tend to displace from solution any metal occurring below it in the list, just as zinc displaces copper from solution in the Daniell cell described above.   This list is given in Table I.*   A number in volts is given opposite each metal such that *the* EMF *of an ideal cell composed of any two metals will be the difference between these voltages, the metal lower in the table furnishing the positive electrode.* These EMF's are additive in the sense that the EMF of a Zn-Ni cell plus the EMF of a Ni-Cu cell will be the EMF of a Zn-Cu cell.

In this table, the voltages are referred to hydrogen as zero.   The metals above hydrogen will displace hydrogen from acid with release of energy; those below hydrogen will not.   The EMF's can actually be measured relative to a 'hydrogen electrode' consisting of spongy platinum which adsorbs hydrogen strongly and is kept 'soaked' with hydrogen gas while immersed in a solution containing hydrogen ions.   If one is careful never to draw more than minute currents while measuring the EMF, this device behaves like a reversible metal electrode.

TABLE I

ELECTROCHEMICAL SERIES

Li	−2.96 volts
Rb	−2.93
K	−2.92
Ca	−2.76
Na	−2.71
Zn	−0.76
Fe	−0.44
Cd	−0.40
Tl	−0.34
Ni	−0.23
Sn	−0.14
Pb	−0.12
H	0
Cu	+0.34
Ag	+0.80
Hg	+0.80
Au	+1.36

We can now see from Table I why electrolytically refined copper is so very pure.   With the exception of silver, all the metals commonly occurring as impurities in crude copper lie above Cu in the electrochemical series.   Hence, these metals tend to displace copper in solution, or tend

* From the *International Critical Tables* (McGraw-Hill, New York, 1926).

to remain in solution in preference to letting copper remain in solution. The voltages used in electrolyzing copper are deliberately kept very low so that the energy necessary to plate out these elements at the expense of copper is not available. This energy is like that which we discussed in connection with plating out zinc and dissolving copper in charging the Daniell cell. The valuable silver impurity is removed from solution, as fast as silver ions enter solution, by the addition to the $CuSO_4$ electrolyte of a small amount of common salt (NaCl) to form a very insoluble precipitate of AgCl.

6. THE REVERSIBLE-HEAT EFFECT

WE HAVE been noticing small but definite discrepancies between measured EMF's and those computed from chemical-reaction energies. The reason is that not all of the chemical energy that disappears when a cell is discharging is turned into electrical energy; a definite small portion of the energy appears as heat. Chemical reactions occur at the electrodes. All the chemical energy would go into electrical energy if it happened that the products of the reaction were left with just such random thermal energy as to have the same temperature as the particles entering the reaction. But usually this does not happen, and the reaction products are left with slightly more than this thermal energy; then the cell tends to become warmer. (*The heat we are discussing is in addition to, and to be sharply distinguished from, any I^2R-heating, and has a direct influence on the generated EMF, or open-circuit voltage, measured by drawing only an infinitesimal current.*) If heat is thus generated, its amount must be subtracted from the chemical energy released to get the electrical energy—in accordance with the law of conservation of energy. The equation is

$$H = nV + h, \qquad \text{(discharge)} \quad (12)$$

where V = generated EMF, in volts,

      n = number of electrons transferred per molecular reaction,

   nV = electrical energy generated, in ev per molecular reaction,

    H = chemical energy released, in ev per molecular reaction,

    h = heat generated, in ev per molecular reaction.

For reasons we shall explain presently, h is called the *reversible heat*.

For the Daniell cell, the chemical energy released is 56.0 kcal/mole, so that $H = 56.0/23.1 = 2.43$ ev/molecule. The quantity h can be determined calorimetrically by putting the cell in a calorimeter and carefully separating the reversible heat, which is directly proportional to the current, from the I^2R-heat which varies as the square of the current. For the Daniell cell, $h = 0.25$ ev/molecule. Hence, $nV = (2 \text{ electrons}) \times V = 2.43$ ev $- 0.25$ ev $= 2.18$ ev, and $V = 1.09$ v, as observed. In this case some 10 per cent of the chemical energy is changed into heat h, 90 per cent into electrical energy.

Now this whole process is exactly reversible. If we charge a Daniell cell, the EMF does not change, so that 2.18 ev of electrical energy is converted to chemical energy (per molecule). But 2.43 ev of chemical energy is gained. The difference, 0.25 ev, must be taken out of thermal energy, and the cell tends to cool correspondingly. This is why h is called *reversible heat*. If some of the chemical energy is changed into heat on discharge, an equal amount of heat is changed into chemical energy on charge. On charge we have the same equation

$$H = nV + h \qquad\qquad \text{(charge)} \quad (13)$$

with reversed meaning for all terms:

$$H = \text{chemical energy created,}$$
$$nV = \text{electrical energy that disappears,}$$
$$h = \text{thermal energy that disappears.}$$

In some cells, h is a *negative* number in equations (12) and (13). In this case, heat disappears on discharge and *more* electrical energy is generated than the amount of chemical energy released; conversely, on charge, heat is generated from a portion of the electrical energy supplied. This situation obtains for the lead-acid cells in the ordinary automobile storage battery.

7. CELLS IN CURRENT USE AS SOURCES OF EMF

MANY DIFFERENT cells have been devised and used in the past. These cells fall into three types, which may be designated as *standard cells, primary cells,* and *storage cells.* Of each type, only one or two examples, which have proven superior to all others, still remain in use as sources of EMF. These examples, which will be described in this section, are

> (a) *Standard cells:*   Weston cadmium cell
> (b) *Primary cells:*   Dry cell
> (c) *Storage cells:*   Lead-acid storage cell
>   Edison alkaline cell

A *battery* consists of a number of primary or storage cells connected in series. Even when this number is only *one*, the source of EMF is commonly called a battery.

(a) *Standard cells.* A standard cell is not intended as a source of energy but for use as a secondary standard of voltage. It is always used in a voltage-comparison circuit such as the potentiometer which was described in Sec. 6 of Chap. 30. It is designed to maintain a very constant voltage over a long period of time, provided no appreciable current is ever drawn from the cell. Therefore, the circuit in which it is used must be so designed that no current of over about $\frac{1}{10000}$ amp ever passes through the cell. Under these conditions, the voltage of the Weston cadmium cell, which is about 1.018 v, can be trusted to remain constant to about 1 part in 100,000, so that this cell furnishes an admirable secondary standard of voltage for use in laboratory calibrations of voltmeters and other instruments.

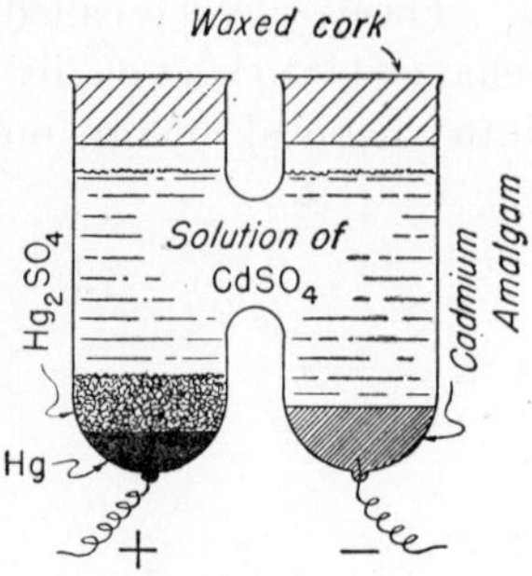

Fig. 4. The Weston standard cell.

The Weston cell (Fig. 4) has as its positive electrode liquid mercury on which floats a paste of mercurous sulfate, Hg_2SO_4, which is an almost insoluble compound. The negative electrode is an amalgam, 10 to 15 per cent of cadmium dissolved in mercury. The electrodes are held in place in the legs of an H-shaped glass vessel by porous porcelain retainers; the construction is delicate and will not permit rough handling. The electrolyte is a solution of $CdSO_4$, either almost saturated or kept saturated by the presence of crystals of solid $CdSO_4$.

The electrode reactions are reversible so long as the current is kept extremely low. On discharge, at the negative electrode cadmium goes into solution as Cd^{++}:

$$Cd_{Metal} \rightarrow 2\varepsilon^- + Cd^{++}. \qquad \text{(negative electrode)}$$

At the positive electrode, neutral mercury is released from the Hg_2SO_4, the SO_4 going into solution:

$$Hg_2SO_4 + 2\varepsilon^- \rightarrow 2\ Hg_{Liq} + SO_4^{--}. \qquad \text{(positive electrode)}$$

Actually, this last reaction must take place in two steps. Since the solubility of Hg_2SO_4 is small but finite, there will be some Hg^+ ions in solution. Two of these ions pick up electrons from the mercury surface and deposit as liquid mercury, and their removal from solution permits another molecule of Hg_2SO_4 to dissolve.

(b) *Primary cells.* A primary cell is one that cannot be 'charged,' because the cell reactions are not reversible or not efficiently reversible in practice. All of the energy that the cell will ever deliver is put in as chemical energy when the cell is made; when this energy is exhausted, the cell is dead. The only cell of this type in general use is the common dry cell, which of course is not really 'dry.' It is merely *unspillable* because the electrolyte is soaked up in sawdust, blotting paper, gelatin, flour, plaster of Paris, or the like, and is tightly sealed in with tar to prevent evaporation.

The negative electrode of a dry cell (Fig. 5) is the zinc can itself. The positive electrode is a stick of carbon, which is inert and does not enter the chemical reaction. The carbon electrode is made with a large surface area so as to keep down the internal resistance of the cell. The electrolyte is a strong solution of sal ammoniac (NH_4Cl). The space between the carbon electrode and the can is filled with a mixture of inert material to absorb the electrolyte, manganese dioxide (MnO_2) to absorb the generated hydrogen, and powdered carbon to further reduce the internal resistance. This mixture is mechanically separated from the zinc can by several layers of blotting paper.

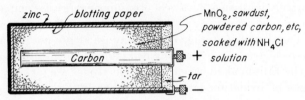

Fig. 5. The dry cell.

When this cell delivers current, zinc goes into solution at the negative electrode. At the inert carbon electrode, NH_4^+ ions are discharged, releasing free ammonia and hydrogen:

$$2 NH_4^+ + 2\varepsilon^- \rightarrow 2 NH_3 + H_2.$$

The ammonia, NH_3, is readily soluble and remains dissolved in the electrolyte. The free hydrogen gas, which would quickly spoil the action of the cell if allowed to collect around the carbon electrode (a phenomenon called, for some reason, *polarization*), is taken up and oxidized by the manganese dioxide:

$$H_2 + 2 MnO_2 \rightarrow H_2O + Mn_2O_3.$$

A dry cell, when new, gives an EMF of slightly over 1.5 volts. The EMF is of course completely independent of the cell size. The internal resistance is comparatively high, varying from something less than 0.1 ohm for the large No. 6 cell to well over 1 ohm for the small cells used in B-batteries. If a cell is short-circuited, the internal resistance rapidly rises and the current drops because of polarization—the MnO_2 does not take up the hydrogen as fast as it is generated under these conditions.

The 'fuel' for this cell is essentially metallic zinc, which is consumed to form zinc ammonium chloride. As the cell is used, the zinc can is eaten up until it begins to leak and the cell becomes worthless. Because of local action caused by impurities in the zinc and other materials, the cell deteriorates even when it is standing on the shelf with no current drawn, and becomes worthless in a matter of a couple of years. The rate of deterioration is accelerated by high temperatures and can be reduced by refrigeration.

(c) *Storage cells.* The energy supplied by a primary cell is in general very expensive compared with energy obtained by burning coal. Zinc to 'burn' is extremely expensive compared with coal to burn. A *storage* cell employs completely reversible chemical reactions so that the chemical energy used up in discharge can be restored by charging. Aside from the initial cost of the cell, which is high, the energy is obtained substantially at the cost of electrical energy used to charge the cell. When the cell is charged from power lines, this energy is obtained from coal or water-power. The automobile storage battery is charged by energy obtained by burning gasoline in the internal-combustion engine. These are all relatively inexpensive ways of obtaining energy as compared with consuming zinc.

Two types of storage cells are in use at present: (1) the lead-acid cell, whose electrodes are lead and lead peroxide in a sulfuric-acid solution, and (2) the Edison akaline cell, whose electrodes are nickel and iron in various stages of oxidation, and whose electrolyte is a solution of the alkali, potassium hydroxide (caustic potash, KOH).

The lead-acid battery has the advantage of extremely low internal resistance, which enables it to supply extremely large currents for short periods of time. It is the only battery suitable for starting automobile motors. On a winter day at 0° F, an automobile starter requires a current of about 300 amp. A 3-cell, 6-volt automobile battery has an internal resistance of about 0.003 ohm, or only 0.001 ohm per cell, and when fully charged is capable of supplying a current of 300 amp steadily for about 3 min when the battery is at 0° F.

The disadvantages of the lead-acid battery are that it is heavy, weak structurally, and comparatively short-lived. The active materials are in the form of pastes held in grids of lead-antimony alloy. The grids are structurally weak and tend to sag or buckle, and the pastes tend to flake off with repeated charging and discharging and to sink to the bottom of the jar.

The Edison alkaline battery is lighter in weight and structurally much stronger and more durable than the lead-acid cell. It is constructed entirely of nickel-plated steel, except for the active materials, which are contained in finely perforated steel tubes or cells. Its high internal resistance (about 10 times that of a comparable lead battery) makes it unsuitable for motor-starting service.

In the lead-acid battery, the active material of the negative plate is metallic lead in a spongy condition so that a large surface area is exposed to the sulfuric-acid electrolyte. On discharge, the metallic lead changes to solid lead sulfate which remains on the surface and in the pores of the spongy-lead electrode. The reaction is

$$Pb_{Metal} + SO_4^{--} \xrightarrow[\text{discharge}]{} 2\epsilon^- + (PbSO_4)_{Solid}. \quad \left(\begin{smallmatrix} \text{negative} \\ \text{electrode} \end{smallmatrix}\right) \quad (14)$$

At the positive plate the reaction is more complex. The active material is lead peroxide, PbO_2, in which the lead is quadrivalent. Two electrons arriving at the positive plate reduce the valence of the Pb and permit one molecule of PbO_2 to combine with one of H_2O and pass into solution as a bivalent Pb^{++} ion and four OH^- ions, so that a net charge of 2 electrons is carried into solution to compensate the net charge of 2 electrons that leaves the solution at the negative plate in (14).   This reaction is

$$(PbO_2)_{Solid} + 2\ H_2O + 2\varepsilon^- \xrightarrow[\text{discharge}]{} Pb^{++} + 4\ OH^-. \quad \left(\begin{smallmatrix}\text{positive}\\\text{electrode}\end{smallmatrix}\right) \quad (15a)$$

But the Pb^{++} ion immediately combines with an SO_4^{--} ion to form insoluble $PbSO_4$ on the surface or within the pores of the lead-peroxide paste:

$$Pb^{++} + SO_4^{--} \xrightarrow[\text{discharge}]{} (PbSO_4)_{Solid}; \qquad (15b)$$

and the OH^- ions combine with H^+ ions to form water:

$$4\ OH^- + 4\ H^+ \xrightarrow[\text{discharge}]{} 4\ (H_2O)_{Liq.} \qquad (15c)$$

The secondary reactions (15b) and (15c) do not involve any transfer of charge to or from the electrode.

The net result of (14) and (15) is that, for each two electrons that flow, one molecule of lead peroxide is changed to lead sulfate at the positive electrode, one atom of lead is changed to lead sulfate at the negative electrode, and two molecules of H_2SO_4 disappear from solution and are replaced by two molecules of water.   The over-all reaction is

$$PbO_2 + Pb + 2\ H_2SO_4 \xrightarrow[\text{discharge}]{} 2\ PbSO_4 + 2\ H_2O, \qquad (16)$$

with a requirement of two faradays of charge transfer if (16) is in moles.

Exactly the reverse of (14), (15), and (16) takes place on charge.

The density of the sulfuric-acid solution decreases as discharge progresses, since heavy sulfuric-acid molecules are replaced by lighter water molecules, according to (16).   Hence, the density of the electrolyte furnishes an indication of the state of charge, and lead-acid batteries can be 'tested' with a hydrometer.   Such batteries are ordinarily used in an operating range between densities of $1.285\ g/cm^3$ (fully charged) and $1.150\ g/cm^3$ (time to recharge).

The energy released in the chemical reaction (16) varies with the concentration of the sulfuric acid, because of variations in the large heat of solution of H_2SO_4 in water; hence, the EMF of the cell will also vary with charge condition and will furnish an indication of the state of charge.   At $25°$ C and a density of $1.285\ g/cm^3$, the EMF is 2.13 volts; whereas at a density of $1.150\ g/cm^3$, the EMF has dropped to 2.01 volts.

Example.   *At an electrolyte density of* $1.200\ g/cm^3$, *the* EMF *of the lead-acid cell is* 2.05 v *and the heat of the reaction* (16) *is* 91.2 kcal/mole.   *On discharge, what percentages of the chemical energy go into electrical energy and into heat?*

From (5), we see that the chemical energy released is

$$H = (91.2/23.1) \text{ ev/molecule} = 3.95 \text{ ev/molecule}.$$

This should more properly be called the energy released per molecular reaction (16). The electrical energy created, since 2 electrons are transferred through 2.05 v per molecular reaction, is

$$nV = (2 \text{ electrons})(2.05 \text{ v}) = 4.10 \text{ ev/reaction}.$$

More electrical energy is created than the chemical energy released. This additional energy comes from thermal energy. In (12) and (13), h is negative and has the value

$$h = -0.15 \text{ ev/reaction}.$$

Thermal energy disappears on discharge and is generated on charge. We could say that on discharge $100 (4.10/3.95) = 104$ per cent of the chemical energy goes into electrical energy and -4 per cent into heat—or that 96 per cent of the electrical energy comes from chemical energy, 4 per cent from thermal energy.

The reactions in the Edison nickel-iron cell are less simple than those in the lead cell. Initially the active material at the positive electrode is a mixture of nickel hydrate and flaked nickel; at the negative electrode, iron oxide; the electrolyte is a solution of KOH. Nickel and iron form many oxides and hydroxides of different valences, and in use various mixtures of Ni, NiO, Ni_2O_3, Ni_3O_4, $Ni(OH)_2$, and $Ni(OH)_3$ are found on the positive plate, with mixtures of Fe, FeO, and $Fe(OH)_2$ on the negative plate. In any case, the chemical energy during discharge is furnished by oxidation of the iron and a corresponding reduction of the nickel.

8. THERMOELECTRIC EFFECTS; THE THERMOCOUPLE

A NUMBER of different thermoelectric effects occur in metals. These effects involve direct reversible interchange between thermal and electrical energy, and certain other types of interactions between temperature gradients and potential gradients. One of these effects, the *Seebeck effect*, is utilized in the thermocouple, a thermometer of great practical importance; it and its inverse, the *Peltier effect*, will be described here. We shall also describe the *Thomson effect*.

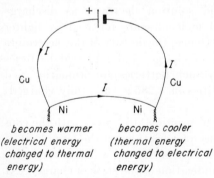

becomes warmer
(electrical energy
changed to thermal
energy)

becomes cooler
(thermal energy
changed to electrical
energy)

Fig. 6. Peltier effect for copper and nickel.

About 1834, Jean Charles Athanase Peltier, in Paris, discovered that when there is a current through a circuit composed of two dissimilar metals, as in Fig. 6, one of the junctions between the metals tends to become warmer and the other junction tends to become cooler. The rate of heat generation or absorption is proportional to the current.   When the current is reversed, the roles of the two junctions are reversed.   The temperature changes associated with this *Peltier effect* appear in addition to temperature increases resulting from the normal I^2R-heating.   The I^2R-heating depends on the square of the current and is independent of current direction.   By use of low-resistance pieces of metal, it is possible, in spite of the I^2R-heating, to get one of the junctions to cool below room temperature.

The dependence of the effect on current direction in the case of the metals Cu and Ni is shown in Fig. 6.

The *Seebeck effect*, discovered in 1821 by Thomas Johann Seebeck in Berlin, is the inverse of the Peltier effect. Here (Fig. 7), holding the two junctions at different temperatures causes a current when no other source of EMF is present. The current in Fig. 7 is in such a direction as to *tend* to equalize the temperature discrepancy.   With the current direction shown, we note from Fig. 6 that the hot junction tends to cool and the cold junction to warm up.   The circuit of Fig. 7 is a heat engine which absorbs heat at the hot junction, converts some of the heat into electrical energy, and rejects the rest of the absorbed heat at the cold junction.

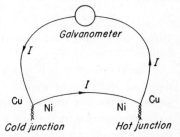

Fig. 7. Seebeck effect. The thermocouple.

When used as a thermometer, the circuit of Fig. 7 is called a *thermocouple*.   The value of the thermocouple as a thermometer depends on the fact that the net EMF developed is directly related to the temperature difference between the junctions.   For small temperature differences, it is approximately proportional to the temperature difference.   Although the net EMF is small (of the order of 10 to 40 microvolts per C deg of temperature difference), a sensitive galvanometer can be calibrated to read temperature differences to an accuracy of $\frac{1}{1000}$ deg.   The cold junction is usually placed in ice water to furnish a constant reference temperature; the hot junction can be in an inaccessible location, for example in the wheat in the middle of a grain elevator, where it would be impossible to read a mercury thermometer.

The proportionality between EMF and temperature difference does not hold over a very wide temperature range.   In fact, for some metal pairs the EMF goes to a maximum and then decreases again as the hot-junction temperature is raised; but metals can be selected in which this reversal does not occur, and temperatures can be read accurately from a calibration curve.

Thermocouples in which the two metals are copper and constantan, or iron and constantan, are widely used in the lower temperature ranges.

For higher temperatures, noble metals of high melting point and low chemical activity must be used; the most satisfactory combination employs platinum as one metal and a rhodium-platinum alloy as the other. Such a couple furnishes a satisfactory thermometer up to a temperature of about 1600° C (2900° F).

In practice, a thermocouple circuit ordinarily consists of at least three metals—the two metals constituting the thermocouple proper, and copper leads to the galvanometer and copper galvanometer windings.   The wir-

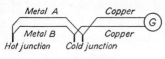

Figure 8

ing is arranged as in Fig. 8.   The two connections to the copper constitute the cold junction; and so long as these two connections are at the same temperature, the EMF developed is exactly the same as if the wires were connected directly together at the cold junction, with no copper in the circuit.

The thermocouple is one of the most sensitive devices for the measurement of radiant energy.   In this usage, the junctions are made small, so as to have low thermal capacity, and blackened.   The radiant energy to be measured is focused by a mirror on one of the junctions.   A sensitive galvanometer can detect the small temperature rise associated with the absorption of very small quantities of radiant energy.   Such an instrument is used for the mapping of spectra in the infrared beyond the limits of the photographic plate.   It is also used in connection with reflecting telescopes for measuring the total amount of radiation of all wavelengths received from a star.   One form, which has several cold and several hot junctions in series so that the EMF's are additive, and is arranged so that the radiation falls on all the hot junctions, is called a *thermopile*.   This instrument is the basis of the *radiation pyrometer*, designed to be pointed at a hole in a furnace and to determine the furnace temperature by measuring the total radiant energy emitted.

The thermoelectric effect is not an unmixed blessing.   In any electrical apparatus in which the circuits contain different metals or even different grades of the same metal, temperature differences arising from any cause will set up small 'thermal EMF's' and 'thermal currents,' as they are called.   In a sensitive apparatus these spurious thermal effects can cause a good deal of trouble, and sometimes great pains are taken to eliminate them by constructing whole pieces of equipment of exactly the same grade of copper.

Even when a piece of electrical equipment is constructed of a single grade of copper, small thermal EMF's exist if there are temperature differences between different portions of the equipment.   These EMF's appear as a result of a phenomenon known as the *Thomson effect*.   If a copper rod is heated at one end and cooled at the other, a difference of potential is observed between the ends.   This *Thomson* difference of potential is approximately proportional to the temperature difference between the ends of the rod. It arises from a temperature dependence of the density of free electrons in the metal. These free electrons have properties analogous to those of gas molecules. If a tube containing gas is heated at one end, the density of the gas decreases at that end since the gas pressure remains constant throughout. The 'electron gas' in a metal behaves similarly, and since the electrons are charged, the ends of the rod become charged, negatively at the low-temperature end where the electron density is greatest.

PROBLEMS

1. Find the speed, in m/sec, of each of the following particles when they are accelerated from rest through a difference of potential of 12,000 v: (a) protons; (b) deuterons; (c) alpha-particles; (d) electrons. (Charges and masses of these particles may be found in Sec. 3 of the Appendix.) Ans: (a) 1.52×10^6 m/sec; (b) 1.07×10^6 m/sec; (c) 1.08×10^6 m/sec; (d) 6.50×10^7 m/sec.

2. A 25-g marble is dropped from a height of 1 m. What is the kinetic energy of this marble in electron-volts just before it strikes the floor?

3. Recalling the discussion of the kinetic theory of gases (p. 315), find the average translational kinetic energy of a nitrogen N_2 molecule in a room where the temperature is 27° C, and express this energy in ev. What is the corresponding energy of an O_2 molecule in the same room? Ans: 0.0388 ev.

4. The Van de Graaff generator is a device that provides a stream of high-energy charged particles for use as projectiles for bombardment of atomic nuclei. A certain Van de Graaff machine provides a 25-μa beam of protons accelerated through 1.5 million volts. How many protons per second are in the beam and what is the energy of each in ev and in joules?

5. The cathode of a silver coulometer increased 0.2105 g in mass during an electrolysis. How many coulombs of electricity passed? Ans: 188.

6. How many coulombs are required to purify 1 kg of electrolytic copper? If an average current of 125 amp is used, how long will it take?

7. Dilute sulfuric acid ionizes to give H^+ and SO_4^{--} ions. On electrolysis with platinum electrodes, hydrogen gas is given off at the cathode and oxygen gas at the anode. Write down the electrode reactions and show that the amount of gas of each type, per faraday, is the same as in the electrolysis of pure water.

8. A current of 0.3 amp passes successively through solutions of hydrochloric acid (HCl), sulfuric acid (H_2SO_4), and phosphoric acid (H_3PO_4) via platinum electrodes. Calculate the weight and volume of hydrogen liberated per hour in each case.

9. What volume of H_2 and O_2 gas (at NTP) are liberated if 0.05 amp passes through dilute sulfuric acid for 20 min? Ans: 6.97 cm³; 3.48 cm³.

10. Chlorine and caustic soda are prepared commercially by electrolyzing a solution of common salt (NaCl), using inert electrodes. At the cathode, caustic soda (NaOH) is formed in solution, with hydrogen evolution. At the anode, chlorine gas (Cl_2) is evolved. Write down the electrode reactions. How many liters of chlorine gas at NTP are evolved per faraday? of hydrogen gas?

11. When a ferric-chloride ($FeCl_3$) solution is electrolyzed by using platinum electrodes, chlorine gas is generated at the anode but iron is not plated out at the cathode. Rather, the solution starts changing to one of ferrous chloride ($FeCl_2$) in the neighborhood of the cathode. Write the electrode reactions.

12. Three electrolytic cells with platinum electrodes are connected in series. The first cell contains Ag^+ and NO_3^- ions; the second, Fe^{++} and Cl^-; the third, K^+ and I^-. In 1 hr, 100 g of silver are deposited. In the same time, how many grams of oxygen are released, iron deposited, chlorine released, and iodine deposited? Compare the number of liters of O_2 and of Cl_2 at NTP.

13. A piece of 'costume jewelry' has a surface area of 90 cm² and is to be covered with a layer of silver 10 microns thick. If the plating process is accomplished electrochemically with a silver-nitrate solution, how long will be required for the process if a current of 5 amp is used?   Ans: 169 sec.

14. A smooth, freshly cleaned sheet of aluminum is to be coated with an extremely thin layer of copper. The sheet is 100 cm in length and 20 cm in width and is to be covered on both sides by a layer of copper equal in thickness to 590 mμ (the wavelength of yellow light). The plating process is accomplished in a $CuSO_4$ cell. How much electric charge is transported during the plating process? How many Cu atoms are deposited?

15. Outline a method of 'weighing' by means of an electrolytic cell. In particular, show how the loss in mass of the positive electrode in a copper-plating bath can be determined from current and time measurements. What mass of copper is removed from the positive electrode in 1 sec by a steady current of 1 amp?   Ans: 3.29×10^{-4} g.

16. By means of a stop watch and milliammeter, how accurately can a quantity of copper be 'weighed' if the stop watch can be read to 0.01 sec and the meter to 0.1 ma?

17. (a) How many coulombs are there in 1 amp·hr? (b) How many ampere-hours are there in 1 faraday?   Ans: (a) 3600 coul; (b) 26.8 amp·hr.

18. (a) In the lead-acid cell, how many grams of PbO_2 are changed to $PbSO_4$ on the positive plate for each faraday (that is, for each 26.8 amp·hr) of charge delivered? (b) How many grams of lead are converted to $PbSO_4$ on the negative plate for each faraday? (c) By how many grams does the mass of the electrolyte decrease for each faraday?

19. The capacity of a lead-acid cell in ampere-hours is limited by the amount of PbO_2 on the positive plate. Before *all* the PbO_2 is converted to $PbSO_4$, the voltage of the cell has dropped and the internal resistance has increased to the point where it is desirable to recharge. A cell with a rated useful capacity of 50 amp·hr has 500 g of PbO_2 on the positive plates. What would be the capacity of this cell if *all* the PbO_2 were converted to $PbSO_4$?   Ans: 112 amp·hr.

20. A 160-amp·hr storage battery maintains an average terminal voltage of 6.15 v during use from 'full charge' to 'complete discharge.' How much energy is delivered to the external circuit?

21. Assuming that there is adequate $CuSO_4$, how many ampere-hours will a Daniell cell deliver before a 400-g zinc cathode is all dissolved?   Ans: 328.

22. The solubility of $CuSO_4$ is 140 g per liter of solution. If a Daniell cell starts with ½ liter of saturated $CuSO_4$ solution and adequate zinc, how many ampere-hours will it deliver before the $CuSO_4$ is used up?

23. In Fig. 8, if metal A is replaced by a copper wire of the same resistance, the galvanometer reads a current I_1; if metal B is replaced by a copper wire of the same resistance, the galvanometer reads a current I_2 in the same direction. Show that for the actual circuit of Fig. 8, the galvanometer will read $I_1 + I_2$.

24. For given hot- and cold-junction temperatures, the *thermoelectric power* of a given metal A is defined as the voltage developed in the circuit of Fig. 8 per degree temperature difference when metal B is lead. If, when the hot junction is at 100° C and the cold junction at 10° C, the thermoelectric power of platinum is 4 $\mu v/C$ deg and that of nickel is 20 $\mu v/C$ deg (EMF in the same sense) what will be the voltage developed by a Pt-Ni thermocouple with the junctions at these temperatures? Explain your reasoning carefully.

25. If the thermoelectric power of iron is -12 $\mu v/C$ deg under the conditions of Prob. 24, what will be the magnitude of the EMF of a Ni-Fe thermocouple with junctions at 10° and 100° C? Ans: 2.88 mv.

26. The thermoelectric power (see Prob. 24) of copper is $+2.7$ $\mu v/C$ deg, while that of constantan is -38.1 $\mu v/C$ deg. If a copper-constantan thermocouple is used with a suspended-coil galvanometer that gives a deflection of 0.1 mm/μv when used with a light beam and scale, what is the minimum temperature difference between junctions that can be detected if a 0.1-mm deflection is the minimum observable?

27. The ionization energies of atmospheric gases are listed in a handbook as follows: N_2, 15.5 ev; O_2, 12.5 ev; and CO_2, 14.4 ev. Taking 15 ev as a rough average ionization energy of an 'air molecule,' compute the number of ion pairs formed when a 4.5 Mev alpha-particle comes to rest after passing through dry air. The number of ion pairs actually observed is 1.4×10^5. What is the average kinetic energy of each ion pair after formation? (Note: the handbook values for ionization energy assume zero kinetic energy of the ions after separation.)

Ans: 3×10^5, 17.1 ev.

28. Consider galvanized iron (iron coated with zinc) from the standpoint of electrolytic action. If a sheet of galvanized iron is in contact with an acidic solution, and the zinc coating is pitted, will zinc or iron dissolve?

29. Taking 15 ev as the ionization energy of an 'air molecule' and assuming that the mean free path (average distance between collisions) of the ions as approximately 10^{-5} cm at NTP, calculate an approximate value for the dielectric strength of air at NTP. Recalling that the actual dielectric strength for dry air is 30,000 v/cm find the effective mean free path of the ions causing breakdown. What are the particles chiefly involved in causing breakdown?

Ans: 150,000 v/cm; 5×10^{-4} cm; electrons.

30. Hydrogen and oxygen are produced commercially by the electrolysis of a solution of H_2SO_4 as in Prob. 7, with inert electrodes. Using the same values of internal resistance, electrical-energy cost, and fixed cost per cell as in the copper-refining example on p. 652, determine the voltage at which these gases can be produced most economically.

31. The bronze screws and steel hull of a ship form a huge short-circuited electrolytic cell. Relative to iron, bronze behaves electrolytically like copper. Diagram the flow of charge in this cell. Do the screws or the hull corrode?

Ans: the hull, and this constitutes a very serious naval problem only partly solved by frequent and careful painting.

32. What percentages of the electrical energy go into chemical energy, reversible heat, and I^2R heat when the cell in Prob. 30 is operated at 2 volts?

CHAPTER 32

MAGNETIC EFFECTS OF ELECTRIC CURRENTS

THE WORD *magnetism* comes from the ancient Greek name for certain naturally occurring iron-oxide stones called *lodestones*. These stones have the property of exerting forces on each other and on bits of iron or steel. They also have the power of imparting their own distinctive properties to pieces of steel that they touch. A piece of steel (for example, a steel needle) that has thus acquired the properties of the lodestone is said to be *magnetized*, and is called a *magnet*.

It was later discovered that a lodestone or a steel magnet experiences a torque that tends to orient it in a particular direction on the earth. This led to the important invention, sometime before the middle of the 12th century A.D., of the mariner's compass.

In 1820, Hans Christian Oersted discovered that forces exist between a magnet and a wire carrying electric current. In the same year, Ampère found that related forces exist between two wires carrying electric currents. Ampère suggested that the forces between magnets arise from the presence of circulating currents ('Amperian whirls') within the magnets. Modern research has shown this hypothesis to be correct, the circulating currents consisting of electrons in motion around the positive atomic nuclei or 'spinning' on their own axes. Thus *all magnetic phenomena are now explained in terms of forces between electric currents*.

Since the forces between currents are fundamental, we begin the study of magnetism with a description of these forces in this chapter, the study of magnetized materials being left for the following chapter. Study of magnetic forces between currents is known as *electromagnetism*, whereas the older subject of *magnetostatics* considered only magnets. Ampère's hypothesis makes magnetostatics a branch of electromagnetism.

Magnetic effects are of extreme technical importance because they are fundamental to the performance of electrical machinery of all types. Electric meters, motors, generators, transformers, relays, lifting magnets, and loudspeakers are all electromagnetic devices. *Electrostatics* by itself would have led to very little technical development of electricity. *Electromagnetism*, together with electrostatics and such subjects as electrochemistry and thermoelectricity, made possible all the present applications of electricity except those depending on twentieth-century developments in *electronics*.

668

1. INTRODUCTION

As AMPÈRE first discovered, wires carrying currents exert on each other forces proportional to the currents, in addition to any electrostatic forces that may exist between the wires.   Since it is possible for a wire carrying a current to be electrostatically neutral—the negative electrostatic charge on the moving electrons being exactly equal and opposite to the fixed positive charge in the wire—these additional forces must be associated with the *motion* of electric charges.   In addition to the electrostatic forces between charges, there is another distinct system of forces associated with the motion of the charges; these are called *magnetic forces.* Magnetic forces exist between two charges only if both charges are in motion, the magnitude of the force being proportional to the product of the speeds of the charges.

> **Magnetic forces** are forces associated with the *motion* of electric charges.

The reader should immediately remark that these ideas seem inconsistent with the principle of relativity. They *are* inconsistent unless we are careful to write '*motion relative to the observer.*' This inconsistency was one of the things that bothered Einstein, and led to his extension of the Newtonian principle of relativity to comprehend electromagnetic phenomena.

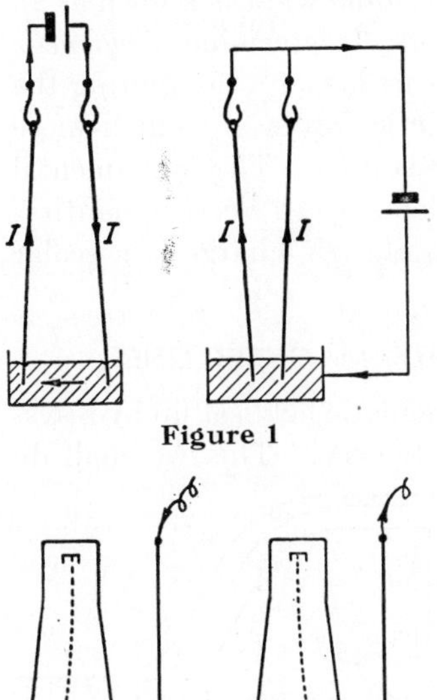

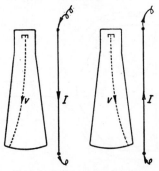

Figure 1

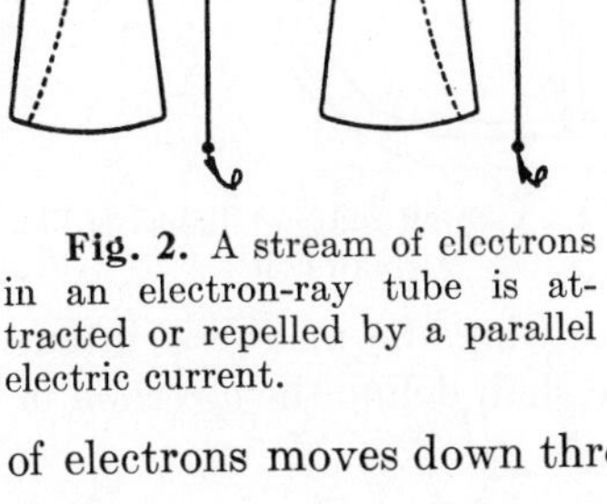

The existence of magnetic forces between parallel wires carrying current can be easily demonstrated with the apparatus sketched in Fig. 1.   Here two stiff .wires hang with their lower ends dipping into a pool of mercury so that the lower ends are free to move.   If currents are sent through the two wires in opposite directions, the wires are mutually repelled; if currents are sent through the two wires in the same direction, the wires are mutually attracted.

That these forces are fundamentally forces between charges in motion can be easily demonstrated by replacing the left-hand wire of Fig. 1 (whose upward current corresponds to *electrons moving down*) by an electron-ray tube in which a beam of electrons moves down through a vacuum.   According to the direction

Fig. 2. A stream of electrons in an electron-ray tube is attracted or repelled by a parallel electric current.

of the current in the fixed parallel wire, the beam of electrons is transversely deflected in the direction corresponding to the motion of the wire in Fig. 1. This experiment is sketched in Fig. 2, the two parts of this figure corresponding to the parts of Fig. 1.

The forces between two *parallel* currents constitute a particularly simple case of a fairly complex system of forces which we need to study in detail. This system of forces is best expressed in terms of the *magnetic intensity* ℬ. The procedure is similar to the determination of electrostatic forces in terms of the electric intensity ℰ. In the electrostatic case we proceeded in two steps. We first learned to compute ℰ from the distribution in space of electrostatic charges. Similarly, we shall learn to compute ℬ from the distribution in space of electric currents. Then as a second step, the force on an electrostatic charge was determined by the magnitude and direction of ℰ at the location of the charge. Similarly the magnetic force on a *current element* (a short length of wire carrying current, or a single moving charge) is determined by the magnitude and direction of ℬ at the location of the current element.

Just as the electric-intensity vectors ℰ determine what is known as an electric field, so the magnetic-intensity vectors ℬ determine a *magnetic field*. The student is warned, however, that the laws for computing the magnetic intensity and for computing magnetic forces are much more complex than the corresponding laws in electrostatics. The fundamental reason for this complexity is that a current element is a vector quantity, having magnitude and direction, whereas an electric charge is a scalar quantity, having only magnitude.

2. THE DIRECTION OF THE MAGNETIC INTENSITY; MAGNETIC LINES

Logically, before we can ask about the magnetic field set up by a system of currents, we must *define* magnetic intensity. This we shall do

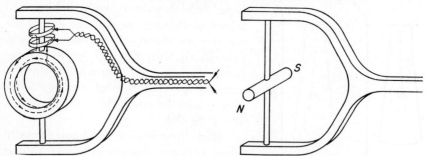

Fig. 3. A small current-carrying coil free to turn about an axle.   **Fig. 4.** A small magnet behaves like a small coil.

operationally by specifying a method of measuring the magnetic intensity ℬ at a point of space. In this section we shall define the *direction* of the intensity; in the next section, its *magnitude*.

A magnetic field (for example, the earth's magnetic field, the field in the vicinity of magnetized iron, or that in the vicinity of conductors carrying current) can be explored by means of either a small magnet mounted as in Fig. 4 so that it is free to rotate about an axle perpendicular to the magnet, or a small current-carrying coil consisting of many turns of wire mounted as in Fig. 3 so that it is free to rotate about an axle in the plane of the coil.   These devices must be carefully balanced so that they will not tend to rotate because of gravitational forces, particularly when the axle is horizontal.   The magnet of Fig. 4, when the axle is vertical, is the prototype of the familiar compass needle.   As a compass, its ends are *north-seeking* and *south-seeking;* by this criterion its ends are designated as *N* and *S*.

At any point in a magnetic field, both the magnet and the coil will tend to orientate in a certain direction.   We specify the orientation of the magnet by means of a vector ***M*** along the axis of the magnet pointing in the direction from the south-seeking end toward the north-seeking end, as in Fig. 5.   We specify the orientation of a coil by a vector ***M*** lying along the *axis* of the coil (not to be confused with

Fig. 5. Direction of the magnetic moment ***M*** of a magnet and of a coil.

the *axle* of Fig 3) and pointing in the direction in which a right-hand screw would advance if its head were turned in the direction of the current in the coil, as in Fig. 5.   A vector in this direction, and of a magnitude to be defined presently, is called the *magnetic moment* of the small magnet or the small coil.   The *right-hand rule*, given above, for determining the direction of the magnetic moment of the coil, is most conveniently applied as follows:

> Let the fingers of your right hand curl around in the direction of the current in a small coil; then the thumb of this hand will point out in the direction of the magnetic-moment vector of the coil.

With these specifications for the direction of the magnetic moment, it is found experimentally that *the small coil and the small magnet behave exactly alike;* at a given point in a magnetic field, either will tend to turn so that its magnetic moment is pointing in the same particular direction.

> The **direction** of the **magnetic intensity** $\mathfrak{B}$ at a point of space is defined as the direction in which the magnetic-moment vector of either a small coil or a small magnet tends to orientate when the small coil or magnet is placed at that point of space.

In this definition, *one should think of the coil or magnet as somehow cleverly mounted so that the magnetic-moment vector is free to turn in every direction*.   In the practical mounting of Figs. 3 and 4, the magnetic-moment vector can only rotate in one plane and define the direction of the

component of the magnetic intensity in that plane.   With such a mounting, successive tests with the axle in various orientations are required to
determine the direction of the magnetic intensity in space.

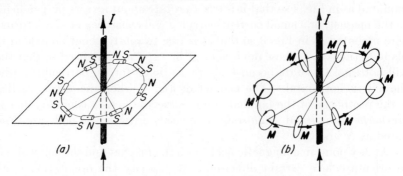

Fig. 6. Exploration of the field near a long straight wire by means of
(a) a small magnet, (b) a small coil.

Thus, at a point in the vicinity of a long straight wire carrying a heavy
current (so that the magnetic intensity arising from this current is large

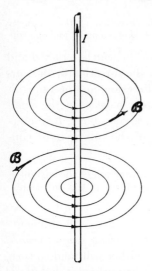

Fig. 7. Representative
magnetic lines in the field
of a long straight wire.

compared with that of the earth's magnetic
field), the small coil or magnet tends to turn
so that its magnetic moment has a direction
perpendicular to the wire and perpendicular
to the radius from the wire to the point.
Thus, the magnetic field set up by the current in the wire is found to have the direction
shown by the magnetic-moment vectors in
Fig. 6.

Just as we defined an electric line as a
directed line whose tangent at any point is in
the direction of the electric intensity $\mathcal{E}$, we
define a *magnetic line* as a directed line whose
tangent is in the direction of the magnetic
intensity $\mathcal{B}$. From the observed directions
given by Fig. 6, we see that the magnetic lines
in the vicinity of a long straight wire are circles
surrounding the wire, as in Fig. 7.

The experimental results of Figs. 6 and 7
also determine the sense of the magnetic-
intensity vector along the circular magnetic lines, in relation to the current direction.   This sense, as shown in Fig. 7, is given by a right-hand
rule of the following type:

Point the thumb of your right hand in the direction of the current in the
wire, and your curled fingers will point in the direction the magnetic intensity
points along the circular magnetic lines.

According to this rule, if the direction of the current is reversed in Fig. 7, the direction of the magnetic intensity and hence that of the magnetic lines will reverse at each point.   By turning Fig. 7 upside down, one can see that this reversal of direction certainly occurs.

The earth has a magnetic field in which, over most of the inhabited surface, the horizontal component vector $\mathfrak{B}_H$ points generally northward.   The earth's magnetic intensity also has a strong downward component throughout most of the northern hemisphere, a strong upward component throughout most of the southern.   The magnetic intensity near San Francisco, for example, has a northward component, an eastward component, and a large downward component, so that the actual vector $\mathfrak{B}$

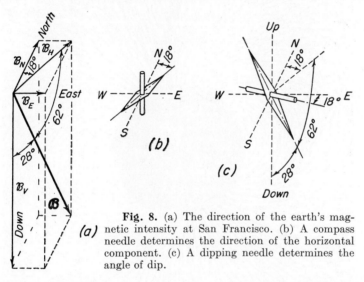

Fig. 8. (a) The direction of the earth's magnetic intensity at San Francisco. (b) A compass needle determines the direction of the horizontal component. (c) A dipping needle determines the angle of dip.

points in the direction shown in Fig. 8(a).   The direction of this intensity could be determined by a small magnet mounted so as to be free to rotate in all directions, but a perfectly balanced, sufficiently frictionless, gimbaled mounting of this type has never been achieved.   Rather, the direction of this or of any other magnetic-intensity vector is determined in two steps, by the use of a single-axle mounting of the type shown in Fig. 4. First a *compass needle*, mounted to rotate about a vertical axle only, is used to determine the direction of the horizontal component $\mathfrak{B}_H$, as in Fig. 8(b).   To assure that the needle moves in a horizontal plane, an accurate compass needle is floated, like a ship's card, on the horizontal surface of a liquid.   Then a second needle, called a *dipping needle*, which rotates in perfect gravitational balance about a horizontal axis, is used as indicated in Fig. 8(c).   The horizontal axis is aligned perpendicular to the horizontal component of the field so that the needle swings accurately in the plane determined by $\mathfrak{B}_H$ and $\mathfrak{B}_V$, which plane contains the vector $\mathfrak{B}$ itself.   This needle then points along $\mathfrak{B}$ and gives the *dip* of the magnetic field below the horizontal.   For example, at San Francisco, the horizontal component points 18° east of north, and the dip is 62°.

The origin of the earth's magnetic field is still a mystery.   The field is presumed to arise from macroscopic currents flowing around inside the earth rather than from permanently magnetized materials, since at the temperatures that probably exist in the interior of the earth, iron, cobalt, and nickel lose their characteristic magnetic properties.

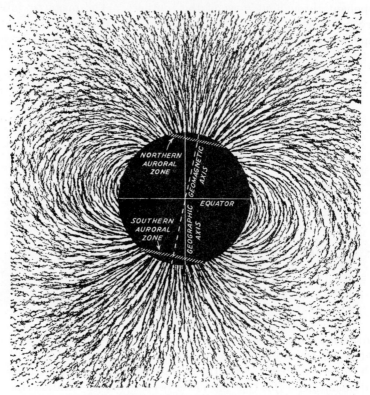

Fig. 9. The magnetic field of the earth. [*J. A. Fleming, Terrestrial Magnetism and Electricity, Dover.*]

The field is much like that of a current-carrying coil or bar magnet at the center of the earth.   The field of such a coil or magnet, mapped by means of iron filings, is shown in Fig. 9.

The earth's field is approximately symmetrical about an axis, called the *geomagnetic axis*, that is tilted 12° with respect to the geographic axis. The great circle in a plane normal to the geomagnetic axis is called the *geomagnetic equator*.   Even when plotted in geomagnetic coordinates, the fields are not entirely symmetrical but show localized variations arising, apparently, from variations in earth structure.   Figure 10 is a map, in

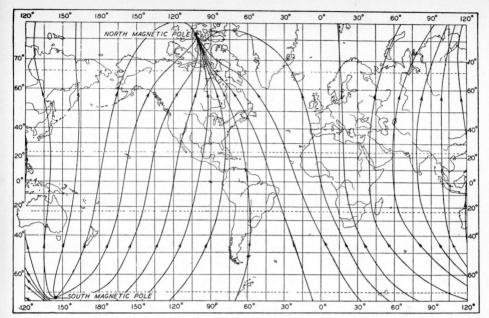

Fig. 10. Lines (called *magnetic meridians*) whose tangents show the direction of the horizontal component vector $\mathfrak{G}_H$ in the earth's magnetic field; that is, the direction in which a compass needle will point.

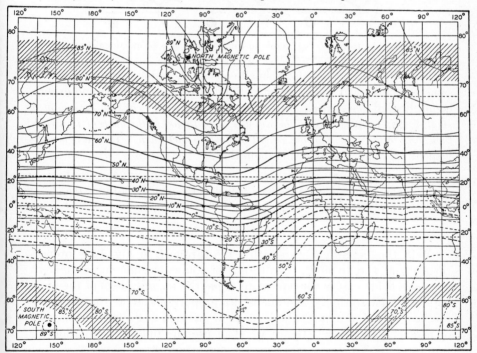

Fig. 11. The *dip* (or *inclination*) of the earth's magnetic field (the angle between the magnetic intensity vector $\mathfrak{G}$ and the horizontal). The hatched areas represent the zones in which auroras are observed on over 80 per cent of the nights. [*Department of Terrestrial Magnetism, Carnegie Institution of Washington.*]

geographic coordinates, showing the direction of the horizontal component of the earth's magnetic intensity; Fig. 11 shows the angle of dip.

3. MAGNITUDE OF THE MAGNETIC INTENSITY

IT IS POSSIBLE to *define* the magnitude $\mathfrak{B}$ of the magnetic intensity in terms of either the torque on a small coil or the force on a current element. We adopt the former course because (a) we have already used it in defining field direction, (b) it is somewhat more fundamental, (c) the defining equation is of simpler form, (d) the operational determination of the magnitude is easier to visualize. Having defined $\mathfrak{B}$ in terms of torque on a small coil, we shall state the somewhat complex relations that govern force on a current element and verify their correctness.

Since a small magnet or a small coil tends to turn so that its magnetic-moment vector M lines up with the magnetic-intensity vector $\mathfrak{B}$; there must exist a torque acting to turn M into $\mathfrak{B}$ when these are not aligned. *This torque is found experimentally to be proportional to the sine of the angle between the two vectors* (see Fig. 12).

Fig. 12. The torque L that tends to turn M into $\mathfrak{B}$ is proportional to $\sin\theta$.

Different small magnets or small coils at the same orientation in the same magnetic field will experience different torques. It is found experimentally that *for a given orientation in a magnetic field, the torque on a small coil is proportional to the number N of turns, to the current I in each turn, and to the area A of the circuit formed by each turn.* Hence it is convenient to adopt the following definition:

> The **magnitude** of the **magnetic moment of a coil** is measured in amp·m², and defined as the product of the number of turns, the current in each turn, and the area of the circuit.

Thus
$$M = NIA. \tag{1}$$

With this definition, we see that the torque L in Fig. 12 is proportional to M and to $\sin\theta$. The torque of course is different in different magnetic fields. It is convenient to *define* the magnitude $\mathfrak{B}$ of the magnetic intensity so that the torque is also proportional to $\mathfrak{B}$; that is, to use torque on a coil of unit magnetic moment oriented at $\theta = 90°$ as a *measure* of magnetic intensity. Hence we shall use the following equation for torque as the *defining equation* for the magnitude $\mathfrak{B}$:

$$L = M\mathfrak{B}\sin\theta. \qquad \left\{ \begin{array}{l} L \text{ in nt·m} \\ M \text{ in amp·m}^2 \\ \mathfrak{B} \text{ in weber/m}^2 \end{array} \right\} \tag{2}$$

The unit of magnetic intensity defined by this equation is given the name *weber per square meter*. We shall later wish to call ℬ the magnetic-flux *density;* the name weber* is given to the unit of magnetic flux and hence weber/m² to the unit of flux density. According to (2):

> The **weber per square meter** is the magnetic intensity that will result in a torque of one newton·meter on a coil of magnetic moment one ampere·meter² placed with its axis perpendicular to the direction of the magnetic intensity.

No new fundamental unit is required to describe magnetic phenomena. All magnetic units can be expressed in terms of mechanical units and the unit of electric charge or current. Thus, from (2), we note that the unit of ℬ can be written as

$$1\,\frac{\text{weber}}{\text{m}^2} = 1\,\frac{\text{nt}}{\text{amp·m}}. \tag{3}$$

Formula (1) gives the correct value for the magnetic moment to be used in (2) regardless of the shape of the coil: the coil may be wound on a circular frame as in Fig. 3, on a rectangular frame, or on a frame of any other shape. If the different turns of the coil have different areas, A is to be taken as the average area.

We should also like to have equation (2) applicable to the case of a small magnet by giving a suitable definition of the magnetic moment of the magnet. The following definition accomplishes this purpose:

> The **magnetic moment of a small magnet** is equal to the magnetic moment of a small coil that would experience the same torque when placed in the same orientation at the same location in the same magnetic field.

The magnetic moment of a magnet is thus measured in amp·m². This unit will seem more reasonable when we see later on how the magnetic moment of the magnet actually arises from the presence of currents circulating within the substance of the magnet.

One type of *magnetometer* measures the three components of the intensity of the earth's field directly in terms of the definition (2) by measuring the torques tending to rotate three mutually perpendicular small magnets mounted on torsion fibers.†

---

* After WILHELM EDWARD WEBER (1804–1891), German physicist who, along with KARL FRIEDRICH GAUSS (1777–1855), German mathematician, devised the absolute systems of electric and magnetic units.

† The magnitude of the horizontal component of the earth's magnetic intensity varies from 3.5×10^{-5} weber/m² at the magnetic equator to zero at the magnetic poles; that of the vertical component varies from zero at the magnetic equator to 7×10^{-5} weber/m² at the magnetic poles. The earth's field is subject to irregular fluctuations. Large fluctuations of intensity are called *magnetic storms*. Such storms occur most frequently in the auroral zones shown on Fig. 11. Sunspots, magnetic storms, and auroras are apparently interrelated phenomena.

Example. *A compass needle experiences a torque of 5×10^{-4} nt·m when it is pointing geographically north at San Francisco, where the horizontal component of intensity of the earth's field is 25×10^{-6} weber/m². What is the magnetic moment of the compass needle?*

Since the compass needle is mounted on a vertical axis, it is only the horizontal component of the earth's magnetic intensity that tends to rotate it. Hence we can substitute the given values of L and $\mathcal{B}_H$ in (2). The value of θ is the angle between geographical north and $\mathcal{B}_H$, given in Fig. 8 as 18°. Therefore the magnetic moment is

$$M = \frac{L}{\mathcal{B}_H \sin\theta} = \frac{5\times10^{-4}\ \text{nt·m}}{(25\times10^{-6}\ \text{weber/m}^2)\ \sin18°}$$

$$= \frac{5\times10^{-4}}{(25\times10^{-6})(0.309)}\ \frac{\text{nt·m}^3}{\text{weber}} = 64.7\ \text{amp·m}^2,$$

where we have utilized (3) in making the shift of units.

4. THE MAGNETIC FORCE ON A CONDUCTOR CARRYING CURRENT

THE TORQUE on a small coil in a magnetic field arises from forces on the different elements of length of the current-carrying conductors in the coil. We now turn to consideration of the forces on such current elements.

By a current element of magnitude $I\ dl$, in ampere·meters, we mean a piece of conductor of length dl carrying current I. The force on such a current element is determined by the magnetic intensity at the location of the current element. The whole force on a conductor is obtained by integrating the forces on the current elements. The formula for the force on a current element can be formally derived from (1) and (2), but the derivation is somewhat involved. We shall state the answer and then verify that it gives values of torque in agreement with (2).

A current element has direction as well as magnitude; the force on a current element depends on its direction relative to that of the magnetic intensity. We first note that, as in Fig. 13(a), *a current element parallel*

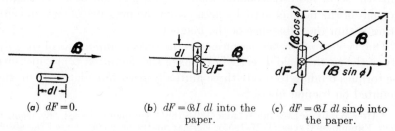

(a) $dF=0$.   (b) $dF=\mathcal{B}I\ dl$ into the   (c) $dF=\mathcal{B}I\ dl\ \sin\phi$ into
                                  paper.   the paper.

Fig. 13. The force on a current element in a magnetic field. (The $\otimes$ represents the tail of an arrow.)

to the magnetic intensity experiences no force; while *a current element perpendicular to the magnetic intensity experiences the force*

$$dF = \mathcal{B}I\ dl, \tag{4}$$

in a direction perpendicular to both the magnetic intensity and the current element, in the sense shown in Fig. 13(b).   In the general case, in Fig. 13(c), when a current element makes an angle ϕ with the magnetic intensity, the magnetic intensity may be resolved into two components: One component is of magnitude $\mathcal{B}\cos\phi$ and parallel to the current; this component occasions no force.   The other component is of magnitude $\mathcal{B}\sin\phi$ and perpendicular to the current; according to (4) this component gives rise to the force

$$\boxed{dF = \mathcal{B}I\ dl\ sin\phi}\qquad \left.\begin{array}{l} F \text{ in nt}\\ \mathcal{B} \text{ in weber/m}^2\\ I \text{ in amp}\\ l \text{ in m} \end{array}\right\} \quad (5)$$

in the direction shown in Fig. 13.

The force is determined by the component of the magnetic intensity perpendicular to the wire, and is in turn perpendicular to both this component and the wire.   There are a number of rules for finding in which of

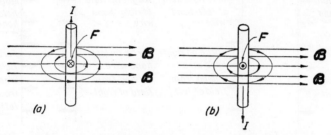

(a)   (b)

Fig. 14. Rule for determining the direction of the force on a current element placed in an external magnetic field $\mathcal{B}$. (a) The field of the current element *strengthens* the field $\mathcal{B}$ in *front* of the wire and *weakens* it behind; the force is *into* the paper, as indicated by the $\otimes$. (b) The field of the current element strengthens the field $\mathcal{B}$ behind the wire and weakens it in front; the force is *out* of the paper, as indicated by the $\odot$.

the two such directions the force acts.   The rule the writers find the simplest to remember is the following:

Apply the right-hand rule as in Fig. 7 to find the sense of the circular magnetic field set up by the current in the wire itself.   This field (see Fig. 14) will be in the same direction as, and will strengthen, the applied field on one side of the wire.   It will be in the direction opposite to, and hence tend to weaken, the applied field on the opposite side of the wire.   *The force on the wire is a vector directed from the side on which the field is strengthened toward the side on which it is weakened.*

As an example of this rule regarding direction of the force, let us reconsider the two parallel wires of Fig. 1.   Each of the wires is in a magnetic field, like that of Fig. 7, set up by the other wire; and the direction of this field determines, according to the above rule, the direction of the force.   This example is illustrated in detail in Fig. 15.

Now let us verify that formulas (4) and (5) give a value of torque on a small coil that is in agreement with (2). We first note that by a *small* coil, we mean one sufficiently small so that the magnetic intensity ℬ does not vary appreciably from one current element of the coil to any other. If the field is uniform, the coil can be of any size we please. We shall assume a uniform field in the following discussion.

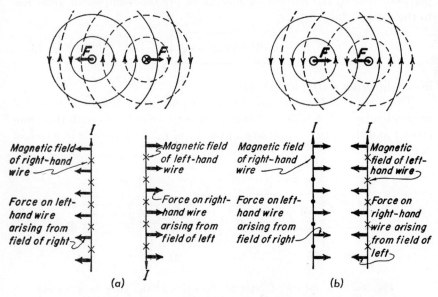

Fig. 15. The forces between parallel wires carrying current arise from the fact that each wire is in the magnetic field of the other. The top view illustrates particularly well that the experimental results of Fig. 1 are in agreement with the rule that the magnetic force is 'from the strengthened toward the weakened part of the field.'

Consider first the N-turn rectangular coil of Fig. 16 with its plane parallel to ℬ. The sides of length l experience forces in the directions indicated by the dot and cross, each of magnitude given by (4) as ℬIl per turn or $F = N$ℬIl total. The lever arm of each of these forces is $\frac{1}{2} w$ about the dotted line through the center of the coil. Hence the torque exerted by these forces is $L = N$ℬIlw. The ends of length w experience no magnetic force. The magnetic moment of the coil has the magnitude $M = NIlw$ and a direction out of the paper toward the reader. The torque computed above has the magnitude $L = M$ℬ and a sense that tends to turn M into ℬ, as we set out to verify.

Now let the magnetic-moment vector of the same coil make angle θ with ℬ, as shown in the end-view, Fig. 17. The forces F have the same magnitude as before, but the lever arms are reduced to $\frac{1}{2} w \sin\theta$. The ends of length w now experience forces (magnitude Nℬ$Iw \cos\theta$ each), but these forces are into and out of the paper in Fig. 17, cancel each other, and do not contribute to the torque. The torque is therefore $L = N\mathfrak{B}Ilw$ $\sin\theta = M\mathfrak{B}\sin\theta$ in a sense that tends to turn M into $\mathfrak{B}$; this agrees with (2).

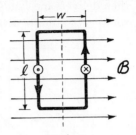

Figure 16

Finally, let us consider a single-turn coil of arbitrary shape having its plane parallel to $\mathfrak{B}$, Fig. 18. Consider the torque of the magnetic forces about the X-axis, perpendicular to $\mathfrak{B}$. These forces will be away from the reader where the current has a leftward component, toward the reader where the current is rightward. Consider the torque of the top half of the coil. The element dX has length $dl = dX/\cos\alpha$ and experiences force $dF = \mathfrak{B}I\,dl\,\cos\alpha = \mathfrak{B}I\,dX$; hence torque $dL = \mathfrak{B}IY\,dX$. The total torque of the top half is $\mathfrak{B}I\int Y\,dX$, in which the integral is just the area of the top half of the coil. A similar consideration for the bottom half shows the total torque to be $\mathfrak{B}IA = \mathfrak{B}M$, where A is the area of the coil.

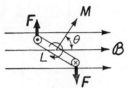

Figure 17

(We have simplified matters by drawing Fig. 18 so that the extreme values of X come at $Y = 0$, but the mathematically inclined student can easily prove the same relation for the more general case.) This is in agreement

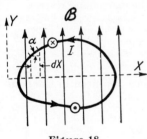

Figure 18

with (2); the agreement in the case where the plane of the coil makes an angle with $\mathfrak{B}$ can be demonstrated by similar but geometrically more complicated arguments.

We can now discuss the principle of the DC electric motor in terms of the simple prototype illustrated in Fig. 19, which shows a single rectangular loop arranged so that it can rotate about a horizontal axle in a uniform magnetic field. The axle carries a commutator arranged to reverse the direction of current in the loop each time the plane of the loop passes through the vertical plane, so that the torque will always have the same sense. As we have already computed in connection with Fig. 17, the total torque is

$$L = \mathfrak{B}Ilw\sin\theta, \qquad (6)$$

always in the clockwise sense.

The torque (6) vanishes when the plane of the coil is normal to the magnetic field and is at a maximum when the plane of the coil is parallel to the magnetic field. The torque of such a one-turn motor would come in spurts during each half-revolution, and the motor would depend on inertia to carry it through the no-torque position ($\theta = 0$). An actual motor contains a number of turns arranged at various angles so that only one turn at a time passes through the no-torque position. Such a motor then delivers mechanical energy at a fairly constant torque but requires a complex commutation system to reverse the current in each turn as it

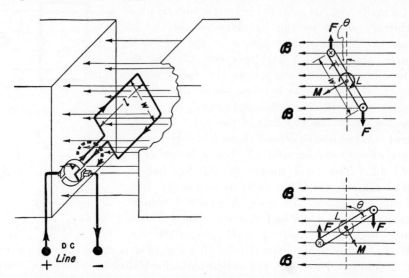

Fig. 19. Prototype of a DC electric motor with commutator. Two positions of the rotating loop are shown at the right. The commutator reverses the current as the plane of the loop passes through the broken center line so that the conductor to the left of this line always has current into the paper and force upward; the conductor to the right always has current out of the paper and force downward; the torque always has the same sense.

passes the no-torque position. Many segments are required in the commutator of a DC motor to do this switching properly.

5. THE D'ARSONVAL GALVANOMETER

THE ESSENTIAL element of DC ammeters and voltmeters is a moving-coil galvanometer of the type shown in Fig. 20. The coil of this galvanometer is supported on hardened steel pivots turning in jeweled bearings. Its rotational motion is restrained by a pair of springs (not shown in Fig. 20), one above and one below the coil, which also serve as current leads to the coil. The position of coil and pointer in Fig. 20 is intended to represent the equilibrium position as determined by the springs, with no current in the coil. In use, the current in the coil is into the paper on the right and out of the paper on the left, so that the magnetic forces in the uniform radial magnetic field create a clockwise torque. The coil moves clockwise until the resisting counterclockwise spring torque equals the clockwise magnetic torque. Since the magnetic torque is proportional to the current in the coil and since the spring torque is proportional to the angle of rotation from the equilibrium position, the angle of rota-

tion is proportional to the current in the coil.   The straightforward
development of the relation between current and angle is left as an exercise.

Pivoted galvanometers of the
type shown in Fig. 20 can be purchased that give full-scale deflection on a current as low as 1
microampere; greater sensitivity
than this cannot be achieved because of friction in the bearings.
To achieve sensitivity, the spring
torque constant must be made
very low, but the spring torque
must still be large compared to
the frictional torque in the bearings if the instrument is to perform properly.   To avoid friction
and to achieve a very low torque
constant, more sensitive instruments, designed to measure currents in the range 10^{-6} to 10^{-10}
amperes, are of the *suspended-coil*

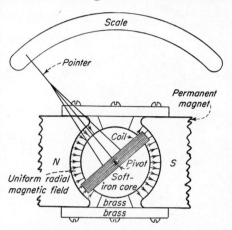

Fig. 20. Schematic drawing of a galvanometer. The drawing is distorted in that
the coil and pole pieces would ordinarily
be much smaller in comparison with the
lengths of the pointer and scale.

type, with the coil suspended from a fiber of phosphor bronze, silver, or
quartz.   Such a suspended-coil instrument is not usually portable.   It
is read by means of a lamp and scale, with the light beam reflected from
a small mirror attached to the coil.

6. MAGNETIC FIELDS SET UP BY ELECTRIC CURRENTS

Now THAT we have defined the magnitude and direction of the magnetic intensity and learned in principle
how to measure it in terms of the torque
exerted on a current-carrying loop, we
turn to the question of the magnitude
and direction of the magnetic intensity
in the field set up by a given system of
electric currents.   First, let us look at
some pictures of the field.   We have
already seen Fig. 7, which gives the
magnetic lines around a long straight
conductor;   Fig. 21 shows the lines
around a circular turn of wire; Fig. 30

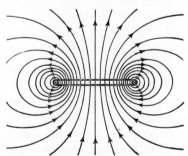

Fig. 21. Magnetic lines linking a
circular turn of wire.

those around a solenoid.   We notice one thing in common in these
pictures, and this is true of all magnetic fields:

*Magnetic lines never begin or end but form continuous closed curves, each
curve linking at least some of the current that sets up the field, the sense
of the linkage being given by the right-hand rule.*

There is no magnetic stuff on which magnetic lines can begin or end in the way in which electric lines begin and end on electric charges. Magnetic lines are always associated with electric currents, and they wrap themselves *around* the currents in the direction of curl of the fingers of the right hand if the thumb points in the direction of the current.

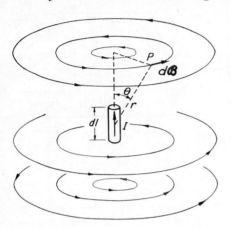

To compute the field of a current, we use a relation known as Ampère's law, which gives the contribution of a current element to the magnetic intensity. The intensity arising from any circuit can then be obtained by integrating the contributions of the elements of the circuit. The inte-

Fig. 22. The field of a current element.

gration is frequently very complicated because each contribution is a little vector, not a scalar, and the contributions must be added vectorially.

Ampère's law gives the contribution $d\mathcal{B}$ that a current element $I\,dl$ makes to the magnetic intensity at a point P (see Fig. 22):

AMPÈRE'S LAW: *The contribution $d\mathcal{B}$ that a current element makes to the magnetic intensity at a point P has a direction perpendicular to both the current element and the line joining the current element to P, in the sense shown in Fig. 22, and has magnitude proportional to the product $I\,dl\,\sin\theta$ and inversely proportional to the square of the distance r, where θ and r are defined as in Fig. 22.*

Thus we can write $\qquad d\mathcal{B} \propto I\,dl\,\sin\theta/r^2$,

or $\qquad\qquad\qquad\qquad d\mathcal{B} = \text{const} \times I\,dl\,\sin\theta/r^2$.

Just as in the case of the Coulomb expression in electrostatics, the constant here has dimensions; to make the dimensions balance, it must be measured in webers/amp·m. Its numerical value is exactly 10^{-7}. In the system of units we are using, the ampere and the coulomb (the ampere·second) are defined so that this particular constant has this exact value; this assignment turns out to give the constant in Coulomb's law the inexact value we have already used—these matters will be discussed in detail in Chap. 36. Thus in the equation above we write

$$\text{const} = 10^{-7} \text{ weber/amp·m} = 10^{-7} \text{ nt/amp}^2 = 10^{-7} \text{ kg·m/coul}^2. \quad (7)$$

Since this constant recurs repeatedly in the discussion of magnetism, we shall abbreviate the units still further and write const $= (10^{-7} \text{ w/a·m})$.

In this notation, Ampère's law takes the form*

$$d\mathcal{B} = (10^{-7} \text{ w/a·m}) \ I \ dl \ \sin\theta/r^2. \qquad \left\{ \begin{array}{l} \mathcal{B} \text{ in weber/m}^2 \\ I \text{ in amp} \\ l,r \text{ in m} \end{array} \right\} \quad (8)$$

Ampère's law is based on experimental observation.   It gives a value of $d\mathcal{B}$ which, when integrated, gives agreement with the observed field of any system of currents.

As a first application of Ampère's law, we compute the intensity contribution of a piece of straight wire of length L carrying current I at a point P opposite one end of the wire and at distance a from it (Fig. 23). The contribution of all current elements of the wire is in the same direction at P (out of the paper).   We obtain the intensity at point P by integrating the contributions (8) to obtain

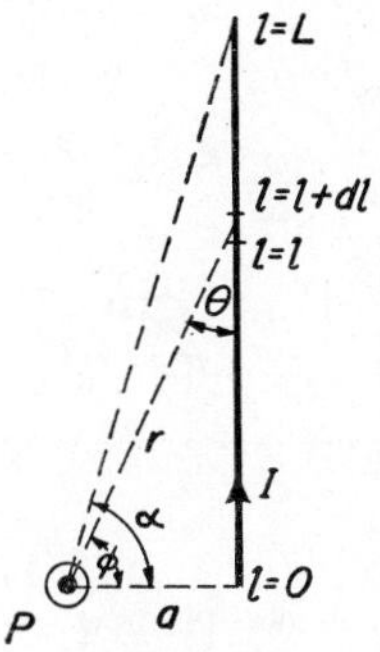

Fig. 23.
$\mathcal{B} = (10^{-7} \text{ w/a·m})$
$\times I \sin\alpha/a.$

$$\mathcal{B} = \int_0^L (10^{-7} \text{ w/a·m})(I \sin\theta/r^2) \ dl.$$

This integral is most easily evaluated in terms of the variable angle ϕ, which runs from 0 to α.   By use of the substitutions

$$\sin\theta = \cos\phi, \quad r = a/\cos\phi, \quad l = a \tan\phi, \quad dl = a \sec^2\phi \ d\phi,$$

the integral becomes

$$\mathcal{B} = (10^{-7} \text{ w/a·m})(I/a) \int_0^\alpha \cos\phi \ d\phi$$

$$= (10^{-7} \text{ w/a·m})(I/a) \left[\sin\phi \right]_0^\alpha = (10^{-7} \text{ w/a·m}) \ I \sin\alpha/a. \quad (9)$$

From this equation, we can easily get the formulas for the general case, when P is not opposite one end of the wire, that are given under Figs. 24 and 25.   In Fig. 24 we have added together the contributions, computed from (9), of two pieces of wire, one subtending an angle α and the other an angle β at P.   In Fig. 25, we have subtracted what would be the contribution of a piece of wire subtending angle β from the contribution of a piece subtending angle α to get that of the remaining piece.

* In advanced textbooks an algebraic symbol is used to indicate that a dimensional constant is involved.   When 'rationalized' units are employed, Ampère's law is written

$$d\mathcal{B} = (\mu_0/4\pi) \ I \ dl \ \sin\theta/r^2,$$

where μ_0 is called the 'rational permeability of free space.'   When 'nonrationalized' units are used, the relation is written

$$d\mathcal{B} = \mu_0' \ I \ dl \ \sin\theta/r^2$$

where μ_0' is called the 'nonrational' or 'unrationalized permeability of free space.' It should be noted that

$$\mu_0/4\pi = \mu_0' = 10^{-7} \text{ weber/amp·m.}$$

Further discussion of systems of units is given in Sec. 2 of the Appendix.

By using the formulas given with Figs. 24 and 25, we can find the field of any circuit composed entirely of straight runs of wire. As an example, the field at the *center* of the square coil of N turns, given in Fig. 26, is obtained from (9), with $\alpha = 45°$, taken $8N$ times over.

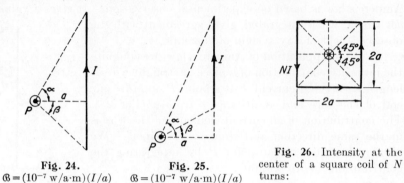

Fig. 24.
$\mathfrak{B} = (10^{-7} \text{ w/a·m})(I/a)$
$\times (\sin\alpha + \sin\beta)$.

Fig. 25.
$\mathfrak{B} = (10^{-7} \text{ w/a·m})(I/a)$
$\times (\sin\alpha - \sin\beta)$.

Fig. 26. Intensity at the center of a square coil of N turns:
$\mathfrak{B} = (10^{-7} \text{ w/a·m}) 4\sqrt{2}\, NI/a$.

The field of a straight infinite wire is obtained from Fig. 24 with $\alpha = \beta = 90°$. This gives

$$\mathfrak{B} = (10^{-7} \text{ w/a·m})\, 2I/a. \quad \text{(infinite straight wire)} \quad (10)$$

From this equation we see that the intensity in Fig. 7 falls off inversely with distance a from the wire. Of course no infinite wire really exists, but we notice from Fig. 24 that so long as a is very small compared to the distance of P from the ends of the wire, α and β will be approximately $90°$, and formula (10) will be closely realized.

Example. *Determine the force per unit length between two parallel wires carrying currents I and I'. What is the force per meter length between two wires 1 m apart each carrying 1 amp?*

Let the distance between the wires be d (in m). Then the magnetic intensity set up by the current I at the location of the other wire (see Fig. 15) is given by (10) as

$$\mathfrak{B} = (10^{-7} \text{ w/a·m})\, 2I/d.$$

The force per unit length on the wire carrying current I' placed in this field, which we shall denote by f, is given by (4) as

$$f = dF/dl = \mathfrak{B}I' = (10^{-7} \text{ w/a·m})\, 2II'/d.$$

The unit of f will be more obviously nt/m when I, I' are in amp and d in m if we write 10^{-7} nt/amp^2 instead of 10^{-7} w/a·m, in accordance with (7). Hence

$$f = (10^{-7} \text{ nt/amp}^2)\, 2II'/d. \quad \left(\begin{smallmatrix}\text{force between}\\\text{parallel wires}\end{smallmatrix}\right) \quad (11)$$

As indicated in Fig. 15, this force is repulsive if the currents are oppositely directed, attractive if the currents are in the same direction.

If $I = I' = 1$ amp, $d = 1$ m,

$$f = (10^{-7} \text{ nt/amp}^2)(2 \text{ amp}^2)/(1 \text{ m}) = 2 \times 10^{-7} \text{ nt/m}.$$

As a next application of Ampère's law, we shall compute the intensity at any point on the axis of a circular turn of radius a (Fig. 27). In this case the current element $I\,dl$ makes an intensity contribution $d\mathcal{B}$ that lies in the axial plane and is perpendicular to r. Its magnitude is given by (8) with $\theta = 90°$. This intensity contribution has a component $d\mathcal{B}$ $\sin\phi$ along the axis and a component $d\mathcal{B}\cos\phi$ normal to the axis. We see from Fig. 27 that the elements $d\mathcal{B}_1$ and $d\mathcal{B}_2$ arising from equal lengths dl on opposite sides of the circle have components normal to the axis that cancel in pairs, so that the result of integration around the circle is an intensity in the axial direction. Since $\sin\phi = a/r$, the axial component arising from dl is

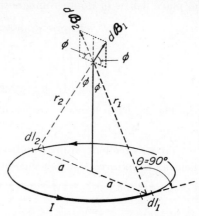

Fig. 27. Intensity contributions on the axis of a circular turn from two current elements $I\,dl_1$ and $I\,dl_2$ of equal length but on opposite sides of the circle. Note that $d\mathcal{B}_1 \perp r_1 \perp dl_1$, and that $d\mathcal{B}_2 \perp r_2 \perp dl_2$.

$$d\mathcal{B}_{\text{Axial}} = (10^{-7}\ \text{w/a·m})\ I\,dl\,\sin\phi/r^2 = (10^{-7}\ \text{w/a·m})\ Ia\,dl/r^3.$$

Integration over dl merely introduces the circumference $2\pi a$ of the circle in place of dl and gives as the total intensity

$$\mathcal{B} = (10^{-7}\ \text{w/a·m})\ 2\pi Ia^2/r^3, \qquad (12a)$$

in the axial direction. The maximum value of this intensity is obtained when r takes on its smallest value, $r = a$, at the center of the coil. The intensity at the center of a circular coil of N turns has the value

$$\mathcal{B} = (10^{-7}\ \text{w/a·m})\ 2\pi NI/a, \qquad \left(\begin{smallmatrix}\text{center of}\\\text{circular coil}\end{smallmatrix}\right)\ (12b)$$

slightly greater than the intensity (Fig. 26) at the center of a square coil of half-side a.

The computation of the field of a square coil at points off the axis involves only the use of the results in Figs. 24 and 25, and a certain amount of geometry and trigonometry. The computation of the field of a circular coil at points off the axis involves complex integrals (elliptic integrals) beyond the scope of a first course in calculus. The magnetic lines for a circular coil were plotted in Fig. 21.

7. MAGNETIC FIELD OF A SOLENOID

A *solenoid* (Greek *solen*, 'tube') is a single layer of wire wound as in Fig. 28 on the surface of a cylinder, not necessarily circular. The wire may be slipped off the cylinder after winding, or the cylinder may remain in place if it is of nonferromagnetic material.

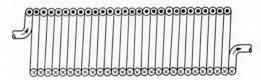

Fig. 28. Cross section of a solenoid with n turns per meter length, each turn carrying current I.

To an excellent approximation, the solenoid has the same magnetic field as a uniform sheet of current flowing around the cylinder. If the

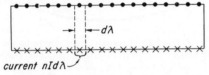

current $nId\lambda$

Fig. 29. A current sheet of nI amp/m or $nI\,d\lambda$ amp in a length $d\lambda$ is equivalent to the solenoid of Fig. 28.

solenoid has n turns per meter length and each turn carries current I, the current around a meter length of the cylinder will be nI, and the current in a length $d\lambda$ will be $nI\,d\lambda$, as indicated in Fig. 29.

The magnetic lines of a solenoid whose length is twice its diameter are shown in Fig. 30. We shall not be able to show how to compute this field in detail, but we shall learn to compute the intensity *on the axis*.

A solenoid is said to be *long* if its length is many times (at least 5 times) its diameter. Long solenoids play an important role in magnetic experimentation because such a solenoid provides a very uniform field

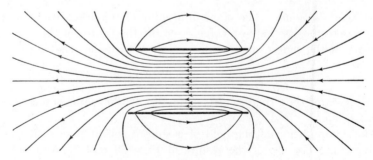

Fig. 30. The field of a solenoid.

over its whole central section to within about two 'diameters' from each end. The treatment below will show where the end effects begin to come in along the axis.

We shall start by computing the intensity on the axis at the very end of a circular solenoid; then, by superpositions analogous to those that led from Fig. 23 to Figs. 24 and 25, we can obtain the intensity at any point on the axis.   In Fig. 31, the intensity at point P arising from the current $nI \, d\lambda$ in the strip of width $d\lambda$ is given by (12a) as

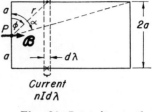

$$d\mathfrak{B} = (10^{-7} \text{ w/a·m}) \, 2\pi \, nI \, d\lambda \, a^2/r^3.$$

This value is to be integrated over the length of the solenoid.   The best integration variable is ϕ, which runs from 0 to α.   We can write

$$r = a/\cos\phi, \quad \lambda = a \tan\phi, \quad d\lambda = a \sec^2\phi \, d\phi,$$

to get

Fig. 31. Intensity on the axis at the end of a circular solenoid of n turns/m:

$$\mathfrak{B} = (10^{-7} \text{ w/a·m}) \, 2\pi nI \sin\alpha.$$

$$\mathfrak{B} = (10^{-7} \text{ w/a·m}) \, 2\pi nI \int_0^\alpha \cos\phi \, d\phi$$

$$= (10^{-7} \text{ w/a·m}) \, 2\pi nI \left[\sin\phi\right]_0^\alpha = (10^{-7} \text{ w/a·m}) \, 2\pi nI \sin\alpha.$$

The arguments that lead to the formulas under Figs. 32 and 33 are now similar to those we have used before.   We note that on the axis

Fig. 32. Intensity on the axis inside a circular solenoid:

$$\mathfrak{B} = (10^{-7} \text{ w/a·m}) \, 2\pi nI \, (\sin\alpha + \sin\beta).$$

Fig. 33. Intensity on the axis outside of a circular solenoid:

$$\mathfrak{B} = (10^{-7} \text{ w/a·m}) \, 2\pi nI \, (\sin\alpha - \sin\beta).$$

inside and well away from the ends of a long solenoid, where we may take $\beta = \alpha = \frac{1}{2}\pi$ in Fig. 32, we have

$$\boxed{\mathfrak{B} = (10^{-7} \text{ w/a·m}) \, 4\pi nI.} \qquad \binom{\text{SOLENOID}}{\text{FORMULA}} \quad (13)$$

It can be shown that this formula gives the intensity in the interior of a long solenoid of any cross-sectional shape, at any point that is well away from the ends.   Away from the ends, the intensity is uniform across the cross section. Formula (13) also gives the intensity at all points in the interior of a 'thin' toroid (Fig. 43), and in a thin 'curved solenoid' (Fig. 42), away from the ends.

The intensity on the axis near the end of a long circular solenoid falls off as in Fig. 34.   This plot is made by taking $\alpha = 90°$ in Fig. 32 or Fig. 33 and plotting $\mathfrak{B}$ against distance from the end of the solenoid expressed in units of the radius a.   The magnetic intensity is expressed as percentage of that inside the solenoid as given by (13).   It will be noticed that the intensity at the end of the solenoid is just half the full intensity, in accordance with the formula of Fig. 31, whereas the intensity is up to 95

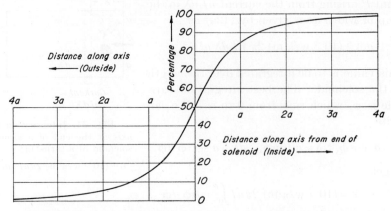

Fig. 34. Magnetic intensity on the axis near the end of a long circular solenoid. Ordinates are percentage of the intensity given by the solenoid formula. Abscissas are distances from the end of the solenoid in terms of the solenoid radius a. The left end of the solenoid lies at the central vertical line of this chart.

per cent of its full value one diameter ($2a$) inside the solenoid, and down to 5 per cent one diameter outside. The general characteristic of a solenoid is that the intensity is large inside, small outside.

8. MAGNETIC FLUX

A *magnetic tube* is an imaginary tube bounded by magnetic lines (see Fig. 35). A magnetic tube is *always* a region of space that is topologically equivalent to a doughnut.

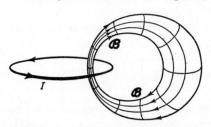

Fig. 35. A magnetic tube in the field of a circular current.

The product of intensity $\mathcal{B}$ by the cross-sectional area A of the tube is called the *flux through the tube*. The flux is usually denoted by Φ, and is measured in *webers:*

$$\Phi = \mathcal{B}A. \qquad \left\{ \begin{array}{l} \Phi \text{ in webers} \\ \mathcal{B} \text{ in webers/m}^2 \\ A \text{ in m}^2 \end{array} \right\}$$

Since $\mathcal{B} = \Phi/A$, $\mathcal{B}$ is frequently called the *flux density*. If $\mathcal{B}$ cannot be considered as constant over the cross section of the tube, we must define Φ as the surface integral

$$\Phi = \iint \mathcal{B} \, dA,$$

taken over the cross section, where dA is an element of area of surface perpendicular to $\mathcal{B}$.

An important law, proved in more advanced texts, is:

The flux through a magnetic tube is constant along the length of the tube.

Thus, magnetic flux obeys a 'conservation' law analogous to that governing the flow (flux) of mass of fluid through a pipe or stream tube. If we were to call the product $\mathcal{E}A$ in equation (17), p. 570, the *electric flux*, we should have an analogous relation for electric flux.

The concept of magnetic flux will prove to be very important when we come to study electromagnetic induction, electric generators, transformers, and similar topics. We note from (3) that the unit of flux can be written as

$$1 \text{ weber} = 1 \frac{\text{nt·m}}{\text{amp}} = 1 \frac{\text{joule}}{\text{coul/sec}} = 1 \text{ volt·sec.} \qquad (14)$$

Thus we shall find later that induced voltage is given by rate of change of flux, in webers/sec, which is seen to be dimensionally correct.

> **Example.** *A solenoid* 3 m *long and* 20 cm *in diameter is wound with* 8 *turns/cm of wire carrying* 90 amp. *Determine the flux threading the center of the solenoid.*
>
> The center of the solenoid is 15 radii away from the ends, so according to Fig. 34 the center is in the region where the intensity is 100 per cent of that given by the solenoid formula, with high accuracy. We have stated that under such circumstances the intensity is uniform across the cross section. We substitute $n = 800$ turns/m and $I = 90$ amp in (13) to find
>
> $$\mathcal{B} = (10^{-7} \text{ weber/amp·m}) \, 4\pi \, (800/\text{m}) \, 90 \text{ amp} = 0.0905 \text{ weber/m}^2.$$
>
> The area of a circle 0.2 m in diameter is 0.0314 m²; hence the flux is
>
> $$\Phi = \mathcal{B}A = (0.0905 \text{ weber/m}^2)(0.0314 \text{ m}^2) = 0.00284 \text{ weber.}$$

9. THE POLE CONCEPT; FORCES ON THIN SOLENOIDS AND THIN MAGNETS

WE NOW introduce a useful concept: that of the *magnetic pole*. A magnetic pole is conceived to be made of some magnetic stuff on which a magnetic field exerts forces, just as an electric field exerts forces on electric charges. *There really is no such magnetic stuff.* A magnetic field exerts forces only on currents, or moving charges, and hence exerts torques on coils carrying currents. A steel magnet is equivalent to a large collection of small coils, each coil consisting of the electrons of a single iron atom. These electrons move in orbits around the nucleus and 'spin' on their own axes, as discussed on p. 709. The magnetic moments of the atoms are systematically oriented so that most of them are pointing along the axis of the magnet. The torque on the magnet is the cumulative effect of the torque on each of the atoms.

The pole concept is not *necessary* to a treatment of magnetism, but it does materially simplify certain important computations of magnetic fields and forces.   In the course of the historical development of magnetic concepts, the older subject of *magnetostatics* dealt with poles exclusively.

The manner in which the torque on a small coil or a small magnet can be expressed in terms of forces on magnetic poles is illustrated in Fig. 36. We suppose that a pole of strength m experiences a force

$$F = m\mathfrak{B}, \quad \text{in newtons,} \tag{15}$$

the force vector being in the direction of the field $\mathfrak{B}$ if m is positive, in the opposite direction if m is negative.   Then equal and opposite poles $\pm m$

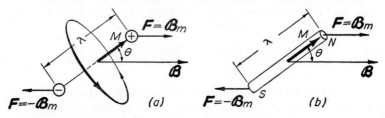

Fig. 36. The torque on a small coil or a small magnet can be computed from the forces on two fictitious magnetic poles on the axis, of strengths $\pm m$, separated by a distance λ such that $M = m\lambda$. The coil shown in (a) is not necessarily circular, but may have any shape.

separated by a short distance λ along the magnetic-moment vector as in Fig. 36 would experience equal and opposite forces, forming a couple with the resultant torque

$$L = \mathfrak{B}m\lambda \sin\theta,$$

which gives the result $L = \mathfrak{B}M \sin\theta$, in agreement with (2), provided that

$$M = m\lambda; \quad m = M/\lambda. \tag{16}$$

In the case of a small magnet, it is customary to take λ as the length of the magnet, as in Fig. 36; m is then determined by (16) if the magnetic moment M of the small magnet is known.   Since M is measured in amp·m², we see from (16) that m is measured in amp·m.

By using the pole concept, it is easy to compute the forces on a long thin solenoid in a magnetic field.   The solenoid is to be so thin that the variation of the magnetic field over the cross section of the solenoid is negligible, but the variation over the length of the solenoid may be as large as we please.

Such a thin solenoid is sketched in Fig. 37.   Consider an (infinitesimal) section of the solenoid of length λ.   This section can be considered as a small coil carrying current $nI\lambda$ (Fig. 29) with magnetic moment $M = nI\lambda A$, where A is the cross-sectional area of the solenoid.   The forces on this small coil can be represented by the forces on a pair of poles separated by the distance λ, and of strength $\pm m$, with, according to (16),

$$m = nIA. \tag{17}$$

This is the strength of the poles indicated by $\oplus$ and $\ominus$ signs in Fig. 37. Now if, as indicated at the right of Fig. 37, we slice the whole solenoid into strips of length λ, with a view to computing the forces on each strip from the forces on $+$ and $-$ poles on its right and left faces, then so far as the net forces on the whole solenoid are concerned, the poles cancel all down the line except at the ends, where we are left with poles of strength $\pm nIA$.

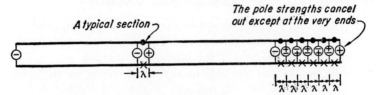

Fig. 37. A long thin solenoid is equivalent to a single pair of poles, of strengths $\pm nIA$.

The net force system acting on the solenoid, considered as a rigid body, is equivalent to just the two forces obtained by imagining the solenoid to have a + pole at one end and a − pole at the other, these poles being acted on by the external magnetic field in accordance with (15). The pole strength is given by (17), and the $+$ or N end of the solenoid is determined by the right-hand rule that gives the direction of the magnetic-moment vector.

A long thin magnet, such as a magnetized steel knitting needle, behaves exactly like a long thin solenoid; the forces in a magnetic field can be considered as arising from poles of strength $+m$ on its N end and $-m$ on its S end.

Thus, there is complete similarity of behavior between a thin solenoid and a thin magnet. In a uniform field, such as that of the earth, each

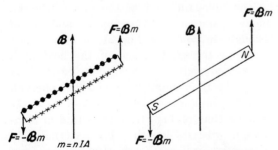

Fig. 38. Forces on a solenoid and a thin magnet in a uniform field as given by the pole picture.

Fig. 39. Actual system of forces on a solenoid in a uniform magnetic field.

behaves as if it were acted on by equal and opposite forces on its two ends, which result in a torque tending to turn it into the direction of the field (Fig. 38). It must be emphasized that this is not at all the system of forces that actually exists. The actual system consists of forces to the right on all current elements going into the paper in Fig. 39, and forces to the left on all current elements coming out of the paper. These forces are to be computed from (5). The computation of the net torque from the force system of Fig. 39 is much more complex than from the pole picture of Fig. 38, which, as we have shown, will give the same answer.

10. EXTERNAL FIELDS OF SOLENOIDS AND MAGNETS

THE TORQUE on a thin solenoid or magnet can be computed from the forces on a pair of fictitious poles at its ends; these same poles can be used to compute the *external* field of the solenoid or magnet.

It can be shown that the field of any small coil is, at distances large compared to the size of the coil, the same as the field which would be computed by an inverse-square law, like Coulomb's law, from the pair of fictitious poles shown in Fig. 36. In the inverse-square law we must, of course, use a different constant from that used in the electrostatic case. We must take the intensity at distance r from a pole of strength m as

$$\mathcal{B} = (10^{-7}\text{ w/a·m})\ m/r^2. \tag{18}$$

The magnetic lines computed in this way for a pair of poles of strengths $+m$ and $-m$ (called a *magnetic dipole*) are shown in Fig. 40. This picture is the same as Fig. 21 but reduced in size so that the coil has become infinitesimal and hence invisible at the center of the picture. So far as the visible parts of Fig. 40 are concerned, we have a correct picture of the field of an infinitesimal coil. However, we know that the picture is incorrect right at the center, because the electric lines of a pair of poles start at one pole and end at the other, whereas magnetic lines actually are endless and thread through the coil as in Fig. 21.

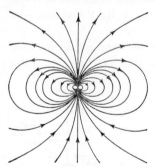

Fig. 40. Field of a magnetic dipole or an infinitesimal coil, with magnetic-moment vector pointing upward.

From the equivalence of the field of a dipole and that of a small coil, everywhere except in their immediate vicinity, one can easily compute the field *outside* a solenoid, such as that of Fig. 37, that is thin in comparison with its length. The external field of each typical section is that of a pair of poles of strength $\pm m = \pm nIA$. In getting the whole external field of the solenoid, the $+$ and $-$ poles cancel, just as in Fig. 37, except at the ends. Hence, *the field of the whole solenoid, external to the solenoid and at a distance from the end large compared with the thickness of the solenoid, is the field computed from* (18) *for a pole of strength $m = nIA$ at one end and a pole of strength $-m = -nIA$ at the other.*

The external field of a thin magnet is exactly like that of a thin solenoid.

Since both the external fields of, and the forces on, thin solenoids and thin magnets are given correctly by the pole concept, with equal and opposite poles at the ends, we see that such solenoids and magnets interact just as if they had poles on their ends that interact by the inverse-square law, the rest of the solenoid or magnet merely furnishing a rigid mechanical connection between the poles. We see from (15) and (18) that on this picture the force between two poles m and m' with separation r is to be taken as

$$F = (10^{-7} \text{ w/a·m}) \, mm'/r^2.$$

The force is repulsive if the poles have like sign, attractive if they have unlike sign.

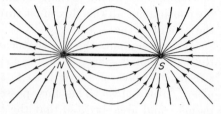

Fig. 41. External field of a thin magnet or solenoid.

The magnetic lines external to a thin solenoid or magnet are illustrated in Fig. 41. These lines are the same as those of Fig. 18, p. 557, for the electrostatic field of a pair of equal and opposite charges.

An argument similar to the above will show that if the solenoid is curved as in Fig. 42, its external field is still representable as the field of $+$ and $-$ poles of strength nIA at its ends. If the solenoid is bent through 360° and closed, to form a toroid as in Fig. 43, the *external*

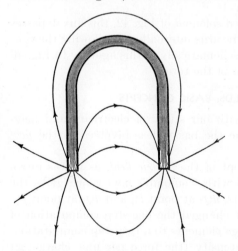

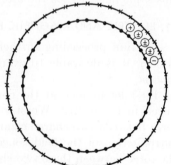

Fig. 42. The field of a thin curved solenoid.

Fig. 43. A toroid has *no* external field.

field entirely disappears since the poles that give the field of each typical section are canceled by the poles of the adjoining sections, *all the way around*. Hence, *the external field of a toroid* is represented by the field of *no* poles, and *is zero*.

It must be emphasized that the arguments of this section apply only to the field outside the solenoid, since the field *close* to the poles representing a typical section is not given at all correctly by the pole picture. The magnetic lines *do not end on the poles*, but are continuous and thread through the solenoid or magnet (see Fig. 42). The field inside a solenoid cannot be obtained from the pole picture. We can, however, compute the flux through the solenoid. A certain amount of flux leaves the $+$ pole and makes its way outside the solenoid around to the $-$ pole. Since flux tubes do not actually begin and end on these fictitious poles but are continuous, all this flux must thread *through* the solenoid *inside*, from the $-$ end to the $+$ end.

We can compute the flux that leaves a $+$ pole by considering the flux through a small sphere of radius r surrounding the pole. At a distance r from a $+$ pole of strength nIA, the flux density is $\mathfrak{B} = (10^{-7} \text{ w/a·m})$ nIa/r^2, from (18). This flux passes normally through the sphere of radius r and area $4\pi r^2$, so that the total flux through the sphere is $\Phi = 4\pi r^2 \cdot \mathfrak{B} = (10^{-7} \text{ w/a·m}) \, 4\pi nIA$. This is the amount of flux that leaves the $+$ end of a thin solenoid and passes externally around to the $-$ end. Hence, the amount of flux threading through a thin solenoid is

$$\Phi = (10^{-7} \text{ w/a·m}) \, 4\pi nIA.$$

This is the same value as is obtained by multiplying the flux density in the solenoid formula (13) by the area A.

We see, then, that in the curved solenoid of Fig. 42, this flux Φ passes externally between the poles and returns internally by following the contour of the solenoid, as indicated schematically in this figure. In Fig. 43 this same flux threads the interior of the toroid.

11. ELECTRIC AND MAGNETIC FIELDS: BASIC CONCEPTS

BEFORE proceeding further with our study of electricity and magnetism, it is desirable to examine the basic ideas involved in the *field concept*.

First let us look at the concept of the *electric field*, as it was introduced in Chap. 27. We started with Coulomb's law, which gives the force between two charge elements, dQ_1 at point P_1 and dQ_2 at point P_2. Introduction of the field concept changed the one-step computation of the force between these two charge elements to a two-step computation: We first compute the electric intensity (the force per unit charge) at point P_2 arising from the charge element dQ_1 at P_1. We then compute the force on dQ_2 by multiplying this electric intensity by the magnitude of the charge. The advantage of this two-step procedure is that, by employing such convenient relations as Gauss's law, we can readily compute the electric intensity at P_2 arising from a whole collection of charge elements constituting body 1, and from this electric intensity compute the force on any charge that may be placed at P_2. We are also enabled to introduce the convenient concepts of *electric lines*, and of *difference of electric potential* as the integral of electric intensity along an electric line.

The initial *observable* physical phenomenon is that electric charges exert forces on each other in accordance with Coulomb's law. The electric field is entirely conceptual: it is a convenient logical tool for visualizing the electrical 'conditions' in the vicinity of charged bodies and for computing electrical forces, differences of potential, etc. The understanding of electrical phenomena would be difficult without this concept, and this understanding took a great step forward when Faraday invented the concept.

Let us look in particular at the steps involved in the computation of the force between two charged bodies, body 1 composed of charge elements dQ_1, and body 2 composed of elements dQ_2. An element of static charge dQ_1 makes the vector contribution

$$d\mathbf{\mathcal{E}}_1 = (9 \times 10^9 \text{ nt·m}^2/\text{c}^2) \, dQ_1/r_{12}^2 \quad \text{radially out or in}$$

to the electric intensity at a point P_2 at distance r_{12} from this charge element. The total intensity from a body 1 at the point P_2 is the vector integral:

$$\mathbf{\mathcal{E}}_1 = \int_{\text{Body 1}} d\mathbf{\mathcal{E}}_1. \qquad \text{(electric field of body 1)}$$

The force $d\mathbf{F}_2$ exerted by the whole of body 1 on a charge element dQ_2 at point P_2 is

$$d\mathbf{F}_2 = \mathbf{\mathcal{E}}_1 \, dQ_2,$$

and the total force on a body 2 made up of charge elements dQ_2 and placed in the field of body 1 is

$$\mathbf{F}_2 = \int_{\text{Body 2}} \mathbf{\mathcal{E}}_1 \, dQ_2. \qquad \text{(electric force on body 2)}$$

The electric-field concept enables us to make such force computations conveniently in two separate steps.

While we could describe electrostatics without the *electric*-field concept, we should have tremendous difficulty in describing magnetism without the *magnetic*-field concept. The basic magnetic relationship, analogous to Coulomb's law, is the law giving the magnetic force between two charges in motion, or between two current elements. But this law is extraordinarily difficult to state in one step—we have not even made an attempt to do so. The complication arises from the fact that, while charge elements are *scalars*, current elements are *vectors*. We have learned to compute the force between two current elements by introducing the field concept *ab initio*. The magnetic intensity at a point P_2 arising from a current element at P_1 is given by Ampère's law; in turn the force on a current element at P_2 is given by the law containing equation (5)—both of these laws express rather complex vectorial relationships.

An element of *steady* current $I_1\,dl_1$ makes the vector contribution

$$d\mathfrak{B}_1 = (10^{-7}\ \text{w/a·m})\ I_1\,dl_1\,\sin\theta_1/r_{12}^2 \quad \text{perpendicular to } r_{12} \text{ and } dl_1$$

to the magnetic intensity at any point P_2 located like P in Fig. 22. The total magnetic intensity at this point from a wire carrying current I_1 is the vector integral

$$\mathfrak{B}_1 = \int_{\text{Wire 1}} d\mathfrak{B}_1 = I_1 \times (\text{geometrical factor}). \qquad \text{(magnetic field of wire 1)}$$

The integral is taken over the entire length of the wire and gives an answer that is proportional to I_1 since each contribution $d\mathfrak{B}_1$ has a magnitude proportional to I_1. The coefficient of I_1 is a purely geometrical factor depending on the shape of wire 1 and the location of the point P_2 at which the intensity is computed.

Formula (5) gives the force $d\mathbf{F}_2$ exerted by the whole current I_1 on a current element $I_2\,dl_2$ of a second wire:

$$d\mathbf{F}_2 = \mathfrak{B}_1 I_2\,dl_2\,\sin\phi_2 \quad \text{perpendicular to } \mathfrak{B}_1 \text{ and } dl_2.$$

The total force on wire 2 is then the vector integral:

$$\mathbf{F}_2 = \int_{\text{Wire 2}} d\mathbf{F}_2 = I_1 I_2 \times (\text{geometrical factor}). \qquad \text{(magnetic force on wire 2)}$$

Since $\mathfrak{B}_1$ is proportional to I_1, $d\mathbf{F}_2$ and hence $\mathbf{F}_2$ are proportional to $I_1 I_2$, the proportionality constant being purely geometrical.

Again we see that we have conveniently reduced the computation of magnetic forces to two separate steps by introduction of the field concept.

While the observation of electrical forces long preceded the development of the concept of the electric field, the concept of the magnetic field was well established long before it was even realized that magnetic forces arise from charges in motion. This historical difference arose from the existence of permanently magnetized bodies such as compass needles and the existence of the magnetic field of the earth. It would be difficult indeed to conceive of computing the torque on a compass needle by a complex multiple vectorial integration of the forces between the circulating current elements that set up the earth's field and the revolving electrons in the compass needle. Although basically the torque arises in this way, the field concept certainly furnishes a much simpler, but logically consistent, way of predicting and computing the observed physical effects.

When we consider *electromagnetic waves* (such as light waves or radio waves), which are traveling sinusoidal waves of electric and magnetic intensity, capable of causing sinusoidally varying forces on electric charges, we realize vividly that a phenomenological description that did *not* employ the field concept in both the electric and the magnetic case would be prohibitively difficult. Such waves result from *oscillating charges*, or their equivalent, *sinusoidally varying currents*. The formulas previously given for electric and magnetic fields apply only to the *static* or *unvarying* case. If charges are accelerated or currents varying, as they are in a radio-transmitter antenna, these formulas must be modified by a factor that expresses the fact that electric and magnetic influences travel outward from their source only with the finite speed of light. In the case of a sinusoidally oscillating source, there is a constant loss of energy, which can be considered as traveling outward into space with the wave because energy can be absorbed by electric charges at a distant point, for example by the electrons in a radio receiving antenna. However, departures from the static formulas are not significant when frequencies are low. We can use the static formulas without error in the following chapters for alternating currents of power frequencies (60 cycles/sec), telephone frequencies in the audio range, and even at radio frequencies *inside* a radio set. Conditions under which departures from these formulas, because of energy radiation, become significant will be discussed in Sec. 1 of Chap. 37.

12. MAGNETIC FORCE ON A MOVING CHARGED PARTICLE

THE FORMULA that gives the force on a single charged particle moving in a magnetic field is of great importance in modern atomic and nuclear research. We can derive this formula by considering that a beam of moving particles constitutes a current, and that the total force on all the particles in length dl of the stream of particles must be given by our previous formulas for the force on a current element.*

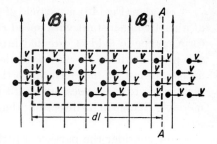

Figure 44

Let us consider the beam of particles shown in Fig. 44. Let each particle have charge Q and speed v. Let there be p particles per meter length of the beam, so that there will be $p\,dl$ particles in the length dl. Counting from the instant at which Fig. 44 is drawn, all these $p\,dl$ particles will cross the plane AA in the time required for the leftmost particles to go a distance dl, that is, in a time $dt = dl/v$. The charge carried across the plane AA in this time is the charge on $p\,dl$ particles, or $pQ\,dl$, in coulombs. The current then is

* Actually, formula (20) for the force on a single moving particle, is the more fundamental formula from which formula (5) for the force on a current element could be derived. We have chosen the historical and operationally more convenient approach.

$$I = \frac{pQ \, dl}{dt} = \frac{pQ \, dl}{dl/v} = pQv. \tag{19}$$

This important formula gives the current represented by a beam containing p particles per unit length of beam, each having charge Q and traveling with speed v.

Now the formula (4), $dF = \mathfrak{B}I \, dl = \mathfrak{B}pQv \, dl$, gives the total force on length dl of the current in Fig. 44. This is the total force on the $p \, dl$ particles in dl. Hence, the force on each particle may be obtained by dividing this expression by $p \, dl$, to get

$$F = \mathfrak{B} \, Q \, v. \qquad \left\{ \begin{array}{l} F \text{ in nt} \\ \mathfrak{B} \text{ in weber}/m^2 \\ Q \text{ in coul} \\ v \text{ in m/sec} \end{array} \right\} \tag{20}$$

This is the force on a single particle moving perpendicular to a magnetic field. The direction of the force is perpendicular to both $\mathfrak{B}$ and $\boldsymbol{v}$, the choice of the two such directions being made by considering the direction of the equivalent current. Thus, in Fig. 44, if Q is positive, the current direction is to the right, and $\boldsymbol{F}$ is out of the paper; if Q is negative, the conventional current is toward the left, and $\boldsymbol{F}$ is into the paper.

If $\mathfrak{B}$ is not perpendicular to $\boldsymbol{v}$, the force is determined, as in the case of ordinary currents, entirely by the magnitude and direction of the component of $\mathfrak{B}$ perpendicular to $\boldsymbol{v}$.

These considerations are fundamental to the theory of the cyclotron, the electron microscope, the mass spectrograph, and various other types of vacuum tubes and electron-ray tubes. For these applications we need to learn about the path of a charged particle in a uniform magnetic field.

Consider (Fig. 45) a particle of positive charge Q and mass m moving at a particular instant with speed v toward the top of the paper in a uniform magnetic field $\mathfrak{B}$ directed into the paper. The magnetic force on this particle will be $F = \mathfrak{B}Qv$ to the left. This force will give the particle an acceleration $a = F/m = \mathfrak{B}Qv/m$ to the left. Since this acceleration is perpendicular to $\boldsymbol{v}$, it does not result in a change in the magnitude of $\boldsymbol{v}$ but merely a change in its direction; that is, the particle is deflected toward the left.

Now consider the particle a little later, when it has reached the position indicated by broken lines. Since the force on the particle and its acceleration are still perpendicular to its velocity, there is still no tendency to change the magnitude of the velocity. Since the field is uniform, the acceleration has the same magnitude as before. Motion at constant speed with a constant acceleration always at right angles to the velocity is known, from mechanics, to be motion in a circle of such radius R that $a = v^2/R$, or, in our case,

$$R = \frac{v^2}{a} = \frac{v^2}{\mathfrak{B}Qv/m} = \frac{mv}{\mathfrak{B}Q}. \tag{21}$$

The radius of the circular path increases in proportion to the momentum mv of the particle and varies inversely as the magnetic intensity and the charge on the particle. A negative particle would have its force and acceleration vectors reversed relative to those of a positive particle. Hence, if Q were negative in Fig. 45, the path would curve to the right instead of to the left.

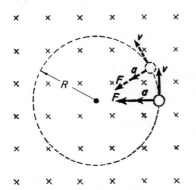

Fig. 45. The force on a positively charged particle moving normally to a uniform magnetic field directed into the paper.

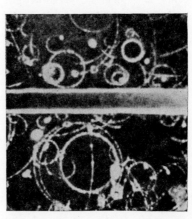

Fig. 46. [*From Rasetti, Elements of Nuclear Physics, Prentice-Hall, 1937.*]

Figure 46 is a cloud-chamber photograph showing paths of electrons in a magnetic field directed into the paper. Such photographs can be used to determine the speed of the particles; the larger the circle the faster the speed in accordance with (21): $v = R\,(\mathfrak{B}Q/m)$.

As we shall see in Chap. 38, the operation of the cyclotron depends on an interesting property of an orbit such as that of Fig. 45, namely, that the time it takes a particular type of particle to go once around the orbit and return to its starting point is independent of the speed v of the particle. A particle of high speed travels rapidly around an orbit of large radius, and one of low speed travels slowly around an orbit of small radius; but since, according to (21), the distance traveled, $2\pi R$, is directly proportional to the speed, the times taken are equal. The time of revolution is $T = 2\pi R/v$, so

$$T = 2\pi m/\mathfrak{B}Q, \tag{22}$$

independent of the speed v. Thus the various electrons shown in Fig. 46, traveling at different speeds proportional to the different radii of their circular orbits, all execute these orbits in the same periodic times.

PROBLEMS

1. If a straight horizontal conductor carrying 50 amp from south to north passes through the magnetic field of a large magnet, the magnetic field being

1.5 webers/m² vertically upward over a length of 1.2 m of the wire, what is the force on the wire in magnitude and direction?   Ans: 90.0 nt toward the east.

2. If 25 cm of a straight conductor is at right angles to a uniform magnetic field of 0.7 weber/m², what current must flow in the conductor in order that the force on this section be 4 nt?

3. In a region where the earth's magnetic field has a downward component of 0.50×10^{-4} weber/m², a northward component of 0.10×10^{-4} weber/m², and no east-west component, what is the force on a meter length of wire carrying 200 amp: (a) horizontally, from S to N? (b) horizontally, from W to E? (c) vertically upward?   Ans: (a) 0.0100 nt westward; (b) 0.0102 nt, northward and upward at an angle of 11°.3 above the horizontal; (c) 0.0020 nt westward.

4. In a region where the northward component of the earth's field is 0.25×10^{-4} weber/m what current would be a #10 aluminum conductor running E and W have to carry in order that the upward magnetic force should equal the downward gravitational force?

5. When the single-turn coil of Fig. 17 is carrying 40 amp and the dimensions of the coil are $l = 20$ cm, $w = 12$ cm, what are the torques on the coil at $\theta = 0°$, 30°, 60°, and 90°, if the magnetic intensity is 0.5 weber/m²?
          Ans: 0, 0.240, 0.416, 0.480 nt·m.

6. If the coil of Fig. 17 is made of 40 concentrated turns, each carrying 10 amp, with dimensions $l = 20$ cm, $w = 12$ cm, in a field of 0.6 weber/m², what will be the torque on the coil at $\theta = 0°$, 30°, 60°, and 90°?

7. Prove that the single-turn coil of Fig. 19, when turning at n revolutions per second, has a mechanical power output of $4n\mathcal{B}lwI$, in watts if l and w are in meters.

8. Show that the period of oscillation of a compass needle, when it is performing small oscillations about the direction of the horizontal component of the earth's magnetic field, is

$$T = 2\pi \sqrt{I/M\mathcal{B}}, \quad \text{in sec,}$$

where I is the moment of inertia in kg·m², M is the magnetic moment in amp·m², and $\mathcal{B}$ is the horizontal field component in weber/m². A measurement of T in a known field will determine I/M for a compass needle; this needle of known I/M can then be used in the same way to determine the horizontal component of an unknown field.

9. In the galvanometer shown in Fig. 20, let N = number of turns in coil, $\mathcal{B}$ = intensity of radial magnetic field (weber/m²), l = effective length of wires in the field (m), r = radius from axis of rotation to coil wires (m), θ = angle of rotation of coil, measured from no-current equilibrium position (rad), C = torque constant of springs (nt·m/rad), I = current in each turn of coil (amp). Show that

$$I = C\theta/2N\mathcal{B}lr.$$

10. A galvanometer coil is wound of No. 30 copper wire (103.2 ohms per thousand feet). Each turn requires 4 inches of wire. What spring torque constant must be used if, in the notation of Prob. 9, $\mathcal{B} = 0.3$ weber/m², $l = 2.5$ cm, $r = 1$ cm, and the meter is to give full-scale (60°) deflection on 1 milliampere and have 1 ohm resistance at 20° C?

11. A galvanometer is wound of No. 33 copper wire (206.9 ohms per thousand feet). Each turn requires 4 inches of wire. What spring torque constant must be used if, in the notation of Prob. 9, $\mathcal{B} = 0.5$ weber/m², $l = 2.5$ cm, $r = 1$ cm, and the meter is to give full-scale (60°) deflection on 1 microampere and have 30 ohms resistance at 20° C?   Ans: 1.04×10^{-7} nt·m/rad.

12. (a) Show that a small bar magnet with magnetic moment pointing geographically north, and mounted on a vertical torsion fiber, can be used to measure fluctuations in the eastward component of the earth's magnetic intensity.   (b) How can a small bar magnet be mounted on a *horizontal* torsion fiber so as to measure fluctuations in the northward component of the earth's magnetic intensity?

13. What is the magnetic intensity in weber/m² at a distance of 1 cm from an infinitely long straight wire carrying 120 amp? at 2 cm? 3 cm? 4 cm?

Ans: 24, 12, 8, 6×10⁻⁴ weber/m².

14. What current must an infinitely long straight wire carry in order that the magnetic intensity at a distance of 2 cm be 0.025 weber/m²?

15. What current must a circular coil of 100 turns and 10 cm radius carry to give a magnetic intensity of 0.001 weber/m² at the center?   Ans: 1.59 amp.

16. What current must a square coil of 100 turns and 10 cm half-side carry to give a magnetic intensity of 0.001 weber/m² at the center?

17. Show that the magnetic intensity at the center of a rectangular coil of sides a and b, in m, is $(10^{-7} \text{ w/a·m}) \, 8NId/ab$, where d is the length of the diagonal. Find the intensity at the center of a rectangular coil of 100 turns with sides 10 cm and 40 cm long, carrying 5 amp.   Ans: 0.00412 weber/m².

18. In the notation of Fig. 47, show that the magnetic intensity at any point on the axis of a square turn carrying current I is
$$\mathcal{B} = (10^{-7} \text{ w/a·m}) \, 8Ia^2/r^2 \sqrt{r^2+a^2}.$$

19. Show that at a large distance, the magnetic intensity of Prob. 18 on the axis of a square coil can be written as $\mathcal{B} = (10^{-7} \text{ w/a·m}) \, 2M/r^3$, where M is the magnetic moment of the coil.

20. Show that the magnetic intensity on the axis of the circular coil of Fig. 27 can be

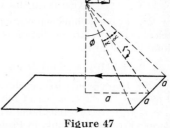

Figure 47

written as $\mathcal{B} = (10^{-7} \text{ w/a·m}) \, 2M/r^3$, where M is the magnetic moment of the coil.

21. Show that the pole picture gives magnetic intensity $\mathcal{B} = (10^{-7} \text{ w/a·m}) \, M/r^3$ *in the plane* of a one-turn coil at distances r large compared to the size of the coil.   Verify this formula at at least one point in the plane of a square coil.

22. The particular arrangement of two coaxial circular coils of radius a with planes separated by distance a shown in Fig. 48 is known as a pair of *Helmholtz coils*.   This particular coil system is useful because it gives an almost uniform field over a fairly large volume at the center as indicated in Fig. 48.   Let X denote the distance from the plane of the lower coil to any point on the axis.   If each turn carries current I, compute the intensity (a) at the center ($X = 0.5\,a$), (b) at $X = 0.4\,a$, $0.6\,a$, (c) at $X = 0.3\,a$, $0.7\,a$, (d) at $X = 0.2\,a$, $0.8\,a$.   The reason for

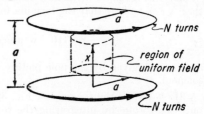

Fig. 48. Helmholtz coils.

the slow variation of the field in the neighborhood of $X = 0.5\,a$ is that with this particular spacing, with distance a between the coils, not only is $d\mathcal{B}/dX = 0$ at $X = 0.5\,a$, but also $d^2\mathcal{B}/dX^2 = 0$ at $X = 0.5\,a$.   Prove this statement.   The second derivative vanishes halfway between the coils only for this particular coil spacing.

23. Let Fig. 31 represent a square solenoid instead of a circular solenoid, with a and r defined as in Fig. 47.   Carry out an integration of the intensity given by the formula of Prob. 18 from $\phi = 0$ to $\phi = \frac{1}{2}\pi$, to show that the field on the axis at the end of a very long square solenoid is $(10^{-7}\text{ w/a·m})\, 2\pi nI$, the same as for a circular solenoid.   Hence, show that the solenoid formula (13) holds for a square solenoid as well as for a circular solenoid.

24. For testing magnetic mines during World War II, large square solenoids were constructed, 2 or 3 ft square and 20 or 30 ft long, which could be used to apply a uniform field to the entire mine case.   The solenoids were wound with 2 turns per inch length.   From the solenoid formula (13), compute the field in webers/m² per ampere current.   Ships' fields are usually specified in a unit called the milligauss (1 milligauss = 10^{-7} weber/m²).   Show that the solenoid constant you have computed is very close to 1 milligauss/milliampere, a very convenient value for test purposes.

25. What is the flux through a circular solenoid 5 cm in radius and 100 cm long wound with 1200 turns of wire carrying 2 amp?   Ans: 23.7 μweber.

26. What is the flux through a long solenoid 3 ft square wound with 2 turns per inch carrying 4 amp?

27. In Fig. 19, p. 682, if $l = 60$ cm, $w = 30$ cm, $\mathcal{B} = 0.6$ weber/m², what is the flux linking (that is, passing through) the rectangular loop when (a) $\theta = 0°$, (b) $\theta = 30°$, (c) $\theta = 60°$, (d) $\theta = 90°$?

          Ans: (a) 0.108 weber; (b) 0.0935 weber; (c) 0.0540 weber; (d) 0.

28. Two telephone wires are parallel to a power wire carrying current I.   The telephone wires are at distances r_1 and r_2 from the power wire.   Show that the total flux from the power wire passing *between* the telephone wires is

$$(10^{-7}\text{ w/a·m})\, 2I \log_e(r_2/r_1), \quad \text{in webers per meter length.}$$

29. Two power wires, each carrying 1000 amp but in opposite directions, are 1 m apart on the crossbar of telephone poles.   On the same poles, on a crossbar 5 m below, are two telephone wires also 1 m apart, each directly below a power wire.   From the formula in Prob. 28, compute the magnetic flux from the power circuit that links the telephone circuit, per kilometer of line.   NOTE: Telephone wires would never be strung just this way.   Such magnetic linkage would be highly undesirable because currents would be induced in the telephone circuit whenever the current in the power circuit changed.   We shall see in Chap. 34 that the magnitude of the induced current depends directly on the flux linkage you have computed.   Ans: 0.00784 weber/km.

30. In Fig. 33, let P be at a distance X from the left end of the solenoid such that $X \gg a$.   Show that the formula for the field at P reduces to

$$\mathcal{B} = (10^{-7}\text{ w/a·m})\, m \left(\frac{1}{X^2} - \frac{1}{(X+l)^2} \right),$$

as would be given by the pole picture.   Here $m = nIA$ and l is the length of the solenoid.

31. Consider the solenoid of Fig. 38 in a uniform magnetic field.   (a) Compute the torque by integrating the torques on the elements of length as given by (2).   (b) Compute the torque on poles of strength (17) at the ends and verify that this gives the same result as (a).   (c) Show that the whole torque is correctly given by (2) if one uses the integrated magnetic moment NIA, where N is the total number of turns.

32. Show that if the solenoid of Fig. 38 is of length l, and has rectangular cross section of height h in the plane of the paper and width w perpendicular to the plane of the paper, then the force system of Fig. 39 has the same torque as the pole picture of Fig. 38, when the solenoid is in a uniform magnetic field.

33. A thin magnet 15 cm long experiences a torque of 0.030 newton·cm when placed perpendicular to a uniform field of 0.045 weber/m². What is the pole strength of the magnet?   Ans: $m = 0.0444$ amp·m.

34. What is the pole strength of a thin solenoid of area 0.6 cm², length 15 cm, wound with a total of 500 turns carrying 0.2 amp?

35. If the magnet of Prob. 33 is placed in the same plane as an infinite straight wire carrying 100 amp, perpendicular to the wire, with its N end 5 cm from the wire and its S end 20 cm from the wire, what is (a) the net force acting on the magnet and (b) the net torque about the center of the magnet?

Ans: (a) 1.33×10^{-5} nt; (b) 1.67×10^{-6} nt·m.

36. If the thin solenoid of Prob. 34 is placed in the same plane as an infinite straight wire carrying 100 amp, perpendicular to the wire, with one end 5 cm from the wire and the other end 20 cm from the wire, what is (a) the net force acting on the solenoid and (b) the net torque about the center of the solenoid?

37. Find the total force with which the two thin solenoids shown below repel each other if each solenoid has a cross-sectional area of 0.5 cm². Ans: 6.25 μnt.

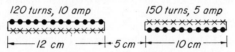

38. Find the total force with which the two thin solenoids shown below attract each other if each solenoid has a cross-sectional area of 0.5 cm².

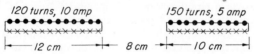

39. An electron moving at a speed of 2×10^7 m/sec in a vacuum chamber enters a uniform magnetic field in which $\mathfrak{B} = 1.13 \times 10^{-3}$ weber/m². The velocity of the electron is at all times perpendicular to $\mathfrak{B}$, and hence the electron describes a circular path like those in Fig. 46. What is the radius of the path?

Ans: 10.0 cm.

40. Determine the time of revolution of the electron in Prob. 39. What is the frequency of the circular motion of the electron?

41. In Fig. 20, p. 558, is shown an electron-ray tube in which the electron beam is deflected by forces exerted by the electric field between two plane plates. Another type of electron-ray tube employs magnetic deflection. In such a tube, two solenoids are employed to set up a substantially uniform field. The two solenoids are end-to-end like those in Prob. 38, except that the gap between the ends would be 1 cm or less; the electron beam then passes through this gap perpendicular to the paper. Show that when such a gap is short compared to the diameters of the two solenoids, the magnetic intensity in the gap is substantially constant. From (21), the radius of curvature of an electron path is $R = mv/\mathfrak{B}e$. Show that the direction of the beam traversing the field is changed by $\theta = P/R$, where P is the length of the curved path of the electrons in the magnetic field.

42. Using the results of Prob. 41 and the data given in the example on p. 558, find the magnetic intensity $\mathfrak{B}$ required to give a deflection of 7.8 cm if the length P is 1 cm,

NOTE: We have seen how high-energy atomic projectiles can be accelerated by having a proton, deuteron, or alpha-particle fall through a large difference of potential in an acceleration tube such as that used in a Van de Graaff machine. There are difficulties involved in producing and maintaining potentials of several millions volts in such a machine.   The cyclotron, which is described in Chap. 38, provides a method of accelerating charged particles without the use of excessively high potentials.   This is done by causing the particles to fall repeatedly through a relatively small difference of potential; the scheme is illustrated in Fig. 9, p. 844.   A rapidly alternating potential is applied to two D-shaped hollow electrodes called 'dees' mounted in a vacuum chamber between the poles of a large electro-magnet.   Equation (22) shows that an ion of mass m and charge Q has a constant period and hence constant frequency of revolution in a magnetic field $\mathcal{B}$ regardless of its speed v.   Thus, if an alternating potential V is applied at just this frequency f, it is possible for an ion to fall through a difference of potential V each time it makes a half revolution.   The following problems based on already familiar principles serve to describe the operation of a cyclotron. (Note that no electric field exists *inside* the hollow dees.)

43. A proton in a large vacuum chamber moves with low speed v in a direction normal to a magnetic field of intensity $\mathcal{B} = 0.656$ weber/m². Using 1.67×10^{-27} kg as the mass of the proton, (a) find the time required for the proton to traverse a complete circular path in the magnetic field.   (b) Determine the frequency of this motion.   (c) If a high frequency alternating potential difference of peak value 20 kilovolts is applied to two hollow D-shaped electrodes mounted in the chamber, how much does the proton's kinetic energy increase each time it makes a complete 'round trip' from one dee to the other dee and back?   (d) Does the proton return to its starting point in making such a round trip?   (e) If the magnetic field is constant over a circular region of diameter 1.5 m, and if a proton starts near the center of the field, what is the kinetic energy of the proton when it traverses a path of maximum radius 0.75 m?   (f) How many times has the proton traversed the gap between the dees by the time its path has maximum radius? (g) How long a time is required for the proton to achieve its maximum kinetic energy?   Ans: (a) 10^{-7} sec; (b) 10^7 sec^{-1}; (c) 4×10^4 ev $= 6.4 \times 10^{-15}$ joule; (e) 18.5×10^{-13} joule $= 11.1$ Mev; (f) 550; (g) 2.25×10^{-5} sec.

44. If a cyclotron with a magnetic field like that described in Problem. 43 were used to accelerate deuterons, what should be the frequency of the alternating high voltage?   What would be the maximum deuteron energy attainable? Answer the same questions for alpha particles.

NOTE: The forces exerted on charged particles moving in a plane perpendicular to a magnetic field are utilized in the *mass spectrograph*, a device used in comparing masses of ions.   The mass spectrograph is described in connection with Fig. 2 on p. 823.

45. A stream of protons and deuterons in a vacuum chamber enters a uniform magnetic field.   Both protons and deuterons have been subjected to the same accelerating potential; hence the kinetic energies of the particles are the same.   If the ion stream is perpendicular to $\mathcal{B}$ and the protons move in a circular path of radius 20 cm, find the radius of the path traversed by the deuterons.

Ans: 28.2 cm.

46. Singly charged ions of the chlorine isotopes 35 and 37 of equal kinetic energy enter a magnetic field in the manner described in Prob. 45.   Find the ratio of the radii of curvature of the paths traversed.   Repeat the calculation for singly charged ions (a) of bromine isotopes 79 and 81 (b) of uranium isotopes 235 and 238.   (The uranium isotopes were separated in large quantity by this method during World War II.)

47. In a cyclotron, energy is given to charged particles by a high-frequency oscillator.   In the microwave oscillator tube called the *magnetron*, the process is reversed; energy is transferred from a large number of electrons to a set of electrodes.   The scheme can be visualized from Fig. 49, which shows a 'bunch' of electrons moving in a circular path normal to a magnetic field $\mathfrak{B}$.   In traversing the circular path, the electrons pass close to electrodes A and B.   Write an expression for the potential V_A of electrode A that arises from a 'bunch' of N electrons at mean distance r from A.   Write an expression for the maximum

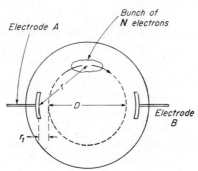

Figure 49

value of the difference $(V_{AB} = V_A - V_B)$ in terms of the distance of nearest approach r_1 of the electron bunch to the electrodes and the diameter D of the electron orbit. How many times per second does the potential difference V_{AB} go through a complete cycle?   Ans: Ne/r; $NeD/(r_1{}^2 + rD)$; $\mathfrak{B}e/2\pi m$.

48. What should be the value of $\mathfrak{B}$ in Prob. 47 if the frequency of V_{AB} is to be 1 megacycle/sec, 1000 megacycles/sec, 10,000 megacycles/sec, 25,000 megacycles/sec?   These latter frequencies are used radar work, the requisite power being produced by magnetrons operating on the principles just described.   The details of magnetron design are discussed in courses on communications.   Energy is derived from electron 'bunches' in klystron oscillators by a somewhat different method.

49. Referring back to Prob. 22 and Fig. 48, let the pair of Helmholtz coils be square, of half-side a, instead of circular.   What now should be the distance between the planes of the two coils in order to satisfy the condition $d^2\mathfrak{B}/dX^2 = 0$ midway between the coils?   Ans: 1.09 a.

50. For the square Helmholtz coils of Prob. 41, compute the magnetic intensity (a) at the center, (b) at a point 0.2 a above or below the center, (c) at a point in the central horizontal plane but displaced 0.2 a horizontally from the center toward one of the sides of the square coils.

CHAPTER 33

MAGNETIC PROPERTIES OF MATTER

ALL MATTER IS composed of atoms with positive nuclei and negative electrons. Since the negative electrons are in continual motion and hence constitute microscopic electric currents, all matter responds more or less to the presence of a magnetic field.

In the absence of an applied magnetic field, the microscopic currents ordinarily have sufficiently random orientation that, though they set up large local magnetic fields on the microscopic (atomic) scale, the net current and the net magnetic moment in any macroscopic volume vanish and no physically observable macroscopic magnetic field is set up by the matter. An *exception* occurs in the case of a 'permanent magnet.'

When matter is placed in a magnetic field from some external source, magnetic forces on the moving electrons will cause some type of reorientation of electron orbits in atoms and of current paths of free electrons in metals, so that the matter will itself set up a macroscopic magnetic field. This field may be either in the same direction as the applied field, in which case the matter is said to be *paramagnetic,* or in the opposite direction, in which case the matter is said to be *diamagnetic.*

However, except for those few substances known as *ferromagnetic materials,* these effects are always very small. The field set up by para- or diamagnetic matter is of the order of 10^{-7} (for gases) or 10^{-6} (for liquids or solids) of the applied field—always a very small fraction of the applied field, and of little or no practical importance. Unlike the case in electrostatics, where all materials except gases have a sufficiently large dielectric constant to have a pronounced electrical effect when placed in an electric field, *all except the few ferromagnetic materials can, for engineering purposes, be treated as magnetically inert and can be considered to behave no differently from a vacuum in the presence of a magnetic field.*

Thus, for engineering purposes, the field of a solenoid may be considered the same whether its core is vacuum, air, brass, or wood. But if the core is iron, or a nickel-iron alloy, the *core* may set up a field hundreds, thousands, or even hundreds of thousands of times greater than the applied field of the *winding* itself. *Ferromagnetism* is thus of tremendous engineering importance and will occupy our attention in this chapter.

Computations of the magnetic effects of ferromagnetic materials are very complex unless the geometry is very simple.   We shall learn the basic principles by using the simplest possible geometry, that of the *toroid;* and shall apply these principles to electromagnets of simple geometry. Application to the complex geometries of practical permanent and electro-magnets receives detailed attention in courses in electrical engineering.

1. FERROMAGNETISM

THE ELECTRONS in matter set up local magnetic fields on a microscopic scale for two reasons.   First, because the charged electron in its orbital motion around the atomic nucleus constitutes a little circulating current that has a magnetic moment.   Second, because the electron has an intrinsic magnetic moment associated with an intrinsic angular momen-tum called the electron *spin*.   The electron behaves as if it is spinning about its own axis like a top.   It has an intrinsic angular momentum of 5.271×10^{-35} kg·m²/sec.   As would be expected from the picture of a charged body spinning like a top, there is a magnetic moment associated with this angular momentum.   The magnetic-moment vector points in the direction opposite to the angular momentum vector because the charge is negative.   The intrinsic magnetic moment of each electron has the magnitude 9.274×10^{-24} amp·m².   A magnetic moment of this magnitude is called one *Bohr magneton.*

The Bohr magneton furnishes a basic unit of magnetic moment for electrons, for not only is the spin magnetic moment one Bohr mag-neton, but the magnetic moment arising from orbital motion of each elec-tron in an atom is a small integral number of Bohr magnetons.   The total magnetic moment of an atom is the vector sum of the spin moments and the orbital moments of all the electrons.   It can be measured by observing the effect of a magnetic field on the spectrum of the atoms, and can be correctly computed by modern atomic theory.

The discussion so far has applied particularly to free individual atoms such as occur in a monatomic gas.   The individual atoms of most ele-ments have sufficient magnetic moment so that if they retained this magnetic moment when put together to form a solid, and if the atomic magnetic moments were all orientated in the same direction, they would set up a very large macroscopic magnetic field (this field is estimated for iron in Prob. 3, p. 725).   Actually, in only a very few materials is any appreciable orientation observed; this fact was not explained satisfactorily until atomic theory had reached an advanced stage of development in 1928.   Only in the few substances called *ferromagnetic* do the electrons ever set up anything but an extremely tiny macroscopic magnetic field. The ferromagnetic substances are *iron, cobalt,* and *nickel;* some but not all alloys of these three metals with each other and with other metals; certain oxides of these metals; one rare earth (*gadolinium*); and certain alloys and compounds of *manganese* and *chromium* (but not the pure metals themselves), in particular, the *Heusler alloys* of Mn, Al, and Cu, and the metallic compound *manganese bismuthide*, MnBi.

These constitute all the substances having ferromagnetic properties at ordinary temperatures. Certain other substances acquire these properties at very low temperature. The list is very restricted because there is a peculiarity in structure that is necessary for a substance to be ferromagnetic. Let us try to get a rough understanding, in the case of solids and liquids, of the conditions necessary for ferromagnetism.

The electrons in an atom occur in 'shells' of different 'radii.' In most elements, all electrons except the 'valence' electrons are in 'complete' shells. The different shells, as we progress outward from the nucleus, may contain at most 2, 8, 18, · · · electrons. When a shell contains all the electrons that are permitted, it is said to be 'complete,' which really means *full;* that is, there is no room for any more passengers.

When a shell is complete, the vector sum of the magnetic moments of the electrons in the shell is zero. A complete shell does not set up an external magnetic field, neither does it respond in any way to any external magnetic field. With no exceptions, it is magnetically inert.

Hence, for most materials, only the magnetic moments of the valence electrons would be available to be oriented by an external magnetic field so that they could set up an appreciable macroscopic field of their own. But in a solid or liquid, the valence electrons play an essential role in the cohesive binding that holds the atoms together. As a result, *the valence electrons in a solid or liquid cannot contribute significantly to a macroscopic magnetic field.* In the formation of a solid, the valence electrons may move from one atom to an adjoining atom to form magnetically inert complete shells in both resulting ions (ionic binding, as in NaCl); the valence electrons from two adjoining atoms may pair to form a magnetically inert homopolar bond in the space between the atoms (like the C atoms in a diamond and in organic compounds); or the valence electrons may become free, as in a metal. In the metallic case, the valence electrons are no longer moving in little orbits with magnetic moments, and it also turns out that in any small region of the metal the spin magnetic moments add up to a vector resultant of zero. In no type of cohesive binding are there appreciable magnetic effects from the valence electrons. The presence of an externally applied magnetic field does have a slight effect on the valence electrons that gives rise to a weak paramagnetism or diamagnetism.

How then do we get any ferromagnetism if it cannot arise from valence electrons and cannot arise from electrons in complete shells? Clearly it must arise from electrons that are neither valence electrons nor in complete shells. Such electrons occur in the 'transition elements' and in the rare earths (see the periodic table in the Appendix, Sec. 9). In these elements we have *two* incomplete shells, with one so buried in the atom that its electrons do not contribute to cohesive binding and remain free to be oriented by a magnetic field. The electronic structure of Fe, Co, and Ni is shown in Fig. 1.

But this exposition does not explain why Fe, Co, Ni, and Gd are the *only* ferromagnetic elements; we might expect the other transition elements and rare earths to be ferromagnetic also. A clue to the explanation is found when one considers that *permanent* magnets can be made of ferromagnetic materials—once magnetized, they tend to retain at least some of their magnetism permanently. Consequently, when the atomic magnetic moments in a ferromagnetic material are once orientated, there must be strong interatomic torques tending to maintain this orientation in spite of the thermal agitation that tends to disarrange the orientation. Weber in 1852 first proposed that each atom is a permanent magnet capable of orientation, and Ewing in 1890 first pointed out the necessity for strong interatomic torques to account for the observed phenomena. The shell structure of the atomic electrons and the fact that the inner incomplete shell is responsible for ferromagnetism were recognized in the period following the fundamental work of Bohr (1913). But not until quantum mechanics was formulated in 1925 was there a satisfactory theory of atomic processes

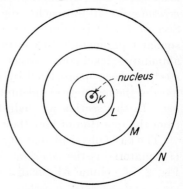

Fig. 1. Electronic structure of iron, cobalt, and nickel:

The K-shell has 2 electrons. It is complete and magnetically inert.

The L-shell has 8 electrons. It is complete and magnetically inert.

The M-shell has 14, 15, 16 electrons in Fe, Co, Ni. It is incomplete since it will hold 18 electrons. The electrons of this shell are responsible for the ferromagnetism.

The incomplete N-shell has 2 electrons that are responsible for the binding forces in the solid.

that permitted computation of interatomic torques. In the years following 1928, Heisenberg and others computed the magnitudes of the torques between the magnetic moments of adjacent atoms. These computations showed that in the case of Fe, Co, and Ni there are strong forces tending to keep the magnetic moments of adjacent atoms lined up parallel to one another, whereas in the case of other transition elements the interatomic forces actually prevent the magnetic moments from lining up and hence prevent these elements from being strongly magnetic. Thus, quantum mechanics finally gave an answer to the old question of why only three common elements of the periodic table are ferromagnetic. Quantum-mechanical theory also accounts satisfactorily for the ferromagnetism of the transition elements manganese and chromium, which occur just before iron in the periodic table, when the atoms are separated by abnormally large distances as they are in the Heusler alloys.

2. PERMANENT MAGNETS

ONCE THE microscopic magnetic moments of the electrons in a ferromagnetic material have been oriented by application of a magnetic field, they tend to a greater or lesser degree to remain orientated and to continue to set up a macroscopic field of their own.   In a material like pure soft iron or mild steel, only a little of the systematic orientation remains after removal of the applied field.   Such a material is said to be *magnetically soft;* it approaches the ideal magnetic material we shall study in Secs. 3–7, and is suitable for use in transformers, dynamos, relays, and similar equipment.   In contrast, the hard alloy steels, particularly the aluminum-nickel-cobalt steels (Alnico) are *magnetically hard.*   Once such steel has been magnetized by application of an external field, it retains most of the magnetism indefinitely and constitutes a good *permanent magnet.*   In this section we shall discuss permanent magnets as such, apart from the question of how they became magnetized.

The basic physical quantity used to describe the state of magnetization of a material is the *magnetic moment per unit volume.*   Consider a cube, Fig. 2, of volume δV small in size compared with the dimensions of a

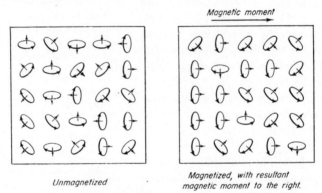

Magnetic moment

Unmagnetized

Magnetized, with resultant magnetic moment to the right.

Fig. 2. A schematic representation of the orientation of the microscopic magnetic moments of unmagnetized and magnetized material.*

magnet, but large enough to contain many billions of atoms.   When the material is unmagnetized, the electron moments (those that are magnetically effective) are orientated with sufficient randomness so that if their magnetic moments were summed vectorially for the whole volume δV, we should get an answer close to zero, as at the left of Fig. 2.   When the material is magnetized, the magnetic moments are orientated with a preference for a particular direction, as shown at the right of Fig. 2.   In

* Discussion of the domain structure of ferromagnetic materials is omitted from this text.   Actually, because of the interatomic forces discussed in the preceding section, whole blocks of atoms ($\sim 10^{-6}$ mm^3 in volume) have their magnetic moments uniformly orientated, even in an unmagnetized sample; and each 'atom' of Fig. 2 should be thought of as representing such a block or 'domain.'

this case the vector sum of the atomic magnetic moments would give a resultant magnetic moment δM for the volume δV. The magnetic moment δM would be proportional to the volume δV, and by dividing the resultant magnetic moment by the volume, we can define a *magnetic moment per unit volume*, which we denote by the vector $\mathfrak{M} = \delta M / \delta V$. The total magnetic moment of the volume δV is $\delta M = \mathfrak{M} \, \delta V$. $\mathfrak{M}$ is called the *intensity of magnetization;* it is measured in amp·m²/m³ = amp/m.

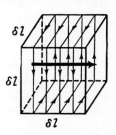

Macroscopically (that is, averaged over the violent microscopic irregularities), the field set up by a magnetized cube is the same as the field of a fictitious current, flowing around the edge of the cube in the direction shown in Fig. 3, that has the same magnetic moment. The magnetic moment of such a current δI would be $\delta I \, \delta l^2$, since the area of the circuit is δl^2. This quantity is equal to the magnetic moment $\mathfrak{M} \, \delta V$:

Fig. 3. The magnetic moment $\mathfrak{M} \, \delta V$ indicated by the heavy arrow sets up the same field as current $\mathfrak{M} \, \delta l$ in the direction shown by the light arrows.

$$\delta I \; \delta l^2 = \mathfrak{M} \; \delta l^3, \quad \text{or} \quad \delta I = \mathfrak{M} \; \delta l.$$

We need a total current $\mathfrak{M} \, \delta l$ around the cube, or current $\delta I / \delta l = \mathfrak{M}$ per unit width in the current sheet.

We are now prepared to calculate the field of a permanent bar magnet uniformly magnetized in the direction of its length, with magnetic

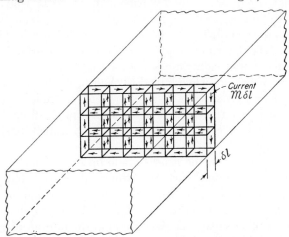

Fig. 4. Part of a uniformly magnetized bar magnet.

moment $\mathfrak{M}$ per unit volume. The macroscopic field of each volume element is the field of the current sheet of Fig. 3. In a slice of length δl across the magnet, these currents will be equivalent to a single current $\mathfrak{M} \, \delta l$ around the periphery, as indicated in Fig. 4.

The whole field of the bar magnet, inside and outside, is exactly like the field of a solenoid with current $nI = \mathfrak{M}$ per meter length.

The external field is the coulomb field of $+$ poles of total strength $\mathfrak{M}A$ spread across the area A of the N-end of the bar, with equal and opposite negative poles at the S-end of the bar. The internal field has magnetic intensity $\mathfrak{B} = (10^{-7} \text{ w/a·m}) \, 4\pi\mathfrak{M}$ at points well away from the ends. The diagram of Fig. 30, p. 688, applies with the correlation $nI = \mathfrak{M}$.

An actual bar magnet is not usually uniformly magnetized, so the magnetic moment per unit volume is not constant. There is some tendency for the magnetic moment per unit volume to decrease toward the ends of the bar. Such a magnet has a field like that of a solenoid whose turns are wound more densely near the center than near the ends.

Example. *A long iron bar is easily magnetized to an intensity of magnetization of 10^6 amp/m. If such a long bar is uniformly magnetized to this intensity, what is the magnetic intensity just outside the end of the bar?*

The whole field of the bar is the same as the field of a solenoid with current $nI = \mathfrak{M}$ per meter length. As we have seen on p. 689, the magnetic intensity just at the end of a long solenoid is $(10^{-7} \text{ w/a·m}) \, 2\pi nI$. Hence the magnetic intensity at the end of the long magnetized bar is

$$(10^{-7} \text{ w/a·m}) \, 2\pi \cdot 10^6 \text{ a/m} = 0.628 \text{ weber/m}^2.$$

3. MAGNETIZATION OF A TOROID

FUNDAMENTAL experiments on the magnetic properties of ferromagnetic materials are usually done by using a thin toroidal ring of the material with a winding applied completely around the outside, as in Fig. 5. The variation in the flux $\Phi = \mathfrak{B}A$ is measured as the current I in the winding is varied. To determine the flux in an iron ring without cutting into the ring seems at first sight impossible; actually, there is an instrument called a *fluxmeter* which, when linked to the ring with a few turns of wire (called a *secondary coil*), will accurately record, in webers, all changes in flux that occur inside the ring. The operation of the fluxmeter depends on the phenomenon of electromagnetic induction, which we shall study in the next chapter.

The flux density $\mathfrak{B}$ in the ring is made up of two parts—that arising directly from the 'external' current in the winding, and that arising from 'internal' currents associated with the orientated spin and orbital motions of the electrons in the ferromagnetic material. From the solenoid formula (13), p. 689, which also gives the field in the interior of a thin toroid, the part of the field arising from 'external' current nI per meter length of winding is $(10^{-7} \text{ w/a·m}) \, 4\pi nI$.

As a result of 'internal' currents, the ferromagnetic core has a magnetic moment $\mathfrak{M}$ per unit volume, which, by symmetry, is in the circumferential direction shown in Fig. 5, is the same all the way around the toroid, and for a thin toroid can be assumed constant across the cross section. Such a distribution of magnetic moments will, by the argument of Sec. 2, set up the same field as a current $\mathfrak{M}$ per meter length around the surface of the core, as indicated in Fig. 5. This fictitious current, from which the field set up by the magnetization of the toroid can be computed, is itself exactly like the current in the winding of a toroid, so it sets up the field $(10^{-7} \text{ w/a·m}) \, 4\pi\mathfrak{M}$.

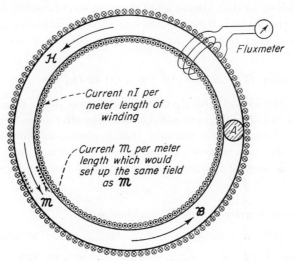

Fig. 5. A toroid with a core of ferromagnetic material, wound with n turns per meter length, each carrying current I.

The total magnetic intensity in the core is the sum of these two contributions:

$$\mathfrak{B}_{\text{Core}} = (10^{-7} \text{ w/a·m}) \, 4\pi n I + (10^{-7} \text{ w/a·m}) \, 4\pi\mathfrak{M}. \quad \binom{\text{ferromag-}}{\text{netic core}} \quad (1)$$

<small>(from external current)   (from internal current)</small>

The total magnetic intensity in the ferromagnetic core is much larger than the magnetic intensity the same current in the winding would produce in a non-ferromagnetic core:

$$\mathfrak{B}_{\text{No core}} = (10^{-7} \text{ w/a·m}) \, 4\pi n I. \quad \binom{\text{no ferromag-}}{\text{netic core}} \quad (2)$$

We define the ratio of (1) to (2) as the *permeability*

$$\mu = \mathfrak{B}_{\text{Core}}/\mathfrak{B}_{\text{No core}}. \quad (3)$$

The **permeability** of a material is the ratio of the magnetic intensity in a toroidal core formed of the material to the intensity the same current in the same winding would produce in a non-ferromagnetic core of the same dimensions.

The permeability of a ferromagnetic material is not a constant—it depends on the magnetic intensity itself and also somewhat on the previous magnetization history of the specimen.   However for the 'soft' magnetic materials used in electromagnetic machinery and transformers (as distinguished from the 'hard' magnetic materials used in permanent magnets), it is approximately constant, provided the magnetization is not too great.   For such materials it has a value very large compared to unity—of the order of 1000 for the irons and steels and 10,000 for the nickel alloys—so that almost all of the magnetic intensity arises from the second term of (1).   We note that the above definition assigns the value $\mu = 1$ (to within one part in 10^6; see p. 708) to a non-ferromagnetic material.

In relation (1), $\mathscr{B}_{\text{Core}} = (10^{-7} \text{ w/a·m}) \, 4\pi \, (nI + \mathfrak{M})$,

while it is the second term that contributes most of the magnetic intensity in a material of high permeability, it is the first term, representing the current and turns in the winding, that is responsible for the existence of the magnetization represented by the second term.   Hence the term nI is called the *magnetizing force* and denoted by the special symbol $\mathscr{H}$:

$$\mathscr{H} = nI. \qquad\qquad \text{(toroid)} \quad (4)$$

We can now rewrite (1) and (2) in the forms

$$\mathscr{B}_{\text{Core}} = (10^{-7} \text{ w/a·m}) \, 4\pi \, (\mathscr{H} + \mathfrak{M}), \quad \mathscr{B}_{\text{No core}} = (10^{-7} \text{ w/a·m}) \, 4\pi\mathscr{H}; \quad (5)$$

and (3) as $\mu = \mathscr{B}_{\text{Core}} / \mathscr{B}_{\text{No core}} = \mathscr{B}_{\text{Core}} / (10^{-7} \text{ w/a·m}) \, 4\pi\mathscr{H}$,

or $$\mathscr{B}_{\text{Core}} = (10^{-7} \text{ w/a·m}) \, 4\pi \, \mu\mathscr{H}. \qquad\qquad (6)$$

This relation shows that the magnetic intensity in the core (in webers/m²) is proportion to the magnetizing force $\mathscr{H}$ (in ampere-turns/meter) and to the permeability μ of the material (dimensionless).

We now note that, in the first of relations (5), $\mathscr{B}$ and $\mathfrak{M}$ represent the magnitudes of *vector* quantities.   Hence it is desirable to think of $\mathscr{H}$ as also representing the magnitude of a vector quantity defined by

$$\mathscr{H} = \frac{(10^7 \text{ amp·m/weber})}{4\pi} \, \mathscr{B} - \mathfrak{M}. \qquad\qquad (7)$$

In the toroidal case, $\mathscr{H}$ will have the same circumferential direction as $\mathscr{B}$ and $\mathfrak{M}$, as indicated by the vector marked $\mathscr{H}$ in Fig. 5.

We have introduced the concept of a *vector* called *magnetizing force* in the particularly simple case of a uniformly wound toroid, where the magnitude of the vector is given by (4) and the vector can be defined by (7). In the case of more complex arrangements of magnetic materials and windings, no such simple relation as (4) exists for the magnitude of $\mathscr{H}$ but (7) is taken as the definition of the vector $\mathscr{H}$:

The **magnetizing force** $\mathscr{H}$ is a vector defined by (7).   Its magnitude is measured in ampere-turns/meter, and for the case of a uniformly wound toroid has the value (4).

In the general case, the physical significance of the vector $\mathfrak{K}$ is obscure, and its mathematical treatment is well beyond the scope of this text, but the convenience of introducing the vector will be illustrated by the examples in the following sections.

We note from (7) that any point where $\mathfrak{M} = 0$, that is, at any point in any material except a ferromagnetic material, $\mathfrak{K}$ and $\mathfrak{B}$ are vectors in the same direction and with magnitudes differing by a constant factor:

$$\mathfrak{K} = \frac{(10^7 \text{ amp·m/weber})}{4\pi} \, \mathfrak{B} \quad \textit{except in ferromagnetic materials.}$$

Because of this relation, the formulas of Chap. 32 for the magnetic effects of electric currents will give $\mathfrak{K}$ instead of $\mathfrak{B}$ if they are multiplied by a factor of $(10^7 \text{ amp·m/weber})/4\pi$, provided that no ferromagnetic materials are present.

Example. *An iron toroid of permeability* 1500 *is wound with* 100 turns/ meter *each carrying* 8 amp. *Determine* $\mathfrak{K}$, $\mathfrak{B}$, $\mathfrak{M}$. *What would be the magnetic intensity* $\mathfrak{B}$ *if the core were not ferromagnetic?*

From (4),　$\mathfrak{K} = nI = (100 \text{ turns/m})(8 \text{ amp}) = 800 \text{ amp-turns/m.}$

From (6),　　$\mathfrak{B}_{\text{Core}} = (10^{-7} \text{ weber/amp·m}) \, 4\pi\mu\mathfrak{K}$

$= 10^{-7} \cdot 4\pi \cdot 1500 \cdot 800 \text{ weber/m}^2 = 1.51 \text{ weber/m}^2.$

On the other hand,

$\mathfrak{B}_{\text{No core}} = (10^{-7} \text{ weber/amp·m}) \, 4\pi nI$

$= 10^{-7} \cdot 4\pi \cdot 800 \text{ weber/m}^2 = 1.01 \times 10^{-3} \text{ weber/m}^2,$

which is $\frac{1}{1500}$ of $\mathfrak{B}_{\text{Core}}$.

4. THE MAGNETIC CIRCUIT

A CLOSED PATH of magnetic material (such as the toroid in Fig. 5) is called a *magnetic circuit*, since the magnetic flux runs through the magnetic material like the electric current in an electric circuit. This analogy explains the terminology of some of the following definitions.

If N is the total number of turns in the winding and l is the average length of the core or winding in meters (the length of bar required to make the toroid if an iron bar is bent into a circle and welded), then $n = N/l$. Using (6) and (4), we can write the formula for the total flux as

$$\Phi = \mathfrak{B}A = (10^{-7} \text{ w/a·m}) \, 4\pi\mu\mathfrak{K}A = \frac{4\pi\mu}{(10^7 \text{ a·m/w})} \, nIA = \frac{4\pi\mu A}{(10^7 \text{ a·m/w}) \, l} \, NI,$$

or　　　　　　　　　　$$\Phi = \frac{NI}{(10^7 \text{ a·m/w}) \, l/4\pi\mu A}.$$

The numerator of this expression is called the *magnetomotive force:*

$$\text{MMF} = NI, \quad \text{in ampere-turns.} \tag{8}$$

The denominator is called the *reluctance* of the magnetic circuit:

$$\mathcal{R} = \frac{(10^7 \text{ a·m/w}) \, l}{4\pi\mu A}, \quad \text{in } \frac{\text{ampere-turns}}{\text{weber}}. \tag{9}$$

With these notations the formula for flux through the magnetic circuit can be written as

$$\Phi = \text{MMF}/\mathcal{R}, \tag{10}$$

in exact analogy with the electric-circuit formula $I = \text{EMF}/R$. Note that from (4), $\mathcal{H} = nI = NI/l = \text{MMF}/l$, so that the relation between MMF and $\mathcal{H}$ is

$$\text{MMF} = \mathcal{H} \, l. \tag{11}$$

Example. *Determine the flux in the core of Fig. 6 when the current in the winding is 1 amp. How does the flux vary with current?*

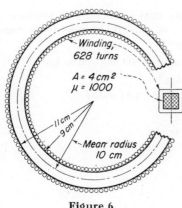

Winding, 628 turns

$A = 4 cm^2$
$\mu = 1000$

11 cm
9 cm

Mean radius
10 cm

Figure 6

Since $N = 628$ turns, and the mean circumference is $l = 2\pi \, (0.1 \text{ m}) = 0.628$ m, $n = N/l = 1000$ turns/m. For $I = 1$ amp, we get

$$\mathcal{H} = nI = 1000 \text{ amp-turn/m}.$$

For this magnetizing force, (5) gives

$$\begin{aligned} \mathcal{B} &= (10^{-7} \text{ w/a·m}) \, 4\pi \, \mu\mathcal{H} \\ &= 4\pi \times 10^{-7} \times 10^3 \times 10^3 \text{ weber/m}^2 \\ &= 1.257 \text{ weber/m}^2. \end{aligned}$$

Since $A = 4 \times 10^{-4} \text{ m}^2$,

$$\begin{aligned} \Phi = \mathcal{B}A &= 1.257 \times 4 \times 10^{-4} \text{ weber} \\ &= 5.03 \times 10^{-4} \text{ weber.} \end{aligned}$$

Alternatively, we can compute Φ from (10) by using the MMF and the reluctance. From (8) or (11),

$$\text{MMF} = NI = \mathcal{H}l = 628 \text{ amp-turn.}$$

From (9), $\quad \mathcal{R} = \dfrac{(10^7 \text{ a·m/w}) \, l}{4\pi\mu A} = \dfrac{(10^7 \text{ a·m/w}) \, 0.628 \text{ m}}{4\pi \, (10^3) \, 4 \times 10^{-4} \text{ m}} = 0.125 \times 10^7 \, \dfrac{\text{amp-turn}}{\text{weber}}.$

Hence, $\quad \Phi = \dfrac{\text{MMF}}{\mathcal{R}} = \dfrac{628 \text{ amp-turn}}{0.125 \times 10^7 \text{ amp-turn/weber}} = 5.02 \times 10^{-4} \text{ weber,}$

which agrees with the previous value. If the current in the winding is x amp instead of 1 amp, the above answers for $\mathcal{H}$, $\mathcal{B}$, MMF, and Φ are multiplied by x; $\mathcal{R}$ is unchanged.

5. A MAGNETIC CIRCUIT OF UNIFORM CROSS SECTION AND PERMEABILITY

IF THE DISTRIBUTED turns on the highly permeable toroid of Fig. 5 are collected into a concentrated coil as indicated in Fig. 7, it is an experimental fact that the flux lines continue to follow the toroid around, and the total flux Φ remains unchanged if the total number of ampere-turns remains unchanged.

If the core were made of wood or brass, the flux patterns of the concentrated winding of Fig. 7 would be entirely different from that of the distributed winding of Fig. 5, and the presence of the toroidal core in Fig. 7 could be completely ignored. But with a core

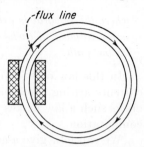

of permeability 1000, the flux in the core of Fig. 5 is 1000 times the flux arising from the winding alone; $^{999}\!/_{1000}$ of the flux arises from the magnetization of the core. And, so long as the core permeability is large compared to unity, the magnetization of the core in Fig. 7 can be shown, experimentally and theoretically, to be the same as the magnetization of the core of Fig. 5, for the same total ampere-turns. Since the bulk of the flux arises from the core magnetization and only a trivial part directly from the current in the winding, most of the

Fig. 7. A toroid with a concentrated winding of N turns and mean circumference l.

flux will follow the iron circuit as indicated on Fig. 7 and the flux will have the same magnitude as for the case of Fig. 5 if the number of ampere-turns in the winding is the same.

All the formulas of the previous section that apply to Fig. 5 can be applied to Fig. 7 except those involving n, the number of turns per unit length, which is meaningless for Fig. 7. The best procedure is to compute MMF from (8), $\Re$ from (9), and Φ from (10). Then $\mathcal{B} = \Phi/A$, and $\mathcal{3C}$ can be obtained from (6) or from (11).

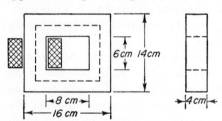

Fig. 8. The mean length of the core is the length of the broken line, $l = (12+12+10+10) = 44$ cm $= 0.44$ m.

This same type of computation can be made for a core of arbitrary shape but constant cross section, with any type of concentrated or distributed winding, if l is the mean length of 'iron' path; for example, for the transformer core of Fig. 8 if l is taken as the length of the broken line, 0.44 m.

6. THE LINE-INTEGRAL LAW FOR $\mathcal{3C}$

IN THE PREVIOUS sections we have seen that for the case of either a concentrated or a distributed winding, MMF $=\mathcal{3C}\,l=NI$, where l is the length of ferromagnetic path and N is the number of turns.

This equation is a special case of a theorem known as *the line-integral law for* $\mathcal{3C}$, which can be rigorously proved from the formal definition of $\mathcal{3C}$ on p. 716. The proof is omitted here. The law is:

If we follow any closed path and take the integral of $\mathcal{3C}_l\,dl$, where dl is an element of length along the path, and $\mathcal{3C}_l$ is the component of $\mathcal{3C}$ in the *direction we are moving along the path, then*

$$\oint \mathfrak{IC}_l \, dl = NI, \tag{12}$$

where the integral is extended completely around the closed path and N is the number of turns of wire, each carrying current I, that are linked by the path.

In this law only 'external' currents in wires are considered, 'internal' currents arising from magnetization are not included. The fact that $\mathfrak{IC}$ obeys such a law makes the vector $\mathfrak{IC}$ very useful from the standpoint of computation.

We can now give a general definition of magnetomotive force:

> The **magnetomotive force** around a closed path is the number of ampere-turns of current in wires that link the path.

That is, MMF $= NI$, which by (12) equals the line integral $\oint \mathfrak{IC}_l \, dl$.

7. SERIES MAGNETIC CIRCUITS

By a *series magnetic circuit* we mean a closed highly permeable path such as that of Fig. 9, which may be made up of pieces of different lengths, different cross-sectional areas, and different permeabilities. A good

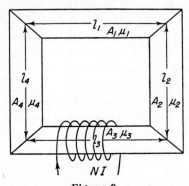

Figure 9

approximation to the flux in such a circuit may be obtained by the following method.

Most of the flux will follow around the ferromagnetic path, because of its high permeability, and it will be satisfactory to consider that *all* the flux follows around this path. Since flux tubes are closed and of constant strength throughout, the flux must be the same in all parts of the circuit:

$$\Phi_1 = \Phi_2 = \Phi_3 = \Phi_4 = \Phi,$$

where subscripts 1, 2, 3, and 4 refer to the four legs of the circuit in Fig. 9. Then

$$\mathfrak{B}_1 A_1 = \mathfrak{B}_2 A_2 = \mathfrak{B}_3 A_3 = \mathfrak{B}_4 A_4 = \Phi, \quad .$$

so that $\mathfrak{B}_1 = \Phi / A_1, \quad \mathfrak{B}_2 = \Phi / A_2, \quad \mathfrak{B}_3 = \Phi / A_3, \quad \mathfrak{B}_4 = \Phi / A_4.$

Now, the line integral occurring in (12) has the value

$$\text{MMF} = \mathfrak{IC}_1 l_1 + \mathfrak{IC}_2 l_2 + \mathfrak{IC}_3 l_3 + \mathfrak{IC}_4 l_4 = NI.$$

In this equation we can substitute the following expressions analogous to equation (6):

$$\mathcal{K}_1 = \frac{(10^7 \text{ a·m/w})}{4\pi\mu_1}\,\mathcal{B}_1, \qquad \mathcal{K}_3 = \frac{(10^7 \text{ a·m/w})}{4\pi\mu_3}\,\mathcal{B}_3,$$

$$\mathcal{K}_2 = \frac{(10^7 \text{ a·m/w})}{4\pi\mu_2}\,\mathcal{B}_2, \qquad \mathcal{K}_4 = \frac{(10^7 \text{ a·m/w})}{4\pi\mu_4}\,\mathcal{B}_4,$$

to obtain

$$\text{MMF} = (10^7 \text{ a·m/w})\,\Phi\left(\frac{l_1}{4\pi\mu_1 A_1} + \frac{l_2}{4\pi\mu_2 A_2} + \frac{l_3}{4\pi\mu_3 A_3} + \frac{l_4}{4\pi\mu_4 A_4}\right) = NI.$$

This equation can be solved for the flux Φ:

$$\Phi = \frac{NI}{(10^7 \text{ a·m/w})\left(\dfrac{l_1}{4\pi\mu_1 A_1} + \dfrac{l_2}{4\pi\mu_2 A_2} + \dfrac{l_3}{4\pi\mu_3 A_3} + \dfrac{l_4}{4\pi\mu_4 A_4}\right)}. \qquad (13)$$

This expression can be written more concisely if we define the reluctances of the various parts of the circuit, in analogy with (9), by

$$\mathcal{R}_1 = \frac{(10^7 \text{ a·m/w})\, l_1}{4\pi\mu_1 A_1}, \qquad \mathcal{R}_2 = \frac{(10^7 \text{ a·m/w})\, l_2}{4\pi\mu_2 A_2}, \quad \text{etc.} \qquad (14)$$

We define the total reluctance of the series magnetic circuit as the sum of these reluctances. Formula (13) then becomes

$$\Phi = \frac{\text{MMF}}{\mathcal{R}_1 + \mathcal{R}_2 + \mathcal{R}_3 + \mathcal{R}_4} = \frac{\text{MMF}}{\mathcal{R}}, \qquad (15)$$

where $\qquad\qquad \text{MMF} = NI, \qquad \mathcal{R} = \mathcal{R}_1 + \mathcal{R}_2 + \mathcal{R}_3 + \mathcal{R}_4.$

This gives the general definition

> The **reluctance** of a magnetic circuit is the ratio of the magneto-motive force around the circuit to the flux through the circuit.

Similar formulas will apply to the case of a magnetic circuit with a *short* air gap. By a *short* gap we mean one whose length (in the direction of the flux lines) is considerably less than its width in either of the other directions.

Example. *Consider the prototype cyclotron magnet of Fig. 10. The dimensions here are typical of a cyclotron (see Chap. 38) designed to produce a beam of protons with an energy of about 3 million electron-volts. A field of 1 weber/m² in the air gap is desired, and a permeability of 500 may be assumed for the iron. Assume that in Fig. 10 the effective length of path in the iron is 7.4 m and the effective cross-sectional area of the iron is constant around the circuit and is equal to the area ¼ π m² of the circular pole pieces of 1-m diameter. Compute the number of ampere-turns required in the winding in order to set up a field of 1 weber/m².*

The reluctance of the iron part of the circuit (length 7.4 m, area ¼ π m², permeability 500) is, from (14),

$$\mathcal{R}_{\text{Iron}} = \frac{(10^7 \text{ a·m/w})(7.4 \text{ m})}{4\pi \ (500)(\tfrac{1}{4} \pi \text{ m}^2)} = 15{,}000 \ \frac{\text{amp-turn}}{\text{weber}}.$$

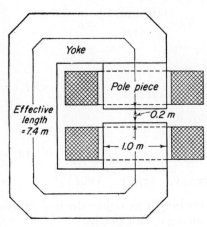

Figure 10

Since the air gap is short compared with its horizontal dimensions, we can use a similar formula to compute the reluctance of the air gap. Such a formula assumes that the flux lines go straight across the gap so that the length of the flux path is just the gap length (0.2 m in our case) and the area of the flux path is just the area of the pole pieces ($\tfrac{1}{4} \pi$ m²). These assumptions are analogous to those involved in the derivation of the parallel-plate condenser formula in electrostatics. They neglect the 'fringing' of the flux at the edges of the poles and are valid only for short gaps. In our case, with $\mu = 1$ for air, we have, for the reluctance of the air gap,

$$\mathcal{R}_{\text{Air gap}} = \frac{(10^7 \text{ a·m/w})(0.2 \text{ m})}{4\pi \ (\tfrac{1}{4} \pi \text{ m}^2)} = 203{,}000 \ \frac{\text{amp-turn}}{\text{weber}}.$$

The total reluctance of the circuit is the sum of these;

$$\mathcal{R} = 218{,}000 \text{ amp-turn/weber.}$$

It will be noticed that most of the reluctance is in the air gap.

The total flux desired is

$$\Phi = \mathcal{B}A = (1 \text{ weber/m}^2) \times \tfrac{1}{4} \pi \text{ m}^2 = 0.785 \text{ weber.}$$

Thus, the MMF required is

$$\text{MMF} = \Phi\mathcal{R} = (0.785 \text{ weber})(218{,}000 \text{ amp-turn/weber}) = 171{,}000 \text{ amp-turn.}$$

Such an enormous number of ampere-turns is usually supplied by coils that surround the pole pieces as in the figure. The coils are wound of heavy copper tubing carrying a very heavy current, and water flows through the tubing to carry off the I^2R-heat.

8. REAL MAGNETIC MATERIALS

IF WE TAKE a ring specimen of a magnetic material with a toroidal winding as in Fig. 5, we can increase the value of $\mathcal{H} = NI/l$ in small steps by increasing the value of the current I in small steps. For each change in $\mathcal{H}$, we can measure the change in flux, and hence the change in $\mathcal{B}$, by means of the fluxmeter. Hence, we can plot a curve of $\mathcal{B}$ against $\mathcal{H}$. If we start with an unmagnetized specimen, a curve obtained in this way is known as a *magnetization curve*. A magnetization curve for annealed iron is shown in Fig. 11. It will be noticed that this real material corresponds only roughly to the concept of a material of constant permeability $\mu = (10^7/4\pi) \ (\mathcal{B}/\mathcal{H}) \text{ a·m/w}$. In the actual case of annealed iron, μ

starts with a value of about 200, determined by the slope of the line marked μ_0 in Fig. 11, which is known as the *initial permeability* μ_0. As the magnetizing force increases, the ratio $\mathcal{B}/\mathcal{3C}$ at first increases, reaching its maximum at about $\mathcal{B} = 1$ weber/m², as indicated by the slope of the line marked μ_M in Fig. 11. The *maximum permeability* μ_M in this case is 5000. The ratio $\mathcal{B}/\mathcal{3C}$ then decreases, and $\mathcal{B}$ slowly approaches the *saturation magnetization* $\mathcal{B}_S$, which in this case is 2.15 weber/m². A plot of

$$\mu = [(10^7/4\pi)\ \mathrm{a\cdot m/w}]\ (\mathcal{B}/\mathcal{3C})$$

is given in Fig. 12.

For many applications of magnetic materials, high flux densities are desired at very low values of magnetizing force. For such applications, which include low-current transformers, low-current relays, inductive 'loading' of telephone cables, and sensitive detectors of small field changes (as in magnetic mines), the best material is the one of highest initial permeability or of highest maximum permeability, depending on the particular application. A great deal of effort has gone into the development of materials of increased permeability during the past few decades, and tremendous progress has been achieved as indicated in the

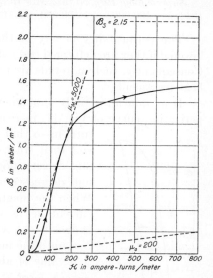

Fig. 11. Magnetization curve for annealed iron of high purity.

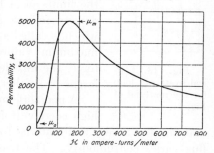

Fig. 12. Permeability *vs.* magnetizing force for the material of Fig. 11.

following tabulation,* which lists type of material, heat-treatment, year of introduction, and presently attainable magnetic characteristics:

Iron, 99.9%, annealed, *1890,* $\mu_0 = 200$, $\mu_M = 5000$, $\mathcal{B}_S = 2.15$ weber/m².

Silicon-iron, 3.3% Si, 96.6% Fe, cold-rolled, then annealed at 800° C, *1900,* $\mu_0 = 600$, $\mu_M = 10{,}000$, $\mathcal{B}_S = 2.0$ weber/m².

78 permalloy, 78% Ni, 21% Fe, heat-treated at 1050° C with rapid cool, *1913,* $\mu_0 = 8{,}000$, $\mu_M = 100{,}000$, $\mathcal{B}_S = 1.0$ weber/m².

4-79 permalloy, 79% Ni, 4% Mo, 16% Fe, heat-treated at 1100° C, *1921,* $\mu_0 = 20{,}000$, $\mu_M = 80{,}000$, $\mathcal{B}_S = 0.87$ weber/m². (*Mumetal,* 75% Ni, 2% Cr. 5% Cu, 18% Fe, has almost identical properties.)

* From Bozorth, REVIEWS OF MODERN PHYSICS, January, 1947.

1040 alloy, 72% Ni, 14% Cu, 3% Mo, 11% Fe, heat-treated in hydrogen at 1100° C, *1934*, $\mu_0 = 40,000$, $\mu_M = 100,000$, $\mathcal{B}_S = 0.6$ weber/m².

Supermalloy, 79% Ni, 5% Mo, 15% Fe, heat-treated in hydrogen at 1300° C, *1944*, $\mu_0 = 100,000$, $\mu_M = 800,000$, $\mathcal{B}_S = 0.8$ weber/m².

The permeability of any of the above materials will be drastically lowered if they are deformed beyond the elastic limit after heat-treatment. Consequently, such materials are fabricated in final size and shape before heat treatment.

If we take an initially unmagnetized sample of iron that has the magnetization curve of Fig. 11, increase the magnetizing force to 160 amp-turn/m so that the flux density becomes 1 weber/m²,

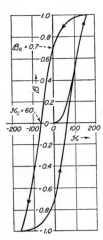

and then start decreasing the magnetizing force, the flux density does not decrease along the same curve but decreases along the curve shown in Fig. 13. When the magnetizing force has dropped to zero (no current in the winding), we still have a *residual flux* of density $\mathcal{B}_R$, which in this case is about 0.7 weber/m². Not until the magnetizing force has assumed the negative value of about -60 amp-turn/m (known as the *coercive force* $\mathcal{H}_C$) does the flux density become zero. If the magnetizing force is repeatedly varied between the limits of $+160$ and -160 amp-turn/m, the flux density follows around the closed curve of Fig. 13, which is called a *hysteresis loop.* For higher or lower maximum values of cyclically applied magnetizing force, the flux density follows around correspondingly larger or smaller hysteresis loops.

Fig. 13. Typical hysteresis loop for the material of Fig. 11.

A magnetic material with a high residual flux and a high coercive force is a very good permanent magnet material but a very bad material for a transformer or a motor where the flux varies continuously. The reason for the latter part of this statement is that the energy of self-inductance expended in setting up the magnetic field (see Chap. 34) is not completely recovered when the field decreases to zero if there is hysteresis. Rather, there is an energy loss in each cycle, if an alternating current is applied, that is proportional to the area of the hysteresis loop on a plot such as that of Fig. 13. Hence, for materials subjected to cyclic magnetization, a very narrow hysteresis loop is highly desirable.

For permanent magnets, a high value of residual flux is desired if the magnet is to have a strong field. Of much more importance, *a permanent-magnet material must have a very high value of coercive force.* Characteristics of permanent-magnet materials have continuously improved from the time of the first introduction of tungsten steel in 1855. This material (6% W, 0.7% Cr, 0.3% Mn. 93% Fe) has a residual flux of 1.05

weber/m² and a coercive force of 5200 amp-turn/m for the hysteresis loop corresponding to magnetization to saturation. One of the Alnicos (Al-Ni-Co steels), Alnico V (8% Al, 14% Ni, 24% Co, 3% Cu, 51% Fe), introduced in 1940, has a residual flux of 1.25 weber/m² and a coercive force of 44,000 amp-turn/m, for magnetization to saturation. In 1952, a coercive force of 270,000 amp-turn/m was reported for manganese bismuthide, with a residual flux of 0.43 weber/m².

PROBLEMS

1. Atomic theory tells us that the electrons responsible for ferromagnetism move in circular orbits around the nucleus with angular momentum h/π, where h is Planck's constant (see Appendix, Sec. 3). Assume that the radius of the orbit is $r = 10^{-10}$ m; this radius is not accurately known. Compute literal and numerical values of the speed v of the electron, the equivalent current I (the charge passing any point in the orbit per second), and the orbital magnetic moment M (defined as I times the area of the orbit). Independent of the value assumed for r, this magnetic moment turns out to be 2 Bohr magnetons.

Ans: $v = h/\pi mr = 2.32 \times 10^6$ m/sec; $I = eh/2\pi^2 mr^2 = 5.90 \times 10^{-4}$ amp; $M = 2(eh/4\pi m) = 18.5 \times 10^{-24}$ amp·m².

2. Show that for a charged particle with charge e and mass m moving in a circular orbit the ratio of the magnetic moment associated with the orbital motion of the charge to the angular momentum of the particle is $e/2m$. This ratio of magnetic moment to angular momentum is called the *gyromagnetic ratio*.

3. (a) If iron has a density of 7870 kg/m³, how many atoms are there per cubic meter? (b) If each atom of iron in a bar magnet has a resultant magnetic moment of 1 Bohr magneton, and these magnetic moments are all orientated in the direction of the length of the magnet, what is the value of $\mathfrak{M}$, the magnetic moment per cubic meter? (c) What is the field strength in the center of a long bar magnet magnetized as in (b)? (d) The saturation magnetization (the maximum field strength that can arise from the oriented atomic moments of the material) of iron is observed to be 2.15 weber/m². To what magnetic moment, in Bohr magnetons per atom, does this value correspond? Ans: (a) 8.49×10^{28}; (b) 7.87×10^5 amp/m; (c) 0.989 weber/m²; (d) 2.17 Bohr magnetons per atom.

4. A cylindrical bar magnet is very long in comparison with its diameter. On the centerline of the magnet, just outside the end of the magnet, the field strength is measured as 0.457 weber/m². Assuming the magnetization to be uniform, compute the intensity of magnetization.

5. If a core of the same dimensions as Fig. 6 is made of laminated annealed sheet steel of permeability 5000 and is wound with 1000 turns of No. 19 wire carrying 0.15 amp, find $\mathfrak{IC}$, $\mathfrak{B}$, MMF, and $\mathfrak{R}$. Compute Φ from both formulas: $\Phi = \mathfrak{B}A$ and $\Phi = \text{MMF}/\mathfrak{R}$, and check. Ans: $\mathfrak{IC} = 239$ amp-turn/m; $\mathfrak{B} = 1.50$ weber/m²; MMF $= 150$ amp-turn; $\mathfrak{R} = 2.50 \times 10^5$ amp-turn/weber; $\Phi = 6.00 \times 10^{-4}$ weber.

6. If a core of the same dimensions as Fig. 6 is made of wrought iron of permeability 8000 and is wound with 500 turns of No. 18 wire carrying 0.15 amp, find $\mathfrak{IC}$, $\mathfrak{B}$, MMF, and $\mathfrak{R}$. Compute Φ from both formulas: $\Phi = \mathfrak{B}A$ and $\Phi = \text{MMF}/\mathfrak{R}$, and check.

7. A toroid is made by bending a circular rod of 3-cm diameter and 1-m length into a circle and welding the ends. The material is mild steel of permeability 1100. It is wound with 150 turns uniformly distributed. What current is necessary to set up a flux density of 1.2 webers/m²? Ans: 5.79 amp.

8. A cast-iron toroid is made by casting a doughnut shape. The mean radius of the toroid is 12 cm, the radius of the section is 1.5 cm. The permeability is 400. It is wound with 400 turns uniformly distributed. What current is necessary to set up a flux density of 0.3 weber/m²?

9. In Prob. 7, what current is necessary to set up a flux of 6×10^{-4} weber?
Ans: 4.09 amp.

10. In Prob. 8, what current is necessary to set up a flux of 1.5×10^{-4} weber?

11. If the air gap of Fig. 10 is decreased to 0.1 m, with a corresponding increase in the length of the iron path, and the permeability of the iron is 500, as in the computation in the example, find the number of ampere-turns required to set up a flux density of 1 weber/m². Ans: 91,600.

12. If the air gap of Fig. 10 is filled with a block of iron of permeability 100, all other constants being as in the example, compute the number of ampere-turns required to set up a flux density of 1 weber/m².

13. In the computation in the example for the magnet of Fig. 10, how many ampere-turns would be required if the yoke were made of better iron, of permeability 1000? Ans: 165,000.

14. In a magnet of the type shown in Fig. 10, if the air gap is of length 0.1 m and cross section 1 m², the pole pieces each of length 0.75 m, cross-section 1 m², and permeability 100, and the yoke of effective length 5.8 m, effective cross section 0.7 m², and permeability 500, what flux density is set up in the air gap with 90,000 ampere-turns in the windings?

15. It is asserted in the text that the area of the hysteresis loop shown in Fig. 13 is proportional to an energy loss. By consideration of the physical dimensions of $\mathcal{B}$ and $\mathcal{K}$, show that the area of the loop has the dimensions of energy per unit volume (joules/m³).

16. It is asserted on p. 714 that the external field of a uniformly magnetized bar is the coulomb field of poles spread uniformly over the ends of the bar. By imagining the bar to be divided lengthwise into long, thin pieces analogous to the thin solenoid of Fig. 37, p. 693, show that this type of computation will give the correct magnetic intensity for any point outside the bar, no matter how close it may be to the end of the bar.

17. In connection with Prob. 16, show, by analogy with the known electric field of a sheet of electric charge, that the distribution of pole strength of $\mathfrak{M}$ per unit area over the end of a bar magnet gives the correct intensity $(10^{-7}$ w/a·m) $2\pi\mathfrak{M}$ just outside the end of the bar.

18. From the picture of Prob. 16, show that the intensity is uniform across the cross section at the center of a long bar magnet or solenoid. Use this picture to determine how long the solenoid must be to have central intensity within about one per cent of that given by the solenoid formula.

CHAPTER 34

ELECTROMAGNETIC INDUCTION

WE HAVE STATED earlier that an electric generator changes mechanical energy into the electrical energy associated with an electric current, and that if current is forced through the generator in the opposite direction, the same machine will act as a motor, changing electrical energy into mechanical energy. We have described the action of the DC motor in Chap. 32, but we have not yet described the action of the generator.

The action of the motor depends on the fact that a wire carrying current in a magnetic field experiences a force and tends to move. The generator action is the reverse; the motion of a wire in a magnetic field sets up an EMF that tends to cause a current. The latter phenomenon is an example of *electromagnetic induction.*

The fact that an EMF is set up in a wire moving in a magnetic field was discovered in 1831 independently by Faraday in London and by Henry* in America. These men first discovered how to change mechanical energy directly into the energy of current electricity.

1. MAGNITUDE AND DIRECTION OF THE INDUCED EMF

CONSIDER a wire, Fig. 1, a length l of which lies in a magnetic field $\mathcal{B}$ and moves with velocity $v.$ The wire, field, and velocity are all three mutually perpendicular.

Although the wire as a whole is macroscopically neutral, each individual microscopic charge Q in the wire is acted on by a force, in the direction shown, of magnitude

$$F = \mathcal{B}Qv$$

in newtons. This expression is the formula for force on a charge moving in a magnetic field, equation (20), p. 700.

Unlike the positive nuclei, the electrons are free to move and will move to the left. If the ends of the wire are open, the movement of the electrons will cause the left end of the wire to become negatively charged and the right end to become positively charged. Motion of the electrons

---

* JOSEPH HENRY (1797–1878), instructor at Albany Academy, Albany, N. Y., where he made this discovery; then professor of natural philosophy at Princeton College, Princeton, N. J.; later the first secretary of the Smithsonian Institution.

continues until the ends of the wire reach such different potentials that the force exerted by the resulting electric field on the electrons exactly

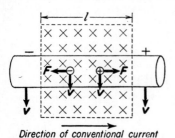

balances the force **F** that acts on the electrons because of the motion of the wire. Since the force on a charge Q in an electric field ε is εQ, this requires that an electric field of magnitude $\varepsilon = \mathcal{B}v$ be set up in the part of the wire in the magnetic field. The electric field must be from right to left to balance the magnetic forces. An electric field ε acting over the length l corresponds to a difference of potential

Fig. 1. Forces on the free electrons and positive nuclei in a wire moving downward through a magnetic field directed into the paper.

Direction of conventional current

$$V = \varepsilon l = \mathcal{B}vl. \qquad \left\{\begin{matrix} V \text{ in volts} \\ \mathcal{B} \text{ in webers/m}^2 \\ v \text{ in m/sec} \\ l \text{ in meters} \end{matrix}\right\} \quad (1)$$

The wire of Fig. 1, if open-circuited, acquires a difference of potential of magnitude $\mathcal{B}vl$ between its ends; the right end being at the higher potential.

On the other hand, suppose the circuit to be closed externally between the ends of the wire. A current will then occur in the direction indicated in Fig. 1. During the passage of the current through the section of wire moving in the magnetic field, work will be done *by* the magnetic forces *on* the charges since the magnetic forces are *in* the direction of motion of the charges. The amount of work will be $Fl = \mathcal{B}Qvl$ on a charge Q. By definition, the EMF is the work in joules per coulomb of charge, or

$$\text{EMF} = V_E = \mathcal{B}vl, \text{ in volts.} \qquad (2)$$

Equation (2) is the fundamental formula for EMF generated in a wire moving in a magnetic field. It is the same as the difference of potential (1) between the ends of the wire in the open-circuit case, but not necessarily the same as the difference of potential in the closed-circuit case because there may be an IR-drop in the wire.

Example. *Verify that in the case where the circuit is closed by an external resistance, as in Fig. 2, the heat generated in the resistance exactly equals the mechanical work that must be done to push the stiff wire through the magnetic field at constant speed v. Assume that the resistance of the straight wire and flexible leads is negligible compared to the external resistance R.*

The EMF (2) will cause current

$$I = \mathcal{B}vl/R, \quad \text{in amp.} \qquad (i)$$

This current will develop heat in the resistance at the rate

$$I^2R = \mathcal{B}^2v^2l^2/R, \quad \text{in watts,} \qquad (ii)$$

by dissipation of electrical energy.   This dissipated energy must come from mechanical energy expended to push the wire.   The need for expenditure of mechanical energy is clear if we note that we now have a wire carrying current in a magnetic field and that therefore there is a magnetic force normal to the wire from the side on which its own field strengthens the applied field toward that on which it weakens it.   This magnetic force is in the direction opposite to the motion, to the left in Fig. 2.   The magnitude of this force is, by (4), p. 678 and by (i),

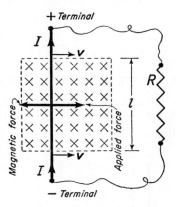

$$F = \mathfrak{B}lI = \mathfrak{B}^2 v l^2/R, \quad \text{in newtons.}$$

Since the wire has no acceleration, the net force on it must be zero; consequently, our applied force in the direction of motion must have the same magnitude F as this magnetic force.   The applied force F then does work at the rate

$$Fv = \mathfrak{B}^2 v^2 l^2/R, \quad \text{in watts,}$$

which is the same as the rate of development of heat in (ii), as we were to verify.

Fig. 2. A prototype electric generator.

Formula (2) is derived for the case where $\mathfrak{B}$, l, and v are mutually perpendicular.   Here l represents a vector along the length of the wire.   It is readily shown that if $\mathfrak{B}$, l, and v are not mutually perpendicular, we must use in (2) the component of v that is perpendicular to l, and the component of $\mathfrak{B}$ in a direction perpendicular to both l and v.

From the above example we see that *the induced current is in such a direction as to produce a magnetic force that opposes the force causing the motion.*   The direction of the induced current can readily be determined directly from this rule and the known rules for the direction of magnetic force.   Alternatively, a very convenient scheme based on Fig. 3 can be used to determine this direction:

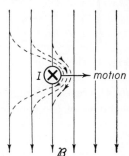

Fig. 3. View of Fig. 2 looking from the bottom toward the top of the page.

Imagine the magnetic lines to be like rubber bands so that they stretch and bend around the wire as it is pushed through them.   Then if the fingers of the right hand are curled around the wire, pointing in the same direction as the magnetic lines wrapped around the wire, the thumb will point in the direction of the induced current.

Example.   *The field in the air gap between the pole pieces and the armature of an electric generator is 1 weber/m². The length of the wires on the armature is 1 meter. How fast must these wires move in order to generate an* EMF *of 1 volt in each armature wire?*

From (2) we find that

$$v = \text{emf}/\mathfrak{B}l = 1 \text{ v}/(1 \text{ w/m}^2)(1 \text{ m}) = 1 \text{ v·m/weber}.$$

This answer does not look at first sight like a *speed*, but we note from (14), p. 691, that 1 weber = 1 volt·sec, so that we get

$$v = 1 \text{ v·m/v·sec} = 1 \text{ m/sec}.$$

Hence a wire 1 meter long moving at a speed of 1 m/sec in a field of **1** weber/ m² generates an emf of **1** volt.

2. THE RELATION BETWEEN EMF AND RATE OF CHANGE OF FLUX

THERE IS another very useful way of writing the emf generated in the closed circuit of Fig. 2. Let the symbol Φ stand for the flux in webers that is *linking* the closed circuit in Fig. 4. Φ then stands for the amount

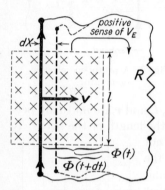

of flux *to the right* of the straight wire in this figure and decreases in time as the wire moves. We shall compute $d\Phi/dt$, which is of course a negative quantity. In time dt, let the wire move to the right a distance dX, so that $dX/dt = v$. Then during the time interval dt, Φ decreases by the amount of flux in an area $l\, dX$. This amount of flux is $\mathfrak{B}l\, dX$, so that we can write

$$d\Phi = -\mathfrak{B}l\, dX.$$

Fig. 4. The circuit of Fig. 2.

If we divide through by dt, we get

$$d\Phi/dt = -\mathfrak{B}l\, dX/dt = -\mathfrak{B}lv$$

for the rate of change of flux. But the expression on the right is just the negative of the generated emf as given by (2). Hence

$$\boxed{\text{EMF} = V_E = -\frac{d\Phi}{dt}.} \qquad (3)$$

The absolute magnitude of generated voltage equals the rate of change of flux linking the closed circuit, in webers/sec.

We have already noted, in connection with (14), p. 691, that this relation-ship is dimensionally correct.

Equation (3) determines the direction of the induced emf by means of the following convention: The flux linking the circuit of Fig. 4 has a direction into the paper. Associate a positive sense of V_E around the closed circuit with the direction of Φ through the circuit in accord-ance with the right-hand rule (point thumb in direction of Φ; curled fingers will point in positive sense of V_E). Then in the case illustrated in Fig. 4, $d\Phi/dt$ on the right side of (3) is a negative number (the flux is decreasing), therefore $V_E = -d\Phi/dt$ is in the sense called positive. If the wire moves to the left instead of to the right, Φ is increasing, $d\Phi/dt$ is positive, and V_E is negative. Therefore V_E, and hence the current, is in the opposite direction to that discussed above.

This sign convention is somewhat tedious. Usually it is convenient to use equation (3) to determine the absolute magnitude of V_E and to determine its direction separately by a convenient rule known as *Lenz's law*. This law can be stated as follows:

LENZ'S LAW: *When the flux linking a closed circuit is changing, the flux set up by the induced current is in such a direction as to tend to prevent the change in the flux linkage.*

Thus, in Fig. 4, the flux Φ linking the circuit is into the paper and decreasing in time. The induced current will be in such a direction that the flux it produces is into the paper through the circuit and therefore *tends to prevent the flux linking the circuit from decreasing*. If v be reversed, Φ will be increasing. Since the induced current must now set up a flux out of the paper to try to prevent Φ from increasing, it must be counterclockwise. These directions are seen to be consistent with those we determined in Sec. 1 from fundamental considerations.

The great convenience of equation (3) and Lenz's law is that they can be shown to apply *whenever* the flux through a closed circuit is changing. For example, in Fig. 5, a single loop of wire is moved toward the north

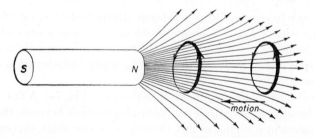

Fig. 5. Motion of a loop of wire in the vicinity of a permanent magnet.

pole of a permanent magnet. The flux Φ through the loop is to the right. The amount of flux is increasing. An EMF is induced whose magnitude is $d\Phi/dt$. The direction of the EMF is determined by Lenz's law. The flux to the right is increasing. The induced current tends to prevent the increase by setting up its own flux *to the left*. Hence, the current must be counterclockwise when viewed from the left as indicated in Fig. 5.

If the loop of Fig. 5 moves to the right, the flux is decreasing; consequently, the induced current is in the opposite direction, tending to set up a flux to the right.

If, in Fig. 5, the loop is stationary and the magnet is moved to the right, exactly the same EMF is induced as when the magnet is stationary and the loop is moved to the left at the same speed, because the rate of change of flux through the loop is the same in the two cases.

If the single loop is replaced by a coil wound with N turns and connected into an external circuit as indicated in Fig. 6, the EMF in each of the N turns in series is $-d\Phi/dt$, and the whole EMF is

Fig. 6. An N-turn coil.

$$\text{EMF} = V_E = -N \frac{d\Phi}{dt}. \qquad (4)$$

Equations (3) and (4) also apply to cases in which the flux through a loop or a coil is changing with no apparent motion. A case of this type is a coil placed in the field between the poles of an electromagnet when the exciting current is changing. The flux through the coil changes as the current in the windings of the electromagnet changes, and an EMF is generated in the coil. Equation (4) gives the magnitude of this EMF, and Lenz's law gives its direction. If the coil is wound around the iron yoke of a magnet, or around an iron toroid as in the case of the fluxmeter coil of Fig. 5, p. 715, these same relations are applicable, and the voltage generated in the coil can be made the basis for a determination of the rate of change of flux within the solid ferromagnetic material.

3. GENERATORS

IT IS EASY to see how to generate an alternating EMF, for example by moving the wire of Fig. 2 back and forth or by spinning the coil of Fig. 6 about its diameter in a magnetic field. Such a rotating coil constitutes a simple AC generator, and it is desirable to study the operation of such a simple generator.

The prototype of an AC generator is shown in Fig. 7. A flat rectangular coil of length l and width w is mounted on a shaft between the poles of a large magnet in a region of flux density $\mathfrak{B}$. The shaft, driven by some source of mechanical power (such as a water wheel or a heat engine), rotates at a frequency of f rev/sec, corresponding to an angular velocity of $\omega = 2\pi f$ rad/sec. As the coil rotates in the magnetic field, an EMF is generated and a difference of potential is produced between the terminals A and B which make contact through 'brushes' with the slip rings connected to the ends of the coil wire.

We shall calculate the generated EMF by means of (3). As the coil rotates in the magnetic field, the flux linking the coil varies from zero, when the plane of the coil is parallel to the field ($\theta = 90°$), to $\Phi_{\text{Max}} = \mathfrak{B}wl$ when the plane of the coil is perpendicular to the field ($\theta = 0°$). The flux linking the coil at angle θ is given by

$$\Phi = \mathfrak{B}wl \cos\theta = \Phi_{\text{Max}} \cos\theta.$$

The generated EMF is given by (3) as

$$V_E = -\frac{d\Phi}{dt} = \mathfrak{B}wl\sin\theta\,\frac{d\theta}{dt} = \Phi_{\text{Max}}\sin\theta\,\frac{d\theta}{dt},$$

or, since $\theta = \omega t = 2\pi ft$ and $d\theta/dt = 2\pi f$,

$$V_E = 2\pi f\,\Phi_{\text{Max}}\sin 2\pi ft = V_M\sin 2\pi ft, \tag{5}$$

where $V_M = 2\pi f\,\Phi_{\text{Max}}$ is the maximum magnitude of V_E reached when the coil is at $\theta = 90°$ and the flux linkage is changing most rapidly. It is left as a problem to show that the same expression for the generated EMF is

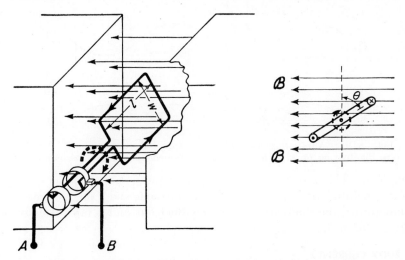

Fig. 7. Prototype AC generator, consisting of a one-turn 'coil.'

obtained if one starts with equation (2). Figure 8(a) shows a plot of V_E as a function of time; V_E is a sinusoidal function of time and, for our simple generator, has the same frequency as the mechanical frequency of rotation of the shaft.

If the coil has N turns, the maximum generated voltage is given by

$$V_M = 2\pi f\,Nwl\,\mathfrak{B}. \tag{6}$$

This is directly proportional to the frequency f, the coil area wl, the flux density $\mathfrak{B}$, and the number of turns. The AC frequency f is usually fixed at some standard value such as 60 cycles/sec; the coil area and the number of turns are limited by considerations of geometry and resistance. The flux density $\mathfrak{B}$ can be increased by winding the coil around a soft iron core of high permeability; this core is usually laminated for reasons given in Sec. 4.

The prototype generator just described is called a two-pole or bipolar generator. Actual generators are made with two, four, six, or more poles, usually at least four, and employ several coils like the single coil we have discussed, wound on a laminated soft-iron armature. As electrical engineering courses devote much attention to practical generator design and operation, we shall not discuss AC generators further here.

In order to obtain DC from our prototype generator, we may replace the slip rings shown in Fig. 7 with a split-ring commutator like the one for the prototype DC motor shown in Fig. 19 on p. 682. Such a commutator can be arranged so that terminal A is always positive with respect to terminal B in Fig. 7; in this case the EMF as measured by the open-circuit difference of potential between A and B would be given by the curve in

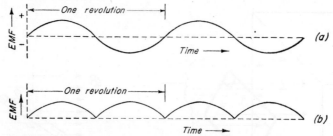

Fig. 8. (a) Alternating EMF obtained from the generator of Fig. 7. (b) Fluctuating DC EMF that would be obtained by adding a commutator.

Fig. 8(b). This EMF has a fluctuating DC value. In the case of a multipolar generator with many sets of armature coils and a many-segmented commutator, the fluctuations are smoothed out and a fairly steady DC EMF is obtained.

4. EDDY CURRENTS

SUPPOSE THAT we have a solid metal cylinder, Fig. 9, rotating in a magnetic field. Consider the longitudinal elements of this cylinder, parallel to the axis of rotation. These elements are conductors moving in a magnetic field. The elements in the left portion of the cylinder are moving up in the magnetic field, and hence an EMF is induced in these elements that tends to drive current in the indicated direction. Conversely, the elements on the right side are moving down in the magnetic field, and an EMF is induced in these elements that tends to drive current in the opposite direction. As a result of these EMF's, a system of circulating currents flows in the metal. These currents are called *eddy currents* because they form closed loops within the metal like eddies within a fluid.

Like the currents in the conductors of a generator, these currents are normal to the magnetic field and experience magnetic forces in the direction opposing the rotation of the cylinder. *The cylinder experiences a counterclockwise magnetic torque in the end view of Fig. 9.* If the cylinder is spinning freely and the magnetic field is brought around it, this torque will stop the rotation very quickly, the kinetic energy of rotation going into heat created by the eddy currents.   If the cylinder is driven at constant speed in the magnetic field, mechanical power equal to the heat produced by the eddy currents must be supplied.   For a given magnetic field, this power can be shown to vary as the square of the speed: (EMF) $\propto$ (speed); (current) $\propto$ (EMF); (heat generated in the form of I^2R losses) $\propto$ (current)^2; and hence (power) $\propto$ (speed)^2.   Or, from an equivalent point of view, (current) $\propto$ (EMF) $\propto$ (speed); (force on current element) $\propto$ (current); hence, (torque) $\propto$ (current) $\propto$ (speed); and (power) $\propto$ (torque) $\times$ (speed) $\propto$ (speed)^2.

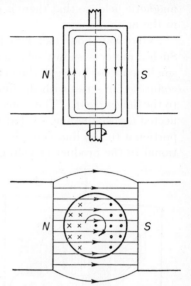

Such eddy currents and eddy-current losses would occur in the armature of a motor or generator if it were a solid-iron cylinder.   The losses would be so large as to be intolerable.   By constructing the armature from steel sheets or laminations only a few hundredths of an inch thick, as shown in Fig. 10, the eddy-current losses can be kept to a negligible

Fig. 9. Top and end views of a solid metal cylinder rotating in a magnetic field.

magnitude.   Lamination of the armature has little effect on the magnetic flux since the flux lines pass through the sheets 'edge-wise' and do not need to cross from one lamination to the next.   The steel laminations are

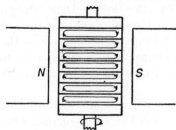

electrically insulated from each other, either by shellac or by nonconducting iron oxide, so that the eddy currents are confined to circulation within each individual steel sheet.   Two factors contribute to the reduction in losses.   First, the length of conductor moving perpendicular to the magnetic field is now just the thickness of the lamina, so that the EMF generated is very small.   Second, the resistance of the eddy-current path is very large because this path is of small cross-sectional area.

This is just one example of a large class of phenomena connected with eddy

Fig. 10. Eddy-current paths in an armature like that of Fig. 9, only laminated. The laminations in an actual armature are very thin. The stack of laminations is held together by bolts that run through them in a direction parallel to the axis of rotation.

currents.   In general, *if there is relative motion between a piece of metal and a magnetic field, eddy currents will be set up in the metal in such a direction that the resulting magnetic forces on the eddy-current elements will tend to stop the relative motion.* The only exception occurs in the case of pure translation of a piece of metal all portions of which are in a constant magnetic field, so that there is no change of flux linking any circuit drawn in the metal.

A DC watt-hour meter makes effective use of an *eddy-current brake.* Such a meter is shown schematically in Fig. 11. It is essentially a very small DC motor in which the magnetic field is set up by low-resistance coils connected in series with the line, so that the magnetic field is proportional to the line current. The armature, in series with a high resistance, is connected across the line, so that the armature receives a small current proportional to the line voltage. The torque of this motor is thus proportional to the product of voltage and current, that is, to the power taken by the load.

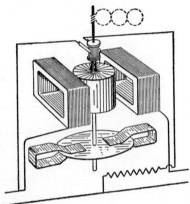

Fig. 11. The DC watt-hour meter. The lines from the power source come in at one side; those to the load whose energy consumption is being measured go out at the other.

The principal resistance to turning of the motor is furnished by an eddy-current brake, consisting of a copper disk that rotates between the poles of permanent magnets. The eddy currents induced in the disk offer a resisting torque that is proportional to the speed of rotation. Since the motor will run at such speed that the motor torque equals the resisting torque, it is seen that the speed of the motor will be proportional to the motor torque, and hence to the power taken by the load. Dials driven through reduction gears thus turn at a speed proportional to power, so the dial readings are proportional to power×time, that is, to energy. The dials are calibrated in watt·hours or kilowatt·hours.

The student should sketch the eddy-current paths in a disk rotating between the poles of one of the magnets shown in Fig. 11 to convince himself that the forces on the eddy currents are in the direction to oppose the rotation.

Another measuring instrument whose satisfactory operation involves eddy currents is the d'Arsonval galvanometer described on pp. 682–683. The combination of coil and spiral springs or fiber in a galvanometer forms a torsion pendulum. Such a pendulum would perform harmonic oscillations about its equilibrium position, making the instrument very inconvenient to use, if a special provision were not made to damp out these oscillations. To provide damping, the coil is wound on a light frame, usually of aluminum, which forms a short-circuited turn. When this *damping frame* rotates in the magnetic field, an EMF, and hence a current, is set up in it by the same action as in Fig. 9. The eddy current that circulates around the damping frame is in such a direction as to experience a magnetic force opposing the rotation. The thickness and resistance of the frame are made such as to introduce enough damping to prevent overshooting and harmonic oscillations, but not enough to make the motion of the pointer unduly sluggish. The *damping frame* has no effect on the position of equilibrium because when the coil has come to rest there is no current in the frame and hence no magnetic force on the frame.

5. AC MOTORS

INDUCED eddy currents are responsible for the operation of the most common type of AC motor, the *induction motor*. Consider what would happen in Fig. 9 if the metal cylinder were standing still but the pole pieces were rotating counterclockwise, so that there was the same relative motion of cylinder and field. Then the same system of eddy currents would be set up in the cylinder, the same counterclockwise torque would be felt by the cylinder, and the cylinder would tend to rotate with the field.

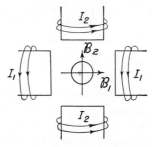

In an induction motor the poles are not actually rotated, but, by exciting two or more windings with currents out of phase, the field is made to rotate just as it would if the poles were rotated. The two-phase (or single splitphase) case is illustrated in Fig. 12. There

Fig. 12. Superposition of two alternating fields at right angles. This figure defines the positive directions of I_1, I_2, $\mathcal{B}_1$, $\mathcal{B}_2$, as used in Fig. 13.

are four poles. An alternating current I_1 sets up an alternating horizontal field $\mathcal{B}_1$. An alternating current I_2 sets up an alternating vertical field $\mathcal{B}_2$. As shown in Fig. 13, if the currents I_1 and I_2 are $\frac{1}{4}$ cycle out

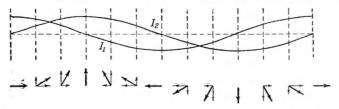

Fig. 13. The *resultant* of a horizontal magnetic field proportional to I_1 and a vertical magnetic field proportional to I_2 is a magnetic field of constant magnitude, rotating one revolution per cycle of the AC. The vectors show the fields $\mathcal{B}_1$ and $\mathcal{B}_2$ of Fig. 12, and the resultant field, in 12 steps during one revolution.

of phase the vector resultant of the two fields is a rotating field of constant magnitude, exactly the same as the field of a single pair of poles carrying DC but rotating around the armature with the frequency of the AC.

In an induction motor, the eddy currents are induced in a 'squirrel cage' (Fig. 14) of heavy copper bars joined at the ends by low-resistance copper rings. To keep down the reluctance of the flux path, the bars of the squirrel cage are embedded in slots in a laminated-iron rotor. For the two-phase motor of Fig. 12, the squirrel-cage rotor will run almost but not quite up to synchronous speed (60 rev/sec for 60-cycle AC). At exactly 60 rev/sec there would be no torque on the rotor because there would be no motion relative to the field, and no eddy currents. At rotor

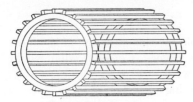

Fig. 14. Squirrel cage.

speeds below 60 rev/sec the eddy-current system and the torque we have been discussing are set up. The slower the speed, the greater is the relative motion and hence the greater is the torque tending to increase the rotor speed. The motor will run at such a speed below 60 rev/sec that the torque will be sufficient to turn the load. This is ordinarily only a few per cent under 60 rev/sec.

Most modern induction motors are three-phase, rather than two-phase. They employ three currents, mutually out of phase by $\frac{1}{3}$ cycle, and a minimum of six poles. The three currents are furnished directly by three-phase power lines. The principle of operation is the same as in the simpler two-phase case we have discussed.

We shall not discuss the AC *synchronous motor* in detail. It is in principle the generator of Fig. 7 run as a motor, with DC in the field, AC in the armature. It runs at synchronous speed, which is such speed that the AC in each conductor reverses each time the loop makes $\frac{1}{2}$ revolution between the poles, that is, the same speed as the generator must turn to generate 60 cycles/sec, if we are talking about 60-cycle AC. Once this motor is turning at synchronous speed, the current in each conductor will be in such a direction as to maintain the speed, and the motor will run synchronously with good torque. But the motor will not run at all *except* at synchronous speed, since at any other speed there will be nothing but a hodgepodge of random torques. Hence, the motor must be brought up to synchronous speed by some other means before it will run as a synchronous motor. This requirement is familiar in the case of non-self-starting synchronous electric-clock motors. Such clock motors use permanent magnets rather than DC for field excitation. Those that are self-starting employ some other principle for starting and only run as synchronous motors after they have been brought up to synchronous speed.

6. MUTUAL INDUCTANCE

CONSIDER THE transformer windings of Fig. 15. Let the iron circuit be an ideal magnetic circuit of high permeability, so that it can be assigned a constant reluctance ℛ, and all flux in the circuit can be assumed to thread both coils.

Current I_1 in coil 1 will set up $\text{MMF} = N_1 I_1$ and flux $\Phi = N_1 I_1/\mathcal{R}$. If I_1 is changing at the rate dI_1/dt, Φ will change at the rate

$$\frac{d\Phi}{dt} = \frac{N_1}{\mathcal{R}} \frac{dI_1}{dt}.$$

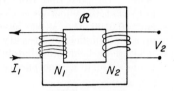

If Φ is changing, an EMF will be induced in coil 2, of magnitude (ignoring sign)

$$V_{E2} = N_2 \frac{d\Phi}{dt} = \frac{N_1 N_2}{\mathcal{R}} \frac{dI_1}{dt}.$$

Figure 15

The EMF in coil 2 is proportional to the rate of change of current in coil 1. The coefficient is known as the *mutual inductance* M_{12}:

$$V_{E2} = M_{12} \frac{dI_1}{dt}, \tag{7}$$

where

$$M_{12} = \frac{N_1 N_2}{\mathcal{R}}, \quad \text{in henrys.} \tag{8}$$

The unit of mutual inductance is given the name *henry*, after Joseph Henry. The mutual inductance is always taken as a positive quantity. As we see from (7), and (14), p. 691,

$$1 \text{ henry} = 1 \text{ volt·sec/amp} = 1 \text{ weber/amp} = 1 \text{ joule/amp}^2. \tag{9}$$

By similar reasoning, we see that if the current in coil 2 is changing there will be an EMF in coil 1 given by

$$V_{E1} = M_{12} \frac{dI_2}{dt}, \tag{10}$$

with the *same* coefficient M_{12} as in (8).

Equations (7) and (10) can be used to define a mutual inductance for any pair of coils, whatever their geometrical configuration and no matter whether or not they are linked by a ferromagnetic circuit. If some of the flux set up by one coil links the second, then a change of current in the first will produce an EMF in the second, and reciprocally.

> The **mutual inductance** of two coils is the EMF induced in one coil by a current changing in the other at the rate of one ampere per second. It is always taken as a positive quantity.

It can be shown rigorously that where no magnetic materials, or only ideal magnetic materials, are involved in the flux paths, one obtains the same value for the mutual inductance no matter which coil is considered to be the primary (the coil in which the current changes) and which the secondary (the coil in which EMF is induced).

Example. *Design a standard* 10-millihenry *mutual inductance by employing a long solenoid as the primary and a winding around its center as the secondary, as indicated in Fig. 16.*

Let us wind the primary long solenoid with gauge No. 19 insulated wire whose diameter is slightly less than 1 mm so that we can wind 1000 turns/ meter. Suppose that from the diameter of the finished primary we compute that the effective cross-sectional area of the solenoid winding is 106 $cm^2 = 0.0106$ m^2. As we have seen in Chap. 32, such a *long* solenoid sets up a uniform field of intensity $(10^{-7}$ w/a·m$)$ $(4\pi nI)$ in the interior of the solenoid, and a field immediately outside the center of the solenoid that can be made as small as one pleases by lengthening the solenoid. Hence one can wind a multi-layered secondary around the center of the solenoid as indicated in Fig. 16, and compute the primary flux linking the secondary from the solenoid formula. We must now compute the number of turns, N_2, required for the secondary.

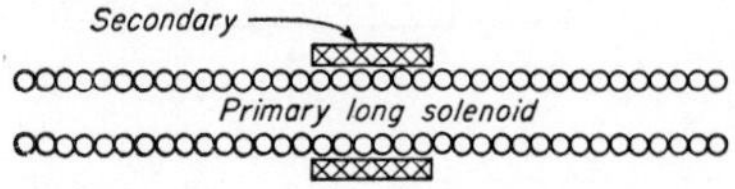

Secondary —

Primary long solenoid

Fig. 16. Schematic diagram of a standard mutual inductance.

Denote the primary current by I_1. The flux threading the secondary is then given by the solenoid formula as

$$\Phi = \mathcal{B}A = (10^{-7} \text{ w/a·m}) \; 4\pi nI_1 A = 10^{-7}\cdot 4\pi \cdot 1000 \times 0.0106 \; I_1 \text{ weber/amp}$$
$$= (13.3 \times 10^{-6} \text{ weber/amp}) \; I_1.$$

Hence $\qquad d\Phi/dt = (13.3 \times 10^{-6} \text{ weber/amp}) \; dI_1/dt.$

The absolute magnitude of the voltage induced in the secondary is given by (4) as

$$V_{E2} = N_2 \; d\Phi/dt = (13.3 \times 10^{-6} \text{ weber/amp}) \; N_2 \; dI_1/dt.$$

By the definition (7) of the mutual inductance,

$$V_{E2} = M_{12} \; dI_1/dt,$$

hence $\qquad M_{12} = 13.3 \times 10^{-6} \; N_2 \text{ weber/amp}.$

Since weber/amp and henry are synonymous, we substitute the desired value $M_{12} = 10^{-2}$ henry to determine

$$N_2 = \frac{10^{-2}}{13.3 \times 10^{-6}} = 752$$

as the number of turns required on the secondary.

7. SELF INDUCTANCE

CONSIDER again coil 1 of Fig. 15. If the current I_1 is changing, an EMF is induced not only in coil 2 but also in coil 1 itself, since the flux through coil 1 is changing. We have $\Phi = N_1 I_1 / \mathcal{R}$, hence

$$V_1 = -N_1 \frac{d\Phi}{dt} = -\frac{N_1^2}{\mathcal{R}} \frac{dI_1}{dt}. \qquad (11)$$

The coefficient is called the *self inductance* in *henrys*, and denoted by $-L_1$:

$$V_{E1} = -L_1 \frac{dI_1}{dt}.$$

The minus sign indicates that the generated EMF is in a direction to oppose the change of current. If the current is increasing, the EMF is in a direction tending to decrease the current, if the current is decreasing, the EMF is in a direction tending to maintain it.

In the same way any circuit, even a simple circuit such as that of Fig. 17, has self inductance. In Fig. 17 a single loop of wire is connected to an AC generator. When the current I has the direction shown, there is a flux linking the circuit in the direction shown. When I increases, Φ increases, and an EMF $V_E = -d\Phi/dt$ is generated in the direction opposing the increase of current.

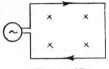

Figure 17

Since the flux Φ is proportional to the current I, $d\Phi/dt \propto dI/dt$, so that we can write $V_E \propto -dI/dt$, or,

$$V_E = -L\frac{dI}{dt}. \qquad (12)$$

> The **self inductance** of a coil is the EMF induced in the coil by the changing magnetic flux it itself sets up when its current is changing at the rate of one ampere per second. It is always taken as a positive quantity.

The self inductance of a simple circuit like Fig. 17 is very small—often negligibly small. The self inductance is greatly increased if the circuit is

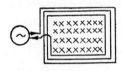

Figure 18

an N-turn 'coil' of the same area, as in Fig. 18. For a given current, each turn of this coil sets up the same flux as in Fig. 17, so that the total flux is multiplied by N. Hence, for given rate of change of current, the EMF generated in *each turn*, $-d\Phi/dt$, is N times as great as in Fig. 17. But the EMF's in the N turns are additive so, for a given rate of change of current, the generated EMF is N^2 times that in Fig. 17. Consequently, the self inductance is N^2 times as great. This dependence of self inductance on the *square* of the number of turns was already found in (11). The self inductance of a coil is greatly increased if the coil is placed around an iron or steel core, because of the great increase in flux.

Self inductance plays a fundamental role in the study of alternating currents, which we shall take up in the next chapter. In this study we shall need equation (13), derived below.

Let us set down carefully the expression for the difference of potential between terminals of a coil or other part of a circuit having self inductance L and resistance R, and carrying a varying current I. Let Fig. 19 define the positive senses of these quantities. Then each coulomb that moves through the circuit from the + to the − terminal loses energy IR to heat but gains energy V_E from the EMF of self inductance. So the *drop* in potential V_T is

$$V_T = IR - V_E.$$

Since, from (12), $V_E = -L\, dI/dt$, we have

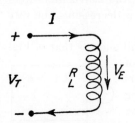

$$V_T = IR + L\frac{dI}{dt}. \qquad (13)$$

Fig. 19. Defining the positive senses of current, I, generated EMF, V_E, and terminal voltage, V_T, for a circuit element.

We can verify the signs in this equation by considering the case where I is positive and increasing (dI/dt positive). Then we must apply to the terminals *more* voltage than is required to overcome the IR-drop, since we must also overcome the EMF of self inductance, which is a back-EMF in this case, opposing the increase in flux and hence opposing the increase in current (V_E is negative in the convention of Fig. 19).

We can now briefly discuss the action of the *transformer* (Fig. 15), which enables one to step AC voltages up and down at will with high efficiency. It is the transformer that makes possible the long-distance transmission of electrical power. When the power is transmitted at very high voltages, 100–300 kv (1 kv = 1000 volts), currents can be kept very small. Hence, IR-drops and I^2R-losses in the lines can be kept small even for very long lines which necessarily have comparatively high R. Since electrical energy can neither be generated nor consumed conveniently at such high voltages, transformers are necessary to step the voltage up and down. Because no DC counterpart of the transformer exists, long-distance transmission of DC is at present entirely impractical.

The transformer has two windings on a common laminated-steel core, as in Fig. 15. The primary winding, of N_1 turns, is where electrical energy is put into the transformer; the secondary winding, of N_2 turns, is where the energy is taken out. The ratio $r = N_2/N_1$ gives the ratio of output voltage to input voltage. This ratio is greater than unity for a step-up transformer, less than unity for a step-down transformer. The winding with the greater number of turns can be made of finer wire than the other, since, being the high-voltage winding, it has to carry less current for the same power. The same transformer will work equally well as a step-up or a step-down transformer, according to which winding is taken as primary, which as secondary.

In the next chapter, we shall discuss the action of the transformer in the case in which power is being drawn from the secondary. Here we shall show that the voltage ratio equals the ratio of the number of turns in the case where the secondary circuit is open, as in Fig. 15. We assume, in the ideal case of no transformer losses, that the resistance of the primary winding is zero. Then, equation (13), the instantaneous terminal voltage of the primary just opposes the generated EMF of self induction and equals

$$V_1 = L_1 \frac{dI_1}{dt} = \frac{N_1^2}{\Re} \frac{dI_1}{dt},$$

by (11).   The EMF generated in the secondary is given by (7) and (8) as

$$V_2 = M_{12} \frac{dI_1}{dt} = \frac{N_1 N_2}{\Re} \frac{dI_1}{dt}.$$

The ratio is at any instant $r = \dfrac{V_2}{V_1} = \dfrac{N_2}{N_1}.$

The fundamental reason for the continued validity of this relationship when current traverses *both* coils is that the induced EMF is proportional to (number of turns) × (rate of change of flux), and the *same* flux traverses *both coils.*

8. ENERGY OF SELF INDUCTANCE

MULTIPLY equation (13) by I to obtain the equation

$$IV_\mathrm{T} \quad = \quad I^2 R \quad + \quad LI \frac{dI}{dt}. \qquad (14)$$

$$\left\{ \begin{matrix} \text{Power} \\ \text{delivered} \\ \text{to circuit} \end{matrix} \right\} = \left\{ \begin{matrix} \text{power} \\ \text{transformed} \\ \text{to heat} \end{matrix} \right\} + \left\{ \begin{matrix} \text{power being} \\ \text{stored in} \\ \text{circuit.} \end{matrix} \right\}$$

When the current is increasing (dI/dt positive), the last term in this equation must represent a rate at which energy is being stored in the circuit, since this amount of power is being delivered to the circuit and is not resulting in the production of heat or mechanical work.   This energy is of some electromagnetic form, and one usually thinks of it as stored in the magnetic field, just as it is possible to think of the energy of a charged condenser as stored in the electric field.   When the current is decreasing (dI/dt negative), more power is transformed to heat than is delivered to the circuit; the magnetic field is giving up its previously stored energy.

Now let us consider the energy balance for a current that increases from 0 at $t=0$ to I_1 at $t=t_1$ and back to 0 at $t=t_2$ as in Fig. 20.   If we

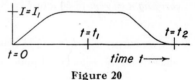

Figure 20

multiply (14) by dt and integrate from $t=0$ to $t=t_1$, we find that

$$\int_0^{t_1} IV_\mathrm{T}\, dt = \int_0^{t_1} I^2 R\, dt + \int_0^{t_1} LI \frac{dI}{dt}\, dt.$$

The last term has the value

$$\int_0^{t_1} LI \frac{dI}{dt}\, dt = L \int_0^{I_1} I\, dI = \tfrac{1}{2} LI_1^2,$$

So that

$$\int_0^{t_1} IV_\mathrm{T}\, dt = \int_0^{t_1} I^2 R\, dt + \tfrac{1}{2} LI_1^2.$$

$$\left\{ \begin{matrix} \text{Energy} \\ \text{supplied} \\ \text{to circuit} \end{matrix} \right\} = \left\{ \begin{matrix} \text{heat de-} \\ \text{veloped} \end{matrix} \right\} + \left\{ \begin{matrix} \text{energy} \\ \text{stored in} \\ \text{circuit.} \end{matrix} \right\}$$

The energy supplied to the circuit is greater than the heat developed by $\frac{1}{2} LI_1^2$, which represents the energy stored in the magnetic field when $I = I_1$. Since I_1 is an arbitrary current value, we conclude that at any current I,

$$\text{energy stored in self inductance} = \frac{1}{2} LI^2. \quad \left\{\begin{array}{c}\text{energy in joules}\\ L \text{ in henrys}\\ I \text{ in amp}\end{array}\right\} \quad (15)$$

This energy is recovered when the current drops back to zero, because if we integrate (14) from t_1 to t_2 (Fig. 20), we find that

$$\int_{t_1}^{t_2} IV_{\mathrm{T}}\, dt = \int_{t_1}^{t_2} I^2 R\, dt + \int_{t_1}^{t_2} LI \frac{dI}{dt}\, dt.$$

The last term now has the value

$$\int_{t_1}^{t_2} LI \frac{dI}{dt}\, dt = L \int_{I_1}^{0} I\, dI = -\frac{1}{2} LI_1^2,$$

so

$$\int_{t_1}^{t_2} IV_{\mathrm{T}}\, dt = \int_{t_1}^{t_2} I^2 R\, dt - \quad \frac{1}{2} LI_1^2.$$

$$\left\{\begin{array}{c}\text{Energy}\\ \text{supplied}\\ \text{to circuit}\end{array}\right\} = \left\{\begin{array}{c}\text{heat de-}\\ \text{veloped}\end{array}\right\} - \left\{\begin{array}{c}\text{energy that had}\\ \text{previously been}\\ \text{stored in circuit.}\end{array}\right\}$$

In this case the heat developed is greater than the energy supplied to the circuit, the difference being the energy of self inductance that had previously been stored in the circuit.

The fact that energy is stored in a circuit containing self inductance and carrying a current is fundamental to a study of oscillating circuits, such as radio oscillators, and to the study of AC circuits.

Example. *How much energy is stored in a magnet of 1-henry self inductance carrying a current of 50 amp?*

From (15),

energy $= \frac{1}{2} LI^2 = \frac{1}{2}$ (1 henry)(50 amp)$^2 = 1250$ henry·amp^2.

Since, from (9), 1 henry $= 1$ joule/amp^2, this becomes

energy $= 1250$ joules.

9. GROWTH AND DECAY OF CURRENT IN INDUCTIVE CIRCUITS

SELF INDUCTANCE gives every circuit a certain degree of sluggishness in the sense that current changes do not instantaneously follow changes in voltage. Consider the battery of voltage V in Fig. 21, which can be connected to the coil by closing switch S_1. With switch S_1 closed and S_2 open, equation (13) gives

$$V = IR + L\, dI/dt, \quad (16)$$

which must hold at any instant. The final value of I is V/R, but I cannot suddenly jump to this value when the switch is closed, because a sudden jump in I would represent an infinite rate of change dI/dt which would set up an infinite back-EMF. Rather, at the instant the switch is closed ($t=0$, say), $I=0$, the first term on the right of (16) is zero, and

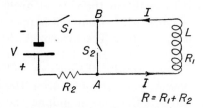

$$V = L\frac{dI}{dt}, \quad \frac{dI}{dt} = \frac{V}{L}. \quad (t=0) \quad (17)$$

The larger the value of L, the slower does the current start increasing at the instant of closing the switch. At later instants, the current increases still less rapidly, since as the IR term in (16) grows, the $L\, dI/dt$ term must decrease. As I approaches the final value V/R, IR approaches V, so that

Fig. 21. (The internal resistance of the battery and the resistance of all leads are negligible compared with R_1 and R_2).

dI/dt approaches zero, and the current reaches its final value only asymptotically, as in Fig. 22.

As is shown by the broken line in Fig. 22, if the current were to go on increasing at its initial rate $dI/dt = V/L$, in amp/sec, it would take a time L/R, in sec, to reach its final value V/R. *The time L/R is known as the time-constant τ of the circuit*, since it gives a measure of the order of magnitude of the build-up time.

Actually, the curve of Fig. 22 is

$$I = \frac{V}{R}(1 - e^{-t/\tau}). \qquad (\tau = L/R) \quad (18)$$

It is easily verified by direct substitution that this function satisfies the differential equation (16), and also that it satisfies the conditions that

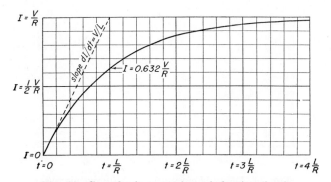

Fig. 22. Growth of current in an inductive circuit.

$I=0$ at $t=0$, $dI/dt = V/L$ at $t=0$, and $I \to V/R$ as $t \to \infty$. Actually, at $t=\tau$, the current has reached only 63.2 per cent ($=1-e^{-1}$) of its final value. It reaches 95 per cent of its final value at $t=3\,\tau$, 99 per cent at $t=4.6\,\tau$, and 99.9 per cent at $t=6.9\,\tau$.

Now suppose that we try to interrupt the current by opening the switch S_1 in Fig. 21. The current cannot instantly drop to zero—in fact, any attempt to make the current drop rapidly will set up whatever voltages, enormous if necessary, are required to maintain the current until the stored energy is dissipated as heat. Ordinarily, what will happen is that across the terminals of the switch S_1 an arc will be drawn which maintains the current while the current dies down. But if the stored energy is large and the switch is pulled too vigorously, the current will flash over through the path of least resistance, perhaps puncturing the windings of the coil itself. Flashover through the person pulling the switch has resulted in death. The moral is, *never* pull a switch that breaks a heavy current through a large inductance; rather, *first shunt the inductance through a suitable resistance.*

Instead of attempting to open switch S_1, let us close switch S_2. Closing this switch is supposed to introduce a perfect short from A to B, so that the voltage across AB becomes 0. (Switch S_1 can be opened shortly after S_2 is closed if it is desired to prevent further discharge of the battery.) V_T in Fig. 19 and equation (13) now is zero, so that in Fig. 21,

$$0 = IR_1 + L\, dI/dt. \tag{19}$$

Let us take $t=0$ as the instant of applying the short and suppose that at this instant $I=I_1$. From (19), the initial rate of decrease of current is

$$\frac{dI}{dt} = -\frac{R_1}{L} I_1. \qquad (t=0)$$

Again, if the current continued to decrease at this rate, it would drop to zero in a time $\tau_1 = L/R_1$, which is known as the *time-constant for decay.*

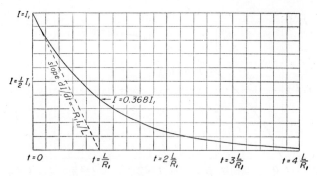

Fig. 23. Decay of current in an inductive circuit.

The actual decay of the current is shown in the curve of Fig. 23, which has the equation

$$I = I_1\, e^{-t/\tau_1}. \qquad (\tau_1 = L/R_1) \quad (20)$$

This equation is seen to satisfy the differential equation (19) and the conditions $I = I_1$ when $t = 0$, $I \rightarrow 0$ when $t \rightarrow \infty$. The curve of Fig. 23 is just the curve of Fig. 22 upside down.

Example. *If, in Fig. 21, $L = 120$ henrys, $R_1 = 60$ ω, $R_2 = 60$ ω, and $V = 120$ v, the switch S_1 is closed at $t = 0$, and the shorting switch S_2 is closed at $t = 5$ sec, determine the time-constants of growth and decay, and plot the current through the inductance as a function of time.*

In this case, $R = R_1 + R_2 = 120$ ω. The time-constant for growth is $\tau = L/R = 1$ sec; the time-constant for decay is $\tau_1 = L/R_1 = 2$ sec. The maximum current would be $V/R = 1$ amp, but from (18) we find that at $t = 5$ sec $= 5\,\tau$, the current has built up to only $(1 - e^{-5})\,V/R = (1 - 0.007)\,V/R = 0.993$ amp. The plot of the growth of current as given by (18) is shown in

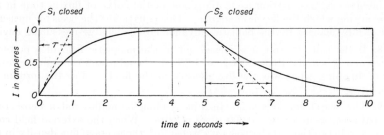

Fig. 24. Growth and decay in an inductive circuit.

Fig. 24, as is the plot of the decay from the maximum of 0.993 amp that is given by (20) with $I_1 = 0.993$ amp.

PROBLEMS

1. A stiff piece of wire 2.4 m long is moved vertically upward in the earth's magnetic field, whose horizontal northward component is 2×10^{-5} weber/m². The wire is horizontal, points east and west, and moves at 50 m/sec. What is the difference of potential between the ends, and which end is positive?

Ans: 0.0024 v; west end.

2. If the wire of Prob. 1 moves horizontally toward the north at the same speed, and the vertical component of the earth's field is 5×10^{-5} weber/m² downward, what is the difference of potential between the ends, and which end is positive?

3. In Fig. 2, let $l = 0.6$ m, $v = 3$ m/sec, $\mathcal{B} = 1.5$ weber/m², and $R = 5$ ohms. (a) What is the generated EMF? (b) What is the current? (c) What is the power expended in heating the resistor? (d) What is the magnitude of the magnetic force? of the applied force? (e) What is the rate at which the applied force does work?   Ans: (a) 2.7 v; (b) 0.54 amp; (c) 1.46 w; (d) 0.486 nt; (e) 1.46 w.

4. In Fig. 2, if $l = 0.6$ m, $\mathcal{B} = 0.8$ weber/m², $R = 9$ ohms, and $F = 0.2$ nt, find (a) the current, (b) the EMF, (c) the speed, (d) the rate of doing work, and (e) the rate of heat generation.

5. A 25-turn coil of the type shown in Fig. 6 has an area of 1 cm². If this coil is moved toward a magnet as in Fig. 5 in such a way that the mean flux density through the coil changes at the rate of 0.3 weber/m²·sec, what voltage is induced in the coil?   Ans: 0.75 mv.

6. A 'harbor loop' is a coil of wire of extensive area laid out on the floor of a harbor entrance to detect the entrance of submarines by means of the voltage induced by the submarine's natural magnetism.

(a) If the flux through the loop changes at the maximum rate of 0.008 weber/ sec as the submarine passes over the near side of the loop, what is the maximum voltage induced in a 50-turn loop?

(b) If the earth's vertical field may be expected to vary as fast as 0.3×10^{-9} weber/m²·sec, what is the maximum area the harbor loop can have if the voltage generated by fluctuations in the earth's field is to be less than 1% of the voltage generated by the submarine in (a)?

7. Show that if the flux linking the coil of Fig. 6 changes in any manner from Φ_1 to Φ_2, then the *charge* that flows through the circuit of total resistance R is given by $Q = N(\Phi_2 - \Phi_1)/R$, in coul. This relation is derived by integrating $I\,dt$ and involves no assumption as to the shape of the curve of flux *vs* time in the period during which the flux is changing. This equation is the basis for measurement of flux changes by the ballistic galvanometer—a charge-measuring device.

8. If the coil of Prob. 5 is jerked out of the magnetic field of a powerful magnet and it is found that a charge of 1.25×10^{-4} coul passes through the resistance of 40 ohms, what was the flux density in the field? (Use the formula of Prob. 7.)

9. The 'search coil' of a magnetic mine is a long permalloy rod of 4 cm² cross-sectional area, wound with 50,000 turns of wire. When the external field component parallel to the rod changes by x weber/m², the average flux density in the rod changes by $5000\,x$ weber/m², provided the externally applied field is sufficiently small—a condition adequately satisfied by the earth's field and by ships' fields. When a ship passes over the mine, the field component parallel to the rod changes by 5×10^{-7} weber/m² during a period of 25 sec. Find the average voltage induced in the search coil during this period.   Ans: 2.00 mv.

10. If the rod of the magnetic mine of Prob. 9 is wound with 100,000 turns of wire and if the field component parallel to the rod changes by 150×10^{-7} weber/m² during a period of 10 sec when a high-speed battleship passes over, find the average induced voltage during this period.

11. Using equation (2), show that the EMF generated by the prototype generator of Fig. 7 is given by $V_E = 2\pi f \cdot \mathcal{B} wl \cdot \sin 2\pi ft$, in agreement with (5).

12. Let a resistance R be connected between A and B in Fig. 7. Neglect the internal resistance of the generator. For a constant angular velocity ω, determine at each instant (angle) (a) the current I; (b) the torque L required to turn the coil; (c) the power $L\omega$ required. (d) Verify that the power in (c) is equal to IV_E as is required by the definition of EMF.

13. If the mutual inductance of the transformer of Fig. 15 is 0.5 henry, find the expression for the voltage induced in the secondary when the primary carries the alternating current $I_1 = 0.6 \sin 120\pi t$ amp.   Ans: $V_{E2} = 36\pi \cos 120\pi t$ volts.

14. If the transformer of Fig. 15 has 200 turns on the primary, 50 turns on the secondary, and a reluctance of 2×10^5 amp-turn/weber, what is the mutual inductance in henrys?

15. If the transformer of Fig. 15 has 200 turns on the primary, 50 turns on the secondary, and an iron path of mean length 110 cm, cross section 10 cm × 10 cm, and permeability 1300, what is the mutual inductance?   Ans: 0.149 henry.

16. A small permalloy toroid has a cross-sectional area of 1 cm², a mean circumference of 10 cm, and a permeability of 50,000 so long as the flux density is small. It has a primary winding of 50 turns and a secondary winding of 100 turns of very fine wire. What is the mutual inductance? If the primary current changes at the rate of 1 milliamp/sec, what voltage is induced in the secondary?

17. A *long* air-core solenoid has a cross-sectional area of 400 cm^2 and is wound with 30 turns per cm. Around the center of the solenoid is wound a secondary coil of 150 turns of wire. (a) What is the mutual inductance between the solenoid winding and the secondary coil? (b) If the solenoid current changes at the rate of 1 amp/sec, what voltage is generated in the secondary winding? (c) If the secondary winding is connected to a source of current and the current in this winding changes at the rate of 1 amp/sec, what voltage is induced in the solenoid winding? Ans: (a) 22.6 millihenrys; 22.6 mv; 22.6 mv.

18. Design a toroid, wound on a non-magnetic core, that will serve as a 1-millihenry self-inductance standard.

19. An induction coil such as is used to set off the spark in an automobile spark plug consists of a primary coil, and a secondary coil of very many more turns of finer wire, both wound around a straight iron core. The primary normally carries a current, which is broken at each instant that a spark is desired. If the primary winding has 200 turns and normally carries a current of 5 amp, and if this current falls to zero in 0.002 sec when the circuit is broken, what must be the mutual inductance if an average of 20,000 v is to be induced in the secondary? If this current sets up a total flux in the core of 10^{-3} weber, how many turns are required on the secondary? Ans: 8 henrys; 40,000.

20. How much energy, over and above that expended in heat, is required to set up a current of 15 amp through a coil of self inductance 0.4 henry?

21. What is the self inductance of the primary winding of the transformer described in Prob. 15? Of the secondary winding? Ans: 0.594, 0.0371 henry.

22. What is the self inductance of the primary winding of the transformer described in Prob. 14? Of the secondary winding?

23. Show that if the total flux linking a coil is Φ when the current is I, then $L = N\Phi/I$, in henrys. Assume ideal magnetic materials.

24. If a current of 5 amp in a 120-turn concentrated coil sets up a total flux of 5×10^{-4} weber linking the coil, find the self inductance of the coil.

25. In Fig. 21, if $R_1 = 2$ ohms, $R_2 = 0.5$ ohm, and $L = 0.8$ henry, what is the time-constant for current growth? for decay? Ans: 0.32 sec; 0.40 sec.

26. In Fig. 21, if $R_1 = 50$ ohms, $R_2 = 1$ ohm, and $L = 100$ henrys, what are the time-constants for current growth and decay?

27. Consider Fig. 25. Again let $R = R_1 + R_2$.

(a) With switch S_2 open, switch S_1 is closed at $t = 0$. To what value does the current I build up, and with what time-constant?

(b) After I has built up to its final value, switch S_2 is closed, and then switch S_1 is opened. What is the time-constant involved in the decrease of I to zero?

Ans: (a) V/R_1, L/R_1; (b) L/R.

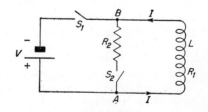

Figure 25

28. In Prob. 27, let S_2 be closed at $t = 2$ sec, S_1 opened at $t = 3$ sec. Take $L = 120$ henrys, $R_1 = 60\ \omega$, $R_2 = 60\ \omega$, $V = 120$ v.

(a) Sketch the plot of I as a function of time.

(b) On the same plot sketch the current through R_2 from B to A.

29. In the circuit described in Prob. 25, and with $V = 6.0$ v, find the current 0.5 sec after switch S_1 is closed. At this time, how much energy is stored in the circuit?   Ans: 1.90 amp; 1.44 joules.

30. In the circuit of Fig. 21 with $V = 12$ v, $R_1 = 0.2$ ohm, $R_2 = 1.8$ ohms, and $L = 2.0$ henry, find the voltage across R_2 after switch S_1 has been closed for 0.4 sec. At this time, what is the power being dissipated in the circuit?

31. Equation (15) gives the expression $\frac{1}{2} LI^2$ for the total energy of self inductance of a coil, and (11) gives the value $N^2/\mathfrak{R}$ for the self inductance. Using these two relations along with the magnetic circuit formula $\Phi = \text{MMF}/\mathfrak{R}$, derive an expression in terms of $\mathfrak{B}$ and μ for the energy per unit volume in the interior of a toroid, if one considers the energy to be stored in the region of magnetic field.   Ans: $(10^7 \text{ a·m/w}) \, \mathfrak{B}^2/8\pi\mu$.

32. The *betatron* (Fig. 26) is a device invented by Kerst for giving extremely high kinetic energies to electrons by making use of electromagnetic induction.

Fig. 26. The betatron [*courtesy of Prof. Donald Kerst*]. The evacuated porcelain 'doughnut' described in Prob. 33 is visible in white at the center of the picture between the poles of the magnet.

In order to understand its operation, consider first a copper ring of radius r. (a) What is the induced EMF in this ring when the magnetic flux through the ring is changing at the rate $d\Phi/dt$? (b) Associated with this induced EMF, there is an electric intensity inside the ring; what are the magnitude and direction of the electric intensity vector? (c) What is the magnitude of the force exerted on a free electron inside the copper ring? (d) How much work would the electric field do in moving an electron entirely around the ring back to its starting point? (e) What becomes of this work?   Ans: (a) $d\Phi/dt$; (b) $(d\Phi/dt)/2\pi r$; (c) $e\,(d\Phi/dt)/2\pi r$; (d) $e\,(d\Phi/dt)$.

33. If the copper ring of Prob. 32 were removed and replaced by a hollow glass or porcelain ring or 'doughnut,' the changing magnetic flux would still produce an electric field $\mathcal{E} = (d\Phi/dt)/2\pi r$ inside the doughnut. This electric field would still exert a tangential force $e\,(d\Phi/dt)/2\pi r$ on an electron inside the tube. If the electron could be constrained to move in a circular path of radius r, the field would do work $e\,(d\Phi/dt)$ as the electron moved completely around the evacuated doughnut. (a) Since there is no resistance to the electron's motion inside the doughnut, what becomes of the work done? (b) What is the increase in the kinetic energy of the electron after it makes N traversals of its circular 'orbit' inside the doughnut?

Ans: (b) $Ne \, (d\Phi/dt)$.

34. In an actual betatron, electrons already moving with almost the speed of light are 'injected' into the evacuated doughnut and are constrained to move in a circular path by a suitably arranged magnetic field. These electrons are subjected for a time Δt to the electric field produced while the magnetic flux at the center of the doughnut is changing and are then ejected from their stable orbits and strike a target. Consider a doughnut of mean radius 50 cm; electrons moving with almost the speed of light enter the doughnut, the flux through the 'hole in the doughnut' increases at an average rate of 24 webers/sec for $\frac{1}{240}$ sec, and then the electrons are ejected. (a) To what electric intensity is each electron subjected? (b) How much work is done on each electron during each revolution around the doughnut? (c) Assuming that each electron maintains a speed approximately equal to the speed of light (see sec. 3, Chap. 38, for justification of this assumption), compute the number of revolutions described before ejection. (d) How much does the kinetic energy of each electron increase before ejection?

Ans: (a) 7.64 v/m, (b) 24 ev, (c) 3.98×10^5, (d) 9.55 Mev.

35. In Fig. 25, let $L=120$ henrys, $R_1=60 \, \omega$, $V=120$ v. With S_1 closed and S_2 open, the current I has built up to its final value; then, instead of closing the shunting switch S_2, an attempt is made to pull S_1. An arc is drawn between the blades of S_1 that has effective resistance 2000 ω. What is the initial voltage between the blades of S_1? What is the initial terminal voltage of the coil?

CHAPTER 35

ALTERNATING-CURRENT CIRCUITS

HAVING STUDIED electromagnetic induction, we are now in a position to determine the current in circuits containing resistance, inductance, and capacitance when alternating voltages are applied. Our study of AC circuits will be applicable not only to ordinary power circuits but also to circuits carrying audio and radio frequencies in connection with telephone, radio, and various other applications of electronics. We conclude the chapter with a discussion of some of the electrical measuring instruments suitable for use in AC power circuits.

1. THE VECTOR DIAGRAM

IN AC-CIRCUIT theory we are concerned with currents and voltages that vary sinusoidally with time at a definite fixed frequency f. For ordinary commercial AC in the United States, the usual value is $f = 60$ sec^{-1}, commonly expressed as $f = 60$ cycles/sec or $f = 60 \sim$. If the function $A(t)$ represents such a current or voltage, it will vary with time according to

$$A(t) = A_M \sin 2\pi ft \tag{1}$$

where A_M represents the maximum value of the sinusoidal function $A(t)$. (For $f = 60 \sim$, $2\pi f = 377$ sec^{-1}.) A plot of the curve (1) is given in Fig. 1. A complete oscillation occurs in the time $1/f$ ($\frac{1}{60}$ sec for $60 \sim$).

In (1), it is customary to think of $2\pi ft$ as an angle in radians, whose sine must be looked up. It is useful to express the equivalent angle in degrees; one speaks in this case of 'electrical degrees.' The various times are expressed in *electrical degrees* as indicated on Fig. 1, and we shall follow the custom of marking the abscissas of our plots only with electrical degrees, the understanding being that these are really plots against time, with the time interval $1/f$ represented by 360 electrical degrees. This usage is very convenient.

Another useful aid in dealing with such sinusoidally varying quantities as $A(t)$ in (1) is to note that $A(t)$ can be thought of at any instant as the *vertical projection* of the rotating vector A, of length A_M, drawn at the left of Fig. 1. A is in the position shown by the heavy arrow at $t = 0$, and it rotates counterclockwise at frequency f. At time t, A has rotated through an angle $\phi = 2\pi ft$, and the *vertical projection* of A is

$$A_M \sin\phi = A_M \sin 2\pi ft.$$

This is seen to be just equal to the expression (1).

At any instant the ordinate of the sine curve of Fig. 1 is equal to the vertical projection of the rotating vector at the left of Fig. 1.

We note that the 'vectors' employed in *vector diagrams* such as Fig. 1 are not true vectors of direct physical significance like those discussed in

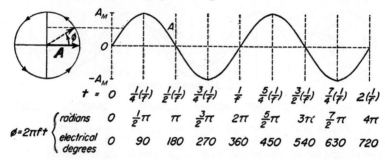

Fig. 1. Representation of the sinusoidally varying quantity in equation (1).

Chap. 1. These 'vectors' are radius vectors in a useful but purely geometrical diagram.

In AC circuits the sine curves representing current and voltage are ordinarily *out of phase*, and the *phase angle* (in electrical degrees) by which

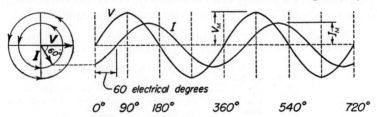

Fig. 2. The current *lags* 60 electrical degrees behind the voltage.

the current leads or lags behind the voltage is an important quantity. Figures 2 and 3 will explain the meanings of the terms used in the preceding sentence. In Fig. 2 are plotted the voltage and current curves:

$$V(t) = V_M \sin 2\pi ft, \qquad I(t) = I_M \sin(2\pi ft - \tfrac{1}{3}\pi). \qquad \left(\begin{smallmatrix}\text{current}\\\text{lagging}\end{smallmatrix}\right)$$

The current is said to *lag behind* the voltage by $\tfrac{1}{3}\pi$ rad, or by a *phase angle* of 60 electrical degrees, because the current reaches its positive maximum of $\tfrac{1}{6}$ cycle *later* than the voltage, passes through zero $\tfrac{1}{6}$ cycle *later*, reaches its negative maximum $\tfrac{1}{6}$ cycle *later*, and so on. At the left of Fig. 2 we place, at $t=0$, a vector V like that in Fig. 1 and a vector I, of length

I_M, 60° *behind* $\mathbf{V}$. If we imagine that both these vectors rotate at frequency f, then at any instant the ordinate of the V-curve is the vertical projection of the vector $\mathbf{V}$ and the ordinate of the I-curve is the vertical projection of the vector $\mathbf{I}$. Similarly, in Fig. 3 we give plots and vector diagrams of

$$V(t) = V_M \sin 2\pi ft, \qquad I(t) = I_M \sin(2\pi ft + \tfrac{1}{6}\pi), \qquad \binom{\text{current}}{\text{leading}}$$

in which the current *leads* the voltage by $\tfrac{1}{6}\pi$ rad, or by a phase angle of 30 electrical degrees.

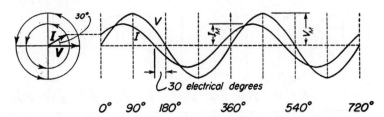

Fig. 3. The current *leads* the voltage by 30 electrical degrees.

The diagrams at the left of Figs. 1, 2, and 3 are known as *vector diagrams*. Properly interpreted, these vector diagrams contain all the information contained in the plots at the right or in the equations of the text, except that the frequency of rotation of the vectors must be specified.

Perhaps the greatest advantage of using the vector diagram is that it leads to a very convenient way of carrying out the arithmetic involved in the trigonometric addition of two sinusoidal curves of different amplitudes and different phases, as illustrated in the following example.

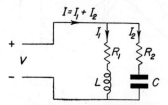

Fig. 4. A parallel AC circuit. The arrows and + and − signs do not give the actual directions of current and voltage, which are alternating, but define the directions and polarity for which I_1, I_2, I, and V are to be considered as positive.

Example. *Consider the circuit of Fig. 4. Let the alternating voltage be*

$$V(t) = 160 \sin(377 \ \text{sec}^{-1} t) \ \text{volts},$$

corresponding to 60 ∼. *As we shall see later, the current in an inductive path will in general lag behind the voltage, so let*

$$I_1(t) = 3 \sin(377 \ \text{sec}^{-1} t - \tfrac{1}{6}\pi) \ \text{amp},$$

corresponding to a phase lag of 30°. *Generally, the current in a capacitive path will lead the voltage, so let*

$$I_2(t) = 4 \sin(377 \ \text{sec}^{-1} t + \tfrac{1}{3}\pi) \ \text{amp},$$

corresponding to a lead angle of 60°. *Find the amplitude and phase of the line current*

I, *which at every instant is the sum* $I(t) = I_1(t) + I_2(t)$.

This problem can be solved by pure trigonometry, but it is much more convenient to use an argument from the vector diagram. The student should learn to understand the following procedure thoroughly before proceeding to later sections because we shall frequently omit plotted curves and merely give vector diagrams. He must clearly visualize the meaning of the vector diagram: that the vectors are drawn to represent the situation at a particular instant $(t=0)$, that the vectors rotate counterclockwise with frequency f, in rev/sec, and that at any instant the magnitude of each quantity is given by the *vertical projection* of its representative vector.

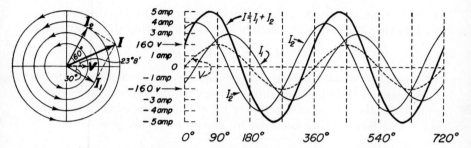

Fig. 5. I_1+I_2 is represented by the rotating vector $I=I_1+I_2$.

In Fig. 5 are plotted V, I_1, and I_2 as given by the above equations. The sum I_1+I_2 is also plotted. On the left are shown the positions at $t=0$ of the rotating vectors whose vertical projections give the values of I_1 and I_2. We shall show that *the sum of I_1 and I_2 is represented by the vertical component of a rotating vector I that is the vector sum of the rotating vectors I_1 and I_2.* If we let the vectors I_1, I_2, and I, where

$$I=I_1+I_2, \tag{i}$$

all rotate together, equation (i) will remain true at every instant. Since the vertical projection of the vector sum of two vectors is the sum of their vertical projections, we shall have at every instant

$$I_Y = I_{1Y} + I_{2Y}.$$

But it is just these vertical projections that represent the current values I, I_1, and I_2 at each instant, hence the statement in italics is valid.

In our case, then, we find the vector representing I by taking the vector sum of I_1 and I_2. With all quantities in amperes,

$I_{1X}=3\cos30°=2.598$	$I_{1Y}=-3\sin30°=-1.500$
$I_{2X}=4\cos60°=2.000$	$I_{2Y}=\ \ \ 4\sin60°=\ \ \ 3.464$
$I_X=\quad\quad\ \ \overline{4.598}$	$I_Y=\quad\quad\quad\ \ \overline{1.964}$

whence,   magnitude of $I=5.000$,   direction of $I=23°\!.1$ above X-axis.

In the equation for I, the magnitude of I appears as the coefficient of the sine; the lead angle $23°\!.1=0.404$ rad appears with $+$ sign as in Fig. 3:

$$I=5.000\sin(377\ \text{sec}^{-1}\,t+0.404)\ \text{amp}.$$

The type of reasoning used in the above example gives a very simple and straightforward scheme for finding the sum of two sinusoidal curves:

The rotating vector that represents the sum of two sinusoidal curves is the vector sum of the rotating vectors that represent the two curves individually.

2. POWER IN AC CIRCUITS; EFFECTIVE VALUES OF VOLTAGE AND CURRENT

THE VOLTAGE across a pure resistance R carrying alternating current $I = I_M \sin 2\pi ft$ is, at any instant

$$V_R = R\,I = R\,I_M \sin 2\pi ft = V_{RM} \sin 2\pi ft, \quad \text{where} \quad V_{RM} = RI_M.$$

At any instant, the rate at which energy is being supplied to the resistance, which in turn is the rate at which heat is being developed, is the product

$$V_R\,I = V_{RM}\,I_M \sin^2 2\pi ft.$$

This quantity, which is never negative, is called the *instantaneous power*.

We can get the whole amount of energy supplied during one cycle by multiplying the instantaneous power by dt and integrating from $t=0$ to $t=1/f$, which is the time occupied by one cycle. This gives

$$\text{energy per cycle} = \int_0^{1/f} V_{RM}\,I_M \sin^2 2\pi ft\,dt = V_{RM}\,I_M \int_0^{1/f} \sin^2 2\pi ft\,dt = \frac{V_{RM}\,I_M}{2f},$$

as may readily be verified by calculus formulas. The whole energy supplied per second, which we call the *power* and denote by P, is then obtained by multiplying the energy per cycle by f, the number of cycles per second:

$$P = \frac{V_{RM}\,I_M}{2} = \frac{I_M^2\,R}{2} = \frac{V_{RM}^2}{2R}. \tag{2}$$

Note that the power does not come smoothly, but in $2f$ spurts per second; P in (2) represents a time-average power.

The occurrence of the 2 in the denominators of the formulas in (2) makes these formulas look different from the corresponding DC formulas. To make the AC power formulas similar in form to the DC, it is customary in specifying AC voltages or currents to give so-called *effective* values V_0 and I_0 rather than maximum values V_M and I_M.

The **effective value** of an alternating voltage or current is defined as $1/\sqrt{2}$ times the maximum value. When AC voltages and currents are specified without qualification, it is always *effective* values that are implied.

Thus $$V_0 = \frac{V_M}{\sqrt{2}}, \quad I_0 = \frac{I_M}{\sqrt{2}}.$$

In our particular case, $V_{R0} = V_{RM}/\sqrt{2}$. The $\sqrt{2}$ is introduced into these definitions so that the power formulas (2) become

$$P = V_{R0}\,I_0 = I_0^2\,R = V_{R0}^2/R, \tag{3}$$

exactly the form of the DC formulas.

When we say that the power company supplies 120 volts AC, we always mean 120 volts effective: $V_0 = 120$ volts; $V_M = 120\sqrt{2}$ volts $= 170$

volts.   Hence, a 120-volt, 60-$\sim$ power circuit has instantaneous voltage

$$V = 170 \sin(377 \text{ sec}^{-1} t) \text{ v.}$$

The fact that the maximum voltage is 170 shows why a 120-volt AC circuit is more dangerous and will give a greater shock than a 120-volt DC circuit; it will send a greater maximum current through the body.

The formula $V_{RM} = RI_M$ becomes $V_{R0}\sqrt{2} = RI_0\sqrt{2}$, or simply

$$V_{R0} = RI_0. \tag{4}$$

Hence, a 40-watt, 120-volt lamp bulb, which has a resistance of 360 ohms, will draw $\frac{1}{3}$ amp DC on 120 volts DC or $\frac{1}{3}$ amp *effective* AC on 120 volts *effective* AC, taking 40 watts of power in either case.   By using effective values in the AC case, we make the ratings of purely resistive circuits, such as lamp bulbs, completely interchangeable between DC and AC.

For the general AC circuit containing inductance and capacitance in addition to resistance, power considerations are more involved.   The instantaneous power supplied by the line is $V I$, where we write

$$V = \sqrt{2}\,V_0 \sin(2\pi ft + \theta), \qquad I = \sqrt{2}\,I_0 \sin 2\pi ft,$$

to indicate that in general V and I are not in phase.   The curve VI is shown in Fig. 6 for the particular case of an inductive circuit with

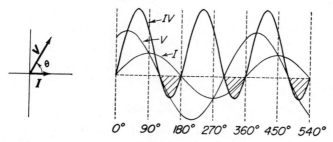

Fig. 6. The product VI of two sinusoidal curves. This is itself a sinusoidal curve of double frequency with axis of ordinates displaced.

$\theta = \frac{1}{3}\pi$ or 60 electrical degrees.   We note that part of the time VI is negative, indicating that during these periods of time (indicated by cross hatching) *energy is being delivered to the line* rather than being received from it.   The same phenomenon occurs in a capacitive circuit, where the current is leading and θ is negative.   In each case during part of the cycle energy that has previously been stored in the inductance or capacitance is being delivered back to the line.

We can integrate the curve VI by straightforward trigonometry and calculus to obtain the average power, but it is easier and more instructive to do the computation as follows: Resolve the rotating vector V in Fig. 6 into two component vectors, V_1 in phase with I, and V_2 ninety degrees out of phase with I.   Then, at any instant

$$V(t) = V_1(t) + V_2(t),$$

where $V_1(t)$ represents a sinusoidal function of time in phase with the sinusoidal function $I(t)$, whereas $V_2(t)$ represents a sinusoidal function 90° out of phase with I.   Then the instantaneous power

$$V I = V_1 I + V_2 I,$$

and the energy supplied in one cycle is

$$\int_0^{1/f} V I \, dt = \int_0^{1/f} V_1 I \, dt + \int_0^{1/f} V_2 I \, dt. \tag{5}$$

Now a glance at Fig. 7 shows that the integral of the product of two sinusoidal curves 90° out of phase vanishes over any cycle, or for that matter, over any half-cycle.   Hence, the last

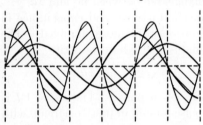

integral in (5) vanishes.   The first integral, of the product of two sinusoidal curves in phase, is like the one we evaluated on p. 756, and gives

$$\text{energy per cycle} = V_{1\text{M}} I_\text{M}/2f.$$

Fig. 7. The product of two sinusoidal curves 90° out of phase is a sinusoidal curve of double frequency. (The time between vertical broken lines is ¼ cycle.)

This value, when multiplied by the number of cycles per second, gives the average power

$$P = V_{1\text{M}} I_\text{M}/2.$$

To express this in terms of line voltage, we notice, from the vector diagram of Fig. 6, that

$$V_{1\text{M}} = V_\text{M} \cos\theta;$$

hence $$P = \tfrac{1}{2} V_\text{M} I_\text{M} \cos\theta = V_0 I_0 \cos\theta. \tag{6}$$

The factor $\cos\theta$ in (6) is called the *power factor*.

> The **power factor** is the factor by which $V_0 I_0$ (in volt·amperes) must be multiplied in order to get power in watts.

As we shall see later, a wattmeter measures actual power P, so power factor can be determined by a simultaneous reading of a wattmeter, an ammeter, and a voltmeter.   This determination is done automatically by a *power-factor meter*.

3. CIRCUIT ELEMENTS CONTAINING CAPACITANCE AND RESISTANCE

IT IS POSSIBLE for a circuit such as that of Fig. 8 to carry an alternating current.   No constant DC could flow in Fig. 8, because charge cannot move through the condenser, but with an alternating current in the lines to the condenser, an alternating charge can pile up on the condenser plates, with the voltage across the plates varying sinusoidally.

Our problem is to find the voltage V required to set up a given alternating current I in the circuit of Fig. 8. The alternating voltage V will be at any instant the sum

$$V = V_C + V_R,$$

where V_C is the voltage across the condenser and V_R that across the resistor.

Let us suppose that the charge on the condenser varies according to the formula

$$Q = Q_M \sin(2\pi ft - \tfrac{1}{2}\pi),$$

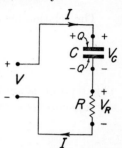

Fig. 8. Circuit containing capacitance and resistance. Arrows and + and − signs define positive senses.

as in Fig. 9. The phase angle is arbitrarily chosen here as $-\tfrac{1}{2}\pi$ in order to make the subsequent discussion more convenient. Then the voltage V_C across the condenser will be

$$V_C = Q/C = (Q_M/C)\sin(2\pi ft - \tfrac{1}{2}\pi) = V_{CM}\sin(2\pi ft - \tfrac{1}{2}\pi),$$

where $V_{CM} = Q_M/C$ is the maximum value of the voltage.

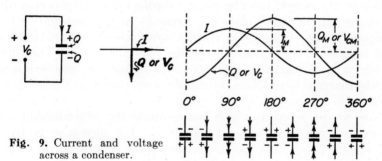

Fig. 9. Current and voltage across a condenser.

The current I entering the condenser equals the rate dQ/dt at which charge is building up. Therefore,

$$I = dQ/dt = 2\pi f Q_M \cos(2\pi ft - \tfrac{1}{2}\pi) = 2\pi f Q_M \sin 2\pi ft$$

since $\cos(x - \tfrac{1}{2}\pi) = \sin x$. If we write this expression as

$$I = I_M \sin 2\pi ft, \tag{7}$$

we have

$$I_M = 2\pi f Q_M = 2\pi f C\, V_{CM}. \tag{8}$$

Thus, if the current in Fig. 9 is $I = I_M \sin 2\pi ft$, the voltage will be

$$V_C = V_{CM}\sin(2\pi ft - \tfrac{1}{2}\pi). \tag{9}$$

The current into a condenser leads the voltage across the condenser by 90 electrical degrees.

The relation between I_M and V_{CM} is given by (8):

$$V_{CM} = \left(\frac{1}{2\pi fC}\right) I_M. \tag{10}$$

This relation is analogous to Ohm's law. The factor $(1/2\pi fC)$ is called the *capacitive reactance*, and is denoted by X_C:

$$V_{CM} = X_C I_M, \quad \text{where} \quad X_C = \frac{1}{2\pi fC}. \tag{11}$$

We can readily verify that the dimensions of X_C are ohms, as they must be according to (10).

> The **capacitive reactance** of a condenser is $X_C = 1/2\pi fC$, and is measured in ohms.

That it is reasonable for the current into a condenser to *lead* the voltage by 90° can be seen from the set of little diagrams below the plotted curves in Fig. 9. These diagrams indicate schematically the actual magnitudes and directions of the current and of the charge or voltage at various times. Evidently, the current must be positive during the whole period in which the charge on the upper plate goes from its maximum negative to its maximum positive value. The current is zero when the charge is a maximum because at this instant the charge is not changing. The current reaches its positive maximum 90° before the charge does because it is then that the charge is increasing most rapidly, even though at this instant the charge itself is zero.

Now we can return to Fig. 8 and complete the determination of the relation between current I and voltage V. For current given by (7), the voltage V_C across the condenser will be given by (9) and (11), and the voltage V_R across the resistance will be given by

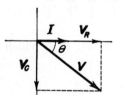

$$V_R = R I = R I_M \sin 2\pi ft = V_{RM} \sin 2\pi ft, \tag{12}$$

where

$$V_{RM} = R I_M. \tag{13}$$

Fig. 10. Vector diagram for the circuit of Fig. 8.

At any instant, the line voltage $V = V_C + V_R$. The determination of V involves the addition of two out-of-phase sinusoidal curves for V_C and V_R. This addition is accomplished in the vector diagram of Fig. 10, in which we see that V_M, the maximum value of V, is given by

$$V_M = \sqrt{V_{CM}^2 + V_{RM}^2}, \tag{14}$$

and that the angle by which the current I leads the voltage V is

$$\theta = \arctan(V_{CM}/V_{RM}). \tag{15}$$

Putting into (14) and (15) the values of V_{CM} and V_{RM} given by (11) and (13), and dividing by $\sqrt{2}$ to get effective values, we find that

$$V_0 = \sqrt{X_C^2 + R^2}\, I_0; \qquad \theta = \arctan(X_C/R). \tag{16}$$

It is customary to write $\qquad V_0 = Z\, I_0, \tag{17}$

where Z is known as the *impedance* of the circuit. In this case

$$Z = \sqrt{X_C^2 + R^2}, \quad \text{in ohms.} \tag{18}$$

The **impedance** of any AC circuit is the ratio of effective voltage to effective current, and is measured in ohms.

As $f \to 0$, $X_C \to \infty$, and $Z \to \infty$; the formulas for any AC circuit reduce to those for a DC circuit as $f \to 0$, and the infinite impedance is consistent with the fact that a circuit containing a condenser will not permit the passage of a direct current.

Example. *Compute the capacitive reactance of a 1-μf condenser at 6, 60, and 600 cycles/sec. Compute the impedance of a circuit containing a 1-μf condenser and a 2000-ohm resistor in series at these same three frequences.*

The capacitive reactance X_C given by (11) decreases as f increases. Direct substitution shows that the reactance of a 1-μf condenser is

$$X_C = 26{,}500 \text{ ohms} \quad \text{at} \quad 6 \sim,$$
$$X_C = 2{,}650 \text{ ohms} \quad \text{at} \quad 60 \sim,$$
$$X_C = 265 \text{ ohms} \quad \text{at} \; 600 \sim.$$

For the 1-μf condenser connected in series with $R = 2000$ ohms, substitution in (18) and (16) shows that the impedance of the circuit and the angle of lead are

$$Z = 26{,}600 \text{ ohms}, \quad \theta = 86°, \quad \text{at} \quad 6 \sim;$$
$$Z = 3{,}330 \text{ ohms}, \quad \theta = 53°, \quad \text{at} \quad 60 \sim;$$
$$Z = 2{,}020 \text{ ohms}, \quad \theta = 7°.5, \quad \text{at} \; 600 \sim.$$

The impedance at $6 \sim$ is almost entirely due to the reactance of the condenser, with $Z \approx X_C$, whereas the impedance at $600 \sim$ is almost entirely due to the resistance, with $Z \approx R$. At low frequencies the circuit appears largely capacitive, with lead angle close to 90°, whereas at high frequencies it appears largely resistive, with lead angle close to zero.

4. CIRCUIT ELEMENTS CONTAINING INDUCTANCE AND RESISTANCE

LET US now consider the circuit element of Fig. 11, containing self inductance L and total resistance R, including the resistance of the coil and any external resistance that may be in series with the coil.

According to the fundamental equation (13), p. 742, we must have at every instant

$$V = I\,R + L\,(dI/dt). \tag{19}$$

It will be convenient to consider the two terms on the right of this equation separately, defining

$$V = V_R + V_L, \quad \text{where} \quad V_R = I\,R, \quad V_L = L\,(dI/dt). \tag{20}$$

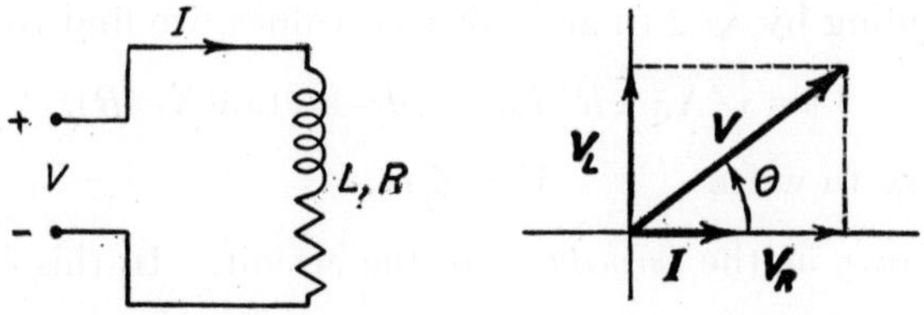

Fig. 11. Circuit containing inductance and resistance.

Let us suppose that the current is $I = I_M \sin 2\pi ft$, as in (7). This current is represented by the vector $\boldsymbol{I}$ in Fig. 11. Then

$$V_R = I\,R = R\,I_M \sin 2\pi ft = V_{RM} \sin 2\pi ft, \quad \text{with} \quad V_{RM} = R\,I_M. \tag{21}$$

Also, $\quad V_L = L\,(dI/dt) = (2\pi fL)\,I_M \cos 2\pi ft = (2\pi fL)\,I_M \sin(2\pi ft + \tfrac{1}{2}\pi);$

or $$V_L = V_{LM} \sin(2\pi ft + \tfrac{1}{2}\pi), \tag{22}$$

with $$V_{LM} = (2\pi fL)\,I_M = X_L\,I_M \tag{23}$$

as the maximum value of V_L. We define the *inductive reactance* by

$$X_L = 2\pi fL, \quad \text{in ohms.} \tag{24}$$

The voltage V_L *leads* the current by 90° and so is represented by the vector $\boldsymbol{V}_L$ drawn in Fig. 11, of length $V_{LM} = X_L\,I_M$.

> The **inductive reactance** of an inductor is $X_L = 2\pi fL$, and is measured in ohms.

In accordance with (20), V is represented by the vector sum of $\boldsymbol{V}_R$ and $\boldsymbol{V}_L$. Hence, we have

$$V_M = \sqrt{V_{LM}^2 + V_{RM}^2} = \sqrt{X_L^2\,I_M^2 + R^2\,I_M^2} = \sqrt{X_L^2 + R^2}\,I_M.$$

Again we write $$V_0 = Z_0\,I_0. \tag{25}$$

where Z is the *impedance:* $\quad Z = \sqrt{X_L^2 + R^2}. \tag{26}$

The current *lags* behind the voltage by

$$\theta = \arctan(V_{LM}/V_{RM}) = \arctan(X_L/R). \tag{27}$$

It is not hard to see why V_L, the out-of-phase component of the voltage, should lead the current by 90°. This component is the part $L(dI/dt)$ of the voltage required to overcome the EMF of self inductance. At $t=0$, the current is zero but is increasing at its maximum rate. Hence, we need the maximum positive value of V_L to overcome the back-EMF that tends to prevent this current increase. One quarter cycle (90°) later, the current has reached its maximum value but is no longer changing, so that V_L is zero.   Thus, V_L has its maximum 90° ahead of the current maximum.

From (24), (26), and (27), we see that as $f \to 0$, $X_L \to 0$, $Z \to R$, $\theta \to 0$, consistent with the fact that self inductance has no effect on a steady direct current.   On the other hand X_L increases in proportion to the frequency, so that a coil of large self inductance can be used as a 'choke coil' to prevent the passage of appreciable AC, but permit the passage of DC; or it can be used to choke off high-frequency AC and permit the passage of low-frequency AC.   One scheme of ringing telephone bells on a two-party line has an appropriate condenser in series with the bell in one phone and a choke coil in series in the other phone.   To ring one phone an AC voltage is used, which passes current through the condenser but very little current through the choke coil.   To ring the other bell, a DC voltage is used, which will not pass current through the condenser but will pass current readily through the choke coil.

Example. *Consider a coil of inductance* 1 henry *and resistance* 377 ohms. *Determine its inductive reactance and its impedance at* $f = 6$, 60, 600 *cycles/sec, and the angle of lag of the current at each of these frequencies.*

Direct substitution in (24), (26), (27) gives

$$X_L = \quad 38 \text{ ohms}, \quad Z = \quad 379 \text{ ohms}, \quad \theta = \ \ 6°, \quad \text{at} \quad 6 \sim;$$
$$X_L = \ 377 \text{ ohms}, \quad Z = \ 534 \text{ ohms}, \quad \theta = 45°, \quad \text{at} \ \ 60 \sim;$$
$$X_L = 3770 \text{ ohms}, \quad Z = 3790 \text{ ohms}, \quad \theta = 84°, \quad \text{at} \ 600 \sim.$$

The inductive reactance approaches zero, the impedance approaches the resistance, and the angle of lag of the current approaches zero as the frequency goes down.   In other words, the lower the frequency, the more closely the circuit resembles a DC circuit.

5. SERIES CIRCUITS CONTAINING RESISTANCE, INDUCTANCE, AND CAPACITANCE; SERIES RESONANCE

WE ARE NOW in a position to consider the general series circuit of Fig. 12.   For a given current I of maximum value I_M and frequency f, the required voltage V will be the sum of three parts:

$$V = V_R + V_L + V_C. \tag{28}$$

The voltage V_R is in phase with the current and has a maximum value given by

$$V_{RM} = R \, I_M.$$

The voltage V_L, necessary to overcome the EMF of self inductance, is 90° ahead of the current and has a maximum value given by

$$V_{LM} = X_L \, I_M = 2\pi f L \, I_M.$$

The voltage V_C across the condenser is 90° behind the current and has a maximum value given by

$$V_{CM} = X_C I_M = \left(\frac{1}{2\pi f C}\right) I_M.$$

These three sinusoidal voltages can be added by adding the rotating vectors at the right of Fig. 12. Two cases arise, according to whether $X_L > X_C$ or $X_C > X_L$. In the first case we have $V_{LM} > V_{CM}$ and the vector diagram (a) of Fig. 12, with current lagging behind voltage (V ahead of I), applies; in this case the inductance is said to predominate. In the second case $V_{CM} > V_{LM}$ as in (b), with current leading voltage (V behind I); capacitance is said to predominate.

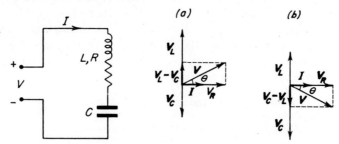

Fig. 12. The general series circuit: (a) $X_L > X_C$, current lags behind voltage; (b) $X_C > X_L$, current leads voltage.

In either case we see from Fig. 12 that

$$V_M = \sqrt{V_{RM}^2 + (V_{LM} - V_{CM})^2} = \sqrt{R^2 I_M^2 + (X_L I_M - X_C I_M)^2}$$

or

$$V_M = \sqrt{R^2 + (X_L - X_C)^2}\ I_M.$$

If we write

$$V_M = Z I_M; \qquad V_0 = Z I_0, \tag{29}$$

where Z is the *impedance* of the circuit, we have

$$Z = \sqrt{R^2 + (X_L - X_C)^2} = \sqrt{R^2 + \left(2\pi f L - \frac{1}{2\pi f C}\right)^2}. \tag{30}$$

Also from Fig. 12, we see that

if $X_L > X_C$, current *lags* by angle $\quad \theta = \arctan \dfrac{V_{LM} - V_{CM}}{V_{RM}} = \arctan \dfrac{X_L - X_C}{R}$;

if $X_C > X_L$, current *leads* by angle $\quad \theta = \arctan \dfrac{V_{CM} - V_{LM}}{V_{RM}} = \arctan \dfrac{X_C - X_L}{R}$. $\left.\begin{array}{c} \\ \\ \\ \\ \end{array}\right\}$ (31)

In deriving these formulas, we have assumed a value for the current and computed the required voltage. The more usual application occurs the other way around: given V_0, we wish to find I_0 and the phase of the current relative to the voltage. I_0 is found by dividing V_0 by Z, in accordance with (29), and the phase is found from (31).

We now turn to a discussion of series resonance:

A series circuit is said to be **resonant** if $X_L = X_C$.

The reason for the word *resonant* will be explained later. We shall first show that the resonance condition $X_L = X_C$ occupies a distinctive position with regard to voltage and current relationships. First we note that

In the case of resonance, the current is in phase with the voltage, and Z = R, so that at the terminals the circuit behaves exactly as if it had no capacitance or inductance, but merely a pure resistance R.

The other distinctive properties of the resonance condition can best be illustrated by specific examples.

Example. *Consider the circuit of Fig. 12 with fixed values $f = 60 \sim$, $V_0 = 1$ volt, $R = 1$ ohm, $L = 1$ henry, $X_L = 377$ ohms, but with variable capacitance C. Compute the effective current I_0 in amperes as a function of the capacitance C in microfarads.*

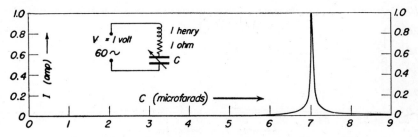

Fig. 13. Current in a series circuit as a function of capacitance, illustrating series resonance at the value of C that makes $X_C = X_L$.

The results of the straightforward computation of I_0 from (29) and (30) are plotted in Fig. 13. The value of C for resonance is given by the following computation, in which 377 sec^{-1} represents the value of $2\pi f$:

$$X_C = X_L, \quad \frac{1}{377 \text{ sec}^{-1} C} = 377 \ \omega, \quad C = \frac{1}{(377)^2 \ \omega \cdot \text{sec}^{-1}} = 7.04 \times 10^{-6} \text{ f} = 7.04 \ \mu\text{f}.$$

The student can easily verify that the dimensions of C in this computation do come out coul/volt or farads.

We notice that in the immediate neighborhood of resonance the current is very large compared with the current for values of C away from resonance, because the impedance Z has its minimum value R at resonance and increases rapidly as the term $X_L - X_C$ in (30) departs from zero either positively or negatively. The sharpness of the peak of a curve such as Fig. 13 depends on the relative values of R and X_L—the smaller the ratio R/X_L, the sharper the peak.

The phenomenon illustrated in Fig. 13 is familiar to everyone in the tuning of the antenna circuit of a radio to an impressed voltage of a given frequency arising from the radio waves broadcast by a given station. The capacitance of a variable condenser is adjusted to obtain maximum current in the antenna circuit. Of course with radio frequencies, which are of the order of 500–1500 kilocycles/second, very much smaller inductances and capacitances are used than those we have been discussing in connection with 60-$\sim$ frequency, since L and C enter all formulas in terms $2\pi fL$ and $2\pi fC$.

Example. *To see how the antenna circuit of a radio can discriminate between stations of different frequency, plot a curve for a circuit like that of Fig. 13, except that C is fixed at 7.04 μf and f varied.*

As we have seen in the previous example, the values of C, L, and R in the circuit of Fig. 14 give resonance at 60 $\sim$. Consider the current when an AC voltage with $V_0 = 1$ volt is applied, for various values of frequency f. Equation (30) gives

$$Z = \sqrt{1 + \left(6.28\,f - \frac{22{,}600}{f}\right)^2} \text{ ohms;}$$

in this relation f is to be considered as a pure number; the units have all been collected. The impedance Z has its minimum value when the parenthesis

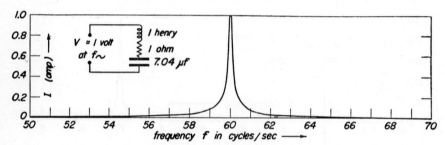

Fig. 14. Current in a series circuit as a function of frequency, illustrating series resonance at the frequency that makes $X_C = X_L$.

vanishes, at $f = 60.0$. At this frequency, $Z = 1$ ohm and $I_0 = V_0/Z = 1$ amp. At any other frequency, Z is greater than 1 ohm and I_0 is less than 1 amp. Figure 14 shows the curve of I_0 as a function of f for a frequency range from 50 to 70 cycles/sec, in the neighborhood of the resonance at 60 $\sim$. This plot also shows a sharp resonance. In connection with the tuned antenna circuits we were discussing above, the same argument shows that if the circuit is tuned to a station of one frequency, the response to stations of other frequencies is greatly attenuated.

The formula for resonance frequency computed by setting $X_L = X_C$,

$$f = 1/(2\pi\,\sqrt{LC}), \qquad \left(\begin{smallmatrix}\text{resonance}\\\text{frequency}\end{smallmatrix}\right) \quad (32)$$

is basic to the discussion of the tuned circuits in radio and television transmitters and receivers.

Near resonance, the voltage across part of a series circuit can become very much larger than the line voltage because, in the vector diagram of Fig. 12, if the vectors V_L and V_C are approximately equal in length, they can both be very much larger than the line voltage V. To illustrate this point, consider the circuit of Fig. 13 or Fig. 14 at resonance, when $I_0 = 1$ amp. Then $X_C = 377$ ohms, so that $V_{C0} = X_C\,I_0 = 377$ volts. Also, $X_L = 377$ ohms and $V_{L0} = 377$ volts. These values are for an impressed voltage of only 1 volt effective. CAUTION: Handle resonant series circuits with care. They can be dangerous both to persons and to apparatus. For example, in the circuit of Fig. 13 or Fig. 14, in spite of the fact that only 1 volt is applied across the circuit, we must use a condenser capable of withstanding 377 volts effective, or 532 volts maximum, without breakdown, if we are to tune for resonance.

In the case of *series resonance*, the circuit operates at power factor unity, with current in phase with voltage and with all the instantaneous power going into heating the resistance. There is appreciable energy $\frac{1}{2}LI^2$ of self-inductance, and appreciable energy $\frac{1}{2}CV_C^2$ stored in the condenser. Since these energies have no effect on the external circuit, they must be just handed back and forth from inductance to capacitance. This transfer must occur twice per cycle, since $\frac{1}{2}LI^2$ is zero each time I is zero, and $\frac{1}{2}CV_C^2$ is zero each time V_C is zero. To verify the validity of this argument, let

$$I = I_M \sin 2\pi ft.$$

Then
$$\frac{1}{2}LI^2 = \frac{1}{2}LI_M^2 \sin^2 2\pi ft;$$

or, since $X_L = 2\pi fL$, we see that

$$\text{energy in inductance} = \frac{X_L}{4\pi f} I_M^2 \sin^2 2\pi ft. \tag{33}$$

Also, from (8), (9), and (11),

$$V_C = X_C I_M \sin(2\pi ft - \frac{1}{2}\pi) = -X_C I_M \cos 2\pi ft,$$

so that
$$\frac{1}{2}CV_C^2 = \frac{1}{2}CX_C^2 I_M^2 \cos^2 2\pi ft.$$

Since $CX_C = 1/2\pi f$, we can write this as

$$\text{energy in condenser} = \frac{X_C}{4\pi f} I_M^2 \cos^2 2\pi ft. \tag{34}$$

We see now that (33) has its maxima at phases $\phi = 2\pi ft = 90°$, $270°$, when (34) vanishes, and that (34) has its maxima at $\phi = 0°$, $180°$, when (33) vanishes. Furthermore, at resonance, when $X_L = X_C$, these maxima are equal. In fact, at resonance the sum of (33) and (34) is a constant, independent of time, since $\sin^2\phi + \cos^2\phi = 1$. This series of calculations shows that in the resonance case the stored energy is precisely handed back and forth from the inductance to the capacitance, or from the magnetic field to the electric field, just as the energy of a pendulum or mechanical oscillator is handed back and forth from kinetic energy of motion to potential energy of position. The term *electrical resonance* is applied to this case because of the analogy with mechanical resonance.

6. THE TRANSFORMER

WE ARE now in position to continue the discussion of the transformer, which we began on p. 742 in the previous chapter. In the earlier discussion, the secondary of the transformer was open. We shall now discuss the simplest case of the *loaded* transformer, the case in which there is a *pure resistance* across the secondary, as in Fig. 15.

We shall consider the ideal case of a transformer with no losses. In an actual transformer the losses can be kept well under one per cent of the power transmitted, so that the actual transformer differs very little in operation from the ideal one. In the ideal case, the windings have zero resistance (no I^2R-losses); the magnetic material is assumed ideal (flux Φ directly proportional to MMF, hence no hysteresis losses); and eddy currents in the core are assumed negligible.

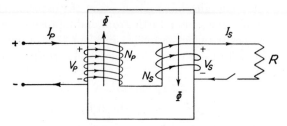

Fig. 15. Diagram of ideal resistanceless transformer with arrows and $+$ and $-$ signs to indicate positive senses of currents, voltages, and flux. V_P and V_S are generated EMF's; in the case of the primary this is of the nature of a *back*-EMF, which opposes the applied voltage in accordance with Kirchhoff's second law.

If we denote the instantaneous primary and secondary currents by I_P and I_S, the core flux Φ will be the sum of the contributions from the two windings:

$$\Phi = \frac{N_P I_P - N_S I_S}{\mathcal{R}}. \tag{35}$$

Here the numerator represents the MMF, the denominator the reluctance, in the formula $\Phi = \text{MMF}/\mathcal{R}$ of Chap. 33. The minus sign comes from the fact that for the particular sign conventions chosen in Fig. 15, a positive I_S sets up a negative flux.

At any instant, the generated EMF's in the two windings will be

$$V_P = N_P \frac{d\Phi}{dt}, \qquad V_S = N_S \frac{d\Phi}{dt}, \tag{36}$$

where the signs are seen to be correct in accordance with Lenz's law for the conventions of Fig. 15. Hence, at every instant,

$$\frac{V_S}{V_P} = \frac{N_S}{N_P} = r. \tag{37}$$

Since the secondary load is purely resistive, we have, at every instant,

$$V_S = RI_S. \tag{38}$$

By combining (38) and (37), we see that V_P, V_S, and I_S are all in phase, with

$$V_S = rV_P \qquad I_S = rV_P/R. \tag{39}$$

Since these equations hold at every instant, the same relations must obtain between the effective values V_{P0}, V_{S0}, I_{S0} of the AC voltages and currents. Equations (39) enable us to obtain all quantities of interest except the primary current I_P.

To obtain the primary current, we compute, by differentiation of (35),

$$V_P = N_P \frac{d\Phi}{dt} = \frac{N_P^2}{\mathcal{R}} \frac{dI_P}{dt} - \frac{N_S N_P}{\mathcal{R}} \frac{dI_S}{dt},$$

or, since $N_P^2/\mathcal{R}$ is the self inductance L_P of the primary,

$$\frac{dI_P}{dt} = \frac{1}{L_P} V_P + r \frac{dI_S}{dt}. \tag{40}$$

To satisfy this equation we must have two components in the primary current: The first component is the one we would obtain if $I_S = 0$ in (40) corresponding to the secondary *open*. This component has effective magnitude V_{P0}/X_{LP} and contributes no power; it is the component that satisfies (40) if the last term on the right is ignored. The second component is obtained by ignoring the first term on the right of (40)—when this term is ignored, (40) is seen to be satisfied by a primary current that is in phase with the secondary current and hence in phase with the primary voltage, and that has effective magnitude rI_{S0}. This component contributes power $rI_{S0}V_{P0}$. Since rV_{P0} is just the secondary voltage V_{S0}, we see that the power contributed is just that delivered by the secondary: $I_{S0}V_{S0}$. The details of the computation of the primary current are illustrated in the following numerical example:

Example. *Consider a step-down transformer (such as sits on a post in the middle of every block in a city) designed to step the 60-cycle/sec power-line voltage of $V_{P0} = 600$ volts down to $V_{S0} = 120$ volts for distribution to the houses. Assume that the transformer has $2\pi f L_P = X_P = 300$ ohms, and that the lighting and heating load serviced is equivalent to a resistance of $R = 2.4$ ohms. Determine the primary current.*

According to (37), the voltage ratio determines the turn ratio r:

$$r = N_S/N_P = V_S/V_P = V_{S0}/V_{P0} = {}^{120}\!/_{600} = 0.2.$$

The secondary load, equivalent to 2.4 ω, determines the secondary current

$$I_{S0} = V_{S0}/R = 120 \text{ v}/2.4 \ \omega = 50 \text{ amp}.$$

The power delivered is $\quad 120 \text{ v} \times 50 \text{ amp} = 6000 \text{ watts}.$

To find the primary current, we first compute the current I_P^{open} that would exist in the primary with the secondary circuit open (no load). In this case, the secondary coil has no influence; the primary current is the same as if the secondary winding were removed entirely from the core of Fig. 15. Consequently, the effective primary current with open secondary is

$$I_{P0}^{\text{Open}} = V_{P0}/X_{LP} = 2 \text{ amp,}$$

lagging the voltage V_P by 90°.

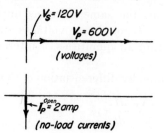

(voltages)

(no-load currents)

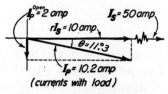

(currents with load)

Fig. 16. Vector diagrams showing effective values of currents and voltages.

This current is represented by the vector in the middle diagram of Fig. 16, marked 'no-load currents.'

The vector addition that determines I_P is accomplished in the diagram at the bottom of Fig. 16. On this diagram, I_P^{Open} is copied from the diagram above; the vector I_S representing 50 amp effective is plotted in phase with V_P; the vector rI_S of 10 amp is along the same line. The vector resultant of I_P^{Open} and rI_S gives I_P of effective value

$$I_{P0} = 10.2 \text{ amp,}$$

lagging the voltage V by

$$\theta = \arctan{\tfrac{2}{10}} = 11°3.$$

The power furnished to the primary is

$$V_{P0} I_{P0} \cos\theta = 600 \,(10.2)(10/10.2) \text{ watts}$$
$$= 6000 \text{ watts,}$$

the same as the power delivered by the secondary.

A similar discussion can be given for the cases in which the secondary is loaded inductively or capacitively. Drawing a current from the secondary tends to cause an alteration in the magnetic flux (35), but this alteration must be prevented by an alteration of the primary current since the flux variation must produce the given back-EMF V_P (36). The power input to the primary exactly equals the power output of the secondary in the ideal case and exceeds it only slightly in the actual case.

Thus, a bell-ringing transformer installed in a home draws an appreciable primary current at no load, but it draws this current so nearly at 90° phase to the primary voltage that the power at no load is too small to turn the kilowatt-hour meter that records energy consumption.

7. THE ELECTRODYNAMOMETER

LET us now discuss measuring instruments for use with AC circuits. Those for use with circuits of ordinary power frequencies usually employ a sensitive element called an *electrodynamometer* (Fig. 17).

The electrodynamometer of Fig. 17 differs from the galvanometer of Fig. 20, p. 683, in that the magnetic field in which the moving coil rotates is created by a pair of fixed coils carrying current supplied from outside through a pair of binding posts separate from those that supply current to the moving coil. With this coil arrangement, a given pointer reading corresponds to a definite value of the *product* $I_1 I_2$ of the currents in the fixed and moving coils, and the scale could be calibrated to read $I_1 I_2$.

While the deflection is not strictly proportional to the product I_1I_2, so that the scale must be calibrated by sending known currents through the coils, the deflection is approximately proportional to I_1I_2, and the marks corresponding to $I_1I_2=0$, $I_1I_2=1$ ma², $I_1I_2=2$ ma², $I_1I_2=3$ ma², and so on, are approximately equally spaced on the scale.

The most important thing to understand is that a given pointer position rigorously corresponds to a definite value of the product I_1I_2 and that the pointer will stand at the position marked $I_1I_2=4$ ma², for example, whether $I_1=2$ ma and $I_2=2$ ma, $I_1=1$ ma and $I_2=4$ ma, $I_1=0.5$ ma and $I_2=8$ ma, or even $I_1=-4$ ma and $I_2=-1$ ma. In Fig. 17, a current

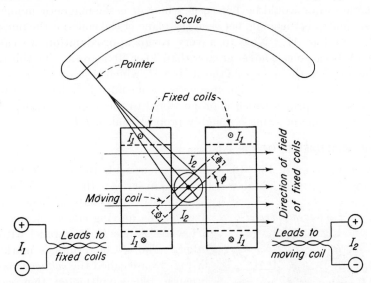

Fig. 17. The electrodynamometer. The pivoted moving coil rotates in the space interior to the fixed coils. A light framework extending through the gap between the fixed coils carries the pointer and the springs supplying the restoring torque. In this diagram the pointer is in the equilibrium position for no current.

I_1 in the fixed coils in the direction shown will set up a magnetic field in the indicated direction. With a current I_2 in the moving coil in the direction shown, the moving coil will have a magnetic moment represented by a vector in the direction perpendicular to its plane and pointing in the same direction as the pointer. The coil in the magnetic field experiences a torque tending to turn its magnetic moment into the direction of the field, that is, a clockwise torque tending to swing the pointer to the right. The pointer will move to the right until the countertorque of the springs just balances the magnetic torque. Suppose now that we increase the current I_1 by a factor k to kI_1, at the same time dropping I_2 by a factor k to I_2/k, so that the product I_1I_2 is unchanged. Then the force on each element of the coil, $\mathfrak{B}I_2\,dl$, will be unchanged because the field $\mathfrak{B}$ at each point is rigorously proportional to I_1, and this field increases by a factor k at the same times that I_2 drops by a factor k.   Hence, the magnetic torque will be unchanged and will still balance the spring torque at the same pointer position.   Similarly, if I_1 and I_2 are both reversed in direction but unchanged in magnitude, the magnetic torque and the pointer position will not change.

Thus, we see that a given pointer position corresponds to a definite value of I_1I_2.   We can now show that the angle of pointer swing from the equilibrium position is *approximately proportional* to the value of I_1I_2. The magnetic field $\mathcal{B}$ is approximately uniform.   For a uniform field, the magnetic torque would be $\mathcal{B}M\cos\phi$, where M is the magnetic moment of the coil and ϕ is the angle between the plane of the coil and the magnetic field as in Fig. 17.   Now to a very rough approximation we can set $\cos\phi = 1$, because ϕ is never greater than 30 or 40 degrees.   To this rough approximation, the magnetic torque is $\mathcal{B}M$, which is *proportional* to I_1I_2, since $\mathcal{B} \propto I_1$ and $M \propto I_2$.   The magnetic torque must balance the restoring torque of the springs which is proportional to the angle of swing.   Consequently, angle of swing is roughly proportional to I_1I_2.

8. THE WATTMETER, DC OR AC

As indicated in Fig. 18, a wattmeter is made from an electrodynamometer by putting a high resistance R_M in series with one of the coils (in

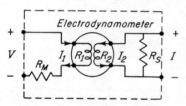

Fig. 18. A *wattmeter* is made from an electrodynamometer.

principle, it is immaterial whether the fixed or the moving coil is selected) and a low resistance R_S in parallel with the other.   The set of terminals marked V in Fig. 18 are called the *voltage terminals* because, like a voltmeter, they can be connected across a circuit and draw very little current.   The set of terminals marked I are called the *current terminals* because the resistance between them is very low and, like an ammeter, they can be connected in series with a circuit without introducing much additional resistance.

The wattmeter is connected to measure the power expended in a load as indicated in Fig. 19, with the voltage terminals in parallel with the load and the whole load current flowing through the current terminals, which are in series with the load.   The instrument will work equally well for DC or AC.   We shall discuss the DC case first.   In this case the current I_1 through the voltage coil of the electrodynamometer is proportional to the voltage V across the load.   The current I_2 through the current coil is proportional to the load current I (actually to the load current plus the current flowing through the voltage terminals of the wattmeter, but the latter current can usually be assumed negligible).   Since the pointer position is a measure of the product $I_1 I_2$ and $I_1 \propto V$ and $I_2 \propto I$, the pointer position is a measure of VI, and the scale can be calibrated in watts. The scale will be approximately linear since the pointer deflection will be approximately proportional to the power in watts.

Let us write $I_1 I_2 = K\,VI$, where K is a constant that depends on the values of the various resistances in Fig. 18.

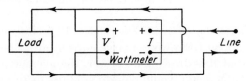

Fig. 19. Connections to a wattmeter to measure the power expended in a load. Arrows indicate current direction for a DC circuit, positive sense of current for an AC circuit.

The ordinary commercial wattmeter will read power correctly on 60-$\sim$ AC as well as on DC, although it will not work on AC of frequency much above 60 cycles/sec. This versatility is possible because the electrodynamometer coils have such low inductive reactance (being air-cored, their self inductance is extremely low) compared to their resistance that even for 60-$\sim$ AC they are the practical equivalent of pure resistances and carry currents in phase with the voltages across them. Consequently, $I_1 I_2 = K\,VI$ for the AC case if the symbols are taken to refer to instantaneous values of currents and voltages. The electrodynamometer movement has sufficient inertia and sufficient damping that it will not follow the rapid variations of magnetic torque that arise when 60-$\sim$ currents are introduced into its coils. Rather, it will set itself at such a position that the spring torque is equal and opposite to the *average* value of the magnetic torque. Since at a given position the instantaneous magnetic torque is proportional to the product $I_1 I_2$, the average magnetic torque will be proportional to the average of this product, which we denote by $\langle I_1 I_2 \rangle_{Av}$. Hence, the scale reading will be a measure of $\langle I_1 I_2 \rangle_{Av}$.

Now let Fig. 19 represent an AC circuit, with instantaneous voltage

$$V = \sqrt{2}\,V_0 \sin 2\pi f t,$$

where V_0 is the *effective* value of the AC voltage. Since the current I will generally differ in phase from the voltage, we write

$$I = \sqrt{2}\,I_0 \sin(2\pi f t + \theta),$$

where I_0 is the *effective* current and the phase angle θ is positive for a leading current, negative for a lagging current. Now, since $I_1 I_2 = K\,VI$,

$$\langle I_1 I_2 \rangle_{Av} = K\,\langle VI \rangle_{Av}.$$

But our computation in Sec. 2 of the power drawn by the load was a computation of $\langle VI \rangle_{\mathrm{Av}}$, and gave

$$P = \langle VI \rangle_{\mathrm{Av}} = V_0 I_0 \cos\theta.$$

Hence $$\langle I_1 I_2 \rangle_{\mathrm{Av}} = K \langle VI \rangle_{\mathrm{Av}} = K P.$$

Since the scale reading is a measure of $\langle I_1 I_2 \rangle_{\mathrm{Av}}$, this equation shows that the same pointer reading will correspond to the same power as in the DC case.

Note that *the wattmeter reads true power* $V_0 I_0 \cos\theta$, not the product $V_0 I_0$. Thus, if a load is drawing a large current at 90° phase angle with the voltage, so that it is drawing no power, the average magnetic torque in the electrodynamometer would be zero, and the meter would read zero.

9. VOLTMETERS AND AMMETERS FOR USE ON AC

For LOW-FREQUENCY (60-$\sim$) AC, an electrodynamometer may be made into a voltmeter or an ammeter by connecting the two coils in series

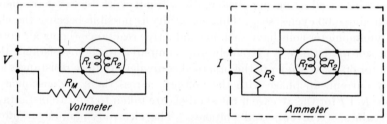

Fig. 20. Conversion of an electrodynamometer into a voltmeter or an ammeter.

and adding either a series or shunt resistance in the same way as in the conversion of a galvanometer to a DC voltmeter or ammeter. This type of instrument is illustrated in Fig. 20. For 60-$\sim$ AC, the coils of the electrodynamometer have negligible reactance and behave like pure resistances. The instruments of Fig. 20 work equally well on DC or 60-$\sim$ AC.

In the voltmeter, the current in each coil is proportional to the applied voltage, so that the pointer swing is a measure of the square of the applied voltage and is approximately proportional to it. For the AC case, the pointer position depends on $\langle V^2 \rangle_{\mathrm{Av}} = V_0^2$, with the result that the same instrument reads either DC voltage or effective value of AC voltage.

Of course the scale is marked with values of voltage rather than of (voltage)^2. This calibration makes the scale extremely nonlinear. For example, if the meter swings full scale on voltage V, voltage $\frac{1}{2}V$ will make it swing only about $\frac{1}{4}$ scale, since the swing is approximately proportional to the square of the voltage. Such a nonlinear scale is illustrated in Fig. 21; it is usually used only for voltages above half the full-scale voltage, because below this point the finer divisions, not shown in Fig. 21, become too close for the scale to be read with accuracy.

The electrodynamometer-type ammeter similarly reads DC current or effective value of AC current on a nonlinear scale like that of Fig. 21.

Electrodynamometer instruments are not ordinarily used for direct currents because they are definitely inferior to the galvanometer type discussed earlier. Since the electrodynamometer element is much less sensitive than the galvanometer element, a galvanometer-

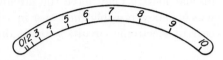

Fig. 21. Typical non-linear scale of an instrument whose swing is proportional to the square of the quantity being measured.

type voltmeter can be made of much higher resistance, and an ammeter of much lower resistance, than the corresponding electrodynamometer type.

A cheaper type of meter, which works on either DC or low-frequency AC, is the *soft-iron* type.   In this type, which is in wide usage for inexpensive instruments, the sensitive element consists of a fixed iron vane and a moving iron vane, both contained within a solenoid as in Fig. 22.   Soft iron with very low hysteresis is used for the vanes.   Current in the

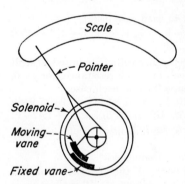

Fig. 22. Sensitive element of soft-iron type of meter.

solenoid sets up a magnetic field perpendicular to the paper in Fig. 22; this field magnetizes both of the vanes in the direction of their length.   The vanes then behave like two bar magnets placed side by side with N poles together and S poles together; they repel each other, causing the pointer attached to the moving vane to swing across the scale.   The motion is resisted by spiral springs.   The scale is not linear but is less distorted than that of Fig. 21.   Ammeters and voltmeters are made by adding shunt or series resistance. When such an instrument is used with DC, the reading is independent of the direction of the current.

The sensitive element of Fig. 22 works on low-frequency AC because the magnetization follows the current.   The polarity of the vanes reverses with the frequency of the current, but the vanes always repel each other because their like poles are always at the same end.

The above instruments cannot be used for high frequencies (audio or radio frequencies).   The sensitive element of a *high-frequency meter* usually depends on the heating effect of a current.   The temperature rise of a fine wire is measured by means of a thermocouple or by means of the linear expansion of a tightly stretched wire.   The temperature rise is a measure of the square of the effective current in the wire. A wattmeter cannot be made on this principle.

There are also various types of electronic voltmeters, some suitable for DC, some for AC. These employ electronic circuits which we shall not discuss here. They have the advantage of extremely high impedance, which makes possible their use in connection with high-resistance, low-current electronic circuits without disturbing the currents in the circuits.

PROBLEMS

1. (a) What is the effective value of the current in a circuit containing a 1-μf condenser in series with a 2000-ω resistor when an alternating voltage of 2000 v effective is applied, with $f=6 \sim$? $60 \sim$? $600 \sim$? (b) Write the equation for the current in each case, if $V=2830 \sin2\pi ft$ v.

Ans: (a) 0.0752, 0.600, 0.990 amp; (b) 0.106 sin(37.7 sec^{-1} $t+1.50$), 0.848 sin(377 sec^{-1} $t+0.925$), 1.40 sin(3770 sec^{-1} $t+0.131$) amp.

2. (a) What is the reactance of a 2-$\mu\mu$f condenser at $10^4 \sim$? at $10^5 \sim$? $10^6 \sim$?
(b) What is the impedance of a 2-$\mu\mu$f condenser in series with a 1-megohm resistor, at $10^4 \sim$? at $10^5 \sim$? at $10^6 \sim$?
(c) What is the effective value (in microamperes) of the alternating current in the circuit of (b) when an alternating voltage of 150 v effective is applied with $f=10^4 \sim$? $10^5 \sim$? $10^6 \sim$?
(d) What is the angle of lead of the current in each case in (c)?
(e) Write the equation of the current in each case in (c) if $V=212 \sin2\pi ft$ volts.

3. (a) What is the effective value of the alternating voltage required to send current $I=0.1 \sin2\pi ft$ amp through a 1-henry coil of 377-ω resistance, for $f=6$, 60, and 600 $\sim$? (b) Write the equation for the voltage in each case.

Ans: (a) 26.8, 37.8, 268 v; (b) 37.9 sin (37.7 sec^{-1} $t+0.105$), 53.4 sin(377 sec^{-1}$t+0.785$), 379 sin(3770 sec^{-1} $t+1.47$) v.

4. (a) What is the inductive reactance of a 1-millihenry coil of 1-megohm resistance, at $10^7 \sim$? at $10^8 \sim$? at $10^9 \sim$?
(b) What is the impedance of this coil at these frequencies?
(c) What is the effective value (in microamperes) of the alternating current that flows through this coil when an alternating voltage of 150 v effective is applied, at $10^7 \sim$? at $10^8 \sim$? at $10^9 \sim$?
(d) What is the angle of lag of the current in each case in (c)?
(e) Write the equation of the current in each case in (c) if $V=212 \sin2\pi ft$ volts.

5. A circuit containing a 15-μf condenser and a 10-ohm resistance in series is connected across a pair of lines. In parallel with this circuit, across the same pair of lines, is a circuit containing a coil of 0.1-henry inductance and 24-ohm resistance.
(a) What is the current through each of these parallel circuits when 24 v DC is applied to the lines?
(b) What is the effective value of the current through each of these parallel circuits when AC of 24 v effective, at 500 $\sim$, is applied to the lines?

Ans: (a) 0, 1 amp; (b) 1.02, 0.076 amp.

6. Two circuits are in parallel across a pair of leads in a radio set. One circuit has capacitance 0.1 μf and resistance 50,000 ohms in series; the other has inductance 5 henrys and resistance 35 ohms. The first circuit is designed to 'pass' both audio and radio frequency, the second circuit to 'choke out' radio frequency.

(a) If an audio-frequency signal of 50 v effective at 1000 $\sim$ is impressed, what is the effective current in microamperes in each of the two circuits?

(b) If a radio-frequency signal of 50 v effective at 1000 kilocycles/sec is impressed, what is the effective current in microamperes in each of the two circuits?

7. A coil having an inductance of 0.6 henry and a resistance of 50 ohms is in series with a resistor of 300 ohms. A 60-$\sim$ voltage of 160 v effective is applied to the combination. (a) What is the current and what is its angle of lag? (b) What is the voltage across the coil, and by what angle does it lead the current? (c) What is the voltage across the resistor, and by what angle does it lead the current? (d) Show current, coil voltage, resistor voltage, and total voltage on a single vector diagram.

Ans: (a) 0.384 amp, 32°.9; (b) 88.9 v, 77°.5; (c) 115 v, 0°.

8. A coil having an inductance of 1.5 henrys and a resistance of 150 ohms is in series with a resistor of 900 ohms. A 60-$\sim$ voltage of 500 v effective is applied to the combination. (a) What is the current and what is its angle of lag? (b) What is the voltage across the coil, and by what angle does it lead the current? (c) What is the voltage across the resistor, and by what angle does it lead the current? (d) Show current, coil voltage, resistor voltage, and total voltage on a single vector diagram.

9. Consider the circuit of Fig. 12, with $X_L = 3$ ohms, $X_C = 1.5$ ohms, and $R = 0.8$ ohm. Compute I_0 for $V_0 = 24$ volts, and compute the angle of lag or lead. Ans: 14.1 amp; current lags by 61°.9.

10. Consider the circuit of Fig. 12, with $X_L = 3$ ohms, $X_C = 4.5$ ohms, and $R = 2.4$ ohms. Compute I_0 for $V_0 = 24$ volts, and compute the power factor.

11. An inductor (a coil having self inductance and resistance), a resistor, and a capacitor (a condenser) are in series. The inductor has self inductance of 0.5 henry and resistance of 100 ohms. The resistor has 80 ohms of resistance and the capacitor has 8 μf of capacitance. An applied 60-$\sim$ voltage causes 1 amp effective through the series circuit.

(a) Compute the total impedance Z.

(b) From Z and the current, compute the effective total voltage, V_0, required, and the phase angle between the voltage and the current.

(c) Compute the effective voltage V_{I0} across the terminals of the inductor; the effective voltage V_{R0} across the terminals of the resistor; and the effective voltage V_{CM} across the terminals of the capacitor. In each case obtain the phase angle between these voltages and the current.

(d) Plot the three voltages V_I, V_R, and V_C on a vector diagram. Add these vectorially to obtain the total voltage vector V, and check the agreement of this voltage in magnitude and phase with the result obtained in (b).

Ans: (a) 230 ω; (b) 230 v, 38°.5 behind current; (c) $V_{I0} = 213$ v, 62°.1 ahead of current; $V_{R0} = 80$ v, in phase with current; $V_{C0} = 332$ v, 90° behind current.

12. Repeat Prob. 11 for the case where the inductor has 5 millihenrys of self inductance and 9 ohms of resistance, the resistor has 8 ohms of resistance, the capacitor has 40 μf of capacitance, and an applied 500-$\sim$ voltage causes 1 amp effective.

13. What is the resonance frequency for the series circuit of Prob. 11? What voltage is required to cause 1 amp at this frequency? Ans: 79.6 $\sim$; 180 v.

14. What is the resonance frequency for the series circuit of Prob. 12? What voltage is required to cause 1 amp effective at this frequency?

15. In the circuit of Fig. 14, if the capacitance and resistance are fixed at 7.04 μf and 1 ohm, but the inductance is adjustable, what value of inductance will bring the circuit into resonance for a 50-$\sim$ applied voltage?   Ans: 1.44 henry.

16. In the circuit of Fig. 14, if the capacitance and resistance are fixed at 7.04 μf and 1 ohm but the inductance is adjustable, what value of inductance will bring the circuit into resonance for a 70-$\sim$ applied voltage?

17. Show that the curve of Fig. 13 applies to a radio antenna circuit if we let the ordinates represent microamperes instead of amperes, the abscissas $\mu\mu$f instead of μf, and change L to 10 millihenrys, R to 100 ohms, V_0 to 0.1 millivolt, and f to 600 kilocycles/sec.

18. Show that the curve of Fig. 14 applies to a radio antenna circuit if we let the ordinates represent microamperes instead of amperes, the abscissas kilocycles/sec instead of cycles/sec, leave L at 1 henry, and change R to 1000 ohms, C to 7.04 $\mu\mu$f, and V_0 to 1 millivolt.

19. A current of 10 amp, lagging by 30°, flows in an AC circuit when 110 volts are applied. What is the power factor? What is the power? Ans: 0.866; 953 w.

20. A current of 0.5 amp, leading by 60°, flows in an AC circuit when 24 volts are applied. What is the power factor? What is the power?

21. What is the power in the circuit of Fig. 14 at resonance frequency? What is the maximum energy stored in the self inductance? in the capacitance?
Ans: 1 w; 1 joule; 1 joule.

22. A series circuit has self inductance, capacitance, and resistance. A fixed AC voltage is applied and the capacitance adjusted until maximum current flows. The maximum current is found to be 2 amp effective. What power is being supplied to the circuit if the total resistance is 15 ohms?

23. A transformer has 50 turns on the primary and 1000 on the secondary. When the primary is connected to 110-v AC mains, what is the voltage of the secondary? Ans: 2420 v.

24. A bell-ringing transformer is designed to step 120 volts down to 4 volts. If the secondary has 12 turns, how many turns should the primary have?

25. A toy transformer for operating an electric train has an input current to the primary of 0.9 amp lagging 15° behind the input voltage of 120 v. The terminal voltage of the secondary is 6.0 v. The load on the secondary has a power factor of 0.707. Under these conditions the actual efficiency of the transformer is 95%. Find the secondary current. Ans: 18.2 amp.

26. A large step-down transformer has a primary input of 5000 kw at 3300 v. The transformer is 99% efficient. The secondary feeds into a load of power factor 0.850 at 550 v. Find the secondary current.

27. Consider an ideal no-loss transformer feeding into a resistive load of 55 ohms, as in Fig. 15. The primary has 20 turns, the secondary 100 turns. The reluctance of the core is 10,000 ampere-turns/weber. The primary is connected to 110-v, 60-$\sim$ lines. Find the secondary voltage, the secondary current, the primary current and its angle of lag, and the power.
Ans: 550 v; 10.0 amp; 50.5 amp, 8°3; 5500 w.

28. Consider an ideal no-loss transformer feeding into a resistive load of 0.55 ohm, as in Fig. 15. The primary has 240 turns, the secondary 40 turns. The reluctance of the core is 2000 ampere-turns/weber. The primary is connected to

3300-v, 60-$\sim$ lines. Find the secondary voltage, the secondary current, the primary current and its angle of lag, and the power.

NOTE: Although in principle it does not matter which of the coils of the electro-dynamometer is used as the current and which as the voltage coil of the watt-meter, in practice it is most convenient to make the fixed coil of low resistance and to use it as the current coil. The fixed coil is made from a few turns of heavy wire and usually has sufficiently low resistance that it can be used without a shunt. The moving coil is made of many turns of fine wire and is used as the potential coil with a multiplier in series.

29. It is desired to make a wattmeter from an electrodynamometer that gives full-scale deflection with $I_1 I_2 = 0.01$ amp^2 by placing a high resistance in series with the moving coil and using this as the potential coil. If the moving coil has a resistance of 200 ohms and the wattmeter is to read 100 watts full-scale, what series resistance is needed? Ans: 9800 ohms.

30. It is desired to make a wattmeter from an electrodynamometer that gives full-scale deflection with $I_1 I_2 = 0.05$ amp^2 by placing a high resistance in series with the moving coil and using this as the potential coil. If the moving coil has a resistance of 500 ohms and the wattmeter is to read 1000 watts full-scale, what series resistance is needed?

31. A wattmeter designed for operation on 110 volts is connected to a load consisting of a condenser in series with a variable resistance, connected to 110 volts AC. As the value of the resistance is decreased, the power reading increases to about half scale on the wattmeter and then begins to decrease—and then the current coil of the wattmeter burns out! Explain this sequence of events.

32. One method of producing 'atomic projectiles' without the use of enormous DC potentials is a *linear accelerator*, in which high frequency AC voltages are applied to the tubular accelerator sections in a tube like that in Fig. 44, p. 583. The focus tube and the second, fourth, sixth, $\cdots$ sections are connected to one ter-minal of the AC 'generator,' while the first, third, fifth, $\cdots$ sections are connected to the other terminal. Thus, a proton emerging from the focus tube when the focus tube has its maximum positive potential is accelerated to the first section and moves into the field-free space inside the tubular electrode. If the length of the first section has the correct value, the proton will emerge when the first section has its maximum positive potential and be again accelerated, this time toward the second accelerator section. This process if repeated numerous times before the proton finally reaches the target. If the maximum difference of potential between electrodes is 100 kv, through how many gaps must the proton pass before attaining an energy of 1 Mev? It is desirable to work at high fre-quencies; in order to see this, make a rough calculation of the length of a 1-Mev linear accelerator with gap voltage 100 kv, when operated at 60 cycles/sec, 1 megacycle/sec, and 100 megacycles/sec.

33. In the linear accelerator designed by Alvarez at Berkeley, a Van de Graaf accelerator serves as the 'ion source.' The accelerator proper is approximately 10 m long and the AC frequency is 200 megacycles/sec. Taking 4×10^7 m/sec as the average speed of a proton in the accelerator, find the length of time spent by a proton in the accelerator. How many voltage cycles take place in this time? Through how many gaps could the proton be accelerated? NOTE: 30 Mev pro-tons have been obtained from such a machine. Ans: 2.5×10^{-7} sec; 50; 100.

CHAPTER 36

THE FUNDAMENTAL ELECTRICAL UNITS

Up to this point we have defined the various electrical units in the most convenient fashion in the order in which they were introduced. Our definition of the coulomb (p. 550) involved a dimensional constant whose numerical value (8.987×10^9) we arbitrarily chose as 10^{-7} times the square of the numerical value of the speed of light in m/sec. We then defined the ampere as one coulomb per second, and stated certain experimental formulas for magnetic forces between currents given in amperes. *Alternatively*, the ampere can be independently defined in terms of forces between currents, in which case the coulomb is defined as one ampere. second and the proportionality constant occurring in Coulomb's law of force becomes experimentally determinable. In this alternative scheme this proportionality constant proves, both experimentally and theoretically (on the basis of Maxwell's electromagnetic theory of light), to be related to the square of the speed of light in the manner of our original definition.

The scheme in which the ampere is defined in terms of forces between currents and the coulomb is defined as one ampere·second is the most convenient for absolute measurements, and is taken as fundamental by the International Committee of Weights and Measures.

In this chapter we shall redefine the basic electrical and magnetic quantities in this manner. Then we shall discuss the way in which the standards are established and maintained at the National Bureau of Standards.

1. DEFINITIONS OF THE AMPERE AND THE WEBER

Experimental observations of the magnetic forces between currents lead to the laws governing the dependence of such forces on geometrical factors, such as the lengths of the current elements and the distance and angle between them. Consistent with such experiments, we can formulate two postulates which together will serve to define the *magnitudes* of both current and magnetic intensity.

We *postulate* that magnetic intensity in webers/m² in an iron-free region can be computed from current in amperes by integrating the vector contribution $d\mathfrak{B}$ whose magnitude is $(10^{-7}$ weber/amp·m$)$ $I\,dl\,\sin\theta/r^2$ and whose direction is normal to both dl and r as discussed on p. 684.   We further *postulate* that the force in newtons on a current element $I\,dl$ in a

magnetic field can be computed from the formula $dF = \mathfrak{B}I\,dl$, where $\mathfrak{B}$ is the intensity component normal to the wire (p. 678).

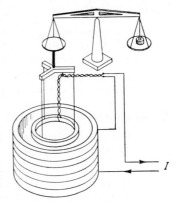

These two postulates together enable us to compute the magnetic force in newtons between any two current elements $I\,dl$ and $I'\,dl'$ in terms of I, I', and geometrical lengths and angles.   By integration, they enable us to compute the whole force in newtons between two coils such as those of Fig. 1.   If the two coils are connected in series as in Fig. 1, so that the currents in the two coils have the *same* value I, these two postulates enable us to compute the force in newtons as a function of the current I.

Fig. 1. Schematic diagram of *current balance.*

Hence, by measurement of the force in Fig. 1, we can use these postulates to define the unit of current, the ampere.   Such a measurement determines a current in amperes by measurements of mechanical units, the meter and the newton.

The fundamental measurement of current is made in this way by measuring the force between two accurately constructed coils carrying the same current.   Such a measurement can be made at the National Bureau of Standards with an accuracy of 1 or 2 parts in a million.

> The unit of current, the **ampere**, is defined by the formulas that give the magnetic force between wires carrying currents.

This definition may seem to be a little vague because the formulas referred to are geometrically complicated and not succinctly repeatable in the definition.   However, the definition, using the formulas given by the two postulates at the beginning of this section, is nonetheless precise. If it were practical to measure the force per meter length between two infinite parallel wires spaced distance a apart and carrying the same current I, one could make use of the formula (11), p. 686:

$$f = 2\,(10^{-7}\text{ nt/amp}^2)\,I^2/a \qquad \left\{ \begin{matrix} f \text{ in nt/m} \\ a \text{ in m} \\ I \text{ in amp} \end{matrix} \right\} \quad (1)$$

to give the following definition of the ampere:

> The **ampere** is that current which when flowing in each of two infinite parallel wires one meter apart will result in a magnetic force of 2×10^{-7} newton per meter length.

After we have used the two postulates together to define the ampere, either postulate by itself will serve to define the unit of magnetic intensity, the weber/m². The unit of flux, the weber, follows at once. For example:

> One **weber per square meter** is the intensity of a magnetic field in which a wire carrying a current of one ampere perpendicular to the field will experience a force of one newton per meter length.

> Flux in **webers** is the integral of the normal component of magnetic intensity in webers per square meter over area in square meters.

2. DEFINITION OF THE VOLT

> The **volt** can be defined in terms of the ampere and the watt by the formula

$$P = IV \tag{2}$$

> for the rate in watts at which heat is generated by current I passing through a resistor. Alternatively, the **volt** can be defined by the formula

$$V = d\Phi/dt \tag{3}$$

> for the EMF induced in a wire cutting flux.

In employing the second definition, the flux is computed from the currents that set up a magnetic field in an iron-free region. These two definitions are logically consistent, since the second formula can be derived from the first and from the definitions given in Sec. 1. The argument is essentially that presented in Secs. 1 and 2 of Chap. 34.

Although (2) and (3) are logically satisfactory as *definitions,* no method of high accuracy has been devised for an absolute measurement of voltage in terms of either of these definitions. In the case of the first definition the limitation on accuracy arises from the fact that the power must be measured calorimetrically, and the mechanical equivalent of heat is not known with high precision.

Since the ohm, which we define next, *can* be measured to high accuracy, accurate absolute measurements of voltage are made by compari on with the IR-drop across an accurately determined resistance.

3. DEFINITION OF THE OHM

> The **ohm** is defined in terms of the volt and the ampere by the relation

$$R = V/I. \tag{4}$$

There are several methods for absolute measurement of the resistance of a wire to an accuracy of a few parts in a million. One method which has been used extensively is illustrated in simplified fashion in Fig. 2. Here a current I sets up a magnetic field $\mathcal{B} = (10^{-7} \text{ w/a·m}) 4\pi nI$ in a *long* solenoid with n turns per meter. A disk rotating in this field has an EMF induced between center and rim of magnitude $V = \Phi/T$, where Φ

is the flux cut by a radius of the disk in one revolution, and T is the period of revolution. Φ is just the flux contained in a circle of area equal to the area of the disk, which we denote by A.   Hence, $\Phi = \mathcal{B}A = (10^{-7}\text{ w/a·m})\,4\pi nIA$, and

$$V = \Phi/T = (10^{-7}\text{ w/a·m})\,4\pi nIA/T. \qquad (5)$$

The resistance R to be determined is included in the circuit as shown, and a galvanometer G is used to indicate whether or not current is flowing through the disk.

Consider first the situation with the disk at rest so that $V = 0$.   The battery current splits, part going down through R and part down through

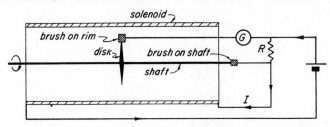

Fig. 2. Apparatus for absolute measurement of the ohm.

the disk.   These currents reunite and the whole battery current goes through the solenoid winding.   Now let the disk start turning in such a direction that the induced EMF is from shaft to rim, opposing the current from the battery.   As the disk speeds up, there will be less and less current through G, until a speed is reached at which the current through G is exactly zero.   When this condition is attained, the period of rotation T is accurately measured.   Under these conditions all the solenoid current I flows through R; and by applying Kirchhoff's second law to the loop containing R, G, and the disk, we see that

$$IR = V,$$

where V is the generated EMF.   Substituting the expression (5) for V in this equation, we have

$$IR = (10^{-7}\text{ w/a·m})\,4\pi nIA/T.$$

The important point is that in this equation the current I cancels, giving the equation

$$R = (10^{-7}\text{ w/a·m})\,4\pi nA/T$$

for the resistance in terms of the number of turns per meter on the solenoid, the area of the disk, and the period of revolution of the disk, all of which can be accurately measured.   The student can verify that this resistance comes out in volts/amp, or ohms.

A refined apparatus of the above type has given very accurate measurements of resistance.   Other accurate methods for absolute determination of resistance employ standard mutual or self inductances. In these methods, as in the method we have described, current magnitude cancels and resistance is determined by a value of inductance and a frequency. It is noted that self and mutual inductance of nonferrous coils can be computed from geometry alone; hence, the standards of inductance used in these methods are accurately constructed coils whose inductances have been computed.

4. DEFINITION OF THE COULOMB; THE PROPORTIONALITY CONSTANT IN COULOMB'S LAW

The **coulomb** is defined in terms of the ampere and the second by the equation

$$Q = It. \tag{6}$$

This definition of Q makes the proportionality constant γ in Coulomb's law for the force between two charges at distance r,

$$F = \gamma \frac{Q_1 Q_2}{r^2} \qquad \begin{cases} F \text{ in nt} \\ \gamma \text{ in nt·m}^2/\text{coul}^2 \\ Q \text{ in coul} \\ r \text{ in m} \end{cases}$$

(p. 550), a matter for experimental determination. In Chap. 27, we gave γ the numerical value $8.9878 \times 10^9 \approx 9 \times 10^9$. This is the value that is found experimentally. It is also the value required by the theory of the speed of propagation of an electromagnetic wave. The details of this theory are beyond the scope of this text, but the result it gives for the numerical value of the speed of an electromagnetic wave (light or radio wave in vacuum) is

$$c = \sqrt{(10^{-7} \text{ coul}^2/\text{nt·sec}^2) \gamma} \quad \text{from which} \quad \gamma = (10^{-7} \text{ nt·sec}^2/\text{coul}^2) c^2.$$

Thus, there are two ways of determining γ: by direct electrostatic-force measurement, and by measurement of the speed of light and application of the theory of electromagnetic waves.

The electrostatic determination of γ is made most accurately, not by a direct measurement of the force between charges, but rather by measurement of the capacitance of a condenser, since the same numerical constant γ ($\approx 9 \times 10^9$ nt·m^2/coul^2) occurs in all formulas for capacitance of a condenser in Chap. 28. Thus, formula (3), p. 586, for the capacitance of a parallel-plate condenser with vacuum dielectric is

$$C = \frac{1}{\gamma} \frac{A}{4\pi d}.$$

Such a condenser can be accurately constructed, and its capacitance can be measured in terms of the definition $Q = It$ of charge by a method that repeatedly charges the condenser to a known voltage and permits it to discharge a large but known number of times per second through a galvanometer calibrated in terms of the definition of the ampere. Thus,

C is measured in terms of the ampere and the volt.   By putting the measured capacitance C in the above formula, γ is determined.

The most accurate value of γ determined by measuring the capacitance of a condenser is

$$\gamma = (2.9978)^2 \times 10^9 \text{ nt·m}^2/\text{coul}^2.$$

This values agrees with that determined from the measured speed of light:

$$\gamma = 10^{-7} \text{ (nt·sec}^2/\text{coul}^2) \ c^2 = (2.9979)^2 \times 10^9 \text{ nt·m}^2/\text{coul}^2.$$

The almost perfect agreement between these two values is overwhelming evidence for the validity of the electromagnetic theory of light.

5. MAINTENANCE OF THE UNITS AT THE NATIONAL BUREAU OF STANDARDS

A HIGHLY accurate measurement of a current or resistance by the method of Fig. 1 or Fig. 2 or by one of the alternatives is not a routine procedure.   Rather, it is an exacting and time-consuming task which is performed only at intervals of a decade or so, to measure or check the values of *concrete standards* of resistance and voltage that are the actual standards in terms of which calibrations are made by comparison methods. By a *concrete* standard is meant one that can be physically stored away in a vault for future reference, as can the standard meter and kilogram.

The concrete standard of resistance at the N.B.S. consists of ten 1-ohm coils of manganin wire, whose resistance has been measured from time to time by an absolute method to an accuracy of a few parts in a million. In the years between measurements, the average resistance of the ten coils is assumed, with good justification, to remain constant.

A concrete standard of current cannot be maintained, but a concrete standard of voltage can, in the form of the Weston standard cell.   Currents can then be determined by comparison of the voltage drop across a standard resistor with the concrete standard of voltage.   At the National Bureau of Standards the concrete standard of voltage is maintained by a group of about twenty standard cells, with others in reserve.   If a cell in the standard group shows a decided change in voltage as compared to the mean of the group, it is replaced by a cell from the reserve group.   The voltage of these cells has been measured from time to time to an accuracy of a few parts in a million by measuring with the current balance the current required to set up an IR-drop in the standard ohm equal to the EMF of the cell.   The IR-drop and the EMF are compared by a potentiometer as described on p. 632.

All electrical and magnetic quantities can be readily measured in terms of the volt, the ohm, the meter, the kilogram, and the second.   Consequently, the concrete standards of resistance and voltage, together with the mechanical standards, are used for calibration purposes at the N.B.S. Concrete standards of capacitance, self inductance, and mutual inductance are also maintained by means of standard capacitors and inductors.

Part VI

MODERN PHYSICS

CHAPTER 37

ELECTROMAGNETIC WAVES;
PHOTONS; ELECTRONS

THE TERM *modern physics* refers to the new physical phenomena and laws that have been discovered since about 1890. At that time most of the physical phenomena we have thus far discussed (with the exception of those involving the nuclear and electronic structure of matter) were well understood. The physics of that time—including Newtonian mechanics, geometrical and physical optics, thermodynamics and the electromagnetic theory of Faraday and Maxwell, known now as *classical physics*—was concerned chiefly with phenomena perceptible directly to the human senses. For treatment of such phenomena, classical physics remains entirely satisfactory. *Modern physics* is concerned largely with phenomena not directly perceptible to the senses—with the particles of which atoms and even atomic nuclei are constructed, and the mechanism of emission and absorption of radiation by atoms and nuclei, as well as with the generation, transmission, and reception of the long-wave radiation used in radio and television.

It has been found that many of the phenomena encountered in modern physics cannot be satisfactorily treated in terms of Newtonian mechanics and the classical electromagnetic theory of Maxwell. In order to treat internal forces in atoms and molecules, it is necessary to use *quantum mechanics*. We shall begin the present chapter with a brief discussion of Maxwell's classical theory of electromagnetic radiation and then shall show how *quantum effects* were first encountered in studies of the emission and absorption of radiation.

Most of the discoveries of modern physics would have been impossible without the development of high-vacuum techniques at the turn of the century. These techniques have made possible the development of the thermionic vacuum tubes that have played so important a part not only in the electronic circuits used in physical research but also in radio and television. More recently, *semiconductors* are taking over many of the functions of thermionic vacuum tubes. We have already discussed the use of semiconductors as rectifiers on p. 613. In Sec. 6 of this chapter we shall discuss *transistors*.   Space does not permit a discussion of how thermionic vacuum tubes and transistors are used as amplifier and oscillators.   However, the student will probably study these and other examples of *applied modern physics* in later courses.

1. ELECTROMAGNETIC WAVES

CLERK MAXWELL's electromagnetic theory of light was published in 1864, before electromagnetic waves had been produced and detected by *electrical methods* (as distinguished from optical methods).   Maxwell's theory indicated that light waves *could* be electromagnetic in character and gave a description of the much longer and at that time unknown electromagnetic waves now used in radio and television.   Long electromagnetic waves were first produced and detected in 1886 by Henrich Hertz, a German physicist, who found that these waves had properties similar to those of light even though his experiments were conducted with waves a meter or more in length; the waves could be reflected, refracted, diffracted, and polarized.   By these and later experiments, Maxwell's theory has been confirmed as to the correct description of the *transmission* of light waves as well as of radio waves.   With respect to *emission* and *absorption* processes, Maxwell's theory gives an accurate description of the long waves produced by oscillating macroscopic charges and currents, but is incapable of describing the processes of emission and absorption by molecules, atoms, and nuclei involved in waves of visible and shorter wavelength.

The experiments of Hertz were rather crude, but the principles involved are the same as those used today in radio.   A 'transmitter' circuit containing inductance L_1 and capacitance C_1 produces electrical oscillations of the resonance frequency $f_1 = 1/(2\pi \sqrt{L_1 C_1})$ given by (32), p. 766.   Electromagnetic waves of this frequency are emitted from a part of the circuit called the *antenna*.   If a receiver circuit containing L_2 and C_2 is supplied with an antenna properly oriented with respect to the transmitter antenna and is 'tuned' so that $f_2 = 1/(2\pi \sqrt{L_2 C_2}) = f_1$, energy will be transferred from the transmitter to the receiver by the electromagnetic waves and can be detected by appropriate methods.

The emission of radiation from an oscillating circuit can be visualized by considering Fig. 1, which gives a schematic diagram of an oscillating dipole antenna.   This type of antenna consists of a straight conductor with a source of high-frequency alternating EMF, usually part of a vacuum-tube oscillator, at its center.   The two halves of the straight conductor can be considered both as the 'plates' of a condenser and as conductors for the movement of charges.

The electric and magnetic fields around this antenna are continually changing, but there are several points in the cycle at which we can get some idea of their configuration from our earlier discussion of electric and magnetic fields.   When the upper half of the dipole has its *maximum* positive charge, as in Fig. 1(a), electric lines pass from the upper half to the lower half, as indicated schematically by the two 𝜀-lines shown; the current is zero, hence there are no 𝔅-lines.   A quarter-cycle later there are no 𝜀-lines, but since the current is directed downward, magnetic lines form circles about the conductor in the manner indicated schematically by the directions of 𝔅 shown in Fig. 1(b).   In (c), the lower half of the antenna is positive and the electric lines extend from the lower half to the upper half as shown by the two 𝜀-lines.   In (d), the current is directed upward and the magnetic lines form circles around the conductor and have the direction indicated by 𝔅.   Thus, an observer looking at the oscillating dipole in Fig. 1 from the left edge of the paper would observe the electric lines on the left side of the dipole as lines *parallel to the dipole* and directed either upward or downward, and the

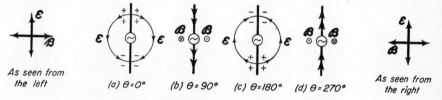

As seen from the left   (a) θ=0°   (b) θ=90°   (c) θ=180°   (d) θ=270°   As seen from the right

Fig. 1. An oscillating-dipole antenna, showing conditions at successive quarter cycles: (a) top positive, bottom negative, current zero; (b) zero charge, maximum downward current; (c) top negative, bottom positive, current zero; (d) zero charge, maximum upward current.

magnetic lines on the left side of the dipole as lines *perpendicular to the dipole*.   The 𝜀-lines and the 𝔅-lines close to the dipole are out of phase by 90° in their sinusoidal variation of intensity with time.

As we have already mentioned on p. 699, the schematic pictures of the magnetic and electric fields we have shown in Fig. 1 are only partially correct, since we have shown the electric fields for *static charge distributions* and the magnetic fields for *steady currents*.   Actually, *the charge distribution and the currents are both changing*.   If the dipole oscillated extremely slowly, the simple pictures we have shown would apply fairly well.   The electric lines would slowly appear while the ends of the antenna were being charged, would slowly disappear while the charges were being neutralized, and then would slowly reappear with reversed direction while the ends of the antenna were being charged with reversed polarity.   Similarly, the magnetic lines would gradually appear while the current was increasing, would slowly disappear while the current was dropping to zero and then would slowly reappear with reversed direction while the reversed current built up.   Actually, the static computations are not accurate for a rapidly oscillating dipole; Maxwell's theory shows that the electric and magnetic lines do not disappear completely, but some of the lines appear to become 'disengaged' from the dipole and move away from the dipole as *electromagnetic radiation*. For given charge and current distributions, as in Fig. 1, the energy so radiated away increases very rapidly with frequency—it varies as the fourth power of the frequency.

The parts of the electric and magnetic fields that do not disappear when the charges or currents decrease to zero but move outward with the speed of light still have the same perpendicular relation between the directions of $\mathcal{E}$ and $\mathfrak{B}$ as in Fig. 1, but the oscillations of $\mathcal{E}$ and $\mathfrak{B}$ are *in phase*, rather than being 90° out of phase as would be concluded from the static picture of Fig. 1. Thus an electromagnetic wave consists of a sinusoidal $\mathcal{E}$-wave always accompanied by a similar $\mathfrak{B}$-wave at right angles, both $\mathcal{E}$ and $\mathfrak{B}$ being perpendicular to the direction of propagation—the wave is transverse. Receivers (absorbers) respond variously to the $\mathcal{E}$ or $\mathfrak{B}$ part

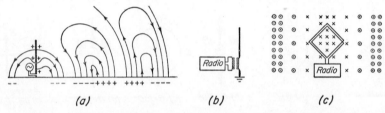

(a)   *(b)*   *(c)*

Fig. 2. (a) A 'half-dipole' transmitting antenna, showing the electric lines of the radiation field schematically. (b) A vertical receiving antenna, which responds to the electric component. (c) A 'loop' antenna, which responds to the rate of change of magnetic flux as the magnetic lines indicated by crosses and dots move past it in their progress outward from the transmitter.

of the wave. Fig. 2 indicates the appropriate orientations of the two familiar types of radio-receiver antennas.

In the case of charges or currents oscillating with frequency f and periodic time $T = 1/f$, Maxwell's theory shows that the *static* formulas are valid out to distances from the apparatus such that the time of transmission at the speed of light is small compared to the periodic time T. Since the time of transmission out to distance d is d/c, where c is the speed of light, we see that this condition on distance can be written as $d/c \ll T$, or $d \ll cT = c/f$, or $d \ll \lambda$, where λ is the wavelength corresponding to frequency f. For ordinary alternating current with $f = 60$ cycles/sec, the wavelength $\lambda = (3 \times 10^8 \text{ m/sec})/(60/\text{sec}) = 5 \times 10^6 \text{ m} = 5000$ km. Hence the static formulas are applicable at distances small compared to 5000 km from the apparatus, and we could without hesitation use the static formulas in our discussion of alternating currents in Chap. 35. Again, *the loss of energy through radiation is negligible so long as the dimensions of the apparatus are small compared to the wavelength λ.* Since all the ordinary alternating-current apparatus we have considered (including the transmission lines) is small in size compared with 5000 km, we can ignore loss of energy by radiation. Thus there is significant radiation only from apparatus comparable in size to the wavelength λ. Thus for radiation of ordinary radio waves of about 300-m wavelength, the transmitting antenna must be very long. At FM and television frequencies (shorter wavelengths), much shorter antennas suffice, while at the wavelengths of visible light, single atoms and molecules can radiate (see Probs. 25 and 26).

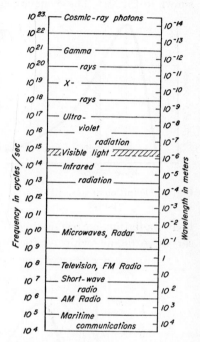

Fig. 3. The electromagnetic spectrum.

The known spectrum of electromagnetic waves covers the great range of wavelengths from about 10^{-14} meters to 10^{+4} meters, as indicated in Fig. 3. The longer waves are generated by oscillating electrical circuits; those of intermediate length, from infrared to X rays, by changes in the extra-nuclear structure of molecules and atoms, as we shall discuss later, or by changes in the energy of rotation or vibration of molecules; gamma rays arise from changes in structure of nuclei of atoms; cosmic-ray photons are of unknown origin, although processes involving the annihilation of matter which will be mentioned in the following chapter are undoubtedly involved.

2. BLACK-BODY RADIATION; PLANCK'S QUANTUM HYPOTHESIS

The STEFAN-BOLTZMANN law, (4), p. 296, gives the emissive power W_0 of a perfect radiator (black body) at absolute temperature T. Thus far we have said nothing concerning the *spectrum* of the radiation emitted by a perfect radiator. We can immediately assert that the spectrum of a perfect radiator is continuous; that is, radiation of all wavelengths is emitted from a black body. In order to discuss the relative abundance of radiation of different wavelengths in the spectrum, it is necessary to introduce the quantity W_λ, called the *spectral emissive power;* this gives a measure of the emissive power of a body for radiation in a unit wavelength range at wavelength λ. This quantity can be determined by means of a spectrograph. What is actually observed is the amount of radiation in a short wavelength interval between λ and $\lambda+\Delta\lambda$. The rate of emission of radiant energy in this wavelength range is given by $W_\lambda \, \Delta\lambda$ as represented by the shaded area in Fig. 4. *The unit in which the spectral emis-*

sive power W_λ is measured is watts/m² per unit wavelength interval; for example watts/m² per millimicron.

Plots of the spectral emissive powers for different temperatures are shown in Fig. 5. These curves, called *black-body radiation curves*, all have

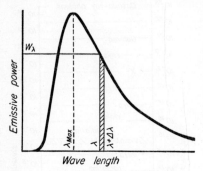

Fig. 4. Definition of spectral emissive power.

certain basic similarities in form. The curves for higher temperatures are always above the curves for lower temperatures; the maxima of the curves are displaced toward shorter wavelengths as the temperature of the black body is increased. The progressive shift of maximum toward the violet end of the spectrum accounts for the change in color of a body from red through white to blue as its temperature is increased. Sunlight has the characteristics of black-body radiation corresponding to a temperature of about 6000° K and serves to define 'white.' Incandescent-lamp filaments are much cooler

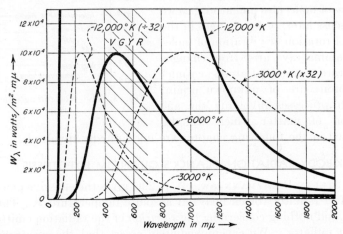

Fig. 5. Accurate plots of Planck black-body radiation curves for temperatures of 3000°, 6000°, and 12,000° K. The ordinates are values of spectral emissive power. Broken lines show the 3000° curve with ordinates multiplied by 32 and the 12,000° curve with ordinates divided by 32; this brings the maxima of these curves to the same value as the maximum of the 6000° curve.

(about 3000° K) and give light that is more orange than daylight. Certain stars, such as Vega (12,000° K) are much hotter and appear blue.

It should be noted that the area under the radiation curve for any absolute temperature T is equal to the total emissive power W_0 and is therefore equal to the value given by the Stefan-Boltzmann law:

$$\int_0^{\infty} W_\lambda \, d\lambda = W_0 = \sigma T^4.$$

Hence the total area under the curves of Fig. 5 varies as the fourth power of the absolute temperature. It turns out that the wavelength λ_M of the maximum of the curve varies inversely as the absolute temperature, according to the law

$$\lambda_M = A/T,$$

where A is a constant whose value is $A = 2.8979 \times 10^6$ mμ·K deg. This relation is called *Wien's displacement law*, after Wilhelm Wien (1864–1928).

Many attempts were made to derive an analytical expression for the detailed shape of the curves of Fig. 5 by application of *classical* electromagnetic theory to the problem of black-body radiation, but all such attempts ended in failure. The correct form of the equation for the spectral emissive power W_λ was first given by Max Planck in 1900 on semiempirical grounds. This expression is

$$W_\lambda = \frac{2\pi \times 10^{-9} \, hc^2}{\lambda^5 (e^{hc/\lambda kT} - 1)}, \tag{1}$$

in watts/m²·mμ, where

λ is the wavelength in *meters*,
$c = 2.99793 \times 10^8$ m/sec is the speed of light,
$k = 1.3804 \times 10^{-23}$ joule/K deg is *Boltzmann's constant*, defined as the gas constant R times the mass of a particle of unit atomic mass,
$h = 6.625 \times 10^{-34}$ joule·sec $= 4.134 \times 10^{-15}$ ev·sec is a new universal constant called *Planck's constant*.

The successful attempt of Planck to derive this expression on theoretical grounds represented the beginning of *quantum* theory, which has revolutionized our concepts of the nature of the processes taking place in the emission and absorption of radiation. The radical assumption that Planck made—an assumption completely contrary to the ideas of classical electromagnetic theory according to which emission and absorption are essentially continuous processes, but an assumption that has since been well confirmed by many lines of experimental evidence—is the following:

PLANCK'S QUANTUM HYPOTHESIS: *Radiation of frequency f cannot be emitted or absorbed in arbitrary amounts but is always emitted or absorbed in a discrete quantity, or quantum, of energy hf, where h is a universal constant. In the radiation field in an enclosure, the radiation of frequency f cannot exist in arbitrary amounts but must consist of an integral number of such energy quanta.*

The complete formulation of the above statement is due partly to Planck and partly to Einstein, who drew his conclusions from an analysis of the photoelectric effect discussed in Sec. 4.

The Planck curves of Fig. 5 are in agreement with experiment. They illustrate the strong dependence of area on temperature (fourth power); the shift of the maximum inversely as the temperature; the variation of the height of the maximum as the fifth power of the temperature; and the way in which the 6000° curve of the sun has its maximum in the visible region (cross-hatched).

Example. *How can one construct the Planck black-body-radiation curve for any temperature, once the* 6000° K *curve of Fig.* 5 *has been computed and plotted?*

In equation (1), denote the constant in the numerator by a, and the constant hc/k occurring in the exponent by b. Then we can write

$$W_\lambda = \frac{a}{\lambda^5(e^{b/\lambda T}-1)} = \frac{aT^5}{(\lambda T)^5(e^{b/\lambda T}-1)}.$$

The denominator is a function of λT only. Apart from the factor T^5 in the numerator that multiplies all ordinates, the curves have the same shape when plotted against λT. The broken curves of Fig. 5 are obtained from the 6000-deg curve by squeezing or expanding the scale of abscissas by a factor of 2 in λ. The T^5 ratio, 32, is then used to multiply or divide all ordinates to get the solid curves. The scheme of going to any other temperature should be clear from this discussion.

3. THE ELECTRON

BEFORE proceeding with a discussion of further applications of quantum theory, we shall discuss some of the properties of the earliest known elementary particle of modern physics—the *electron*. Although an 'atom of electricity' had been suggested much earlier in explanations of Faraday's laws of electrolysis, the existence of the electron as a charged material particle was not proved until near the beginning of the twentieth century when J. J. Thomson and R. A. Millikan determined its charge and mass. We have thus far in this book *assumed* the existence of the electron and have seen that metallic conduction can be satisfactorily explained as the movement of 'free' electrons within the metal. The first indication of the existence of these particles came with the discovery of the phenomenon of *thermionic emission*, in which electrons actually escape from the surface of metals heated in a vacuum.

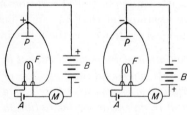

(a) Current from plate to filament   (b) No current from filament to plate

Fig. 6. Edison's discovery.

Thermionic emission was first observed by Thomas Edison in the course of experiments (1879–1885) concerned with the development of the incandescent lamp. Edison found that if a plate P were sealed into an *evacuated* lamp in the manner indicated in Fig. 6 a current could pass from this plate to the heated filament *F* but could not be made to flow in the reverse direction. In the arrangement shown in this figure, battery *A* of small EMF (commonly called the *A-battery*) is used to heat the filament to incandescence, and battery *B* of large EMF (commonly called the *B-battery*) is connected between the plate and the filament. When the plate is positive with respect to the filament as in part (a) of the figure, the meter *M* indicates a current from the plate to the filament; when the plate is negative with respect to the filament as in part (b), there is no current between filament and plate.

These observed effects can be explained if we assume that the current consists of electrons that are emitted from the hot filament. When the plate is positive with respect to the filament, the emitted negative electrons are pulled to the plate, and the meter indicates an electric current from the plate to the filament; when the plate is negative with respect to the filament, electrons emitted from the filament are repelled by the plate, and hence there is no current. The cold plate furnishes no electrons for the process of conduction through the tube. Likewise, if the A-battery is removed and the filament becomes cold, no current will flow in either direction through the evacuated tube (unless extremely high voltages are applied).

Since conduction in metals takes place by movement of 'free' electrons, it might be thought that a free electron coming toward a metal surface from within the metal could readily pass through the metal surface and escape. The results of the Edison experiment indicate that appreciable numbers of electrons can ordinarily escape from a metal *only when the metal is hot*. Electrons within a metal can be regarded as 'free' so far as electric current *within* the metal is concerned, but they are confronted by a 'barrier' at the surface of the metal. In order to escape from the metal, an electron must have sufficient energy to pass through the surface barrier. The minimum energy an electron must have in order to escape may be called the 'height of the potential barrier' at the metal surface. If an electron has just the minimum energy necessary to pass through the barrier, it will have no kinetic energy when it reaches the outside of the metal; electrons having more than the minimum energy will have appreciable kinetic energies after penetrating the barrier. The escape of electrons from a metal is quite analogous to the escape of the molecules of a liquid in evaporation, where there are also barrier forces tending to prevent the escape (see pp. 325 and 338).

Experiment shows that the electrons emitted from hot filaments can be deflected by electric and magnetic fields. The results of experiments on these 'thermionic' electrons show that these electrons have a characteristic charge $-e$ and mass m. Electrons can also be ejected from matter by ultraviolet light and by X rays; electrons are spontaneously ejected from radioactive materials. Investigation has shown that electrons from all sources have the same properties, and hence we are justified in considering the existence a *unique* electron as firmly established.

Between 1909 and 1917, R. A. Millikan carefully determined the electronic charge itself by observations of charged oil droplets in an electric field. A schematic diagram of Millikan's apparatus is shown in Fig. 7. Oil droplets from an atomizer are introduced into the space between the parallel plates. X rays passing through the air produce ionization of the air molecules, releasing electrons that become attached to the oil droplets. The motion of one of the oil droplets of mass M is observed by

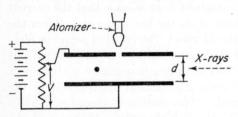

Fig. 7. Schematic diagram of Millikan's oil-droplet apparatus.

means of a microscope. Let us suppose that the oil droplet has a single electron attached. If the condenser plates are not charged, the oil droplet is subjected to a gravitational force $w = Mg$ and will move downward; owing to the viscosity of the air, the downward motion will be slow. From the rate of fall, the weight of the oil droplet can be determined by known laws of hydrodynamics—a tiny sphere falls at the constant velocity for which the viscous resistance of the air just balances the force of gravity. After the rate of fall of a particular droplet has been determined, the plates are charged so as to exert an upward electrostatic force just sufficient to make the downward motion of the droplet cease. When there is no resultant vertical motion, the upward force $e\mathcal{E}$ is exactly equal and opposite to the gravitational force. Hence,

$$e\mathcal{E} = Mg, \quad \text{and} \quad e = Mg/\mathcal{E} = Mgd/V,$$

where V is the voltage between the plates and d is their separation.

The values of charge obtained by Millikan were not the same on all droplets, but the value was always a small integer (from 1 to 9) times the least charge observed. This least charge could then be assumed to be the charge on a single electron, with some of the droplets carrying more than one electron. By careful measurements, Millikan was able to obtain a very accurate value of the charge e.

If we know the charge e on the electron, its mass m can be obtained by determining e/m in an experiment that superposes electric and magnetic deflecting fields on an electron beam. The electric and magnetic fields are arranged as in Fig. 8 so that the forces they exert on the electrons in the beam are in opposite directions, and the fields are adjusted so as to produce no deflection. When there is no resultant deflection, the force $F = e\mathcal{E}$ exerted by the electric field is equal and opposite to the force $F = \mathcal{B}ev$ exerted by the magnetic field:

$$e\mathcal{E} = \mathcal{B}ev, \quad \text{or} \quad \mathcal{E} = \mathcal{B}v,$$

where v is the speed of the electrons.   The speed can be written in terms of the accelerating voltage V used in the electron gun.   For ordinary accelerating voltages of a few kv, relativistic effects (Sec. 3, Chap. 38) do not need to be considered, and we can use the classical relation

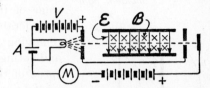

$$\tfrac{1}{2}mv^2 = eV, \quad \text{or} \quad v^2 = 2eV/m.$$

Substitution of this value for v^2 in $\mathcal{E}^2 = \mathcal{B}^2 v^2$ leads to the formula

$$e/m = \mathcal{E}^2 / 2V\mathcal{B}^2,$$

Fig. 8. Schematic diagram of apparatus for measuring e/m. The electron beam, indicated by broken lines, is in an evacuated enclosure.

where the electric field $\mathcal{E}$, the magnetic field $\mathcal{B}$, and the accelerating voltage V are all easily determinable quantities.   The first accurate value of e/m was obtained by J. J. Thomson.

The experiments we have discussed, and other more recent experiments of various types, give as the present 'best' values of the electronic charge and mass

$$e = 1.6021 \times 10^{-19} \text{ coul}, \qquad m = 9.1085 \times 10^{-31} \text{ kg}. \qquad (2)$$

The most accurate determination of Avogadro's number is made by measuring the faraday in coulombs electrochemically and dividing by the charge on the electron.

4. THE PHOTOELECTRIC EFFECT

Now THAT we have seen some evidence for the existence of the electron and have seen how electrons are emitted from hot filaments, let us consider certain quantum effects that are involved in electron emission.

Electrons can acquire sufficient energy to escape from cold metal if the metal is illuminated with light of sufficiently short wavelength.   In this process, the energy needed for escape is furnished by the energy of a light quantum.   This phenomenon is known as the *photoelectric effect* and was first discovered in 1887 by Heinrich Hertz, who noticed that a spark would jump more readily between two charged spheres when their surfaces were illuminated by light from another spark.

An arrangement that can be used for observing the photoelectric effect is shown schematically in Fig. 9.   A beam of light strikes a metal surface S in an evacuated tube.   Electrons are emitted by the surface and are drawn to the collector C, normally maintained at a positive voltage with respect to S.   The current can be measured by the galvanometer G.   It is found that for a given surface S, the frequency of the incident light must be greater than a certain frequency, called the *threshold frequency*, before any electrons are emitted by the surface at all. The threshold frequency for most metals is in the ultraviolet, but for some materials like potassium and cesium oxide it is in the visible region.

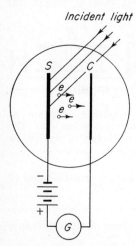

Incident light

Fig. 9. Photoelectric cell. Light striking the metal surface *S* ejects electrons which are drawn to the collector *C*.

For light frequencies well above the threshold, some of the electrons are emitted from *S* with considerable speed, as can be demonstrated by removing the battery from the circuit in Fig. 9 and noting that there is still a small current. The speed of the fastest electrons can be determined by finding the *negative* voltage that must be applied to the collector *C* in order to stop the current completely. Experiments show that *the maximum speed of the emitted electrons depends only on the frequency of the incident light*. The number of electrons emitted per second (as determined from current measurements) depends on the intensity of the incident light, but the maximum speed of the electrons is independent of the intensity of the incident light and depends only on the frequency.

The correct explanation of the photoelectric effect was given by Einstein in 1906. Einstein used the quantum theory that had been proposed earlier by Planck to account for the shape of the black-body-radiation curves. According to this theory, light is not emitted and absorbed continuously, but in small bundles or quanta, called *photons*.

A **photon** is a single quantum of electromagnetic radiation.

The energy *E* of each photon is proportional to the frequency and is given by Planck's relation $E = hf$.

According to Einstein's explanation, when a photon is absorbed at a metal such as *S* in Fig. 9, its total energy hf is imparted to a single electron within the metal. The energy acquired by the electron may enable it to penetrate the potential barrier at the surface of the metal and escape if it is moving toward the barrier with sufficient speed. In penetrating the barrier, the electron loses a certain energy ϕ, called the *work function* of the surface; if the energy hf received from the incident light quantum is greater than ϕ, the electron retains kinetic energy after leaving the surface. Since electrons absorb photons at various depths within the metal, and acquire initial velocities in various directions, there will be a distribution of energy of the electrons emerging from the surface. But the maximum kinetic energy $\frac{1}{2} mv_{\text{Max}}^2$ of electrons emitted from a metal on which light of frequency *f* is incident is given by the Einstein *photo-*

electric equation $\tfrac{1}{2} \, mv_{\text{Max}}^2 = hf - \phi,$ (3)

as illustrated in Fig. 10. The experimental results are described accurately and completely by this expression, which is based on quantum theory and cannot be explained by classical electromagnetic theory. For a particular metal, the plot of maximum energy against light frequency is a straight line whose slope gives a measure of the quantum constant h. The maximum energy becomes zero at the *threshold frequency* where $hf = \phi$; below this frequency no electrons are emitted because absorption of a photon does not impart sufficient energy to an electron for it to pass the potential barrier at the metal surface. The

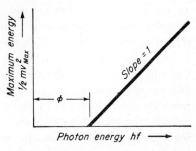

Fig. 10. Plot of the photoelectric equation when the same energy scales are used for ordinates and abscissas.

photoelectric effect furnished the first and one of the most direct proofs of the quantum hypothesis.

Example. *When ultraviolet light of 300-mμ wavelength falls on a metal surface, as in Fig. 9, a retarding potential of 0.5 v must be applied to keep the most energetic electrons from reaching the collector.   Determine the work function, the wavelength of the photoelectric threshold, and the retarding potential required for light of 200-mμ wavelength.*

In (3), the maximum kinetic energy is 0.5 ev since this is the potential energy increase of an electron passing through 0.5 v of retarding field, and equals its loss of kinetic energy.   The frequency f is obtained from

$$f = (c/\lambda) = (3 \times 10^8 \text{ m/sec})/(300 \times 10^{-9} \text{ m}) = 10^{15}/\text{sec}.$$

Hence $hf = (4.13 \times 10^{-15} \text{ ev·sec})(10^{15}/\text{sec}) = 4.13 \text{ ev},$

and $\phi = hf - \tfrac{1}{2} \, mv_{\text{max}}^2 = 4.13 \text{ ev} - 0.5 \text{ ev} = 3.63 \text{ ev}.$

The photoelectric threshold occurs at $hf = \phi = 3.63$ ev, or $f = 0.878 \times 10^{15}/\text{sec}$, corresponding to $\lambda = c/f = 342$ mμ. Light of *longer* wavelength than this will give no photoelectric emission since the quantum energy will be less than the work function.

The quantum energy of 200-mμ light will be $\tfrac{3}{2}$ that for 300-mμ, or $hf = \tfrac{3}{2}$ (4.13 ev) = 6.20 ev. For this light, $hf - \phi = (6.20 - 3.63)$ ev = 2.57 ev, so a retarding potential of 2.57 v would be required to stop all collection.

5. THERMIONIC VACUUM TUBES

THE PHENOMENON of *thermionic emission* of electrons provides the basis for the operation of the 'vacuum tubes' that play such an important role in modern life.   Although the subject of 'engineering electronics' is a highly specialized one and we shall not be able to discuss the details of circuits employing thermionic vacuum tubes, it is desirable to give a brief account of the basic ideas and principles involved in the construction and operation of the two simplest tubes: the *diode* and the *triode*.

The escape of electrons from the surface of a heated metal electrode in a vacuum tube leaves the metal positively charged. The electrons that have escaped are therefore attracted by the metal and form a 'negative charge cloud' or *space charge* around the electrode. Ordinarily, an equilibrium is quickly established between the number of electrons escaping from a metal surface and the number returning to the surface from the space charge. If, however, as in Edison's experiment, a second near-by electrode is maintained at a higher potential than the first, electrons in the space charge are attracted to it; and as long as the potential difference is maintained, there will be a steady movement of electrons from the first electrode to the second. The first electrode is called the *cathode;* the second is called the *anode* or *plate*. A vacuum tube containing two electrodes of this type is called a *diode*. The cathode may be a hot *filament* or a cylindrical electrode heated by an internal hot-wire called a *heater*.

In order to study the characteristics of a diode, the arrangement shown shown in Fig. 11 may be used. In this circuit the milliameter MA gives the plate current I_P for various values of plate voltage V_P, which can be

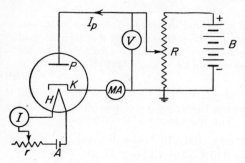

varied by means of the indicated voltage-divider arrangement popularly called a 'potentiometer' and can be read from the voltmeter V. If the potential difference V_P between plate and cathode is small, only a few of the emitted electrons reach the plate. Most of the emitted electrons penetrate only a short distance into the space charge and then return to the cathode. As the plate potential

Fig. 11. Circuit for obtaining characteristic curves of plate current *vs* plate voltage for a diode in which an indirectly-heated cathode K is used.

is increased, more and more of the emitted electrons reach the plate, and with sufficiently high potential difference *all* the emitted electrons arrive at the plate. Further increase of the plate voltage V_P does not increase the plate current, which is said to be *saturated*.

Typical graphs of plate current I_P as a function of plate voltage V_P are shown in Fig. 12. As indicated, the plate current I_P is not quite zero even when the plate voltage V_P is zero; some of the emitted electrons still have appreciable kinetic energy after penetrating the potential barrier at the cathode surface, and the more rapidly moving ones are able to penetrate the space charge and reach the plate even when there is no accelerating potential. A small retarding potential Oa (exaggerated in the figure) is sufficient to prevent these fastest electrons from reaching the plate.

The saturation current I_s is equal to the total emission current from the cathode.

As indicated in Fig. 12, the magnitude of the saturation current increases when the cathode temperature is increased by increasing the heater current. The relation between satura-

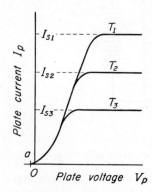

tion or total emission current and cathode temperature is given by a formula derived first by O. W. Richardson and later in a different manner by Saul Dushman:

$$J_s = A\ T^2\ e^{-\phi/kT}, \qquad (4)$$

where J_s is the total emission current per unit area at the cathode surface, A is a constant that is characteristic of the cathode surface, T is the absolute temperature of the cathode sur-

Fig. 12. Characteristic curves of a diode for three cathode temperatures $T_1 > T_2 > T_3$.

face, k is the Boltzmann constant (see p. 795), and ϕ is the *work function* of the surface. The constant A appearing in Richardson's equation is approximately the same for all pure metal surfaces: $A = 60.2$ amp/cm^2·(K deg)^2.

A plot of the Richardson equation (4) for a pure tungsten filament is shown in Fig. 13. For tungsten the work function ϕ is 4.52 electron-volts and ϕ/k is 52,500° K, since $k = 8.617 \times 10^{-5}$ ev/K deg. The controlling factor in (4) is the exponential, which prevents the expression from having appreciable values until T is about $\frac{1}{20}$ of ϕ/k.

To obtain high emission at easily attainable temperatures, it can be seen from (4) that the work function should be *small*. The cathode materials in regular use are tungsten, thoriated tungsten, and metals coated with alkaline-earth or rare-earth oxides.

Even casual inspection of Fig. 12 suggests the possibility of using a diode as a rectifier, since for positive plate voltages the plate current is

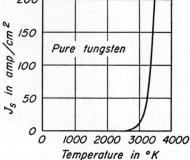

Fig. 13. Saturation current density *vs* temperature for a tungsten filament.

appreciable whereas for negative plate voltages the plate current is negligible. The use of diodes as 'half-wave' and 'full-wave' rectifiers is treated in Probs. 21 and 22 at the end of this chapter.

Before saturation has been attained, the plate current I_P in a diode can be varied by changing the plate voltage V_P. Lee De Forest, in 1907, discovered that if a third electrode called a *control grid* be inserted between the cathode and plate, the potential of this third electrode exerts much greater 'control' over the plate current than does the plate voltage itself. The grid is an open mesh of fine wire, which allows the electrons to pass

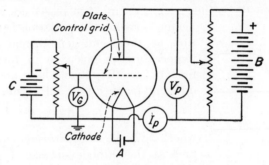

Fig. 14. Arrangement for obtaining characteristic curves of a triode.

through the openings.   A schematic diagram of a tube containing a control grid is shown in Fig. 14.   Since small variations in grid voltage produce relatively large variations in plate current, the three-electrode tube or *triode* can be used as an *amplifier*.

Commercial triodes are usually operated at potentials much lower than would be required to draw saturation current.   The plate current of

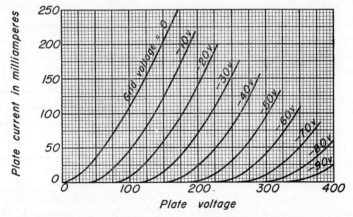

Fig. 15. Average plate characteristics for a 2A3 triode with filament heated by an A-battery of 2.5 volts.

a triode is a function of cathode temperature, plate voltage, and grid voltage.   It cannot be expressed conveniently as an algebraic function of these variables but is customarily expressed by graphs of characteristic curves like those shown in Fig. 15 for a 2A3 tube.   The filament or heater of a commercial tube is usually operated by a fixed voltage prescribed by the manufacturer, and hence the curves in the graph give the plate current for various grid and plate voltages measured relative to the cathode

at a fixed A-battery voltage.   The individual curves show plate current
as functions of plate voltage when the control-grid voltage is kept constant.   For example, when the grid voltage is -20 v and the plate voltage is 200 v, the plate current is 140 ma.   The data represented by the
curves in Fig. 15 are obtained by means of the arrangement shown schematically in Fig. 14.   The battery from which the grid voltages are
obtained is traditionally called the 'C-battery.'

The interrelations between various electrode potentials and currents
are commonly expressed in terms of *tube factors*, the values of which can
be determined from the characteristic curves.   The most useful of the
tube factors are (a) the *amplification factor μ*, (b) the *plate conductance G_P*
(or its reciprocal, the *plate resistance R_P*), and (c) the *transconductance*
G_M.   These tube factors are defined in the following way:

(a) The *amplification factor μ* is defined as the negative of the ratio of a small
change in plate voltage to a small change in grid voltage when the plate current
is kept constant.   It measures the ratio of the effectiveness of a change in control-grid voltage and of a change in plate voltage in controlling the plate current.
The amplification factor is given by the relation

$$\mu = -\Delta V_P/\Delta V_G \quad (I_P = \text{const}), \tag{5}$$

where the small changes ΔV_P and ΔV_G are read from a plot of the characteristic
curves such as that shown in Fig. 15.   The amplification factor of the 2A3 is
approximately 4 for the straight portions of the curves.

(b) The *plate conductance G_P* is defined as the ratio of a small change in plate
current to a small change in plate voltage when the grid voltage is kept constant.
The plate resistance R_P is the reciprocal of the plate conductance and is evaluated
from the relation

$$R_P = 1/G_P = \Delta V_P/\Delta I_P \quad (V_G = \text{const}), \tag{6}$$

where the small changes may be read directly from the appropriate characteristic
curve.   The plate conductance is a measure of the effect of changes in plate
voltage on plate current.   The plate resistance of the 2A3 is in the neighborhood
of 500 ohms for the straight portions of the curves of Fig. 15.

(c) The *transconductance G_M* is defined as the ratio of a small change in plate
current to a small change in grid voltage at constant plate voltage:

$$G_M = \Delta I_P/\Delta V_G \quad (V_P = \text{const}), \tag{7}$$

where ΔI_P and ΔV_G are read from a plot similar to that in Fig. 15.   The transconductance is a measure of the effect of changes of grid voltage on plate current.
The transconductance of the 2A3 is approximately 0.008 mho for the straight
portions of the characteristic curves.

The plate current increases with increase of either the plate potential
V_P or the grid potential V_G.   For small changes in these potentials we can
write, in accordance with (6) and (7),

$$\Delta I_P = \frac{\Delta V_P}{R_P} + G_M \, \Delta V_G. \tag{8}$$

If we alter both V_P and V_G so that I_P remains constant ($\Delta I_P = 0$), we have, from (8),

$$0 = \frac{\Delta V_P}{R_P} + G_M \, \Delta V_G$$

or

$$-\frac{\Delta V_P}{\Delta V_G} = G_M \, R_P.$$

But, from (5), this ratio equals the amplification factor μ, so the three tube factors are connected by the relation

$$\mu = G_M \, R_P.$$

Equation (8) can now be rewritten in the form

$$\Delta I_P = \frac{\Delta V_P + \mu \, \Delta V_G}{R_P}, \qquad (9)$$

which shows again that grid-voltage changes have μ times as much effect on plate current as equal plate-voltage changes.

We shall not be able to go into the details of circuits employing triodes. The important circuits are of two types, *amplifiers* and *oscillators*. An amplifier is so arranged that small oscillating voltages applied to the grid so influence the plate current that amplified oscillating voltages appear across a resistance or an inductance in the plate circuit. If the tube is operated on the straight part of the characteristics, the amplification can be faithful (of high fidelity). In a radio receiver the weak antenna signal is ordinarily amplified several times at radio frequency, then transformed by rectification and filtering to audio frequency, and then again amplified several times at audio frequency before being applied to the loudspeaker.

One of the important applications of vacuum tubes is in circuits for the *generation* of high-frequency electrical oscillations. We have noted that the application of small AC voltages to the grid of a triode can result in the production of larger AC voltages in the plate circuit of the triode. If a part of the AC voltage in the plate circuit is returned to the grid in proper phase through a 'feed-back network,' larger grid voltages are produced and these larger grid voltages will in turn produce still larger plate voltages. If the plate and grid are both properly coupled to LC circuit elements, the circuits begin to oscillate. An LC circuit will oscillate at its resonance frequency $1/2\pi \sqrt{LC}$ computed in (32), p. 766. To maintain steady oscillation, it is necessary that energy be supplied to the circuit at the same rate as energy is removed from the circuit by resistance heating or other dissipative losses. The triode is able to acquire the needed energy from its B-supply when properly connected.

Shortly after De Forest introduced the control grid, it was found that additional grids could be used to advantage in thermionic vacuum tubes. A treatment of these multi-element tubes is beyond the scope of our present interest, but it might be remarked that vacuum tubes with as many as eight electrodes are now in common use.

6. TRANSISTORS

ONE OF the essential characteristics of vacuum tubes is that they are 'non-linear' circuit elements. By a nonlinear element, we mean an element in which the current is not directly proportional to applied voltage. That vacuum tubes are certainly not linear devices is illustrated by the quite different behavior of plate current when positive and negative plate voltages are applied. Since thermionic vacuum tubes have proved so useful, the question arises as to whether useful nonlinear elements cannot be provided in still other ways. Work in recent years has shown that the properties of semiconductors can be used to advantage in constructing nonlinear circuit elements.

In Chap. 29 we have pointed out how a rectifier can be constructed by making *two* connections to a semiconducting material. One of the two connections is made in such a way that a rectifying barrier is formed; electrons move freely through the barrier in one direction and with great difficulty in the other direction. The behavior of such a circuit element is therefore similar to that of a thermionic *diode*.

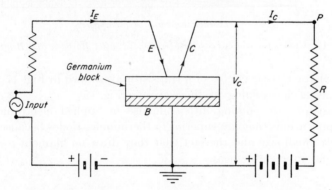

Fig. 16. Schematic diagram of transistor. Small input voltages produce large variations in potential across the resistor.

The possibility of making *three* connections to a semiconductor and having the resulting device behave as a *triode* is immediately apparent. Such a device was developed at the Bell Telephone Laboratories in 1948 and is called a *transistor*. A schematic diagram of a transistor is shown in Fig. 16. The transistor consists of a tiny block of germanium with three electrodes: the base electrode B, electrode E called the *emitter*, and electrode C called the *collector*. Electrodes E and C make rectifying contacts with the germanium block; the barriers at the rectifying contacts readily pass currents in the directions shown by the arrows but not in the reverse directions. The rectifying contacts are close together on the surface of the germanium block.

When the emitter is biased to establish current in the direction shown, the input current I_E is found to control the output current I_C in a manner that is analogous to the way in which grid voltage controls plate current in a thermionic triode. Thus, an input signal consisting of a small variation ΔI_E in emitter current will produce a large variation ΔI_C in collector current. This property makes it possible to use the transistor as an amplifier.

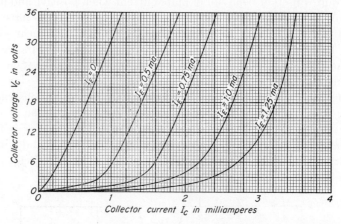

Fig. 17. Characteristic curves for a transistor [*after Bardeen and Brattain*].

The characteristic curves of a transistor are shown in Fig. 17. These curves have a close analogy to those given in Fig. 15.

Transistors are coming into wide use in applied electronics. For many applications they are superior to thermionic triodes because of their extremely small size and the fact that they draw no filament power and produce no appreciable heat.

7. X RAYS

INCIDENT photons cause the emission of electrons in the photoelectric effect. The inverse process—the emission of photons by a metal when electrons are incident—results in the production of X rays.

In 1895, Wilhelm Konrad Roentgen discovered that when high-speed electrons impinge upon the walls of discharge tubes or upon metal electrodes, penetrating radiation is given off. The name *X rays* was applied because the nature of the radiation was not known. Today we know that X rays are electromagnetic radiation like light, but of much shorter wavelengths and higher frequencies than visible light.

When an electron with an energy of several thousand electron-volts strikes a metal target, X rays are emitted from the surface.   There is a distribution of energy among the emitted photons, but the maximum energy, corresponding to the maximum frequency f_{Max} of the emitted radiation, can be obtained from the photoelectric equation (3) as

$$hf_{\text{Max}} = \tfrac{1}{2}mv^2, \tag{10}$$

where v is the speed of the incident electrons.   In the case of X rays the magnitude of the work function ϕ is so small compared with the photon energy that it can be neglected in the photoelectric equation.   The target in an X-ray tube emits X rays of all frequencies below the *maximum* frequency, and the spectrum of the emitted X rays extends indefinitely from the wavelength corresponding to f_{Max} toward longer wavelengths.

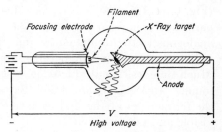

Fig. 18. X-ray tube. Electrons emitted by the filament strike the metal target on the anode. X rays are emitted from the target.

X rays are emitted by nonmetals as well as metals, although for convenience the target in a commercial X-ray tube (Fig. 18) is always metallic.   The spectrum emitted from a heavy element is continuous, but superimposed on this continuous spectrum are 'bright lines' corresponding to *characteristic* X rays.   The frequencies of the bright lines are determined by the element of which the target is made.   Spectral series of characteristic X rays arise from changes in energy of the inner electrons of the atoms.   Just as the atoms of every element have characteristic emission lines in the visible spectrum when properly excited, so the atoms of the heavy elements have characteristic lines in the X-ray spectrum.   As pointed out in the next section, visible spectra appear as the result of energy changes of a few electron-volts involving the *outer electrons;* X-ray spectra appear as the result of energy changes of thousands of electron-volts involving the *inner electrons*.

The penetrating properties of X rays are so well known that they will not be discussed here.   They are widely utilized in the fields of medicine and surgery and in location of imperfections in metal structures.

The wavelengths of X rays are much shorter than those of visible light and are small enough to be comparable to the interatomic distances in crystals.   Hence, crystal lattices can act as 'gratings' for X rays in much the same manner as ruled gratings are used in the visible region.   From the observed X-ray diffraction patterns, interatomic distances in crystals can be accurately measured when the wavelength of the X rays is known (see Fig. 20, p. 815).

8. LINE SPECTRA; QUANTUM MECHANICS

The quantum theory was initially developed to account for the shape of the black-body radiation curves giving spectral emissive power as a function of wavelength; it was next used to explain the photoelectric effect.   Now let us see how this theory can be applied to another emission process—the emission of *line spectra* by atoms.   In this case, we have to account for the discrete frequencies present in the observed spectra.

The simplest in appearance of all atomic spectra is that of hydrogen (Fig. 6, p. 536); the spectra of other atoms are much less regular (compare the Fe lines in Fig. 9, p. 539).   There are no frequency sequences analogous to the fundamental and overtones that might be expected if a radiating atom were comparable in any way with an electrical oscillator. Much time was spent in looking for sequences of this type, but none were found.   In 1885, Johann Jakob Balmer found a simple formula that gives the frequencies of the hydrogen lines appearing in Fig. 6, p. 536, in the visible and near ultraviolet:

$$f = cR \left(\frac{1}{4} - \frac{1}{n^2} \right), \tag{11}$$

where c is the speed of light, R is a quantity called the *Rydberg constant* whose value is 10,967,758 m^{-1}, and n is a number that takes the integral values 3, 4, 5, 6, $\cdots$ for the various lines of the series.   The frequencies of the lines in this series increase with increasing n and converge to the limit $\frac{1}{4} cR$ as n becomes large.   Further examination of the spectrum of atomic hydrogen in regions outside the visible region revealed the existence of several similar spectral series which have been named for their discoverers:

Lyman series: $f = cR \left(\dfrac{1}{1^2} - \dfrac{1}{n^2} \right)$,   where $n = 2, 3, 4, \cdots$ (ultraviolet)

Balmer series: $f = cR \left(\dfrac{1}{2^2} - \dfrac{1}{n^2} \right)$,   where $n = 3, 4, 5, \cdots$ (visible)

Paschen series: $f = cR \left(\dfrac{1}{3^2} - \dfrac{1}{n^2} \right)$,   where $n = 4, 5, 6, \cdots$ (infrared)

Brackett series: $f = cR \left(\dfrac{1}{4^2} - \dfrac{1}{n^2} \right)$,   where $n = 5, 6, 7, \cdots$ (infrared)

Pfund series: $f = cR \left(\dfrac{1}{5^2} - \dfrac{1}{n^2} \right)$,   where $n = 6, 7, 8, \cdots$ (infrared)

Humphreys series: $f = cR \left(\dfrac{1}{6^2} - \dfrac{1}{n^2} \right)$,   where $n = 7, 8, 9, \cdots$ (far infrared)

The frequencies of *all* observed lines of atomic hydrogen are contained in the above series.

It will be noted that the frequency of any observed spectral line of hydrogen can be written as the difference of two frequencies, called *term frequencies*.   The term frequencies are

$$f_n = (1/n^2)\, cR. \qquad (n = 1, 2, 3, \cdots) \qquad (12)$$

The number of term frequencies is considerably smaller than the number of lines; every possible difference between two term frequencies gives the frequency of a spectral line. In the case of hydrogen, the term frequencies are represented by the positions of the horizontal lines in Fig. 19 measured down from the line marked 0.   The lengths of the various vertical lines in Fig. 19 represent term differences and are proportional to the frequencies of the spectral lines in the various series as indicated.   The term values are plotted down from a zero at the top for a reason that will be made clear in a moment.

Similar regularities were found in other spectra more complicated than that of hydrogen, and resulted in the formulation by Ritz in 1908 of the *combination principle*, according to which each atom may be characterized by a set of numbers called *term frequencies*, such that the actual frequencies of the spectral lines are given by the differences between these term frequencies.

It remained for Niels Bohr in 1913 to suggest that each term represents an *energy level* of the atom. This hypothesis was the beginning of the *quantum mechanics* of atomic structure, as distinguished from the quantum theory of radiation which we have discussed earlier.   According

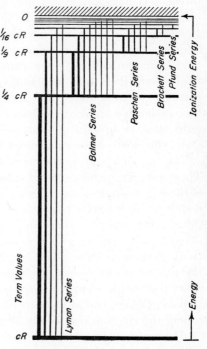

Fig. 19. The spectrum of atomic hydrogen. The horizontal lines represent allowed energy levels of the atom, associated with $n = 1, 2, \cdots, \infty$ as we go from the lowest level up to the ionization energy. When the atom makes a transition from one energy level to a lower one in this diagram, it emits radiation of frequency proportional to the energy difference, that is, proportional to the *length* of the vertical line connecting the two energy levels.

to quantum mechanics, an atom (or a molecule) cannot have an arbitrary amount of internal energy; rather, it must at any time be in one of a discrete set of states, each having a particular value of energy.   When it is not in its state of lowest energy, it will spontaneously make a transition to one of the states of lower energy, the energy released appearing as a single

quantum of radiation of frequency f such that the energy released equals
hf.   Correspondingly, if radiation falls on the atom it can absorb a single
quantum, but of only such frequencies f that the quantum energy hf is
exactly the energy needed to excite the atom to one of its possible states
of higher energy.

These ideas can be clarified by returning to the term diagram for
hydrogen, Fig. 19.   The horizontal lines can now be interpreted as energy
levels.   At normal temperatures all the hydrogen atoms are in the state
of lowest energy at the bottom of the diagram, called the *ground state*.
In the ground state the electron is at an average distance of about
0.5×10^{-10} m from the nucleus, which is a single proton in the most common hydrogen isotope.   According to any classical theory of the negatively charged electron revolving around the positively charged proton in
planetary fashion under the influence of the electrical force of attraction,
the accelerated charged electron would radiate away its energy and fall
right into the proton, but this does not happen.   When in this ground
state, the electron loses no energy by radiation.

The possible states of motion of the electron are said to be *quantized*.
There are only certain allowed states; and when the electron is in any one
of these states it does not radiate—it radiates or absorbs energy only when
it shifts from one state to another.   The states above the ground state are
called *excited states*.   These are states of higher energy; and since energy
is required to pull the electron away from the proton, it is accurate to
think of them as states in which the electron is farther and farther from
the proton as the energy increases.   The allowed states get closer and
closer together in energy in accordance with our previous discussion of the
terms and finally end at the ionization energy, which is the energy required
to pull the electron completely away from the proton.

Hydrogen molecules can be dissociated into atoms and the atoms
raised to excited states so as to excite the emission spectrum by either (a)
raising the temperature of the gas sufficiently, (b) using an electrical discharge, or (c) illuminating the gas with ultraviolet light of frequency
corresponding to that of one of the lines in the Lyman series.

Emission of radiation corresponds to transitions downward in Fig. 19;
absorption of radiation corresponds to transitions upward.   In each case
the frequency of radiation is exactly proportional to the energy change,
the proportionality factor being Planck's constant h.   Hence, the frequency of the radiation is proportional to the length of the vertical lines
in Fig. 19, since this length represents the magnitude of the energy change.
If we call the ionization energy zero, as is most convenient, the term
frequency f_n must be associated with the *negative* energy $E_n = -hf_n$.
When the atom makes a transition from state n to state n' ($n > n'$ for
emission), the energy released is $E_n - E_{n'} = -h(f_n - f_{n'})$.   For example,
the first Balmer line involves a change from $n = 3$ to $n' = 2$, releasing energy

given by (12) as

$$E_3 - E_2 = -h(f_3 - f_2) = h(f_2 - f_3) = h\, cR \left(\frac{1}{4} - \frac{1}{9} \right),$$

corresponding to the quantum energy of a photon of the first Balmer frequency ($n = 3$ in Eq. (11)).

There is a large body of experimental evidence of various types, all confirming the correctness of the above picture. We shall describe only one type of experiment, first performed by James Franck and Gustav Hertz in 1913, that gives very direct confirmation of the energy-level interpretation of spectral terms. A beam of hydrogen atoms (not molecules) in the ground state is sent down a vacuum tube; the beam is bombarded from the side by electrons of known and controlled energy, and a spectrograph is focused on the beam. A bombarding electron is capable of imparting some or all of its kinetic energy to a hydrogen atom when it collides with the atom. But when the bombarding electrons have energy below the quantum energy hf of the first line of the Lyman series (compare Fig. 19), no spectrum appears, because the hydrogen atom in its ground state is incapable of absorbing *less* than this energy. When the electron energy exceeds the quantum energy of the first Lyman line but is less than that of the second, only the first Lyman line appears in the spectrum. When the energy exceeds the quantum energy of the second Lyman line but is less than that of the third, the first two Lyman lines *and* the first Balmer line appear in the spectrum. And so on. Similar experiments performed with a large number of different types of atoms completely confirm the correspondence of energy levels and term frequencies.

Each element of the periodic table has an energy-level diagram similar to Fig. 19, in which the energy differences correspond to observed spectral lines. In no other case is this diagram so simple as that for hydrogen. The energy values, and hence the spectral-line frequencies, for any atom are given by the formulas of the *quantum mechanics* initiated by Schrödinger and Heisenberg in 1925.

Each diatomic or polyatomic molecule also has a characteristic energy-level diagram, in which the energy levels occur in closely spaced groups, so the lines also occur in closely spaced groups called bands—hence the term *band spectrum* (see Fig. 8, p. 538).

9. PHOTONS; WAVES ASSOCIATED WITH MATERIAL PARTICLES

In our discussion of the quantum theory of radiation, we have pointed out that energy is always emitted or absorbed in discrete units or quanta. If the frequency of the radiation is f, the energy E of a single quantum is given by $E = hf$. When the frequency is low, the energy of a single quantum is so small that it is impossible for any physical instrument to detect a single quantum.

Thus, for low radio frequencies a large number of quanta must be received in order for any detecting instrument to give a response. The reception of large numbers of quanta with the energy of each quantum extremely small gives the impression of a *continuous* process of reception, analogous to our feeling that light energy enters our eyes and produces stimuli continuously and not by discontinuous processes.

At X-ray frequencies, the quantum energy is about 10^{12} times as high as that for AM radio (see Fig. 3), and *a single quantum can easily be detected*, even by a relatively insensitive detector. This fact gives us further evidence that emission and absorption are actually quantum processes. The individual photons in the X-ray and γ-ray regions have such distinctive properties that they have many of the characteristics of particles.

At X-ray frequencies, the interaction of individual photons with matter can easily be studied. Arthur H. Compton, in 1924, discovered that when a monochromatic beam of X rays of frequency f is scattered by a gas, *two* frequencies are present in the scattered beam. One frequency f is equal to the frequency of the original unscattered X rays in the incident beam; this frequency was to be expected on the basis of the classical electromagnetic theory of scattering. The other frequency f', not expected from classical theory, is always less than the frequency of the incident X rays and is dependent on the scattering angle θ.

Compton was able to account for the change in frequency of the scattered radiation by considering the incident photon as a 'particle' with energy hf and with momentum of magnitude hf/c. Scattering is assumed to take place as a result of a collision between the incident photon and an electron in the scattering material. The energy of the incident photon is large compared to the energy binding the electron into the atom, so the electron can be considered as essentially free in this collision. As a result of the collision, a part of the energy and momentum of the incident photon is transferred to the electron, so that the final energy hf' and momentum hf'/c of the scattered photon are less than those of the incident photon. By writing the conservation-of-energy and the conservation-of-momentum relations for a collision of this type, Compton was able to account exactly for the observed frequency changes. We shall not go through the calculation, but shall merely point out that *we can explain the results of Compton's scattering experiment by treating the X-ray photon as a particle of energy hf having momentum of magnitude $hf/c = h/\lambda$*. Observations of the recoil electrons knocked out of the gas have shown that they do indeed have the momentum and energy to be expected from the momentum and energy equations for a collision with a particle with the initial momentum and energy assumed for the photon.

On the basis of this *Compton effect*, we might be led to the conclusion that X rays consist of particles and are not waves at all. However, there are other X-ray phenomena that can be explained only on the basis of wave properties.   The wavelength of X rays is of the same order of magnitude as the distance between the atoms or ions in crystals, and crystals can be used as three-dimensional diffraction gratings for X rays.   The diffraction pattern produced when a pencil of X rays passes through powdered steel is shown in Fig. 20. Such diffraction phenomena give abundant evidence that X rays also have wave characteristics.

This dual nature of X rays—particle nature in the Compton effect and wave nature in diffraction—is completely contrary to classical ideas, but this dualism is now regarded as characteristic not only of electromagnetic radiation but of matter as well. Just as we were accustomed to think of *light* as consisting of *waves*, so also we were accustomed to think of *matter* as consisting of *particles*.   Visible light and radio waves do not have a

Fig. 20. X-ray diffraction pattern of powdered steel. [*From Clark, Applied X-rays (McGraw-Hill).*]

readily observable particle nature, and particles large enough to be seen do not have a readily observable wave nature.   However, as we have seen in the preceding section, the behavior of tiny 'particles' such as electrons, atoms, and molecules cannot be completely described in terms of the 'classical' principles of motion and electromagnetic theory.

In 1924, Louis Victor de Broglie suggested that *the motion of an electron or of any other material particle is associated with a wave motion of wavelength*

$$\lambda = h/mv,$$

where h is Planck's constant, m is the mass of the particle, and v is its speed.   For an electron having an energy E, in ev, the wavelength in $m\mu$ given by the above expression is $\lambda = 1.2263 \ (m\mu \cdot ev^{1/2})/\sqrt{E}$.   Thus, an electron with an energy of 100 ev would, according to de Broglie, have a characteristic wavelength of 0.12263 $m\mu$.   This wavelength is comparable to the wavelengths of X rays.   Therefore, if de Broglie's hypothesis is correct, an electron beam passing through a thin film of powdered crystal or through a metal film should experience diffraction similar to that experienced by an X-ray beam.   Diffraction of an electron beam was first observed in 1927 by C. J. Davisson and L. H. Germer.   A photograph of an electron diffraction pattern is shown in Fig. 21.   The essential similarity between this diffraction pattern and the X-ray diffraction pattern shown in Fig. 20 is at once apparent.   We are led to the conclusion that the de Broglie hypothesis is correct.   Consideration of the above expression for the de Broglie wavelength reveals that for particles of large mass, the associated wavelength is so small, even for the low speeds of thermal agitation, that no diffraction phenomena can be observed, and hence the wave nature of large particles cannot be readily detected.

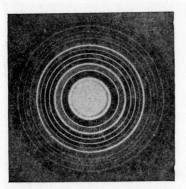

The de Broglie hypothesis was taken over by Erwin Schrödinger and Werner Heisenberg, who used it in the development of modern *quantum mechanics*, or, as it is sometimes called, *wave mechanics*. The quantum mechanics of Schrödinger and Heisenberg enables us to predict correctly the characteristic energy levels of an atom or molecule from certain perfectly general equations.   When quantum mechanics is applied to a system involving macroscopic bodies, the number of characteristic energy levels is so great and the levels are so close together that the results become equivalent to those obtained by classical Newtonian mechanics.

Fig. 21. Electron diffraction pattern of cesium iodide. [*From Stranathan, Particles of Modern Physics (Blakiston).*]

Thus, we see that both matter and photons have properties of the character that we ordinarily ascribe to 'particles,' and properties of the character that we ordinarily ascribe to 'waves.'   The 'particle' properties of radio-frequency photons are not apparent because only a very large number of photons can be detected.   The 'wave' properties of macroscopic matter are not apparent because the wavelength is undetectably small.   In the X-ray region, photons show both 'particle' and 'wave' properties very strikingly; in the γ-ray region, only the 'particle' properties of the photons are apparent because again the wavelength is undetectably small.   Slow-speed electrons and neutrons have detectably large wavelengths, so their 'wave' properties are apparent.

Both photons and material particles have energy, momentum, and wavelength.   'Wave' properties are apparent only if the wavelength is detectable, which means in practice that it is at least sufficiently large to be comparable to the 'grating' spacing of crystals.   Properties ordinarily associated with 'particles' are apparent only if the energy and momentum are sufficiently large so that individuals can be detected.

The above discussion is not intended to imply that there is not a fundamental difference between photons and material particles.   In spite of the fact they they share similar physical properties such as energy, momentum, and wavelength, there is one fundamental difference: a photon always moves with the speed c of light, whereas a material particle always moves with a speed that is less than c. It is always possible to imagine an observer for whom any material particle would be at rest, but a photon cannot be at rest for any observer. There are other fundamental differences in the manner of interaction with material charged particles that justify the conclusion that the 'wave' associated with photons is electromagnetic in nature whereas the 'wave' associated with material particles is of quite another character unspecifiable in terms of ordinary macroscopic physical quantities.

PROBLEMS

1. If the wavelength of the radiation in Hertz's apparatus was 5.4 m and the capacitance was 1.33 $\mu\mu$f, what was the inductance?   Ans: 6.17 μhenry.

2. With a capacitance of 1.33 $\mu\mu$f, what is the inductance in Hertz's apparatus, if the wavelength of the radiation is 6.5 m?

3. At what wavelength does the black-body emission curve have its maximum at room temperature (27° C)?   Ans: 9.657 μ.

4. The melting point of tungsten is 3400° C. At what wavelength does the black-body radiation curve for this temperature have its maximum?

5. The maximum of the radiation curve for the sun occurs at 480 mμ. What would be the temperature of a black body for which the radiation curve would have a maximum at this wavelength?   Ans: 6160° K.

6. What would be the temperature of a black body for which the intensity maximum occurred in the infrared at 1000 mμ? in the ultraviolet at 100 mμ?

7. From Planck's formula, compute the relative spectral emissive powers for black-body radiation at 400 mμ (deep violet), 500 mμ (green), and 600 mμ (orange), setting the emissive power at 500 mμ equal to 1 in each case, for (a) a tungsten filament at 3000° K, (b) the sun at 6000° K, (c) Vega at 12,000° K.
Ans: (a) 0.28:1:1.99; (b) 0.91:1:0.90; (c) 1.60:1:0.63.

8. Compare Betelgeuse (3000° K) and Vega (12,000° K) with the sun (6000° K) with regard to (a) total emissive power, (b) spectral emissive power at 600 mμ, (c) spectral emissive power at 100 mμ. Assume that all three stars radiate like black bodies.

9. By counting squares under the 6000° curve of Fig. 5, estimate the total emissive power and compare with the value 7.4×10^7 watts/m² given by the Stefan-Boltzmann formula.

10. From the Planck formula (1), derive the Stefan-Boltzmann law and Wien's displacement law.

11. In an oil-droplet experiment, the condenser plates are 1.60 cm apart, the radius of the oil droplet is 2.8×10^{-4} cm, and the density of the oil is 0.92 g/cm³. If a single excess electron is attached to the droplet, what voltage should be applied between the condenser plates in order to counterbalance the weight of the oil droplet?   Ans: 5.18×10^4 v.

12. With the apparatus described in Prob. 11, what voltage should be applied between the condenser plates in order to support an oil droplet of radius 5.52×10^{-4} cm if two excess electrons are attached to the droplet?

13. In an arrangement for measuring e/m for the electron, the accelerating voltage is 10 kv. The distance between the deflecting plates is 0.8 cm and the voltage between the deflecting plates is 500 volts. Find the intensity of the magnetic field that must be applied in the region between the deflecting plates in order to give zero deflection. Ans: 1.05×10^{-3} weber/m².

14. If the accelerating voltage used in the arrangement described in the preceding problem were reduced to 5 kv, what should be the value of the magnetic intensity if the voltage between the deflecting plates is maintained at 500 volts?

15. The photoelectric threshold of tungsten is 273 mμ. Determine the maximum kinetic energy of the electrons ejected from a tungsten surface by ultraviolet light of wavelength 180 mμ. Ans: 2.35 ev.

16. What is the maximum kinetic energy of electrons ejected from tungsten by ultraviolet light of wavelength 100 mμ if the photoelectric threshold is 273 mμ?

17. When a copper surface is illuminated by light of wavelength 253.7 mμ from a mercury arc, the value of the retarding potential required to stop the emission of electrons is 0.59 volt. What is the photoelectric threshold for copper? Ans: 288 mμ.

18. When a copper surface with photoelectric threshold at 288 mμ is illuminated by light of wavelength 200 mμ, what retarding potential is required to stop the collection of electrons?

19. If the photoelectric threshold of tungsten is 273 mμ, what is its work function in electron-volts? Ans: 4.58 ev.

20. If the photoelectric threshold of copper is 288 mμ, what is its work function in electron-volts?

21. For a diode connected to a transformer as in Fig. 22, make a sketch of the current through resistor R as a function of time for a case in which saturation current is never approached and for a case in which saturation current is reached.

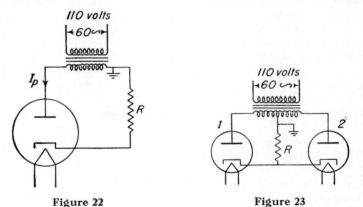

Figure 22   Figure 23

22. For two diodes connected to a transformer as in Fig. 23, make a sketch of the current through resistor R as a function of time for a case in which saturation is never approached and for a case in which saturation is reached. How could you use a large capacitor C to maintain a nearly constant DC voltage across R? How could a large inductor L be used for this purpose?

23. Calculate the minimum energy in ev that a bombarding electron must have in order to produce X rays of wavelength 0.1 mμ. Ans: 12,400 ev.

24. What is the shortest wavelength produced in an X-ray tube operated at 1 million volts?

25. The most intense line radiated by the hydrogen atom (the first Lyman line in the ultraviolet, see Fig. 19) has a frequency of 2.5×10^{15} cycles/sec. When this line is being radiated, the electron orbit has a diameter of 2×10^{-10} m. What is the ratio of the wavelength to the diameter of the orbit? A typical gamma ray radiated by a nucleus of diameter 10^{-15} m has a frequency of 5×10^{20} cycles/sec. What is the ratio of the wavelength to the diameter of the nucleus?

Ans: 600; 600.

26. For efficient radiation, radio transmitting antennas are usually made at least one-quarter wavelength long. What is the length of a quarter-wave antenna at the following frequencies: 15 kilocycles/sec (naval communications); 1000 kc/sec (AM radio); 100 Mc/sec (television); 10,000 Mc/sec (microwave radio).

27. What is the wavelength of the first line of the Lyman series in the spectrum of hydrogen? In what spectral region is it found? Ans: 122 mμ.

28. What is the wavelength of the first line in the Balmer series of hydrogen? In what spectral region does it occur?

29. What minimum energy, in ev, must an electron have in order to excite the first Lyman line of hydrogen in the Franck-Hertz experiment? What is the quantum energy in joules of the radiation in the first Lyman line?

Ans: 10.2 ev; 1.63×10^{-18} joule.

30. What minimum energy, in ev, must an electron have in order to excite the first Balmer line in the Franck-Hertz experiment? What is the quantum energy in joules of the radiation of the first Balmer line?

31. How many quanta of visible light of wavelength 500 mμ would have a total energy equivalent to the energy of a single quantum of X radiation of wavelength 0.1 mμ? Ans: 5000.

32. How many quanta of radiation of 30 m wavelength would have a total energy equal to the energy of a single X-ray quantum of wavelength 2 mμ?

33. The distance between adjacent planes in a certain crystal is 0.15 mμ. Taking this distance as the equivalent grating interval, find the angle at which the first-order diffraction maximum would occur if X rays of wavelength 0.075 mμ strike the hypothetical grating at normal incidence. Ans: 30°.

34. At what angle would the first-order diffraction pattern from the crystal grating of Prob. 31 be observed if X radiation of 0.1-mμ wavelength struck the grating at normal incidence?

35. Calculate the energy and momentum of a photon of X radiation of wavelength 0.1 mμ. Ans: 1.99×10^{-15} joule; 6.62×10^{-24} kg·m/sec.

36. Find the energy and momentum of a photon of X radiation of wavelength 0.03 mμ.

37. From the expression for the de Broglie wavelength, $\lambda = h/mv$, verify the correctness of the relation $\lambda = 1.2263 \, (\text{m}\mu \cdot \text{ev}^{1/2})/\sqrt{E}$ for the wavelength associated with an electron of energy E in electron-volts.

38. Calculate the wavelengths associated with electrons that have been accelerated through potential differences of 1 volt, 10 volts, 100 volts, and 1000 volts.

39. From the de Broglie relation, calculate the wavelength associated with a 'thermal' neutron of kinetic energy $\frac{1}{30}$ ev. Ans: 0.157 mμ.

40. When X rays of wavelength 10^{-10} m impinge on matter, the X rays that are scattered at 90° to the original beam have wavelength 1.0242×10^{-10} m. Determine the magnitude and direction of the velocity of the recoiling electron in order that momentum be conserved. Compute the energies of the original photon, the scattered photon, and the electron, and verify that energy is conserved within the accuracy of your computation.

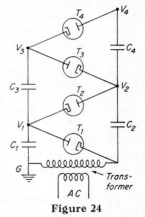

41. The rectifying properties of diodes are used in the Cockcroft-Walton machine for obtaining high voltages for use in obtaining high-energy charged particles in an acceleration tube like that shown in Fig. 44, p. 583. The first few sections of a Cockcroft-Walton circuit are shown in Fig. 24. The diodes T_1, T_2, T_3, and T_4 act as electronic switches. Trace the current paths (a) when the right-hand end of the transformer secondary is negative and (b) when it is positive. If the secondary voltage at the transformer is 100,000 volts, show that condenser C_1 is charged to 100,000 volts in case (a) and shares its charge with C_2 in case (b). Show that the difference of potential between the plates of C_2 is 200,000 volts after several cycles.

Figure 24

The combination of C_1, C_2, T_1, and T_2 is called a voltage doubler section. Find the potential of point V_4 with respect to ground. What is the maximum difference of potential between the plates of C_4?   Ans: 400 kv, 200 kv.

42. How would you arrange the diodes in Fig. 24 if you wish to use the difference of potential between V_4 and G to accelerate deuterons? electrons? If you are given 40 large diodes capable of withstanding a peak voltage of 60 kv and 40 condensers capable of withstanding 50 kv, design a Cockcroft-Walton circuit to give maximum positive voltage above ground. What should be the secondary voltage on the transformer you must purchase for use on a 120-v, 60-$\sim$ line?

43. Electron 'lenses' are regions of strongly non-uniform electric or magnetic fields that are capable of 'focusing' an electron beam, as indicated in Fig. 25. In an electron microscope a divergent beam of electrons from a filament is rendered parallel by a 'condensing' lens; then passes through the 'object' in the form of a thin film, or is reflected from the surface of a solid object; the beam is focused by an 'objective' lens and again by a 'camera' lens onto a photographic plate. The result is a 'picture' of the object enlarged as much as 30,000 times. Wave properties of the electron are not involved in the image formation, just as the wave properties of light are not involved in ray optics. But just as in optics, wave properties control the angular resolution.

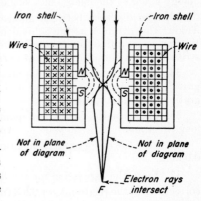

Fig. 25. A modern magnetic lens.

Compare the angular resolutions of light and electron microscopes of the same objective 'aperture' if 100-ev electrons are used.

CHAPTER 38

NUCLEAR PHYSICS

ALTHOUGH nineteenth-century scientists regarded atoms of a given element as indestructible and immutable units, developments that took place during the closing days of the nineteenth century did much to alter this view. The clear recognition of the electron as an elementary particle which could be removed from material bodies by thermal and photoelectric emission processes indicated that the electron is a constituent part of atoms. The discovery of natural radioactivity indicated that the atoms of the heaviest elements such as uranium, thorium, and radium are spontaneously disintegrating to produce elements of lower atomic mass and in the process are emitting charged particles at high speed. The charged particles emitted were identified as electrons (called *beta particles*) and positively charged helium nuclei (called *alpha particles*). These discoveries indicated that atoms are not really indivisible, as the name *atom* implies, but are composed of simpler elementary particles, of which the electron was the first to be discovered.

In this chapter we shall discuss briefly the nuclear model of the atom, and nuclear reactions that result in changes in atomic species. Nuclear reactions give rise to transformation of mass to energy (so-called *atomic energy*); to understand this transformation we must explain the basic ideas of the theory of relativity. The chapter concludes with a brief description of the present status of knowledge of elementary particles.

1. THE NUCLEAR MODEL OF THE ATOM

THE APPROXIMATE sizes of the atoms and lighter molecules (diameters of the order of 0.1 mμ or 10^{-10} m) were known at the beginning of the present century from interpretation of the observed properties of gases on the basis of kinetic theory. After the discovery that electrons formed a part of the structure of atoms, J. J. Thomson proposed a model of the atom in which the electrons were embedded in a matrix of positive electric charge like plums in a pudding. Vibration of the electrons about their equilibrium positions was supposed to result in the emission of light. The Thomson model was not satisfactory, and was discarded in 1911 in favor of a nuclear model proposed by Ernest Rutherford (1871–1937).

Rutherford proposed the nuclear model to account for results obtained in his experiments on the scattering of high-speed, doubly charged helium atoms (alpha particles) by matter. A schematic diagram of the experimental arrangement he used is shown in Fig. 1. Alpha particles emitted by a naturally radioactive source were allowed to pass through a hole in a metal shield and strike a thin gold foil which acted as a scatterer. The alpha particles scattered at various angles θ with the incident beam were counted by observing the scintillations produced when the particles impinged upon a fluorescent screen. On the basis of the Thomson model, there should be no electric fields near or within the gold atoms intense enough to produce scattering at large angles. In the experiment, however, it was observed that some of the alpha particles were scattered through angles even greater than 90°; that is, some alpha particles emerged from the gold foil on the same side they entered. In order to explain such large-angle scattering of high-speed alpha particles, Rutherford was forced to assume the existence of an intense electric field within the atom. To provide such an intense field, Rutherford assumed that the entire positive charge of the atom was concentrated in a very small nucleus and that electrons occupied the space outside the nucleus. Subsequent careful scattering experiments substantiated Rutherford's theory and showed that the positive charge Ze on the nucleus of an atom must be concentrated within a region of the order of 10^{-15} m in diameter (only 1/100,000 of the diameter of the atom), in order to give a sufficiently intense repulsive field to account for the observed scattering. Further evidence of the essential correctness of the Rutherford model was obtained when Bohr successfully used it in his theory of the hydrogen spectrum. The analysis of the spectra of the atoms of other elements has enabled us to obtain detailed information on the arrangement of the extranuclear electrons in various atoms and has given ample evidence for the correctness of the nuclear model.

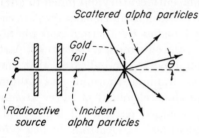

Figure 1

One can thus visualize an atom of atomic number Z as a tiny nucleus of positive charge Ze (which we shall see contains most of the mass of the atom), around which Z negatively charged electrons move in planetary fashion in much the same way as the planets move around the sun. The atomic numbers of all known elements are shown in the tables of sections 4 and 9 of the Appendix.

In the same way that the mass of the electron can be determined by e/m measurements once e had been determined, the masses of atoms can be determined or compared from analogous Q/m measurements on

ions of known charge Q.   A device for making such measurements, called
a *mass spectrograph*, is shown in Fig. 2.   Positive ions (charge $Q = +e$) of
the element being studied are formed in a discharge tube; after acceleration, a narrow beam of high-speed ions passes through slits S_1 and S_2 into
an evacuated region containing a uniform magnetic field of flux density
$\mathscr{B}'$ directed away from the reader, and containing a uniform electric field
$\mathscr{E}$ set up by the plates of a parallel-plate condenser.   By varying the
voltage on the condenser plates, the force $\mathscr{E}Q$ exerted on the ions by the
electric field can be made equal and opposite to the force $\mathscr{B}'Qv$ exerted by
the magnetic field on ions having speed v; when this is done, all ions with
speed $v = \mathscr{E}/\mathscr{B}'$ will pass through the third slit S_3 regardless of differences

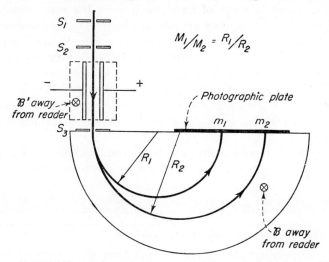

Fig. 2. A mass spectrograph of the Bainbridge type.

in mass.   These ions enter a second uniform magnetic field $\mathscr{B}$ directed
away from the reader and traverse a circular path of radius R.   The force
acting on an ion of mass m is given by

$$\mathscr{B}Qv = mv^2/R.$$

Solving this equation for m, we may write

$$m = (\mathscr{B}Q/v) \times R = \text{const} \times R,$$

which indicates that ions of a given charge Q traverse circular paths of
radii proportional to their masses.   With the arrangement shown in Fig.
2, the ions strike a photographic plate after traversing one semicircle
and produce darkened traces on the photographic plate.   From the position of the trace on the plate, R can be accurately determined.   If $\mathscr{B}$, Q,
and v are also accurately known, the absolute value of the ion mass m can
be calculated.

Such experiments show that the mass of the ordinary hydrogen atom is 1838 times the mass of the electron, so that $^{1837}\!/_{1838}$ of the mass is contained in the nucleus (the proton). In all other atoms, the nucleus contains an even larger fraction of the mass.

One discovery made by J. J. Thomson in 1913 with a prototype of the mass spectrograph was that not all the atoms of a given element have the same mass. Most of the elements have two or more *isotopes*.*

Isotopes are atoms of different mass but equal nuclear charge.

The **isotopic mass** is the mass, on the physical atomic-mass scale, of a neutral isotope (nucleus plus Z electrons).

Since the different isotopes of an element have the same number and arrangement of electrons, they are almost identical in chemical behavior. The isotopes of an element differ but little in either chemical or physical properties, hence quantity separation of the isotopes is always a laborious and expensive process. Separation can be effected by taking advantage of slight differences in *rate of diffusion*, *rate of evaporation*, *rate of electrolysis*, or *rate of chemical reaction*. Isotopes are also separated in quantity at Oak Ridge by using a device that is in principle a mass spectrograph.

Some elements have numerous isotopes; for example, tin has ten isotopes. Figure 3 is a photograph of the mass spectrum of tin.

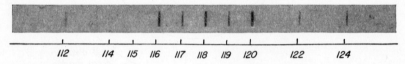

112	114	115	116	117	118	119	120	122	124

Fig. 3. The mass spectrum of tin, showing the traces of the ten isotopes, and their approximate isotopic masses [*courtesy of K. T. Bainbridge*].

It is impossible to make a very accurate determination of the relative abundances of the different isotopes of an element from a photographic record such as that of Fig. 3, but by adapting the mass spectrograph to electrical recording of the total charge on the ions collected at various radii R, it is possible to make accurate abundance measurements.

Hydrogen has an isotope called *deuterium* of approximately twice the mass of the ordinary hydrogen atom; the hydrogen isotopes are of particular interest because of their large mass ratio. The deuterium nucleus, called the *deuteron*, has the simplest known nuclear structure except for the proton itself. About 1 atom in 6000 in ordinary hydrogen is a deuterium isotope. There is also an unstable hydrogen isotope of approximately three times the mass of ordinary hydrogen, called *tritium*.

* The literal meaning of the word *isotope* is 'same place.' The term indicates that the *isotopes* occupy the *same place in the periodic table;* they have the same atomic number Z.

Tritium does not occur in natural hydrogen, but can be formed by nuclear reactions (see Sec. 2).

Oxygen has three stable isotopes, of masses approximately 16, 17, and 18 times the mass of hydrogen. As we have already remarked in Chap. 31, physicists have adopted an atomic-mass scale in which the mass of the O^{16} isotope is given the atomic mass $M = 16$ exactly. The atomic-mass scale is a scale of relative masses, and it is most convenient to consider the atomic mass M as dimensionless, as we have done consistently. However, in this chapter we need to work with actual masses of atoms, ions, and nuclei. For example, the mass m occurring above in the description of the mass spectrograph was the actual mass of an ion. We need to be able to compute actual masses in kg from atomic masses. To facilitate this computation, we introduce the *atomic mass unit* (amu), defined as the actual mass of a hypothetical atom of atomic mass 1. A better definition is

The **atomic mass unit (amu)** is $\frac{1}{16}$ the mass of the O^{16} atom.

We see from this definition that

The actual mass of an atom of atomic mass M is $m = M$ amu.

We could in principle obtain the value of the amu in kg by measuring the mass of the O^{16} ion in kg in a mass spectrograph, adding the known mass of one electron to get the mass of the neutral atom, and dividing by 16. In practice, this technique does not give a very accurate value, because mass spectrographs measure mass ratios with much more accuracy than they measure absolute masses. But Avogadro's number $\mathfrak{N}$ is known to high accuracy from measurements of the faraday and the charge on the electron. And 16 g of O^{16} atoms contain $\mathfrak{N}$ atoms, each of mass 16 amu. Hence 16 g $= 16\ \mathfrak{N}$ amu, and

$$1 \text{ amu} = (1/\mathfrak{N}) \text{ g} = (1/6.0247 \times 10^{23}) \text{ g} = 1.6597 \times 10^{-24} \text{ g} = 1.6597 \times 10^{-27} \text{ kg}. \quad (1)$$

The isotopic masses in all cases are very close to integers. No known isotopic mass differs from an integer by more than 0.06. We shall see why this is so when we learn how nuclei are built from protons and neutrons, each of atomic mass very close to unity, and when we remember that almost all the mass of an isotope is contained in the nucleus. It is convenient to distinguish different isotopes of an element by means of the *mass number:*

The **mass number** of an isotope is the integer nearest to its isotopic mass.

For example, Fig. 3 shows the mass numbers of the ten isotopes of tin; the mass numbers of the three isotopes of hydrogen are 1, 2, and 3; while those of the three isotopes of oxygen are 16, 17, and 18.

2. NUCLEAR REACTIONS

THE NUCLEUS of an atom of a particular *element* is characterized by a particular value of the *atomic number Z*. (The charge on the nucleus is *Ze.*) The different nuclei of the isotopes of this element (remember that isotopes differ only in that they have nuclei of different masses) are characterized by different *mass numbers A*. (The mass number is the approximate mass of the nucleus in amu, as well as the approximate mass of the neutral isotope, since almost all the mass of an atom resides in the nucleus.) To discuss nuclear reactions conveniently, we need to have a *symbol* for a *nucleus*. Specification of Z and A would be sufficient, but it is convenient to append these numbers to the chemical symbol X, writing $_Z X^A$. Thus the three types of oxygen *nuclei* are denoted by $_8 O^{16}$, $_8 O^{17}$, and $_8 O^{18}$, while the symbol $_{92} U^{238}$ denotes the uranium *nucleus* with $Z = 92$, $A = 238$.

The earliest source of information concerning the structure of the nucleus was the phenomenon of natural radioactivity, discovered by Henri Becquerel in 1896. Practically all of the naturally occurring *radioactive* elements have atomic numbers between $Z = 81$ and $Z = 92$. Two types of natural radioactive-disintegration processes have been observed for the elements in this range. One of these involves the emission of *alpha particles* (helium nuclei). An example of this type of process is the disintegration of uranium 238; this nucleus spontaneously emits, after an average lifetime of 10^9 years, an alpha particle and becomes a thorium nucleus of mass number 234. The equation for the disintegration of uranium 238 can be written as

$$_{92} U^{238} \rightarrow {}_{90} Th^{234} + {}_2 He^4,$$

where *the left-hand subscripts give the atomic numbers and the superscripts give the mass numbers*. The effect of alpha-particle emission is to decrease the mass number of the parent nucleus by 4 units and the atomic number by 2 units. In equations of this kind the sum of the mass numbers of the product nuclei on the right is equal to the mass number of the original nucleus on the left; the same is true of the atomic numbers, since the atomic numbers measure charge, and electric charge is conserved. It might be noted, however, that the product nuclei have kinetic energy and also that a heavy product nucleus like $_{90} Th^{234}$ may be left in an excited energy state and reach its lowest or ground state only by the emission of one or more high-energy quanta called *gamma rays*. Gamma radiation is similar in character to high-frequency X radiation.

The second type of naturally occurring disintegration involves the emission of *beta particles*, which are high-energy electrons. A typical beta-emission process occurs when the *radium* isotope of mass number 228 disintegrates to form an actinium isotope of mass number 228 and an electron.   The descriptive equation may be written as

$$_{88}\text{Ra}^{228} \rightarrow {_{89}}\text{Ac}^{228} + {_{-1}}\epsilon^0,$$

where the electron ϵ is assigned an atomic number of -1 because of its negative charge and a mass number 0 because its mass is only 0.0005 amu. When a beta particle is emitted, the atomic number of the product nucleus is always 1 greater than that of the parent nucleus, and the mass number is unchanged.   The product nucleus may be left in an excited state and reach its ground state by gamma-ray emission.

Observations of the energies of the emitted beta particles show that, if energy and momentum are conserved in beta-emission processes, it is necessary to assume that another particle called a *neutrino* is emitted along with the beta particle.   The neutrino has no charge and has a mass that is much smaller than the electron mass.   Although this particle has never been observed directly, the above equation should probably be written as

$$_{88}\text{Ra}^{228} \rightarrow {_{89}}\text{Ac}^{228} + {_{-1}}\epsilon^0 + {_0}\nu^0$$

where the symbol $_0\nu^0$ represents the neutrino.

The *neutrino* is regarded as a fundamental particle.   That it has never been directly observed is not surprising, because an extremely light particle of no charge would be extraordinarily difficult to detect.   The physicists of today accept its existence because of several different lines of evidence that require either the existence of such a particle or radical revision of some of the most fundamental principles of physics, such as the laws of conservation of energy, momentum, and angular momentum.

The rate at which radioactive processes take place is usually measured by a quantity called the *half-life* of the material.

> The **half-life** of a radioactive material is the time required for the activity of a sample of the material to decrease to one-half of its initial value, or, what amounts to the same thing, the time for half the atoms of the sample to disintegrate.

The half-lives of naturally occurring radioactive substances vary from 10^{10} years to 10^{-11} seconds.   The three natural series start from $_{92}\text{U}^{238}$, $_{92}\text{U}^{235}$, and $_{90}\text{Th}^{232}$, and after a chain of about twelve alpha- and beta-emissions with various half-lives, all end in different stable isotopes of lead.

Further knowledge of the properties of atomic nuclei has been obtained by using the alpha particles from radioactive materials as projectiles for the bombardment of other nuclei.   As we have seen, Rutherford used alpha particles in his studies of scattering and was thus led to the nuclear model of the atom.   Rutherford also used alpha particles to produce *nuclear reactions*.

> A **nuclear reaction** is a reaction involving a change from one nuclear species to another.

Because of their high energy, alpha particles can approach very close to the atomic nuclei of the lighter elements.   In certain cases alpha particles can 'penetrate' the nucleus of an atom and cause a change to another type of nucleus.   On the basis of a theory advanced by Bohr, a nuclear reaction of this type may be thought of as consisting of two steps.   The first involves the capture of the bombarding alpha particles by a nucleus and the formation of a compound nucleus.   The second is the almost immediate breaking up of the compound nucleus into the final products. As an example, let us consider one of the earliest observed alpha-particle reactions.   When high-energy alpha particles pass through nitrogen gas, the following reaction occurs:

$$_7N^{14} + {}_2He^4 \rightarrow ({}_9F^{18}) \rightarrow {}_8O^{17} + {}_1H^1.$$

The penetration of the alpha particle into the nitrogen nucleus produces the compound nucleus $_9F^{18}$, an unstable isotope of fluorine, which immediately breaks up into an isotope of oxygen and a proton.   Many reactions of this type, in which an alpha particle is captured and a proton emitted, have been observed.

The capture of an alpha particle by a nucleus does not always result in the emission of a proton by the compound nucleus formed as a result of this capture.   In one reaction observed in the bombardment of beryllium by alpha particles, a very penetrating type of particle is emitted by the newly formed compound nucleus.   Chadwick showed in 1932 that the emitted particles are *neutral particles of mass very nearly equal to that of the proton*.   These particles are called *neutrons* and are formed as a result of the reaction

$$_4Be^9 + {}_2He^4 \rightarrow ({}_6C^{13}) \rightarrow {}_6C^{12} + {}_0n^1,$$

where $_0n^1$ is the symbol for the neutron, showing that it has zero charge and mass number unity.   Thus was discovered a new fundamental particle, the *neutron*.

The discovery of the neutron gave further insight into the structure of the nucleus.   Prior to the neutron's discovery, it had been thought that the nucleus consisted of protons and electrons, but this assumption was very unsatisfactory for a number of reasons.   According to presently accepted theory:

The nucleus is composed of protons and neutrons.

The number of protons in a given nucleus is equal to its atomic number Z and the number of neutrons $(A - Z)$ is just sufficient to make up the remainder of the mass number A; for example, the $_2He^4$ nucleus contains 2 protons and 2 neutrons, while the $_{92}U^{238}$ nucleus contains 92 protons and 146 neutrons.   The neutrons and protons that compose the nucleus are together called *nucleons*.

A **nucleon** is a constituent particle of atomic nuclei, a proton or a neutron.

The mass number is the number of nucleons in a nucleus.

The neutrons emitted by a nucleus in a process such as described above behave quite differently from charged particles such as electrons, protons, and alpha particles. As a result of their charges, charged particles interact strongly with the planetary electrons of atoms and usually fritter away their energy by ionizing the atoms or molecules of the materials through which they pass; they lose energy very rapidly and are brought to rest and neutralized after passage through only a few centimeters of air

or through thin metal foils. Neutrons, possessing no electric charge, have very little interaction with the extranuclear portion of atoms and are consequently more penetrating than charged particles of comparable energy. Neutrons interact strongly only with nuclei; a neutron may have elastic collisions with nuclei, but eventually it is captured by a nucleus. One type of capture process is that in which a neutron is captured by nitrogen as described in the equation

$$_7N^{14} + {_0}n^1 \rightarrow ({_7}N^{15}) \rightarrow {_6}C^{14} + {_1}H^1.$$

In this process, the product nucleus $_6C^{14}$ is unstable and eventually achieves stability by the beta-emission process

$$_6C^{14} \rightarrow {_7}N^{14} + {_{-1}}\varepsilon^0 + {_0}\nu^0.$$

These two processes are illustrated schematically in Fig. 4.

When slow neutrons collide with nuclei, many reactions are observed in which the neutron is captured and the product nucleus achieves stability by emission of a gamma-ray photon of energy hf. This

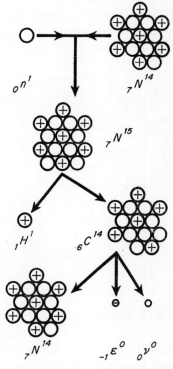

Fig. 4. The neutron-capture reaction of nitrogen.

process is called *radiative capture*.   A typical radiative-capture reaction is

$$_{48}Cd^{113} + {_0}n^1 \rightarrow {_{48}}Cd^{114} + hf.$$

Neutron-capture processes in which an alpha particle is ejected are also observed.

On the presently accepted picture in which nuclei are believed to contain only neutrons and protons, the electrons that are emitted when a nucleus undergoes a beta process must be thought of as *created* when a neutron changes to a proton in the nucleus.   When a neutron changes to a proton, an electron must be emitted in order that the total charge may be conserved.   The reverse process, in which a proton changes into a neutron and a *positron* (a particle of electronic mass but charge $+e$) will be considered in Sec. 4.

A free neutron (one not in a nucleus) is unstable and eventually spontaneously changes to a proton and an electron (plus a neutrino, probably).   This process, which is analogous to natural beta radioactivity, has a half-life of 18 minutes.

3. THE THEORY OF RELATIVITY

BEGINNING in 1906, Kaufmann, Bücherer, and others conducted experiments that showed that the charge-to-mass ratio, e/m, for the high-speed electrons (beta particles) emitted from radioactive substances is less than the ratio for electrons of moderate speed.   The ratio was found to decrease as the speed increased.   If this decrease is interpreted as an increase of mass with speed, charge being constant, the experimental data on the mass of the electron as a function of speed are given by the points of Fig. 5.

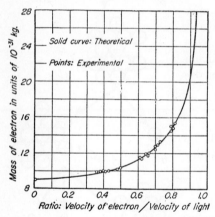

Fig. 5. Electron mass as a function of speed.

This departure from the Newtonian idea of an invariant mass is one of the predictions of the *theory of relativity*, formulated by Albert Einstein in 1905.   Einstein made a critical re-examination of the fundamental principles of mechanics and electrodynamics in the light of available experimental data and concluded that our basic philosophical ideas of space and time were in need of complete revision.   Einstein concluded that distances and time intervals between 'events' would be given different values by different 'observers' moving relative to each other, even though these observers were using identically constructed meter sticks and clocks. The difference must be such that

Any observer will always find the same value, $c = 3 \times 10^8$ m/sec, for the speed of light relative to himself, regardless of the direction of travel of the light beam.

This statement was an experimental conclusion from the observations of Michelson and Morley who, in 1881, showed by a careful interferometric technique that the observed speed of light is a constant, unaffected by the earth's high orbital speed around the sun at any time of the day or year for any direction of propagation relative to the earth. If the statement above were not true, it would be possible to find an *absolute* velocity for an observer. All experimental evidence leads to the conclusion that only relative velocities are observable, and hence to Einstein's extension of the Newtonian principle of relativity:

PRINCIPLE OF RELATIVITY: *If the laws of physics are valid in one coordinate system, they are equally valid in a coordinate system in motion at constant velocity relative to it; hence there is no way of determining absolute motion—only relative motion can be measured.*

We cannot go here into the details of the theory of relativity, but it is necessary that we learn some of the results of this theory that are fundamental to an understanding of modern particle physics. The theory requires a revision of Newton's second principle, but the effect of the revision is undetectably small for bodies whose speed is small compared to the speed of light (say less than $\frac{1}{100} c = 3 \times 10^6$ m/sec $= 6,000,000$ mi/hr), but the revision is very significant for particles moving at speeds close to that of light.

By logical arguments, Einstein not only predicted the observed increase of mass with speed, but made other startling predictions, such as that of the equivalence of mass and energy. This equivalence, which was not verified until much later, is fundamental to an understanding of the release of atomic energy in nuclear reactions. We shall state Einstein's expression for the variation of mass with velocity and then discuss briefly the equivalence of mass and energy.

The mass of a particle is not a constant but increases with increasing speed in such a way as to approach infinity as the speed of the particle approaches that of light, according to the relation

$$m = \frac{m_0}{\sqrt{1 - (v^2/c^2)}}. \qquad (2)$$

Here m_0, called the *rest mass*, is the Newtonian mass—the apparent mass of the particle when at rest or when moving with a speed small compared to the speed of light. A plot of (2) for the electron, with $m_0 = 9.1 \times 10^{-31}$ kg, is given in the solid curve of Fig. 5, which is seen to agree with the experimental points.

The first and third of Newton's principles remain the same in relativistic mechanics as in Newtonian. The second principle must be written as the vector equation

$$\boldsymbol{F} = \frac{d}{dt}(m\boldsymbol{v}) \qquad (3)$$

—force equals time rate of change of momentum. This equation has the same outward form as the one applicable in Newtonian mechanics, but now if the speed is increasing with time, the mass is also increasing with time, and we must keep the m inside the differentiation symbol; we *cannot* take m outside and set force equal to mass times acceleration as we did in Newtonian theory where mass was constant.

Just as in Newtonian mechanics, *work* is defined as the force component in the direction of motion times distance moved, and the *kinetic energy* of a particle at speed v is defined as the work necessary to increase the speed of the particle from 0 to v. From formulas (2) and (3), we find (see Prob. 43):

$$\text{K.E.} = \int F_s \, dS = c^2(m - m_0). \tag{4}$$

The kinetic energy of a particle equals c^2 times the difference between its mass and its rest mass.

That this strange formula does reduce to the Newtonian expression $\tfrac{1}{2} m_0 v^2$ for kinetic energy at low speeds we can easily verify. By expanding (2) in a series of powers of v^2/c^2, we find

$$m = m_0 \left[1 - \frac{v^2}{c^2} \right]^{-\frac{1}{2}} = m_0 \left[1 + \tfrac{1}{2}\frac{v^2}{c^2} + \tfrac{3}{8}\frac{v^4}{c^4} + \cdots \right];$$

whence

$$\text{K.E.} = c^2(m - m_0) = \tfrac{1}{2} m_0 v^2 + \tfrac{3}{8} m_0 \frac{v^4}{c^2} + \cdots = \tfrac{1}{2} m_0 v^2 \left[1 + \tfrac{3}{4}\frac{v^2}{c^2} + \cdots \right].$$

The Newtonian formula $\tfrac{1}{2} m_0 v^2$ is valid when v/c is sufficiently small that the second term in the last bracket is negligible in comparison with unity.

The fact that the kinetic energy of a particle is directly proportional to the difference between the mass of the particle and its rest mass leads one to suspect that perhaps mass and energy are just two different measures of the same physical quantity, the conversion factor being c^2. Further consideration along these lines led Einstein to the conclusion that this is indeed so—that mass is associated with all forms of energy: kinetic, potential, elastic, thermal, chemical, nuclear, and electromagnetic—and that *whenever a body changes in energy it changes in mass correspondingly.* The conversion factor in all cases is c^2, the change in energy ΔE in joules being related to the change in mass Δm in kg by

$$\Delta E = c^2 \, \Delta m, \tag{5}$$

with c in m/sec. Thus, *mass and energy are measures of the same physical quantity,* the equivalent changes in mass and energy being

$$\left. \begin{aligned} 1 \text{ kg} &\sim c^2 \text{ joules} \sim 8.987 \times 10^{16} \text{ joules}; \\ 1 \text{ joule} &\sim 1.113 \times 10^{-17} \text{ kg}. \end{aligned} \right\} \tag{6}$$

The extremely small size of the factor 1.1×10^{-17} accounts for the fact that it is impossible to detect the mass changes associated with ordinary energy changes such as occur in thermal heating and chemical reactions. Thus, to heat 1 kg of water from $0°$ C to $100°$ C, we must add 418,500 joules of energy, which increases the mass of the water by only 5×10^{-12} kg. Again, the energy release in the complete combustion of *3 tons* of carbon makes the combustion products only *1 milligram* lighter than the *11 tons* of carbon and oxygen entering the reaction.

Only since 1932 has there been direct experimental confirmation of the relation (5). This relation has now been accurately confirmed in many nuclear reactions in which the release of energy is so large that the accompanying mass changes are readily measured in a mass spectrograph.

There is energy E associated with any mass m, and mass m associated with any energy E, the relation between energy and mass being $E = mc^2$.

By this identification of mass and energy, the *principle of conservation of energy* and the *principle of conservation of mass* become *one and the same physical principle*, not two distinct principles as in classical theory.
not two distinct laws as in classical theory.

The *total energy* of a particle is mc^2; from (4) we have

$$mc^2 = m_0 c^2 + \text{K.E.} \tag{7}$$

The term $m_0 c^2$ is called the *rest energy* of the particle (energy associated with the rest mass of the particle). Thus

$$\text{total energy} = \text{rest energy} + \text{kinetic energy.} \tag{7a}$$

The above considerations would assign mass hf/c^2 to a *photon* of energy hf. Since the photon moves at speed c, it would have momentum $(hf/c^2)c = hf/c$. This is the value of momentum that had to be assigned to the photon to explain the experimental observations in the Compton effect, which we discussed on p. 814.

4. THE POSITRON; ANNIHILATION AND CREATION OF MATTER

UNTIL 1932, there was no experimental evidence that the *rest* energy of a particle could ever change to another form of energy, but since the discovery of the *positron* in 1932 the process of the 'annihilation' of material particles (electrons and positrons) with the complete conversion of their rest energy into the energy of light quanta has become familiar, as has the inverse process, that of the 'materialization' of the energy of light quanta as the rest energy of electrons and positrons.

The rest masses of various particles with which we shall be concerned have the following values:

electron:	0.0005488 amu	deuteron:	2.01418 amu
neutron:	1.00898 amu	H^2 atom:	2.01473 amu
proton:	1.00759 amu	α-particle:	4.00276 amu
H^1 atom:	1.00814 amu	He^4 atom:	4.00386 amu.

The energies of nuclear reactions are ordinarily specified in Mev, so that we need to know the relativistic equivalence between mass in amu and energy in Mev. From (1), (6), and (1), p. 643, we find the equivalence factor

$$1 \text{ amu} \sim 931.2 \text{ Mev.}$$

Thus the energy equivalents of the rest masses of the electron and proton are

electron: 0.511 Mev,   proton: 938 Mev.

This equivalent, for the electron, is directly observed in connection with annihilation and creation of electrons and positrons, as we shall now discuss.

In 1932, Carl D. Anderson discovered a new elementary particle in the cosmic radiation. This particle is called a *positron;* it has a mass equal to that of the electron and a *positive* charge equal in absolute magnitude to the electron's negative charge. The positron has a transitory existence on the earth, and therefore had not been previously observed in investigations of atomic structure. Anderson found that positrons are created in a process called *pair production*, in which *a gamma-ray photon disappears and an electron-positron pair is created.* In other words, *the radiant energy of the photon is converted into matter.* The energy relationship for this process is

$$(hf)_{\text{Photon}} = (m_0 c^2 + \text{K.E.})_{\text{Electron}} + (m_0 c^2 + \text{K.E.})_{\text{Positron}}.$$

Since the rest energies of the positron and the electron are each equal to 0.511 Mev, the energy of the photon must be greater than 1.02 Mev before pair production can occur.

When traversing matter, a positron is ultimately annihilated, along with an electron, by a process with the following energy balance:

$$(m_0 c^2)_{\text{Positron}} + (m_0 c^2)_{\text{Electron}} = 2 \ (hf)_{\text{Photon}}.$$

It is observed that *two* photons appear as the result of the annihilation of the positron-electron pair; each photon has an energy of approximately 0.5 Mev, which indicates that the electron and positron have little kinetic energy when they are annihilated. Hence K.E. terms have been omitted on the left of the above equation.

Energy (including rest energy), momentum, and electric charge are all conserved in the processes of pair production and annihilation. *Pair production takes place only in the vicinity of some heavy nucleus* such as that of lead; recoil of the heavy nucleus in connection with the pair-production process is necessary in order to satisfy the condition for conservation of momentum. In annihilation, the two photons travel in opposite directions, as would be expected from momentum considerations since the electron and positron velocities are small at the time when annihilation occurs. Charge conservation requires that electrons and positrons be created or annihilated in pairs, not individually.

It is interesting to note that the existence of the positron, and all of its properties, had been predicted several years before its discovery, by P. A. M. Dirac, as a necessary consequence of *quantum mechanics*. The same type of reasoning would predict that research at very much higher energies (thousands of Mev) will lead to the discovery of a 'negative proton' bearing the same relation to the proton as the positron does to the electron, and that creation and annihilation of these heavier particles will be observed.

Positrons are also observed as a result of many nuclear reactions. The simplest occurs in the collision of a high-speed proton with another proton. One of the protons changes to a neutron, and the neutron and the other proton combine to form the nucleus of heavy hydrogen $_1H^2$, which is called the *deuteron*. In this change, a positron is created and emitted in a process that is analogous to beta-emission. The reaction is

$$_1H^1 + _1H^1 \rightarrow (_2He^2) \rightarrow _1H^2 + _{+1}\varepsilon^0 + _0\nu^0.$$

5. MASS-ENERGY TRANSFORMATIONS IN NUCLEAR REACTIONS

WE HAVE SEEN above that the energies involved in ordinary chemical reactions like the combustion of carbon are so small that there is no experimentally detectable difference between the rest mass of the reactants (carbon and oxygen) and the rest mass of the reaction product (CO_2). Now let us consider the analogous problem of the formation of a stable atomic nucleus from protons and neutrons. Although we cannot, in general, produce stable nuclei from neutrons and protons in the laboratory in a manner comparable with the way in which we can produce carbon dioxide from carbon and oxygen, we can make very accurate comparisons of atomic masses by means of the mass spectrograph; and from these masses we can determine the energy that would be released in the formation of a nucleus from neutrons and protons.

The rest energy $M_0 c^2$ of a nucleus is not equal to the sum of the rest energies the constituent nucleons (protons and neutrons) would have if free, because there are also the internal kinetic and potential energies to be considered. If we denote the internal energy by I.E., we have

$$M_0 c^2 = \sum_{\text{Nucleons}} m_0 c^2 + \text{I.E.} \qquad (8)$$

The internal energy I.E. *is always a negative quantity* because of the negative potential energy of the strong attractive forces between nucleons that hold the nucleus together. Hence, *the rest mass of a nucleus is less than the sum of the rest masses of the constituent nucleons.* The mass (energy) difference would be released in the process of formation of the nucleus from the nucleons; the difference would have to be supplied in order to break the nucleus up into its constituent nucleons. This energy difference, which in this case is so large as to be capable of being measured as a mass difference, is quite analogous to a chemical heat of reaction.

A neutral atom of atomic number Z and mass number A is built of Z protons and $A - Z$ neutrons in the nucleus, and Z extranuclear electrons. Since the binding energy of the extranuclear electrons is quite negligible when expressed in amu, we can consider that this atom would have the same mass as Z neutral H^1 atoms and $A - Z$ neutrons were it not for the internal energy of the nucleus. If we call the rest mass of the neutral atom M, that of the H^1 atom m_H, and that of the neutron m_n, the internal energy of the nucleus is given, in amu, by

$$\text{I.E.} = M - Z\, m_H - (A - Z)\, m_n.$$

The values of m_H (determined mass-spectroscopically) and m_n (determined indirectly from the energetics of various nuclear reactions) were given on p. 833.

Example. *Determine the total internal energy and the internal energy per nucleon for the $_8O^{16}$ nucleus.*

Since, by definition, the mass of the O^{16} atom is exactly 16 amu, we have, from the last equation above,

$$\text{I.E.} = [16.0000 - 8(1.00814) - 8(1.00898)]\ \text{amu}$$
$$= [16.0000 - 8.0651 - 8.0718]\ \text{amu} = -0.1369\ \text{amu}.$$

The O^{16} nucleus has 0.1369 amu or 127.5 Mev *less energy* than its constituent particles—this amount of energy would be released on formation of O^{16} from its constituent particles. Division by 16 gives internal energy of -8.0 Mev per nucleon, as in Fig. 6.

The negative of the internal energy is frequently called the *binding energy*—this is the energy that would have to be supplied to the nucleus to break it up into its constituent parts; thus the binding energy of the O^{16} nucleus is 0.1369 amu or 127.5 Mev.

Figure 6 shows the internal energies of various nuclei plotted against mass number. One curve shows the total internal energy in Mev, computed as in the example above. For the other curve, the internal energy is divided by the mass number A to give the internal energy per nucleon. This second curve is of the greatest interest because it shows that those nuclei with mass numbers between 50 and 80 give the lowest internal energy per nucleon and hence represent the most stable arrangements of nucleons. Both lighter and heavier nuclei are relatively less stable.

If we could develop some method of causing two or more light nuclei to combine to form a nucleus with intermediate mass number, a great deal of energy would be released; similarly, by splitting a heavy nucleus into two or more nuclei with intermediate mass numbers, we could also release large amounts of energy.

Reactions of the second type, in which heavy nuclei are split into nuclei of intermediate mass number with consequent release of energy of about 1 Mev per nucleon as indicated in Fig. 6 are called *fission* reactions, since a heavier nucleus divides to form lighter nuclei.   Such reactions are

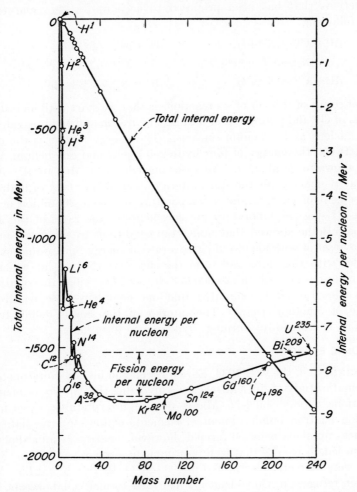

Fig. 6. Total internal energy and internal energy per nucleon as functions of mass number. While the points show representative nuclei, all nuclei lie close to these curves.

used in the chain-reacting pile and in the ordinary atomic bomb (see Sec. 6).

Reactions of the first type are called *fusion* reactions, since lighter nuclei *combine* or *fuse* to form heavier nuclei.   These reactions form the basis of the 'fusion' or 'thermonuclear' bomb.   They also occur in the interiors of stars where temperatures are sufficiently high for the thermal velocities of nuclei to be sufficient to initiate such nuclear reactions, and account for the continued release of stellar energy. The origin of the solar energy is probably a series of nuclear reactions, the net result of which is the formation of one helium nucleus from four protons. One set of reactions that has been proposed to account for the solar energy is the following:

$$_1H^1 + {}_6C^{12} \rightarrow {}_7N^{13} + hf, \qquad\qquad _1H^1 + {}_7N^{14} \rightarrow {}_8O^{15} + hf,$$

$$_7N^{13} \rightarrow {}_6C^{13} + {}_{+1}\varepsilon^0 + {}_0\nu^0, \qquad\qquad _8O^{15} \rightarrow {}_7N^{15} + {}_{+1}\varepsilon^0 + {}_0\nu^0,$$

$$_1H^1 + {}_6C^{13} \rightarrow {}_7N^{14} + hf, \qquad\qquad _1H^1 + {}_7N^{15} \rightarrow {}_6C^{12} + {}_2He^4.$$

The net result of this set of six reactions is that we start with an ordinary nucleus of C^{12} and four nuclei of ordinary hydrogen and end up again with a C^{12} nucleus and a helium nucleus. The energy release is the difference between the energy of four hydrogen nuclei and one helium, which Fig. 6 shows to be about 6.5 Mev per nucleon or 26 Mev total. Astrophysical evidence gives the sun's interior about 35 per cent of hydrogen, one per cent of carbon, and a temperature of about 20 million degrees Kelvin. Using the laboratory measurements of the rates of the above reactions, Bethe showed that under the conditions in the solar interior the above set of reactions would give a rate of energy release that exactly coincides with that observed from the sun. At the rate at which the above reactions go with the 20,000,000-degree Maxwellian distribution of proton velocities, it is computed that one complete cycle requires an average of 5 million years. The interior of the sun is definitely not *exploding*, it is steadily 'burning' hydrogen to form helium.

6. ATOMIC ENERGY

BEGINNING in the year 1934, Enrico Fermi and his collaborators began a systematic study of nuclear reactions involving the capture of neutrons by various atomic nuclei. Many readily interpretable experiments involving neutron bombardment of elements of low, intermediate, and high mass numbers were performed; however, neutron bombardment of uranium led to results that were not immediately interpretable. These results were correctly interpreted in 1939 by O. R. Frisch and Lise Meitner, then refugees in Copenhagen, when their former collaborators, Otto Hahn and F. Strassmann in Berlin, chemically identified *barium* as one of the reaction products appearing when uranium is bombarded by neutrons. The appearance of barium as a reaction product was interpreted as evidence that the uranium nucleus on capturing a neutron split into two nuclei of intermediate mass number and thus resulted in the discovery of *nuclear fission*. Since the energy per nucleon of nuclei of intermediate mass number is, as indicated in Fig. 6, about 1 Mev less than the energy per nucleon of uranium, about 235 Mev of energy is released from each U^{235} nucleus that undergoes fission. This enormous quantity of energy

is released when a slow neutron with only room-temperature thermal energy (approximately $\frac{1}{30}$ ev) is captured by a uranium nucleus; hence, it was immediately obvious that if large numbers of thermal neutrons were available, the fission process could be used in power production.

Further studies of uranium fission showed that it was the relatively rare isotope $_{92}U^{235}$ that was split by slow neutrons and that *in addition to two elements of intermediate mass number, several neutrons are usually present among the reaction products.* For example, the following fission reaction might occur:

$$_{92}U^{235} + _0n^1 \rightarrow {}_{56}Ba^{144} + {}_{36}Kr^{89} + 3\ _0n^1.$$

The fission products $_{56}Ba^{144}$ and $_{36}Kr^{89}$ are both unstable since their mass numbers are larger than those associated with atomic numbers 56 and 36 in stable elements; in other words, these two isotopes contain too many neutrons and too few protons. However, by a series of beta-particle emissions, they eventually achieve stability, since the emission of a beta particle results in a reduction of the number of neutrons by 1 and an increase in the number of protons by 1 in a nucleus. It should be noted that the reaction given above is only one of many possible fission reactions. The known fission products are elements near the middle of the periodic table having atomic numbers in the range from $Z=34$ to $Z=58$ and mass numbers in the range from $A=70$ to $A=166$, somewhat to the right of the minimum in Fig. 6. Careful measurements indicate that the average initial kinetic energy of fission products is in the neighborhood of 160 Mev, and that about 40 Mev of additional energy appears as kinetic energy of the neutrons and as energy associated with beta and gamma radiation from the fission products, making a total of about 200 Mev per fission.

The uranium isotope $_{92}U^{235}$ seems to be the only known naturally occurring nucleus that undergoes a fission reaction produced by neutrons of very low energy. However, two other nuclei, which have been produced as a result of radiative capture of neutrons, can also be split by slow neutrons. One of these is the uranium isotope $_{92}U^{233}$ formed when neutrons are captured by $_{90}Th^{232}$ to form $_{90}Th^{233}$, which undergoes two beta-emission processes to form U^{233}:

$$_{90}Th^{232} + _0n^1 \rightarrow {}_{90}Th^{233}, \quad _{90}Th^{233} \rightarrow {}_{91}Pa^{233} + _{-1}\varepsilon^0, \quad _{91}Pa^{233} \rightarrow {}_{92}U^{233} + _{-1}\varepsilon^0.$$

The other artificially produced fissionable nucleus is $_{94}Pu^{239}$ (*plutonium*), which can be produced as a result of radiative capture of slow neutrons by the most abundant uranium isotope $_{92}U^{238}$ in the following reactions:

$$_{92}U^{238} + _0n^1 \rightarrow {}_{92}U^{239}, \quad _{92}U^{239} \rightarrow {}_{93}Np^{239} + _{-1}\varepsilon^0, \quad _{93}Np^{239} \rightarrow {}_{94}Pu^{239} + _{-1}\varepsilon^0.$$

The elements neptunium Np ($Z=93$) and Pu ($Z=94$) are called *transuranic elements.* Six more transuranic elements have now been arti ficially produced by nuclear reactions. These are $Z = 95$, 96, 97, 98, 99, and 100 (americium, curium, berkelium, and californium, with elements 99 and 100 as yet unnamed).

The fission processes produced when samples containing $_{92}U^{233}$ and $_{94}Pu^{239}$ are irradiated with slow neutrons are similar in essentials to the fission processes we have described for $_{92}U^{235}$.

We pointed out above that it was early realized that nuclear fission could be used for power production, provided an abundant supply of neutrons were available to initiate fission processes. When it was found that two or three neutrons are released in every fission process, it became apparent that nuclear *chain reactions** might be produced by using these released neutrons to produce additional fissions. In order to understand how this process is possible, consider the schematic diagram in Fig. 7. In part (a) of this figure, a single neutron produces fission of a $_{92}U^{235}$ nucleus in a block of uranium metal, and, in addition to the fission product nuclei, three neutrons are assumed to be released. These neutrons are 'lost' either by escaping from the space occupied by the uranium or in radiative capture by $_{92}U^{238}$ or some other nucleus that may be present. Hence, this reaction is not self-sustaining.
In part (b) of this figure is shown

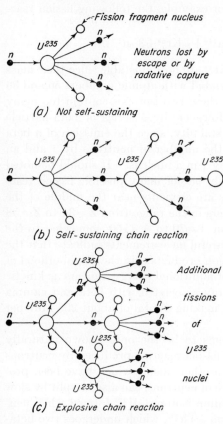

(a) Not self-sustaining

(b) Self-sustaining chain reaction

(c) Explosive chain reaction

Figure 7

a chain reaction that is just self-sustaining. In each fission, on the average, one of the released neutrons produces the fission of another $_{92}U^{235}$ nucleus and two are lost by escape or by radiative capture. In part (c) is shown a chain reaction which involves high 'multiplication'; in this case, every neutron released by a fission process produces additional fission of a $_{92}U^{235}$ nucleus. Hence, assuming 3 neutrons per fission,

---

* The term *chain reaction* has long been used by chemists to describe a series of individual reactions in which a reaction product of the first reaction produces a second reaction, a reaction product of the second reaction produces a third, etc.

we would expect 3^N fissions in the Nth 'generation'; remembering that 200 Mev energy is released during each process, we see that a great deal of energy would be produced in a very short time.   The reaction shown schematically in part (b) of Fig. 7 would be the type in a nuclear *reactor* or 'pile' designed for sustained power production or for production of Pu by using the excess neutrons to initiate the last series of reactions listed above.   In this case, when the number of fission chains had reached some value corresponding to the desired power level, each chain should be just self-sustaining on the average.   The reaction shown schematically in part (c) is the type to be desired in an atomic bomb or other device in which enormous amounts of energy are to be released in a very short time.

The neutrons that are created in a fission reaction are initially *fast*, with energies of several Mev.   While, in a nuclear reactor, the neutrons are slowed down before producing additional fissions, if we wish to make a bomb that will detonate with explosive violence, we must utilize a *fast neutron* fission reaction.   Not only U^{235} and Pu^{239} but also the common isotope U^{238} undergo fission with *fast* neutrons.   If *more than one* of the neutrons generated by fission were, while still fast, to cause a new fission, the rate of energy generation would build up.   Apparently this build-up will not take place with U^{238} because of competition of the radiative-capture process; either Pu^{239}, separated U^{235}, or presumably U^{233} from thorium, must be used for a bomb.

When a fission process takes place within the material of a bomb, let us see what may happen to the two or three neutrons that are generated. They may be radiatively captured in the bomb material or in an impurity; they may be elastically scattered and start to slow down; they may escape from the material—none of these processes is useful in generating an explosion.   Finally, K of the two or three neutrons may cause another fast-neutron fission. K is known as the reproduction factor; and if K is appreciably greater than 1, the bomb will explode.   Let us consider a spherical mass of U^{235} or Pu^{239}, free from impurities, and consider what happens as we gradually increase the radius and the mass of material in this sphere.   When the sphere is very small, the neutrons initiated in the fission processes that are continuously being induced by cosmic rays will largely escape.   The mean free path of a neutron, before it initiates a fission, will be large compared to the radius of the sphere; under this condition the reproduction factor will be less than unity.   As we increase the size of the sphere, the probability of neutron loss by escape decreases; at a certain size, the neutrons generated by each fission will, on the average, produce one additional fission.   The mass of fissionable material in such a sphere, which has $K = 1$, is called the *critical mass*.

In order to be useful as an explosive device, fissionable material must be assembled into a *supercritical* mass with K substantially greater than 1, so that a great deal of energy can be released by fission processes before the assembly is blown apart. Presumably the method of detonation of the atomic bomb consists in the rapid assembly of subcritical masses into a supercritical mass at the instant detonation is desired.

In an atomic bomb, sufficient energy is released to convert the uranium or plutonium metal into a highly compressed gas at a temperature of about 10 million degrees Kelvin. In expanding, this compressed gas forms a blast wave of enormous intensity in the surrounding atmosphere. The highly compressed, high-temperature gas expands as a 'ball of fire' which gives off intense ultraviolet, visible, and infrared radiation capable of igniting combustible material and causing severe burns at a distance of the order of a mile. Gamma rays and highly radioactive fission products in lethal quantities are also produced when an atomic bomb is detonated.

In view of the momentary high temperatures produced during the explosion of a uranium or plutonium fission bomb, it is possible to use a *fission* bomb as a detonator for a *nuclear fusion bomb* that utilizes the energy released when the nuclei of very light elements combine or fuse to form a single nucleus of greater mass. Such fusion reactions are called *thermonuclear reactions* because they would depend on a very high temperature to start them off and keep them going, just as a high temperature is required for ignition and combustion of carbon in oxygen. Several such reactions involving hydrogen isotopes have been suggested for a fusion bomb, which therefore is popularly termed a 'hydrogen bomb.' Some of the suggested reactions with the resulting energy releases are:

$$_1H^2 + _1H^2 \rightarrow _1H^3 + _1H^1 + 4 \text{ Mev}, \qquad _1H^3 + _1H^3 \rightarrow _2He^4 + 2\ _0n^1 + 11 \text{ Mev},$$
$$_1H^2 + _1H^2 \rightarrow _2He^3 + _0n^1 + 4 \text{ Mev}, \qquad _1H^3 + _1H^2 \rightarrow _2He^4 + _0n^1 + 18 \text{ Mev}.$$

Other reactions involving heavier nuclei such as those of lithium would also release substantial amounts of energy in a fusion process.

Any of these reactions could, in principle, be used, provided sufficiently high temperatures—tens of millions of degrees—were available to *start* the reaction; once started, the reaction (like a TNT chemical reaction) could be self-sustaining until the bomb blew itself apart.

7. PARTICLE ACCELERATORS

FOR LABORATORY study of nuclear reactions under controlled conditions, there has been increasing demand for generation of bombarding ions of higher and higher energy and in good quantity. In this section we shall describe some of the 'machines' that have been and are being developed to satisfy this demand.

The use of alpha particles from naturally radioactive sources as projectiles for nuclear bombardment produced valuable results in the Rutherford scattering experiments and in the discovery of the first nuclear reactions. However, the numbers of alpha particles obtainable per second from natural radioactive sources is relatively small compared with the numbers of charged particles present in electron or ion beams, and the alpha-particle energies are limited to 10 million electron-volts (10 Mev). These limitations of natural radioactive sources were soon recognized, and much effort has gone into the development of devices—the so-called 'atom smashers'—that accelerate charged particles, such as protons, deuterons, and electrons, to be used as projectiles in the study of nuclei. These 'accelerators' provide abundant sources of charged particles for use in the study of nuclear reactions.

In principle, the simplest method of producing high-energy projectiles is to allow charged particles such as protons to pass in an evacuated tube from a region of very high potential to a region of low potential. This process is used in the *Van de Graaff generator* illustrated in Fig. 8, in which a charged belt discharges completely (by electrostatic principles) to the outside of a sphere, thereby raising the sphere to a high negative or positive potential. Potentials as high as 5 million volts have been attained, and the voltage of the sphere can be maintained constant to 0.1 per cent. In accelerating positive ions, the voltage from the high-voltage electrode is applied to a long vacuum tube, one end of which is in the sphere itself and contains an ion source that supplies protons, deuterons, or doubly charged helium ions (see Fig. 44, p. 583). The other end of the vacuum tube is at ground potential and contains the 'target' to be bombarded. To accelerate electrons, the sphere is made negative; very penetrating

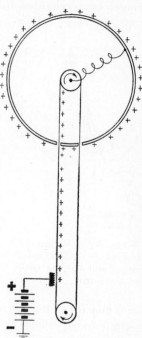

Fig. 8. Schematic diagram of the Van de Graaff electrostatic generator.

X rays for medical purposes are obtained from electrons accelerated in this way.

Ions of higher energy are obtained with the *cyclotron* developed by E. O. Lawrence. In this device, positive ions are made to pass repeatedly through the same accelerating potential and finally to acquire energies corresponding to a fall through a potential many times greater than that actually applied at any one time between the electrodes. The arrangement of the electrodes in the cyclotron is illustrated schematically in Fig. 9. Two semicircular hollow copper boxes, called 'dees' because of their shape, are arranged in the manner indicated. The dees are placed in an evacuated enclosure between the pole faces of a huge magnet so that there is a strong magnetic field perpendicular to the flat faces of the dees. An alternating potential of the order of 10 kv is applied between the dees at a frequency of the order of 20 megacycles/sec.

A supply of low-energy positive ions is generated at point P midway between the dees by electron bombardment of gas introduced at low pressure; the gas is usually hydrogen, deuterium, or helium. During a half-cycle these ions will be accelerated toward one of the dees B. Once these ions enter the hollow electric-field-free space within the dee, they will no longer be accelerated by the alternating electric field and will move at constant *speed*. However, since they are traveling perpendicular to a

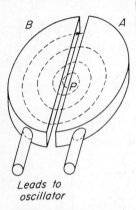

constant magnetic field $\mathcal{B}$, they will traverse a circular path and will finally return to the gap between the dees. If the frequency of the alternating potential is such that the time required to describe this semicircle corresponds to one half-cycle then the ions will arrive at the gap at just the proper time to be further accelerated by the now reversed electric field. The ions are now moving faster after entering the second dee A and will therefore traverse a circular path of greater radius. However, as we have seen on p. 701, the *time* required for an ion to traverse a circular path, or half a circular path, in a magnetic field is independent of the speed of the ion. The time for a half-revolution is given by $\pi m/\mathcal{B}Q$, where m and Q are the mass and charge of the ion.

Fig. 9. Schematic diagram of the electrodes (dees) and the ion path in a cyclotron.

Thus, for an ion to arrive at the gap between the dees at just the proper instant to experience further acceleration after each half-revolution, the oscillator must have a period equal to the time of two half-revolutions of the ion, or $2\pi m/\mathcal{B}Q$, in seconds, corresponding to a frequency of $\mathcal{B}Q/2\pi m$, in cycles/sec. For a proton of mass 1.67×10^{-27} kg and charge 1.60×10^{-19} coul, with a field of 1.5 weber/m², this is a frequency of 23 megacycles/sec. The ions describe a series of semicircles of increasing radius, gradually spiraling outward and finally emerging at the outer edge of the dees, where they may be concentrated on a target by means of an electrostatic deflecting plate. The ions emerge with an energy equivalent to a fall through a potential many times higher than that used in the accelerating process.

The practical energy limit for protons from such a standard cyclotron has been found to be about 10 Mev. The limitation arises from the fact that the mass of an ion begins to increase appreciably at high speeds, and the time of revolution no longer remains independent of speed. Within the dees, the speed v of a particle is not changing; the magnetic force on the particle is $\mathcal{B}Qv$; the acceleration is v^2/R; hence the relativistic form of Newton's second principle gives $\mathcal{B}Qv = mv^2/R$; and

$$\text{time of half-revolution} = \pi R/v = \pi m/\mathcal{B}Q. \tag{9}$$

While this expression for the time of half-revolution has the same form as in nonrelativistic theory, we must now use the relativistic mass, which increases with energy at high energies, so the time of half-revolution no longer remains constant.

The first attempt to remove this relativistic difficulty resulted in the design of the *synchrocyclotron*. In this accelerator, which looks exactly like a cyclotron (see Fig. 10), a pulse of ions is emitted for a short period

Fig. 10. The 184-inch synchrocyclotron. [*Courtesy of Radiation Laboratory, University of California.*]

at the center; the frequency of the oscillator supplying the accelerating voltage is held constant until the masses of the ions in this pulse, and hence the times of half-revolution, begin to increase; then the oscillator is *frequency-modulated* so that the frequency drops in accordance with the increasing times; when this pulse of ions has been collected at the edge of the dees, a new pulse is emitted and the process repeated. The most powerful synchrocyclotron, at the University of Chicago, has pole pieces 170 inches in diameter and produces proton energies of 450 Mev.

The synchrocyclotron is very wasteful of iron in setting up a magnetic field throughout a large volume, only a small part of which is occupied by the ion pulse at any one time. More recent machines, designed for still higher energies, keep the *radius of curvature* of the ion pulse constant by increasing the magnetic intensity in proportion the increase of the momentum mv of the particles as they are accelerated. In such machines, called *synchrotrons*, the ion pulse repeatedly follows the same path in a vacuum tube that usually has four straight sections and four 90-degree

curves.   A pulse of ions is injected into the path at fairly high energy
from some other form of accelerator, is then repeatedly accelerated by
suitable oscillators in the straight sections, and deflected through 90
degrees by an array of magnets in the curved sections and finally deflected
onto a target.   To keep the radii of curvature constant, the magnetic
intensity must increase in proportion to the momentum mv of the particles.   Since the times of traversing both the straight sections and the
curved sections are inversely proportional to the speed v of the particles,
the frequency of the oscillator must increase in proportion to this speed.

Figure 11. Bevatron with 135-ft diameter magnet that produces 6.25-Bev
protons. [*Courtesy of Radiation Laboratory, University of California.*]

However, if the particles are injected at a speed that is, say, $\frac{1}{10}$ the speed
of light, the speed can increase by a factor of only 10, so the oscillator frequency need rise only by a factor of 10.   The first synchrotron to give
protons of over one billion electron-volts (1 Bev) was the 'cosmotron'
at the Brookhaven National Laboratory, while the 'bevatron' at the
University of California has more recently given protons an energy of
6 Bev.   The synchrotron principle is also applicable to the acceleration
of electrons, and the California Institute of Technology has an electron
synchrotron operating at 1 Bev.   Figure 11 shows a photograph of the
bevatron at the University of California.

This discussion of particle accelerators is far from complete; we have
omitted discussion of important types known as Cockroft-Walton generators, linear accelerators, and betatrons.   These have, however,
received some consideration in problem sets in preceding chapters.

8. NUCLEAR FORCES; ELEMENTARY PARTICLES

THUS FAR, we have described the nucleus only by saying that it is composed of protons and neutrons; we have said very little about the forces that hold these particles together.   Actually, very little is known about the nature of these forces.   The known facts are these: (a) a proton at a relatively large distance $r > 10^{-15}$ m from a nucleus of charge Ze is acted on only by the force of ordinary electrostatic repulsion, but at a shorter distance the proton is strongly attracted by so-called *short-range forces;* (b) a neutron at a large distance $r > 10^{-15}$ m from a nucleus experiences no appreciable force, but at a shorter distance the neutron is strongly attracted by forces similar to those experienced by a proton.   These short-range forces, called *nuclear forces*, are different from and much stronger than any forces that could arise from gravitational, electrostatic, or magnetic effects.

The short-range nuclear forces show *saturation effects* analogous to the saturation of valence forces in chemical compounds.   In the case of valence forces, we say that a carbon atom has four valence bonds and is *saturated* when all four of these bonds are utilized in forming links with atoms of other elements, as in methane (CH_4).   Similarly, nuclear forces in light nuclei tend to become saturated when two protons and two neutrons combine to form an alpha particle.   These saturation effects account for the particular stability in Fig. 6 of the nuclei $_2He^4$, $_6C^{12}$, and $_8O^{16}$, which are composed of 1, 3, and 4 alpha particles, respectively.

In 1935, Hideki Yukawa, a Japanese physicist, developed a theory that pictured short-range forces between particles in nuclei as forces similar to the chemical forces between adjacent atoms in homopolar compounds.   In a homopolar chemical bond between two atoms, electrons are *shared* between the two atoms.   In order to account for the saturation characteristic of the short-range nuclear forces, Yukawa postulated the existence of a particle of mass *intermediate* between the electron and proton masses.   From the known range of the strong forces, calculation showed that the mass of the hypothetical particle should be about 300 times that of the electron.   Because this mass is *intermediate*, the particle was called a *meson*.

In the years following 1935, conclusive evidence was found for the existence of a particle of intermediate mass in cosmic radiation.   However this particle, now called the μ-meson, had a mass of 207 electron masses, and did not have the properties predicted by Yukawa.   However, another meson having properties more nearly like those predicted by Yukawa was found in 1947.   It is called a π-meson and its mass is 273 electron masses.   The validity of Yukawa's theory of nuclear forces has not yet been completely either proved or disproved.

Since 1947, the balance of the wierd array of unstable particles shown in Table I, all lighter than the deuteron, have been observed either in the cosmic radiation or in the laboratory. These particles all decay spontaneously to electrons, positrons, protons, photons (and presumably neutrinos), which are the only particles not subject to spontaneous decay.

TABLE I

OBSERVED PARTICLES

Class	Name	Symbol	Mass	Charge	Spontaneous decay products	Mean life (sec)
Light	electron	$_{-1}\varepsilon^0$	m	$-e$	stable	stable
	positron	$_{+1}\varepsilon^0$	m	$+e$	stable	stable
Mesons	μ-meson	$_{-1}\mu$	$207\ m$	$-e$	$_{-1}\varepsilon^0 + 2\,_0\nu^0$	2×10^{-6}
	μ-meson	$_{+1}\mu$	$207\ m$	$+e$	$_{+1}\varepsilon^0 + 2\,_0\nu^0$	2×10^{-6}
	π-meson	$_0\pi$	$264\ m$	o	$\left\{\begin{array}{l}_{+1}\varepsilon^0 +_{-1}\varepsilon^0 + hf\\ \text{or } 2\ hf\end{array}\right\}$	5×10^{-15}
	π-meson	$_{-1}\pi$	$273\ m$	$-e$	$_{-1}\mu +_0\nu^0$	3×10^{-8}
	π-meson	$_{+1}\pi$	$273\ m$	$+e$	$_{+1}\mu +_0\nu^0$	3×10^{-8}
	K-particles $\left\{\vphantom{\begin{array}{c}1\\2\\3\\4\end{array}}\right.$	$_{+1}K$	$934\ m$	$+e$	$_{+1}\mu +_0\nu^0$	$\sim10^{-8}$
		$_{+1}\theta$	$966\ m$	$+e$	$_{+1}\pi +_0\pi$	$\sim10^{-9}$
		$_0\theta$	$966\ m$	o	$_{+1}\pi +_{-1}\pi$	2×10^{-10}
		$_{+1}\tau$	$966\ m$	$+e$	$\left\{\begin{array}{l}2\,_{+1}\pi +_{-1}\pi\\ \text{or }_{+1}\pi + 2\,_0\pi\end{array}\right\}$	2×10^{-8}
Nucleons	proton	$_1H^1$	$1836\ m$	$+e$	stable	stable
	anti-proton	$_{-1}H^1$	$1836\ m$	$-e$	stable	stable
	neutron	$_0n^1$	$1839\ m$	o	$_1H^1 +_{-1}\varepsilon^0 +_0\nu^0$	1,080
Hyperons		$_0\Lambda$	$2181\ m$	o	$_1H^1 +_{-1}\pi$	4×10^{-10}
		$_{-1}\Sigma$	$2340\ m$	$-e$	$_0n^1 +_{-1}\pi$	4×10^{-11}
		$_{+1}\Sigma$	$2340\ m$	$+e$	$\left\{\begin{array}{l}_0n^1 +_{+1}\pi\\ \text{or }_1H^1 +_0\pi\end{array}\right\}$	4×10^{-11}
		Ξ or Ω	$2582\ m$	$-e$	$_0\Lambda +_{-1}\pi$	$\sim10^{-10}$

Primary cosmic radiation, consisting of protons, alpha-particles, and some heavier nuclei, with energies up to 10^{17} ev, enters the top of the earth's atmosphere. These extremely energetic particles collide with nuclei in the atmosphere, producing secondary protons, neutrons, and mesons. The spontaneous disintegration of neutral π-mesons produces photons. The photons are materialized to produce electrons and positrons, the latter in turn being annihilated to form photons of lower energy. The μ-mesons are longer lived than the π-mesons; they do not interact strongly with nuclei and hence furnish the most abundant and most penetrating component of the cosmic rays observed at sea level and even many hundreds of feet under earth or water.

Many types of particles exist in the cosmic radiation because of the repeated events—nuclear reactions of all types, annihilations, and materializations—that take place as the primaries and extremely high-energy secondaries penetrate the atmosphere. There is good evidence for the presence of other mesons, called K-particles, heavier than pi-mesons, and of 'hyperons' intermediate in mass between the neutron and the deuteron.

Experimentation with cosmic rays is very slow and unsatisfactory because of the very small chance of having an event of interest take place where it can be observed—in a cloud chamber or in a photographic emulsion. Experiments on artificially produced mesons have greatly added to the knowledge of their properties.

Mesons were first produced in the laboratory by bombardment of matter with 380-Mev protons from the 184-inch synchrocyclotron at Berkeley in 1948. They have since been produced by bombardment with high-energy neutrons and gamma rays. For example, charged and neutral π-mesons can be produced when gamma rays interact with protons and neutrons as follows:

$$hf + {}_1H^1 \rightarrow {}_0n^1 + {}_{+1}\pi, \qquad hf + {}_1H^1 \rightarrow {}_1H^1 + {}_0\pi,$$

$$hf + {}_0n^1 \rightarrow {}_1H^1 + {}_{-1}\pi, \qquad hf + {}_0n^1 \rightarrow {}_0n^1 + {}_0\pi.$$

In each case, since the rest masses of the proton and neutron are approximately equal, the gamma-ray energy hf must approximately equal the rest energy of the meson that 'materializes'; this rest energy is about 140 Mev.

At present we are only beginning studies of the behavior of particles having energies approaching a billion electron-volts (Bev). The directions being taken in these studies are twofold. First, exhaustive studies of cosmic rays are in progress. Second, studies of nuclear reactions produced by the much more abundant projectiles available with recently developed new types of accelerators are in progress. With these accelerators entering the billion-electron-volt range, one should be able to study under controlled laboratory conditions the many strange and little-understood phenomena observed occasionally with cosmic rays. Such studies should add much to the knowledge of elementary particles and of the forces that bind them into nuclei. The Bev-range is critical because here for the first time one reaches energies above the rest energies of the proton and the neutron. The discovery of the *negative proton* or *anti-proton* was announced in October 1955 by the Radiation Laboratory of the University of California. This particle bears the same relation to the proton as the positron does to the electron. Processes analogous to annihilation and pair production of electrons and positrons occur with these *heavy* elementary particles, but the energies involved are 1836 times as great.

PROBLEMS

1. What is the electric charge of the oxygen nucleus in electronic-charge units? in coulombs?   Ans: $+8e$; 1.28×10^{-18} coul.

2. How many planetary electrons are present in a neutral atom of helium? of chlorine? of bromine? of lead?

3. Chlorine has two isotopes of masses 34.980 and 36.978 amu. If the radius of the path described by the lighter isotope in the Bainbridge spectrograph is

5 cm, find the separation between the traces produced by the two isotopes on the photographic plate.   Ans: 0.571 cm.

4. Find the plate separation for the lithium isotopes of mass numbers 6 and 7 if the radius of the path of the lighter isotope in a Bainbridge mass spectrograph is 5 cm. The isotopic masses are 6.017 and 7.018.

5. Find the average mass of an oxygen atom in kg.   Ans: 2.66×10^{-26} kg.

6. How many U^{235} atoms are there in 1 kg of U^{235}?

7. The thorium isotope Th^{234} spontaneously disintegrates by beta-particle emission. Write the equation describing this process.

8. The isotope produced by the process mentioned in Prob. 7 is a beta emitter. Write the equation describing this second beta process.

9. Natural radium is $_{88}Ra^{226}$. After 1600 years, half the atoms in a sample of radium will have decayed to stable $_{82}Pb^{206}$. The radium first changes to radon by alpha emission; then the radon changes to the above isotope of lead by a succession of eight decay processes that altogether require only 25 years for half the radon to change to lead. From radium to stable lead, the chain of nine decay processes leads through the following elements, including two unstable isotopes of lead: (1) Ra→Rn, (2) →Po, (3) →Pb, (4) →Bi, (5) →Po, (6) →Pb, (7) →Bi, (8) →Po, (9) →Pb. Write the equation describing each of these nine nuclear disintegrations.

10. Experiment shows that for a given radioactive material the number of disintegrations occurring per unit time, dN/dt, depends only on the total number N of radioactive atoms present in the sample, and is proportional to this number. Thus, $dN/dt = -\lambda N$, where the proportionality constant λ is called the *decay constant*. Show that if we start with N_0 radioactive atoms at $t = 0$, the number remaining at any later time is given by $N = N_0 e^{-\lambda t}$, and that the half-life of the radioactive material is $0.693/\lambda$.

11. When boron is bombarded with alpha particles, a reaction involving B^{10} results in the ejection of protons. Write an equation describing this reaction.

12. When boron is bombarded with alpha particles, a reaction involving B^{11} results in the ejection of neutrons. Write the equation describing this reaction.

13. Calculate the mass of an electron moving at 0.9 of the speed of light. Give the result in terms of the rest mass m_0 and in kg.
$$\text{Ans: } 2.29 \ m_0; \ 2.09 \times 10^{-30} \text{ kg.}$$

14. What is the mass of an electron moving at a speed of $0.95 \ c$? $0.99 \ c$? Give the results in terms of the rest mass and in kg.

15. What is the total energy E associated with an electron moving with a speed of $0.9 \ c$? What is the classical value for the kinetic energy of this electron? What is the relativistic value for the kinetic energy of this electron?
$$\text{Ans: } 1.88 \times 10^{-13} \text{ joule; } 0.331 \times 10^{-13} \text{ joule; } 1.06 \times 10^{-13} \text{ joule.}$$

16. At what speed, in mi/sec, will the mass of a body be increased by one part in a million?

17. By measurement of tracks in a Wilson cloud chamber, it is found that the total kinetic energy of an electron-positron pair is 6.25 Mev. What was the energy of the original photon responsible for the production of the electron-positron pair?   Ans: 7.27 Mev.

18. Compute the total binding energy for the sulfur isotope $_{16}S^{32}$, of isotopic mass 31.9825. What is the binding energy per nucleon?

19. Compute the binding energy per nucleon of $_6C^{12}$ and $_7N^{14}$ in Mev. The masses of the neutral atoms are 12.00388 and 14.00753 amu, respectively. The higher binding energy per nucleon for $_6C^{12}$ is an example of the saturation effects for nuclear forces when the nucleus is composed of a whole number of alpha particles.   Ans: $_6C^{12}$, 7.67 Mev; $_7N^{14}$, 7.47 Mev.

20. The isotope $_{83}Bi^{209}$ has mass 209.056 amu, $_{36}Kr^{82}$ has 81.938 amu. What is the *difference* in Mev of binding energy per nucleon for these two nuclei, one near the right of the curve in Fig. 6 and one near the minimum?

21. Calculate the total energy released in the series of reactions described on p. 838 if four moles of protons combine to form a single mole of helium.
$$\text{Ans: } 2.58 \times 10^{12} \text{ joules.}$$

22. Calculate the total energy in joules released if a mole of $_1H^1$ atoms combines with a mole of $_3Li^7$ atoms to form two moles of helium atoms. The isotopic mass of $_3Li^7$ is 7.01816.

23. If $_4Be^9$ (9.01496 amu) is bombarded with 3.00-Mev alpha particles to form $_6C^{12}$ (12.00388 amu) and a neutron in accordance with the reaction on p. 828, find the resulting kinetic energy. This kinetic energy will be shared between the neutron and the recoil carbon but will mostly reside in the lighter neutron.   Ans: 8.57 Mev.

24. When $_7N^{14}$ (14.00753 amu) is bombarded with 3.00-Mev alpha particles to form $_8O^{17}$ (17.00450 amu) and a proton, as in the reaction on p. 828, find the resulting energy in Mev. This kinetic energy will be shared between the proton and the recoil oxygen, but will mostly reside in the lighter proton.

25. Taking 200 Mev as the energy released during the fission of a single U^{235} nucleus, compute the number of fission processes taking place each second in a reactor operating at a power level of 1 kilowatt.   Ans: 3.12×10^{13}.

26. How much U^{235} (mass 235 amu) is consumed each day in a nuclear reactor operating at a power level of 1 kilowatt? How much bituminous coal (heat of combustion 7500 cal/g) would be required to release this amount of energy?

27. What is the total decrease each day in the total *mass* of the material in a uranium pile operating at a power level of 1 kilowatt?   Ans: 9.61×10^{-7} g.

28. If a reactor designed for ship propulsion delivers 50,000 kw of power continuously, what is the consumption of U^{235} in kilograms per day? What is the equivalent consumption of coal (7500 cal/g) in kg/day? Assume 100 per cent efficiency in each case.

29. The fuel value of coal is measured by the heat of combustion. Using 200 Mev as the energy release per fission, calculate the 'heat of fission' for pure U^{235} in joules/kg and in cal/g.   Ans: 8.21×10^{13} joules/kg; 1.96×10^{10} cal/g.

30. To how many tons of coal (7500 cal/g) is one pound of U^{235} equivalent in fuel value?

31. According to official estimates, the atomic bomb at Hiroshima was equivalent to 20,000 tons of TNT. Assuming 3.8×10^9 joules as the energy released by detonation of 1 ton of TNT, find the number of fissions occurring, the total amount of U^{235} consumed, and the total mass decrease involved in the explosion of the bomb.   Ans: 2.37×10^{24}; 0.925 kg; 8.45×10^{-4} kg.

32. In a normal-uranium reactor, thin uranium rods are embedded in a 'pile' of graphite. Most of the high-energy fission neutrons from U^{235} escape from the rods into the graphite. If the graphite is sufficiently pure, these neutrons are slowed down to thermal energies by collisions with carbon nuclei without undergoing any nuclear reaction. If the pile is sufficiently large, these thermal neutrons have a high probability of re-entering a uranium rod before escaping from the surface of the pile. This slowing-down process is necessary because the high-energy fission neutrons would have such a high probability of radiative capture by U^{238} that a chain reaction could not be sustained, whereas it has been demonstrated that the above graphite pile will sustain a chain reaction and produce power and plutonium. Show that in principle such a pile can be designed to produce one atom of Pu for each atom of U^{235} that undergoes fission, so that the supply of 'fuel' is continuously renewed. Show that such a pile effectively uses all of the normal uranium, not just U^{235} as fuel. A reactor designed in this way is called a 'breeder.' Note that many of the fission products have high affinity for neutrons, so that these products would gradually contaminate the graphite; this difficulty is solved in recent proposals for breeder reactors that employ a 'moderator' such as water that is more easily replaced or purified than is graphite.

33. The high-voltage electrode in a Van de Graaff generator is maintained at a potential of 4 million volts. Calculate the maximum energies that can be imparted to protons, deuterons, and alpha particles by this machine.

Ans: 4 Mev; 4 Mev; 8 Mev.

34. If an ion source could be devised that would completely strip the electrons from atoms, what kinetic energies could be imparted to the 'projectiles' obtained when (a) lithium, (b) carbon, and (c) sulfur nuclei were accelerated by the generator of Prob. 33?

35. In a certain cyclotron the radio-frequency oscillator operates at a frequency of 10 megacycles/sec and applies a peak voltage of 10 kv between the dees. Find the time required for protons to describe a semicircular path inside one of the dees. What should be the flux density of the magnetic field in this cyclotron? If the effective diameter of the pole faces measured to the periphery of the dees in this cyclotron is 1.5 m, what is the maximum kinetic energy that can be imparted to protons?   Ans: 5×10^{-8} sec; 0.656 webers/m²; 11.6 Mev.

36. If the frequency and the peak value of the voltage in the cyclotron of Prob. 35 were maintained constant, what should be the magnetic-field strength if deuterons are to be accelerated? What would be the maximum kinetic energy imparted to the deuterons? Make a similar calculation for doubly charged helium ions.

37. Why is a cyclotron not useful for the acceleration of *electrons* to high energies? At what energy in ev would the time of a half-revolution of an electron in a cyclotron increase by one per cent over its value for slow electrons.

Ans: 2500 ev.

38. At what energy in Mev would the times of half-revolution of protons, deuterons, and alpha-particles in a cyclotron increase by one per cent over their values for slow particles?

39. Show that at low energies, the magnetic intensity required to bend charged particles into a circle of given radius is proportional to the square root of the energy of the particles, whereas at extremely high energies, it is proportional to the energy itself.

40. If the maximum usable magnetic field is 1 weber/m², what radius of curvature must be allowed in a synchrotron designed to accelerate protons to an energy of 1 Bev? of 100 Bev?

41. If the maximum usable magnetic field is 1 weber/m², what radius of curvature must be allowed in a synchrotron designed to accelerate electrons to an energy of 1 Bev?   Ans: 3.3 m.

42. At what energies do the speeds of electrons, protons, deuterons, and alpha-particles reach 99 per cent of their maximum possible speeds?

43. Derive the expression (4), $K.E. = c^2(m - m_0)$, by the following steps: From (3) show that $K.E. = \int [mv(dv/dt) + v^2(dm/dt)] \, dt$. Differentiate (2) to obtain dm/dt. Compute $(c^2 - v^2)(dm/dt)$, and from this expression show that the bracketed integrand above is just $c^2(dm/dt)$, and hence that $K.E. = c^2 \int dm$.

44. In the Compton effect, the wavelength λ_θ of X rays scattered at angle θ with the direction of the original beam of X rays of wavelength λ is

$$\lambda_\theta = \lambda + (h/cm_0)(1 - \cos\theta),$$

where m_0 is the rest mass of the electron. Derive this formula from the principles of conservation of energy and momentum, using the relativistic expressions for these quantities throughout.

45. From the formula in Prob. 44, show that Compton scattering at 90° is always accompanied by a wavelength increase of 0.0242×10^{-10} m.

APPENDIX

In this Appendix, we begin with a discussion of the various systems of mechanical, electrical, and magnetic units that are encountered in the literature. We then give tables of accurate values of the fundamental physical constants and of physical properties of the elements, including atomic masses. Mathematical tables of trigonometric functions, logarithms, and exponentials, and an extensive set of tables of conversion factors that the student should find useful throughout his work in science and engineering follow. The Appendix concludes with the periodic table of the elements.

1. SYSTEMS OF MECHANICAL UNITS

Several systems of mechanical units are used in scientific and engineering work. Scientists and electrical engineers prefer the metric absolute system. Mechanical and civil engineers find it convenient to use the force units that occur in gravitational systems.

Once the length and time units have been selected, the key relationship involved in setting up a consistent system of units is the form of Newton's second principle used to give the relationship between force units and mass units. Thus, if we express the second principle in the form

$$F = ma, \tag{1}$$

the force unit is *defined* by this equation in terms of the mass unit, or conversely. In the meter-kilogram-second (MKS) system, the acceleration is given in meters per second per second, the mass unit is the kilogram, and the force unit to be used is the *newton*, which is defined by (1) as the resultant force that will give a mass of 1 kg an acceleration of 1 m/sec². In the centimeter-gram-second (CGS) system, the acceleration is given in centimeters per second per second, the mass unit is the gram, and (1) defines another force unit, the *dyne;* the dyne is the resultant force required to give a mass of 1 g an acceleration of 1 cm/sec².* In the foot-pound-second (FPS) system, the foot per second per second is the acceleration unit, the pound is the mass unit, and (1) defines a force unit called the

---

* In the CGS system, the unit of energy, the cm·dyne, is called the *erg*. From their definitions, we find that

$$1 \text{ newton} = 1 \text{ kg·m/sec}^2 = 10^5 \text{ g·cm/sec}^2 = 10^5 \text{ dynes},$$
$$1 \text{ joule} = 1 \text{ nt·m} = 10^5 \text{ dyne·}10^2 \text{ cm} = 10^7 \text{ ergs}.$$

855

poundal, which is the resultant force required to give a one-pound mass an acceleration of 1 ft/sec². These are the *absolute* systems in current use; other units in these systems are listed in Table I. There is no reference to the strength of the earth's gravitational field in the definition of any of the units in these absolute systems.

Equation (1) will also apply when systems of gravitational units of one type (which we call Type I) are used. In systems of this type, a gravitational force unit is chosen and then (1) is used to *define* a gravitational mass unit. In the gravitational system we have used in this book (called British Type I in Table I), the force unit in (1) is taken as the pound, defined as the force of gravity on a one-pound mass at a location where the acceleration of gravity has its standard value

$$g_0 = 9.80665 \text{ m/sec}^2 = 32.17398 \text{ ft/sec}^2.$$

With this force unit, and ft/sec² for the acceleration unit, (1) is used to define a mass unit, the *slug*, as the mass to which a force of 1 lb will give an acceleration of 1 ft/sec². This mass unit has the value 1 slug = 32.174 lb-mass. There is also a metric gravitational system of Type I in occasional use on the European continent. In this system, which we do not list in Table I, the force unit is the kilogram-force, the acceleration unit is the m/sec², and the mass unit defined by (1) has the magnitude 9.8 kg-mass.

TABLE I

SYSTEMS OF MECHANICAL UNITS

	Absolute systems			Gravitational systems		
	MKS	CGS	FPS	British Type I	British Type II	Metric Type II
Newton's second principle:	$F = ma$	$F = ma$	$F = ma$	$F = ma$	$g_0 F = ma$ $(g_0 = 32.174)$	$g_0 F = ma$ $(g_0 = 9.80665)$
Length.....	meter	centimeter	foot	foot	foot	meter
Mass.......	kilogram	gram	pound	slug	pound-mass	kilogram-mass
Time.......	second	second	second	second	second	second
Force......	newton	dyne	poundal	pound	pound-force	kilogram-force
Velocity....	m/sec	cm/sec	ft/sec	ft/sec	ft/sec	m/sec
Acceleration	m/sec²	cm/sec²	ft/sec²	ft/sec²	ft/sec²	m/sec²
Torque.....	nt·m	dyne·cm	pdl·ft	lb·ft	lbf·ft	kgf·m
Moment of inertia...	kg·m²	g·cm²	lb·ft²	slug·ft²	lbm·ft²	kgm·m²
Pressure....	nt/m²	dyne/cm²	pdl/ft²	lb/ft²	lbf/ft²	kgf/m²
Energy.....	joule	erg	ft·pdl	ft·lb	ft·lbf	m·kgf
Power......	watt	erg/sec	ft·pdl/sec	ft·lb/sec	ft·lbf/sec	m·kgf/sec
Momentum.	kg·m/sec	g·cm/sec	lb·ft/sec	slug·ft/sec	lbm·ft/sec	kgm·m/sec
Impulse....	nt·sec	dyne·sec	pdl·sec	lb·sec	lbf·sec	kgf·sec

Since Newton's second principle has been used in the form (1) throughout this book, the equations derived in this book will in general apply only when one of the systems of units discussed above is used. *Any of the first four systems given in Table I may be used in any of the equations of this volume, except in equations containing electrical or magnetic quantities (which require* MKS *mechanical units).* In these four systems, the quantities appearing in Newton's principle have the following units:

System	F	$=$ m	a
MKS:	newton	kg	m/sec²
CGS:	dyne	g	cm/sec²
FPS:	poundal	lb	ft/sec²
British Type I:	lb	slug	ft/sec².

Some engineers prefer to use the pound-mass (lbm) as the mass unit and the pound-force (lbf) as the force unit. This can be done, provided Newton's second principle is written in the form

$$g_0 F = m a, \qquad\qquad (2)$$

where g_0 is a *dimensionless* constant having the value 32.174 when F is in lbf, m is in lbm, and a is in ft/sec². Similarly, continental engineers sometimes use the kilogram-mass (kgm) as the mass unit and the kilogram-force (kgf) as the force unit; they do this by writing Newton's principle in the form (2) where the constant g_0 has the value 9.80665 when F is in kgf, m in kgm, and a in m/sec². These gravitational systems are designated as Type II in the last two columns of Table I. *The relations derived in this book do not in general hold in these systems of Type II.*

2. SYSTEMS OF ELECTRICAL AND MAGNETIC UNITS

IN THE COURSE of the historical development of electricity and magnetism, three different systems of units were introduced: a CGS *electrostatic system* for handling problems in *electrostatics;* a CGS *electromagnetic system* for handling problems in *magnetism;* and the *practical system* employed by engineers for problems in *current electricity.* Since these three subjects are not at all independent, it was formerly necessary to learn not only all three systems of units, but a complex set of relations between them. The practical units—the coulomb, ampere, ohm, and volt—had been chosen as certain multiples of the *electromagnetic* units that would be of convenient practical size. It was Giorgi, in 1901, who first pointed out that if an MKS, rather than a CGS, system of fundamental mechanical units were employed, a single complete and consistent system of electrical and magnetic units could be devised that would embody the practical units of current, voltage, and resistance. This MKS system has been approved by various international physical and electrotechnical bodies, and is rapidly replacing the older CGS systems in scientific and technical work.   It is this system, in the so-called 'rationalized' form, that we have employed in this book.   Since, however, all the older treatments of the subject employ the CGS systems, it is desirable to see how the latter are set up and to give the relations between the units in these systems and those in the MKS system.*

THE *electrostatic unit* (ESU) of charge is defined by the equation

$$F = (1 \text{ dyne·cm}^2/\text{statcoul}^2) \, Q_1 Q_2 / d^2 \qquad (3)$$

for the force between charges.   With F in dynes and d in cm, Q is in *statcoulombs*.   By comparison of (3) with (2), p. 551, we see from the definitions of the CGS mechanical units given in Sec. 1 that

$$1 \text{ coulomb} = 3 \times 10^9 \text{ statcoulombs.}†$$

Current in *statamperes* is defined as statcoulombs per second, so

$$1 \text{ ampere} = 3 \times 10^9 \text{ statamperes.}†$$

Difference of potential in *statvolts* is defined by the equation $W = QV$, with W in ergs.   Comparison with the definition of the volt as the joule/coulomb shows that

$$1 \text{ statvolt} = 300 \text{ volts.}†$$

Finally, the *statohm* and the *statfarad* are defined by $R = V/I$ and $C = QV$, and we see that

$$1 \text{ statohm} = 9 \times 10^{11} \text{ ohms,}†$$

and $$1 \text{ farad} = 9 \times 10^{11} \text{ statfarads.}†$$

Instead of the above names with the prefix 'stat-,' units in this system are frequently designated as ESU of charge, current, potential, and so forth.

THE *electromagnetic unit* (EMU) of current, the *abampere*, may be defined by using the formula

$$f = (2 \text{ dyne/abamp}^2) \, I^2/d \qquad (4)$$

for the force in dynes per cm length between two infinite parallel wires a distance d (in cm) apart, each carrying current I in abamperes.   When (4) is compared with (11), p. 686, we see that

$$1 \text{ abampere} = 10 \text{ amperes.}$$

* In earlier writings, the constants in (3) and (4) were taken as dimensionless, thus making the ESU of charge and the EMU of current expressible in terms of units of length, mass, and time.   That this is basically incorrect is immediately apparent from the fact that it gives charge or current different physical dimensions in terms of length, mass, and time in the two systems.   Equations (3) and (4) as written recognize this fact, which was not clearly understood when the CGS systems were set up.

† Throughout this section the number '3' stands for 2.99793, the numerical constant occurring in the metric value of the speed of light, and '9' stands for the square of this constant.   Conversion factors accurate to four figures are given in the tables of Sec. 8.

TABLE II
ELECTRICAL AND MAGNETIC UNITS IN THE THREE SYSTEMS

	Practical MKS unit	*Electromagnetic* EMU	*Electrostatic* ESU
Length l	1 meter	1 centimeter	1 centimeter
Mass m	1 kilogram	1 gram	1 gram
Time t	1 second	1 second	1 second
Force f	1 newton = 1 kg·m/sec²	1 dyne = 1 g·cm/sec²	1 dyne = 1 g·cm/sec²
Energy W	1 joule = 1 m·nt	1 erg = 1 cm·dyne	1 erg = 1 cm·dyne
Power P	1 watt = 1 joule/sec	1 erg/sec	1 erg/sec
Charge Q	1 coul	1 abcoul	1 statcoul
Current $I = Q/t$	1 amp = 1 coul/sec	1 abamp = 1 abcoul/sec	1 statamp = 1 statcoul/sec
Electric potential $V = W/Q$	1 volt = 1 joule/coul	1 abvolt = 1 erg/abcoul	1 statvolt = 1 erg/statcoul
Resistance $R = V/I$	1 ohm = 1 joule·sec/coul²	1 abohm = 1 erg·sec/abcoul²	1 statohm = 1 erg·sec/statcoul²
Electric intensity $\mathcal{E} = V/l = f/Q$	1 volt/meter = 1 nt/coul	1 abvolt/cm = 1 dyne/abcoul	1 statvolt/cm = 1 dyne/statcoul
Capacitance $C = Q/V$	1 farad = 1 coul/v = 1 coul²/joule	1 abf = 1 abcoul/abv = 1 abcoul²/erg	1 statf = 1 statcoul/stav = 1 statcoul²/erg
Dielectric displacement $\mathfrak{D}$*	1 coul/m²	1 EMU = $(1/4\pi)$ abcoul/cm²	1 ESU = $(1/4\pi)$ statcoul/cm²
Electric inductive capacity $\epsilon_\epsilon = \mathfrak{D}/\mathcal{E}$*	1 farad/meter = 1 coul²/joule·m	1 EMU = $(1/4\pi)$ abcoul²/erg·cm	1 ESU = $(1/4\pi)$ statcoul²/erg·cm
Magnetic flux density $\mathfrak{B} = f/lI$	1 weber/m² = 1 nt/amp·m	1 gauss = 1 dyne/abamp·cm	1 ESU = 1 dyne/statamp·cm
Magnetic flux $\Phi = \mathfrak{B}A$	1 weber = 1 joule/amp	1 maxwell = 1 erg/abamp	1 ESU = 1 erg/statamp
Magnetic moment $M = IA$	1 amp·m²	1 abamp·cm²	1 statamp·cm²
Magnetization $\mathfrak{M} = M/v$	1 amp/m	1 abamp/cm	1 statamp/cm
Magnetizing force $\mathcal{H}$	1 amp-turn/meter	1 oersted = $(1/4\pi)$ abamp-turn/cm	1 ESU = $(1/4\pi)$ statamp-turn/cm
Magnetomotive force MMF $= \mathcal{H}l$	1 ampere-turn	1 gilbert = $(1/4\pi)$ abamp-turn	1 ESU = $(1/4\pi)$ statamp-turn
Reluctance $\mathfrak{R} = $ MMF$/\Phi$	1 amp-turn/weber = 1 amp²/joule	1 gilbert/maxwell = $(1/4\pi)$abamp²/erg	1 ESU = $(1/4\pi)$ statamp²/erg
Inductance L or M $= V/(dI/dt)$	1 henry = 1 ohm·sec = 1 joule/amp²	1 abhenry = 1 abohm·sec = 1 erg/abamp²	1 stathenry = 1 statohm·sec = 1 erg/statamp²
Magnetic inductive capacity $\epsilon_m = \mathfrak{B}/\mathcal{H}$*	1 henry/meter = 1 nt/amp²	1 gauss/oersted = 4π abhenry/cm = 4π dyne/abamp²	1 ESU = 4π stathenry/cm = 4π dyne/statamp²
Dielectric constant K	dimensionless and equal in the three systems		
Permeability μ	dimensionless and equal in the three systems		

*These quantities are not defined in this text. The factors containing 4π that occur in these and other lines arise because the MKS units are 'rationalized,' the CGS units 'unrationalized'; the meaning of the term 'rationalization' is explained in more advanced texts.

Defining the *abcoulomb* from $Q = It$, with t in sec, the *abvolt* from $W = QV$, with W in ergs, and the *abohm* from $R = V/I$, we see that

$$1 \text{ abcoulomb} = 10 \text{ coulombs,}$$
$$1 \text{ volt} = 10^8 \text{ abvolts,} \qquad (5)$$
$$1 \text{ ohm} = 10^9 \text{ abohms}$$

In this electromagnetic system, we may define the magnetic field strength $\mathcal{B}$ in *gausses* by means of the formula $F = \mathcal{B}lI$, in dynes, for the force on a length l (in cm) of wire carrying current I (in abamperes) perpendicular to the field. Comparison of this formula with (5), p. 679, shows that

$$1 \text{ weber/m}^2 = 10^4 \text{ gausses.}$$

Flux in *maxwells* is given by $\Phi = \mathcal{B}A$, with A in cm^2; hence

$$1 \text{ weber} = 10^8 \text{ maxwells.} \qquad (6)$$

The magnetizing force $\mathcal{H}$ in *oersteds* is defined in this system by the equation

$$\mathcal{H} = \mathcal{B} \text{ (oersted/gauss)} - 4\pi\mathcal{M},$$

with magnetic moment per unit volume $\mathcal{M}$ in abampere·cm^2/cm^3. Comparison with (1), p. 614, shows that

$$1 \text{ ampere-turn/meter} = 4\pi \times 10^{-3} \text{ oersted.}$$

It is noted that in this system $\mathcal{B}$ and $\mathcal{H}$ are numerically equal except in ferromagnetic materials. For a toroid, MMF $= \mathcal{H}l$, with l in cm. The unit of MMF is called the *gilbert*. Hence

$$1 \text{ ampere-turn} = 0.4\,\pi \text{ gilberts.}$$

Permeability is defined by $\mathcal{B} = \mu\mathcal{H}$ gauss/oersted, so that the permeability is unity for nonmagnetic materials just as in the MKS system of Chap. 33; hence permeability has the same value in the two systems. With reluctance defined by $\mathcal{R} = \text{MMF}/\Phi$, the reluctance of a toroid is $\mathcal{R} = (l/\mu A)$ (oersted/gauss) with l in cm, A in cm^2. The relation between the reluctance units is seen to be

$$1 \frac{\text{ampere-turn}}{\text{weber}} = \frac{4\pi}{10^9} \frac{\text{gilbert}}{\text{maxwell}}.$$

In the electromagnetic system, electromotive force is given by rate of change of flux, just as in the practical system, since the same factor 10^8 relates the flux units (6) and the EMF units (5).

Table II gives the units of all electrical and magnetic quantities in terms of mechanical units and the units of charge or current. The relations between the units in the three systems can be obtained from this table by using the above relations between the charge and current units and the relations between the mechanical quantities.

3. FUNDAMENTAL PHYSICAL CONSTANTS

THE MOST accurate values of the fundamental physical constants are derived from a critical analysis of all precision data that give either the value of a constant directly, or the value of a combination of such constants, such as the ratio e/m of charge to mass of an electron. Such analyses lead to an estimate of the *probable error*, indicated by the $\pm$ quantities in the following list. In principle, a physicist stating a probable error is willing to bet even money that his value is not off by more than this error from the true value.

The following table is based on the most recent critical analyses of J. W. M. DuMond and E. R. Cohen. All data in this table are on the physical scale of atomic masses (see p. 644).

Gravitation constant (G) .... $(6.670 \pm 0.005) \times 10^{-11}$ nt·m^2/kg^2

Volume of mole of ideal gas at NTP .... $(22{,}420.7 \pm 0.6)$ cm^3

Standard atmosphere .... $(101{,}324.6 \pm 0.4)$ nt/m^2

Ice-point .... $273.16° \pm 0.01°$ K

Mechanical equivalent of heat .... (4185.5 ± 0.4) joules/kcal

Avogadro's number (number of particles in one mole) .... $(6.0247 \pm 0.0004) \times 10^{23}$

Atomic mass of natural oxygen on physical scale .... 16.00436 ± 0.00009

Ratio of atomic masses on physical scale to those on chemical scale $(16.00436/16)$ .. 1.000272 ± 0.000005

Atomic mass unit (amu) .... $(1.6597 \pm 0.0001) \times 10^{-27}$ kg

Density of mercury at NTP .... $(13{,}595.04 \pm 0.06)$ kg/m^3

Universal gas constant (R) .... (8316.6 ± 0.4) joules/kg·K deg
$= (1.9870 \pm 0.0002)$ cal/g·K deg

Boltzmann's constant (k) .... $(1.3804 \pm 0.0001) \times 10^{-23}$ joule/K deg

Speed of light (c) .... $(2.997929 \pm 0.000008) \times 10^{8}$ m/sec

Faraday (charge carried by 1 mole of monovalent ions) .... $(96{,}520 \pm 2)$ coul

Electronic charge (e) .... $(1.60207 \pm 0.00007) \times 10^{-19}$ coul

Electron-volt (ev) .... 1.60207×10^{-19} joule

Planck's constant (h) .... $(6.6252 \pm 0.0005) \times 10^{-34}$ joule·sec
$= 4.134 \times 10^{-15}$ ev·sec

Constant in Stefan-Boltzmann law (σ) .... $(5.6686 \pm 0.0005) \times 10^{-8}$ watt/(K deg)^4·m^2

Constant in Wien's displacement law (A) . $(2.8979 \pm 0.0005) \times 10^{-3}$ m·K deg

Rest energy corresponding to 1 amu ...... (931.16 ± 0.02) Mev

Particles:

	atomic mass	mass	charge
electron	$(5.4876 \pm 0.0001) \times 10^{-4}$	$(9.1085 \pm 0.0006) \times 10^{-31}$ kg	$-e$
proton	1.007593 ± 0.000003	$(1.6724 \pm 0.0001) \times 10^{-27}$ kg	$+e$
neutron	1.008982 ± 0.000003	$(1.6747 \pm 0.0001) \times 10^{-27}$ kg	0
deuteron	2.014176 ± 0.000006	$(3.3429 \pm 0.0002) \times 10^{-27}$ kg	$+e$
α-particle	4.00276 ± 0.00003	$(6.6434 \pm 0.0004) \times 10^{-27}$ kg	$+2e$

4. PHYSICAL PROPERTIES OF THE ELEMENTS

Average atomic masses are expressed on the physical scale.
Other data courtesy of W. F. Meggers, from a 1953 compilation for *Key to Periodic Chart of the Atoms*, W. M. Welch Scientific Co.

Element	Symbol	Atomic number	Average atomic mass	Density at 20° C (g/cm³)	Melting point (° C)	Boiling point (° C)	Electrical resistivity (10⁻⁸ ohm·m)
Actinium......	Ac	89	227	—	(1600)	—	—
Aluminum....	Al	13	26.99	2.699	660.1	2060	2.65 (20° C)
Americium....	Am	95	[243]	11.7	>850	—	—
Antimony....	Sb	51	121.79	6.62	630.5	1440	39.0 (0° C)
Argon........	A	18	39.955	1.663×10^{-3}	−189.4	−185.8	gaseous
Arsenic.......	As	33	74.93	5.73	subl.	610	35 (0° C)
Astatine.....	At	85	[210]	—	—	—	—
Barium.......	Ba	56	137.40	3.5	704	1640	—
Berkelium....	Bk	97	[245]	—	—	—	—
Beryllium.....	Be	4	9.015	1.82	1280	2770	5.88 (0° C)
Bismuth......	Bi	83	209.06	9.80	271.3	1420	107 (0° C)
Boron........	B	5	10.82	2.3	2300	2550	10^{12} (0° C)
Bromine......	Br	35	79.938	3.12	−7.2	58	liquid
Cadmium.....	Cd	48	112.44	8.65	320.9	765	6.83 (0° C)
Calcium......	Ca	20	40.09	1.55	850	1487	3.43 (0° C)
Californium...	Cf	98	[246]	—	—	—	—
Carbon....... (graphite)	C	6	12.013	2.22	3700	4830	1370 (0° C)
Cerium.......	Ce	58	140.17	6.9	600	1400	78 (20° C)
Cesium.......	Cs	55	132.95	1.9	28	690	18.8 (0° C)
Chlorine......	Cl	17	35.467	2.995×10^{-3}	−101	−34.7	gaseous
Chromium....	Cr	24	52.02	7.19	1930	2500	13 (28° C)
Cobalt........	Co	27	58.96	8.9	1492	2900	6.24 (20° C)
Copper.......	Cu	29	63.56	8.96	1083.0	2600	1.67 (20° C)
Curium.......	Cm	96	[243]	—	—	—	—
Dysprosium...	Dy	66	162.50	8.56	—	—	—
Erbium.......	Er	68	167.2	9.16	—	—	—
Europium.....	Eu	63	152.0	5.24	—	—	—
Fluorine......	F	9	19.01	0.790×10^{-3}	−220	−188.2	gaseous
Francium.....	Fr	87	[223]	—	—	—	—
Gadolinium...	Gd	64	156.9	7.95	—	—	—
Gallium......	Ga	31	69.74	5.91	29.8	2070	53.4 (0° C)
Germanium...	Ge	32	72.62	5.36	960	2700	10^5 (0° C)
Gold.........	Au	79	197.3	19.32	1063.0	2970	2.19 (0° C)
Hafnium	Hf	72	178.6	11.4	(1700)	>3700	—
Helium.......	He	2	4.004	0.166×10^{-3}	−271.4	−268.9	gaseous
Holmium.....	Ho	67	164.98	10.12	—	—	—
Hydrogen....	H	1	1.0083	0.0838×10^{-3}	−259.4	−252.7	gaseous
Indium......	In	49	114.79	7.31	156.4	1450	8.37 (0° C)
Iodine........	I	53	126.94	4.93	114	183	10^{15} (20° C)
Iridium.......	Ir	77	193.2	22.5	2443	~5300	5.3 (20° C)
Iron..........	Fe	26	55.87	7.87	1539	2740	9.71 (20° C)
Krypton......	Kr	36	83.82	3.488×10^{-3}	−157	−152	gaseous
Lanthanum...	La	57	138.96	6.15	826	1800	59 (18° C)
Lead.........	Pb	82	207.27	11.34	327.3	1740	20.6 (20° C)
Lithium......	Li	3	6.942	0.53	186	1370	8.55 (0° C)
Lutetium.....	Lu	71	175.04	9.74	—	—	—
Magnesium...	Mg	12	24.33	1.74	650	1110	4.46 (20° C)
Manganese...	Mn	25	54.94	7.43	1245	2150	185 (20° C)

Element	Symbol	Atomic number	Average atomic mass	Density at 20° C (g/cm³)	Melting point (° C)	Boiling point (° C)	Electrical resistivity (10⁻⁸ ohm·m)
Mercury......	Hg	80	200.66	13.55	−38.9	356.6	94.1 (0° C)
Molybdenum..	Mo	42	95.98	10.2	2620	4800	5.17 (0° C)
Neodymium...	Nd	60	144.31	7.05	840	—	79 (18° C)
Neon.........	Ne	10	20.188	0.839×10^{-3}	−248.6	−246.0	gaseous
Neptunium...	Np	93	[237]	19.5	640		
Nickel........	Ni	28	58.71	8.9	1453	2730	6.84 (20° C)
Niobium......	Nb	41	92.94	8.57	2420	3300	13.1 (18° C)
Nitrogen......	N	7	14.012	1.165×10^{-3}	−210.0	−195.8	gaseous
Osmium......	Os	76	190.3	22.5	2700	~5500	9.5 (20° C)
Oxygen.......	O	8	16.0044	1.332×10^{-3}	−218.8	−183.0	gaseous
Palladium.....	Pd	46	106.7	12.0	1552	4000	10.8 (20° C)
Phosphorus... (yellow)	P	15	30.983	1.82	44.1	280	10^{17} (11° C)
Platinum.....	Pt	78	195.28	21.45	1769	4410	9.83 (0° C)
Plutonium....	Pu	94	[242]	—	—	—	—
Polonium.....	Po	84	210	9.24	254	—	42
Potassium....	K	19	39.111	0.86	63	770	6.15 (0° C)
Praseodymium.	Pr	59	140.96	6.63	940	—	88 (18° C)
Promethium...	Pm	61	[145]	—	—	—	
Protactinium..	Pa	91	231	—	(3000)	—	—
Radium......	Ra	88	226.11	5.0	700	1140	metallic
Radon........	Rn	86	222	9.07×10^{-3}	−71	−61.8	gaseous
Rhenium.....	Re	75	186.36	20.5	3170	~5900	—
Rhodium.....	Rh	45	102.94	12.44	1960	~4500	4.5 (20° C)
Rubidium.....	Rb	37	85.50	1.53	39	680	12.5 (20° C)
Ruthenium....	Ru	44	101.7	12.2	2500	~4900	7.6 (0° C)
Samarium.....	Sm	62	150.47	7.7	>1300	—	—
Scandium.....	Sc	21	44.96	2.5	1200	2400	—
Selenium.....	Se	34	78.98	4.81	220	680	10^{13} (20° C)
Silicon........	Si	14	28.10	2.33	1430	2300	10^{5} (0° C)
Silver........	Ag	47	107.909	10.49	960.8	2210	1.59 (20° C)
Sodium.......	Na	11	23.003	0.97	97.7	892	4.2 (0° C)
Strontium.....	Sr	38	87.65	2.6	770	1380	23 (20° C)
Sulfur........ (rhombic)	S	16	32.075	2.07	119.0	444.6	10^{23} (20° C)
Tantalum.....	Ta	73	180.93	16.6	3000	~6100	12.4 (18° C)
Technetium...	Tc	43	[99]	11.46	(2700)	—	—
Tellurium.....	Te	52	127.64	6.24	450	1390	10^{5} (20° C)
Terbium......	Tb	65	159.2	8.33	327	—	—
Thallium.....	Tl	81	204.45	11.85	300	1460	18 (0° C)
Thorium......	Th	90	232.18	11.5	1800	~5200	19 (20° C)
Thulium......	Tm	69	169.4	9.35	—	—	—
Tin..........	Sn	50	118.73	7.298	231.9	2270	11.5 (20° C)
Titanium.....	Ti	22	47.91	4.54	1800	~5100	80 (0° C)
Tungsten.....	W	74	183.97	19.3	3380	5930	5.5 (20° C)
Uranium......	U	92	238.13	18.7	1133	~4300	60 (18° C)
Vanadium....	V	23	50.96	6.0	1740	3400	26 (20° C)
Xenon........	Xe	54	131.3	5.49×10^{-3}	−112	−108.0	gaseous
Ytterbium....	Yb	70	173.09	7.01	—	—	—
Yttrium......	Y	39	88.94	5.51	1500	~4600	—
Zinc..........	Zn	30	65.40	7.133	419.5	906	5.92 (20° C)
Zirconium....	Zr	40	91.24	6.5	1800	~5000	41.0 (0° C)
Einsteinium ..	E	99	—	—	—	—	—
Fermium.....	Fm	100	—	—	—	—	—

5. NATURAL TRIGONOMETRIC FUNCTIONS

sin

	.0	.1	.2	.3	.4	.5	.6	.7	.8	.9		
0°	.0000	.0017	.0035	.0052	.0070	.0087	.0105	.0122	.0140	.0157	.0175	89°
1°	.0175	.0192	.0209	.0227	.0244	.0262	.0279	.0297	.0314	.0332	.0349	88°
2°	.0349	.0366	.0384	.0401	.0419	.0436	.0454	.0471	.0488	.0506	.0523	87°
3°	.0523	.0541	.0558	.0576	.0593	.0610	.0628	.0645	.0663	.0680	.0698	86°
4°	.0698	.0715	.0732	.0750	.0767	.0785	.0802	.0819	.0837	.0854	.0872	85°
5°	.0872	.0889	.0906	.0924	.0941	.0958	.0976	.0993	.1011	.1028	.1045	84°
6°	.1045	.1063	.1080	.1097	.1115	.1132	.1149	.1167	.1184	.1201	.1219	83°
7°	.1219	.1236	.1253	.1271	.1288	.1305	.1323	.1340	.1357	.1374	.1392	82°
8°	.1392	.1409	.1426	.1444	.1461	.1478	.1495	.1513	.1530	.1547	.1564	81°
9°	.1564	.1582	.1599	.1616	.1633	.1650	.1668	.1685	.1702	.1719	.1736	80°
10°	.1736	.1754	.1771	.1788	.1805	.1822	.1840	.1857	.1874	.1891	.1908	79°
11°	.1908	.1925	.1942	.1959	.1977	.1994	.2011	.2028	.2045	.2062	.2079	78°
12°	.2079	.2096	.2113	.2130	.2147	.2164	.2181	.2198	.2215	.2233	.2250	77°
13°	.2250	.2267	.2284	.2300	.2317	.2334	.2351	.2368	.2385	.2402	.2419	76°
14°	.2419	.2436	.2453	.2470	.2487	.2504	.2521	.2538	.2554	.2571	.2588	75°
15°	.2588	.2605	.2622	.2639	.2656	.2672	.2689	.2706	.2723	.2740	.2756	74°
16°	.2756	.2773	.2790	.2807	.2823	.2840	.2857	.2874	.2890	.2907	.2924	73°
17°	.2924	.2940	.2957	.2974	.2990	.3007	.3024	.3040	.3057	.3074	.3090	72°
18°	.3090	.3107	.3123	.3140	.3156	.3173	.3190	.3206	.3223	.3239	.3256	71°
19°	.3256	.3272	.3289	.3305	.3322	.3338	.3355	.3371	.3387	.3404	.3420	70°
20°	.3420	.3437	.3453	.3469	.3486	.3502	.3518	.3535	.3551	.3567	.3584	69°
21°	.3584	.3600	.3616	.3633	.3649	.3665	.3681	.3697	.3714	.3730	.3746	68°
22°	.3746	.3762	.3778	.3795	.3811	.3827	.3843	.3859	.3875	.3891	.3907	67°
23°	.3907	.3923	.3939	.3955	.3971	.3987	.4003	.4019	.4035	.4051	.4067	66°
24°	.4067	.4083	.4099	.4115	.4131	.4147	.4163	.4179	.4195	.4210	.4226	65°
25°	.4226	.4242	.4258	.4274	.4289	.4305	.4321	.4337	.4352	.4368	.4384	64°
26°	.4384	.4399	.4415	.4431	.4446	.4462	.4478	.4493	.4509	.4524	.4540	63°
27°	.4540	.4555	.4571	.4586	.4602	.4617	.4633	.4648	.4664	.4679	.4695	62°
28°	.4695	.4710	.4726	.4741	.4756	.4772	.4787	.4802	.4818	.4833	.4848	61°
29°	.4848	.4863	.4879	.4894	.4909	.4924	.4939	.4955	.4970	.4985	.5000	60°
30°	.5000	.5015	.5030	.5045	.5060	.5075	.5090	.5105	.5120	.5135	.5150	59°
31°	.5150	.5165	.5180	.5195	.5210	.5225	.5240	.5255	.5270	.5284	.5299	58°
32°	.5299	.5314	.5329	.5344	.5358	.5373	.5388	.5402	.5417	.5432	.5446	57°
33°	.5446	.5461	.5476	.5490	.5505	.5519	.5534	.5548	.5563	.5577	.5592	56°
34°	.5592	.5606	.5621	.5635	.5650	.5664	.5678	.5693	.5707	.5721	.5736	55°
35°	.5736	.5750	.5764	.5779	.5793	.5807	.5821	.5835	.5850	.5864	.5878	54°
36°	.5878	.5892	.5906	.5920	.5934	.5948	.5962	.5976	.5990	.6004	.6018	53°
37°	.6018	.6032	.6046	.6060	.6074	.6088	.6101	.6115	.6129	.6143	.6157	52°
38°	.6157	.6170	.6184	.6198	.6211	.6225	.6239	.6252	.6266	.6280	.6293	51°
39°	.6293	.6307	.6320	.6334	.6347	.6361	.6374	.6388	.6401	.6414	.6428	50°
40°	.6428	.6441	.6455	.6468	.6481	.6494	.6508	.6521	.6534	.6547	.6561	49°
41°	.6561	.6574	.6587	.6600	.6613	.6626	.6639	.6652	.6665	.6678	.6691	48°
42°	.6691	.6704	.6717	.6730	.6743	.6756	.6769	.6782	.6794	.6807	.6820	47°
43°	.6820	.6833	.6845	.6858	.6871	.6884	.6896	.6909	.6921	.6934	.6947	46°
44°	.6947	.6959	.6972	.6984	.6997	.7009	.7022	.7034	.7046	.7059	.7071	45°
	.9	.8	.7	.6	.5	.4	.3	.2	.1	.0		

cos

sin

	.0	.1	.2	.3	.4	.5	.6	.7	.8	.9	
45°	.7071	.7083	.7096	.7108	.7120	.7133	.7145	.7157	.7169	.7181	.7193	44°
46°	.7193	.7206	.7218	.7230	.7242	.7254	.7266	.7278	.7290	.7302	.7314	43°
47°	.7314	.7325	.7337	.7349	.7361	.7373	.7385	.7396	.7408	.7420	.7431	42°
48°	.7431	.7443	.7455	.7466	.7478	.7490	.7501	.7513	.7524	.7536	.7547	41°
49°	.7547	.7559	.7570	.7581	.7593	.7604	.7615	.7627	.7638	.7649	.7660	40°
50°	.7660	.7672	.7683	.7694	.7705	.7716	.7727	.7738	.7749	.7760	.7771	39°
51°	.7771	.7782	.7793	.7804	.7815	.7826	.7837	.7848	.7859	.7869	.7880	38°
52°	.7880	.7891	.7902	.7912	.7923	.7934	.7944	.7955	.7965	.7976	.7986	37°
53°	.7986	.7997	.8007	.8018	.8028	.8039	.8049	.8059	.8070	.8080	.8090	36°
54°	.8090	.8100	.8111	.8121	.8131	.8141	.8151	.8161	.8171	.8181	.8192	35°
55°	.8192	.8202	.8211	.8221	.8231	.8241	.8251	.8261	.8271	.8281	.8290	34°
56°	.8290	.8300	.8310	.8320	.8329	.8339	.8348	.8358	.8368	.8377	.8387	33°
57°	.8387	.8396	.8406	.8415	.8425	.8434	.8443	.8453	.8462	.8471	.8480	32°
58°	.8480	.8490	.8499	.8508	.8517	.8526	.8536	.8545	.8554	.8563	.8572	31°
59°	.8572	.8581	.8590	.8599	.8607	.8616	.8625	.8634	.8643	.8652	.8660	30°
60°	.8660	.8669	.8678	.8686	.8695	.8704	.8712	.8721	.8729	.8738	.8746	29°
61°	.8746	.8755	.8763	.8771	.8780	.8788	.8796	.8805	.8813	.8821	.8829	28°
62°	.8829	.8838	.8846	.8854	.8862	.8870	.8878	.8886	.8894	.8902	.8910	27°
63°	.8910	.8918	.8926	.8934	.8942	.8949	.8957	.8965	.8973	.8980	.8988	26°
64°	.8988	.8996	.9003	.9011	.9018	.9026	.9033	.9041	.9048	.9056	.9063	25°
65°	.9063	.9070	.9078	.9085	.9092	.9100	.9107	.9114	.9121	.9128	.9135	24°
66°	.9135	.9143	.9150	.9157	.9164	.9171	.9178	.9184	.9191	.9198	.9205	23°
67°	.9205	.9212	.9219	.9225	.9232	.9239	.9245	.9252	.9259	.9265	.9272	22°
68°	.9272	.9278	.9285	.9291	.9298	.9304	.9311	.9317	.9323	.9330	.9336	21°
69°	.9336	.9342	.9348	.9354	.9361	.9367	.9373	.9379	.9385	.9391	.9397	20°
70°	.9397	.9403	.9409	.9415	.9421	.9426	.9432	.9438	.9444	.9449	.9455	19°
71°	.9455	.9461	.9466	.9472	.9478	.9483	.9489	.9494	.9500	.9505	.9511	18°
72°	.9511	.9516	.9521	.9527	.9532	.9537	.9542	.9548	.9553	.9558	.9563	17°
73°	.9563	.9568	.9573	.9578	.9583	.9588	.9593	.9598	.9603	.9608	.9613	16°
74°	.9613	.9617	.9622	.9627	.9632	.9636	.9641	.9646	.9650	.9655	.9659	15°
75°	.9659	.9664	.9668	.9673	.9677	.9681	.9686	.9690	.9694	.9699	.9703	14°
76°	.9703	.9707	.9711	.9715	.9720	.9724	.9728	.9732	.9736	.9740	.9744	13°
77°	.9744	.9748	.9751	.9755	.9759	.9763	.9767	.9770	.9774	.9778	.9781	12°
78°	.9781	.9785	.9789	.9792	.9796	.9799	.9803	.9806	.9810	.9813	.9816	11°
79°	.9816	.9820	.9823	.9826	.9829	.9833	.9836	.9839	.9842	.9845	.9848	10°
80°	.9848	.9851	.9854	.9857	.9860	.9863	.9866	.9869	.9871	9874	.9877	9°
81°	.9877	.9880	.9882	.9885	.9888	.9890	.9893	.9895	.9898	.9900	.9903	8°
82°	.9903	.9905	.9907	.9910	.9912	.9914	.9917	.9919	.9921	.9923	.9925	7°
83°	.9925	.9928	.9930	.9932	.9934	.9936	.9938	.9940	.9942	.9943	.9945	6°
84°	.9945	.9947	.9949	.9951	.9952	.9954	.9956	.9957	.9959	.9960	.9962	5°
85°	.9962	.9963	.9965	.9966	.9968	.9969	.9971	.9972	.9973	.9974	.9976	4°
86°	.9976	.9977	.9978	.9979	.9980	.9981	.9982	.9983	.9984	.9985	.9986	3°
87°	.9986	.9987	.9988	.9989	.9990	.9990	.9991	.9992	.9993	.9993	.9994	2°
88°	.9994	.9995	.9995	.9996	.9996	.9997	.9997	.9997	.9998	.9998	.9998	1°
89°	.9998	.9999	.9999	.9999	.9999	1.000	1.000	1.000	1.000	1.000	1.000	0°
	.9	.8	.7	.6	.5	.4	.3	.2	.1	.0		

cos

tan

	.0	.1	.2	.3	.4	.5	.6	.7	.8	.9		
0°	.0000	.0017	.0035	.0052	.0070	.0087	.0105	.0122	.0140	.0157	.0175	89°
1°	.0175	.0192	.0209	.0227	.0244	.0262	.0279	.0297	.0314	.0332	.0349	88°
2°	.0349	.0367	.0384	.0402	.0419	.0437	.0454	.0472	.0489	.0507	.0524	87°
3°	.0524	.0542	.0559	.0577	.0594	.0612	.0629	.0647	.0664	.0682	.0699	86°
4°	.0699	.0717	.0734	.0752	.0769	.0787	.0805	.0822	.0840	.0857	.0875	85°
5°	.0875	.0892	.0910	.0928	.0945	.0963	.0981	.0998	.1016	.1033	.1051	84°
6°	.1051	.1069	.1086	.1104	.1122	.1139	.1157	.1175	.1192	.1210	.1228	83°
7°	.1228	.1246	.1263	.1281	.1299	.1317	.1334	.1352	.1370	.1388	.1405	82°
8°	.1405	.1423	.1441	.1459	.1477	.1495	.1512	.1530	.1548	.1566	.1584	81°
9°	.1584	.1602	.1620	.1638	.1655	.1673	.1691	.1709	.1727	.1745	.1763	80°
10°	.1763	.1781	.1799	.1817	.1835	.1853	.1871	.1890	.1908	.1926	.1944	79°
11°	.1944	.1962	.1980	.1998	.2016	.2035	.2053	.2071	.2089	.2107	.2126	78°
12°	.2126	.2144	.2162	.2180	.2199	.2217	.2235	.2254	.2272	.2290	.2309	77°
13°	.2309	.2327	.2345	.2364	.2382	.2401	.2419	.2438	.2456	.2475	.2493	76°
14°	.2493	.2512	.2530	.2549	.2568	.2586	.2605	.2623	.2642	.2661	.2679	75°
15°	.2679	.2698	.2717	.2736	.2754	.2773	.2792	.2811	.2830	.2849	.2867	74°
16°	.2867	.2886	.2905	.2924	.2943	.2962	.2981	.3000	.3019	.3038	.3057	73°
17°	.3057	.3076	.3096	.3115	.3134	.3153	.3172	.3191	.3211	.3230	.3249	72°
18°	.3249	.3269	.3288	.3307	.3327	.3346	.3365	.3385	.3404	.3424	.3443	71°
19°	.3443	.3463	.3482	.3502	.3522	.3541	.3561	.3581	.3600	.3620	.3640	70°
20°	.3640	.3659	.3679	.3699	.3719	.3739	.3759	.3779	.3799	.3819	.3839	69°
21°	.3839	.3859	.3879	.3899	.3919	.3939	.3959	.3979	.4000	.4020	.4040	68°
22°	.4040	.4061	.4081	.4101	.4122	.4142	.4163	.4183	.4204	.4224	.4245	67°
23°	.4245	.4265	.4286	.4307	.4327	.4348	.4369	.4390	.4411	.4431	.4452	66°
24°	.4452	.4473	.4494	.4515	.4536	.4557	.4578	.4599	.4621	.4642	.4663	65°
25°	.4663	.4684	.4706	.4727	.4748	.4770	.4791	.4813	.4834	.4856	.4877	64°
26°	.4877	.4899	.4921	.4942	.4964	.4986	.5008	.5029	.5051	.5073	.5095	63°
27°	.5095	.5117	.5139	.5161	.5184	.5206	.5228	.5250	.5272	.5295	.5317	62°
28°	.5317	.5340	.5362	.5384	.5407	.5430	.5452	.5475	.5498	.5520	.5543	61°
29°	.5543	.5566	.5589	.5612	.5635	.5658	.5681	.5704	.5727	.5750	.5774	60°
30°	.5774	.5797	.5820	.5844	.5867	.5890	.5914	.5938	.5961	.5985	.6009	59°
31°	.6009	.6032	.6056	.6080	.6104	.6128	.6152	.6176	.6200	.6224	.6249	58°
32°	.6249	.6273	.6297	.6322	.6346	.6371	.6395	.6420	.6445	.6469	.6494	57°
33°	.6494	.6519	.6544	.6569	.6594	.6619	.6644	.6669	.6694	.6720	.6745	56°
34°	.6745	.6771	.6796	.6822	.6847	.6873	.6899	.6924	.6950	.6976	.7002	55°
35°	.7002	.7028	.7054	.7080	.7107	.7133	.7159	.7186	.7212	.7239	.7265	54°
36°	.7265	.7292	.7319	.7346	.7373	.7400	.7427	.7454	.7481	.7508	.7536	53°
37°	.7536	.7563	.7590	.7618	.7646	.7673	.7701	.7729	.7757	.7785	.7813	52°
38°	.7813	.7841	.7869	.7898	.7926	.7954	.7983	.8012	.8040	.8069	.8098	51°
39°	.8098	.8127	.8156	.8185	.8214	.8243	.8273	.8302	.8332	.8361	.8391	50°
40°	.8391	.8421	.8451	.8481	.8511	.8541	.8571	.8601	.8632	.8662	.8693	49°
41°	.8693	.8724	.8754	.8785	.8816	.8847	.8878	.8910	.8941	.8972	.9004	48°
42°	.9004	.9036	.9067	.9099	.9131	.9163	.9195	.9228	.9260	.9293	.9325	47°
43°	.9325	.9358	.9391	.9424	.9457	.9490	.9523	.9556	.9590	.9623	.9657	46°
44°	.9657	.9691	.9725	.9759	.9793	.9827	.9861	.9896	.9930	.9965	1.000	45°
	.9	.8	.7	.6	.5	.4	.3	.2	.1	.0		

cot

tan

	.0	.1	.2	.3	.4	.5	.6	.7	.8	.9	
45°	1.000	1.003	1.007	1.011	1.014	1.018	1.021	1.025	1.028	1.032	1.036	44°
46°	1.036	1.039	1.043	1.046	1.050	1.054	1.057	1.061	1.065	1.069	1.072	43°
47°	1.072	1.076	1.080	1.084	1.087	1.091	1.095	1.099	1.103	1.107	1.111	42°
48°	1.111	1.115	1.118	1.122	1.126	1.130	1.134	1.138	1.142	1.146	1.150	41°
49°	1.150	1.154	1.159	1.163	1.167	1.171	1.175	1.179	1.183	1.188	1.192	40°
50°	1.192	1.196	1.200	1.205	1.209	1.213	1.217	1.222	1.226	1.230	1.235	39°
51°	1.235	1.239	1.244	1.248	1.253	1.257	1.262	1.266	1.271	1.275	1.280	38°
52°	1.280	1.285	1.289	1.294	1.299	1.303	1.308	1.313	1.317	1.322	1.327	37°
53°	1.327	1.332	1.337	1.342	1.347	1.351	1.356	1.361	1.366	1.371	1.376	36°
54°	1.376	1.381	1.387	1.392	1.397	1.402	1.407	1.412	1.418	1.423	1.428	35°
55°	1.428	1.433	1.439	1.444	1.450	1.455	1.460	1.466	1.471	1.477	1.483	34°
56°	1.483	1.488	1.494	1.499	1.505	1.511	1.517	1.522	1.528	1.534	1.540	33°
57°	1.540	1.546	1.552	1.558	1.564	1.570	1.576	1.582	1.588	1.594	1.600	32°
58°	1.600	1.607	1.613	1.619	1.625	1.632	1.638	1.645	1.651	1.658	1.664	31°
59°	1.664	1.671	1.678	1.684	1.691	1.698	1.704	1.711	1.718	1.725	1.732	30°
60°	1.732	1.739	1.746	1.753	1.760	1.767	1.775	1.782	1.789	1.797	1.804	29°
61°	1.804	1.811	1.819	1.827	1.834	1.842	1.849	1.857	1.865	1.873	1.881	28°
62°	1.881	1.889	1.897	1.905	1.913	1.921	1.929	1.937	1.946	1.954	1.963	27°
63°	1.963	1.971	1.980	1.988	1.997	2.006	2.014	2.023	2.032	2.041	2.050	26°
64°	2.050	2.059	2.069	2.078	2.087	2.097	2.106	2.116	2.125	2.135	2.145	25°
65°	2.145	2.154	2.164	2.174	2.184	2.194	2.204	2.215	2.225	2.236	2.246	24°
66°	2.246	2.257	2.267	2.278	2.289	2.300	2.311	2.322	2.333	2.344	2.356	23°
67°	2.356	2.367	2.379	2.391	2.402	2.414	2.426	2.438	2.450	2.463	2.475	22°
68°	2.475	2.488	2.500	2.513	2.526	2.539	2.552	2.565	2.578	2.592	2.605	21°
69°	2.605	2.619	2.633	2.646	2.660	2.675	2.689	2.703	2.718	2.733	2.747	20°
70°	2.747	2.762	2.778	2.793	2.808	2.824	2.840	2.856	2.872	2.888	2.904	19°
71°	2.904	2.921	2.937	2.954	2.971	2.989	3.006	3.024	3.042	3.060	3.078	18°
72°	3.078	3.096	3.115	3.133	3.152	3.172	3.191	3.211	3.230	3.251	3.271	17°
73°	3.271	3.291	3.312	3.333	3.354	3.376	3.398	3.420	3.442	3.465	3.487	16°
74°	3.487	3.511	3.534	3.558	3.582	3.606	3.630	3.655	3.681	3.706	3.732	15°
75°	3 732	3.758	3.785	3.812	3.839	3.867	3.895	3.923	3.952	3.981	4.011	14°
76°	4.011	4.041	4.071	4.102	4.134	4.165	4.198	4.230	4.264	4.297	4.331	13°
77°	4.331	4.366	4.402	4.437	4.474	4.511	4.548	4.586	4.625	4.665	4.705	12°
78°	4.705	4.745	4.787	4.829	4.872	4.915	4.959	5.005	5.050	5.097	5.145	11°
79°	5.145	5.193	5.242	5.292	5.343	5.396	5.449	5.503	5.558	5.614	5.671	10°
80°	5.671	5.730	5.789	5.850	5.912	5.976	6.041	6.107	6.174	6.243	6.314	9°
81°	6.314	6.386	6.460	6.535	6.612	6.691	6.772	6.855	6.940	7.026	7.115	8°
82°	7.115	7.207	7.300	7.396	7.495	7.596	7.700	7.806	7.916	8.028	8.144	7°
83°	8.144	8.264	8.386	8.513	8.643	8.777	8.915	9.058	9.205	9.357	9.514	6°
84°	9.514	9.677	9.845	10.02	10.20	10.39	10.58	10.78	10.99	11.20	11.43	5°
85°	11.43	11.66	11.91	12.16	12.43	12.71	13.00	13.30	13.62	13.95	14.30	4°
86°	14.30	14.67	15.06	15.46	15.89	16.35	16.83	17.34	17.89	18.46	19.08	3°
87°	19.08	19.74	20.45	21.20	22.02	22.90	23.86	24.90	26.03	27.27	28.64	2°
88°	28.64	30.14	31.82	33.69	35.80	38.19	40.92	44.07	47.74	52.08	57.29	1°
89°	57.29	63.66	71.62	81.85	95.49	114.6	143.2	191.0	286.5	573.0	∞	0°
		.9	.8	.7	.6	.5	.4	.3	.2	.1	.0	

cot

6. TABLE OF LOGARITHMS TO BASE 10

N	0	1	2	3	4	5	6	7	8	9	P. P. 1	2	3	4	5
10	0000	0043	0086	0128	0170	0212	0253	0294	0334	0374	4	8	12	17	21
11	0414	0453	0492	0531	0569	0607	0645	0682	0719	0755	4	8	11	15	19
12	0792	0828	0864	0899	0934	0969	1004	1038	1072	1106	3	7	10	14	17
13	1139	1173	1206	1239	1271	1303	1335	1367	1399	1430	3	6	10	13	16
14	1461	1492	1523	1553	1584	1614	1644	1673	1703	1732	3	6	9	12	15
15	1761	1790	1818	1847	1875	1903	1931	1959	1987	2014	3	6	8	11	14
16	2041	2068	2095	2122	2148	2175	2201	2227	2253	2279	3	5	8	11	13
17	2304	2330	2355	2380	2405	2430	2455	2480	2504	2529	2	5	7	10	12
18	2553	2577	2601	2625	2648	2672	2695	2718	2742	2765	2	5	7	9	12
19	2788	2810	2833	2856	2878	2900	2923	2945	2967	2989	2	4	7	9	11
20	3010	3032	3054	3075	3096	3118	3139	3160	3181	3201	2	4	6	8	11
21	3222	3243	3263	3284	3304	3324	3345	3365	3385	3404	2	4	6	8	10
22	3424	3444	3464	3483	3502	3522	3541	3560	3579	3598	2	4	6	8	10
23	3617	3636	3655	3674	3692	3711	3729	3747	3766	3784	2	4	5	7	9
24	3802	3820	3838	3856	3874	3892	3909	3927	3945	3962	2	4	5	7	9
25	3979	3997	4014	4031	4048	4065	4082	4099	4116	4133	2	3	5	7	9
26	4150	4166	4183	4200	4216	4232	4249	4265	4281	4298	2	3	5	7	8
27	4314	4330	4346	4362	4378	4393	4409	4425	4440	4456	2	3	5	6	8
28	4472	4487	4502	4518	4533	4548	4564	4579	4594	4609	2	3	5	6	8
29	4624	4639	4654	4669	4683	4698	4713	4728	4742	4757	1	3	4	6	7
30	4771	4786	4800	4814	4829	4843	4857	4871	4886	4900	1	3	4	6	7
31	4914	4928	4942	4955	4969	4983	4997	5011	5024	5038	1	3	4	6	7
32	5051	5065	5079	5092	5105	5119	5132	5145	5159	5172	1	3	4	5	7
33	5185	5198	5211	5224	5237	5250	5263	5276	5289	5302	1	3	4	5	6
34	5315	5328	5340	5353	5366	5378	5391	5403	5416	5428	1	3	4	5	6
35	5441	5453	5465	5478	5490	5502	5514	5527	5539	5551	1	2	4	5	6
36	5563	5575	5587	5599	5611	5623	5635	5647	5658	5670	1	2	4	5	6
37	5682	5694	5705	5717	5729	5740	5752	5763	5775	5786	1	2	3	5	6
38	5798	5809	5821	5832	5843	5855	5866	5877	5888	5899	1	2	3	5	6
39	5911	5922	5933	5944	5955	5966	5977	5988	5999	6010	1	2	3	4	6
40	6021	6031	6042	6053	6064	6075	6085	6096	6107	6117	1	2	3	4	5
41	6128	6138	6149	6160	6170	6180	6191	6201	6212	6222	1	2	3	4	5
42	6232	6243	6253	6263	6274	6284	6294	6304	6314	6325	1	2	3	4	5
43	6335	6345	6355	6365	6375	6385	6395	6405	6415	6425	1	2	3	4	5
44	6435	6444	6454	6464	6474	6484	6493	6503	6513	6522	1	2	3	4	5
45	6532	6542	6551	6561	6571	6580	6590	6599	6609	6618	1	2	3	4	5
46	6628	6637	6646	6656	6665	6675	6684	6693	6702	6712	1	2	3	4	5
47	6721	6730	6739	6749	6758	6767	6776	6785	6794	6803	1	2	3	4	5
48	6812	6821	6830	6839	6848	6857	6866	6875	6884	6893	1	2	3	4	4
49	6902	6911	6920	6928	6937	6946	6955	6964	6972	6981	1	2	3	4	4
50	6990	6998	7007	7016	7024	7033	7042	7050	7059	7067	1	2	3	3	4
51	7076	7084	7093	7101	7110	7118	7126	7135	7143	7152	1	2	3	3	4
52	7160	7168	7177	7185	7193	7202	7210	7218	7226	7235	1	2	2	3	4
53	7243	7251	7259	7267	7275	7284	7292	7300	7308	7316	1	2	2	3	4
54	7324	7332	7340	7348	7356	7364	7372	7380	7388	7396	1	2	2	3	4

NOTE:
$$\log_e N = \log_e 10 \, \log_{10} N = 2.3026 \log_{10} N$$
$$\log_{10} e^x = x \log_{10} e = 0.43429\, x$$

N	0	1	2	3	4	5	6	7	8	9	P.P. 1	2	3	4	5
55	7404	7412	7419	7427	7435	7443	7451	7459	7466	7474	1	2	2	3	4
56	7482	7490	7497	7505	7513	7520	7528	7536	7543	7551	1	2	2	3	4
57	7559	7566	7574	7582	7589	7597	7604	7612	7619	7627	1	2	2	3	4
58	7634	7642	7649	7657	7664	7672	7679	7686	7694	7701	1	1	2	3	4
59	7709	7716	7723	7731	7738	7745	7752	7760	7767	7774	1	1	2	3	4
60	7782	7789	7796	7803	7810	7818	7825	7832	7839	7846	1	1	2	3	4
61	7853	7860	7868	7875	7882	7889	7896	7903	7910	7917	1	1	2	3	4
62	7924	7931	7938	7945	7952	7959	7966	7973	7980	7987	1	1	2	3	3
63	7993	8000	8007	8014	8021	8028	8035	8041	8048	8055	1	1	2	3	3
64	8062	8069	8075	8082	8089	8096	8102	8109	8116	8122	1	1	2	3	3
65	8129	8136	8142	8149	8156	8162	8169	8176	8182	8189	1	1	2	3	3
66	8195	8202	8209	8215	8222	8228	8235	8241	8248	8254	1	1	2	3	3
67	8261	8267	8274	8280	8287	8293	8299	8306	8312	8319	1	1	2	3	3
68	8325	8331	8338	8344	8351	8357	8363	8370	8376	8382	1	1	2	3	3
69	8388	8395	8401	8407	8414	8420	8426	8432	8439	8445	1	1	2	3	3
70	8451	8457	8463	8470	8476	8482	8488	8494	8500	8506	1	1	2	2	3
71	8513	8519	8525	8531	8537	8543	8549	8555	8561	8567	1	1	2	2	3
72	8573	8579	8585	8591	8597	8603	8609	8615	8621	8627	1	1	2	2	3
73	8633	8639	8645	8651	8657	8663	8669	8675	8681	8686	1	1	2	2	3
74	8692	8698	8704	8710	8716	8722	8727	8733	8739	8745	1	1	2	2	3
75	8751	8756	8762	8768	8774	8779	8785	8791	8797	8802	1	1	2	2	3
76	8808	8814	8820	8825	8831	8837	8842	8848	8854	8859	1	1	2	2	3
77	8865	8871	8876	8882	8887	8893	8899	8904	8910	8915	1	1	2	2	3
78	8921	8927	8932	8938	8943	8949	8954	8960	8965	8971	1	1	2	2	3
79	8976	8982	8987	8993	8998	9004	9009	9015	9020	9025	1	1	2	2	3
80	9031	9036	9042	9047	9053	9058	9063	9069	9074	9079	1	1	2	2	3
81	9085	9090	9096	9101	9106	9112	9117	9122	9128	9133	1	1	2	2	3
82	9138	9143	9149	9154	9159	9165	9170	9175	9180	9186	1	1	2	2	3
83	9191	9196	9201	9206	9212	9217	9222	9227	9232	9238	1	1	2	2	3
84	9243	9248	9253	9258	9263	9269	9274	9279	9284	9289	1	1	2	2	3
85	9294	9299	9304	9309	9315	9320	9325	9330	9335	9340	1	1	2	2	3
86	9345	9350	9355	9360	9365	9370	9375	9380	9385	9390	1	1	2	2	3
87	9395	9400	9405	9410	9415	9420	9425	9430	9435	9440	0	1	1	2	2
88	9445	9450	9455	9460	9465	9469	9474	9479	9484	9489	0	1	1	2	2
89	9494	9499	9504	9509	9513	9518	9523	9528	9533	9538	0	1	1	2	2
90	9542	9547	9552	9557	9562	9566	9571	9576	9581	9586	0	1	1	2	2
91	9590	9595	9600	9605	9609	9614	9619	9624	9628	9633	0	1	1	2	2
92	9638	9643	9647	9652	9657	9661	9666	9671	9675	9680	0	1	1	2	2
93	9685	9689	9694	9699	9703	9708	9713	9717	9722	9727	0	1	1	2	2
94	9731	9736	9741	9745	9750	9754	9759	9763	9768	9773	0	1	1	2	2
95	9777	9782	9786	9791	9795	9800	9805	9809	9814	9818	0	1	1	2	2
96	9823	9827	9832	9836	9841	9845	9850	9854	9859	9863	0	1	1	2	2
97	9868	9872	9877	9881	9886	9890	9894	9899	9903	9908	0	1	1	2	2
98	9912	9917	9921	9926	9930	9934	9939	9943	9948	9952	0	1	1	2	2
99	9956	9961	9965	9969	9974	9978	9983	9987	9991	9996	0	1	1	2	2

7. TABLE OF EXPONENTIALS

$$e^x$$

x	0	1	2	3	4	5	6	7	8	9
0.0	1.000	1.010	1.020	1.031	1.041	1.051	1.062	1.073	1.083	1.094
0.1	1.105	1.116	1.127	1.139	1.150	1.162	1.174	1.185	1.197	1.209
0.2	1.221	1.234	1.246	1.259	1.271	1.284	1.297	1.310	1.323	1.336
0.3	1.350	1.363	1.377	1.391	1.405	1.419	1.433	1.448	1.462	1.477
0.4	1.492	1.507	1.522	1.537	1.553	1.568	1.584	1.600	1.616	1.632
0.5	1.649	1.665	1.682	1.699	1.716	1.733	1.751	1.768	1.786	1.804
0.6	1.822	1.840	1.859	1.878	1.896	1.916	1.935	1.954	1.974	1.994
0.7	2.014	2.034	2.054	2.075	2.096	2.117	2.138	2.160	2.181	2.203
0.8	2.226	2.248	2.270	2.293	2.316	2.340	2.363	2.387	2.411	2.435
0.9	2.460	2.484	2.509	2.535	2.560	2.586	2.612	2.638	2.664	2.691
1.0	2.718	2.746	2.773	2.801	2.829	2.858	2.886	2.915	2.945	2.974
1.1	3.004	3.034	3.065	3.096	3.127	3.158	3.190	3.222	3.254	3.287
1.2	3.320	3.353	3.387	3.421	3.456	3.490	3.525	3.561	3.597	3.633
1.3	3.669	3.706	3.743	3.781	3.819	3.857	3.896	3.935	3.975	4.015
1.4	4.055	4.096	4.137	4.179	4.221	4.263	4.306	4.349	4.393	4.437
1.5	4.482	4.527	4.572	4.618	4.665	4.712	4.759	4.807	4.855	4.904
1.6	4.953	5.003	5.053	5.104	5.155	5.207	5.259	5.312	5.366	5.419
1.7	5.474	5.529	5.585	5.641	5.697	5.755	5.812	5.871	5.930	5.989
1.8	6.050	6.110	6.172	6.234	6.297	6.360	6.424	6.488	6.554	6.619
1.9	6.686	6.753	6.821	6.890	6.959	7.029	7.099	7.171	7.243	7.316
2.0	7.389	7.463	7.538	7.614	7.691	7.768	7.846	7.925	8.004	8.085
2.1	8.166	8.248	8.331	8.415	8.499	8.585	8.671	8.758	8.846	8.935
2.2	9.025	9.116	9.207	9.300	9.393	9.488	9.583	9.679	9.777	9.875
2.3	9.974	10.07	10.18	10.28	10.38	10.49	10.59	10.70	10.80	10.91
2.4	11.02	11.13	11.25	11.36	11.47	11.59	11.70	11.82	11.94	12.06
2.5	12.18	12.30	12.43	12.55	12.68	12.81	12.94	13.07	13.20	13.33
2.6	13.46	13.60	13.74	13.87	14.01	14.15	14.30	14.44	14.59	14.73
2.7	14.88	15.03	15.18	15.33	15.49	15.64	15.80	15.96	16.12	16.28
2.8	16.44	16.61	16.78	16.95	17.12	17.29	17.46	17.64	17.81	17.99
2.9	18.17	18.36	18.54	18.73	18.92	19.11	19.30	19.49	19.69	19.89
3.0	20.09	20.29	20.49	20.70	20.91	21.12	21.33	21.54	21.76	21.98
3.1	22.20	22.42	22.65	22.87	23.10	23.34	23.57	23.81	24.05	24.29
3.2	24.53	24.78	25.03	25.28	25.53	25.79	26.05	26.31	26.58	26.84
3.3	27.11	27.39	27.66	27.94	28.22	28.50	28.79	29.08	29.37	29.67
3.4	29.96	30.27	30.57	30.88	31.19	31.50	31.82	32.14	32.46	32.79

x	.0	.1	.2	.3	.4	.5	.6	.7	.8	.9
3	20.09	22.20	24.53	27.11	29.96	33.12	36.60	40.45	44.70	49.40
4	54.60	60.34	66.69	73.70	81.45	90.02	99.48	109.9	121.5	134.3
5	148.4	164.0	181.3	200.3	221.4	244.7	270.4	298.9	330.3	365.0
6	403.4	445.9	492.7	544.6	601.8	665.1	735.1	812.4	897.8	992.3
7	1097	1212	1339	1480	1636	1808	1998	2208	2441	2697
8	2981	3295	3641	4024	4447	4915	5432	6003	6634	7332
9	8103	8955	9897	10938	12088	13360	14765	16318	18034	19930

$$\log_{10} e^x = x \log_{10} e = 0.43429\, x$$

Time

	yr	day	hr	min	sec
1 year =	1	365.2	8.766×10^3	5.259×10^5	3.156×10^7
1 day =	2.738×10^{-3}	1	24	1440	8.640×10^4
1 hour =	1.141×10^{-4}	4.167×10^{-2}	1	60	3600
1 minute =	1.901×10^{-6}	6.944×10^{-4}	1.667×10^{-2}	1	60
1 second =	3.169×10^{-8}	1.157×10^{-5}	2.778×10^{-4}	1.667×10^{-2}	1

1 year = 365.24219879 days

Density

	slug/ft³	lb/ft³	lb/in³	kg/m³	g/cm³
1 slug per ft³ =	1	32.17	1.862×10^{-2}	515.4	0.5154
1 pound per ft³ =	3.108×10^{-2}	1	5.787×10^{-4}	16.02	1.602×10^{-2}
1 pound per in³ =	53.71	1728	1	2.768×10^4	27.68
1 kilogram per m³ =	1.940×10^{-3}	6.243×10^{-2}	3.613×10^{-5}	1	0.001
1 gram per cm³ =	1.940	62.43	3.613×10^{-2}	1000	1

Speed

	ft/sec	km/hr	m/sec	mi/hr	knot
1 foot per second =	1	1.097	0.3048	0.6818	0.5925
1 kilometer per hour =	0.9113	1	0.2778	0.6214	0.5400
1 meter per second =	3.281	3.6	1	2.237	1.944
1 mile per hour =	1.467	1.609	0.4470	1	0.8689
1 knot =	1.688	1.852	0.5144	1.151	1

1 knot = 1 nautical mile/hr   1 mi/min = 88 ft/sec = 60 mi/hr

e^{-x}

x		0	1	2	3	4	5	6	7	8	9
0.0		1.000	.9900	.9802	.9704	.9608	.9512	.9418	.9324	.9231	.9139
0.1		.9048	.8958	.8869	.8781	.8694	.8607	.8521	.8437	.8353	.8270
0.2		.8187	.8106	.8025	.7945	.7866	.7788	.7711	.7634	.7558	.7483
0.3		.7408	.7334	.7261	.7189	.7118	.7047	.6977	.6907	.6839	.6771
0.4		.6703	.6637	.6570	.6505	.6440	.6376	.6313	.6250	.6188	.6126
0.5		.6065	.6005	.5945	.5886	.5827	.5769	.5712	.5655	.5599	.5543
0.6		.5488	.5434	.5379	.5326	.5273	.5220	.5169	.5117	.5066	.5016
0.7		.4966	.4916	.4868	.4819	.4771	.4724	.4677	.4630	.4584	.4538
0.8		.4493	.4449	.4404	.4360	.4317	.4274	.4232	.4190	.4148	.4107
0.9		.4066	.4025	.3985	.3946	.3906	.3867	.3829	.3791	.3753	.3716
1.0		.3679	.3642	.3606	.3570	.3535	.3499	.3465	.3430	.3396	.3362
1.1		.3329	.3296	.3263	.3230	.3198	.3166	.3135	.3104	.3073	.3042
1.2		.3012	.2982	.2952	.2923	.2894	.2865	.2837	.2808	.2780	.2753
1.3		.2725	.2698	.2671	.2645	.2618	.2592	.2567	.2541	.2516	.2491
1.4		.2466	.2441	.2417	.2393	.2369	.2346	.2322	.2299	.2276	.2254
1.5		.2231	.2209	.2187	.2165	.2144	.2122	.2101	.2080	.2060	.2039
1.6		.2019	.1999	.1979	.1959	.1940	.1920	.1901	.1882	.1864	.1845
1.7		.1827	.1809	.1791	.1773	.1755	.1738	.1720	.1703	.1686	.1670
1.8		.1653	.1637	.1620	.1604	.1588	.1572	.1557	.1541	.1526	.1511
1.9		.1496	.1481	.1466	.1451	.1437	.1423	.1409	.1395	.1381	.1367
2.0		.1353	.1340	.1327	.1313	.1300	.1287	.1275	.1262	.1249	.1237
2.1		.1225	.1212	.1200	.1188	.1177	.1165	.1153	.1142	.1130	.1119
2.2		.1108	.1097	.1086	.1075	.1065	.1054	.1043	.1033	.1023	.1013
2.3		.1003	*9926	*9827	*9730	*9633	*9537	*9442	*9348	*9255	*9163
2.4	0.0	9072	8982	8892	8804	8716	8629	8544	8458	8374	8291
2.5	0.0	8208	8127	8046	7966	7887	7808	7730	7654	7577	7502
2.6	0.0	7427	7353	7280	7208	7136	7065	6995	6925	6856	6788
2.7	0.0	6721	6654	6587	6522	6457	6393	6329	6266	6204	6142
2.8	0.0	6081	6020	5961	5901	5843	5784	5727	5670	5613	5558
2.9	0.0	5502	5448	5393	5340	5287	5234	5182	5130	5079	5029
3.0	0.0	4979	4929	4880	4832	4783	4736	4689	4642	4596	4550
3.1	0.0	4505	4460	4416	4372	4328	4285	4243	4200	4159	4117
3.2	0.0	4076	4036	3996	3956	3916	3877	3839	3801	3763	3725
3.3	0.0	3688	3652	3615	3579	3544	3508	3474	3439	3405	3371
3.4	0.0	3337	3304	3271	3239	3206	3175	3143	3112	3081	3050

x		.0	.1	.2	.3	.4	.5	.6	.7	.8	.9
3	0.0	4979	4505	4076	3688	3337	3020	2732	2472	2237	2024
4	0.0	1832	1657	1500	1357	1228	1111	1005	*9095	*8230	*7447
5	0.00	6738	6097	5517	4992	4517	4087	3698	3346	3028	2739
6	0.00	2479	2243	2029	1836	1662	1503	1360	1231	1114	1008
7	0.000	9119	8251	7466	6755	6112	5531	5004	4528	4097	3707
8	0.000	3355	3035	2747	2485	2249	2035	1841	1666	1507	1364
9	0.000	1234	1117	1010	*9142	*8272	*7485	*6773	*6128	*5545	*5017
10	0.0000	4540	4108	3717	3363	3043	2754	2492	2254	2040	1846

$$\log_{10} e^{-x} = -x \log_{10} e = -0.43429\, x$$

8. TABLES OF CONVERSION FACTORS

Plane Angle

	°	′	″	rad	rev
1 degree =	1	60	3600	1.745×10^{-2}	2.778×10^{-3}
1 minute =	1.667×10^{-2}	1	60	2.909×10^{-4}	4.630×10^{-5}
1 second =	2.778×10^{-4}	1.667×10^{-2}	1	4.848×10^{-6}	7.716×10^{-7}
1 radian =	57.30	3438	2.063×10^{5}	1	0.1592
1 revolution =	360	2.16×10^{4}	1.296×10^{6}	6.283	1

1 rev $= 2\pi$ rad $= 360°$ $1° = 60′ = 3600″$
1 artillery mil $= \frac{1}{6400}$ rev $= 0.0009817$ rad $= 0°05625$

Solid Angle
1 sphere $= 4\pi$ steradians $= 12.57$ steradians

Length

	cm	m	km	in	ft	mi
1 centimeter =	1	10^{-2}	10^{-5}	0.3937	3.281×10^{-2}	6.214×10^{-6}
1 meter =	100	1	10^{-3}	39.37	3.281	6.214×10^{-4}
1 kilometer =	10^{5}	1000	1	3.937×10^{4}	3281	0.6214
1 inch =	2.540	2.540×10^{-2}	2.540×10^{-5}	1	8.333×10^{-2}	1.578×10^{-5}
1 foot =	30.48	0.3048	3.048×10^{-4}	12	1	1.894×10^{-4}
1 statute mile =	1.609×10^{5}	1609	1.609	6.336×10^{4}	5280	1

1 foot $= \frac{1200}{3937}$ meter   1 micron $(\mu) = 10^{-6}$ m   1 fathom $= 6$ ft
1 meter $= \frac{3937}{1200}$ feet   1 millimicron $(m\mu) = 10^{-9}$ m   1 yard $= 3$ ft
1 angstrom (A) $= 10^{-10}$ m   1 light-year $= 9.4600 \times 10^{12}$ km   1 rod $= 16.5$ ft
1 X-unit $= 10^{-13}$ m   1 parsec $= 3.084 \times 10^{13}$ km   1 mil $= 10^{-3}$ in
1 nautical mile $= 1852$ m $= 1.1508$ statute miles $= 6076.10$ ft

Area

	m²	cm²	ft²	in²	circ mil
1 square meter =	1	10^{4}	10.76	1550	1.974×10^{9}
1 square centimeter =	10^{-4}	1	1.076×10^{-3}	0.1550	1.974×10^{5}
1 square foot =	9.290×10^{-2}	929.0	1	144	1.833×10^{8}
1 square inch =	6.452×10^{-4}	6.452	6.944×10^{-3}	1	1.273×10^{6}
1 circular mil =	5.067×10^{-10}	5.067×10^{-6}	5.454×10^{-9}	7.854×10^{-7}	1

1 square mile $= 27,878,400$ ft² $= 640$ acres   1 acre $= 43,560$ ft²
1 barn $= 10^{-28}$ m²

Volume

	m³	cm³	l	ft³	in³
1 cubic meter =	1	10^{6}	1000	35.31	6.102×10^{4}
1 cubic centimeter =	10^{-6}	1	1.000×10^{-3}	3.531×10^{-5}	6.102×10^{-2}
1 liter =	1.000×10^{-3}	1000	1	3.531×10^{-2}	61.02
1 cubic foot =	2.832×10^{-2}	2.832×10^{4}	28.32	1	1728
1 cubic inch =	1.639×10^{-5}	16.39	1.639×10^{-2}	5.787×10^{-4}	1

1 U.S. fluid gallon $= 4$ U.S. fluid quarts $= 8$ U.S. fluid pints
$= 128$ U.S. fluid ounces $= 231$ in³.

1 British Imperial gallon $=$ the volume of 10 lb of water at 62° F $= 277.42$ in³.
1 liter $=$ the volume of 1 kg of water at its maximum density $= 1000.028$ cm³.

Mass

	g	kg	oz	lb	slug	ton
1 gram =	1	0.001	3.527×10^{-2}	2.205×10^{-3}	6.852×10^{-5}	1.102×10^{-6}
1 kilogram =	1000	1	35.27	2.205	6.852×10^{-2}	1.102×10^{-3}
1 ounce (Avoirdupois) =	28.35	2.835×10^{-2}	1	6.250×10^{-2}	1.943×10^{-3}	3.125×10^{-5}
1 pound (Avoirdupois) =	453.6	0.4536	16	1	3.108×10^{-2}	0.0005
1 slug =	1.459×10^{4}	14.59	514.8	32.17	1	1.609×10^{-2}
1 ton =	9.072×10^{5}	907.2	3.2×10^{4}	2000	62.16	1

1 Avoirdupois pound $= 7000$ grains
1 Troy or Apothecaries' pound $= 12$ Troy or Apothecaries' ounces
$= 5760$ grains $= 0.8229$ Avoirdupois pound

1 long ton $= 2240$ lb   1 stone $= 14$ lb   1 hundredweight (cwt) $= 112$ lb
1 metric ton $= 1000$ kg $= 2205$ lb   1 carat $= 0.2$ g   1 pennyweight (dwt) $= 24$ grains
1 lb $= 453.5924277$ g   1 kg $= 2.2046223$ lb   1 slug $= 32.17398$ lb

1 atomic mass unit (amu) $= 1.6597 \times 10^{-27}$ kg

Force

	dyne	gf	kgf	nt	lb	pdl
1 dyne =	1	1.020×10^{-3}	1.020×10^{-6}	10^{-5}	2.248×10^{-6}	7.233×10^{-5}
1 gram-force =	980.7	1	0.001	9.807×10^{-3}	2.205×10^{-3}	7.093×10^{-2}
1 kilogram-force =	9.807×10^5	1000	1	9.807	2.205	70.93
1 newton =	10^5	102.0	0.1020	1	0.2248	7.233
1 pound =	4.448×10^5	453.6	0.4536	4.448	1	32.17
1 poundal =	1.383×10^4	14.10	1.410×10^{-2}	0.1383	3.108×10^{-2}	1

$$1 \text{ kgf} = 9.80665 \text{ nt} \qquad 1 \text{ lb} = 32.17398 \text{ pdl}$$

Pressure

	atm	dyne/cm²	inch of water	cm Hg	kgf/m²	nt/m²	lb/in²	lb/ft²
1 atmosphere =	1	1.013×10^6	406.8	76	1.033×10^4	1.013×10^5	14.70	2116
1 dyne per cm² =	9.869×10^{-7}	1	4.015×10^{-4}	7.501×10^{-5}	1.020×10^{-2}	0.1	1.450×10^{-5}	2.089×10^{-3}
1 inch of water at 4° C* =	2.458×10^{-3}	2491	1	0.1868	25.40	249.1	3.613×10^{-2}	5.202
1 centimeter of mercury at 0° C* =	1.316×10^{-2}	1.333×10^4	5.353	1	136.0	1333	0.1934	27.85
1 kilogram-force per m² =	9.678×10^{-5}	98.07	3.937×10^{-2}	7.356×10^{-3}	1	9.807	1.422×10^{-3}	0.2048
1 newton per m² =	9.869×10^{-6}	10	4.015×10^{-3}	7.501×10^{-4}	0.1020	1	1.450×10^{-4}	2.089×10^{-2}
1 pound per in² =	6.805×10^{-2}	6.895×10^4	27.68	5.171	703.1	6.895×10^3	1	144
1 pound per ft² =	4.725×10^{-4}	478.8	0.1922	3.591×10^{-2}	4.882	47.88	6.944×10^{-3}	1

* Where the acceleration of gravity has the standard value 9.80665 m/sec².

$$1 \text{ bar} = 10^6 \text{ dyne/cm}^2 \qquad 1 \text{ millibar} = 10^3 \text{ dyne/cm}^2$$

Energy, Work, Heat

	BTU	erg	ft·lb	hp·hr	joule	kcal	kwh
1 British thermal unit =	1	1.055×10^{10}	777.9	3.929×10^{-4}	1055	0.2520	2.930×10^{-4}
1 erg =	9.481×10^{-11}	1	7.376×10^{-8}	3.725×10^{-14}	10^{-7}	2.389×10^{-11}	2.778×10^{-14}
1 foot·pound =	1.285×10^{-3}	1.356×10^{7}	1	5.051×10^{-7}	1.356	3.239×10^{-4}	3.766×10^{-7}
1 horsepower·hour =	2545	2.685×10^{13}	1.980×10^{6}	1	2.685×10^{6}	641.4	0.7457
1 joule =	9.481×10^{-4}	10^{7}	0.7376	3.725×10^{-7}	1	2.389×10^{-4}	2.778×10^{-7}
1 kilocalorie =	3.968	4.186×10^{10}	3087	1.559×10^{-3}	4186	1	1.163×10^{-3}
1 kilowatt·hour =	3413	3.6×10^{13}	2.655×10^{6}	1.341	3.6×10^{6}	860.1	1

See table of relativistic mass-energy equivalents on p. 760.

1 m·kgf = 9.807 joules
1 watt·sec = 1 joule = 1 m·nt
1 cm·dyne = 1 erg

Power

	BTU/hr	ft·lb/min	ft·lb/sec	hp	kcal/sec	kw	w
1 British thermal unit per hour =	1	12.97	0.2161	3.929×10^{-4}	7.000×10^{-5}	2.930×10^{-4}	0.2930
1 foot·pound per minute =	7.713×10^{-2}	1	1.667×10^{-2}	3.030×10^{-5}	5.399×10^{-6}	2.260×10^{-5}	2.260×10^{-2}
1 foot·pound per second =	4.628	60	1	1.818×10^{-3}	3.239×10^{-4}	1.356×10^{-3}	1.356
1 horsepower =	2545	3.3×10^{4}	550	1	0.1782	0.7457	745.7
1 kilocalorie per second =	1.429×10^{4}	1.852×10^{5}	3087	5.613	1	4.186	4186
1 kilowatt =	3413	4.425×10^{4}	737.6	1.341	0.2389	1	1000
1 watt =	3.413	44.25	0.7376	1.341×10^{-3}	2.389×10^{-4}	0.001	1

1 watt = 1 joule/sec

Energy, Work, Heat

	BTU	erg	ft·lb	hp·hr	joule	kcal	kwh
1 British thermal unit =	1	1.055×10^{10}	777.9	3.929×10^{-4}	1055	0.2520	2.930×10^{-4}
1 erg =	9.481×10^{-11}	1	7.376×10^{-8}	3.725×10^{-14}	10^{-7}	2.389×10^{-11}	2.778×10^{-14}
1 foot·pound =	1.285×10^{-3}	1.356×10^{7}	1	5.051×10^{-7}	1.356	3.239×10^{-4}	3.766×10^{-7}
1 horsepower·hour =	2545	2.685×10^{13}	1.980×10^{6}	1	2.685×10^{6}	641.4	0.7457
1 joule =	9.481×10^{-4}	10^{7}	0.7376	3.725×10^{-7}	1	2.389×10^{-4}	2.778×10^{-7}
1 kilocalorie =	3.968	4.186×10^{10}	3087	1.559×10^{-3}	4186	1	1.163×10^{-3}
1 kilowatt·hour =	3413	3.6×10^{13}	2.655×10^{6}	1.341	3.6×10^{6}	860.1	1

See table of relativistic mass-energy equivalents on p. 760.

1 m·kgf = 9.807 joules

1 watt·sec = 1 joule = 1 m·nt

1 cm·dyne = 1 erg

Power

	BTU/hr	ft·lb/min	ft·lb/sec	hp	kcal/sec	kw	w
1 British thermal unit per hour =	1	12.97	0.2161	3.929×10^{-4}	7.000×10^{-5}	2.930×10^{-4}	0.2930
1 foot·pound per minute =	7.713×10^{-2}	1	1.667×10^{-2}	3.030×10^{-5}	5.399×10^{-6}	2.260×10^{-5}	2.260×10^{-2}
1 foot·pound per second =	4.628	60	1	1.818×10^{-3}	3.239×10^{-4}	1.356×10^{-3}	1.356
1 horsepower =	2545	3.3×10^{4}	550	1	0.1782	0.7457	745.7
1 kilocalorie per second =	1.429×10^{4}	1.852×10^{5}	3087	5.613	1	4.186	4186
1 kilowatt =	3413	4.425×10^{4}	737.6	1.341	0.2389	1	1000
1 watt =	3.413	44.25	0.7376	1.341×10^{-3}	2.389×10^{-4}	0.001	1

1 watt = 1 joule/sec

Force

	dyne	gf	kgf	nt	lb	pdl
1 dyne =	1	1.020×10^{-3}	1.020×10^{-6}	10^{-5}	2.248×10^{-6}	7.233×10^{-5}
1 gram-force =	980.7	1	0.001	9.807×10^{-3}	2.205×10^{-3}	7.093×10^{-2}
1 kilogram-force =	9.807×10^5	1000	1	9.807	2.205	70.93
1 newton =	10^5	102.0	0.1020	1	0.2248	7.233
1 pound =	4.448×10^5	453.6	0.4536	4.448	1	32.17
1 poundal =	1.383×10^4	14.10	1.410×10^{-2}	0.1383	3.108×10^{-2}	1

$$1 \text{ kgf} = 9.80665 \text{ nt} \qquad 1 \text{ lb} = 32.17398 \text{ pdl}$$

Pressure

	atm	dyne/ cm²	inch of water	cm Hg	kgf/m²	nt/m²	lb/in²	lb/ft²
1 atmosphere =	1	1.013×10^6	406.8	76	1.033×10^4	1.013×10^5	14.70	2116
1 dyne per cm² =	9.869×10^{-7}	1	4.015×10^{-4}	7.501×10^{-5}	1.020×10^{-2}	0.1	1.450×10^{-5}	2.089×10^{-3}
1 inch of water at 4° C* =	2.458×10^{-3}	2491	1	0.1868	25.40	249.1	3.613×10^{-2}	5.202
1 centimeter of mercury at 0° C* =	1.316×10^{-2}	1.333×10^4	5.353	1	136.0	1333	0.1934	27.85
1 kilogram-force per m² =	9.678×10^{-5}	98.07	3.937×10^{-2}	7.356×10^{-3}	1	9.807	1.422×10^{-3}	0.2048
1 newton per m² =	9.869×10^{-6}	10	4.015×10^{-3}	7.501×10^{-4}	0.1020	1	1.450×10^{-4}	2.089×10^{-2}
1 pound per in² =	6.805×10^{-2}	6.895×10^4	27.68	5.171	703.1	6.895×10^3	1	144
1 pound per ft² =	4.725×10^{-4}	478.8	0.1922	3.591×10^{-2}	4.882	47.88	6.944×10^{-3}	1

* Where the acceleration of gravity has the standard value 9.80665 m/sec².

$$1 \text{ bar} = 10^6 \text{ dyne/cm}^2 \qquad 1 \text{ millibar} = 10^3 \text{ dyne/cm}^2$$

Volume

	m³	cm³	l	ft³	in³
1 cubic meter =	1	10^6	1000	35.31	6.102×10^4
1 cubic centimeter =	10^{-6}	1	1.000×10^{-3}	3.531×10^{-5}	6.102×10^{-2}
1 liter =	1.000×10^{-3}	1000	1	3.531×10^{-2}	61.02
1 cubic foot =	2.832×10^{-2}	2.832×10^4	28.32	1	1728
1 cubic inch =	1.639×10^{-5}	16.39	1.639×10^{-2}	5.787×10^{-4}	1

1 U.S. fluid gallon = 4 U.S. fluid quarts = 8 U.S. fluid pints
　= 128 U.S. fluid ounces = 231 in³.

1 British Imperial gallon = the volume of 10 lb of water at 62° F = 277.42 in³.

1 liter = the volume of 1 kg of water at its maximum density = 1000.028 cm³.

Mass

	g	kg	oz	lb	slug	ton
1 gram =	1	0.001	3.527×10^{-2}	2.205×10^{-3}	6.852×10^{-5}	1.102×10^{-6}
1 kilogram =	1000	1	35.27	2.205	6.852×10^{-2}	1.102×10^{-3}
1 ounce (Avoirdupois) =	28.35	2.835×10^{-2}	1	6.250×10^{-2}	1.943×10^{-3}	3.125×10^{-5}
1 pound (Avoirdupois) =	453.6	0.4536	16	1	3.108×10^{-2}	0.0005
1 slug =	1.459×10^4	14.59	514.8	32.17	1	1.609×10^{-2}
1 ton =	9.072×10^5	907.2	3.2×10^4	2000	62.16	1

1 Avoirdupois pound = 7000 grains

1 Troy or Apothecaries' pound = 12 Troy or Apothecaries' ounces
　= 5760 grains = 0.8229 Avoirdupois pound

1 long ton = 2240 lb　　　1 stone = 14 lb　　　1 hundredweight (cwt) = 112 lb
1 metric ton = 1000 kg = 2205 lb　1 carat = 0.2 g　　1 pennyweight (dwt) = 24 grains
1 lb = 453.5924277 g　　　　1 kg = 2.2046223 lb　1 slug = 32.17398 lb

1 atomic mass unit (amu) = 1.6597×10^{-27} kg

Time

	yr	day	hr	min	sec
1 year =	1	365.2	8.766×10^3	5.259×10^5	3.156×10^7
1 day =	2.738×10^{-3}	1	24	1440	8.640×10^4
1 hour =	1.141×10^{-4}	4.167×10^{-2}	1	60	3600
1 minute =	1.901×10^{-6}	6.944×10^{-4}	1.667×10^{-2}	1	60
1 second =	3.169×10^{-8}	1.157×10^{-5}	2.778×10^{-4}	1.667×10^{-2}	1

1 year = 365.24219879 days

Density

	slug/ft³	lb/ft³	lb/in³	kg/m³	g/cm³
1 slug per ft³ =	1	32.17	1.862×10^{-2}	515.4	0.5154
1 pound per ft³ =	3.108×10^{-2}	1	5.787×10^{-4}	16.02	1.602×10^{-2}
1 pound per in³ =	53.71	1728	1	2.768×10^4	27.68
1 kilogram per m³ =	1.940×10^{-3}	6.243×10^{-2}	3.613×10^{-5}	1	0.001
1 gram per cm³ =	1.940	62.43	3.613×10^{-2}	1000	1

Speed

	ft/sec	km/hr	m/sec	mi/hr	knot
1 foot per second =	1	1.097	0.3048	0.6818	0.5925
1 kilometer per hour =	0.9113	1	0.2778	0.6214	0.5400
1 meter per second =	3.281	3.6	1	2.237	1.944
1 mile per hour =	1.467	1.609	0.4470	1	0.8689
1 knot =	1.688	1.852	0.5144	1.151	1

1 knot = 1 nautical mile/hr   1 mi/min = 88 ft/sec = 60 mi/hr

8. TABLES OF CONVERSION FACTORS

Plane Angle

	°	′	″	rad	rev
1 degree =	1	60	3600	1.745×10^{-2}	2.778×10^{-3}
1 minute =	1.667×10^{-2}	1	60	2.909×10^{-4}	4.630×10^{-5}
1 second =	2.778×10^{-4}	1.667×10^{-2}	1	4.848×10^{-6}	7.716×10^{-7}
1 radian =	57.30	3438	2.063×10^{5}	1	0.1592
1 revolution =	360	2.16×10^{4}	1.296×10^{6}	6.283	1

$$1 \text{ rev} = 2\pi \text{ rad} = 360° \qquad 1° = 60' = 3600''$$
1 artillery mil $= \frac{1}{6400}$ rev $= 0.0009817$ rad $= 0°\!.05625$

Solid Angle
$$1 \text{ sphere} = 4\pi \text{ steradians} = 12.57 \text{ steradians}$$

Length

	cm	m	km	in	ft	mi
1 centimeter =	1	10^{-2}	10^{-5}	0.3937	3.281×10^{-2}	6.214×10^{-6}
1 meter =	100	1	10^{-3}	39.37	3.281	6.214×10^{-4}
1 kilometer =	10^{5}	1000	1	3.937×10^{4}	3281	0.6214
1 inch =	2.540	2.540×10^{-2}	2.540×10^{-5}	1	8.333×10^{-2}	1.578×10^{-5}
1 foot =	30.48	0.3048	3.048×10^{-4}	12	1	1.894×10^{-4}
1 statute mile =	1.609×10^{5}	1609	1.609	6.336×10^{4}	5280	1

1 foot $= \frac{1200}{3937}$ meter   1 micron $(\mu) = 10^{-6}$ m   1 fathom = 6 ft
1 meter $= \frac{3937}{1200}$ feet   1 millimicron $(m\mu) = 10^{-9}$ m   1 yard = 3 ft
1 angstrom (A) $= 10^{-10}$ m   1 light-year $= 9.4600 \times 10^{12}$ km   1 rod = 16.5 ft
1 X-unit $= 10^{-13}$ m   1 parsec $= 3.084 \times 10^{13}$ km   1 mil $= 10^{-3}$ in
1 nautical mile $= 1852$m $= 1.1508$ statute miles $= 6076.10$ ft

Area

	m²	cm²	ft²	in²	circ mil
1 square meter =	1	10^{4}	10.76	1550	1.974×10^{9}
1 square centimeter =	10^{-4}	1	1.076×10^{-3}	0.1550	1.974×10^{5}
1 square foot =	9.290×10^{-2}	929.0	1	144	1.833×10^{8}
1 square inch =	6.452×10^{-4}	6.452	6.944×10^{-3}	1	1.273×10^{6}
1 circular mil =	5.067×10^{-10}	5.067×10^{-6}	5.454×10^{-9}	7.854×10^{-7}	1

1 square mile $= 27,878,400$ ft² $= 640$ acres   1 acre $= 43,560$ ft²
1 barn $= 10^{-28}$ m²

$$e^{-x}$$

x	0	1	2	3	4	5	6	7	8	9
0.0	1.000	.9900	.9802	.9704	.9608	.9512	.9418	.9324	.9231	.9139
0.1	.9048	.8958	.8869	.8781	.8694	.8607	.8521	.8437	.8353	.8270
0.2	.8187	.8106	.8025	.7945	.7866	.7788	.7711	.7634	.7558	.7483
0.3	.7408	.7334	.7261	.7189	.7118	.7047	.6977	.6907	.6839	.6771
0.4	.6703	.6637	.6570	.6505	.6440	.6376	.6313	.6250	.6188	.6126
0.5	.6065	.6005	.5945	.5886	.5827	.5769	.5712	.5655	.5599	.5543
0.6	.5488	.5434	.5379	.5326	.5273	.5220	.5169	.5117	.5066	.5016
0.7	.4966	.4916	.4868	.4819	.4771	.4724	.4677	.4630	.4584	.4538
0.8	.4493	.4449	.4404	.4360	.4317	.4274	.4232	.4190	.4148	.4107
0.9	.4066	.4025	.3985	.3946	.3906	.3867	.3829	.3791	.3753	.3716
1.0	.3679	.3642	.3606	.3570	.3535	.3499	.3465	.3430	.3396	.3362
1.1	.3329	.3296	.3263	.3230	.3198	.3166	.3135	.3104	.3073	.3042
1.2	.3012	.2982	.2952	.2923	.2894	.2865	.2837	.2808	.2780	.2753
1.3	.2725	.2698	.2671	.2645	.2618	.2592	.2567	.2541	.2516	.2491
1.4	.2466	.2441	.2417	.2393	.2369	.2346	.2322	.2299	.2276	.2254
1.5	.2231	.2209	.2187	.2165	.2144	.2122	.2101	.2080	.2060	.2039
1.6	.2019	.1999	.1979	.1959	.1940	.1920	.1901	.1882	.1864	.1845
1.7	.1827	.1809	.1791	.1773	.1755	.1738	.1720	.1703	.1686	.1670
1.8	.1653	.1637	.1620	.1604	.1588	.1572	.1557	.1541	.1526	.1511
1.9	.1496	.1481	.1466	.1451	.1437	.1423	.1409	.1395	.1381	.1367
2.0	.1353	.1340	.1327	.1313	.1300	.1287	.1275	.1262	.1249	.1237
2.1	.1225	.1212	.1200	.1188	.1177	.1165	.1153	.1142	.1130	.1119
2.2	.1108	.1097	.1086	.1075	.1065	.1054	.1043	.1033	.1023	.1013
2.3	.1003	*9926	*9827	*9730	*9633	*9537	*9442	*9348	*9255	*9163
2.4	0.0 9072	8982	8892	8804	8716	8629	8544	8458	8374	8291
2.5	0.0 8208	8127	8046	7966	7887	7808	7730	7654	7577	7502
2.6	0.0 7427	7353	7280	7208	7136	7065	6995	6925	6856	6788
2.7	0.0 6721	6654	6587	6522	6457	6393	6329	6266	6204	6142
2.8	0.0 6081	6020	5961	5901	5843	5784	5727	5670	5613	5558
2.9	0.0 5502	5448	5393	5340	5287	5234	5182	5130	5079	5029
3.0	0.0 4979	4929	4880	4832	4783	4736	4689	4642	4596	4550
3.1	0.0 4505	4460	4416	4372	4328	4285	4243	4200	4159	4117
3.2	0.0 4076	4036	3996	3956	3916	3877	3839	3801	3763	3725
3.3	0.0 3688	3652	3615	3579	3544	3508	3474	3439	3405	3371
3.4	0.0 3337	3304	3271	3239	3206	3175	3143	3112	3081	3050

x	.0	.1	.2	.3	.4	.5	.6	.7	.8	.9
3	0.0 4979	4505	4076	3688	3337	3020	2732	2472	2237	2024
4	0.0 1832	1657	1500	1357	1228	1111	1005	*9095	*8230	*7447
5	0.00 6738	6097	5517	4992	4517	4087	3698	3346	3028	2739
6	0.00 2479	2243	2029	1836	1662	1503	1360	1231	1114	1008
7	0.000 9119	8251	7466	6755	6112	5531	5004	4528	4097	3707
8	0.000 3355	3035	2747	2485	2249	2035	1841	1666	1507	1364
9	0.000 1234	1117	1010	*9142	*8272	*7485	*6773	*6128	*5545	*5017
10	0.0000 4540	4108	3717	3363	3043	2754	2492	2254	2040	1846

$$\log_{10}e^{-x} = -x \log_{10}e = -0.43429\,x$$

Quantity of Electricity, Electric Charge

	abcoul	amp·hr	coul	faraday	statcoul
1 abcoulomb (1 EMU) =	1	2.778×10^{-3}	10	1.036×10^{-4}	2.998×10^{10}
1 ampere·hour =	360	1	3600	3.730×10^{-2}	1.079×10^{13}
1 coulomb =	0.1	2.778×10^{-4}	1	1.036×10^{-5}	2.998×10^{9}
1 faraday =	9652	26.81	9.652×10^{4}	1	2.893×10^{14}
1 statcoulomb (1 ESU) =	3.336×10^{-11}	9.266×10^{-14}	3.336×10^{-10}	3.456×10^{-15}	1

1 electronic charge $= 1.602 \times 10^{-19}$ coul

Electric Current

	abamp	amp	statamp
1 abampere (1 EMU) =	1	10	2.998×10^{10}
1 ampere =	0.1	1	2.998×10^{9}
1 statampere (1 ESU) =	3.336×10^{-11}	3.336×10^{-10}	1

Electric Potential, Electromotive Force

	abv	v	statv
1 abvolt (1 EMU) =	1	10^{-8}	3.336×10^{-11}
1 volt =	10^{8}	1	3.336×10^{-3}
1 statvolt (1 ESU) =	2.998×10^{10}	299.8	1

Electric Resistance

	abohm	ohm	statohm
1 abohm (1 EMU) =	1	10^{-9}	1.113×10^{-21}
1 ohm =	10^{9}	1	1.113×10^{-12}
1 statohm (1 ESU) =	8.987×10^{20}	8.987×10^{11}	1

Electric Resistivity

	abohm·cm	μohm·cm	ohm·cm	statohm·cm	ohm·m	ohm·circ mil/ft
1 abohm·centimeter (1 EMU) =	1	0.001	10^{-9}	1.113×10^{-21}	10^{-11}	6.015×10^{-3}
1 microhm·centimeter =	1000	1	10^{-6}	1.113×10^{-18}	10^{-8}	6.015
1 ohm·centimeter =	10^9	10^6	1	1.113×10^{-12}	0.01	6.015×10^6
1 statohm·centimeter (1 ESU) =	8.987×10^{20}	8.987×10^{17}	8.987×10^{11}	1	8.987×10^9	5.406×10^{18}
1 ohm·meter =	10^{11}	10^8	100	1.113×10^{-10}	1	6.015×10^8
1 ohm·circular mil per foot =	166.2	0.1662	1.662×10^{-7}	1.850×10^{-19}	1.662×10^{-9}	1

Capacitance

	abf	f	μf*	statf
1 abfarad (1 EMU) =	1	10^9	10^{15}	8.987×10^{20}
1 farad =	10^{-9}	1	10^6	8.987×10^{11}
1 microfarad =	10^{-15}	10^{-6}	1	8.987×10^5
1 statfarad (1 ESU) =	1.113×10^{-21}	1.113×10^{-12}	1.113×10^{-6}	1

* This unit is frequently abbreviated mf.

Inductance

	abhenry	henry	microhenry	millihenry	stathenry
1 abhenry (1 EMU) =	1	10^{-9}	0.001	10^{-6}	1.113×10^{-21}
1 henry =	10^9	1	10^6	1000	1.113×10^{-12}
1 microhenry =	1000	10^{-6}	1	0.001	1.113×10^{-18}
1 millihenry =	10^6	0.001	1000	1	1.113×10^{-15}
1 stathenry (1 ESU) =	8.987×10^{20}	8.987×10^{11}	8.987×10^{17}	8.987×10^{14}	1

Magnetic Flux

	maxwell	kiloline	weber
1 maxwell (1 line or 1 EMU) =	1	0.001	10^{-8}
1 kiloline =	1000	1	10^{-5}
1 weber =	10^8	10^5	1

1 ESU = 299.8 weber

Magnetic Flux Density $\mathfrak{B}$

	gauss	kiloline/in^2	weber/m^2	milligauss	γ
1 gauss (line per square centimeter) =	1	6.452×10^{-3}	10^{-4}	1000	10^5
1 kiloline per square inch =	155.0	1	1.550×10^{-2}	1.550×10^5	1.550×10^7
1 weber per square meter =	10^4	64.52	1	10^7	10^9
1 milligauss =	0.001	6.452×10^{-6}	10^{-7}	1	100
1 gamma =	10^{-5}	6.452×10^{-8}	10^{-9}	0.01	1

$$1 \text{ ESU} = 2.998 \times 10^6 \text{ weber/m}^2$$

Magnetomotive Force

	abamp-turn	amp-turn	gilbert
1 abampere-turn =	1	10	12.57
1 ampere-turn =	0.1	1	1.257
1 gilbert =	7.958×10^{-2}	0.7958	1

$$1 \text{ pragilbert} = 4\pi \text{ amp-turn} \qquad 1 \text{ ESU} = 2.655 \times 10^{-11} \text{ amp-turn}$$

Magnetizing Force $\mathfrak{H}$

	abamp-turn/cm	amp-turn/cm	amp-turn/in	amp-turn/m	oersted
1 abampere-turn per centimeter =	1	10	25.40	1000	12.57
1 ampere-turn per centimeter =	0.1	1	2.540	100	1.257
1 ampere-turn per inch =	3.937×10^{-2}	0.3937	1	39.37	0.4947
1 ampere-turn per meter =	0.001	0.01	2.540×10^{-2}	1	1.257×10^{-2}
1 oersted =	7.958×10^{-2}	0.7958	2.021	79.58	1

1 oersted = 1 gilbert/cm
1 pra-oersted = 4π amp-turn/m $\qquad$ 1 ESU = 2.655×10^{-9} amp-turn/m

Relativistic Mass-Energy Equivalents

	kg	amu	joule	Mev
1 kilogram =	1	6.025×10^{26}	8.987×10^{16}	5.610×10^{29}
1 atomic mass unit =	1.660×10^{-27}	1	1.492×10^{-10}	931.0
1 joule =	1.113×10^{-17}	6.705×10^9	1	6.242×10^{12}
1 million electron-volts =	1.783×10^{-30}	1.074×10^{-3}	1.602×10^{-13}	1

9. PERIODIC TABLE OF THE ELEMENTS

								He 2
H 1								
Li 3	Be 4	B 5	C 6	N 7	O 8	F 9	Ne 10	
Na 11	Mg 12	Al 13	Si 14	P 15	S 16	Cl 17	A 18	

Transition elements

K 19	Ca 20	Sc 21	Ti 22	V 23	Cr 24	Mn 25	Fe 26	Co 27	Ni 28	Cu 29	Zn 30	Ga 31	Ge 32	As 33	Se 34	Br 35	Kr 36
Rb 37	Sr 38	Y 39	Zr 40	Nb 41	Mo 42	Tc 43	Ru 44	Rh 45	Pd 46	Ag 47	Cd 48	In 49	Sn 50	Sb 51	Te 52	I 53	Xe 54
Cs 55	Ba 56	Lu 71	Hf 72	Ta 73	W 74	Re 75	Os 76	Ir 77	Pt 78	Au 79	Hg 80	Tl 81	Pb 82	Bi 83	Po 84	At 85	Rn 86
Fr 87	Ra 88																

Rare earths

La 57	Ce 58	Pr 59	Nd 60	Pm 61	Sm 62	Eu 63	Gd 64	Tb 65	Dy 66	Ho 67	Er 68	Tm 69	Yb 70
Ac 89	Th 90	Pa 91	U 92	Np 93	Pu 94	Am 95	Cm 96	Bk 97	Cf 98	E 99	Fm 100		

INDEX

A

X

W

Y

Z